Authors

Series Authors

Dan Kennedy, Ph.D., is a classroom teacher and the Lupton Distinguished Professor of Mathematics at the Baylor School in Chattanooga, Tennessee. A frequent speaker at professional meetings on the subject of mathematics education reform, Dr. Kennedy has conducted more than 50 workshops and institutes for high school teachers. He is coauthor of textbooks in calculus and precalculus, and from 1990 to 1994, he chaired the College Board's AP Calculus Development Committee. He is a 1992 Tandy Technology Scholar and a 1995 Presidential Award winner.

Randall I. Charles, Ph.D., is Professor Emeritus in the Department of Mathematics and Computer Science at San Jose State University, San Jose, California. He began his career as a high school mathematics teacher, and was a mathematics supervisor for five years. Dr. Charles has been a member of several NCTM committees and is the former Vice President of the National Council of Supervisors of Mathematics. Much of his writing and research has been in the area of problem solving. He has authored more than 75 mathematics textbooks for kindergarten through college.

Basia Hall currently serves as Manager of Instructional Programs for the Houston Independent School District. With 30 years teaching experience, Ms. Hall has served as a department chair, instructional specialist, instructional supervisor, a school improvement facilitator, and a professional development (TEXTEAMS) trainer. Ms. Hall has developed curriculum for Algebra 1, Geometry, and Algebra 2, and contributed to the development of the Texas Essential Knowledge and Skills. A recipient of the 1992 Presidential Award for Excellence in Mathematics Teaching, Ms. Hall is also a past president of the Texas Association of Supervisors of Mathematics, and she is a state representative for the National Council of Supervisors of Mathematics (NCSM).

…nowledgments appear on pages 707–708, which constitute an extension of this copyright page.

ISBN 0-13-203121-3
2 3 4 5 6 7 8 9 10   11 10 09 08 07

Prentice Hall Mathematics

Need help with your homework? Prentice Hall has the answer!

Homework Video Tutors—Real teachers, reviewing every lesson!

These narrated, interactive tutorials review the key concepts of every lesson, providing unparalleled homework help. With over 1,000 videos for grades 6–12, we've got the help you need.

See for yourself!

1. Go to PHSchool.com
2. Enter Web Code **bae-0775**
3. Click Go!

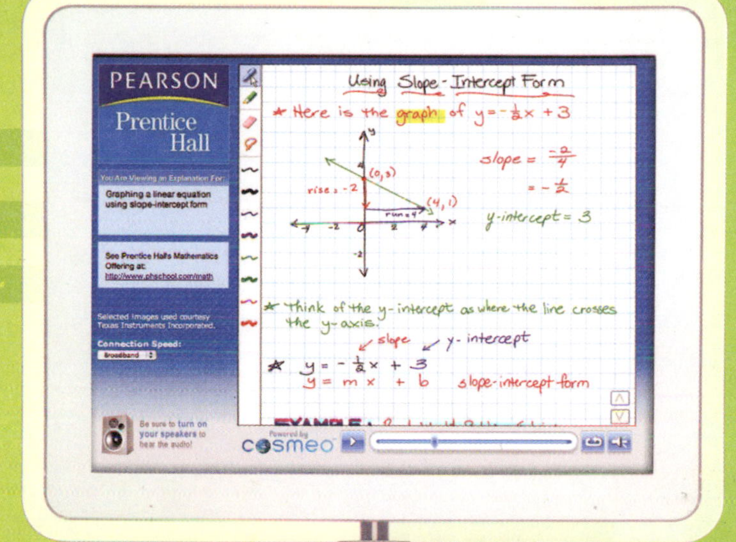

Additional support at PHSchool.com includes

- Vocabulary Quizzes
- Lesson Quizzes
- Data Updates
- Chapter Tests
- California Standards Tutorials

See page CA27 for a complete list!

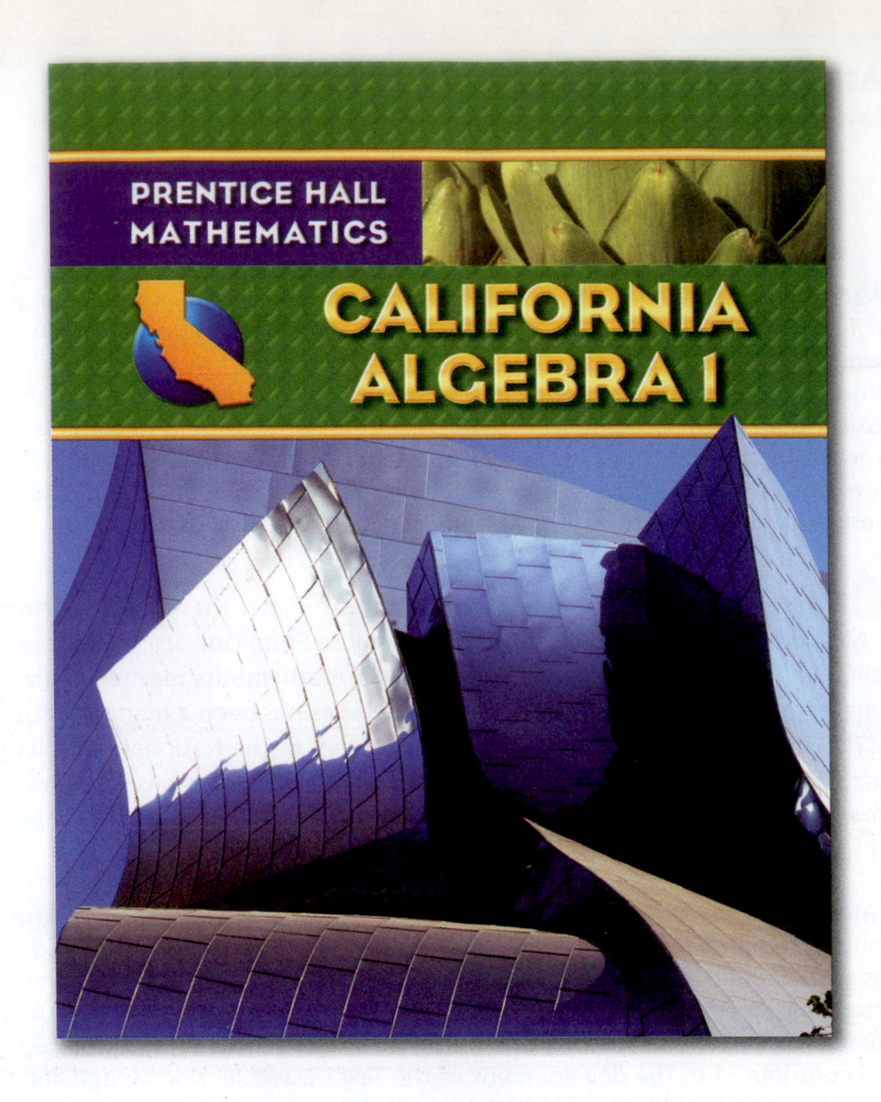

Allan E. Bellman
Sadie Chavis Bragg
Randall I. Charles
Basia Hall
William G. Handlin, Sr.
Dan Kennedy

Boston, Massachusetts
Upper Saddle River, New Jersey

Algebra 1 and Algebra 2 Authors

Allan E. Bellman is a Lecturer/Supervisor in the School of Education at the University of California, Davis. Before coming to Davis, he was a mathematics teacher for 31 years in Montgomery County, Maryland. He has been an instructor for both the Woodrow Wilson National Fellowship Foundation and the T^3 program. Mr. Bellman has a particular expertise in the use of technology in education and speaks frequently on this topic. He was a 1992 Tandy Technology Scholar.

Sadie Chavis Bragg, Ed.D., is Senior Vice President of Academic Affairs at the Borough of Manhattan Community College of the City University of New York. A former professor of mathematics, she is a past president of the American Mathematical Association of Two-Year Colleges (AMATYC), co-director of the AMATYC project to revise the standards for introductory college mathematics before calculus, and an active member of the Benjamin Banneker Association. Dr. Bragg has coauthored more than 50 mathematics textbooks for kindergarten through college.

William G. Handlin, Sr., is a classroom teacher and Department Chairman of Technology Applications at Spring Woods High School in Houston, Texas. Awarded Life Membership in the Texas Congress of Parents and Teachers for his contributions to the well-being of children, Mr. Handlin is also a frequent workshop and seminar leader in professional meetings throughout the world.

Geometry Authors

Laurie E. Bass is a classroom teacher at the 9–12 division of the Ethical Culture Fieldston School in Riverdale, New York. Ms. Bass has a wide base of teaching experience, ranging from grade 6 through Advanced Placement Calculus. She was the recipient of a 2000 Honorable Mention for the RadioShack National Teacher Awards. She has been a contributing writer of a number of publications, including software-based activities for the Algebra 1 classroom. Among her areas of special interest are cooperative learning for high school students and geometry exploration on the computer. Ms. Bass has been a presenter at a number of local, regional, and national conferences.

Art Johnson, Ed.D., is a professor of mathematics education at Boston University. He is a mathematics educator with 32 years of public school teaching experience, a frequent speaker and workshop leader, and the recipient of a number of awards. Dr. Johnson received the Tandy Prize for Teaching Excellence in 1995, a Presidential Award for Excellence in Mathematics Teaching in 1992, and New Hampshire Teacher of the Year, also in 1992. He was profiled by the Disney Corporation in the American Teacher of the Year Program.

California Mathematics Program Advisors

Prentice Hall wishes to thank the following educators for their ongoing advice in the development of this California Edition of Prentice Hall Mathematics. Their valuable insights have helped ensure that this mathematics series meets the needs of California students and their teachers.

Danelle Almaraz
Pre-Algebra Teacher
East Whittier City School District
Whittier, California

Catherine Barker
Algebra Teacher
Los Angeles USD
Long Beach, California

Eric Bitter
Pre-Algebra & Algebra Teacher
Clovis USD
Clovis, California

Joe Brumfield
Consultant
Pasadena, California

Lynn Cevallos
Consultant
Hacienda Heights, California

Manuel E. Chavez
AP Calculus Teacher/Math Coach
Los Angeles USD
Huntington Park, California

Edward Ford
Consultant
Escondido, California

Courtney Glass
Algebra 2 & Pre-Calculus Teacher
Monrovia City USD
Monrovia, California

Bernice Levens
Former Teacher/Consultant
Hacienda Heights, California

Sia Lux
Algebra & Calculus Teacher
Coachella Valley USD
Indio, California

Christy McAloney
Algebra & Calculus Teacher
Grossmont Union High School District
Spring Valley, California

Brian McElfish
Pre-Algebra & Algebra Teacher
Saddleback Valley USD
Lake Forest, California

Paul Dennis McLaughlin
Algebra Teacher
Walnut Valley USD
Walnut, California

Shawn Neal
Pre-Algebra & Algebra Teacher
Visalia USD
Visalia, California

Jason Rose
Algebra Teacher
Temple City USD
Temple City, California

Keith Smith
Pre-Algebra & Algebra Teacher
Grant Joint USD
Sacramento, California

Sarah Thomson
Calculus Teacher & Math Coach
San Bernardino City USD
San Bernardino, California

Contents in Brief

California Mathematics Student Handbook

Tools of Algebra

Student Support

Instant Check System

Vocabulary

GO Online

California Standards

Algebra 1

1.0, 1.1, 2.0, 4.0, 10.0, 24.1, 24.3, 25.0, 25.1, 25.2

Standards Mastery and Assessment

CHAPTER 2

Solving Equations

Standards Mastery and Assessment

Student Support

Instant Check System

Vocabulary

GO Online

California Standards

Algebra 1

2.0, 4.0, 5.0, 15.0, 25.0, 25.3

page 93

Solving Inequalities

Standards Mastery and Assessment

Student Support

Instant Check System

Vocabulary

Go Online

California Standards

Algebra 1

3.0, 4.0, 5.0, 24.0, 24.2, 24.3, 25.2, 25.3

page 134

Graphs and Functions

Standards Mastery and Assessment

Student Support

Instant Check System

Vocabulary

GO Online

California Standards

Algebra 1

15.0, 16.0, 17.0, 18.0, 24.1

page 203

Linear Equations and Their Graphs

Student Support

Instant Check System

Vocabulary

GO Online

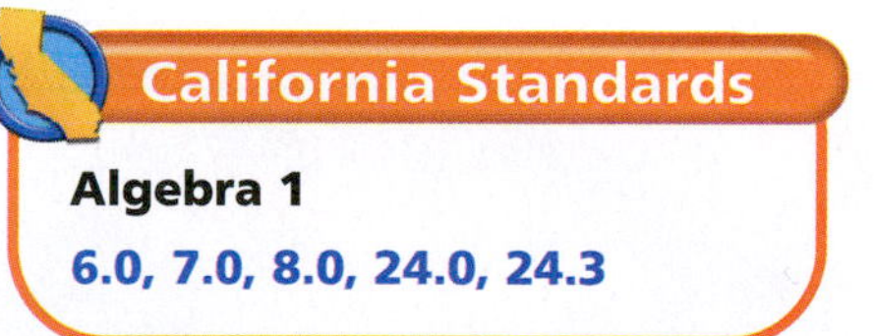

Algebra 1

6.0, 7.0, 8.0, 24.0, 24.3

Standards Mastery and Assessment

page 259

Systems of Equations and Inequalities

Standards Mastery and Assessment

Student Support

Instant Check System

Vocabulary

GO Online

California Standards

Algebra 1

6.0, 9.0, 15.0

page 284

Exponents

Standards Mastery and Assessment

Student Support

Instant Check System

Vocabulary

GO Online

California Standards

Algebra 1

2.0, 10.0

page 327

Polynomials and Factoring

Student Support

Instant Check System

Vocabulary

GO Online

California Standards

Algebra 1
10.0, 11.0

Standards Mastery and Assessment

page 389

Quadratic Equations and Functions

Student Support

Instant Check System

Vocabulary

GO Online

California Standards

Algebra 1

2.0, 14.0, 17.0, 19.0, 20.0, 21.0, 22.0, 23.0, 24.0, 25.1, 25.3

Standards Mastery and Assessment

page 435

Radical Expressions and Equations

Standards Mastery and Assessment

Student Support

Instant Check System

Vocabulary

GO Online

California Standards

Algebra 1

2.0, 17.0, 24.2, 25.0, 25.2

page 508

Rational Expressions and Equations

Student Support

Instant Check System

Vocabulary

GO Online

California Standards

Algebra 1

2.0, 10.0, 12.0, 13.0, 15.0

page 548

Learning the California Standards

Your *Prentice Hall Algebra 1* textbook is designed to help you fully understand and learn the California Mathematics Standards. Here are some features of your textbook that will support your learning throughout the year.

California Check System

Look for the ✓ in each lesson. These questions are opportunities for you and your teacher to make sure you understand the mathematics – so you can be successful with each day's lesson.

GO for Help

Look for this Go for Help arrow throughout every lesson to point you to where you can get help or review important concepts. Be an independent learner – and go for help when you're having trouble.

Get Ready to Learn

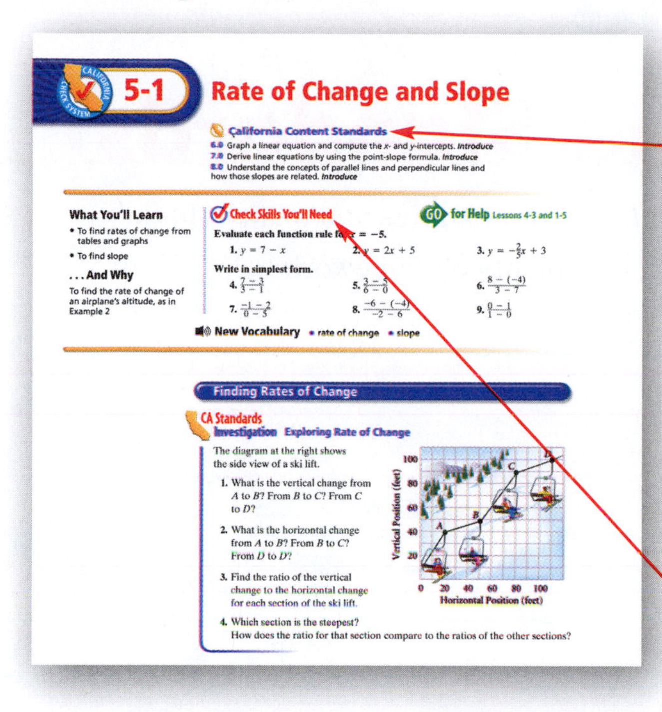

5-1 Rate of Change and Slope

California Content Standards

6.0 Graph a linear equation and compute the x- and y-intercepts. *Introduce*
7.0 Derive linear equations by using the point-slope formula. *Introduce*
8.0 Understand the concepts of parallel lines and perpendicular lines and how those slopes are related. *Introduce*

What You'll Learn

- To find rates of change from tables and graphs
- To find slope

. . . And Why

To find the rate of change of an airplane's altitude, as in Example 2

Check Skills You'll Need

GO for Help Lessons 4-3 and 1-5

Evaluate each function rule for $x = -5$.

1. $y = 7 - x$
2. $y = 2x + 5$
3. $y = -\frac{2}{5}x + 3$

Write in simplest form.

4. $\frac{7-3}{3-1}$
5. $\frac{3-5}{6-0}$
6. $\frac{8-(-4)}{3-7}$
7. $\frac{-1-2}{0-5}$
8. $\frac{-6-(-4)}{-2-6}$
9. $\frac{0-1}{1-0}$

New Vocabulary • rate of change • slope

Finding Rates of Change

CA Standards Investigation Exploring Rate of Change

The diagram at the right shows the side view of a ski lift.

1. What is the vertical change from A to B? From B to C? From C to D?
2. What is the horizontal change from A to B? From B to C? From D to D?
3. Find the ratio of the vertical change to the horizontal change for each section of the ski lift.
4. Which section is the steepest? How does the ratio for that section compare to the ratios of the other sections?

California Content Standards

Your textbook identifies which California standards you'll be covering each day. You'll also know whether you are being introduced to this standard for the first time, developing your understanding of it, or showing your mastery of it.

Check Skills You'll Need

These questions make sure you're ready to start the lesson by reviewing important skills and vocabulary words you'll need. Need help? Go for Help points you to the lesson you can review.

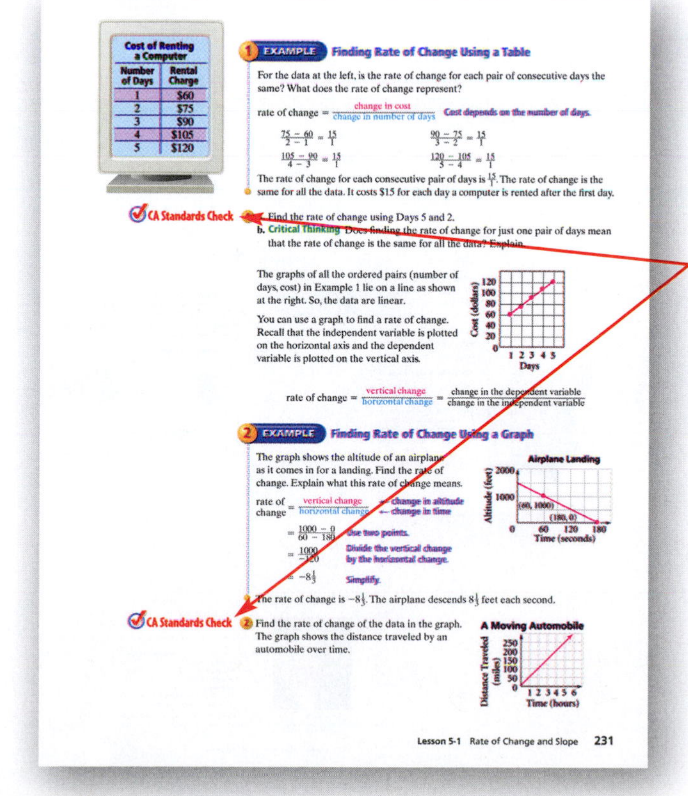

Cost of Renting a Computer

Number of Days	Rental Charge
1	\$60
2	\$75
3	\$90
4	\$105
5	\$120

1 EXAMPLE Finding Rate of Change Using a Table

For the data at the left, is the rate of change for each pair of consecutive days the same? What does the rate of change represent?

$$\text{rate of change} = \frac{\text{change in cost}}{\text{change in number of days}}$$ Cost depends on the number of days.

$\frac{75-60}{2-1} = \frac{15}{1}$ $\quad$ $\frac{90-75}{3-2} = \frac{15}{1}$

$\frac{105-90}{4-3} = \frac{15}{1}$ $\quad$ $\frac{120-105}{5-4} = \frac{15}{1}$

The rate of change for each consecutive pair of days is $\frac{15}{1}$. The rate of change is the same for all the data. It costs \$15 for each day a computer is rented after the first day.

CA Standards Check 1 a. Find the rate of change using Days 5 and 2.
b. **Critical Thinking** Does finding the rate of change for just one pair of days mean that the rate of change is the same for all the data? Explain.

The graphs of all the ordered pairs (number of days, cost) in Example 1 lie on a line as shown at the right. So, the data are linear.

You can use a graph to find a rate of change. Recall that the independent variable is plotted on the horizontal axis and the dependent variable is plotted on the vertical axis.

$$\text{rate of change} = \frac{\text{vertical change}}{\text{horizontal change}} = \frac{\text{change in the dependent variable}}{\text{change in the independent variable}}$$

2 EXAMPLE Finding Rate of Change Using a Graph

The graph shows the altitude of an airplane as it comes in for a landing. Find the rate of change. Explain what this rate of change means.

$\text{rate of change} = \frac{\text{vertical change}}{\text{horizontal change}}$ ← change in altitude ← change in time

$= \frac{1000-0}{60-180}$ Use two points.

$= \frac{1000}{-120}$ Divide the vertical change by the horizontal change.

$= -8\frac{1}{3}$ Simplify.

The rate of change is $-8\frac{1}{3}$. The airplane descends $8\frac{1}{3}$ feet each second.

CA Standards Check 2 Find the rate of change of the data in the graph. The graph shows the distance traveled by an automobile over time.

Lesson 5-1 Rate of Change and Slope 231

CA Standards Check

These questions, after every example, help you and your teacher make sure you understand the example – and the California Standards being taught.

Practicing the California Standards

Your *Prentice Hall Algebra 1* textbook gives you plenty of opportunities to practice, with plenty of homework help along the way.

Each lesson's Standards Practice gives you different levels of exercises.

- **A** Practice by Example: These exercises give you practice with the examples you just learned. Go for Help points you back to the example for easy reference.
- **B** Apply Your Skills: These exercises give you a chance to practice everything you learned in the day's lesson.
- **C** Challenge: This problem extends your learning and gives you a more challenging problem.

What if you need help with your homework? These tutorials show real teachers reviewing each lesson. Your Prentice Hall textbook gives you a unique source for more help – called Homework Video Tutors. Log on to PHSchool.com and enter the Web Code provided – you'll get the homework help you need!

Mastering the California Standards

Your *Prentice Hall Algebra 1* textbook provides opportunities for you to ensure you've mastered the standards after every lesson and every chapter in your textbook.

Standards Mastery After Every Lesson

Multiple Choice Practice and Mixed Review

The final part of each day's exercises includes practice with multiple choice problems and a chance to review skills you learned earlier in your course. This will help keep your skills sharp and help you receive lots of practice with multiple choice questions. All questions are correlated to the California Standards.

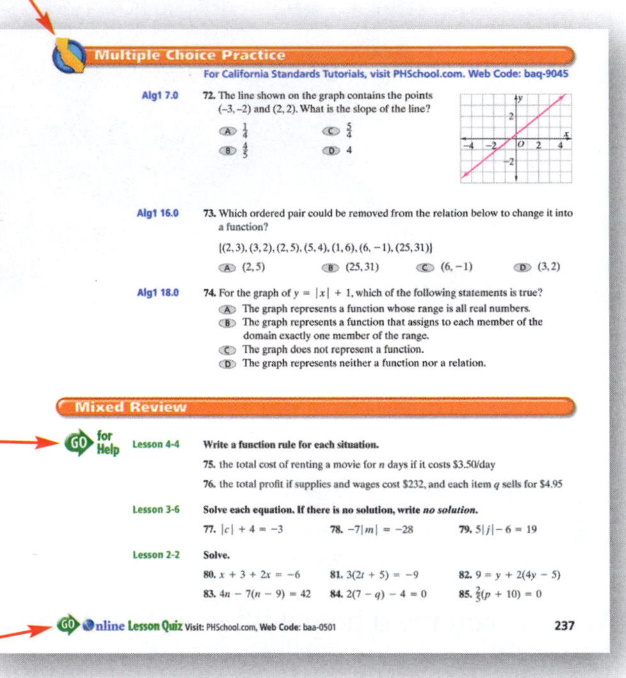

Multiple Choice Practice

For California Standards Tutorials, visit PHSchool.com. Web Code: baq-9045

Alg1 7.0 — **72.** The line shown on the graph contains the points (–3, –2) and (2, 2). What is the slope of the line?

(A) $\frac{1}{4}$ (B) $\frac{4}{5}$ (C) $\frac{5}{4}$ (D) 4

Alg1 16.0 — **73.** Which ordered pair could be removed from the relation below to change it into a function?

$\{(2, 3), (3, 2), (2, 5), (5, 4), (1, 6), (6, -1), (25, 31)\}$

(A) (2, 5) (B) (25, 31) (C) (6, –1) (D) (3, 2)

Alg1 18.0 — **74.** For the graph of $y = |x| + 1$, which of the following statements is true?

(A) The graph represents a function whose range is all real numbers.
(B) The graph represents a function that assigns to each member of the domain exactly one member of the range.
(C) The graph does not represent a function.
(D) The graph represents neither a function nor a relation.

Mixed Review

GO for Help

Lesson 4-4 — **Write a function rule for each situation.**

75. the total cost of renting a movie for n days if it costs $3.50/day

76. the total profit if supplies and wages cost $232, and each item q sells for $4.95

Lesson 3-6 — **Solve each equation. If there is no solution, write *no solution*.**

77. $|c| + 4 = -3$ **78.** $-7|m| = -28$ **79.** $5|j| - 6 = 19$

Lesson 2-2 — **Solve.**

80. $x + 3 + 2x = -6$ **81.** $3(2t + 5) = -9$ **82.** $9 = y + 2(4y - 5)$

83. $4n - 7(n - 9) = 42$ **84.** $2(7 - q) - 4 = 0$ **85.** $\frac{2}{5}(p + 10) = 0$

GO Online Lesson Quiz Visit: PHSchool.com, Web Code: baa-0501

237

The Go for Help arrow points to the lesson you can review. You can also go online and take a lesson quiz – another chance to make sure you've mastered the California Standards you learned.

Standards Mastery after Every Chapter

After every chapter, Standards Mastery Cumulative Practice provides an opportunity to demonstrate your understanding of all the California Standards covered so far.

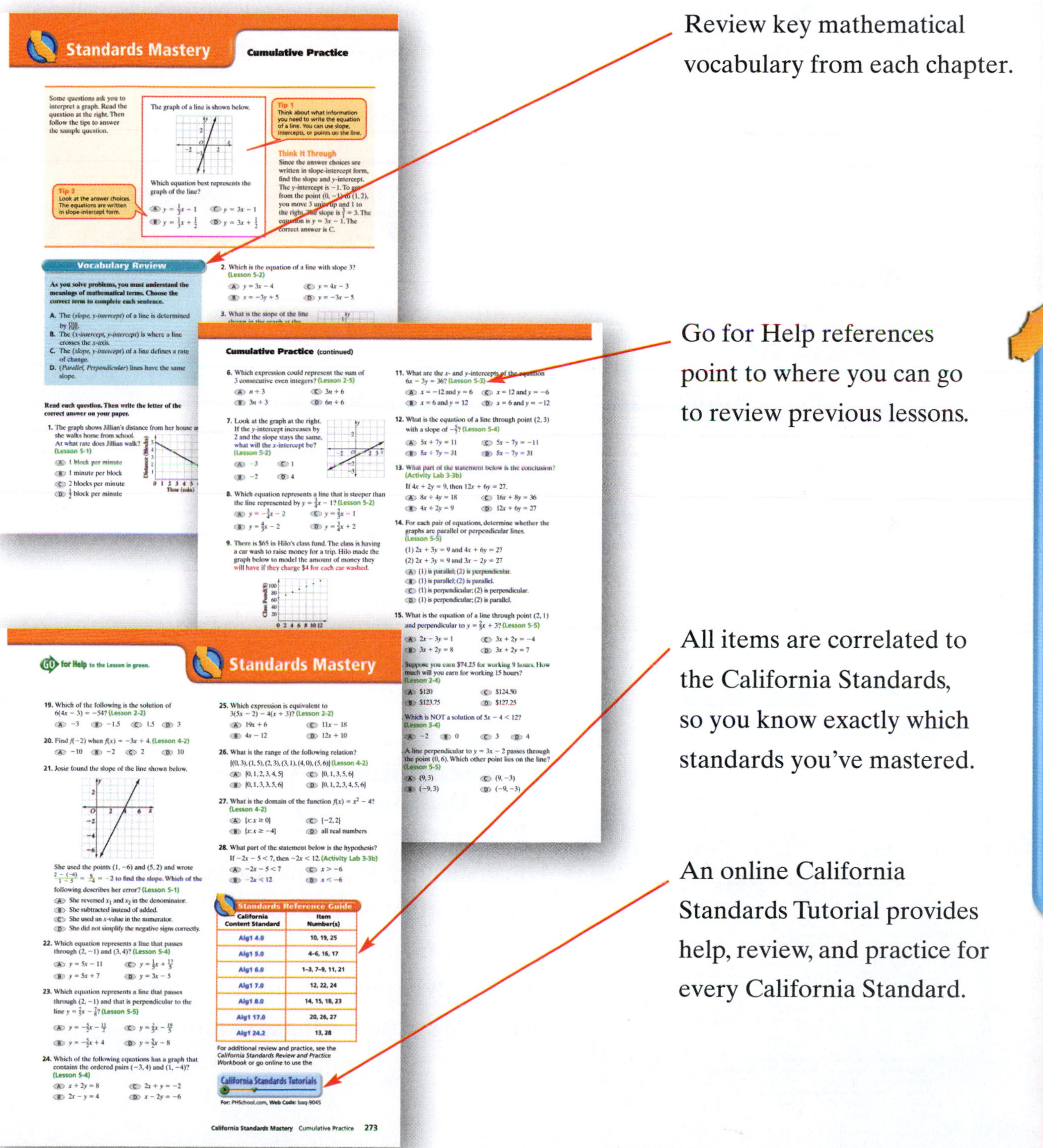

Review key mathematical vocabulary from each chapter.

Go for Help references point to where you can go to review previous lessons.

All items are correlated to the California Standards, so you know exactly which standards you've mastered.

An online California Standards Tutorial provides help, review, and practice for every California Standard.

Standards Mastery in Your Book

Mastering the California Standards

There are other types of features in your *Prentice Hall Algebra 1* textbook that will help you learn the mathematics and be successful in your class.

These features provide opportunities for you to engage with the mathematics being taught. Each feature states the California Standards being covered.

Activity Lab — Rational Exponents

For Use With Lesson 10-1

2.0 Understand and use such operations as taking a root and raising to a fractional power. Understand and use the rules of exponents. *Develop*

You can have roots other than square roots. The third root of a number x is written as $\sqrt[3]{x}$. For example, $\sqrt[3]{8} = 2$ because $2^3 = 8$. You can also express roots using exponents. The expression $a^{\frac{1}{n}}$ is defined as $\sqrt[n]{a}$. An example is $9^{\frac{1}{2}} = \sqrt[2]{9} = 3$.

Rational exponents follow the same rules as integer exponents, so $9^{\frac{1}{2}} \cdot 9^{\frac{1}{2}} = 9^{\left(\frac{1}{2} + \frac{1}{2}\right)} = 9^1 = 9$, just as $\sqrt{9} \cdot \sqrt{9} = 9$.

1 EXAMPLE

Simplify $16^{\frac{1}{4}}$.

$16^{\frac{1}{4}} = 2$ — $16 = 2 \cdot 2 \cdot 2 \cdot 2$, so $\sqrt[4]{16} = 2$

An exponent can be any rational number. You can simplify rational exponents using the property of raising a power to a power, $a^{mn} = (a^m)^n$.

2 EXAMPLE

Simplify $8^{\frac{2}{3}}$.

a.		b.
$8^{\frac{2}{3}} = 8^{\frac{1}{3} \cdot 2}$	Write $\frac{2}{3}$ as a product of 2 and $\frac{1}{3}$.	$8^{\frac{2}{3}} = 8^{2 \cdot \frac{1}{3}}$
$= (8^{\frac{1}{3}})^2$	Use the property of raising a power to a power.	$= (8^2)^{\frac{1}{3}}$
$= (2)^2$	Simplify within the parentheses.	$= (64)^{\frac{1}{3}}$
$= 4$	Simplify.	$= 4$

3 EXAMPLE

Simplify $(x^{\frac{3}{4}})^5 (y^{\frac{1}{2}}) y^{\frac{2}{5}}$.

$(x^{\frac{3}{4}})^5 (y^{\frac{1}{2}}) y^{\frac{2}{5}} = (x^{\frac{15}{4}})(y^{\frac{1}{2}} \cdot y^{\frac{2}{5}})$ — Multiply exponents in $(x^{\frac{3}{4}})^5$.

$= x^{\frac{15}{4}}(y^{\frac{1}{2} + \frac{2}{5}})$ — Add exponents of powers with the same base.

$= x^{\frac{15}{4}} y^{\frac{9}{10}}$ — Simplify fractions. $\frac{1}{2} + \frac{2}{5} = \frac{9}{10}$. Leave $\frac{15}{4}$ as an improper fraction.

EXERCISES

Simplify each expression.

1. $100^{\frac{1}{2}}$ 2. $25^{\frac{1}{2}}$ 3. $8^{\frac{1}{3}}$ 4. $(49^{\frac{1}{2}})^3$
5. $(8^{\frac{1}{3}})^2$ 6. [illegible] 7. $25^{\frac{3}{2}}$ 8. [illegible]
9. [illegible] 10. $(b^{\frac{1}{2}})^4$ 11. [illegible] 12. [illegible]

492 Activity Lab Rational Exponents

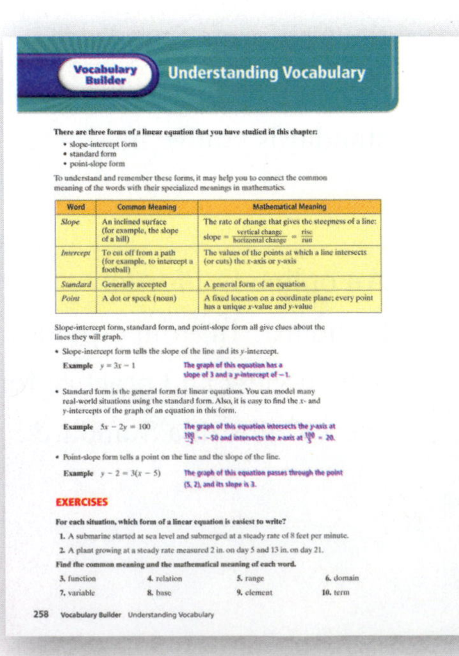

Vocabulary Builder — Understanding Vocabulary

There are three forms of a linear equation that you have studied in this chapter:

- slope-intercept form
- standard form
- point-slope form

To understand and remember these forms, it may help you to connect the common meaning of the words with their specialized meanings in mathematics.

Word	Common Meaning	Mathematical Meaning
Slope	An inclined surface (for example, the slope of a hill)	The rate of change that gives the steepness of a line: slope = $\frac{\text{vertical change}}{\text{horizontal change}} = \frac{\text{rise}}{\text{run}}$
Intercept	To cut off from a path (for example, to intercept a football)	The values of the points at which a line intersects (or cuts) the x-axis or y-axis
Standard	Generally accepted	A general form of an equation
Point	A dot or speck (noun)	A fixed location on a coordinate plane; every point has a unique x-value and y-value

Slope-intercept form, standard form, and point-slope form all give clues about the lines they will graph.

- Slope-intercept form tells the slope of the line and its y-intercept.

  Example $y = 3x - 1$ — The graph of this equation has a slope of 3 and a y-intercept of -1.

- Standard form is the general form for linear equations. You can model many real-world situations using the standard form. Also, it is easy to find the x- and y-intercepts of the graph of an equation in this form.

  Example $5x - 2y = 100$ — The graph of this equation intersects the y-axis at $\frac{100}{-2} = -50$ and intersects the x-axis at $\frac{100}{5} = 20$.

- Point-slope form tells a point on the line and the slope of the line.

  Example $y - 2 = 3(x - 5)$ — The graph of this equation passes through the point (5, 2), and its slope is 3.

EXERCISES

For each situation, which form of a linear equation is easiest to write?

1. A submarine started at sea level and submerged at a steady rate of 8 feet per minute.
2. A plant growing at a steady rate measured 2 in. on day 5 and 13 in. on day 21.

Find the common meaning and the mathematical meaning of each word.

3. function 4. relation 5. range 6. domain
7. variable 8. base 9. element 10. term

258 Vocabulary Builder Understanding Vocabulary

Understanding mathematical vocabulary is an important part of your success in any mathematics class. These features give you even more practice and support in learning these vocabulary words.

GPS Guided Problem Solving

These features give you more support in becoming a good problem solver.

- We provide a great model for talking through the problem-solving process.
- "Think It Through" questions get more in-depth.
- The first two exercises present the steps you should take to solve the problem. They often contain a visual model of the problem.
- The remaining exercises provide independent practice.

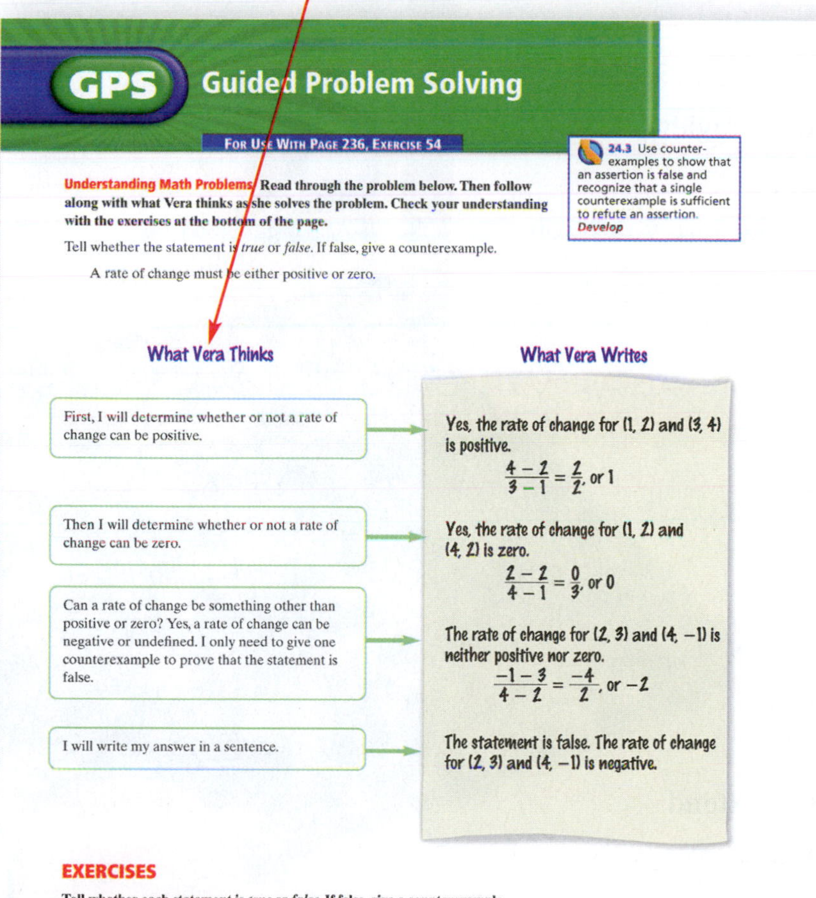
GPS Guided Problem Solving

FOR USE WITH PAGE 236, EXERCISE 54

24.3 Use counterexamples to show that an assertion is false and recognize that a single counterexample is sufficient to refute an assertion. *Develop*

Understanding Math Problems **Read through the problem below. Then follow along with what Vera thinks as she solves the problem. Check your understanding with the exercises at the bottom of the page.**

Tell whether the statement is *true* or *false*. If false, give a counterexample.

A rate of change must be either positive or zero.

What Vera Thinks	What Vera Writes
First, I will determine whether or not a rate of change can be positive.	Yes, the rate of change for (1, 2) and (3, 4) is positive. $\frac{4-2}{3-1} = \frac{2}{2}$, or 1
Then I will determine whether or not a rate of change can be zero.	Yes, the rate of change for (1, 2) and (4, 2) is zero. $\frac{2-2}{4-1} = \frac{0}{3}$, or 0
Can a rate of change be something other than positive or zero? Yes, a rate of change can be negative or undefined. I only need to give one counterexample to prove that the statement is false.	The rate of change for (2, 3) and (4, −1) is neither positive nor zero. $\frac{-1-3}{4-2} = \frac{-4}{2}$, or −2
I will write my answer in a sentence.	The statement is false. The rate of change for (2, 3) and (4, −1) is negative.

EXERCISES

Tell whether each statement is *true* or *false*. If false, give a counterexample.

1. A line always passes through three quadrants.
2. A vertical line always crosses the y-axis.
3. You can use any two points on a line to determine its slope.

238 Guided Problem Solving Understanding Math Problems

California

Student Center

Your Prentice Hall Student Center is your one-stop spot for reviewing the math you learned in class and completing your homework.

Interactive Text

Your complete textbook – electronically!
Also includes:

- Stepped examples for you to review
- Activities and Videos to review your lesson
- Self-Check tests to make sure you're on the right track.

Student Worksheets

All the additional resources your teacher might assign you to extend your learning.

Web Resources

Links out to helpful sites to extend your understanding of math concepts.

Student Center available online and on CD-ROM

Throughout this book you will find links to the Prentice Hall Web site. Use the Web Codes provided with each link to gain direct access to online material. Here's how to ***Go Online***:

1. **Go to PHSchool.com**
2. **Enter the Web Code**
3. **Click Go!**

Lesson Web Codes

Lesson Quiz Web Codes: There is an online quiz for every lesson. Access these quizzes with Web Codes baa-0101 through baa-1105 for Lesson 1-1 through Lesson 11-5.

Lesson Quizzes	
Web Code format: baa-0204	
02 = Chapter 2	04 = Lesson 4

Homework Video Tutor Web Codes: For every lesson, there is additional support online to help students complete their homework. Access the Homework Video Tutors with Web Codes bae-0101 through bae-1105 for Lesson 1-1 through Lesson 11-5.

Homework Video Tutor	
Web Code format: bae-0605	
06 = Chapter 6	05 = Lesson 5

Chapter Web Codes

Chapter	Vocabulary Quizzes	Chapter Tests	California Standards Tutorial
1	baj-0151	baa-0152	baq-9045
2	baj-0251	baa-0252	baq-9045
3	baj-0351	baa-0352	baq-9045
4	baj-0451	baa-0452	baq-9045
5	baj-0551	baa-0552	baq-9045
6	baj-0651	baa-0652	baq-9045
7	baj-0751	baa-0752	baq-9045
8	baj-0851	baa-0852	baq-9045
9	baj-0951	baa-0952	baq-9045
10	baj-1051	baa-1052	baq-9045
11	baj-1151	baa-1152	baq-9045

Additional Web Codes

Video Tutor Help:
Use Web Code bae-0775 to access engaging online instructional videos to help bring math concepts to life.

Data Updates:
Use Web Code bag-9041 to get up-to-date government data for use in examples and exercises.

California Mathematics Content Standards

Here is a complete list of the Mathematics Content Standards for Algebra 1. Use this section as a reference guide as you explore the topics in each chapter.

1.0 Students identify and use the arithmetic properties of subsets of integers and rational, irrational, and real numbers, including closure properties for the four basic arithmetic operations where applicable:

1.1 Students use properties of numbers to demonstrate whether assertions are true or false.

2.0 Students understand and use such operations as taking the opposite, finding the reciprocal, taking a root, and raising to a fractional power. They understand and use the rules of exponents.

3.0 Students solve equations and inequalities involving absolute values.

4.0 Students simplify expressions before solving linear equations and inequalities in one variable, such as $3(2x - 5) + 4(x - 2) = 12$.

What It Means to You

In Chapter 2, you will solve problems involving equations.

A gardener is planning a rectangular garden area in a community garden. His garden will be next to an existing 12-ft fence. The gardener has 44 ft of fencing to build the other three sides of his garden. How long will the garden be if the width is 12 ft?

Where You'll Learn This

You will study these standards in Chapters 1, 2, 3, 7, and 10.

5.0 Students solve multistep problems, including word problems, involving linear equations and linear inequalities in one variable and provide justification for each step.

6.0 Students graph a linear equation and compute the x- and y-intercepts (e.g., graph $2x + 6y = 4$). They are also able to sketch the region defined by linear inequalities (e.g., they sketch the region defined by $2x + 6y < 4$).

7.0 Students verify that a point lies on a line, given an equation of the line. Students are able to derive linear equations by using the point-slope formula.

8.0 Students understand the concepts of parallel lines and perpendicular lines and how their slopes are related. Students are able to find the equation of a line perpendicular to a given line that passes through a given point.

What It Means to You

In Chapter 5, you will use the equation of a line to determine whether or not a given point lies on that line.

Determine whether (8, 4) lies on the graph of the line defined by the equation $3y = 2x - 1$.

Determine whether (8, 4) lies on the graph of $3y = 2x - 1$.

$3y = 2x - 1$

$3(\ ) \stackrel{?}{=} 2(8) - 1$ **Substitute 8 for *x* and 4 for *y*.**

$12 \stackrel{?}{=} 16 - 1$ **Multiply.**

$12 \neq 15$ ✗ **Subtract.**

(8, 4) is *not* a solution.

Where You'll Learn This

You will study these standards in Chapters 2, 3, 5, and 6.

Your Guide to the Standards

9.0 Students solve a system of two linear equations in two variables algebraically and are able to interpret the answer graphically. Students are able to solve a system of two linear inequalities in two variables and to sketch the solution sets.

10.0 Students add, subtract, multiply, and divide monomials and polynomials. Students solve multistep problems, including word problems, by using these techniques.

11.0 Students apply basic factoring techniques to second- and simple third-degree polynomials. These techniques include finding a common factor for all terms in a polynomial, recognizing the difference of two squares, and recognizing perfect squares of binomials.

12.0 Students simplify fractions with polynomials in the numerator and denominator by factoring both and reducing them to the lowest terms.

What It Means to You

In Chapter 6, you will solve systems of equations using various methods, including graphing and algebraic types.

Suppose you want to combine two solutions to make 100 milliliters of 34% acid solution. Solution A is 25% acid and solution B is 40% acid.

Copy and complete the table below.

	Solution A 25% Acid	Solution B 40% Acid	Mixture 34% Acid
Solution (mL)	■	■	■
Acid (mL)	■	■	■

Write and solve a system of equations to find out how much of each solution you need to use.

Where You'll Learn This

You will study these standards in Chapters 6, 7, 8, and 11.

13.0 Students add, subtract, multiply, and divide rational expressions and functions. Students solve both computationally and conceptually challenging problems by using these techniques.

14.0 Students solve a quadratic equation by factoring or completing the square.

15.0 Students apply algebraic techniques to solve rate problems, work problems, and percent mixture problems.

What It Means to You

In Chapter 4, you will solve various types of real world problems using algebraic equations.

The force you must apply to lift an object is proportional to the object's weight. You would need to apply 0.625 lb of force to a windlass to lift a 28-lb weight. How much force would you need to lift 100 lb?

Relate $\frac{\text{force}}{\text{weight}} = \frac{0.625}{28}$, which is about 0.0223.

Define Let n = the force you need to lift 100 lb.

Write Let w = the weight and f = the force.

$f = 0.0223w$ **Write an equation.**

$f = 0.0223(100)$ **Substitute 100 for *w*.**

$f = 2.23$ **Simplify.**

You need about 2.2 lb of force to lift 100 lb.

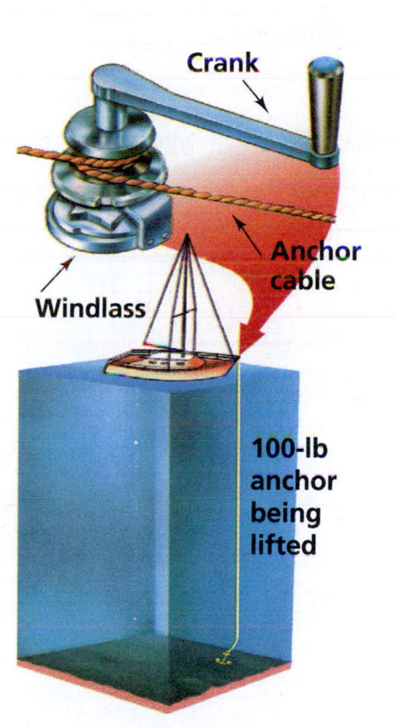

Where You'll Learn This

You will study these standards in Chapters 2, 4, 6, 9, and 11.

Your Guide to the Standards

16.0 Students understand the concepts of a relation and a function, determine whether a given relation defines a function, and give pertinent information about given relations and functions.

17.0 Students determine the domain of independent variables and the range of dependent variables defined by a graph, a set of ordered pairs, or a symbolic expression.

18.0 Students determine whether a relation defined by a graph, a set of ordered pairs, or a symbolic expression is a function and justify the conclusion.

What It Means to You

In Chapter 4, you will examine the characteristics of a function using equations, tables, and graphs.

Model the function rule $y = -\frac{1}{2}x + 1$ using a table of values and a graph.

Step 1 Choose input values for x.
Evaluate to find y.

x	$y = -\frac{1}{2}x + 1$	(x, y)
-4	$y = -\frac{1}{2}(-4) + 1 = 3$	$(-4, 3)$
0	$y = -\frac{1}{2}(0) + 1 = 1$	$(0, 1)$
2	$y = -\frac{1}{2}(2) + 1 = 0$	$(2, 0)$

Step 2 Plot points for the ordered pairs.

Step 3 Connect the points.

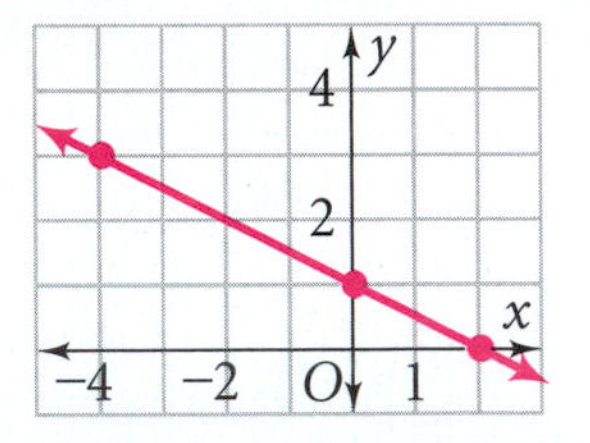

Where You'll Learn This

You will study these standards in Chapters 4, 9, and 10.

19.0 Students know the quadratic formula and are familiar with its proof by completing the square.

20.0 Students use the quadratic formula to find the roots of a second-degree polynomial and to solve quadratic equations.

21.0 Students graph quadratic functions and know that their roots are the x-intercepts.

22.0 Students use the quadratic formula or factoring techniques or both to determine whether the graph of a quadratic function will intersect the x-axis in zero, one, or two points.

23.0 Students apply quadratic equations to physical problems, such as the motion of an object under the force of gravity.

What It Means to You

In Chapter 9, you will examine the characteristics of quadratic functions and use algebraic techniques to solve problems.

Suppose you see an eagle flying over a canyon. The eagle is 30 ft above the level of the canyon's edge when it drops a stick from its claws. The force of gravity causes the stick to fall toward Earth. The function $h = -16t^2 + 30$ gives the height of the stick h in feet after t seconds. Graph this quadratic function.

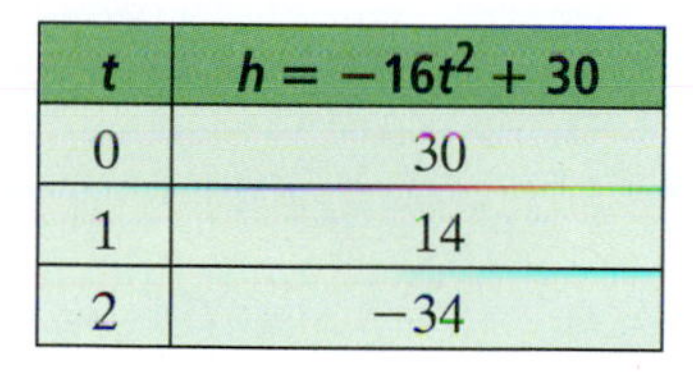

t	$h = -16t^2 + 30$
0	30
1	14
2	−34

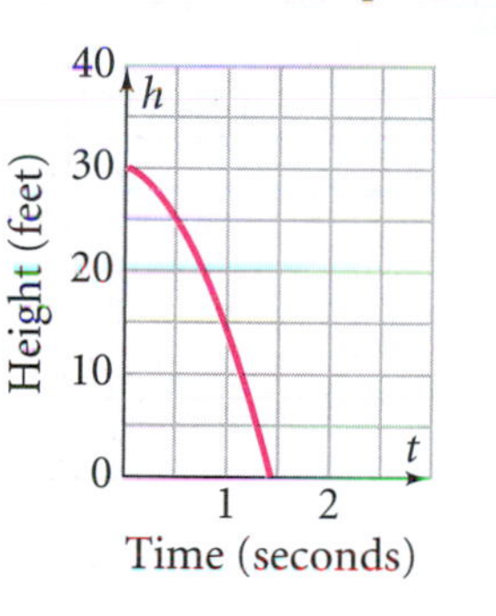

Height h is dependent on time t. Graph t on the x-axis and h on the y-axis. Use nonnegative values for t.

Where You'll Learn This

You will study these standards in Chapter 9.

24.0 Students use and know simple aspects of a logical argument:

24.1 Students explain the difference between inductive and deductive reasoning and identify and provide examples of each.

24.2 Students identify the hypothesis and conclusion in logical deduction.

24.3 Students use counterexamples to show that an assertion is false and recognize that a single counterexample is sufficient to refute an assertion.

What It Means to You

In Chapter 1, you will begin to apply counterexamples to show that an assertion is false.

Is each statement *true* or *false*? If it is false, give a counterexample.

a. All whole numbers are rational numbers.
Every whole number can be written in the form $\frac{n}{1}$, so all whole numbers are rational numbers. The statement is true.

b. The square of a number is always greater than the number.
The square of 0.5 is 0.25, and 0.25 is *not* greater than 0.5. The statement is false.

Where You'll Learn This

You will study these standards throughout this book.

25.0 Students use properties of the number system to judge the validity of results, to justify each step of a procedure, and to prove or disprove statements.

25.1 Students use properties of numbers to construct simple, valid arguments (direct and indirect) for, or formulate counterexamples to, claimed assertions.

25.2 Students judge the validity of an argument according to whether the properties of the real number system and the order of operations have been applied correctly at each step.

25.3 Given a specific algebraic statement involving linear, quadratic, or absolute value expressions or equations or inequalities, students determine whether the statement is true sometimes, always, or never.

What It Means to You

In Chapter 2, you will examine special cases of equations like the examples shown below.

a. Solve $10 - 8a = 2(5 - 4a)$.

$10 - 8a = 2(5 - 4a)$	
$10 - 8a = 10 - 8a$	**Use the Distributive Property.**
$10 - 8a + 8a = 10 - 8a + 8a$	**Add $8a$ to each side.**
$10 = 10$	**Always true!**

This equation is true for every value of *a*, so the equation is an identity.

b. Solve $6m - 5 = 7m + 7 - m$.

$6m - 5 = 7m + 7 - m$	
$6m - 5 = 6m + 7$	**Combine like terms.**
$6m - 5 - 6m = 6m + 7 - 6m$	**Subtract $6m$ from each side.**
$-5 = 7$	**Not true for any value for *m*!**

This equation has no solution.

Where You'll Learn This

You will study these standards throughout this book.

Your Guide to the Standards

Entry-Level Assessment

Read each equation. Then write the letter of the correct answer on your paper.

1. What is the value of this expression if $m = 4$ and $k = 2$?

$$m \cdot \left(7k - \frac{20}{m}\right)$$

(A) 16 (B) 20 (C) 36 (D) 51

2. Which expression has a value of 144?

(A) $2^3 \cdot 3^3$
(B) $3^4 \cdot 4^3$
(C) $2^4 \cdot 3^2$
(D) $3^2 \cdot 4^3$

3. Evaluate $-t^2 + (5 - t)^3$ for $t = 3$.

(A) -3 (B) -1 (C) 15 (D) 17

4. Topsoil sells for $2.48 per cubic foot. How much does $10\frac{1}{2}$ cubic feet of topsoil cost?

(A) $4.23 (B) $12.98 (C) $20.48 (D) $26.04

5. Two thirds of the girls at a summer camp like to jump rope. If 162 girls attend the camp, how many like to jump rope?

(A) 54 (B) 62 (C) 108 (D) 243

6. Simplify the following expression.

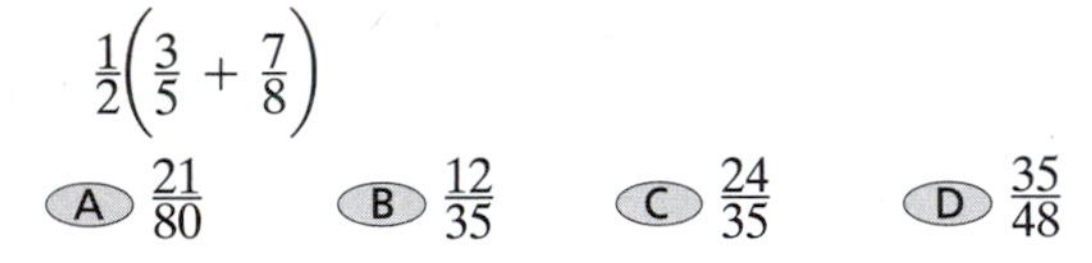

$$\frac{1}{2}\left(\frac{3}{5} + \frac{7}{8}\right)$$

(A) $\frac{21}{80}$ (B) $\frac{12}{35}$ (C) $\frac{24}{35}$ (D) $\frac{35}{48}$

7. A train traveled 357 miles in $8\frac{1}{2}$ hours. What was the train's average speed?

(A) 29 miles per hour
(B) 30 miles per hour
(C) 42 miles per hour
(D) 45 miles per hour

8. Which of the following is an irrational number?

(A) $\frac{4}{3}$ (B) $\sqrt{16}$ (C) $-\frac{1}{8}$ (D) $\sqrt{3}$

9. Which of the following is a rational number?

(A) π
(B) 0.345345345…
(C) 0.212112111…
(D) $\sqrt{7}$

10. The repeating decimal $0.\overline{27}$ is equivalent to what fraction?

(A) $\frac{27}{100}$ (B) $\frac{3}{11}$ (C) $\frac{2}{7}$ (D) $\frac{9}{11}$

11. Which fraction is equivalent to 0.15?

(A) $\frac{15}{10}$ (B) $\frac{3}{20}$ (C) $\frac{6}{10}$ (D) $\frac{1}{15}$

12. A video game that regularly costs $29.95 is on sale for 15% off. What is the sale price of the video game?

(A) $25.46 (B) $28.38 (C) $29.50 (D) $34.4

13. A jewelry store marks up the price of a topaz ring 215%. If the ring cost the store $70.00, what is the selling price of the ring?

(A) $91.50
(B) $150.50
(C) $161.50
(D) $220.50

14. Inez buys a pair of boots on sale for $32.20. The sale price is 20% off the regular price. What is the regular price of the boots?

(A) $34.20
(B) $38.64
(C) $40.25
(D) $57.96

15. Laura deposits $1,500 in an account with a simple interest rate of 6% per year. How much interest will the account earn in 3 years?

(A) $90 (B) $180 (C) $270 (D) $300

16. Ben deposits $320 in an account that earns 3.5% simple interest per year. What is the balance in the account after 4 years?

(A) $322.80
(B) $331.20
(C) $364.80
(D) $432.00

17. A business invests $25,000 in an account that earns 5% interest compounded annually. What is the balance in the account after 2 years?

(A) $25,062.50
(B) $26,250.00
(C) $27,500.00
(D) $27,562.50

18. There are $3\frac{3}{4}$ cups of flour, $1\frac{1}{2}$ cups of sugar, $\frac{2}{3}$ cup of brown sugar, and $\frac{1}{4}$ cup of oil in a cake mix. How many cups of ingredients are there in all?

(A) $4\frac{1}{2}$ cups
(B) $5\frac{1}{6}$ cups
(C) $5\frac{1}{2}$ cups
(D) $6\frac{1}{6}$ cups

19. What value of t makes the following equation true?

$3\frac{1}{8} + t = -\frac{3}{4}$

(A) $-3\frac{7}{8}$ (B) $-2\frac{3}{8}$ (C) $2\frac{3}{8}$ (D) $3\frac{7}{8}$

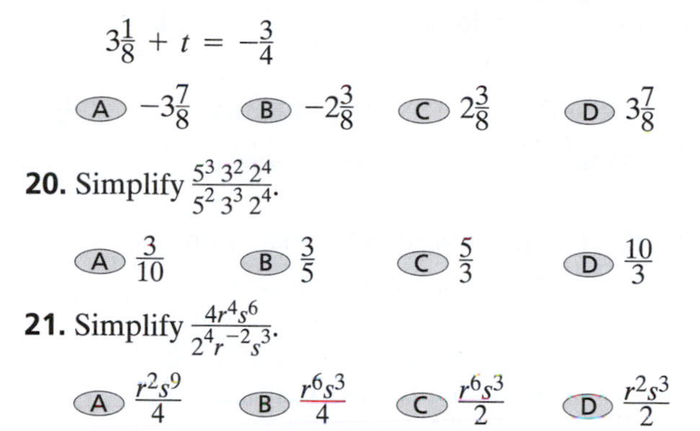

20. Simplify $\frac{5^3\,3^2\,2^4}{5^2\,3^3\,2^4}$.

(A) $\frac{3}{10}$ (B) $\frac{3}{5}$ (C) $\frac{5}{3}$ (D) $\frac{10}{3}$

21. Simplify $\frac{4r^4s^6}{2^4r^{-2}s^3}$.

(A) $\frac{r^2s^9}{4}$ (B) $\frac{r^6s^3}{4}$ (C) $\frac{r^6s^3}{2}$ (D) $\frac{r^2s^3}{2}$

22. Which of the following is equivalent to the expression $\frac{4^3}{4^6}$?

(A) $\frac{1}{4^3}$ (B) $\frac{1}{4^2}$ (C) 4^2 (D) 4^3

23. Which expression has the greatest value?

(A) -9
(B) $|-12|$
(C) $-|-15|$
(D) $|14 - 3|$

24. Which list of numbers is ordered from least to greatest?

(A) $|-5|, -4, -2$
(B) $-11, -12, |-13|$
(C) $-3, 0, |-15|$
(D) $|1|, 0, |-1|$

25. Which property is shown by the equation below?

$-3.2 + 6.8 = 6.8 + (-3.2)$

(A) Identity Property
(B) Associative Property
(C) Distributive Property
(D) Commutative Property

26. Which expression uses the Distributive Property to find $6 \cdot 4.97$?

(A) $6(5) - 0.30$
(B) $6(5 - 0.30)$
(C) $6(5 - 0.03)$
(D) $6(5) - 0.03$

27. Which property is illustrated by the equation $n + (-n) = 0$?

(A) Identity Property
(B) Inverse Property
(C) Symmetric Property
(D) Commutative Property

28. What is the slope of the line graphed below?

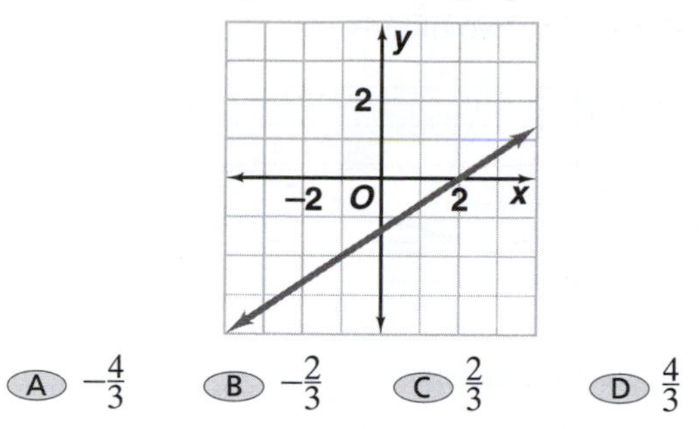

(A) $-\frac{4}{3}$ (B) $-\frac{2}{3}$ (C) $\frac{2}{3}$ (D) $\frac{4}{3}$

29. Which table of values was used to make the following graph?

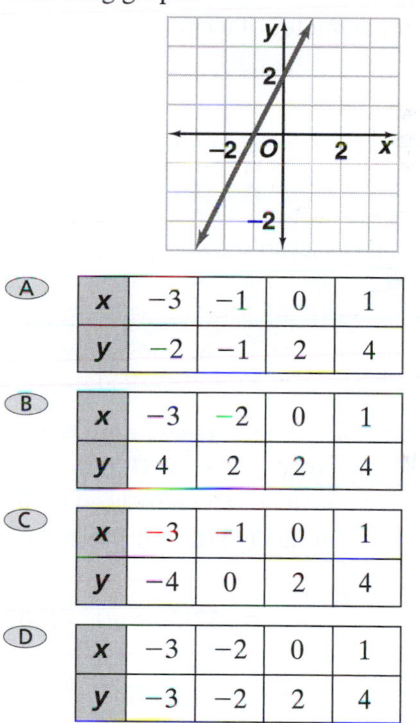

(A)

x	−3	−1	0	1
y	−2	−1	2	4

(B)

x	−3	−2	0	1
y	4	2	2	4

(C)

x	−3	−1	0	1
y	−4	0	2	4

(D)

x	−3	−2	0	1
y	−3	−2	2	4

30. What is the slope of a line that passes through the points with coordinates $(-2, -5)$ and $(1, 4)$?

(A) -3 (B) $-\frac{1}{3}$ (C) $\frac{1}{3}$ (D) 3

31. Which three points lie on the same line?

(A) $(1, 3), (3, 4), (7, 7)$
(B) $(-2, -4), (0, 1), (-4, -8)$
(C) $(3, -1), (5, -4), (-1, 5)$
(D) $(-4, 6), (8, -10), (0, 1)$

32. A linear function of x has a value of 4 when $x = 1$ and a value of 10 when $x = 2.5$. What is the value of the function when $x = 5.5$?

(A) 13 (B) 16 (C) 18.5 (D) 22

33. The graph below represents the relationship between which two quantities?

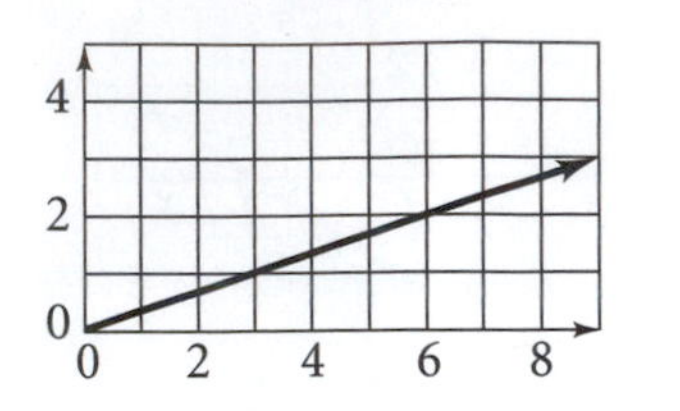

Ⓐ yards and inches

Ⓑ circumference and diameter of a circle

Ⓒ side length and area of a square

Ⓓ radius and diameter of a circle

34. Solve $-5 + \frac{x}{-3} = 28$.

Ⓐ −99 Ⓒ −79

Ⓑ −89 Ⓓ −69

35. What is the solution set to the inequality $3.4x - 5.1 < 10.2$?

Ⓐ $\{x: x < 1.5\}$ Ⓒ $\{x: x < 4.5\}$

Ⓑ $\{x: x < 2.1\}$ Ⓓ $\{x: x < 8.1\}$

36. A sound studio charges a $52 reservation fee and $26 per hour. Felipe paid a total of $130 to use the sound studio. Which equation can be used to find the total number of hours (h) during which Felipe used the studio?

Ⓐ $26 + 52h = 130$ Ⓒ $52(26 + h) = 130$

Ⓑ $52 + 26h = 130$ Ⓓ $26(h + 52) = 130$

37. To make a beaded necklace Jaime bought a bag containing 24 silver beads and 3 bags of colored beads. Each bag of colored beads contained the same number of beads. Jaime bought a total of 78 beads to make the necklace. How many beads were in each bag of colored beads?

Ⓐ 18 Ⓑ 26 Ⓒ 50 Ⓓ 54

38. Cathy ran for 30 minutes at a rate of 5.5 miles per hour. Then she ran for 15 minutes at a rate of 6 miles per hour. How many miles did she run in all?

Ⓐ 2.55 miles Ⓒ 4.25 miles

Ⓑ 4.375 miles Ⓓ 5.75 miles

39. Ryan earns $16 for working 2 hours at his job. At this rate, how long will he have to work to earn $120?

Ⓐ 3.75 hours Ⓒ 15 hours

Ⓑ 7.5 hours Ⓓ 60 hours

40. The chart below describes the maximum speeds of four different remote control cars.

Car	Speed
Car A	45 miles per hour
Car B	30 miles every 2 hours
Car C	30 meters per second
Car D	72 kilometers per hour

Which car is the fastest? (*Hint:* 1 mi = 1609 m)

Ⓐ Car A Ⓒ Car C

Ⓑ Car B Ⓓ Car D

41. Suppose electricity costs 12 cents per kilowatt-hour. How much will it cost to use ten 75-watt light bulbs for 8 hours? (*Hint:* 1 kilowatt = 1000 watts)

Ⓐ $.07 Ⓒ $1.72

Ⓑ $.72 Ⓓ $7.20

42. What is the side length of an isosceles right triangle with a hypotenuse of $\sqrt{18}$?

Ⓐ 3 Ⓒ $6\sqrt{3}$

Ⓑ $3\sqrt{2}$ Ⓓ 9

43. A right triangle has side lengths of 3.5 ft and 12 ft. What is the length of the hypotenuse?

Ⓐ 10.5 Ⓒ 13

Ⓑ 12.5 Ⓓ 15

44. Which triangle with the given side lengths is a right triangle?

Ⓐ 12, 13, 17 Ⓒ 3.2, 5.6, 6.4

Ⓑ 14, 20, 24 Ⓓ 10, 24, 26

45. In the diagram below, $ABCD \cong FGHI$. Which statement is NOT true?

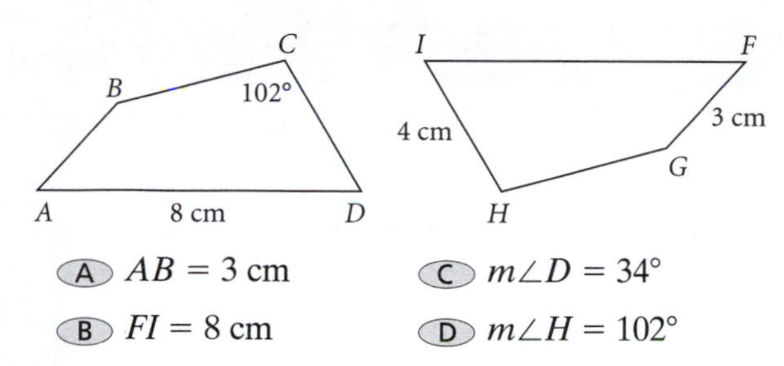

Ⓐ $AB = 3$ cm

Ⓑ $FI = 8$ cm

Ⓒ $m\angle D = 34°$

Ⓓ $m\angle H = 102°$

46. By which method is the pair of triangles below congruent?

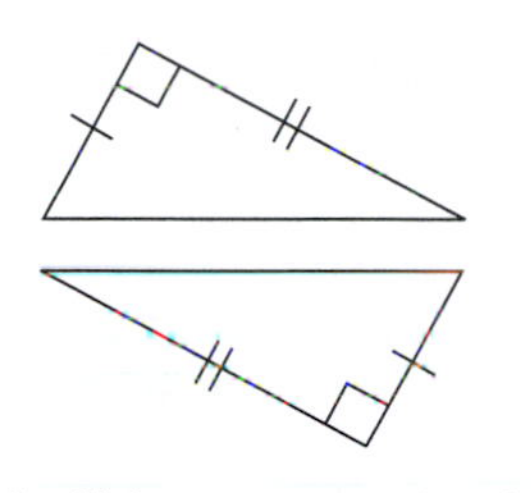

Ⓐ Side-Side-Side

Ⓑ Side-Angle-Side

Ⓒ Angle-Side-Angle

Ⓓ Angle-Angle-Angle

47. Which triangle is congruent to the triangle below by the Angle-Side-Angle method?

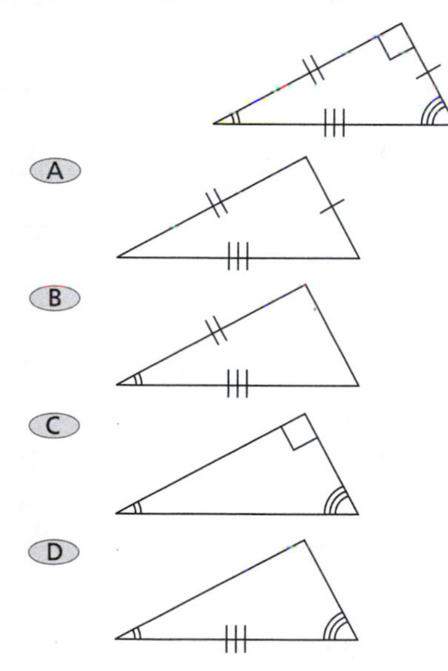

48. Which statement is false?

Ⓐ Two planes can intersect in a line.

Ⓑ Two planes can intersect in a point.

Ⓒ Three planes can intersect in two parallel lines.

Ⓓ Three planes can intersect in a point.

49. Which of the following represents a diagonal of the rectangular prism below?

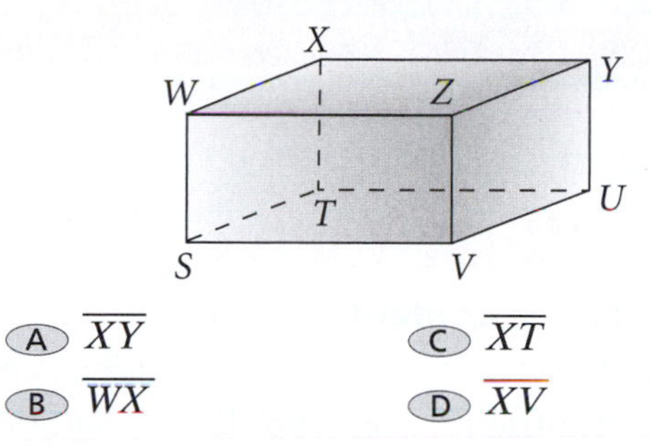

Ⓐ $\overline{XY}$

Ⓑ $\overline{WX}$

Ⓒ $\overline{XT}$

Ⓓ $\overline{XV}$

50. A data set has a lower quartile value of 8 and median value of 15. The data set contains 6 values that range from 8 to 15. Which of the following could represent the total number of values in the data set?

Ⓐ 12

Ⓑ 13

Ⓒ 18

Ⓓ 24

51. The number of points scored by a basketball team during the first 8 games of the season is shown below. What is the upper quartile score?

65, 58, 72, 74, 82, 67, 75, 71

Ⓐ 65.25

Ⓑ 70.5

Ⓒ 74.5

Ⓓ 75.75

52. The table below shows the monthly mean air temperatures for a town in northern California. What is the median temperature?

Month	Temperature (°F)
June	63
July	65
August	69
September	61
October	59

Ⓐ 61°F

Ⓑ 63°F

Ⓒ 63.4°F

Ⓓ 69°F

Tools of Algebra

What You've Learned

California Content Standards

7AF 1.0 Express quantitative relationships using algebraic expressions.

7AF 1.2 Use the correct order of operations to evaluate algebraic expressions.

7NS 1.2 Add, subtract, multiply, and divide rational numbers (integers, fractions, and terminating decimals).

7AF 1.3 Simplify numerical expressions by applying properties of rational numbers and justify the process used.

Check Your Readiness

for Help to the Lesson in green.

Simplifying Fractions (Skills Handbook page 598)

Write in simplest form.

1. $\frac{12}{15}$ **2.** $\frac{20}{28}$ **3.** $\frac{33}{77}$ **4.** $\frac{8}{56}$ **5.** $\frac{48}{52}$

Adding and Subtracting Fractions (Skills Handbook page 600)

Add or subtract. Write each answer in simplest form.

6. $\frac{1}{8} + \frac{1}{6}$ **7.** $\frac{27}{33} - \frac{6}{22}$ **8.** $\frac{3}{4} + \frac{7}{10}$ **9.** $\frac{12}{13} - \frac{1}{3}$

10. $5\frac{7}{10} + 6\frac{7}{8}$ **11.** $7\frac{5}{6} - 3\frac{1}{4}$ **12.** $3\frac{5}{12} - 1\frac{7}{12}$ **13.** $4\frac{5}{7} + 8\frac{3}{4}$

Multiplying and Dividing Fractions (Skills Handbook page 601)

Multiply or divide. Write each answer in simplest form.

14. $\frac{2}{3} \cdot \frac{5}{8}$ **15.** $\frac{5}{6} \div \frac{3}{4}$ **16.** $\frac{4}{5} \cdot \frac{5}{7}$ **17.** $\frac{7}{8} \div \frac{1}{2}$

18. $2\frac{3}{4} \cdot 1\frac{1}{5}$ **19.** $3\frac{2}{3} \div \frac{3}{8}$ **20.** $4\frac{5}{6} \cdot 2\frac{1}{2}$ **21.** $4\frac{2}{5} \div 1\frac{1}{3}$

Using Exponents (Skills Handbook page 603)

Write using exponents.

22. $9 \cdot 9 \cdot 9 \cdot 9 \cdot 9$ **23.** $5 \cdot 7 \cdot 7 \cdot 7 \cdot 7 \cdot 7 \cdot 7$ **24.** $2 \cdot 2 \cdot 3 \cdot 3 \cdot 3 \cdot 3 \cdot 3 \cdot 3$

25. $4 \cdot 4 \cdot 4 \cdot 4 \cdot 7 \cdot 7$ **26.** $5 \cdot 5 \cdot 5 \cdot 8 \cdot 8 \cdot 3$ **27.** $2 \cdot 6 \cdot 6 \cdot 6 \cdot 2 \cdot 6 \cdot 6 \cdot 2$

Write in standard form.

28. 5^3 **29.** 8^4 **30.** 11^2 **31.** $9^2 \cdot 6^1$ **32.** $4^3 \cdot 2^2$

What You'll Learn Next

▲ In this chapter, you will use operations with real numbers to solve problems involving height.

California Content Standards

1.0 Identify and use the arithmetic properties of subsets of integers and rational, irrational, and real numbers, including closure properties for the four basic arithmetic operations where applicable.

2.0 Understand and use such operations as taking the opposite and finding the reciprocal.

25.0 Use properties of the number system to judge the validity of results, to justify each step of a procedure, and to prove or disprove statements.

New Vocabulary

English and Spanish Audio Online

- **absolute value** (p. 20)
- **additive inverse** (p. 24)
- **algebraic expression** (p. 4)
- **counterexample** (p. 18)
- **deductive reasoning** (p. 54)
- **Distributive Property** (p. 45)
- **equation** (p. 5)
- **exponent** (p. 9)
- **inequality** (p. 19)
- **integers** (p. 17)
- **multiplicative inverse** (p. 41)
- **opposites** (p. 20)
- **order of operations** (p. 10)
- **real numbers** (p. 18)
- **reciprocal** (p. 41)

Academic Vocabulary

- **evaluate** (p. 10)
- **simplify** (p. 9)

1-1 Using Variables

California Content Standards

Reviews 7AF 1.1 Use variables and appropriate operations to write an expression or an equation that represents a verbal description. ***Grade 7***

What You'll Learn

- To model relationships with variables
- To model relationships with equations

. . . And Why

To model the relationship between the number and the cost of CDs, as in Example 3

Check Skills You'll Need

Skills Handbook page 597

Estimate to find whether each answer is reasonable.

1. \$154.38
22.45
276.12
+28.98
\$481.93

2. 478.23
−199.30
378.93

3. 76.425
18.94
182.6
+54.769
232.729

4. \$316.24
−48.76
\$267.48

Modeling Relationships With Variables

Vocabulary Tip

Each expression below means 6.50 multiplied by h.

$6.50 \times h$
$6.50 \cdot h$
$6.50(h)$
$(6.50)h$
$6.50h$
$(6.50)(h)$

If you earn an hourly wage of \$6.50, your pay is the number of hours you work multiplied by 6.50.

Hours Worked	Pay (dollars)
1	6.50×1
2	6.50×2
3	6.50×3
h	$6.50 \times h$

In the table at the right, the variable h stands for the number of hours you worked. A **variable** is a symbol, usually a letter, that represents one or more numbers. The expression $6.50h$ is an algebraic expression. An **algebraic expression** is a mathematical phrase that can include numbers, variables, and operation symbols.

Algebraic expressions are sometimes called variable expressions.

1 EXAMPLE Writing an Algebraic Expression

Write an algebraic expression for each phrase.

a. seven more than n

$n + 7$ "More than" indicates addition. Add the first number 7 to the second number n.

b. the difference of n and 7

$n - 7$ "Difference" indicates subtraction. Begin with the first number n. Then subtract the second number 7.

c. the product of seven and n

$7n$ "Product" indicates multiplication. Multiply the first number 7 by the second number n.

d. the quotient of n and seven

$\frac{n}{7}$ "Quotient" indicates division. Divide the first number n by the second number 7.

CA Standards Check **1** Write an algebraic expression for each phrase.

a. the quotient of 4.2 and c **b.** t minus 15

To translate an English phrase into an algebraic expression, you may need to define one or more variables first.

2 EXAMPLE Writing an Algebraic Expression

Problem Solving Tip

In math, you write the phrase "seven less than twelve" as $12 - 7$. The order of the numbers in the math phrase is different than the order of the numbers in the English phrase.

Define a variable and write an algebraic expression for each phrase.

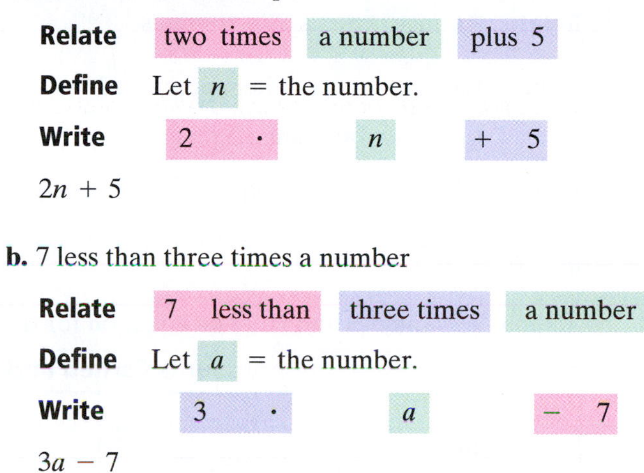

a. two times a number plus 5

Relate two times | a number | plus 5

Define Let n = the number.

Write $2 \cdot$ | n | $+ 5$

$2n + 5$

b. 7 less than three times a number

Relate 7 less than | three times | a number

Define Let a = the number.

Write $3 \cdot$ | a | $- 7$

$3a - 7$

CA Standards Check **2** Define a variable and write an algebraic expression for each phrase.

a. 9 less than a number

b. the sum of twice a number and 31

Modeling Relationships With Equations

An **equation** is a mathematical sentence that uses an equal sign. If an equation is true, then the two expressions on either side of the equal sign represent the same value. An equation that contains one or more variables is an **open sentence.** In everyday language, the word "is" suggests an equal sign in the associated equation.

Over 700 million CDs are shipped from manufacturers to retail stores per year in the United States.

3 EXAMPLE Writing an Equation

Track One Media sells all CDs for \$12 each. Which equation best represents the cost c of a given number of CDs n?

Ⓐ $12 + c = n$

Ⓑ $n + 12 = c$

Ⓒ $12c = n$

Ⓓ $c = 12n$

Relate The total cost | is | \$12 | times | the number of CDs bought.

Define Let n = the number of CDs bought.

Let c = the total cost.

Write $c = 12 \cdot n$

The equation is $c = 12n$, so D is the correct answer.

CA Standards Check **3** **a.** Suppose the manager at Track One Media raises the price of each CD to \$15. Write an equation to find the cost of n CDs.

b. Critical Thinking Suppose the manager at Track One Media uses the equation $c = 10.99n$. What could this mean?

When you write an equation for data in a table, it may help to write a short sentence describing the relationship between the data. Then translate the sentence into an equation. Be sure to tell what each variable represents.

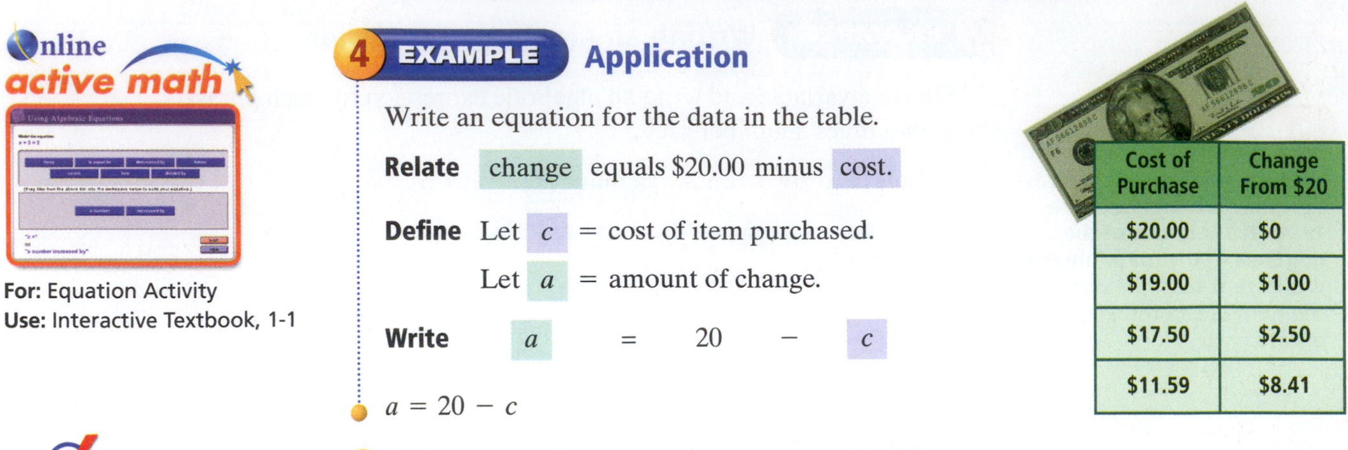

Online active math

For: Equation Activity
Use: Interactive Textbook, 1-1

4 EXAMPLE Application

Write an equation for the data in the table.

Cost of Purchase	Change From \$20
\$20.00	\$0
\$19.00	\$1.00
\$17.50	\$2.50
\$11.59	\$8.41

Relate change equals \$20.00 minus cost.

Define Let c = cost of item purchased.

Let a = amount of change.

Write $a \quad = \quad 20 \quad - \quad c$

$a = 20 - c$

CA Standards Check 4 Define the variables and write an equation for the data in the table.

Amounts Earned and Saved

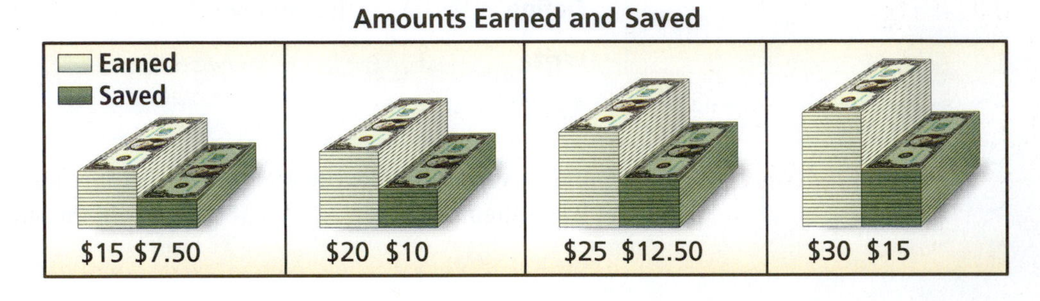

EXERCISES
Standards Practice

For more exercises, see *Extra Skills and Word Problem Practice.*

A Practice by Example

GO for Help Example 1 (page 4)

Write an algebraic expression for each phrase.

1. 4 more than p
2. y minus 12
3. 12 minus m
4. the product of 15 and c
5. the quotient of n and 8
6. the quotient of 17 and k
7. 23 less than x
8. the sum of v and 3

Example 2 (page 5)

Define a variable and write an expression for each phrase.

9. 2 more than twice a number
10. a number minus 11
11. 9 minus a number
12. a number divided by 82
13. the product of 5 and a number
14. the sum of 13 and twice a number
15. the quotient of a number and 6
16. the quotient of 11 and a number

Example 3 (page 5)

Define variables and write an equation to model each situation.

17. The total cost is the number of cans times \$.70.
18. The perimeter of a square equals 4 times the length of a side.
19. The total length of rope, in feet, used to put up tents is 60 times the number of tents.
20. How many slices are left from an 8-slice pizza after you have eaten some slices?

Example 4 (page 6)

Define variables and write an equation to model the relationship in each table.

21.

Number of Workers	Number of Radios Built
1	13
2	26
3	39
4	52

22.

Number of Tapes	Cost
1	\$8.50
2	\$17.00
3	\$25.50
4	\$34.00

23.

Number of Sales	Total Earnings
5	\$2.00
10	\$4.00
15	\$6.00
20	\$8.00

24.

Number of Hours	Total Pay
4	\$32
6	\$48
8	\$64
10	\$80

B Apply Your Skills

Write an expression for each phrase.

25. the sum of 9 and k minus 17

26. 6.7 more than 5 times n

27. 9.85 less than the product of 37 and t

28. the quotient of $3b$ and 4.5

29. 15 plus the quotient of 60 and w

30. 7 minus the product of v and 3

31. the product of 5 and m, minus the quotient of t and 7

32. the sum of the quotient of p and 14, and the quotient of q and 3

33. 8 minus the product of 9 and r

Visit: PHSchool.com
Web Code: bae-0101

Write a phrase for each expression.

34. $q + 5$ **35.** $3 - t$ **36.** $9n + 1$ **37.** $\frac{y}{5}$ **38.** $7hb$

Define variables and write an equation to model the relationship in each table.

39.

Number of Days	Change in Height (meters)
1	0.165
2	0.330
3	0.495
4	0.660

40.

Time (months)	Length (inches)
1	4.1
2	8.2
3	12.3
4	16.4

In the United States, homeowners spend an average of 40 hours per year mowing their lawns.

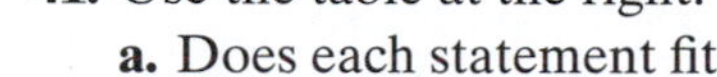

41. Use the table at the right.

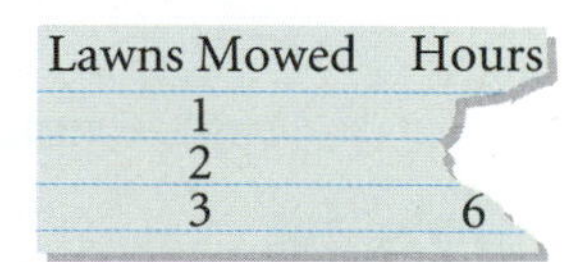

Lawns Mowed	Hours
1	
2	
3	6

a. Does each statement fit the data in the table?

i. hours worked = lawns mowed · 2

ii. hours worked = lawns mowed + 3

b. Writing Which statement in part (a) better describes the relationship between hours worked and lawns mowed? Explain.

42. Which equation best describes the relationship between the amount of money a in a bag of quarters and the number of quarters q?

Ⓐ $a = 0.25q$ Ⓑ $a = 0.25 + q$ Ⓒ $q = 0.25a$ Ⓓ $q = 0.25 + q$

The table at the left shows the height of the first bounce when a ball is dropped from different heights.

Drop Height (ft)	Height of First Bounce (ft)
1	$\frac{1}{2}$
2	1
3	$1\frac{1}{2}$
4	2
5	$2\frac{1}{2}$

43. a. Write an equation to describe the relationship between the height of the first bounce and the drop height.

b. Suppose you drop the ball from a window 20 ft above the ground. Predict how high the ball will bounce.

44. Suppose the second bounce is $\frac{1}{4}$ of the original drop height. Write an equation to relate the height of the second bounce to the drop height.

Describe a real-world situation that each equation could represent. Include a definition for each variable.

45. $d = 5t$ **46.** $a = b + 3$ **47.** $c = \frac{40}{h}$

Multiple Choice Practice

For California Standards Tutorials, visit PHSchool.com. Web Code: baq-9045

7AF 1.1 **48.** Which is an algebraic expression for "the product of 10 and a"?

(A) $a + 10$ (B) $a - 10$ (C) $10a$ (D) $\frac{a}{10}$

7AF 1.1 **49.** Which is an algebraic expression for "9 more than v"?

(A) $v + 9$ (B) $v - 9$ (C) $9 - v$ (D) $9v$

7AF 1.2 **50.** What is the value of $12 + 10 \div 2$?

(A) 20 (B) 17 (C) 11 (D) 6

7NS 1.2 **51.** What is the value of $0.25 \cdot 15$?

(A) 14.75 (B) 10.25 (C) 3.75 (D) 1.5

7AF 1.0 **52.** Sara planted rows of tulips in her garden, as shown in the table. Which equation best describes the relationship between the row number, r, and the number of tulips, t?

(A) $r = 3t$ (C) $\frac{r}{t} = 3$

(B) $t = r + 3$ (D) $t = 3r$

Row Number	Number of Tulips
1	3
2	6
3	9
4	12

Mixed Review

Skills Handbook

GO for Help

Simplify.

53. $\frac{3}{5} + \frac{2}{7}$ **54.** $3\frac{1}{2} + 1\frac{5}{9}$ **55.** $\frac{7}{8} - \frac{5}{12}$ **56.** $5\frac{1}{4} - 2\frac{5}{6}$

57. $\frac{7}{10} \cdot \frac{4}{9}$ **58.** $4\frac{2}{3} \cdot 3\frac{1}{2}$ **59.** $\frac{4}{9} \div \frac{1}{6}$ **60.** $6\frac{3}{4} \div \frac{5}{8}$

Write in expanded form using exponents.

61. 486 **62.** 2957 **63.** 36,021 **64.** 113,845

Exponents and Order of Operations

California Content Standards

25.2 Judge the validity of an argument according to whether the order of operations has been applied correctly at each step. ***Introduce***

What You'll Learn

- To simplify and evaluate expressions and formulas
- To simplify and evaluate expressions containing grouping symbols

. . . And Why

To find the total cost of sneakers including sales tax, as in Example 3

Check Skills You'll Need

GO for Help Skills Handbook page 595

Find the greatest common factor of each set of numbers.

1. 4 and 8 **2.** 12 and 15 **3.** 5 and 7

4. 8 and 12 **5.** 14 and 21 **6.** 12 and 20

Find the least common multiple of each set of numbers.

7. 4 and 8 **8.** 12 and 15 **9.** 5 and 7

10. 3 and 9 **11.** 6 and 9 **12.** 9 and 12

New Vocabulary • simplify • exponent • base • power • order of operations • evaluate

Using the Order of Operations With Exponents

CA Standards Investigation Order of Operations

Two formulas for the perimeter of a rectangle are $P = 2\ell + 2w$ and $P = 2(\ell + w)$.

1. The length ℓ of a rectangle is 8 in. and its width w is 3 in. Find the perimeter of the rectangle using each of the formulas.
2. When you used $P = 2\ell + 2w$, did you add first or multiply first?
3. When you used $P = 2(\ell + w)$, did you add first or multiply first?
4. Which formula do you prefer to use? Why?

Problem Solving Tip

Drawing a diagram may help you understand the problem.

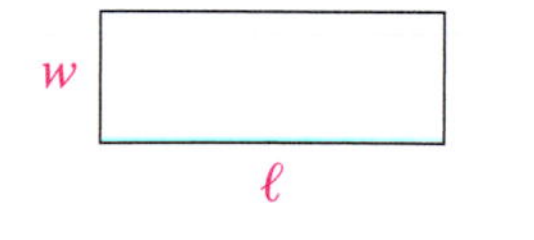

To **simplify** a numerical expression, you replace it with its simplest name. The simplest name for $2 \cdot 8 + 2 \cdot 3$ and for $2(8 + 3)$ is 22.

Expressions may include exponents. Using an exponent provides a shorthand way to show a product of equal factors.

exponent ↓ base → $2^4 = 2 \cdot 2 \cdot 2 \cdot 2$ ← power

An **exponent** tells how many times a number, the **base,** is used as a factor. A **power** has two parts, a base and an exponent.

You read the expression 2^4 as "two to the fourth power." To simplify 2^4, you replace it with its simplest name, 16. There are special names for 2^3, "two cubed," and 2^2, "two squared."

Look at the expression below. It is simplified in two ways.

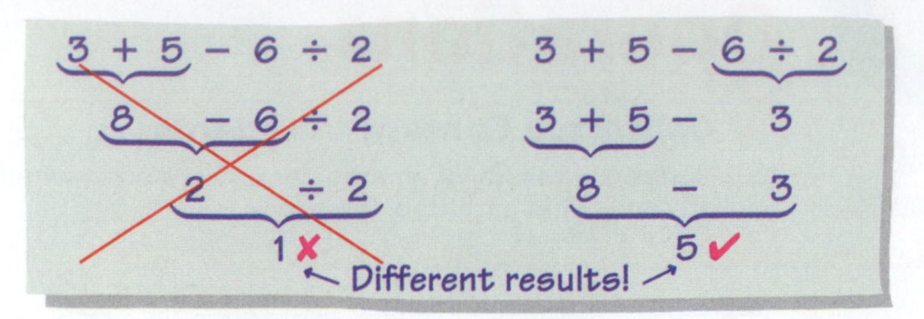

To avoid having two different results when simplifying the same expression, mathematicians have agreed on an order for doing operations.

Summary **Order of Operations**

1. Perform any operation(s) inside grouping symbols.
2. Simplify powers.
3. Multiply and divide in order from left to right.
4. Add and subtract in order from left to right.

GO Online

Video Tutor Help
Visit: PHSchool.com
Web Code: bae-0775

1 EXAMPLE Simplifying a Numerical Expression

Simplify $25 - 8 \cdot 2 + 3^2$.

$25 - 8 \cdot 2 + 3^2 = 25 - 8 \cdot 2 + 9$ **Simplify the power: $3^2 = 3 \cdot 3 = 9$.**

$= 25 - 16 + 9$ **Multiply 8 and 2.**

$= 9 + 9$ **Add and subtract in order from left to right.**

$= 18$ **Add.**

CA Standards Check 1 Simplify each expression.

a. $6 - 10 \div 5$ **b.** $3 \cdot 6 - 4^2 \div 2$ **c.** $4 \cdot 7 + 4 \div 2^2$

You **evaluate** an algebraic expression by substituting a given number for each variable. Then simplify the numerical expression using the order of operations.

2 EXAMPLE Evaluating an Algebraic Expression

Evaluate $3a - 2^3 \div b$ for $a = 7$ and $b = 4$.

$3a - 2^3 \div b = 3 \cdot 7 - 2^3 \div 4$ **Substitute 7 for *a* and 4 for *b*.**

$= 3 \cdot 7 - 8 \div 4$ **Simplify the power.**

$= 21 - 2$ **Multiply and divide from left to right.**

$= 19$ **Subtract.**

CA Standards Check 2 Evaluate each expression for $c = 2$ and $d = 5$.

a. $4c - 2d \div c$ **b.** $d + 6c \div 4$ **c.** $c^4 - d \cdot 2$

You can use expressions with variables to model many real-world situations.

3 EXAMPLE Application

The equation $c = p + 0.0725p$ represents the cost c of a pair of sneakers with price p and sales tax of 7.25%. Use a table to find the cost for \$20, \$32, \$48, and \$60 pairs of sneakers.

Price p	$p + 0.0725p$	Cost c
\$20	$20 + 0.0725(20)$	\$21.45
\$32	$32 + 0.0725(32)$	\$34.32
\$48	$48 + 0.0725(48)$	\$51.48
\$60	$60 + 0.0725(60)$	\$64.35

CA Standards Check 3 The equation $c = p + 0.05p$ represents the cost c of an item with a price p and a 5% sales tax. Make a table to find the cost of items with prices \$5, \$10, \$15, and \$20.

Using the Order of Operations With Grouping Symbols

When you simplify expressions with parentheses, work within the parentheses first. Inside parentheses, use the order of operations.

4 EXAMPLE Simplifying an Expression With Parentheses

Simplify $15(13 - 7) \div (8 - 5)$.

$15(13 - 7) \div (8 - 5) = 15(6) \div 3$ **Simplify within parentheses first.**

$= 90 \div 3$ **Multiply and divide from left to right.**

$= 30$ **Divide.**

CA Standards Check 4 Simplify each expression.

a. $(5 + 3) \div 2 + (5^2 - 3)$ **b.** $8 \div (9 - 7) + (13 \div 2)$

The base for an exponent is the number, variable, or expression directly to the left of the exponent. For $(cd)^2$, cd is the base. For cd^2, d is the base. Grouping symbols show which part of the expression is the base of the power.

5 EXAMPLE Evaluating Expressions With Exponents

Evaluate each expression for $c = 15$ and $d = 12$.

a. $(cd)^2$

$(cd)^2 = (15 \cdot 12)^2$ **← Substitute 15 for *c* and 12 for *d*. →**

$= (180)^2$ **← Simplify within parentheses.**

$= 32{,}400$ **← Simplify. →**

b. cd^2

$cd^2 = 15 \cdot 12^2$

$= 15 \cdot 144$

$= 2160$

CA Standards Check 5 Evaluate each expression for $r = 9$ and $t = 14$.

a. rt^2 **b.** r^2t **c.** $(rt)^2$

You can also use brackets [ ] as grouping symbols. When an expression has several grouping symbols, simplify the innermost expression first.

6 EXAMPLE Simplifying an Expression

Simplify $2[(13 - 7)^2 \div 3]$.

$2[(13 - 7)^2 \div 3] = 2[(6)^2 \div 3]$ First simplify (13 − 7).

$= 2[36 \div 3]$ Simplify the power.

$= 2[12]$ Divide within the brackets.

$= 24$ Multiply.

CA Standards Check 6 Simplify each expression.

a. $5[4 + 3(2^2 + 1)]$ **b.** $12 + 3[18 - 5(16 - 13)]$ **c.** $5 + [(2 + 1)^3 - 3]$

A fraction bar is also a grouping symbol. For an expression like $\frac{2+8}{5-3}$, do the calculations above and below the fraction bar before simplifying the fraction.

7 EXAMPLE Application

A neighborhood association turned a vacant lot into a park. The park is shaped like the trapezoid below. Use the formula $A = h\left(\frac{b_1 + b_2}{2}\right)$ to find the area of the lot.

$A = h\left(\frac{b_1 + b_2}{2}\right)$

$= 130\left(\frac{100 + 200}{2}\right)$ Substitute 130 for h, 100 for b_1, and 200 for b_2.

$= 130\left(\frac{300}{2}\right)$ Simplify the numerator.

$= 130(150)$ Simplify the fraction.

$= 19{,}500$ Multiply.

$b_1 = 100$ ft

$h = 130$ ft

$b_2 = 200$ ft

The area of the park is 19,500 ft^2.

CA Standards Check 7 Find the area of a trapezoid with height $h = 300$ ft and bases $b_1 = 250$ ft and $b_2 = 170$ ft.

EXERCISES

For more exercises, see *Extra Skills and Word Problem Practice.*

Standards Practice Alg1 25.2

A Practice by Example

Simplify each expression.

Example 1 (page 10)

GO for Help

1. $5 + 6 \cdot 9$ **2.** $40 - 2 \cdot 3^2$ **3.** $8 + 12 \div 6 - 3$

4. $8 \cdot 4 + 9^2$ **5.** $5 \cdot 3^2 - 13$ **6.** $21 + 49 \div 7 + 1$

Example 2 (page 10)

Evaluate each expression for $a = 5$, $b = 12$, and $c = 2$.

7. $a + b + 2c$ **8.** $2b \div c + 3a$ **9.** $b^2 - 4a$

10. $ca + a$ **11.** $abc + ab$ **12.** $5a + 12b$

Example 3 (page 11)

13. The equation $s = p - 0.15p$ represents the sale price s of an item with an original price p, after a 15% discount. Make a table to find the discount prices for items with original prices of \$12, \$16, \$20, and \$25.

14. The equation $a = \frac{1}{2}(8)h$ represents the area a of a triangle with base of 8 cm and a height of h cm. Make a table to find the areas of triangles with heights of 6 cm, 7 cm, 8 cm, and 9 cm.

Example 4 (page 11)

Simplify each expression.

15. $2(5 + 9) - 6$
16. $(17 - 7) \div 5 + 1$
17. $(2 + 9) \cdot (8 - 4)$
18. $(7^2 - 3^2) \div 8$
19. $17 - 5^2 \div (2^4 + 3^2)$
20. $(10^2 - 4 \cdot 8) \div (8 + 9)$

Example 5 (page 11)

Evaluate each expression for $s = 11$ and $v = 8$.

21. sv^2
22. $(sv)^2$
23. $s^2 + v^2$
24. $(s + v)^2$
25. $s^2 - v^2$
26. $(s - v)^2$
27. $2s^2v$
28. $(2s)^2v$

Example 6 (page 12)

Simplify each expression.

29. $6[13 - 2(4 + 1)]$
30. $[3(7 + 4) - 2]6$
31. $20 - [4(3 + 2)]$
32. $1^{11} + 3\left[\left(\frac{22}{11} + 8\right) \div 5\right]$
33. $27[5^2 \div (4^2 + 3^2) + 2]$
34. $9 + [4 - (10 - 9)^2]^3$

Example 7 (page 12)

Evaluate the formula $V = \frac{Bh}{3}$ for each pair of values.

35. $B = 4 \text{ cm}^2, h = 6 \text{ cm}$
36. $B = 21 \text{ in.}^2, h = 13 \text{ in.}$
37. $B = 7 \text{ ft}^2, h = 9 \text{ ft}$
38. $B = 8.4 \text{ cm}^2, h = 10 \text{ cm}$
39. $B = 500 \text{ ft}^2, h = 90 \text{ ft}$
40. $B = 118 \text{ m}^2, h = 66 \text{ m}$

B Apply Your Skills

Simplify each expression.

41. $(2 + 3)^2 - 10$
42. $2^3 + 3^2 - 10$
43. $(2^3 + 3)^2 - 10$
44. $(2^3 + 3^2) - 16$
45. $(5.2 - 1) \cdot 12$
46. $4^3 \div 8 - 1 + 5 \div 8$

47. A student wrote that $(a + b)^2 = a^2 + b^2$.
    a. Evaluate each side of the equation for $a = 0$ and $b = 1$.
    b. Evaluate each side of the equation for $a = 1$ and $b = 1$.
    c. Choose another pair of values for a and b. Evaluate each side of the equation for those values.
    d. **Writing** An equation is true if each side of the equation simplifies to the same value or expression. Is the equation $(a + b)^2 = a^2 + b^2$ sometimes, always, or never true? Explain.

48. The frame at the right is 2 in. wide. The outer height h is 17 in., and the outer width w is 14 in. Use the formula $A = (h - 4)(w - 4)$ to find the area of the picture.

    (A) 130 in.^{2} (C) 180 in.^{2}
    (B) 169 in.^{2} (D) 238 in.^{2}

2 in.
2 in.

Homework Video Tutor

Visit: PHSchool.com
Web Code: bae-0102

Evaluate each expression for $m = 3, p = 7$, and $q = 4$.

49. $mp - q$
50. $m(p - q)$
51. $mp^2 - q$
52. $m(p^2 - q)$
53. $(mp^2) - q$
54. $m(p - q)^2$
55. $m \div q + 2p$
56. $qp^2 + pq^2$

GO for Help

For a guide to solving Exercise 57, see p. 16.

57. Error Analysis Find the mistake in the student's work at the right. Then simplify the expression correctly.

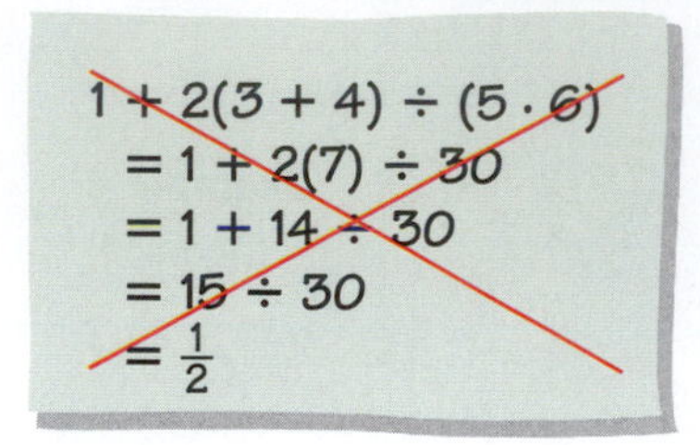

58. Writing Suppose you have a numerical expression. Is there only one number that is the simplest form of the expression? Explain.

59. a. The formula for the volume of a sphere with radius r is $V = \frac{4\pi r^3}{3}$. Find the volume of an orange with radius 5 cm to the nearest hundredth of a cubic centimeter.

b. Suppose the peel of the orange is 0.5 cm thick. What volume of the orange is edible? Round your answer to the nearest hundredth of a cubic centimeter.

Complete each table.

60.

h	$(5h^2 - 4)$
3	■
7	■
8	■
10	■

61.

a	$\frac{(5 \cdot 2 - a + 4)}{10}$
2	■
5	■
9	■
12	■

62. a. The formula for the volume of a cylinder is $V = \pi r^2 h$. What is the volume of the cylinder at the right? Round your answer to the nearest hundredth of a cubic inch.

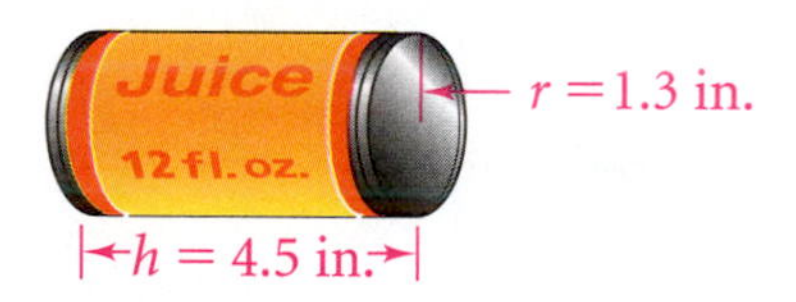

b. Critical Thinking About how many cubic inches does an ounce of juice fill? Round your answer to the nearest tenth of a cubic inch.

c. The formula for the surface area of a cylinder is $SA = 2\pi r(r + h)$. What is the surface area of the cylinder? Round your answer to the nearest hundredth of a square inch.

C Challenge

Use grouping symbols to make each equation true.

63. $10 + 6 \div 2 - 3 = 5$
64. $14 - 2 + 5 - 3 = 4$
65. $3^2 + 9 \div 9 = 2$
66. $6 - 4 \div 2 = 1$

67. a. Simplify $12 + (3 + 7)$ and $(12 + 3) + 7$.

b. Does it seem that the placement of the parentheses affects the value of an expression when only addition is involved? Explain.

68. a. Simplify $(12 - 3) + 7$ and $12 - (3 + 7)$.

b. Does it seem that the placement of the parentheses affects the value of the expression when both addition and subtraction are involved? Explain.

69. Use the numbers 1, 2, 4, and 5 in any order to write expressions equal to each integer from 1 to 20. (Examples: $(2 \cdot 4) + 1^5 = 9$; $4(5 - 2) + 1 = 13$)

70. a. A trapezoid has height $h = 8$ ft, and bases $b_1 = 4$ ft and $b_2 = 5.5$ ft. Use the formula $A = h\left(\frac{b_1 + b_2}{2}\right)$ to find the area of the trapezoid.

b. **Critical Thinking** Does the area of the trapezoid double if the height doubles? If one base doubles? If both bases double? Explain your answers.

Multiple Choice Practice

For California Standards Tutorials, visit PHSchool.com. Web Code: baq-9045

Alg1 25.2

71. Nancy is simplifying the expression below.

$$12 + 3 - (5 - 2)^2 \times 4$$

Which operation should she perform first?

(A) addition (B) division (C) subtraction (D) multiplication

Alg1 25.2

72. The table at the right shows Taylor's work for simplifying $4^3 - 15 \div 7 + 2$. In which step did Taylor first make a mistake?

Step 1	$64 - 15 \div 7 + 2$
Step 2	$49 \div 7 + 2$
Step 3	$7 + 2$
Step 4	9

(A) Step 1
(B) Step 2
(C) Step 3
(D) Taylor did not make a mistake.

Alg1 25.3

73. Which values for x and y could Amanda use to show that $(x + y)^2 = x^2 + y^2$ is NOT always true?

(A) $x = 0, y = 0$
(B) $x = 1, y = 0$
(C) $x = 0, y = 1$
(D) $x = 1, y = 1$

7AF 1.1

74. Juan saw a total of 8 movies during June and July. If m represents the number of movies he saw in June, which expression best represents the number of movies he saw in July?

(A) $8m$ (B) $8 + m$ (C) $8 - m$ (D) $8 \div m$

Mixed Review

GO for Help

Lesson 1-1

Write an expression for each phrase.

75. 2 more than c
76. the product of 36 and m
77. the difference of t and 21
78. the quotient of y and 5

Skills Handbook

Write each decimal as a percent.

79. 0.5 80. 0.34 81. 0.95 82. 1.45 83. 0.06

Skills Handbook

Add or subtract. Write each answer in simplest form.

84. $\frac{3}{10} + \frac{1}{5}$
85. $\frac{3}{8} - \frac{1}{4}$
86. $\frac{5}{12} + \frac{2}{3}$
87. $\frac{3}{4} - \frac{1}{3}$
88. $\frac{5}{8} + \frac{5}{12}$
89. $\frac{7}{8} - \frac{2}{3}$

GPS Guided Problem Solving

For Use With Lesson 1-2

25.2 Judge the validity of an argument according to whether the order of operations has been applied correctly at each step. ***Develop***

Analyzing Errors **Read through the problem below. Then follow along with what Gina thinks as she solves the problem. Check your understanding with the exercise at the bottom of the page.**

Error Analysis Find the mistake in the student's work at the right. Then simplify the expression correctly.

$1 + 2(3 + 4) \div (5 \cdot 6)$
$= 1 + 2(7) \div 30$
$= 1 + 14 \div 30$
$= 15 \div 30$
$= \frac{1}{2}$

What Gina Thinks	What Gina Writes
I am going to simplify the expression and see where my work differs from the student's work. First, I will simplify the expressions inside the parentheses.	$1 + 2(3 + 4) \div (5 \cdot 6) = 1 + 2(7) \div 30$
There are no powers to simplify, so I will next multiply and divide in order from left to right. I'll multiply 2 by 7. So far, our work agrees.	$= 1 + 14 \div 30$
I'll divide 14 by 30 by writing the quotient as a fraction. I'll simplify the fraction and then add it to 1. My solution is different from the student's!	$= 1 + \frac{7}{15}$ $= 1\frac{7}{15}$
The student added 1 to 14 before dividing by 30. That's the mistake, because you should divide before you add.	
I will write my answer in a sentence.	The student performed addition before division instead of division before addition.

EXERCISE

Find and correct the mistake in the work at the right.

$5 \cdot [4^2 - (6 - 2) \cdot 3]$
$= 5 \cdot [4^2 - 4 \cdot 3]$
$= 5 \cdot [16 - 4 \cdot 3]$
$= 5 \cdot [16 - 12]$
$= 80 - 12$
$= 68$

1-3 Exploring Real Numbers

California Content Standards

1.0 Identify and use the arithmetic properties of real numbers. ***Introduce***

1.1 Use properties of numbers to demonstrate whether assertions are true or false. ***Introduce***

2.0 Understand and use such operations as taking the opposite. ***Introduce***

24.3 Use counterexamples to show that an assertion is false and recognize that a single counterexample is sufficient to refute an assertion. ***Introduce***

25.1 Use properties of numbers to formulate counterexamples to claimed assertions. ***Introduce***

What You'll Learn

- To classify numbers
- To compare numbers

. . . And Why

To determine which sets of numbers are appropriate for real-world situations, as in Example 2

Check Skills You'll Need

GO for Help Skills Handbook page 602

Write each decimal as a fraction and each fraction as a decimal.

1. 0.5 **2.** 0.05 **3.** 3.25 **4.** 0.325

5. $\frac{2}{5}$ **6.** $\frac{3}{8}$ **7.** $\frac{2}{3}$ **8.** $3\frac{5}{9}$

New Vocabulary

- natural numbers
- whole numbers
- integers
- rational number
- irrational number
- real numbers
- counterexample
- inequality
- opposites
- absolute value

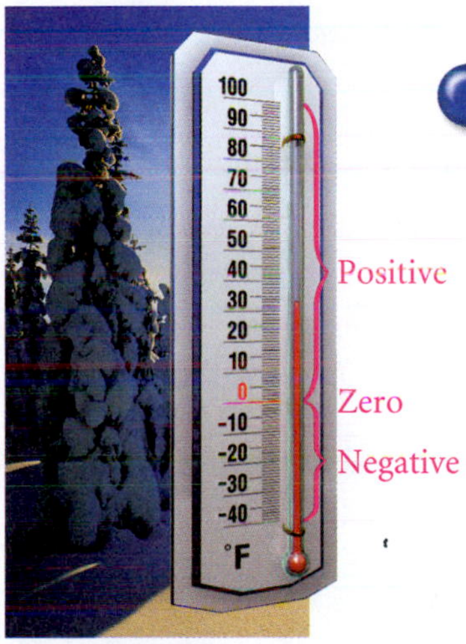

The thermometer shows positive numbers, zero, and negative numbers.

Classifying Numbers

Each of the graphs below shows a set of numbers on a number line.

Natural numbers $1, 2, 3, \ldots$

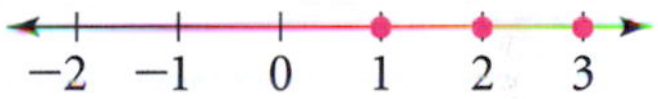

Whole numbers $0, 1, 2, 3, \ldots$

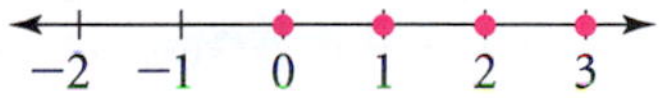

Integers $\ldots -2, -1, 0, 1, 2, \ldots$

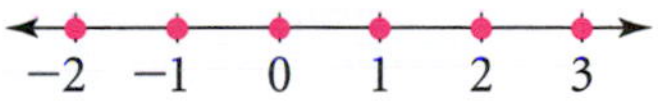

A **rational number** is any number that you can write in the form $\frac{a}{b}$, where a and b are integers and $b \neq 0$. A rational number in decimal form is either terminating, such as 6.27, or repeating, such as 8.222 . . . , which you can write as $8.\overline{2}$.

All integers are rational numbers because you can write any integer n as $\frac{n}{1}$.

1 EXAMPLE Classifying Numbers

Name the set(s) of numbers to which each number belongs.

a. $-\frac{17}{31}$ rational numbers

b. 23 natural numbers, whole numbers, integers, rational numbers $\left(\frac{23}{1}\right)$

c. 0 whole numbers, integers, rational numbers $\left(\frac{0}{1}\right)$

d. 4.581 rational numbers $\left(\frac{4581}{1000}\right)$

CA Standards Check 1 Name the set(s) of numbers to which each number belongs.

a. -12 **b.** $\frac{5}{12}$ **c.** -4.67 **d.** 6

You may need to determine the set of numbers that is reasonable for a given situation. For example, suppose 110 students are going on a field trip. Each bus can hold 40 students. To find the number of buses needed, divide 110 by 40. The answer is a rational number, 2.75. However, it is not the number of buses you would need. You would need a whole number of buses, or 3 buses.

2 EXAMPLE **Application**

Which set of numbers is most reasonable for each situation?

a. the number of students who will go on the class trip — whole numbers

b. the height of the door frame in your classroom — rational numbers

CA Standards Check **2** Which set of numbers is most reasonable for the cost of a scooter?

An **irrational number** cannot be expressed in the form $\frac{a}{b}$, where a and b are integers. Here are three irrational numbers.

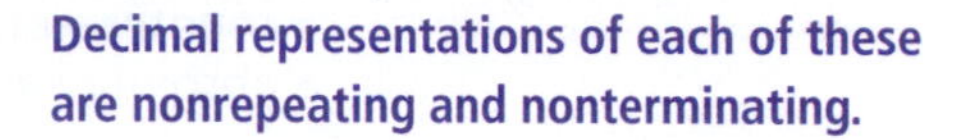

Decimal representations of each of these are nonrepeating and nonterminating.

Together, rational numbers and irrational numbers form the set of **real numbers.**

The Venn diagram below shows the relationships of the sets of numbers that make up the real numbers.

Take Note

Summary **Real Numbers**

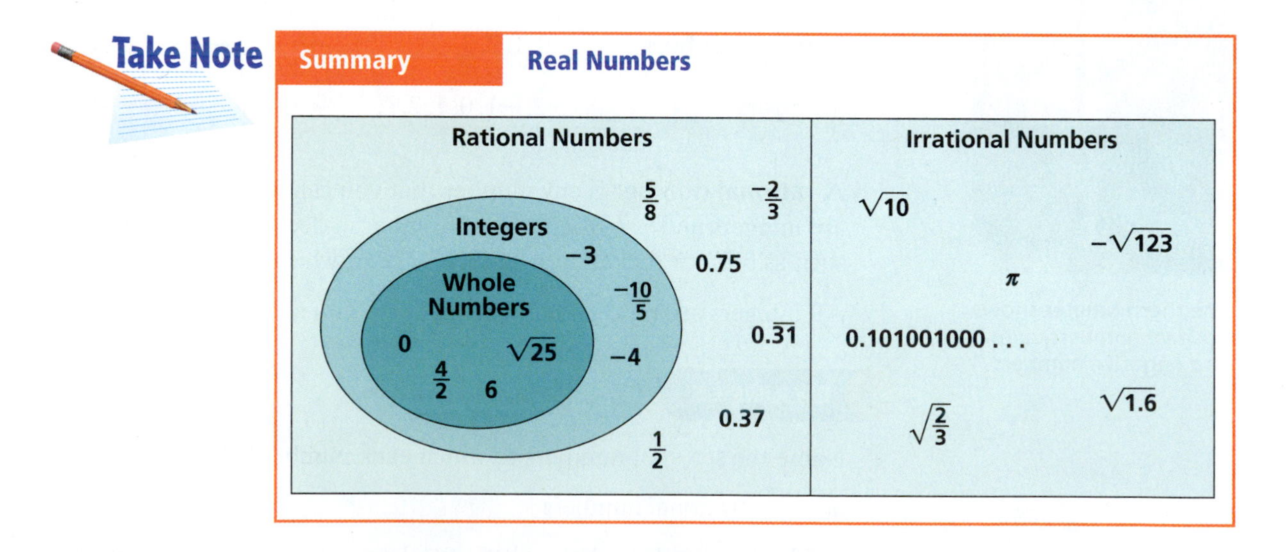

Suppose a friend says that all integers are whole numbers. You respond that −3 is an integer but not a whole number. You are using a counterexample to prove that a statement is false.

Any example that proves a statement false is a **counterexample.** You need only one counterexample to prove that a statement is false, while a proof to show that a statement is true may be more complicated.

3 EXAMPLE Using Counterexamples

Is each statement *true* or *false*? If it is false, give a counterexample.

a. All whole numbers are rational numbers.
Every whole number can be written in the form $\frac{n}{1}$, so all whole numbers are rational numbers. The statement is true.

b. The square of a number is always greater than the number.
The square of 0.5 is 0.25, and 0.25 is *not* greater than 0.5. The statement is false.

CA Standards Check 3 **Critical Thinking** Is each statement true or false? If it is false, give a counterexample.

a. All whole numbers are integers. **b.** No fractions are whole numbers.

Comparing Numbers

Vocabulary Tip

You can read an inequality from left to right or right to left. $3 < 5$ means "3 is less than 5" and "5 is greater than 3." So $3 < 5$ and $5 > 3$ have the same mathematical meaning.

An **inequality** is a mathematical sentence that compares the values of two expressions using an inequality symbol, such as $<$ or $>$.

When you compare two real numbers, only one of these can be true:

$a < b$	or	$a = b$	or	$a > b$
is less than		is equal to		is greater than

There are three other symbols that compare two values.

$a \le b$	or	$a \ne b$	or	$a \ge b$
is less than or equal to		is not equal to		is greater than or equal to

The number line below shows how values of numbers increase as you go to the right on a number line.

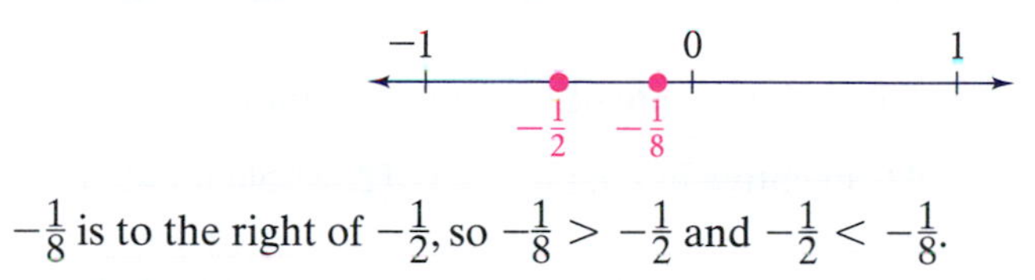

$-\frac{1}{8}$ is to the right of $-\frac{1}{2}$, so $-\frac{1}{8} > -\frac{1}{2}$ and $-\frac{1}{2} < -\frac{1}{8}$.

To compare fractions, you may find it helpful to write the fractions as decimals and then compare the decimals.

4 EXAMPLE Ordering Fractions

Write $-\frac{3}{8}$, $-\frac{1}{2}$, and $-\frac{5}{12}$ in order from least to greatest.

$-\frac{3}{8} = -0.375$ Write each fraction as a decimal.

$-\frac{1}{2} = -0.5$

$-\frac{5}{12} = -0.4166\ldots = -0.41\overline{6}$

$-0.5 < -0.41\overline{6} < -0.375$ Order the decimals from least to greatest.

From least to greatest, the fractions are $-\frac{1}{2}$, $-\frac{5}{12}$, and $-\frac{3}{8}$.

Online active math

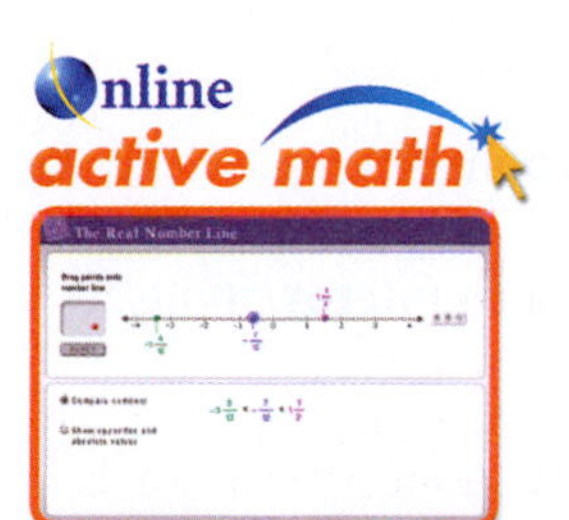

For: Number Line Activity
Use: Interactive Textbook, 1-3

CA Standards Check 4 Write $\frac{1}{12}$, $-\frac{2}{3}$, and $-\frac{5}{8}$ in order from least to greatest.

The two teams pull in opposite directions. Depending on direction, a pull on the rope results in a positive or a negative direction for your team.

Two numbers that are the same distance from zero on a number line but lie in opposite directions are **opposites.**

−3 and 3 are the same distance from 0. So −3 and 3 are opposites.

The **absolute value** of a number is its distance from 0 on a number line. Both −3 and 3 are 3 units from zero. Both have an absolute value of 3. You write "the absolute value of −3" as $|-3|$.

5 EXAMPLE Finding Absolute Value

Find each absolute value.

a. $|12|$ 12 is 12 units from 0 on a number line. $|12| = 12$

b. $\left|-\frac{2}{3}\right|$ $-\frac{2}{3}$ is $\frac{2}{3}$ units from 0 on a number line. $\left|-\frac{2}{3}\right| = \frac{2}{3}$

c. $|0|$ 0 is at 0 on a number line. $|0| = 0$

CA Standards Check 5 Find each absolute value.

a. $|5|$ **b.** $|-4|$ **c.** $|-3.7|$ **d.** $\left|\frac{5}{7}\right|$

EXERCISES

Standards Practice

For more exercises, see *Extra Skills and Word Problem Practice.*

Alg1 1.0, 1.1, 2.0, 24.3, 25.1

A Practice by Example

GO for Help

Example 1 (page 17)

Name the set(s) of numbers to which each number belongs.

1. -1 **2.** $\frac{1}{3}$ **3.** -4.8 **4.** 7 **5.** $-\frac{32}{95}$

6. $-\frac{20}{4}$ **7.** 0 **8.** -7.34 **9.** $\frac{7}{1239}$ **10.** $\sqrt{5}$

Give an example of each kind of number.

11. negative integer **12.** whole number **13.** positive real number

Example 2 (page 18)

Are *whole numbers, integers,* or *rational numbers* the most reasonable for each situation?

14. your shoe size **15.** the number of siblings you have

16. a temperature in a news report

17. the number of quarts of paint you need to buy to paint a room

18. the number of quarts of paint you use when you paint a room

Example 3 (page 19)

Is each statement *true* or *false*? If the statement is false, give a counterexample.

19. All integers are rational numbers.

20. All negative numbers are integers.

21. Every multiple of 3 is odd.

22. No positive number is less than its absolute value.

23. No negative number is less than its absolute value.

Example 4
(page 19)

Use <, =, or > to compare.

24. $\frac{2}{3}$ ■ $\frac{1}{6}$ **25.** $-\frac{2}{3}$ ■ $-\frac{1}{6}$ **26.** $\frac{15}{8}$ ■ $1\frac{6}{8}$ **27.** $\frac{3}{5}$ ■ 0.6

Order the numbers in each group from least to greatest.

28. 2.01, 2.1, 2.001 **29.** $-9\frac{2}{3}, -9\frac{7}{12}, -9\frac{3}{4}$ **30.** $-\frac{5}{6}, -\frac{1}{2}, \frac{2}{3}$

31. −1.01, −1.001, −1.0009 **32.** $\frac{7}{11}$, 0.63, 0.636 **33.** $\frac{22}{25}, \frac{8}{9}$, 0.8888

Example 5
(page 20)

Find each absolute value.

34. $|4|$ **35.** $|-9|$ **36.** $\left|\frac{-9}{14}\right|$ **37.** $|-0.5|$

38. $\left|\frac{3}{5}\right|$ **39.** $|0|$ **40.** $|-1295|$ **41.** $\left|-\frac{4}{5}\right|$

B Apply Your Skills

Write each number in the form $\frac{a}{b}$ using integers to show that it is a rational number.

42. 0.2 **43.** 5 **44.** 21.3 **45.** 1.034 **46.** −4

Name the set(s) of numbers to which each number belongs.

47. $\left|\frac{93}{3}\right|$ **48.** $|-782|$ **49.** $|-1.93|$ **50.** $\left|\frac{37}{59}\right|$

Use <, =, or > to compare.

51. $|19|$ ■ $|-19|$ **52.** $|-18|$ ■ $|-17|$ **53.** $\left|\frac{1}{2}\right|$ ■ $|-0.51|$

54. $|-3.121|$ ■ $|3.12|$ **55.** $\left|\frac{-8}{10}\right|$ ■ $\left|\frac{-16}{20}\right|$ **56.** $\left|\frac{1}{3}\right|$ ■ $|-0.333|$

Simplify each expression. (*Hint:* Absolute value symbols are grouping symbols.)

57. $4 + |3 - 1|$ **58.** $-|41 - 38| + 6$ **59.** $|a - a| + a$

60. $-(|24| - |-4|)$ **61.** $|12| \cdot (-|-4|)$ **62.** $-|-6 + 4| + |3|$

63. a. In the cartoon below, what type of number is pi (π)?
b. Will the football ever be hiked? Explain.

FoxTrot by Bill Amend

64. If the distance between each tick mark is one unit and R and T are opposites, what is the value of Q?

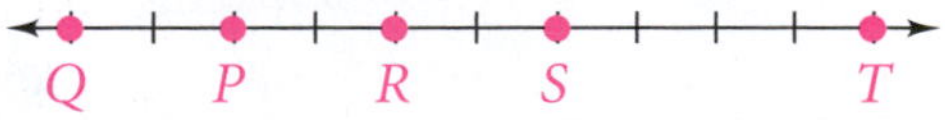

Ⓐ 7 Ⓑ 0 Ⓒ −3 Ⓓ −7

65. Writing Are natural numbers, whole numbers, and integers also rational numbers? Explain.

Homework Video Tutor
Visit: PHSchool.com
Web Code: bae-0103

Problem Solving Tip

Test each statement using a variety of numbers.

Math Reasoning **Determine whether each statement is *sometimes*, *always*, or *never* true. If the statement is not always true, give a counterexample.**

66. The difference of two rational numbers is an integer.

67. The product of two numbers is greater than either number.

68. The opposite of a number is less than the number.

69. The quotient of two nonzero integers is a rational number.

Evaluate each expression for $c = 5$, $d = 1$, and $e = 6$.

70. $-|c + d|$ **71.** $2e + \left|\frac{c}{d}\right|$ **72.** $\frac{|e - d|}{c}$ **73.** $|d + 2| + |-7|$

C Challenge

74. a. Use the formula $d = \frac{m}{v}$ to find the density d of each substance in the table below.

Densities of Some Substances

	Mass (m)	Volume (v)	Density (d)
Aluminum	38.5 g	14 cm^3	■
Gold	38.6 g	2 cm^3	■
Silver	42 g	4 cm^3	■
Diamond	1.75 g	0.5 cm^3	■

b. List the substances from least to greatest density.

75. a. Find a number between -2 and -3 on a number line.

b. Find a number between -2.8 and -2.9.

c. Find a number between $-2\frac{1}{16}$ and $-2\frac{3}{8}$.

d. Critical Thinking On a number line, is it possible to find a number between any two different given numbers? Explain.

Multiple Choice Practice

For California Standards Tutorials, visit PHSchool.com. Web Code: baq-9045

Alg1 25.2

76. Angela simplified the expression below for homework.

$$12 \div 6 - 8 \times 2 + 3$$

When she checked her answer the next day in class, Angela discovered that she had miscopied the problem. She would have had to subtract first to get the correct answer. Which is most likely the expression Angela should have copied for homework?

Ⓐ $12 - 6 \div 8 \times 2 + 3$
Ⓑ $12 \div (6 - 8) \times 2 + 3$
Ⓒ $12 - (6 \div 8 \times 2 + 3)$
Ⓓ $(12 \div 6) - (8 \times 2 + 3)$

Alg1 1.0

77. In which set of numbers does 0 NOT belong?

Ⓐ integers
Ⓑ whole numbers
Ⓒ natural numbers
Ⓓ rational numbers

Alg1 2.0

78. Which number has the same value as $-\left|-\frac{3}{4}\right|$?

Ⓐ -0.75 Ⓑ -0.34 Ⓒ 0.34 Ⓓ 0.75

Alg1 25.3

79. Suppose a is a nonzero integer. Which statement is never true?

Ⓐ $a > -a$ Ⓑ $a < -a$ Ⓒ $|a| = -a$ Ⓓ $|a| = -|a|$

Alg1 1.0

80. Which set of numbers does NOT contain 1000?

Ⓐ whole numbers
Ⓑ irrational numbers
Ⓒ integers
Ⓓ real numbers

Alg1 24.3, 25.1

81. Suppose your brother says that fractions are rational numbers, but fractions are not integers. Which number is a counterexample for this statement?

Ⓐ $\frac{10}{3}$ Ⓑ $\frac{5}{3}$ Ⓒ $-\frac{5}{3}$ Ⓓ $-\frac{9}{3}$

Mixed Review

Lesson 1-2

GO for Help

Simplify each expression.

82. $3 + 5 \cdot 6$ **83.** $(3 + 5)6$ **84.** $3 + 52 \cdot 6$

85. $(33 + 9) \div 6$ **86.** $\frac{12 - 4 \cdot 3}{7 + 13 \cdot 15}$ **87.** $8 - 3 \div 6$

Lesson 1-1

Define variables and write an equation to model the relationship in each table.

88.

Number of Hours	Distance Traveled
1	7 mi
2	14 mi
3	21 mi
4	28 mi

89.

Number of Books	Total Cost
1	$3.50
2	$7.00
3	$10.50
4	$14.00

Checkpoint Quiz 1 — Lessons 1-1 through 1-3

Write a variable expression for each phrase.

1. the sum of b and 4

2. the quotient of c and 2

3. the product of a and 4.3

4. b plus c plus twice a

Evaluate each expression for $a = 3$ and $b = 7$.

5. $(b - a)b$

6. $a^2 + b^2$

7. $ba^2 - a$

8. $(2a)^2b$

9. Is it true that a number is always greater than its opposite? Explain.

10. What set of numbers is reasonable to use for the number of loaves of bread a bakery bakes in one day?

1-4 Adding Real Numbers

California Content Standards

1.0 Identify and use the arithmetic properties of real numbers. ***Develop***
2.0 Understand and use such operations as taking the opposite. ***Develop***

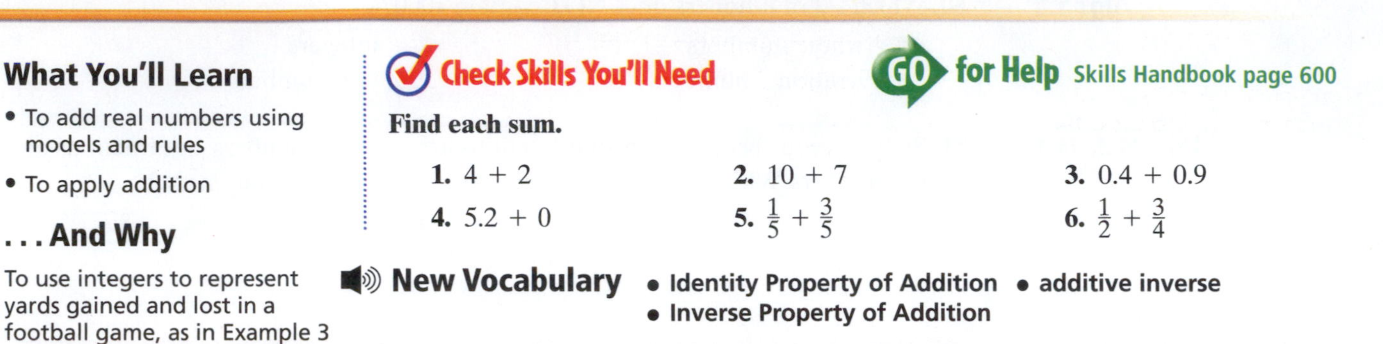

What You'll Learn

- To add real numbers using models and rules
- To apply addition

. . . And Why

To use integers to represent yards gained and lost in a football game, as in Example 3

Check Skills You'll Need

GO for Help Skills Handbook page 600

Find each sum.

1. $4 + 2$ **2.** $10 + 7$ **3.** $0.4 + 0.9$
4. $5.2 + 0$ **5.** $\frac{1}{5} + \frac{3}{5}$ **6.** $\frac{1}{2} + \frac{3}{4}$

New Vocabulary

- Identity Property of Addition
- Inverse Property of Addition
- additive inverse

Adding Real Numbers

In this chapter, you will learn about the properties of real numbers. The examples here use rational numbers—integers and fractions. However, the properties also apply to irrational numbers such as $\sqrt{2}$, which you will study later in the book.

Take Note

Property **Identity Property of Addition**

For every real number n, $n + 0 = n$ and $0 + n = n$.

Examples $-5 + 0 = -5$ $0 + 5 = 5$

The opposite of a number is its **additive inverse.** The number line shows the sum of $4 + (-4)$.

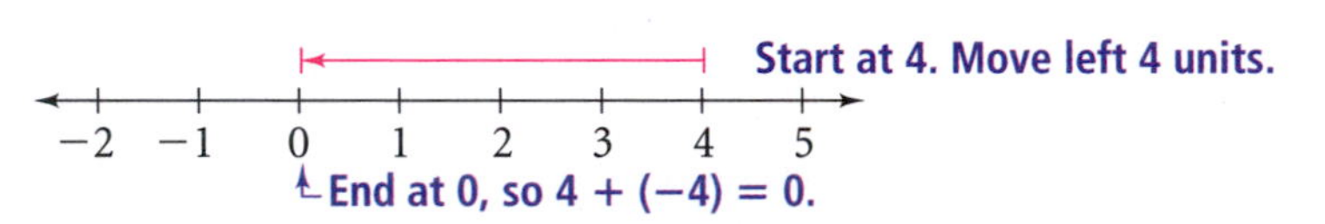

The additive inverse of a negative number is a positive number. The number line below shows the sum of $-5 + 5$.

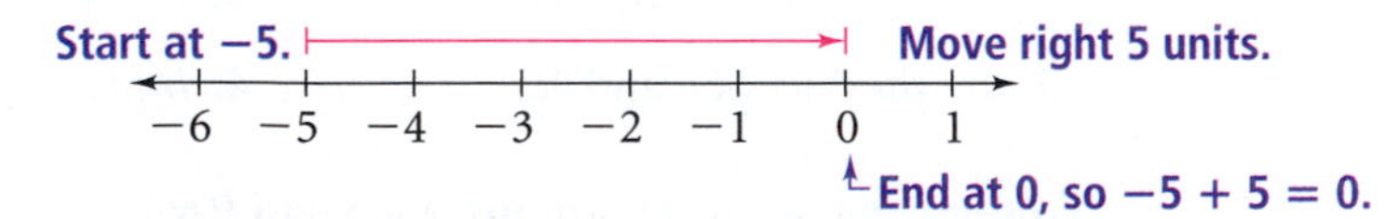

Take Note

Property **Inverse Property of Addition**

For every real number n, there is an additive inverse $-n$ such that $n + (-n) = 0$.

Examples $17 + (-17) = 0$ $-17 + 17 = 0$

You can use number lines as models to add integers.

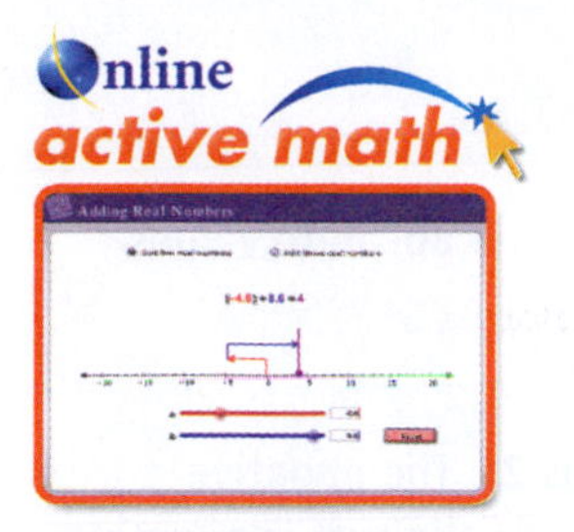

For: Addition Activity
Use: Interactive Textbook, 1-4

1 EXAMPLE Using a Number Line Model

Simplify each expression.

a. $2 + 6$

Start at 2. Move right 6 units.

0 2 4 6 8 10

$2 + 6 = 8$

b. $2 + (-6)$

Start at 2. Move left 6 units.

−8 −6 −4 −2 0 2

$2 + (-6) = -4$

c. $-2 + 6$

Start at −2. Move right 6 units.

−4 −2 0 2 4 6

$-2 + 6 = 4$

d. $-2 + (-6)$

Start at −2. Move left 6 units.

−10 −8 −6 −4 −2 0

$-2 + (-6) = -8$

CA Standards Check 1 Use a number line to find each sum.

a. $-6 + 4$ **b.** $4 + (-6)$

c. $-3 + (-8)$ **d.** $9 + (-3)$

You can also find the sums in Example 1 using rules. Recall that numbers being added are called addends.

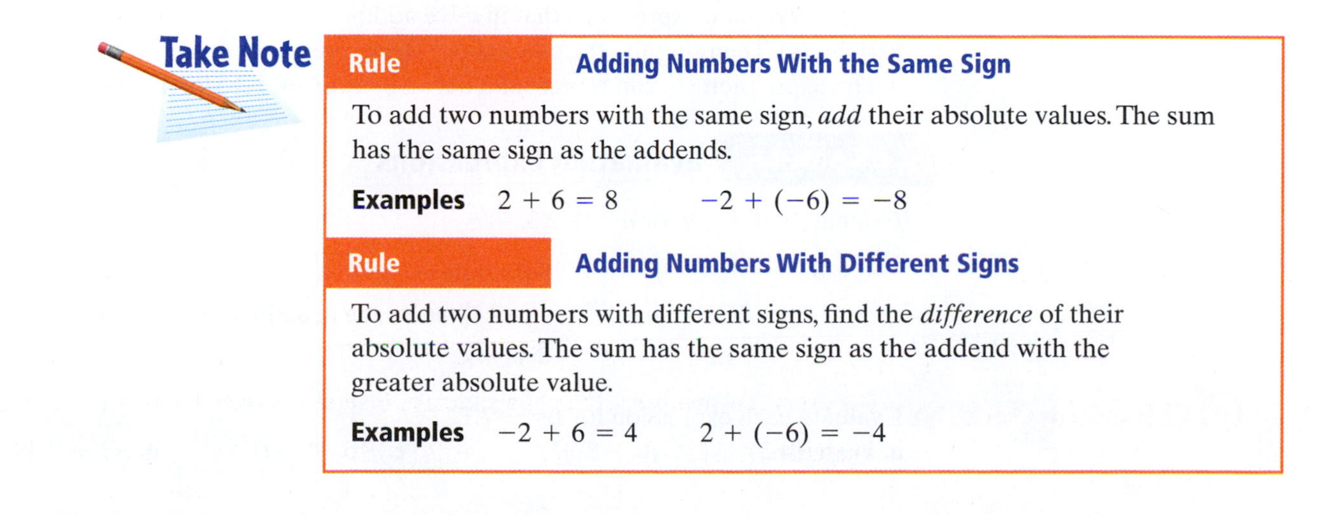

Take Note

Rule **Adding Numbers With the Same Sign**

To add two numbers with the same sign, *add* their absolute values. The sum has the same sign as the addends.

Examples $2 + 6 = 8$ $-2 + (-6) = -8$

Rule **Adding Numbers With Different Signs**

To add two numbers with different signs, find the *difference* of their absolute values. The sum has the same sign as the addend with the greater absolute value.

Examples $-2 + 6 = 4$ $2 + (-6) = -4$

2 EXAMPLE Adding Numbers

Simplify each expression.

a. $-5 + (-6)$

$-5 + (-6) = -11$ — **Since both addends are negative, add their absolute values. The sum is negative.**

b. $13 + (-34)$

$13 + (-34) = -21$ — **The difference of the absolute values is 21. The negative addend has the greater absolute value, so the sum is negative.**

c. $3.4 + 9.7$

$3.4 + 9.7 = 13.1$ — **Since both addends are positive, add their absolute values. The sum is positive.**

d. $-1.5 + 3.4$

$-1.5 + 3.4 = 1.9$ — **The difference of the absolute values is 1.9. The positive addend has the greater absolute value, so the sum is positive.**

CA Standards Check 2 Find each sum.

a. $-7 + (-4)$ **b.** $-26.3 + 8.9$ **c.** $-\frac{3}{4} + \left(-\frac{1}{2}\right)$ **d.** $\frac{8}{9} + \left(-\frac{5}{6}\right)$

You can use negative numbers to model real-world situations.

3 EXAMPLE Application

A football team gains 2 yd and then loses 7 yd in two plays. You express a loss of 7 yd as -7. Use addition to find the result of the two plays.

$2 + (-7) = -5$

The result of the two plays is a loss of 5 yd.

CA Standards Check 3 The temperature falls 15 degrees and then rises 18 degrees. Use addition to find the change in temperature.

Applying Addition

You can evaluate expressions that involve addition. Substitute a value for the variable(s). Then simplify the expression. The expression $-n$ means the opposite of n. The expression $-n$ can represent a negative number, zero, or a positive number.

4 EXAMPLE Evaluating Expressions

Evaluate $-n + 8.9$ for $n = -2.3$.

$-n + 8.9 = -(-2.3) + 8.9$	**Substitute −2.3 for *n*.**
$= 2.3 + 8.9$	**−(−2.3) means the opposite of −2.3, which is 2.3.**
$= 11.2$	**Simplify.**

CA Standards Check 4 Evaluate each expression for $t = -7.1$.

a. $t + (-4.3)$ **b.** $-2 + t$ **c.** $8.5 + (-t)$ **d.** $-t + 7.49$

The elevations of the Sequoia and Kings Canyon National Parks range from 1300 ft to over 14,000 ft.

You can write and evaluate expressions to model real-world situations.

5 EXAMPLE Application

A rock climber climbs a mountain that has a base 132 ft below sea level.

a. Write an expression to represent the climber's height below or above sea level.

Relate 132 ft below sea level plus number of feet climbed

Define Let h = number of feet climbed.

Write $-132 \quad + \quad h$

$-132 + h$

b. Find the climber's height above sea level at 485 ft above the base of the mountain.

$-132 + h = -132 + 485$ **Substitute 485 for *h*.**

$= 353$ **Simplify.**

The climber's height is 353 ft above sea level.

CA Standards Check **5** The temperature one winter morning is −14°F. Define a variable and write an expression to find the temperature after it changes. Then evaluate your expression for a decrease of 11 degrees Fahrenheit.

EXERCISES

Standards Practice

For more exercises, see *Extra Skills and Word Problem Practice*.

Alg1 1.0, 2.0, 25.1

A Practice by Example

Example 1 (page 25)

GO for Help

Write the expression modeled by each number line. Then find the sum.

1. 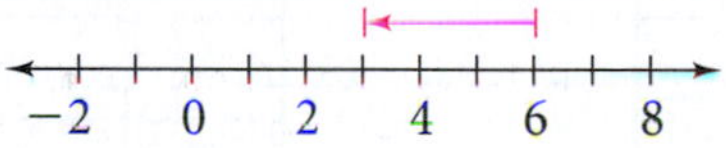

2. 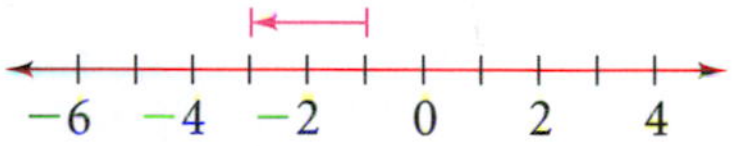

3. 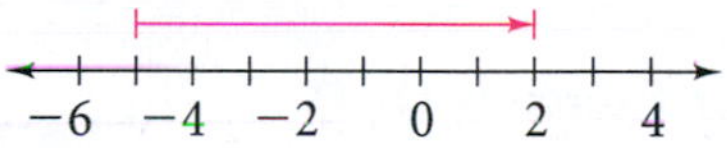

4. 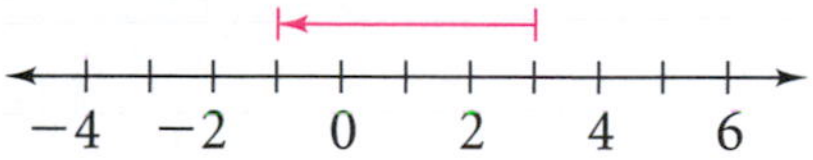

Example 2 (page 26)

Simplify.

5. $3 + 12$

6. $-7 + (-4)$

7. $-8.7 + (-10.3)$

8. $5.04 + 7.1$

9. $5 + (-9)$

10. $-8 + 13$

11. $-27 + 19$

12. $45 + (-87)$

13. $-2.3 + 4.5$

14. $-8.05 + 7.4$

15. $9.51 + (-17)$

16. $3.42 + (-2.09)$

17. $\frac{4}{5} + \frac{2}{15}$

18. $-\frac{5}{9} + \left(-\frac{1}{3}\right)$

19. $2\frac{1}{4} + 3\frac{15}{16}$

20. $-4\frac{3}{8} + \left(-1\frac{3}{4}\right)$

21. $-\frac{2}{3} + \frac{4}{6}$

22. $\frac{1}{9} + \left(-\frac{5}{6}\right)$

23. $-5\frac{7}{12} + 10\frac{3}{4}$

24. $\frac{9}{7} + \left(-2\frac{3}{14}\right)$

Example 3 (page 26)

25. A diver dives 47 ft below the surface of the water and then rises 12 ft. Use addition to find the diver's depth.

26. On two football plays, a team gains 8 yd, and then loses 5 yd. Use addition to find the result of the two plays.

27. One morning in Detroit, Michigan, the temperature at 6 A.M. was -6°F. The temperature rose 13 degrees Fahrenheit by noon. Use addition to find the temperature at noon.

Example 4 (page 26)

Evaluate each expression for $n = 3.5$.

28. $5.2 + n$ **29.** $-5.2 + n$ **30.** $-n + 5.2$ **31.** $-n + (-5.2)$

32. $9.1 + n$ **33.** $-9.1 + n$ **34.** $-n + 9.1$ **35.** $-9.1 + (-n)$

Example 5 (page 27)

36. The temperature one winter morning is -8°F. Define a variable and write an expression to find the temperature after each change below. Then evaluate your expression for each change.

a. a rise of 7°F **b.** a decrease of 3°F

c. a rise of 19°F **d.** a decrease of 12°F

37. You have $74 in a checking account. Define a variable and write an expression to find the balance in your account after each deposit or withdrawal below. Then evaluate your expression for each change.

a. a deposit of $18 **b.** a withdrawal of $29

c. a withdrawal of $47 **d.** a deposit of $120

B Apply Your Skills

Copy and complete each table.

38.

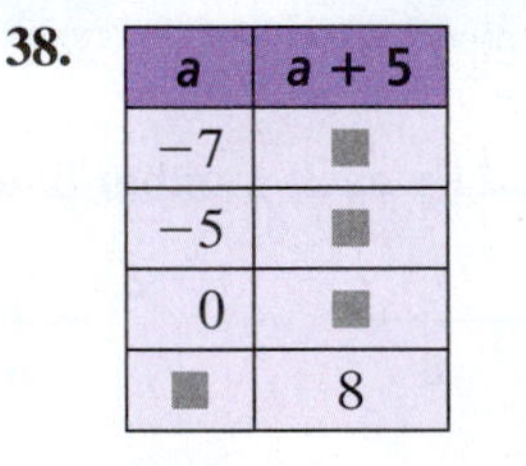

a	$a + 5$
-7	■
-5	■
0	■
■	8

39.

x	$-3 + x$
-2	■
0	■
$1\frac{1}{2}$	■
■	6

40.

n	$n + (-7)$
-4	■
-1	■
3	■
■	-1

Use the table for Exercises 41–43.

Number of People Who Participate in Art Activities (millions)

Ages	Drawing	Pottery	Weaving	Photography	Creative Writing
18–24	9.2	5.0	5.2	6.6	7.6
25–34	7.2	6.8	10.0	7.2	5.2
35–44	6.8	8.2	13.1	8.2	5.4
45–54	4.4	6.1	9.8	6.1	3.4
55–64	1.9	2.1	6.1	2.1	1.0

SOURCE: *Statistical Abstract of the United States*

41. How many people aged 18 to 34 participate in photography?

42. How many people aged 45 to 64 draw?

43. Which of the activities is most popular? Explain how you found your answer.

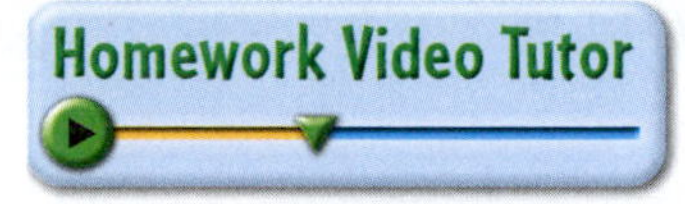

Visit: PHSchool.com
Web Code: bae-0104

44. a. Write a fraction to compare the number of people aged 25 to 34 who weave to the number of people aged 18 to 64 who weave.
b. Write your answer from part (a) as a decimal to the nearest hundredth.
c. What percent of the people who weave are aged 25 to 34?

Evaluate each expression for $a = -2$, $b = 3$, and $c = -4$.

45. $-a + 2 + c$ **46.** $-|a|$ **47.** $a + b$ **48.** $a + (-b)$

49. $a + 3b$ **50.** $c + 3b$ **51.** $c + a + 5$ **52.** $-(c + a + 5)$

53. Writing Without calculating, which is greater, the sum of -227 and 319 or the sum of 227 and -319? Explain.

54. Reasoning Explain what is wrong with the reasoning in the statement: *Since 20 is the opposite of −20, then 20°F must be very hot, because −20°F is very cold.*

Evaluate each expression for $b = -3.5$.

55. $b + 3.2$ **56.** $-9 + b + (-1.2)$

57. $b + |-2.9|$ **58.** $8.5 + b + 3.7$

59. $|b| + (-3.4)$ **60.** $-5.6 + b + 7.2$

61. A charged atom of magnesium has 12 protons and 10 electrons. Each proton has a charge of $+1$, and each electron has a charge of -1. What is the total charge of the atom?
Ⓐ -2 Ⓑ -1 Ⓒ $+1$ Ⓓ $+2$

Copy and complete each table.

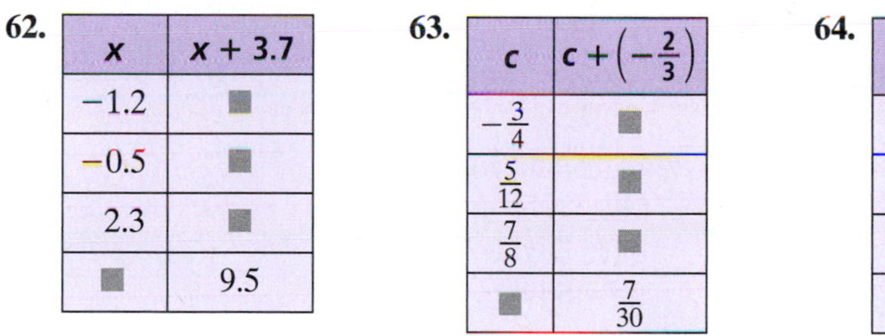

62.

x	$x + 3.7$
-1.2	■
-0.5	■
2.3	■
■	9.5

63.

c	$c + \left(-\frac{2}{3}\right)$
$-\frac{3}{4}$	■
$\frac{5}{12}$	■
$\frac{7}{8}$	■
■	$\frac{7}{30}$

64.

m	$-1\frac{1}{2} + m$
$-2\frac{5}{6}$	■
$1\frac{2}{5}$	■
$2\frac{5}{9}$	■
■	$1\frac{13}{14}$

65. Suppose you overdrew your bank account. You have a balance of $-\$34$. You then deposit checks for \$17 and \$49. At the same time the bank charges you a \$25 fee for overdrawing your account. What is your balance?

66. a. What is the value of $-n$ when $n = -4$?
b. What is the value of $-n$ when $n = 4$?
c. Reasoning For what values of n will $-n$ be positive? Negative?

Simplify each expression.

67. $\frac{w}{5} + \left(-\frac{w}{10}\right)$ **68.** $-\frac{c}{4} + \left(-\frac{c}{4}\right)$

69. $3\left(\frac{a}{7}\right) + 7\left(\frac{a}{3}\right)$ **70.** $-1\left(\frac{b}{9}\right) + \left(-\frac{b}{9}\right)$

71. $\frac{-x}{4} + \frac{x}{3}$ **72.** $\frac{x}{4} + \left(-\frac{x}{3}\right)$

Math Reasoning **Tell whether each sum is *positive*, *negative*, or *zero*. Explain.**

73. n is positive and m is negative. $n + (-m)$ is __?__.

74. n is positive, and m is negative. $-n + m$ is __?__.

75. $|n| = |m|$, n is positive, and m is negative. $n + (-m)$ is __?__.

76. $|n| = |m|$, n is positive, and m is negative. $-n + (-m)$ is __?__.

Multiple Choice Practice

For California Standards Tutorials, visit PHSchool.com. Web Code: baq-9045

Alg1 1.0

77. Simplify $10 + |-3| + (-3)$.

(A) 16
(B) 10
(C) 7
(D) 4

Alg1 2.0

78. Which of the following expressions does NOT have the same value as $-[-(-27)]$?

(A) $-29 + 2$
(B) $-12.8 + (-14.2)$
(C) $-42 + 17$
(D) $8 + (-35)$

Alg1 1.0

79. Which equation illustrates the Identity Property of Addition?

(A) $12 + (-12) = 0$
(B) $2 + 0 = 0 + 2$
(C) $1 \cdot 0 = 0$
(D) $0 + 256 = 256$

Alg1 1.0

80. Which equation illustrates the Inverse Property of Addition?

(A) $-1 = -1 + 0$
(B) $-1 \cdot (-1) = 1$
(C) $1 + (-1) = 0$
(D) $1 + (-1) = -1 + 1$

Alg1 25.2

81. Which is the first step in simplifying the expression $6 + 3 \cdot 8^2 - (4 - 20 \div 5)$?

(A) Add 3 to 6.
(B) Subtract 20 from 4.
(C) Divide 20 by 5.
(D) Square 8.

Mixed Review

GO for Help

Lesson 1-3

Use <, =, or > to compare.

82. $-1.23 \blacksquare -1.18$

83. $1\frac{2}{4} \blacksquare 1\frac{5}{10}$

84. $|-5| \blacksquare |-6|$

85. $|-4.1| \blacksquare |-3.9|$

86. $\left|-\frac{3}{10}\right| \blacksquare \left|\frac{2}{9}\right|$

87. $|1.2| \blacksquare \left|-\frac{6}{5}\right|$

Lesson 1-2

Simplify each expression.

88. $(5 - 2)^2$

89. $-4 + 3.1(2)$

90. $9[5 + (-3)]$

91. $4^2 + 3^2 - 2^2$

Vocabulary Builder

Learning Vocabulary

As you study mathematics this year, make your own mathematics dictionary of new vocabulary terms. Use the following guide for each new term.

- Write the vocabulary term, its part of speech, and its pronunciation.
- Write the definition. Include any symbols for the term. If possible, draw a diagram.
- Give one or more examples of the term.
- Give one or more "nonexamples" of the term.
- Include details using other related terms you know.

EXAMPLE

Write an entry for your dictionary for the term *additive inverse*.

additive inverse (noun) AD uh tiv in VURS

Definition: The opposite of a number; the sum of additive inverses is 0

Example: −1 and 1 $\quad -\frac{1}{2}$ and $\frac{1}{2}$

Nonexamples: 3 and $\frac{1}{3}$ $\quad$ 4 and 0.4

Write the term, part of speech, and pronunciation.

Write the definition.

Give examples.

Give nonexamples.

EXERCISES

Write an entry for your dictionary for each term.

1. variable
2. algebraic expression
3. equation
4. simplify
5. order of operations
6. evaluate
7. integers
8. counterexample
9. absolute value

10. Error Analysis A student wrote a dictionary entry for *whole numbers.* Which parts are incorrect? Explain.

Whole numbers (noun) hohl NUM burz

Definition: The positive integers

Examples: 1, 5, 16, 21, 38

Nonexamples: 0, −7, $\frac{3}{4}$, 2.5, $\sqrt{10}$

1-5 Subtracting Real Numbers

California Content Standards

1.0 Identify and use the arithmetic properties of real numbers. ***Develop***
2.0 Understand and use such operations as taking the opposite. ***Develop***

What You'll Learn

- To subtract real numbers
- To apply subtraction

. . . And Why

To find stock prices, as in Example 5

Check Skills You'll Need

GO for Help Lessons 1-3 and 1-4

Find the opposite of each number.

1. 6 **2.** −7 **3.** 3.79 **4.** $-\frac{7}{19}$

Simplify.

5. $3 + (-2)$ **6.** $9.5 + (-3.5)$ **7.** $13 + (-8)$ **8.** $\frac{2}{3} + \left(-\frac{1}{6}\right)$

Subtracting Real Numbers

You have learned to add real numbers and to find the opposite of a number. You can use these two concepts to understand how to subtract real numbers.

1 EXAMPLE Using a Number Line Model

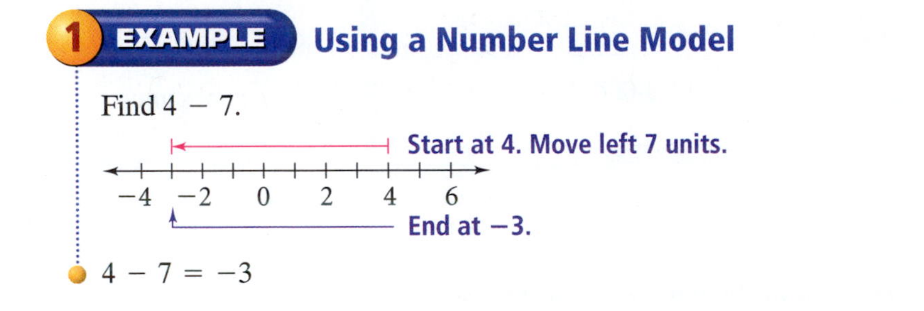

Find $4 - 7$.

$4 - 7 = -3$

CA Standards Check **1** Use a number line to find each difference.

a. $2 - 6$ **b.** $-1 - 4$ **c.** $-3 - 8$ **d.** $7 - 2$

The number line below models the sum $2 + (-6)$ *and* the difference $2 - 6$.

Start at 2. Move left 6 units.

−4 −2 0 2

Both $2 + (-6)$ and $2 - 6$ have the same value, -4. This illustrates the following rule for subtracting real numbers.

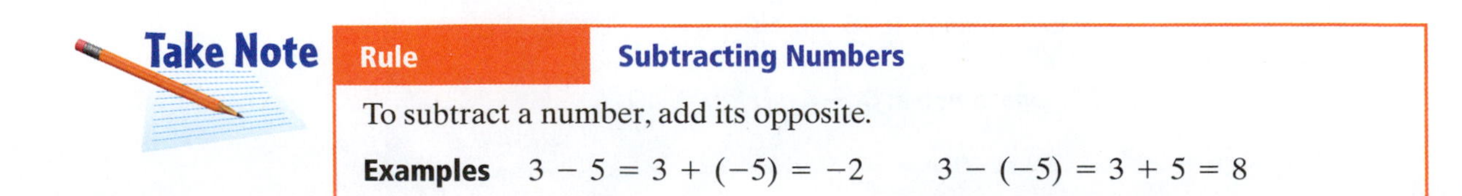

Take Note

Rule **Subtracting Numbers**

To subtract a number, add its opposite.

Examples $3 - 5 = 3 + (-5) = -2$ $3 - (-5) = 3 + 5 = 8$

2 EXAMPLE Subtracting Real Numbers

GO Online
Video Tutor Help
Visit: PHSchool.com
Web Code: bae-0775

Simplify each expression.

a. $-4 - (-9)$

$-4 - (-9) = -4 + 9$ The opposite of -9 is 9.

$= 5$ Add.

b. $\frac{3}{4} - \left(-\frac{11}{12}\right)$

$\frac{3}{4} - \left(-\frac{11}{12}\right) = \frac{3}{4} + \frac{11}{12}$ The opposite of $-\frac{11}{12}$ is $\frac{11}{12}$.

$= \frac{9}{12} + \frac{11}{12}$ Use common denominators.

$= \frac{20}{12}$ Add.

$= \frac{5}{3}$ or $1\frac{2}{3}$ Write $\frac{20}{12}$ in simplest form.

CA Standards Check 2 Find each difference.

a. $-6 - 2$ **b.** $8 - (-4)$ **c.** $3.7 - (-4.3)$ **d.** $-\frac{8}{9} - \left(-\frac{5}{6}\right)$

Applying Subtraction

Recall that when you simplify an expression, you work within grouping symbols first. Absolute value symbols are grouping symbols, so find the value of an expression within the absolute value symbols before finding the absolute value.

3 EXAMPLE Absolute Values

Simplify $|5 - 11|$.

$|5 - 11| = |-6|$ Subtract within absolute value symbols.

$= 6$ Find the absolute value.

CA Standards Check 3 Simplify each expression.

a. $|8 - 7|$ **b.** $|7 - 8|$ **c.** $|-10 - (-4)|$ **d.** $|-4 - (-10)|$

You evaluate expressions that involve subtraction by substituting for the variable. Then simplify the expression.

4 EXAMPLE Evaluating Expressions

Evaluate $-a - b$ for $a = -3$ and $b = -5$.

$-a - b = -(-3) - (-5)$ Substitute -3 for *a* and -5 for *b*.

$= 3 - (-5)$ The opposite of -3 is 3.

$= 3 + 5$ To subtract -5, add its opposite, 5.

$= 8$ Add.

CA Standards Check 4 Evaluate each expression for $t = -2$ and $r = -7$.

a. $r - t$ **b.** $t - r$ **c.** $-t - r$ **d.** $-r - (-t)$

You can write expressions to model real-world situations.

5 EXAMPLE Application

Find the closing price of stock XYZ on Wednesday by subtracting the change in price from the closing price on Thursday.

Stock (TICKER)	Thurs Close	Change	% Change	Volume (100)
ABC	32.79	+0.32	+0.98	95173
PQR	14.23	−1.23	−8.64	63183
XYZ	17.37	−0.87	−5.01	62272

$17.37 - (-0.87) = 17.37 + 0.87$ **Add the opposite.**

$= 18.24$ **Simplify.**

The closing share price on Wednesday was $18.24.

CA Standards Check 5 Find the closing price of stocks ABC and PQR on Wednesday.

EXERCISES Standards Practice

For more exercises, see *Extra Skills and Word Problem Practice.*

Alg1 1.0, 2.0, 24.3, 25.3

A Practice by Example

GO for Help

Example 1 (page 32)

Draw a number line or tiles to model each difference. Then find each difference.

1. $1 - 2$ **2.** $7 - 9$ **3.** $-4 - 2$ **4.** $-2 - 3$

5. $-5 - (-6)$ **6.** $-3 - 8$ **7.** $5 - (-9)$ **8.** $-1 - (-4)$

Example 2 (page 33)

Simplify each expression.

9. $3 - 7$ **10.** $2 - (-9)$ **11.** $-4 - 6$

12. $-5 - (-1)$ **13.** $6.2 - 8.3$ **14.** $-7.4 - 1.8$

15. $5.3 - (-8.4)$ **16.** $-3.6 - (-7.1)$ **17.** $\frac{1}{3} - \frac{1}{2}$

18. $-\frac{2}{5} - \frac{7}{10}$ **19.** $\frac{2}{12} - \left(-\frac{3}{4}\right)$ **20.** $-\frac{5}{12} - \left(-\frac{1}{10}\right)$

Example 3 (page 33)

21. $|5 - 2|$ **22.** $|-7 - 1|$ **23.** $|4 - 10|$

24. $|-3 - (-5)|$ **25.** $|-6 - 7|$ **26.** $|8 - 6|$

27. $|3 - 9|$ **28.** $|-11 - (-8)|$ **29.** $|9 - (-12)|$

Example 4 (page 33)

Evaluate each expression for $x = 3$, $y = -4$, and $z = 6$.

30. $y - z$ **31.** $x - y$ **32.** $-y - x$ **33.** $-x - y$

34. $z - x$ **35.** $2x - z$ **36.** $x + y - z$ **37.** $-z + y - x$

Example 5 (page 34)

38. On Friday, the closing price of a KJL company share was $51.72. It had risen $1.08 from the previous day. Find the closing price of KJL on Thursday.

Evaluate each expression for $a = -2, b = 3.5$, and $c = -4$.

39. $a - b + c$
40. $-c - b + a$
41. $-|a|$
42. $|a| + |b|$
43. $|a + b|$
44. $-|3 + a|$
45. $4b - a$
46. $-4b - |a|$
47. $|c + a - 5|$
48. $|c + a + 5|$
49. $|a - c| - |c|$
50. $|a| + |3b|$

51. Archaeologists found a 1500-year-old ship at the bottom of the Black Sea. The ship is well preserved because oxygen could not make the ship decay. The ship is at a depth of 1000 ft below the surface. This is about 350 ft below the boundary between surface water, which has oxygen, and water below, which does not have oxygen. About how deep is the boundary?

 A 650 ft C 1150 ft
 B 750 ft D 1350 ft

Visit: PHSchool.com
Web Code: bae-0105

Math Reasoning **Decide if each statement is always true. If the statement is not always true, give a counterexample.**

52. The difference of two numbers is less than the sum of those two numbers.
53. The difference of two numbers is less than each of those two numbers.
54. A number minus its opposite is twice the number.
55. Use the data in the table below.

City-Wide Participation in Sports Activities (thousands)

	Sport	Elementary	High School	College
2000	Basketball	5.5	8.2	4.9
	Tennis	1.4	3.2	3.9
	Soccer	4.2	3.8	1.3
	Volleyball	1.6	5.2	5.1

	Sport	Elementary	High School	College
2005	Basketball	6.8	7.9	4.9
	Tennis	1.0	1.8	1.7
	Soccer	5.6	4.1	1.3
	Volleyball	1.8	4.9	2.9

Problem Solving Tip

Subtract corresponding elements in the two tables. For example, the change in participation for basketball in elementary schools was 6800 – 5500, or 1300.

 a. Find the change in participation for tennis at each school level.
 b. Find the change in participation for soccer at each school level.
 c. **Writing** Suppose you invest in sporting goods. In which sport would you invest? Explain.

56. **Critical Thinking** Use examples to illustrate your answers.
 a. Is $|a - b|$ always equal to $|b - a|$?
 b. Is $|a + b|$ always equal to $|a| + |b|$?

GO Online Lesson Quiz Visit: PHSchool.com, Web Code: baa-0105

Challenge

Simplify each expression.

57. $1 - \frac{1}{2} - \frac{1}{3} - \frac{1}{4} - \frac{1}{5} - \frac{1}{6}$

58. $1 - \left(\frac{1}{2} - \left(\frac{1}{3} - \left(\frac{1}{4} - \left(\frac{1}{5} - \frac{1}{6}\right)\right)\right)\right)$

59. $-8t - 5m + 3m - 7t - (-3t) + m$

60. Order the expressions $|x + y|$, $|x - y|$, $|x| - |y|$, and $x - y$ from least to greatest for $x = -8$ and $y = -10$.

Multiple Choice Practice

For California Standards Tutorials, visit PHSchool.com. Web Code: baq-9045

Alg1 1.0

61. While a scientist was collecting soil samples in Death Valley, CA, a helicopter flew overhead to take pictures. If the scientist was at an elevation of –282 feet, and the helicopter was flying at an elevation of 420 feet, which picture best describes the distance between the scientist and the helicopter?

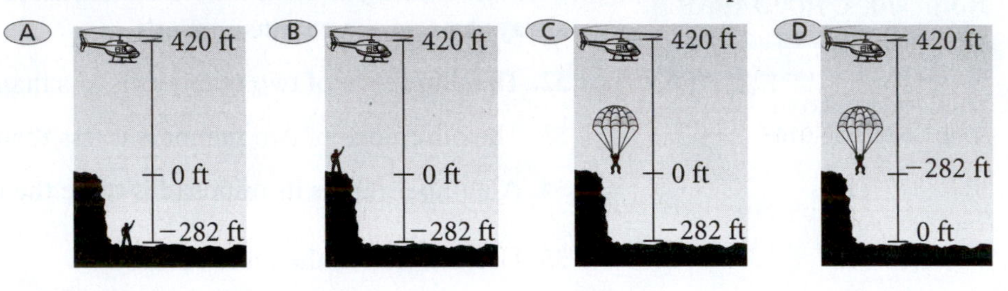

Alg1 2.0

62. What is the opposite of the value of $12 + (-7)$?

Ⓐ 5 Ⓑ –5 Ⓒ $\frac{1}{5}$ Ⓓ $-\frac{1}{5}$

Alg1 1.0

63. Which expression could be used to find the value of 5×13?

Ⓐ $5(10 + 3)$ Ⓑ $5(10) + 3$ Ⓒ $5(10 - 3)$ Ⓓ $5(10) - 5(3)$

Mixed Review

GO for Help

Lesson 1-4

Simplify each expression.

64. $6 + (-2)$ **65.** $-5 + (-4)$ **66.** $-3.4 + 2.7$ **67.** $5.9 + (-10)$

Lesson 1-3

Are *whole numbers, integers,* or *rational numbers* the most reasonable for each situation?

68. your height in feet

69. the number of pages in your math text

70. the low temperature in degrees Celsius for Barrow, Alaska, on January 15

Lesson 1-1

Define variables and write an equation to model each situation.

71. The total cost equals the number of pounds of pears times $1.19/lb.

72. You have $20. Then you buy a bouquet. How much do you have left?

73. You go out to lunch with five friends and split the check equally. What is your share of the check?

Multiplying and Dividing Real Numbers

California Content Standards

1.0 Identify and use the arithmetic properties of real numbers. ***Develop***

1.1 Use properties of numbers to demonstrate whether assertions are true or false. ***Develop***

2.0 Understand and use such operations as taking the opposite and finding the reciprocal. ***Develop***

What You'll Learn

- To multiply real numbers
- To divide real numbers

. . . And Why

To find the change in temperature with an increase in altitude, as in Example 3

Check Skills You'll Need

GO for Help Lessons 1-4 and 1-5

Simplify each expression.

1. $-2 + (-2) + (-2) + (-2)$
2. $-5 + (-5) + (-5) + (-5) + (-5)$
3. $-6 - 6 - 6 - 6$
4. $-12 - 12 - 12 - 12 - 12 - 12$

New Vocabulary

- Identity Property of Multiplication
- Multiplication Property of Zero
- Multiplication Property of -1
- Inverse Property of Multiplication
- multiplicative inverse
- reciprocal

Multiplying Real Numbers

CA Standards Investigation Multiplying Integers

1. **Patterns** Use patterns to complete each statement.

a.
$2 \cdot 3 = \blacksquare$
$2 \cdot 2 = \blacksquare$
$2 \cdot 1 = \blacksquare$
$2 \cdot 0 = \blacksquare$
$2(-1) = \blacksquare$
$2(-2) = \blacksquare$
$2(-3) = \blacksquare$

b.
$3(-2) = \blacksquare$
$2(-2) = \blacksquare$
$1(-2) = \blacksquare$
$0(-2) = \blacksquare$
$-1(-2) = \blacksquare$
$-2(-2) = \blacksquare$
$-3(-2) = \blacksquare$

2. **Make a Conjecture** From the patterns you found in Question 1, what seems to be the sign of the product of a positive number and a negative number?

3. **Make a Conjecture** From the patterns you found in Question 1, what seems to be the sign of the product of two negative numbers?

The product of a number and 1 is the original number. It does not matter whether the original number is positive or negative. The product of 0 and a number is 0. The product of -1 and a number is the opposite of the original number.

Take Note

Property **Identity Property of Multiplication**

For every real number n, $1 \cdot n = n$ and $n \cdot 1 = n$.

Examples $1 \cdot (-5) = -5$ $\quad -5 \cdot 1 = -5$

Property **Multiplication Property of Zero**

For every real number n, $n \cdot 0 = 0$ and $0 \cdot n = 0$.

Examples $35 \cdot 0 = 0$ $\quad 0 \cdot 35 = 0$

Property **Multiplication Property of −1**

For every real number n, $-1 \cdot n = -n$ and $n \cdot -1 = -n$.

Examples $-1 \cdot 5 = -5$ $\quad 5 \cdot (-1) = -5$

From the examples for the properties above, you can see a pattern for multiplying positive and negative numbers.

Multiplying Numbers With the Same Sign

$1 \cdot 5 = 5$

positive · positive = positive

$-1 \cdot (-5) = 5$

negative · negative = positive

Multiplying Numbers With Different Signs

$1 \cdot (-5) = -5$

positive · negative = negative

$-1 \cdot 5 = -5$

negative · positive = negative

This pattern also holds true when multiplying by numbers other than 1 and −1.

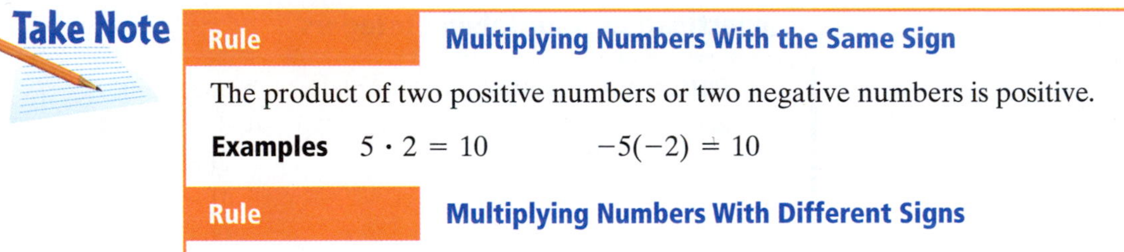

Take Note

Rule **Multiplying Numbers With the Same Sign**

The product of two positive numbers or two negative numbers is positive.

Examples $5 \cdot 2 = 10$ $\quad -5(-2) = 10$

Rule **Multiplying Numbers With Different Signs**

The product of a positive number and a negative number, or a negative number and a positive number, is negative.

Examples $3(-6) = -18$ $\quad -3 \cdot 6 = -18$

1 EXAMPLE Multiplying Numbers

Simplify each expression.

a. $-9(-4) = 36$ The product of two negative numbers is positive.

b. $5\left(-\frac{2}{3}\right) = -\frac{10}{3}$ The product of a positive number and a negative number is negative.

$= -3\frac{1}{3}$ Write $-\frac{10}{3}$ as a mixed number.

CA Standards Check 1 Simplify each expression.

a. $4(-6)$ **b.** $-10(-5)$ **c.** $-4.9(-8)$ **d.** $-\frac{2}{3}\left(\frac{3}{4}\right)$

When you simplify or evaluate expressions with three or more negative numbers, you must be careful to account for all of the negative signs as you multiply.

2 EXAMPLE Evaluating Expressions

Evaluate $-2xy$ for $x = -20$ and $y = -3$.

$-2xy = -2(-20)(-3)$ **Substitute −20 for *x* and −3 for *y*.**

$= -120$ **−2(−20) results in a positive number, 40. 40(−3) results in a negative number, −120.**

CA Standards Check 2 Evaluate each expression for $c = -8$ and $d = -7$.

a. $-(cd)$ **b.** $(-2)(-3)(cd)$ **c.** $c(-d)$

You can use expressions involving multiplication to model real-world situations.

3 EXAMPLE Application

You can use the expression $t = -5.5\left(\frac{a}{1000}\right)$ to calculate the change in temperature t in degrees Fahrenheit for an increase in altitude a, measured in feet. A hot-air balloon starts on the ground and then rises 8000 ft. What is the change in temperature at the altitude of the balloon?

Ⓐ 44°F Ⓑ 40°F Ⓒ −40°F Ⓓ −44°F

$-5.5\left(\frac{a}{1000}\right) = -5.5\left(\frac{8000}{1000}\right)$ **Substitute 8000 for *a*.**

$= -5.5(8)$ **Divide within parentheses.**

$= -44$ **Multiply.**

The change in temperature is −44 degrees Fahrenheit. The answer is D.

CA Standards Check 3 **a.** Find the change in temperature if a balloon rises 4500 ft from the ground.

b. Suppose the temperature is 40°F at ground level. What is the approximate air temperature at the altitude of the balloon?

The expression -3^4 means the opposite of 3^4. The exponent 4 applies to the base 3. The negative sign is not part of the base. In the expression $(-3)^4$, the negative sign is part of the base −3. The exponent 4 applies to the base −3.

4 EXAMPLE Simplifying Exponential Expressions

Vocabulary Tip

Remember that an exponent tells how many times a number is used as a factor.

Use the order of operations to simplify each expression.

a. -3^4

$-3^4 = -(3 \cdot 3 \cdot 3 \cdot 3)$ **Write as repeated multiplication.**

$= -81$ **Simplify.**

b. $(-3)^4$

$(-3)^4 = (-3)(-3)(-3)(-3)$ **Write as repeated multiplication.**

$= 81$ **Simplify.**

CA Standards Check 4 Simplify each expression.

a. -4^3 **b.** $(-2)^4$ **c.** $(-0.3)^2$ **d.** $-\left(\frac{3}{4}\right)^2$

Dividing Real Numbers

The rules for finding the sign when dividing real numbers are the same as the rules for finding the sign when multiplying real numbers.

Take Note

Rule **Dividing Numbers With the Same Sign**

The quotient of two positive numbers or two negative numbers is positive.

Examples $6 \div 3 = 2$ $\quad -6 \div (-3) = 2$

Rule **Dividing Numbers With Different Signs**

The quotient of a positive number and a negative number, or a negative number and a positive number, is negative.

Examples $-6 \div 3 = -2$ $\quad 6 \div (-3) = -2$

You can use the rules for dividing numbers to simplify expressions.

5 EXAMPLE Dividing Numbers

Simplify each expression.

a. $12 \div (-4) = -3$ — The quotient of a positive number and a negative number is negative.

b. $-12 \div (-4) = 3$ — The quotient of a negative number and a negative number is positive.

CA Standards Check 5 Simplify each expression.

a. $-42 \div 7$ **b.** $-8 \div (-2)$ **c.** $8 \div (-8)$ **d.** $-39 \div (-3)$

You can evaluate expressions that involve division.

6 EXAMPLE Evaluating Expressions

Vocabulary Tip

A fraction bar means divide: $\frac{15}{5} = 15 \div 5$.

Evaluate $\frac{-x}{-4} + 2y \div z$ for $x = -20$, $y = 6$, and $z = -1$.

$\frac{-x}{-4} + 2y \div z = \frac{-(-20)}{-4} + 2(6) \div (-1)$ — Substitute −20 for *x*, 6 for *y*, and −1 for *z*.

$= -5 + (-12)$ — Divide and multiply.

$= -17$ — Add.

CA Standards Check 6 Evaluate each expression for $x = 8$, $y = -5$, and $z = -3$.

a. $3x \div (2z) + y \div 10$ **b.** $\frac{2z + x}{2y}$ **c.** $3z^2 - 4y \div x$

A number and its multiplicative inverse have a special relationship.

Take Note

Property **Inverse Property of Multiplication**

For every nonzero real number a, there is a multiplicative inverse $\frac{1}{a}$ such that $a\left(\frac{1}{a}\right) = 1$.

Examples $5\left(\frac{1}{5}\right) = 1$ $\quad -5\left(-\frac{1}{5}\right) = 1$

The **multiplicative inverse,** or **reciprocal,** of a nonzero rational number $\frac{a}{b}$ is $\frac{b}{a}$. Zero does not have a reciprocal. Division by zero is undefined.

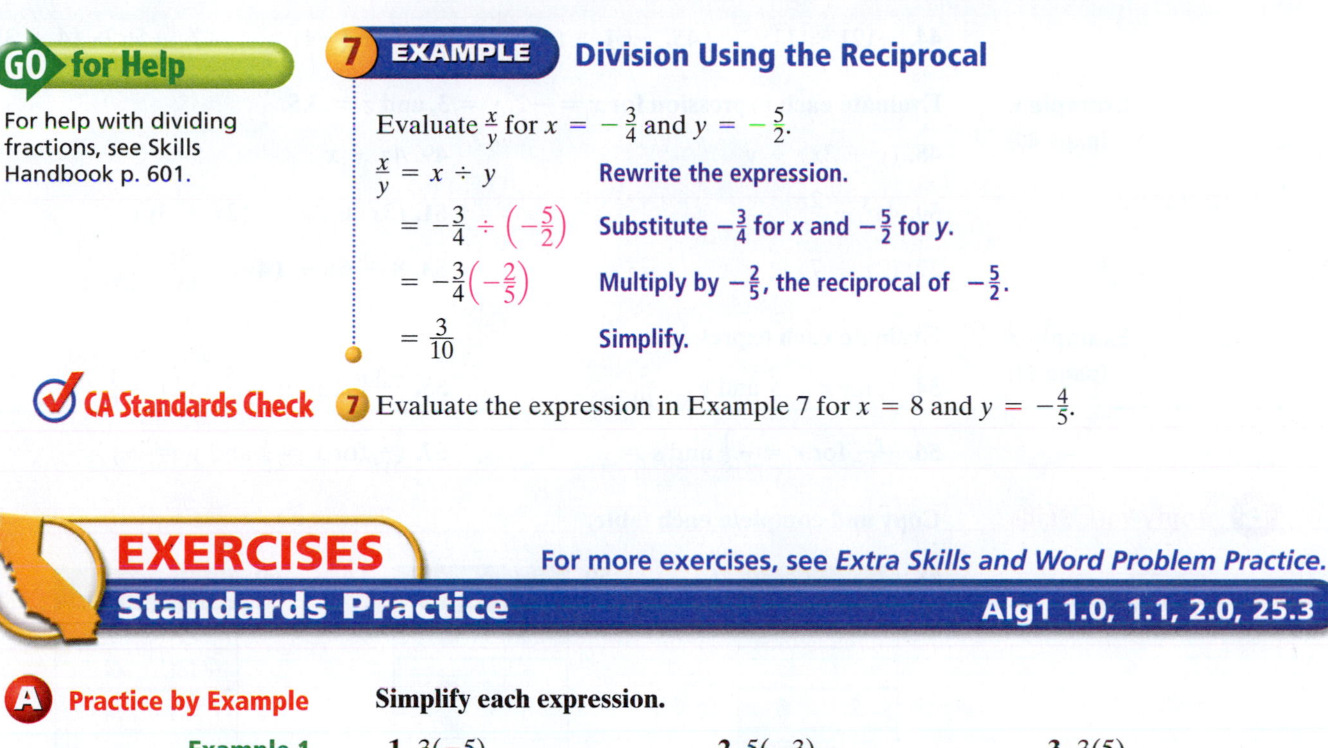

GO for Help

For help with dividing fractions, see Skills Handbook p. 601.

7 EXAMPLE Division Using the Reciprocal

Evaluate $\frac{x}{y}$ for $x = -\frac{3}{4}$ and $y = -\frac{5}{2}$.

$\frac{x}{y} = x \div y$	Rewrite the expression.
$= -\frac{3}{4} \div \left(-\frac{5}{2}\right)$	Substitute $-\frac{3}{4}$ for x and $-\frac{5}{2}$ for y.
$= -\frac{3}{4}\left(-\frac{2}{5}\right)$	Multiply by $-\frac{2}{5}$, the reciprocal of $-\frac{5}{2}$.
$= \frac{3}{10}$	Simplify.

CA Standards Check 7 Evaluate the expression in Example 7 for $x = 8$ and $y = -\frac{4}{5}$.

EXERCISES
Standards Practice

For more exercises, see *Extra Skills and Word Problem Practice*.

Alg1 1.0, 1.1, 2.0, 25.3

A Practice by Example

GO for Help

Example 1 (page 38)

Simplify each expression.

1. $3(-5)$ **2.** $5(-3)$ **3.** $3(5)$

4. $-3(-5)$ **5.** $8(-4.3)$ **6.** $9\left(-\frac{5}{18}\right)$

7. $10(-12)$ **8.** $7(-15)$ **9.** $-4(20)$

10. $-20(-4)$ **11.** $13(-6)$ **12.** $-9(-9)$

Example 2 (page 39)

Evaluate each expression for $m = -4$, $n = 3$, and $p = -1$.

13. mn **14.** $-mn$ **15.** $3m - n$

16. $-5p$ **17.** $2m$ **18.** $7p - 2n$

19. $8p \cdot (-2n)$ **20.** $p \cdot (m + n)$ **21.** mnp

22. $m \cdot (3 + p)$ **23.** $4n^3 \cdot m$ **24.** $m \cdot p + (-n)$

Example 3 (page 39)

Evaluate each expression for $x = -12$ and $y = 4$.

25. $xy - 4y$ **26.** $2xy + 9$ **27.** $x + 4y$

28. $-x + 3y$ **29.** $3y - 2x$ **30.** $6y + x$

31. The expression $w = -22 + \frac{13}{10}t$, where t is the actual air temperature, gives the approximate wind chill temperature w when the wind speed is 20 mi/h. Find the approximate wind chill temperature for the given air temperatures with a 20 mi/h wind.

a. 10°F **b.** −24°F **c.** −8°F **d.** 5°F

Example 4 (page 39)

Simplify each expression.

32. $(-1)^5$ **33.** $-(-2)^3$ **34.** -5^2 **35.** $(-9)^2$

36. -9^2 **37.** $3(-4)^3$ **38.** $-5(-1)^4$ **39.** $-5^2(-3)^3$

Example 5 (page 40)

Simplify each expression.

40. $\frac{6}{-3}$ **41.** $\frac{-36}{9}$ **42.** $\frac{3-14}{-2}$ **43.** $-18 \div (-3)$

44. $-121 \div 11$ **45.** $-64 \div (-5)$ **46.** $2^3 \div (-4)$ **47.** $-56 \div (4 + 3)$

Example 6 (page 40)

Evaluate each expression for $x = -2, y = 3$, and $z = 3.5$.

48. $(y + 3x) \div y$ **49.** $4z \div x$

50. $4x^3 - \frac{2z}{x}$ **51.** $(3x + 2y) \div (2x + 3y)$

52. $(2z + 7) \div y$ **53.** $8 + 6x \div (4y) - \frac{3z}{y}$

Example 7 (page 41)

Evaluate each expression.

54. $\frac{x}{y}$, for $x = \frac{2}{5}$ and $y = \frac{3}{10}$ **55.** $\frac{-3m}{t}$, for $m = \frac{5}{6}$ and $t = \frac{1}{6}$

56. $\frac{r}{-3s}$, for $r = -\frac{1}{8}$ and $s = \frac{3}{4}$ **57.** $\frac{3x}{5y}$, for $x = \frac{1}{5}$ and $y = -\frac{1}{2}$

B Apply Your Skills

Copy and complete each table.

58.

m	$-5m$
−4	■
−1	■
2	■
■	−25

59.

p	$\frac{3}{4}p - 5$
−4	■
−3	■
2	■
■	−2

60.

n	$\lvert 2n - 3 \rvert$
−5	■
−1	■
0	■
4	■

61. a. Find each product.

i. $(-1)(-1)$ **ii.** $(-1)(-1)(-1)$

iii. $(-1)(-2)$ **iv.** $(-1)(-2)(-3)$

v. $(-1)(-2)(-3)(-4)$ **vi.** $(-1)(-2)(-3)(-4)(-5)$

b. Patterns For an even number of negative factors, the product will be __?__.

c. For an odd number of negative factors, the product will be __?__.

d. Writing For a product that includes negative and positive factors, do the positive factors affect the sign of the product? Explain.

62. Suppose a and b are integers.

a. When is the product ab positive?

b. When is the product ab negative?

Evaluate each expression for the given value(s).

63. $\frac{3}{4}w - 7$, for $w = 1\frac{1}{3}$ **64.** $\frac{x}{2y}$, for $x = 3.6$ and $y = -0.4$

65. $\frac{n}{m}$, for $n = -\frac{4}{5}$ and $m = 8$ **66.** $\frac{3a}{b} + c$, for $a = -2, b = -5$, and $c = -1$

Use $a = -3, b = 2$, and $c = -5$ to write an algebraic expression that has each value.

67. 17 **68.** 0 **69.** −1 **70.** 1 **71.** 7

72. A toll bridge in Maine in the early 1900s charged 2¢ per person and $6\frac{1}{4}$¢ for a dozen sheep.

a. How much would the toll for 3 people and 4 dozen sheep have been?

b. If the toll was 56¢ and there were 8 dozen sheep, how many people were there?

Visit: PHSchool.com
Web Code: bae-0106

73. **Reasoning** Does $|ab|$ always equal $|a| \cdot |b|$? Explain.

74. a. Simplify each expression.

$(-2)^2$ $\quad(-2)^3$ $\quad(-2)^4$ $\quad(-2)^5$

$(-3)^2$ $\quad(-3)^3$ $\quad(-3)^4$ $\quad(-3)^5$

b. **Make a Conjecture** Do you think a negative number raised to an even power will be positive or negative? Explain.

c. What is the sign of a negative number raised to an odd power? Explain.

75. Is -10 or 0.1 the multiplicative inverse of 10? Explain.

76. Explain why the reciprocal of a nonzero number is *not* the same as the opposite of the number.

Math Reasoning **Is each statement *always, sometimes,* or *never* true? If a statement is not always true, give a counterexample.**

77. The quotient of two negative numbers is positive.

78. The product of two positive numbers is negative.

79. The opposite of the product of two numbers is negative.

80. The reciprocal of a nonzero number is less than 1.

81. A number *cannot* be its own multiplicative inverse.

82. As riders plunge down the hill of a roller coaster, you can approximate the height h, in feet, above the ground of their roller-coaster car. Use the formula $h = 155 - 16t^2$, where t is the number of seconds since the start of the descent.

a. How far is a rider from the bottom of the hill after 1 second? 2 seconds?

b. **Critical Thinking** Does it take more than or less than 4 seconds to reach the bottom? Explain.

83. The formula $C = \frac{5}{9}(F - 32)$ changes a temperature reading from the Fahrenheit scale F to the Celsius scale C. Which Celsius temperature is equivalent to -13°F?

Ⓐ 25°C Ⓑ 15°C Ⓒ -15°C Ⓓ -25°C

Evaluate each expression for $b = -\frac{1}{2}$.

84. b^3 85. b^4 86. b^5 87. b^6 88. $-b^6$

89. What is the greatest integer n for which $(-n)^3$ is positive and the value of the expression has a 2 in the ones place?

Rewrite each expression using the symbol ÷. Then find each quotient.

Sample $\frac{\frac{-7}{12}}{4} = \frac{-7}{12} \div 4$ Rewrite as $\frac{-7}{12} \div 4$.

$= \frac{-7}{12} \cdot \left(\frac{1}{4}\right)$ Multiply by $\frac{1}{4}$, the reciprocal of 4.

$= -\frac{7}{48}$

90. $\frac{5}{\frac{4}{9}}$ 91. $\frac{\frac{3}{8}}{\frac{-2}{3}}$ 92. $\frac{\frac{-5}{6}}{8}$ 93. $\frac{\frac{-2}{5}}{\frac{-4}{5}}$

Multiple Choice Practice

For California Standards Tutorials, visit PHSchool.com. Web Code: baq-9045

Alg1 2.0

94. Samantha's friend cannot remember what the relationship is between the numbers -2 and $-\frac{1}{2}$. What should Samantha tell her friend?

(A) The numbers are additive inverses.
(B) The numbers are negative reciprocals.
(C) The numbers are multiplicative inverses.
(D) The numbers are multiplicative identities.

Alg1 2.0

95. Simplify $-(-3)(-3)(2)(2)(-1)$.

(A) -36 (B) -6 (C) 6 (D) 36

Alg1 1.1, 25.0

96. By which property is the equation $1 \cdot 0 \cdot (-1) = 0$ true?

(A) Identity Property of Multiplication
(B) Multiplication Property of Zero
(C) Multiplication Property of -1
(D) Inverse Property of Addition

Alg1 2.0

97. Evaluate $-ac - [-(-bc)]$ for $a = -2, b = 6$, and $c = -3$.

(A) -24 (B) -12 (C) 12 (D) 24

Alg1 2.0

98. Which expression does NOT have the same value as $-(1 \cdot 11) - [-3 \cdot (-11)]$?

(A) $-11 + (-11) + (-11) + (-11)$
(B) $4(-11)$
(C) $-(-11)^4$
(D) $33 - 77$

Alg1 25.3

99. When is the following statement true?

The reciprocal of a nonzero number is greater than the original number.

(A) The statement is always true.
(B) The statement is never true.
(C) The statement is true for positive numbers less than 1 and for negative numbers greater than -1.
(D) The statement is true for positive numbers less than 1 and for negative numbers less than -1.

Mixed Review

GO for Help

Lesson 1-5 **Subtract.**

100. $6 - 8$ **101.** $-3 - 17$ **102.** $-2.3 - (-3.1)$

103. $7 - (-2.8)$ **104.** $1\frac{3}{4} - \left(-\frac{1}{2}\right)$ **105.** $-\frac{7}{8} - \left(-\frac{8}{9}\right)$

Lesson 1-3 **Find each absolute value.**

106. $|4.95|$ **107.** $|-56|$ **108.** $|-4.59|$ **109.** $\left|-\frac{3}{4}\right|$

Lesson 1-2 **Evaluate each expression for $a = 4$ and $b = 7$.**

110. $a^2 + b$ **111.** $(a + b)^2$ **112.** ab^2

1-7

The Distributive Property

California Content Standards

1.0 Identify and use the arithmetic properties of real numbers. ***Develop***
4.0 Simplify expressions before solving linear equations. ***Introduce***
10.0 Add, subtract, and multiply monomials. ***Introduce***

What You'll Learn

- To use the Distributive Property
- To simplify algebraic expressions

. . . And Why

To calculate costs when shopping, as in Example 2

Check Skills You'll Need

Use the order of operations to simplify each expression.

1. $3(4 + 7)$ **2.** $-2(5 + 6)$ **3.** $-1(-9 + 8)$

4. $-0.5(8 - 6)$ **5.** $\frac{1}{2}t(10 - 4)$ **6.** $m(-3 - 1)$

New Vocabulary

- Distributive Property
- term
- constant
- coefficient
- like terms

Using the Distributive Property

You can use the Distributive Property to multiply a sum or difference by a number.

Take Note

Property **Distributive Property**

For every real number a, b, and c,

$a(b + c) = ab + ac$ $(b + c)a = ba + ca$

$a(b - c) = ab - ac$ $(b - c)a = ba - ca$

Examples $5(20 + 6) = 5(20) + 5(6)$ $(20 + 6)5 = 20(5) + 6(5)$

$9(30 - 2) = 9(30) - 9(2)$ $(30 - 2)9 = 30(9) - 2(9)$

You can use the Distributive Property to multiply some numbers using mental math. For instance, you can think of 102 as $100 + 2$ and 98 as $100 - 2$.

1 EXAMPLE Simplifying a Numerical Expression

Use the Distributive Property to simplify 34(102).

$34(102) = 34(100 + 2)$ **Rewrite 102 as 100 + 2.**

$= 34(100) + 34(2)$ **Use the Distributive Property.**

$= 3400 + 68$ **Simplify.**

$= 3468$

CA Standards Check **1** Simplify each expression.

a. 13(103) **b.** 21(101) **c.** 24(98) **d.** 15(99)

You can also use the Distributive Property and mental math to calculate costs.

2 EXAMPLE Using Mental Math

Find the cost of 8 sandwiches that cost $5.95 each.

$$
\begin{aligned}
5.95(8) &= (6 - 0.05)8 && \text{Write 5.95 as } 6 - 0.05. \\
&= (6)8 - (0.05)8 && \text{Use the Distributive Property.} \\
&= 48 - 0.40 && \text{Simplify.} \\
&= 47.60
\end{aligned}
$$

The cost of 8 sandwiches is $47.60.

CA Standards Check 2 Find the total cost of 6 pairs of socks that are $2.95 per pair.

Simplifying Algebraic Expressions

You can use the Distributive Property to simplify an algebraic expression. An algebraic expression in simplest form has no grouping symbols.

3 EXAMPLE Simplifying an Expression

Simplify each expression.

a. $2(5x + 3)$

$$
\begin{aligned}
2(5x + 3) &= 2(5x) + 2(3) && \text{Use the Distributive Property.} \\
&= 10x + 6 && \text{Simplify.}
\end{aligned}
$$

b. $(3b - 2)\left(\frac{1}{3}\right)$

$$
\begin{aligned}
(3b - 2)\left(\tfrac{1}{3}\right) &= 3b\left(\tfrac{1}{3}\right) - 2\left(\tfrac{1}{3}\right) && \text{Use the Distributive Property.} \\
&= b - \tfrac{2}{3} && \text{Simplify.}
\end{aligned}
$$

CA Standards Check 3 Simplify each expression

a. $2(3 - 7t)$ **b.** $(0.4 + 1.1c)(3)$

To simplify an expression like $-(6x + 4)$, rewrite the expression as $-1(6x + 4)$, using the Multiplication Property of -1.

4 EXAMPLE Using the Multiplication Property of −1

Simplify $-(6x + 4)$.

$$
\begin{aligned}
-(6x + 4) &= -1(6x + 4) && \text{Rewrite the expression using } -1. \\
&= -1(6x) + (-1)(4) && \text{Use the Distributive Property.} \\
&= -6x - 4 && \text{Simplify.}
\end{aligned}
$$

CA Standards Check 4 Simplify each expression.

a. $-(2x + 1)$ **b.** $(3 - 8a)(-1)$

In an algebraic expression, a **term** is a number, a variable, or the product of a number and one or more variables.

$6a^2 - 5ab + 3b - 12$ ← A **constant** is a term that has no variable.

A **coefficient** is a numerical factor of a term.

Think of $3b - 12$ as $3b + (-12)$ to determine that the constant is -12.

Like terms have exactly the same variable factors.

Like Terms	Not Like Terms
$3x$ and $-2x$	$8x$ and $7y$
$-5x^2$ and $9x^2$	$5y$ and $2y^2$
xy and $-xy$	$4y$ and $5xy$
$-7x^2y^3$ and $15x^2y^3$	x^2y and xy^2

An algebraic expression in simplest form has no like terms. You can use the Distributive Property to combine like terms when simplifying an expression. Think of the Distributive Property as $ba + ca = (b + c)a$.

5 EXAMPLE Combining Like Terms

Simplify each expression.

a. $3x^2 + 5x^2$

$3x^2 + 5x^2 = (3 + 5)x^2$ Use the Distributive Property.

$= 8x^2$ Simplify.

b. $-5c + c$

$-5c + c = -5c + 1c$ Rewrite c as $1c$.

$= (-5 + 1)c$ Use the Distributive Property.

$= -4c$ Simplify.

Problem Solving Tip

Identity Property of Multiplication: $c = 1 \cdot c$ or $1c$

CA Standards Check 5 Simplify each expression.

a. $7y + 6y$ **b.** $3t - t$ **c.** $-9w^3 - 3w^3$ **d.** $8d + d$

You can write an expression from a verbal phrase. The word *quantity* indicates that two or more terms are within parentheses.

6 EXAMPLE Writing an Expression

Write an expression for "3 times the quantity x minus 5."

Relate	3	times	the quantity x minus 5
Write	3	$\cdot$	$(x - 5)$

$3(x - 5)$

CA Standards Check 6 Write an expression for each phrase.

a. -2 times the quantity t plus 7

b. the product of 14 and the quantity 8 plus w

EXERCISES
Standards Practice

For more exercises, see *Extra Skills and Word Problem Practice.*

Alg1 1.0, 4.0, 10.0

A Practice by Example

GO for Help

Example 1 (page 45)

Simplify each expression using the Distributive Property.

1. 12(201) **2.** 51(13) **3.** 11(499) **4.** 8(306)

5. 7(98) **6.** 3(999) **7.** 41(502) **8.** 24(1020)

Example 2 (page 46)

Mental Math Use the Distributive Property to find each price.

9. 4($.99) **10.** 6($1.97) **11.** 5($5.91) **12.** 7($29.93)

13. The school librarian got money to buy reference works on CDs. She bought three CDs for $32.99 each. How much did she spend in all?

14. You stopped on your way to basketball practice and bought four cans of fruit punch for $.69 each. How much did you spend in all?

Example 3 (page 46)

Simplify each expression.

15. $7(t - 4)$ **16.** $-2(n - 6)$ **17.** $3(m + 4)$

18. $(5b - 4)\frac{1}{5}$ **19.** $-2(x + 3)$ **20.** $\frac{2}{3}(6y + 9)$

21. $0.25(6q + 32)$ **22.** $(3n - 7)(6)$ **23.** $(8 - 3r)\frac{5}{16}$

24. $-4.5(b - 3)$ **25.** $\frac{2}{5}(5w + 10)$ **26.** $(9 - 4n)(-4)$

Example 4 (page 46)

27. $-(x + 3)$ **28.** $-(x - 3)$ **29.** $-(3 + x)$

30. $-(3 - x)$ **31.** $-(6k + 5)$ **32.** $-(7x - 2)$

33. $-(2 - 7x)$ **34.** $(4 - z)(-1)$ **35.** $(-4m + 8)(-1)$

Example 5 (page 47)

36. $4t - 7t$ **37.** $12k^2 + 8k^2$ **38.** $9x - 2x$

39. $w + 23w$ **40.** $-18v^2 + 23v^2$ **41.** $7m - m$

42. $13q - 30q$ **43.** $x - 46x$ **44.** $-9p^3 - 6p^3$

Example 6 (page 47)

Write an expression for each phrase.

45. 3 times the quantity *m* minus 7 **46.** −4 times the quantity 4 plus *w*

47. twice the quantity *b* plus 9 **48.** 2 times the quantity 3 times *c* plus 9

B Apply Your Skills

Simplify each expression.

49. 9(4998) **50.** 12(7.001) **51.** 7(2.003)

52. $144\left(\frac{15}{16}b + \frac{8}{9}\right)$ **53.** $3(6.2 + 5m)$ **54.** $\frac{7}{8}\left(\frac{10}{14}d - 48\right)$

Copy and complete each table.

55.

k	$2(k - 4)$
−10	■
−5	■
2.5	■
■	0

56.

n	$-(2n + 5)$
−3	■
−1	■
2	■
■	−15

57.

a	$-3(2 - a)$
−4	■
0	■
2	■
■	9

Write an expression for each phrase.

58. $2\frac{1}{4}$ times the quantity $5\frac{1}{2}$ minus k

59. $6\frac{7}{100}$ times the quantity 8 plus $\frac{4}{3}p$

60. the product of $\frac{11}{20}$ and the quantity b minus $\frac{13}{30}$

61. 17 divided by the quantity z minus 34

62. $4\frac{1}{3}$ times the quantity x minus $\frac{11}{12}$

63. Which expression represents the perimeter of the figure?

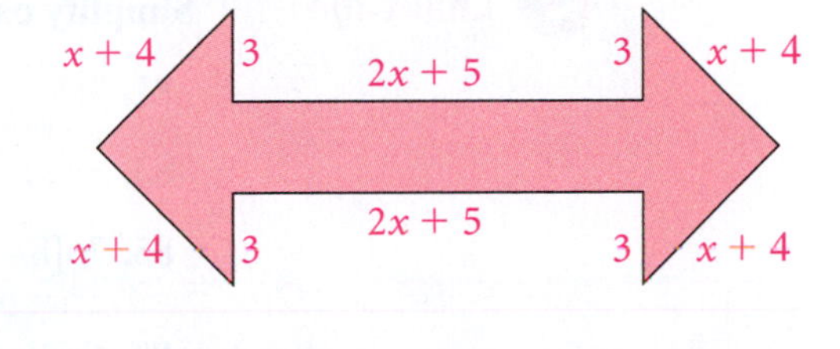

(A) $8x + 38$

(B) $46x$

(C) $4x + 38$

(D) $8x$

Problem Solving Tip

For Exercise 64, test positive and negative values of *a* and *b* as well as zero before writing your conclusion.

64. **Writing** Does $2ab = 2a \cdot 2b$? Explain.

65. **Error Analysis** A student rewrote $4(3x + 10)$ as $12x + 10$. Explain the student's error.

66. Write a variable expression that you could simplify using the Distributive Property. Then simplify your expression.

Simplify each expression.

67. $4.78d + 0d$

68. $-21p - 76p^2 - 9 + p$

69. $3.3t^2 + 8.7t - 9.4t^2 + 5t$

70. $1.5m - 4.2m - 12.5v + 4.2m$

71. $\frac{6}{7}n + n^3 - \left(-\frac{5}{6}n\right)$

72. $-\frac{16}{15}k + \frac{3}{20}h + \frac{7}{40}k$

73. $8m^2 - 5mz + 4mz - m^2 + 4$

74. $9 - 4t + 6y - 3t + 10$

75. $1.4b - 3b^2 + 4c - 2b^2 + c$

76. $8xyz + 4xy - 12yzx + 2xy$

77. Identify the terms, the coefficients, and the constant(s) in the expression $-7t + 6v + 7 - 19y$.

78. A high school basketball court is 84 ft long by 50 ft wide. A college basketball court is 10 ft longer than a high school court but has the same width.

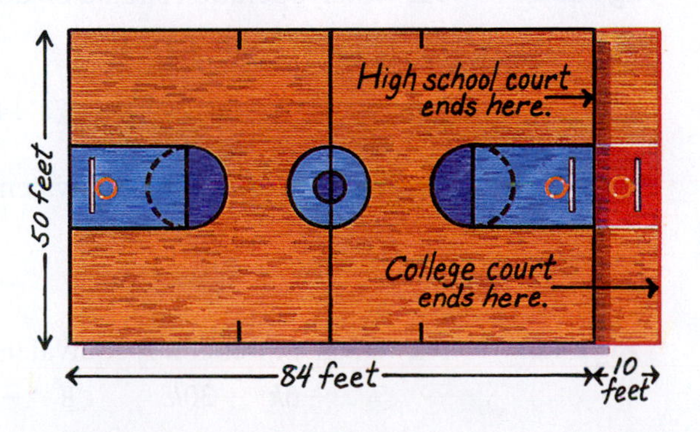

a. Write an expression using parentheses for the area of a college basketball court.

b. Simplify your expression.

Visit: PHSchool.com
Web Code: bae-0107

79. A student searched the pockets of his jeans before doing laundry and found the following numbers of coins: 4 pennies, 2 nickels, and a quarter; 3 quarters and 6 pennies; 1 dime and 5 nickels. How many of each type of coin does the student have?

80. Suppose you buy 4 cans of tomatoes at $1.02 each, 3 cans of tuna for $.99 each, and 3 boxes of pasta at $.52 each. Write an expression to model this situation. Then use the Distributive Property to find the total cost.

C Challenge

Simplify each expression.

81. $9(5 + t) - 6(t + 3)$

82. $4(r + 8) - 5(2r - 1)$

83. $-(m + 3) - 2(m + 3)$

84. $a[2 + b(2 + c)]$

85. $7b[8 + 6(b - 1)]$

86. $-[-5(y + 2z) - 3z]$

87. **Critical Thinking** If $y = 3x - 10$, what is an expression for $\frac{y}{3}$?

88. a. Evaluate $(a + b) \div c$ and $a \div c + b \div c$ for $a = -10$, $b = 6$, and $c = -2$.
b. Evaluate each expression for $a = -9$, $b = -3$, and $c = 6$.
c. **Reasoning** Does it appear that $(a + b) \div c = a \div c + b \div c$? Explain.

89. a. Evaluate $a \div (b + c)$ and $a \div b + a \div c$ for $a = -60$, $b = 3$, and $c = -5$.
b. Evaluate each expression for $a = -24$, $b = -4$, and $c = 2$.
c. **Reasoning** Does it appear that $a \div (b + c) = a \div b + a \div c$? Explain.

Multiple Choice Practice

For California Standards Tutorials, visit PHSchool.com. Web Code: baq-9045

Alg1 4.0

90. Which expression is equivalent to $3(x + 2) - 2(x + 3)$?

A x
B $x + 5$
C $x + 10$
D $x + 12$

Alg1 1.0

91. Which equation illustrates the Distributive Property?

A $4[10 + (c - 2)] = 4[(c - 2) + 10]$
B $5j + 3k + 2j + k = 5j + 2j + 3k + k$
C $0.25 \cdot (4 \cdot 7) = (0.25 \cdot 4) \cdot 7$
D $3(12 - 8) = 3(12) - 3(8)$

Alg1 25.2

92. Which operation should be done first to simplify this expression?

$123 - [18 - (14 + 7)]$

A $232 - 18$
B $14 + 7$
C $18 - 7$
D $18 - 14$

Alg1 10.0

93. Which expression is equivalent to $14x - 21x$?

A $-7x^2$
B $7x^2(2 - 3x)$
C $7x(2x - 3)$
D $-7x$

Alg1 4.0

94. Which expression is equivalent to $-6(k - 5)$?

A $-6k^2 - 30k$
B $-6k + 30$
C $-6k - 5$
D $-6k^2 + 5$

Alg1 10.0

95. Which expression is equivalent to $3.75d + 6c - 9d + 2.5c$?

A $-5.25d + 8.5c$
B $9.75d + 11.5c$
C $5.25d - 4.5c$
D $12.25cd$

Alg1 2.0 **96.** Simplify $-\frac{4}{9} \div \left(-\frac{2}{3}\right)$.

Ⓐ $\frac{8}{27}$ Ⓒ $\frac{3}{2}$

Ⓑ $\frac{2}{3}$ Ⓓ $\frac{27}{8}$

Alg1 10.0 **97.** Simplify $7q + 8pq - 4pq - 9q$.

Ⓐ $-2q + 12pq$ Ⓒ $16q + 4pq$

Ⓑ $-2q + 4pq$ Ⓓ $16q + 12pq$

Mixed Review

Lessons 1-5, 1-6

GO for Help

Simplify each expression.

98. $8(-7) + 4(-3)$

99. $8 + (-4) \cdot 3$

100. $(-3)^2 + (-5)$

101. $(9^2 - 60) \div 3$

102. $\frac{-7 + 5}{-7 - 5}$

103. $\frac{7 - 2}{-12 + 8}$

104. $\frac{1 + (-4)}{21 - 6}$

105. $-3^4 \div 9 - 4 \cdot 2$

Lesson 1-4

Simplify each expression.

106. $6.034 + (-8.42)$

107. $9.73 + 2.397$

108. $-54.1 + 99.4$

109. $|-28.2| + 17.5$

110. $-6.45 + |-9.02|$

111. $3.02 + (-2.1)$

112. $-5.7 + (-3.9)$

113. $14.7 + |-8.3|$

Lesson 1-1

114. a. Write an expression for the phrase "4 more than the quotient of m and 3."

b. Evaluate your expression for $m = 9, m = 3$, and $m = 12$.

Checkpoint Quiz 2

Lessons 1-4 through 1-7

Simplify each expression.

1. $\left(-\frac{1}{3}\right) + \left(\frac{2}{9}\right)$

2. $-3 + (-17)$

3. $|-5| + (-5) + 5$

4. $-10 + 8 - (-13)$

Evaluate each expression for $a = 4$ and $b = -5$.

5. $2a \cdot (-3b)$

6. $-b - a$

7. $(2a^2) \div (4b)$

8. The temperature one day in Sacramento is 74°F. Define a variable and write an expression to find the temperature after it changes. Then evaluate your expression for an increase of 13 degrees Fahrenheit.

Use the Distributive Property to simplify each expression.

9. $\frac{1}{3}(24x - 36)$

10. $6t + 43t$

1-8 Properties of Numbers

CALIFORNIA CHECK SYSTEM

California Content Standards

1.0 Identify and use the arithmetic properties of real numbers. ***Develop***
1.1 Use properties of numbers to demonstrate whether assertions are true or false. ***Master***
24.1 Explain the difference between inductive and deductive reasoning. ***Introduce***
25.0 Use properties of the number system to justify each step of a procedure. ***Introduce***
25.2 Judge whether properties have been applied correctly. ***Develop***

What You'll Learn

- To identify properties
- To use deductive reasoning

. . . And Why

To find total costs mentally, as in Example 2

Check Skills You'll Need

GO for Help Lessons 1-4 and 1-6

Simplify each expression.

1. $8 + (9 + 2)$ **2.** $3 \cdot (-2 \cdot 5)$ **3.** $0.25 \cdot 3 \cdot 4$

4. $3 + x - 2$ **5.** $2t - 8 + 3t$ **6.** $-5m + 2m - 4m$

New Vocabulary

- deductive reasoning

Identifying and Using Properties

The summary below reviews properties of real numbers.

Take Note

Property **Properties of Real Numbers**

For every real number a, b, and c,

Commutative Property of Addition
$a + b = b + a$ **Example** $3 + 7 = 7 + 3$

Commutative Property of Multiplication
$a \cdot b = b \cdot a$ **Example** $3 \cdot 7 = 7 \cdot 3$

Associative Property of Addition
$(a + b) + c = a + (b + c)$ **Example** $(6 + 4) + 5 = 6 + (4 + 5)$

Associative Property of Multiplication
$(a \cdot b) \cdot c = a \cdot (b \cdot c)$ **Example** $(6 \cdot 4) \cdot 5 = 6 \cdot (4 \cdot 5)$

Identity Property of Addition
$a + 0 = a$ **Example** $9 + 0 = 9$

Identity Property of Multiplication
$a \cdot 1 = a$ **Example** $6 \cdot 1 = 6$

Inverse Property of Addition
For every a, there is an additive inverse $-a$ such that $a + (-a) = 0$. **Example** $5 + (-5) = 0$

Inverse Property of Multiplication
For every a $(a \neq 0)$, there is a multiplicative inverse $\frac{1}{a}$ such that $a\left(\frac{1}{a}\right) = 1$. **Example** $5 \cdot \frac{1}{5} = 1$

Symmetric Property
If $a = b$, then $b = a$. **Example** $2 \cdot 3 = 6$, so $6 = 2 \cdot 3$

The following summary reviews some additional properties of real numbers.

Take Note

Property | **Properties of Real Numbers**

For every real number a, b, and c,

Distributive Property	**Examples**
$a(b + c) = ab + ac$	$5(4 + 2) = 5 \cdot 4 + 5 \cdot 2$
$a(b - c) = ab - ac$	$5(4 - 2) = 5 \cdot 4 - 5 \cdot 2$

Multiplication Property of Zero

For every real number n, $n \cdot 0 = 0$.	$-35 \cdot 0 = 0$

Multiplication Property of -1

For every real number n, $-1 \cdot n = -n$.	$-1 \cdot (-5) = 5$

1 EXAMPLE Identifying Properties

Name the property that each equation illustrates. Explain.

a. $9 + 7 = 7 + 9$ — Commutative Property of Addition, because the order of the addends changes

b. $(d \cdot 4) \cdot 3 = d \cdot (4 \cdot 3)$ — Associative Property of Multiplication, because the grouping of the factors changes

c. $t + 0 = t$ — Identity Property of Addition, because the sum of a number and zero is the number

d. $-q = -1q$ — Multiplication Property of -1, because the opposite of a value is the same as -1 times the value

CA Standards Check 1 Name the property that each equation illustrates. Explain.

a. $1m = m$ **b.** $(-3 + 4) + 5 = -3 + (4 + 5)$ **c.** $(3 \cdot 8)0 = 3(8 \cdot 0)$
d. $2 + 0 = 2$ **e.** $np = pn$ **f.** $p + q = q + p$

You can also use the properties to reorganize the order of numbers in sums or products so that you can calculate more easily.

2 EXAMPLE Application

Suppose you buy the school supplies shown at the left. Find the total cost of the supplies.

$0.85 + 2.50 + 5.15 = 2.50 + 0.85 + 5.15$ **Commutative Property of Addition**

$= 2.50 + (0.85 + 5.15)$ **Associative Property of Addition**

$= 2.50 + 6$ **Add within parentheses first.**

$= 8.50$ **Simplify.**

The total cost of the supplies is $8.50.

CA Standards Check 2 You buy a package of cheese for $2.50, a loaf of bread for $2.15, a cucumber for $.65, and some tomatoes for $3.50. Find the total cost of the groceries.

Using Deductive Reasoning

Deductive reasoning is the process of reasoning logically from given facts to a conclusion. Using deductive reasoning, you justify each step in simplifying an expression with reasons such as properties, definitions, or rules.

3 EXAMPLE Justifying Steps

Simplify each expression. Justify each step.

a. $-4b + 9 + b$

Step	Reason
$-4b + 9 + b = -4b + 9 + 1b$	Identity Property of Multiplication
$= -4b + 1b + 9$	Commutative Property of Addition
$= (-4 + 1)b + 9$	Distributive Property
$= -3b + 9$	addition

b. $7z - 5(3 + z)$

Step	Reason
$7z - 5(3 + z) = 7z - 15 - 5z$	Distributive Property
$= 7z + (-15) + (-5z)$	definition of subtraction
$= 7z + (-5z) + (-15)$	Commutative Property of Addition
$= [7 + (-5)]z + (-15)$	Distributive Property
$= 2z + (-15)$	addition
$= 2z - 15$	definition of subtraction

Problem Solving Tip

To use the Commutative Property of Addition, write subtraction as addition of the opposite.

CA Standards Check 3 Simplify each expression. Justify each step.

a. $5a + 6 + a$ **b.** $2(3t - 1) + 2$

EXERCISES Standards Practice

For more exercises, see *Extra Skills and Word Problem Practice.*

Alg1 1.0, 1.1, 24.1, 25.0, 25.2

A Practice by Example

Example 1 (page 53)

GO for Help

Name the property that each equation illustrates. Explain.

1. $-\frac{6}{7} + 0 = -\frac{6}{7}$
2. $1 \cdot \frac{21}{23} = \frac{21}{23}$
3. $(-7 + 4) + 1 = -7 + (4 + 1)$
4. $-0.3 + 0.3 = 0$
5. $9(7.3) = 7.3(9)$
6. $5(12 - 4) = 5(12) - 5(4)$
7. $8(9 \cdot 11) = (8 \cdot 9) \cdot 11$
8. $-0.5 \cdot (-2) = 1$

Example 2 (page 53)

Mental Math Simplify each expression.

9. $47 + 39 + 3 + 11$
10. $25 \cdot 74 \cdot 2 \cdot 2$
11. $4.75 + 2.95 + 1.25 + 6$
12. $10 \cdot 6 \cdot 7 \cdot 10$
13. $2(5 - 3.5) - 8$
14. $6\frac{1}{2} + 4\frac{1}{3} + 1\frac{1}{2} + \frac{2}{3}$
15. You buy 3 grapefruits for \$1.50, a pound of apples for \$.79, some grapes for \$2.50, and some bananas for \$1.21. Find the total cost of the fruit.

Example 3 (page 54)

Give a reason to justify each step.

16. a. $3y - 5y = 3y + (-5y)$ __?__
b. $= [3 + (-5)]y$ __?__
c. $= -2y$ __?__

17. a. $3 \cdot (12 \cdot 10) = 3 \cdot (10 \cdot 12)$ __?__
b. $= (3 \cdot 10) \cdot 12$ __?__
c. $= 30 \cdot 12$ __?__
d. $= 360$ __?__

Simplify each expression. Justify each step.

18. $25 \cdot 1.7 \cdot 4$
19. $-5(7y)$
20. $8 + 9m + 7$
21. $12x - 3 + 6x$
22. $29c + (-29c)$
23. $43\left(\frac{1}{43}\right) + 1$

B Apply Your Skills

Simplify each expression. Justify each step.

24. $2 + g\left(\frac{1}{g}\right)$
25. $36jkm - 36mjk$
26. $(3^2 - 2^3)(8759)$
27. $(7^6 - 6^5)(8 - 8)$
28. $4 + 6(8 - 3m)$
29. $5\left(w - \frac{1}{5}\right) - w(9)$

30. Suppose you are buying soccer equipment: a pair of cleats for $31.50, a soccer ball for $14.97, and shin guards for $6.50. Use mental math to find the total cost.

Tell whether the expressions in each pair are equivalent.

31. $6m + 1$ and $1 \cdot 6 + m$
32. $9y$ and $9 + y$
33. $mp + nq$ and $mq + np$
34. $-(5 - 9)$ and $9 - 5$
35. $8 - 4c$ and $4c - 8$
36. $3(5 + z)$ and $15 + z$
37. $6t - 4$ and $2[(2 + 1)t - 2]$
38. $vwx \cdot yz$ and $v \cdot w \cdot zxy$

Reasoning **Explain your answer to each question.**

39. Is subtraction commutative?
40. Is subtraction associative?
41. Is division commutative?
42. Is division associative?

43. Give a reason to justify each step.
a. $5t + 6 + 3(t + 2) = 5t + 6 + 3t + 6$ __?__
b. $= 5t + 3t + 6 + 6$ __?__
c. $= 5t + 3t + (6 + 6)$ __?__
d. $= 5t + 3t + 12$ __?__
e. $= (5 + 3)t + 12$ __?__
f. $= 8t + 12$ __?__

44. **Reasoning** The Distributive Property states that $a(b + c) = ab + ac$. Use this and the other properties to explain why $(b + c)a = ba + ca$ is also true.

45. A member of the track team records the distance she runs each day. How many miles did she run in all?
Ⓐ 14.2 miles
Ⓑ 14.1 miles
Ⓒ 13.9 miles
Ⓓ 13.8 miles

Day	Distance (miles)
Sunday	4.2
Monday	0
Tuesday	1.5
Wednesday	1.8
Thursday	2.5
Friday	0
Saturday	3.9

46. **Writing** Do you think a peanut butter and jelly sandwich tastes the same regardless of whether the jelly is on top or the peanut butter is on top? Relate your answer to one of the properties of real numbers.

Visit: PHSchool.com
Web Code: bae-0108

C Challenge **Refer to the properties of real numbers on pages 52 and 53. Which properties do *not* hold true for each set of numbers?**

47. integers **48.** natural numbers **49.** whole numbers

Multiple Choice Practice

For California Standards Tutorials, visit PHSchool.com. Web Code: baq-9045

Alg1 1.0

50. Which property guarantees the truth of this statement?

$-3(7x + 5y - 4) = -21x - 15y + 12$

(A) Commutative Property of Multiplication
(B) Identity Property of Multiplication
(C) Distributive Property
(D) Associative Property of Multiplication

Alg1 1.0

51. Simplify $-4 + 17 - 29 + 4 + 29 - 3$.

(A) 14 (B) 20 (C) 22 (D) 72

Alg1 2.0

52. Which of the following has the same result as dividing a number by $\frac{5}{2}$ and then multiplying by $\frac{1}{2}$?

(A) multiplying by 2
(B) multiplying by 5
(C) dividing by 2
(D) dividing by 5

Alg1 2.0

53. The variable a is an integer. Which of the following could NOT equal a^3?

(A) -27 (B) -16 (C) 8 (D) 64

Alg1 10.0

54. Which expression is equivalent to $-2h - (5 - 3h)$?

(A) h (B) $-4h$ (C) $h - 5$ (D) $-5h - 5$

Alg1 1.0

55. Which term best describes the number 0.5?

(A) integer (B) rational (C) irrational (D) whole

Mixed Review

GO for Help

Lesson 1-7 **Simplify each expression.**

56. $5(1.2 + k)$ **57.** $\frac{1}{3}(33 - b)$ **58.** $-2.5(4p + 14)$

59. $4(7 - n)$ **60.** $-(-7.4m + 0.05)$ **61.** $(3v - 5.2)(-6)$

Lesson 1-4 **Simplify.**

62. $12 + (-5)$ **63.** $9.2 + (-27.5)$ **64.** $\frac{5}{8} + \left(-\frac{7}{8}\right)$

65. $-4\frac{6}{10} + 3\frac{2}{5}$ **66.** $-11 + (-124)$ **67.** $|-2.4| + |6.8|$

Lesson 1-1 **Write an expression for each phrase.**

68. 7 plus the sum of m and -17

69. one half of the quotient of b and 4

Activity Lab Closure Properties

FOR USE WITH LESSON 1-8

1.0 Identify and use the arithmetic properties of real numbers, including closure properties for the four basic arithmetic operations. ***Develop***
25.1 Use properties of numbers to construct simple, valid arguments for, or formulate counterexamples to, claimed assertions. ***Develop***

The **closure properties** for real numbers assure that the sum and product of any two real numbers in a given set of numbers are also in the set of numbers.

Closure Property of Addition

For every real number a and b, $a + b$ is a real number.

Closure Property of Multiplication

For every real number a and b, ab is a real number.

1 EXAMPLE

Is the set of negative numbers closed for addition? Is the set of negative numbers closed for multiplication? If not, give a counterexample.

Yes, the set of negative numbers is closed for addition; the sum of any two negative numbers is always a negative number.

No, the set of negative numbers is not closed for multiplication; the product of any two negative numbers is always positive. For example, $(-4)(-5) = 20$ and 20 is not in the set of negative numbers.

2 EXAMPLE

Suppose a set contains only the numbers 0 and 1. Is the set closed for multiplication? Write a valid argument or give a counterexample.

Yes; all the possible products of 0 and 1 are in the set: $0 \cdot 0 = 0$, $0 \cdot 1 = 0$, and $1 \cdot 1 = 1$.

EXERCISES

Is each set closed for addition and for multiplication? If not, give a counterexample.

1. rational numbers
2. integers
3. whole numbers
4. positive numbers
5. odd numbers
6. even numbers
7. real numbers
8. prime numbers

Write a valid argument or give a counterexample.

9. Is the set of whole numbers closed for subtraction?
10. Is the set of even numbers closed for division?
11. Suppose a set contains only the numbers -1, 0, and 1. Is the set closed for addition and for multiplication?

Test-Taking Strategies

Choosing the Process

Not all questions ask you to find the solution to a problem. Some questions simply ask how you would solve a problem. To answer these questions, you must choose a process.

EXAMPLE

To simplify the expression $5 \cdot (12 - 4) + 6 \cdot 3^2$, first simplify inside the parentheses: $12 - 4 = 8$. Which should be the next step?

(A) Multiply 5 by 8.

(B) Add 6 to 8.

(C) Square 3.

(D) Multiply 6 by 3.

The expression inside the parentheses has been simplified. According to the order of operations, you should next simplify powers. So the next step is to square 3. The correct answer is C.

Multiple Choice Practice

1. Rasia is carpeting her living room. The diagram below shows the dimensions of the room.

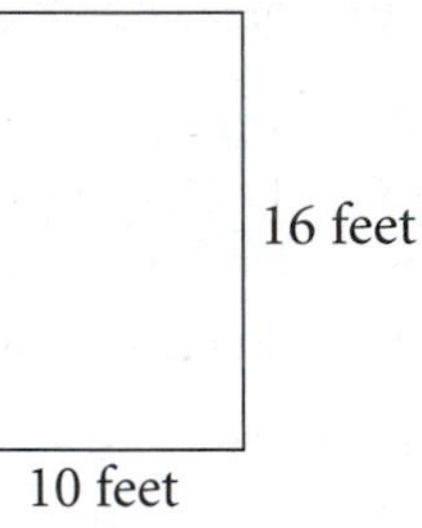

The carpet she is using costs $2.50 per square foot. How can Rasia find the total cost of the carpet?

(A) Double the sum of 10 and 16, and then multiply by 2.50.

(B) Multiply 2.50 by the sum of 10 and 16.

(C) Find the sum of 10, 16, and 2.50.

(D) Find the product of 10, 16, and 2.50.

2. Beth buys a hat for $15.99, including tax. She pays with a $20 bill. How can she determine the amount of change she receives?

(A) Add 20 and 15.99.

(B) Subtract 15.99 from 20.

(C) Multiply 20 and 15.99.

(D) Divide 20 by 15.99.

Chapter 1 Review

Vocabulary Review

English and Spanish Audio Online

absolute value (p. 20)
additive inverse (p. 24)
algebraic expression (p. 4)
base (p. 9)
coefficient (p. 47)
constant (p. 47)
counterexample (p. 18)
deductive reasoning (p. 54)
Distributive Property (p. 45)
equation (p. 5)
evaluate (p. 10)
exponent (p. 9)
Identity Property of Addition (p. 24)
Identity Property of Multiplication (p. 38)
inequality (p. 19)
integers (p. 17)
Inverse Property of Addition (p. 24)
Inverse Property of Multiplication (p. 40)
irrational number (p. 18)
like terms (p. 47)
Multiplication Property of Zero (p. 38)
Multiplication Property of −1 (p. 38)
multiplicative inverse (p. 41)
natural numbers (p. 17)
open sentence (p. 5)
opposites (p. 20)
order of operations (p. 10)
power (p. 9)
rational number (p. 17)
real numbers (p. 18)
reciprocal (p. 41)
simplify (p. 9)
term (p. 47)
variable (p. 4)
whole numbers (p. 17)

For: Vocabulary quiz
Web Code: baj-0151

Choose the term that correctly completes each sentence.

1. A (*constant, term*) is a number, variable, or the product of a number and one or more variables.
2. (*Evaluate, Simplify*) an algebraic expression by substituting a given number for each variable.
3. A mathematical phrase that uses numbers, variables, and operation symbols is an (*algebraic expression, equation*).
4. The number $-\frac{5}{8}$ belongs to the set of (*irrational, rational*) numbers.
5. The (*absolute value, opposite*) of a number is its distance from 0 on a number line.
6. You express the fraction of a pizza you have eaten by using a(n) (*rational number, integer*).
7. The (*reciprocal, additive inverse*) of a number is its opposite.
8. Use the (*Distributive Property, Identity Property of Multiplication*) to write the expression $-4(2x - 3)$ as $-8x + 12$.
9. To change the order of addends in a sum use the (*Associative, Commutative*) Property of Addition.
10. Simplify a(n) (*power, exponent*) by multiplying the base by itself the indicated number of times.
11. To prove a statement is false, you need only one (*counterexample, open sentence*).
12. Dividing by a nonzero number is the same as multiplying by its (*complement, reciprocal*).
13. The set of nonnegative integers is called (*whole, natural*) numbers.
14. A (*variable, coefficient*) is a symbol, usually a letter, that represents one or more numbers.
15. $2x$ and $\frac{1}{2}x$ are (*multiplicative inverses, like terms*).

Skills and Concepts

Lessons 1-1 and 1-2
- To model relationships with variables (p. 4)
- To model relationships with equations and formulas (p. 5)
- To simplify and evaluate expressions and formulas (p. 9)
- To evaluate expressions containing grouping symbols (p. 11)

7AF 1.1, Alg1 25.2

A **variable** represents one or more numbers. To **evaluate** a variable expression, you substitute a given number for each variable. Then you **simplify** the expression using the **order of operations.**

Order of Operations

1. Perform any operation(s) inside grouping symbols.
2. Simplify powers.
3. Multiply and divide in order from left to right.
4. Add and subtract in order from left to right.

Define a variable and write an expression for each phrase.

16. the sum of 5 and three times a number

17. 30 minus a number

18. the quotient of 7 and a number

19. the product of a number and 12

Evaluate each expression. Use $a = 3, b = 2$, and $c = 1$.

20. $2a^2 - (4b + c)$ **21.** $9(a + 2b) + c$ **22.** $\frac{2a + b}{2}$ **23.** $4a - b^2$

Lesson 1-3
- To classify numbers (p. 17)
- To compare numbers (p. 19)

Alg1 1.0, 1.1, 2.0, 24.3, 25.1

Real numbers can be classified as either rational numbers or irrational numbers. A **rational number,** like $\frac{5}{8}$, is a ratio of two integers. An **irrational number,** like π or $\sqrt{2}$, cannot be written as a ratio of integers. Rational numbers include **natural numbers** $(1, 2, 3, \ldots)$, **whole numbers** $(0, 1, 2, 3, \ldots)$, and **integers** $(\ldots, -2, -1, 0, 1, 2, \ldots)$.

Name the set(s) of numbers to which each number belongs.

24. -3.21 **25.** $\sqrt{7}$ **26.** $-\frac{1}{2}$ **27.** 18 **28.** $\frac{35}{5}$

Lessons 1-4 and 1-5
- To add real numbers using models and rules (p. 24)
- To apply addition (p. 26)
- To subtract real numbers (p. 32)
- To apply subtraction (p. 33)

Alg1 1.0, 2.0

To add real numbers with the same sign, add their absolute values. The sum has the same sign as the real numbers. To add real numbers with different signs, find the difference of their absolute values. The sum has the sign of the real number with the greater absolute value. To subtract a real number, add its opposite.

Simplify each expression.

29. $(-13) + (-4)$ **30.** $-12 - (-7)$ **31.** $-12.4 + 22.3$

32. $|54.3 - 29.4|$ **33.** $5 - 17$ **34.** $-3^2 + (-3)^2$

35. $-\frac{3}{10} - \left(-\frac{4}{5}\right)$ **36.** $2\frac{1}{3} + \left(-3\frac{5}{6}\right)$ **37.** $|-17.9 + 11.2|$

Lesson 1-6

- To multiply real numbers (p. 37)
- To divide real numbers (p. 40)

Alg1 1.0, 1.1, 2.0

To multiply or divide real numbers, multiply or divide the absolute values of the numbers. If the numbers have the same sign, the product or quotient is positive. If the numbers have different signs, the product or quotient is negative.

Simplify each expression.

38. $4 - 3(-2)$

39. $5(4)(-2)$

40. $\left(\frac{5}{6}\right)\left(-\frac{2}{3}\right)$

41. $\frac{4 - (-2)}{3}$

42. $\frac{5}{6} \div \left(-\frac{2}{3}\right)$

43. $\frac{5}{6} \div \left(-\frac{2}{3}\right)^2$

44. $-2^4(3^2)$

45. $4^3 - \frac{5(6)}{3}$

Lesson 1-7

- To use the Distributive Property (p. 45)
- To simplify algebraic expressions (p. 46)

Alg1 1.0, 4.0, 10.0

Terms with exactly the same variable factors are **like terms.** You can combine like terms and use the distributive property to simplify expressions.

Distributive Property For all real numbers a, b, and c, $a(b + c) = ab + ac$ and $a(b - c) = ab - ac$.

Simplify each expression.

46. $9m - 5m + 3$

47. $2b + 8 - b + 2$

48. $-5(w - 4)$

49. $9(4 - 3j)$

50. $-(3 - 10y)$

51. $-2\left(r - \frac{1}{2}\right)$

52. $(7b + 1)(5)$

53. $7 - 16v - 9v$

54. $\frac{3}{5}(15t - 2)$

55. $(6 - 3m)(-3)$

56. $-(4 - x)$

57. $0.5(20g + 3)$

Lesson 1-8

- To identify properties (p. 52)
- To use deductive reasoning (p. 54)

Alg1 1.0, 1.1, 24.1, 25.0, 25.2

Use properties of numbers to simplify expressions. Use the **Commutative Property** to change order. Use the **Associative Property** to change grouping.

Which property does each equation illustrate?

58. $62 + 15 + 38 = 62 + (15 + 38)$

59. $62 + 0 + (15 + 38) = 62 + (15 + 38)$

60. $50 \cdot 17 \cdot 2 = 50 \cdot 2 \cdot 17$

61. $9(2^3 - 4^2) = 9(2^3) - 9(4^2)$

Simplify each expression. Justify each step.

62. $19 + 56\left(\frac{1}{56}\right)$

63. $-12p + 45 - 7p$

64. $2(7 - v) - 3v$

65. $24abc - 24bac$

66. $4 \cdot 13 \cdot 25 \cdot 1$

67. $4[m - 2(2m + 3)]$

Chapter 1 Test

Go Online PHSchool.com For: Chapter Test Web Code: baa-0152

Define variables and write an equation to model the relationship in each table.

1.

Number	Cost
1	$2.30
2	$4.60
3	$6.90

2.

Payment	Change
$1	$9
$2	$8
$3	$7

Simplify each expression.

3. $3 + 5 - 4$

4. $8 - 2^4 \div 2$

5. $\frac{2 \cdot 3 - 1}{3^2}$

6. $36 - (4 + 5 \cdot 4)$

Explain why each statement is true or false.

7. All rational numbers are integers.

8. The absolute value of a number is always positive.

Write an expression for each phrase.

9. ten times the result of eleven minus two

10. the quantity p minus five eighths times the result of one fourth plus p

11. 3 plus the product of 14 and k

12. 5 divided by the quantity m plus 6

13. Write four rational numbers. Use a number line to order them from least to greatest.

14. The price p of a CD is $17.95. The sales tax rate r is 7.5%. Use the formula $C = p + rp$ to find the total cost C of the CD.

Simplify each expression.

15. $-1.8 + 12.1 + (-7.6)$

16. $6.3 - 3.9 + 3.7$

17. $1\frac{7}{8} + 14\frac{1}{8}$

18. $-7\frac{7}{8} + \left(-2\frac{1}{2}\right)$

19. $-8\frac{5}{6} + 4\frac{1}{2}$

20. $3 + 5 - 4$

21. $2\frac{2}{3} - \frac{3}{4}$

22. $10.4 + 3.7 - 5.1$

23. On four plays, a football team gained 22 yd, lost 18 yd, gained 8 yd, and lost 14 yd. What is the total number of yards gained or lost on the four plays?

24. Marcus had $163 in his checking account. On Monday, he wrote a check for $315. How much does Marcus need to deposit into his account to prevent the account balance from dipping below the minimum of $25?

Evaluate each expression for $x = 3$, $y = -1$, and $z = 2$.

25. $2x + 3y + z$

26. $-xyz$

27. $-3x - 2z - 7$

28. $-z^3 - 2z + z$

29. $\frac{xy - 3z}{-5}$

30. $|y - x| - z$

31. $x^2 + (-x)^2$

32. $y^2 - (-y)^2$

Simplify each expression.

33. $9(-5)$

34. $8 - 2^4 \div 2$

35. $-4\left(-\frac{2}{3}\right)$

36. $3\frac{1}{6} \div \left(-4\frac{2}{3}\right)$

37. $\frac{2 \cdot 3 - 1}{3^2}$

38. $36 - (4 + 5 \cdot 4)$

39. $3^3 \cdot 11 \div 9$

40. $-12 \div (-4) - 3$

41. Writing Tell if each of the subtraction sentences would *always, sometimes,* or *never* be true. Support your answer with two examples.

a. $(+) - (+) = (+)$

b. $(+) - (-) = (-)$

c. $(-) - (-) = (-)$

d. $(-) - (+) = (+)$

Simplify each expression.

42. $m(-3 + n)$

43. $6(2d - 5)$

44. $\frac{y}{5}(10 - x)$

45. $(7 - 42a)\left(-\frac{3}{7}\right)$

46. $-4(3v - 8)$

47. $\frac{5}{6}(6b + 12)$

48. $2.5(10 - 3h)$

49. $(9 + 5t)(-7)$

Simplify each expression. Justify each step.

50. $10x + 3\left(\frac{1}{3} - x\right)$

51. $2(25a - 5) - 100a$

52. $(3^3 - 3^3)(1 - 2^2)$

53. $-36 \div (-12)$

54. $27rst + 27tsr$

55. $6a - 5 + 3(3 - a)$

56. $5 + h\left(\frac{6}{h}\right) - h$

57. $4c - 6 - (-2c)$

58. Writing Explain why $\left|\frac{a}{b}\right| = \frac{a}{b}$ is *not* always true.

Cumulative Practice

Some questions ask you to determine which situation can be represented by a given equation. Read the question at the right. Then follow the tips to answer the sample question.

Tip 2
Read each answer choice to find a situation where you must add 3 to a number to get 21.

Which problem is best represented by the number sentence $21 = x + 3$?

(A) Rob bought some coasters for \$3 each. How many coasters did he buy?

(B) Andrea has 21 pairs of earrings, and she bought 3 more pairs. How many pairs of earrings does Andrea have now?

(C) Kyle had 3 pages of his term paper written yesterday, and now he has 21 pages written. How many pages did he write between yesterday and today?

(D) Sierra poured 3 cups of water from a jug, and now there are 21 cups left. How many cups of water were in the jug before she poured?

Tip 1
Determine whether the number sentence uses addition, subtraction, multiplication, or division.

Think It Through

The situation in choice A is modeled by multiplication, not addition. The equation $x = 21 + 3$ can be used to find the number of pairs of earrings in choice B. In choice C, Kyle had 3 pages then he wrote more for a total of 21. The equation $21 = x + 3$ describes this situation, so C is the correct answer.

Vocabulary Review

As you solve problems, you must understand the meanings of mathematical terms. Match each term with its mathematical meaning.

A. expression
B. equation
C. evaluate
D. variable
E. simplify

I. substitute a given number for each variable, and then simplify
II. replace an expression with its simplest form
III. a math phrase with operations and numbers or variables
IV. a symbol that represents one or more numbers
V. a math sentence stating two quantities have the same value

Read each question. Then write the letter of the correct answer on your paper.

1. If $x = 2$, $y = 3$, and $z = 4$, which expression has the greatest value? **(Lesson 1-2)**

(A) $z(x - y)$
(B) $z(x - y)^2 - x$
(C) $z(x - y)^3 + x$
(D) $z \div x - x \times y$

2. Which values for x and y will make the statement $5(x - y)^2 = 5x^2 - y^2$ true? **(Lesson 1-2)**

(A) $x = 0, y = 3$
(B) $x = 1, y = 1$
(C) $x = 3, y = 5$
(D) $x = 5, y = 1$

3. Patti is solving a math puzzle. She knows that the solution is an integer. Look at the diagram below.

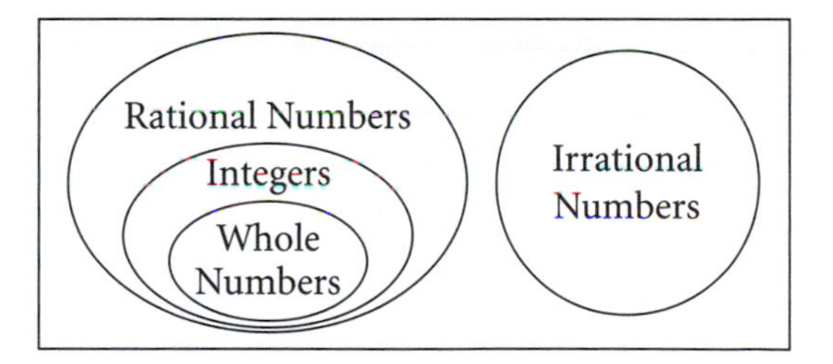

Which of the following must also be a correct conclusion about the solution? **(Lesson 1-3)**

(A) The solution is a rational number.
(B) The solution is a whole number.
(C) The solution is a fraction.
(D) The solution is an irrational number.

4. Which expression is equivalent to $3a + 2 + (3 - a)$? **(Lesson 1-8)**

(A) $2a + 5$
(B) $2a + 6$
(C) $4a + 5$
(D) $4a + 6$

Cumulative Practice (continued)

5. Simplify the algebraic expression $10x - (5x - 1)$. **(Lesson 1-7)**

- (A) $2x - 1$
- (B) $2x + 1$
- (C) $5x - 1$
- (D) $5x + 1$

6. Simplify the algebraic expression $3(2n + 1) + 4(n - 2)$. **(Lesson 1-7)**

- (A) $9n + 1$
- (B) $10n + 1$
- (C) $9n + 5$
- (D) $10n - 5$

7. Tara drew a diagram to represent the statement "Every counting number is an integer." Which of the following could be Tara's diagram? **(Lesson 1-3)**

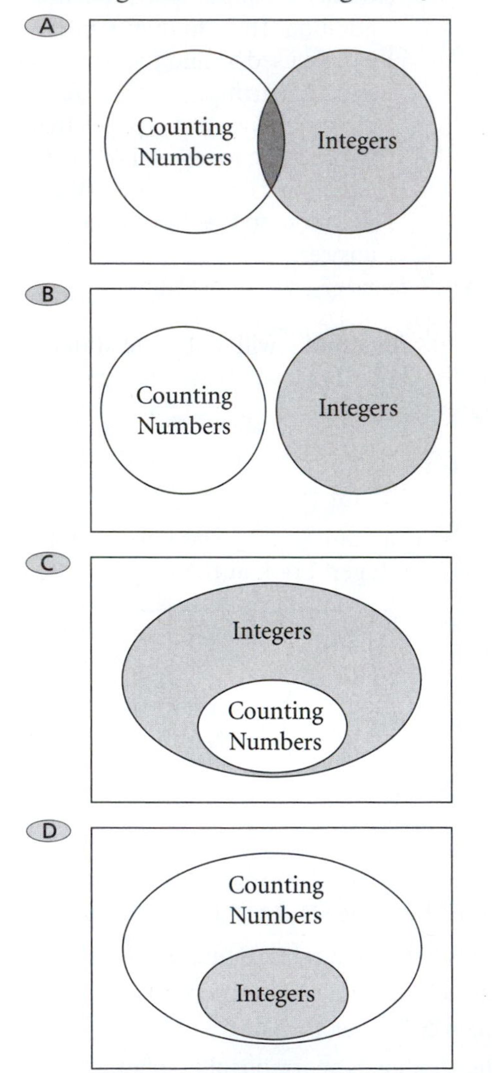

8. Name the property illustrated by the equation $(8 + 2) + 7 = (2 + 8) + 7$. **(Lesson 1-8)**

- (A) Commutative Property of Addition
- (B) Associative Property of Addition
- (C) Distributive Property
- (D) Identity Property of Addition

9. Simplify $2(5 - 3)^2 + 4 \div 2$. **(Lesson 1-2)**

(A) 6 (B) 8 (C) 10 (D) 18

10. Evaluate $\frac{3x - (-4)}{7}$ for $x = -6$. **(Lesson 1-2)**

(A) -3 (B) -2 (C) 2 (D) 3

11. Evaluate $2y + 7$ for $y = 4$. **(Lesson 1-2)**

(A) 11 (B) 15 (C) 22 (D) 31

12. Which product equals $9h - 36$? **(Lesson 1-7)**

- (A) $4(h - 9)$
- (B) $(4 - h)9$
- (C) $(9 - h)4$
- (D) $9(h - 4)$

13. Evaluate $\frac{4a^2}{2b-3}$ for $a = 3$ and $b = 6$. **(Lesson 1-2)**

(A) 3 (B) 4 (C) 6 (D) 16

14. Which property is shown by the equation $5 \times (3 \times 6) = (5 \times 3) \times 6$? **(Lesson 1-8)**

- (A) Commutative Property of Addition
- (B) Associative Property of Addition
- (C) Commutative Property of Multiplication
- (D) Associative Property of Multiplication

15. Evaluate $2a^2$ for $a = 3$. **(Lesson 1-2)**

- (A) 6
- (B) 12
- (C) 18
- (D) 36

16. Simplify the expression $3(2x + 7) + 7(5x + 2)$. **(Lesson 1-8)**

- (A) $17x + 24$
- (B) $41x + 35$
- (C) $41x + 9$
- (D) $76x$

17. Robin worked x hours on Saturday and 3 times as many hours on Monday. Write an expression for the total number of hours Robin worked. **(Lesson 1-1)**

- (A) $x + 3$ hours
- (B) $x + 4x$ hours
- (C) 4 hours
- (D) $4x$ hours

18. Use the formula $A = \frac{1}{2}bh$ to find the area of a triangle with $b = 3.2$ feet and $h = 7.5$ feet. **(Lesson 1-2)**

- (A) 10.7 ft^2
- (B) 11.2 ft^2
- (C) 12 ft^2
- (D) 24 ft^2

19. Sean deposited \$78.35 into his savings account. The next day he withdrew \$29.59. What is the difference between the deposit and the withdrawal? **(Lesson 1-1)**

- (A) \$49.76
- (B) \$49.24
- (C) \$48.76
- (D) \$48.24

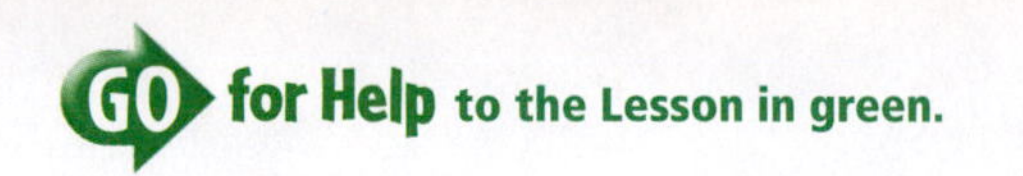

Standards Mastery

20. Evaluate $ac^4 + (a - b)c$ for $a = 4, b = 5$, and $c = -2$. **(Lesson 1-2)**

(A) 66 (C) 18
(B) 62 (D) 14

21. Which phrase can be represented by the expression $\frac{n^2}{3} + 8$? **(Lesson 1-1)**

(A) Three less than the sum of a number squared and eight.
(B) Eight more than the quotient of a number squared and three.
(C) Three less than the quotient of a number squared and eight.
(D) Eight more than the difference between a number squared and three.

22. Which expression is equivalent to $(4a + 6) - (2 - a)$? **(Lesson 1-8)**

(A) $2a + 5$ (C) $4a + 3$
(B) $3a + 4$ (D) $5a + 4$

23. Which problem is best represented by the equation $19.2 = 3.2x$? **(Lesson 1-1)**

(A) Elizabeth had \$3.20. She then received her paycheck for \$19.20. How much does she have now?
(B) Jack has \$19.20. He bought some boxes of cereal at the store for \$3.20 each. How much did he spend on cereal?
(C) Mia spent \$19.20 on socks. If each pair of socks cost \$3.20, how many pairs did she buy?
(D) Amos had \$19.20 and spent \$3.20 on lunch. How much money did Amos have after lunch?

24. Bill has a \$10 coupon for the party store. He needs to buy 25 balloons for a birthday party. If each balloon costs \$1.99, and Bill uses his coupon, what should he do to find the total cost of his purchase? **(Lesson 1-1)**

(A) Find the sum of 10 and 25, and add 1.99.
(B) Find the sum of 25 and 1.99, and subtract 10.
(C) Find the quotient of 25 and 1.99, and add 10.
(D) Find the product of 25 and 1.99, and subtract 10.

25. Simplify the expression $2(5n + 3) - 3(2n - 4)$. **(Lesson 1-8)**

(A) $4n - 1$ (C) $4n - 6$
(B) $4n + 7$ (D) $4n + 18$

26. Which equation best represents the statement "Two more than twice a number is the number squared"? **(Lesson 1-1)**

(A) $2 + n = n^2$ (C) $n^2 + n = 2n$
(B) $2 + 2n = n^2$ (D) $n^2 + n = n$

27. Which operation should you do first when simplifying $2 + 5 - 3 \times 4 \div 2$? **(Lesson 1-2)**

(A) Addition (C) Multiplication
(B) Subtraction (D) Division

28. Which phrase can be represented by the expression $2b - 3$? **(Lesson 1-1)**

(A) Three less than the sum of a number and two.
(B) Two more than the difference of a number and three.
(C) Three less than twice a number.
(D) Two times three less than a number.

29. Which operation should you do last when simplifying $5 + 1 - 4 \times 6 \div 3$? **(Lesson 1-2)**

(A) Addition (C) Multiplication
(B) Subtraction (D) Division

Standards Reference Guide

California Content Standard	Item Number(s)
7AF 1.1	17, 19, 21, 23, 26, 28
Alg1 1.0	3, 7, 8, 14, 24
7AF 1.2	1, 2, 9–11, 13, 15, 18, 20
Alg1 4.0	4–6, 12, 16, 22, 25
Alg1 25.2	27, 29

For additional review and practice, see the *California Standards Review and Practice Workbook* or go online to use the

Visit: PHSchool.com, **Web Code:** baq-9045

Solving Equations

What You've Learned

California Content Standards

1.0 Identify and use the arithmetic properties of subsets of integers and rational, irrational, and real numbers, including closure properties for the four basic arithmetic operations.

1.1 Use properties of numbers to demonstrate whether assertions are true or false.

25.1 Use properties of numbers to construct simple, valid arguments for, or formulate counterexamples to, claimed assertions.

Writing an Equation (Lesson 1-1)

Write an equation to model each situation.

1. The total cost of n cartons of milk is \$3.60. Each carton costs \$.45.
2. The perimeter of an equilateral triangle is 3 times the length of a side s. The perimeter is 124 in.

Adding and Subtracting Real Numbers (Lessons 1-4 and 1-5)

Simplify each expression.

3. $6 + (-3)$ **4.** $-4 - 6$ **5.** $-5 - (-13)$ **6.** $-7 + (-1)$

7. $-4.51 + 11.65$ **8.** $8.5 - (-7.9)$ **9.** $\frac{3}{10} - \frac{3}{4}$ **10.** $\frac{1}{5} + \left(-\frac{2}{3}\right)$

Multiplying and Dividing Real Numbers (Lesson 1-6)

Simplify each expression.

11. $-85 \div (-5)$ **12.** $7\left(-\frac{6}{14}\right)$ **13.** $4^2(-6)^2$ **14.** $22 \div (-8)$

Combining Like Terms (Lesson 1-7)

Simplify each expression.

15. $14k^2 - (-2k^2)$ **16.** $4xy + 9xy$ **17.** $6t + 2 - 4t$ **18.** $9x - 4 + 3x$

Identifying Properties (Lesson 1-8)

Name the property that each equation illustrates.

19. $(6 \cdot 8) \cdot 3 = 6 \cdot (8 \cdot 3)$ **20.** $7(2 - 4) = 7 \cdot 2 - 7 \cdot 4$ **21.** $21 + 15 = 15 + 21$

What You'll Learn Next

California Content Standards

5.0 Solve multi-step problems, including word problems, involving linear equations in one variable and provide justification for each step.

15.0 Apply algebraic techniques to solve rate problems and percent mixture problems.

25.0 Use properties of the number system to judge the validity of results, to justify each step of a procedure, and to prove or disprove statements.

▲ Math models and equations are used to meet a variety of industrial challenges. Some relate to vehicle design and production.

New Vocabulary

English and Spanish Audio Online

- **Addition Property of Equality** (p. 68)
- **consecutive integers** (p. 101)
- **cross products** (p. 94)
- **Division Property of Equality** (p. 68)
- **equivalent equations** (p. 68)
- **identity** (p. 86)
- **inverse operations** (p. 68)
- **Multiplication Property of Equality** (p. 68)
- **proportion** (p. 94)
- **rate** (p. 92)
- **set** (p. 75)
- **solution of an equation** (p. 68)
- **subset** (p. 75)
- **Subtraction Property of Equality** (p. 68)
- **uniform motion** (p. 101)

Review

Solving One-Step Equations

FOR USE WITH LESSON 2-1

Prepares for 5.0 Solve multi-step problems involving linear equations in one variable.

A **solution of an equation** is the value (or values) of the variable that makes the equation true. To find a solution, you can use properties of equality to form equivalent equations. **Equivalent equations** are equations that have the same solution (or solutions).

Addition Property of Equality

For all real numbers a, b, and c, if $a = b$, then $a + c = b + c$.

Example $8 = 5 + 3$

$8 + 4 = 5 + 3 + 4$

Subtraction Property of Equality

For all real numbers a, b, and c, if $a = b$ then $a - c = b - c$.

Example $8 = 5 + 3$

$8 - 2 = 5 + 3 - 2$

Multiplication Property of Equality

For all real numbers a, b, and c, if $a = b$, then $a \cdot c = b \cdot c$.

Example $\frac{6}{2} = 3$

$\frac{6}{2} \cdot 2 = 3 \cdot 2$

Division Property of Equality

For all real numbers a, b, and c, with $c \neq 0$, if $a = b$ then $\frac{a}{c} = \frac{b}{c}$.

Example $3 + 1 = 4$

$\frac{3 + 1}{2} = \frac{4}{2}$

One way to find the solution of an equation is to get the variable alone on one side of the equal sign. You can do this using **inverse operations,** which are operations that undo one another. Addition and subtraction are inverse operations. Multiplication and division are also inverse operations.

EXAMPLE Solving Using Inverse Operations

a. Solve $x - 3 = -8$.

$x - 3 + 3 = -8 + 3$ Add 3 to each side of the equation.

$x = -5$ Simplify.

b. Solve $g + 7 = 11$.

$g + 7 - 7 = 11 - 7$ Subtract 7 from each side of the equation.

$g = 4$ Simplify.

c. Solve $\frac{3}{4}x = 9$.

$\frac{4}{3}\left(\frac{3}{4}x\right) = \frac{4}{3}(9)$ Multiply each side by $\frac{4}{3}$, the reciprocal of $\frac{3}{4}$.

$x = 12$ Simplify.

d. Solve $-96 = 4c$.

$\frac{-96}{4} = \frac{4c}{4}$ Divide each side by 4.

$-24 = c$ Simplify.

Solve each equation.

1. $x - 8 = 0$

2. $c - 4 = 9$

3. $-4 = \frac{2}{5}a$

4. $-8n = -64$

5. $b + 5 = -13$

6. $6 = x + 2$

7. $-7y = 28$

8. $-101 = -\frac{r}{3}$

9. $67 = w - 65$

10. $5b = 145$

11. $\frac{m}{7} = 12$

12. $-4 = k + 19$

Solving Two-Step Equations

California Content Standards

5.0 Solve multi-step problems, including word problems, involving linear equations in one variable and provide justification for each step. ***Introduce***

25.0 Use properties of the number system to justify each step of a procedure. ***Develop***

What You'll Learn

- To solve two-step equations
- To use deductive reasoning

. . . And Why

To solve a problem involving ordering from a catalog, as in Example 2

Check Skills You'll Need

GO for Help Review page 68

Solve each equation and tell which property of equality you used.

1. $x - 5 = 14$
2. $x + 3.8 = 9$
3. $-7 + x = 7$
4. $x - 13 = 20$
5. $\frac{x}{4} = 8$
6. $9 = 3x$

Solve each equation.

7. $10x = 2$
8. $\frac{2}{3}x = -6$
9. $x + 2\frac{3}{4} = 6\frac{1}{2}$

Solving Two-Step Equations

A two-step equation involves two operations. Models can help you understand how to solve equations. In the model below, since ■ represents −1 and ■ represents 1, ■ ■ is a zero pair representing zero. A green rectangle represents a variable.

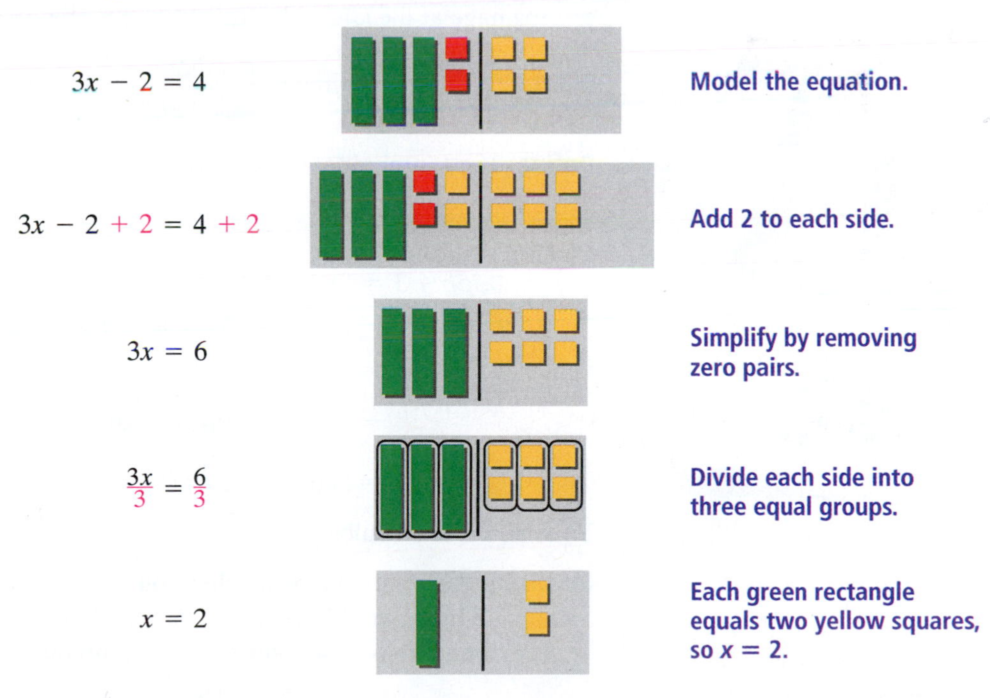

Using the addition, subtraction, multiplication, and division properties of equality, you can form equivalent equations. The equations $3x - 2 = 4$, $3x = 6$, and $x = 2$ are all equivalent equations.

To solve equations, you use the properties of equality repeatedly to get the term with a variable alone on one side of the equation and with a coefficient of 1.

1 EXAMPLE Solving a Two-Step Equation

Solve $10 = \frac{m}{4} + 2$.

$$10 = \frac{m}{4} + 2$$

$$10 - 2 = \frac{m}{4} + 2 - 2 \quad \text{Subtract 2 from each side.}$$

$$8 = \frac{m}{4} \quad \text{Simplify.}$$

$$4 \cdot 8 = 4 \cdot \frac{m}{4} \quad \text{Multiply each side by 4.}$$

$$32 = m \quad \text{Simplify.}$$

Check $10 = \frac{m}{4} + 2$

$$10 \stackrel{?}{=} \frac{32}{4} + 2 \quad \text{Substitute 32 for } m.$$

$$10 \stackrel{?}{=} 8 + 2$$

$$10 = 10 \checkmark$$

CA Standards Check 1 Solve each equation. Check your answer.

a. $7 = 2y - 3$ **b.** $\frac{x}{9} - 15 = 12$ **c.** $-x + 15 = 12$

You can write two-step equations to model real-world situations.

2 EXAMPLE Application

You are ordering tulip bulbs from a flower catalog. You have $14 to spend. Use the catalog page at the left to determine the number of bulbs that you can order.

Relate	cost per tulip bulb	times	number of tulip bulbs	plus	shipping	equals	amount to spend
Define	Let b = number of bulbs you can order.						
Write	0.75	$\cdot$	b	+	3	=	14

$$0.75b + 3 = 14$$

$$0.75b + 3 - 3 = 14 - 3 \quad \text{Subtract 3 from each side.}$$

$$0.75b = 11 \quad \text{Simplify.}$$

$$\frac{0.75b}{0.75} = \frac{11}{0.75} \quad \text{Divide each side by 0.75.}$$

$$b = 14.\overline{6} \quad \text{Simplify.}$$

You can order 14 bulbs.

Check Is the solution reasonable? You can only order whole tulip bulbs. Since 15 bulbs would cost $15 \cdot \$.75 = 11.25$ plus $3 for shipping, which is more than $14, you can only order 14 tulip bulbs.

CA Standards Check 2 Suppose tulips are on sale for $.60 per bulb. What number of bulbs can you order?

In some equations, the variable may have a negative sign in front of it, such as $-x = 3$. To help you solve these equations, recall that $x = 1 \cdot x$ and $-x = -1 \cdot x$. You can solve for x by multiplying by -1 or dividing by -1.

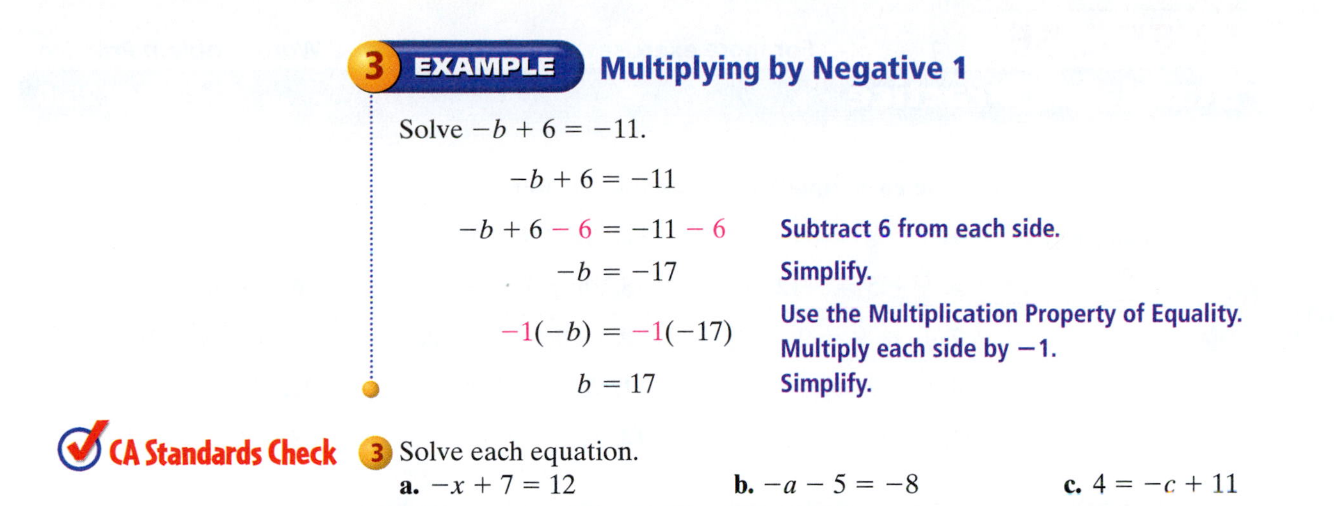

3 EXAMPLE Multiplying by Negative 1

Solve $-b + 6 = -11$.

$-b + 6 = -11$	
$-b + 6 - 6 = -11 - 6$	Subtract 6 from each side.
$-b = -17$	Simplify.
$-1(-b) = -1(-17)$	Use the Multiplication Property of Equality. Multiply each side by -1.
$b = 17$	Simplify.

CA Standards Check 3 Solve each equation.

a. $-x + 7 = 12$ **b.** $-a - 5 = -8$ **c.** $4 = -c + 11$

Using Deductive Reasoning

You can use deductive reasoning and the properties of equality to justify steps as you solve an equation.

4 EXAMPLE Using Deductive Reasoning

For help with deductive reasoning, see p. 54.

Solve $1 = \frac{k}{12} + 5$. Justify each step.

Steps	Reasons
$1 = \frac{k}{12} + 5$	original equation
$1 - 5 = \frac{k}{12} + 5 - 5$	Subtraction Property of Equality
$-4 = \frac{k}{12}$	Simplify.
$(12)(-4) = (12)\frac{k}{12}$	Multiplication Property of Equality
$-48 = k$	Simplify.

CA Standards Check 4 Solve $\frac{3}{5}w + 9 = -1$. Justify each step.

Remember that an expression like $8 - 3y$ can be rewritten as $8 + (-3y)$ using the definition of subtraction.

5 EXAMPLE Using Deductive Reasoning

Solve $8 - 3y = 14$. Justify each step.

Steps	Reasons
$8 - 3y = 14$	original equation
$8 + (-3y) = 14$	definition of subtraction
$8 + (-3y) - 8 = 14 - 8$	Subtraction Property of Equality
$-3y = 6$	Simplify.
$\frac{-3y}{-3} = \frac{6}{-3}$	Division Property of Equality
$y = -2$	Simplify.

CA Standards Check 5 Solve $-9 - 4m = 3$. Justify each step.

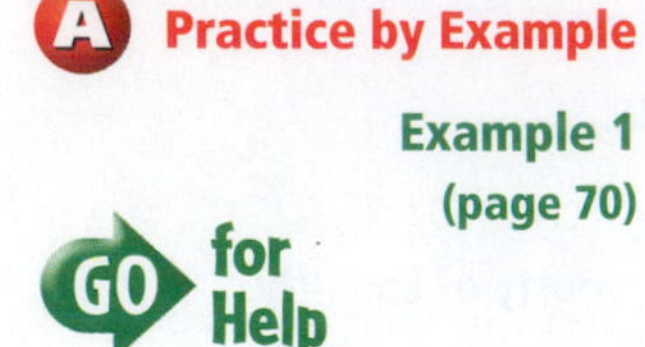

EXERCISES

For more exercises, see *Extra Skills and Word Problem Practice.*

Standards Practice

Alg1 5.0, 25.0

A Practice by Example

Example 1 (page 70)

GO for Help

Solve each equation. Check your answer.

1. $1 + \frac{a}{5} = -1$ **2.** $2n - 5 = 7$ **3.** $-1 = 3 + 4x$

4. $\frac{y}{2} + 5 = -12$ **5.** $3b + 7 = -2$ **6.** $\frac{x}{3} - 9 = 0$

7. $14 + \frac{h}{5} = 2$ **8.** $-10 = -6 + 2c$ **9.** $\frac{m}{8} + 4 = 16$

10. $\frac{a}{4} - 21 = 7$ **11.** $3x - 1 = 8$ **12.** $10 = 2n + 1$

13. $35 = 3 + 5x$ **14.** $41 = \frac{2}{5}x - 7$ **15.** $-3 + \frac{m}{3} = 12$

Example 2 (page 70)

Define a variable and write an equation for each situation. Then solve.

16. A library receives a large cash donation and uses the funds to double the number of books it owns. Then a book collector gives the library 4028 books. After this, the library has 51,514 books. How many books did the library have before the cash donation and the gift of books?

17. Suppose you are helping to prepare a large meal. You can peel 2 carrots per minute. You need 60 peeled carrots. How long will it take you to finish if you have already peeled 18 carrots?

Example 3 (page 71)

Solve each equation. Check your solution.

18. $-b + 5 = -16$ **19.** $-p - 24 = -8$ **20.** $-7 = -c - 29$

21. $-y - 52 = 33$ **22.** $-m + 2 = 1$ **23.** $-9 = -a + 16$

Examples 4, 5 (page 71)

Justify each step.

24.
$$\begin{aligned} \frac{x}{5} + 9 &= 11 \\ \frac{x}{5} + 9 - 9 &= 11 - 9 \\ \frac{x}{5} &= 2 \\ 5\left(\frac{x}{5}\right) &= 5(2) \\ x &= 10 \end{aligned}$$

25.
$$\begin{aligned} -y - 5 &= 11 \\ -y - 5 + 5 &= 11 + 5 \\ -y &= 16 \\ -1(-y) &= -1(16) \\ y &= -16 \end{aligned}$$

26.
$$\begin{aligned} 18 - n &= 21 \\ 18 - n - 18 &= 21 - 18 \\ -n &= 3 \\ -1(-n) &= -1(3) \\ n &= -3 \end{aligned}$$

27.
$$\begin{aligned} 12 - 2h &= 8 \\ 12 - 2h - 12 &= 8 - 12 \\ -2h &= -4 \\ \frac{-2h}{-2} &= \frac{-4}{-2} \\ h &= 2 \end{aligned}$$

B Apply Your Skills

Solve each equation.

28. $\frac{5}{7}x + \frac{1}{7} = 3$ **29.** $\frac{a}{5} + 15 = 30$ **30.** $-\frac{1}{5}t - 2 = 4$

31. $-6 + 6z = 0$ **32.** $3.5 + 10m = 7.32$ **33.** $7 = -2x + 7$

34. $\frac{1}{2} = \frac{2}{5}c - 3$ **35.** $10.7 = -d + 4.3$ **36.** $0.4x + 9.2 = 10$

37. $4x + 92 = 100$ **38.** $-t - 0.4 = -3$ **39.** $-10t - 4 = -30$

Solve each equation. Justify each step.

40. $8 + \frac{c}{-4} = -6$ **41.** $7 - 3k = -14$ **42.** $\frac{-y}{2} + 14 = -1$

Visit: PHSchool.com
Web Code: bae-0201

43. Beneath Earth's surface, the temperature increases 10°C every kilometer. Suppose that the surface temperature is 22°C, and the temperature at the bottom of a coal mine is 45°C. Which equation could be used to find the depth d of the coal mine?

(A) $10d + 22 = 45$
(B) $d = 22 + 10$
(C) $45d - 10 = 22$
(D) $22 = 10d + 45$

Define a variable and write an equation for each situation. Then solve.

44. One health insurance policy pays people for claims by multiplying the claim amount by 0.8 and then subtracting \$500. Find the claim amount for an insurance payment of \$4650.

45. The Library of Congress in Washington, D.C., is the largest library in the world. It contains nearly 128 million items. The library adds about 10,000 items to its collection daily. Find the number of days it will take the library to reach about 150 million items.

Solve each equation.

Problem Solving Tip

For Exercises 46–54, multiply each side by the denominator of the fraction as your first step.

46. $\frac{x + 2}{9} = 5$ **47.** $\frac{y + 1}{3} = 2$ **48.** $\frac{a - 10}{-4} = 2$

49. $\frac{b - 7}{2} = 6$ **50.** $\frac{x - 5}{2} = 10$ **51.** $\frac{x - 3}{7} = 12$

52. $\frac{x + 4}{3} = -8$ **53.** $\frac{x + 6}{4} = -7$ **54.** $\frac{c - 4}{-6} = 9$

In each triangle, the measure of $\angle A$ = the measure of $\angle B$. Find the value of x.

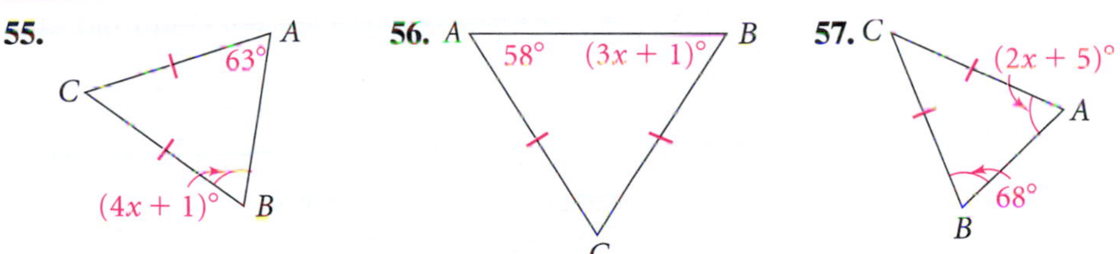

58. Writing Miles has saved \$40. He wants to buy a CD player for \$129 in about four months. To find how much he should save each week, he writes $40 + 16x = 129$. Explain his equation.

Error Analysis **What is the error in the work? Solve each equation correctly.**

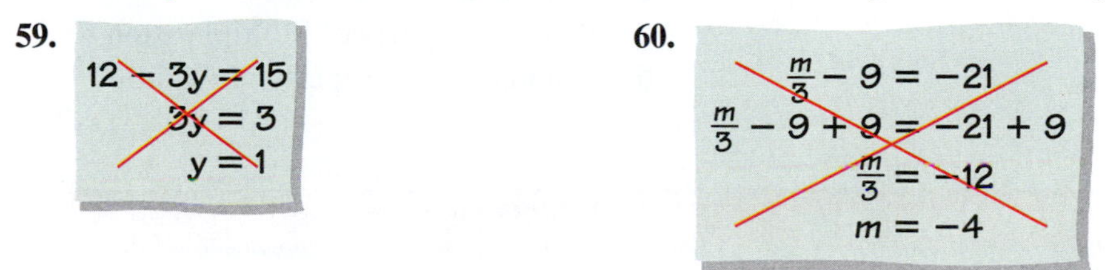

61. Write a problem that you can model with a two-step equation. Write an equation and solve the problem.

62. Critical Thinking If you multiply each side of $0.24r + 5.25 = -7.23$ by 100, the result is an equivalent equation. Explain why it might be helpful to do this.

Use the table at the right for Exercises 63 and 64.

63. A formula for converting a temperature from Celsius C to Fahrenheit F is $F = 1.8C + 32$. Copy and complete the table. Round to the nearest degree.

Fahrenheit	Celsius	Description of Temperature
212°	■	boiling point of water
■	37°	human body temperature
68°	■	room temperature
■	0°	freezing point of water
■	−40°	

64. a. Estimation Use the formula $F = 2C + 30$ to estimate the Fahrenheit temperatures not shown in the table.

b. Critical Thinking Compare your estimated values with the actual values. How good is your formula at estimating the actual temperatures? Explain.

C Challenge

Solve the first equation for x. Then substitute your result into the second equation and solve for y.

65. $x + y = 8$
$2x + 3y = 21$

66. $x + 2y = 1$
$6x - y = -20$

67. $x + y = 12$
$2x + y = 17$

Multiple Choice Practice

For California Standards Tutorials, visit PHSchool.com. Web Code: baq-9045

Alg1 5.0

68. Last season, Everett scored 48 points. This is 6 less than twice the number of points Max scored. How many points did Max score?

(A) 30 (B) 27 (C) 21 (D) 16

Alg1 5.0

69. A cable television company charges $24.95 a month for basic cable service and $6.95 a month for each additional premium channel. If Sami's monthly bill is $45.80, how many premium channels is he receiving?

(A) 1 (B) 2 (C) 3 (D) 4

Alg1 5.0, 25.0

70. To solve $9x + (4 - 3x) = 34$, you first rewrite the equation as $9x + (-3x + 4) = 34$. What property justifies this step?

(A) Associative Property of Addition
(B) Distributive Property
(C) Inverse Property of Multiplication
(D) Commutative Property of Addition

Mixed Review

GO for Help

Lesson 1-6

Simplify each expression.

71. $-6(-4)$ **72.** $2(-5.5)$ **73.** $\frac{45}{-3}$ **74.** $\frac{-5 - 31}{-9}$

Lesson 1-4

Simplify.

75. $-2 + 6$ **76.** $9 + (-3)$ **77.** $-7 + (-4)$ **78.** $16 + (-4)$

Activity Lab Set Notation

FOR USE WITH LESSON 2-1

1.0 Identify and use the arithmetic properties of subsets of integers and rational, irrational, and real numbers, including closure properties for the four basic arithmetic operations. ***Master***

The word *set* often indicates a group of things, like a set of dishes or set of luggage. In mathematics, the word **set** indicates a well-defined collection of **elements,** usually numbers. Below are two ways to write the set of integers.

Roster Notation	Set-Builder Notation
$Z = \{\ldots -3, -2, -1, 0, 1, 2, 3, \ldots\}$	$Z = \{x: x \text{ is an integer}\}$

The content within braces lists the elements of a set or tells how a set is built. You read $Z = \{x: x \text{ is an integer}\}$ as "The set Z equals all the values of x such that x is an integer." The notation $3 \in Z$ means 3 is an element of the set Z. Set $A = \{1, 2, 3\}$ is a **subset** of set Z because every element of set A is an element of set Z.

1 EXAMPLE

Write the set B of positive integers in roster notation and in set-builder notation.

$B = \{1, 2, 3, 4, \ldots\}$ $\qquad$ $B = \{x: x \text{ is an integer and } x > 0\}$

The **intersection** of two sets is the set of all elements that are common to both sets. $A \cap B$ means "A intersection B." The **union** of two sets is the set of all elements that are in either of the sets. $A \cup B$ means "A union B." The empty set, or **null set,** has no elements, and is indicated by { } or $\emptyset$.

2 EXAMPLE

a. Find $C \cap D$, where $C = \{9, 12, 15, 18, 21\}$ and $D = \{x: x \text{ is a positive odd integer}\}$.

$C \cap D = \{9, 15, 21\}$ The numbers in set C that are positive odd integers are 9, 15, and 21.

b. Find $P \cup Q$, where $P = \{5, 10, 15, 20\}$ and $Q = \{8, 10, 18, 20\}$.

$P \cup Q = \{5, 8, 10, 15, 18, 20\}$ List the numbers of both sets in order from least to greatest. If a number appears in both sets, list the number only once.

EXERCISES

Write each set in roster notation and in set-builder notation.

1. set E = negative integers

2. set F = whole numbers greater than 10

3. set G = even prime numbers

4. set H = multiples of 3 less than 30

Let $A = \{2, 5, 8\}$, $B = \{5, 7, 9\}$, $C = \{2, 7, 8\}$, and $D = \{x: x \text{ is a positive even integer less than } 9\}$. Find the union and intersection of each of the following sets.

5. A and B

6. B and C

7. C and D

8. A and C

9. B and D

10. A and D

11. Is the set $\{-1, 0, 1\}$ closed for addition and for multiplication? Explain.

2-2 Solving Multi-Step Equations

California Content Standards

2.0 Understand and use such operations as finding the reciprocal. ***Develop***
4.0 Simplify expressions before solving linear equations. ***Develop***
5.0 Solve multi-step problems, including word problems, involving linear equations in one variable and provide justification for each step. ***Develop***

What You'll Learn

- To use the Distributive Property when combining like terms
- To use the Distributive Property when solving equations

. . . And Why

To solve a problem involving construction, as in Example 2

Check Skills You'll Need

GO for Help Lessons 1-2 and 1-7

Simplify each expression.

1. $2n - 3n$
2. $-4 + 3b + 2 + 5b$
3. $9(w - 5)$
4. $-10(b - 12)$
5. $3(-x + 4)$
6. $5(6 - w)$

Evaluate each expression.

7. $28 - a + 4a$ for $a = 5$
8. $8 + x - 7x$ for $x = -3$
9. $(8n + 1)3$ for $n = -2$
10. $-(17 + 3y)$ for $y = 6$

Using the Distributive Property to Combine Like Terms

You can solve equations that require more than two steps. If there are like terms on one side of an equation, first use the Distributive Property to combine them.

Problem Solving Tip

You use the Distributive Property whenever you add or subtract like terms.

$$x + 4x = 1x + 4x = (1 + 4)x = 5x$$

1 EXAMPLE Combining Like Terms

Solve each equation.

a. $2c + c + 12 = 78$

$2c + c + 12 = 78$

$3c + 12 = 78$ — Combine like terms.

$3c + 12 - 12 = 78 - 12$ — Subtract 12 from each side.

$3c = 66$ — Simplify.

$\frac{3c}{3} = \frac{66}{3}$ — Divide each side by 3.

$c = 22$ — Simplify.

b. $8b + 16 - 2b = 46$

$8b + 16 - 2b = 46$

$8b - 2b + 16 = 46$ — Use the Commutative Property of Addition.

$6b + 16 = 46$ — Combine like terms.

$6b + 16 - 16 = 46 - 16$ — Subtract 16 from each side.

$6b = 30$ — Simplify.

$\frac{6b}{6} = \frac{30}{6}$ — Divide each side by 6.

$b = 5$ — Simplify.

CA Standards Check 1 Solve $7 = 4m - 2m + 1$. Check your answer.

You can model real-world situations using multi-step equations.

2 EXAMPLE Application

A gardener is planning a rectangular garden area in a community garden. His garden will be next to an existing 12-ft fence. The gardener has 44 ft of fencing to build the other three sides of his garden. How long will the garden be if the width is 12 ft?

(A) 32 ft (B) 24 ft (C) 22 ft (D) 16 ft

Relate length of side plus 12 ft plus length of side equals amount of fencing

Define Let x = length of a side adjacent to the fence.

Write x + 12 + x = 44

$$x + 12 + x = 44$$

$$2x + 12 = 44 \quad \text{Combine like terms on the left side of the equation.}$$

$$2x + 12 - 12 = 44 - 12 \quad \text{Subtract 12 from each side.}$$

$$2x = 32 \quad \text{Simplify.}$$

$$\frac{2x}{2} = \frac{32}{2} \quad \text{Divide each side by 2.}$$

$$x = 16 \quad \text{Simplify.}$$

The garden will be 16 ft long. So D is the correct answer.

CA Standards Check 2 A carpenter is building a rectangular fence for a playground. One side of the playground is the wall of a building 70 ft wide. He plans to use 340 ft of fencing material. What is the length of the playground if the width is 70 ft?

Using the Distributive Property to Solve Equations

In the equation $-2(b - 4) = 12$, the parentheses indicate multiplication. Use the Distributive Property to multiply each term within the parentheses by -2. Then use the properties of equality to solve the equation.

3 EXAMPLE Solving an Equation With Grouping Symbols

Study Tip

Remember to multiply the number outside the parentheses by both terms inside the parentheses.

Solve $-2(b - 4) = 12$.

$$-2(b - 4) = 12$$

$$-2b + 8 = 12 \quad \text{Use the Distributive Property.}$$

$$-2b + 8 - 8 = 12 - 8 \quad \text{Subtract 8 from each side.}$$

$$-2b = 4 \quad \text{Simplify.}$$

$$\frac{-2b}{-2} = \frac{4}{-2} \quad \text{Divide each side by } -2.$$

$$b = -2 \quad \text{Simplify.}$$

CA Standards Check 3 Solve each equation.

a. $3(k + 8) = 21$ **b.** $15 = -3(x - 1) + 9$

Following are two ways you can solve an equation like $\frac{2x}{3} + \frac{x}{2} = 7$.

4 EXAMPLE Solving an Equation That Contains Fractions

Quick Tip

$\frac{x}{2}$ and $\frac{1}{2}x$ both represent $x \div 2$.
$\frac{2x}{3}$ and $\frac{2}{3}x$ both represent $2x \div 3$.

Solve $\frac{2x}{3} + \frac{x}{2} = 7$.

Method 1 Adding fractions

$\frac{2x}{3} + \frac{x}{2} = 7$

$\frac{2}{3}x + \frac{1}{2}x = 7$ **Rewrite the equation with fractions as coefficients.**

$\frac{4}{6}x + \frac{3}{6}x = 7$ **Write the fractions with a denominator of 6.**

$\frac{7}{6}x = 7$ **Combine like terms.**

$\frac{6}{7}\left(\frac{7}{6}x\right) = \frac{6}{7}(7)$ **Multiply each side by $\frac{6}{7}$, the reciprocal of $\frac{7}{6}$.**

$x = 6$ **Simplify.**

Method 2 Multiplying to clear fractions

$\frac{2x}{3} + \frac{x}{2} = 7$

$6\left(\frac{2x}{3} + \frac{x}{2}\right) = 6(7)$ **Multiply each side by 6, a common multiple of 3 and 2.**

$6\left(\frac{2x}{3}\right) + 6\left(\frac{x}{2}\right) = 6(7)$ **Use the Distributive Property.**

$4x + 3x = 42$ **Multiply.**

$7x = 42$ **Combine like terms.**

$\frac{7x}{7} = \frac{42}{7}$ **Divide each side by 7.**

$x = 6$ **Simplify.**

CA Standards Check 4 Solve each equation. Explain why you chose the method you used.

a. $\frac{m}{4} + \frac{m}{2} = \frac{5}{8}$ **b.** $\frac{2}{3}x - \frac{5}{8}x = 26$

Quick Review

Powers of 10:
$10^1 = 10$
$10^2 = 100$
$10^3 = 1000$
$10^4 = 10{,}000$

You can clear an equation of decimals by multiplying by a power of 10. In the equation $0.5a + 8.75 = 13.25$, the greatest number of digits to the right of a decimal point is 2. To clear the equation of decimals, multiply each side of the equation by 10^2, or 100.

5 EXAMPLE Solving an Equation That Contains Decimals

Solve $0.5a + 8.75 = 13.25$.

$100(0.5a + 8.75) = 100(13.25)$ **Multiply each side by 10^2, or 100.**

$100(0.5a) + 100(8.75) = 100(13.25)$ **Use the Distributive Property.**

$50a + 875 = 1325$ **Simplify.**

$50a + 875 - 875 = 1325 - 875$ **Subtract 875 from each side.**

$50a = 450$ **Simplify.**

$\frac{50a}{50} = \frac{450}{50}$ **Divide each side by 50.**

$a = 9$ **Simplify.**

CA Standards Check 5 Solve each equation.

a. $0.025x + 22.95 = 23.65$ **b.** $1.2x - 3.6 + 0.3x = 2.4$

Keep the steps in the summary below in mind as you solve equations that have variables on one side of the equation.

Take Note

Summary **Steps for Solving a Multi-Step Equation**

Step 1 Clear the equation of fractions and decimals.

Step 2 Use the Distributive Property to remove parentheses on each side.

Step 3 Combine like terms on each side.

Step 4 Undo addition or subtraction.

Step 5 Undo multiplication or division.

EXERCISES Standards Practice

For more exercises, see *Extra Skills and Word Problem Practice.*

Alg1 2.0, 4.0, 5.0

A Practice by Example

Example 1 (page 76)

GO for Help

Solve each equation. Check your answer.

1. $4n - 2n = 18$
2. $y + y + 2 = 18$
3. $a + 6a - 9 = 30$
4. $5 - x - x = -1$
5. $72 + 4 - 14c = 36$
6. $9 = -3 + n + 2n$
7. $7m - 3m - 6 = 6$
8. $-13 = 2b - b - 10$
9. $-2y + 5 + 5y = 14$
10. $-3z + 8 + (-2z) = -12$

Example 2 (page 77)

Write an equation to model each situation. Solve your equation.

11. Two friends are renting an apartment. They pay the landlord the first month's rent. The landlord also requires them to pay an additional half of a month's rent for a security deposit. The total amount they pay the landlord before moving in is $1725. What is the monthly rent?

12. You are fencing a rectangular puppy kennel with 25 ft of fence. The side of the kennel against your house does not need a fence. This side is 9 ft long. Find the dimensions of the kennel.

Example 3 (page 77)

Solve each equation. Check your answer.

13. $2(8 + p) = 22$
14. $5(a - 1) = 35$
15. $15 = -3(2q - 1)$
16. $26 = 6(5 - a)$
17. $m + 5(m - 1) = 7$
18. $-4(x + 6) = -40$
19. $48 = 8(x + 2)$
20. $5(y - 3) = 19$
21. $5(2 + y) = 77$

Example 4 (page 78)

22. $\frac{a}{7} - \frac{5}{7} = \frac{6}{7}$
23. $x - \frac{5}{8} = \frac{7}{8}$
24. $\frac{m}{6} - 7 = \frac{2}{3}$
25. $\frac{2}{3} + \frac{3k}{4} = \frac{71}{12}$
26. $4 + \frac{m}{8} = \frac{3}{4}$
27. $\frac{a}{2} + \frac{1}{5} = 17$
28. $\frac{1}{2} + \frac{7x}{10} = \frac{13}{20}$
29. $\frac{9y}{14} + \frac{3}{7} = \frac{9}{14}$
30. $\frac{1}{5} + \frac{3w}{15} = \frac{4}{5}$

Solve each equation. Check your answer.

Example 5 (page 78)

31. $3m + 4.5m = 15$
32. $7.8y + 2 = 165.8$
33. $3.5 = 12s - 5s$
34. $1.06y - 3 = 0.71$
35. $0.11p + 1.5 = 2.49$
36. $25.24 = 5y + 3.89$
37. $1.12 + 1.25y = 8.62$
38. $1.025x + 2.458 = 7.583$
39. $0.25m + 0.1m = 9.8$
40. $0.36p + 0.26 = 3.86$

B Apply Your Skills

Solve each equation.

41. $0.5t - 3t + 5 = 0$
42. $-(z + 5) = -14$
43. $\frac{a}{15} + \frac{4}{15} = \frac{9}{15}$
44. $0.5(x - 12) = 4$
45. $8y - (2y - 3) = 9$
46. $\frac{2}{3} + y = \frac{3}{4}$
47. $2 + \frac{a}{-4} = \frac{3}{5}$
48. $\frac{1}{4}(m - 16) = 7$
49. $x + 3x - 7 = 29$
50. $4x + 3.6 + x = 1.2$
51. $2(1.5c + 4) = -1$
52. $26.54 - p = 0.5(50 - p)$

53. **Error Analysis** Explain the error in the student's work at the right.

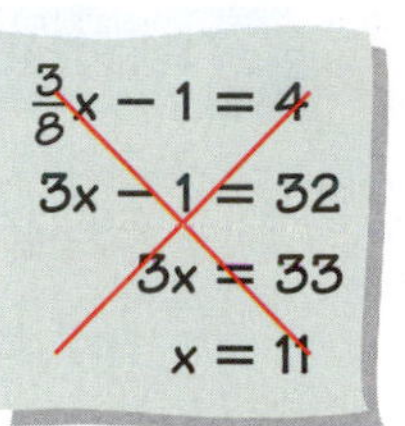

54. **Critical Thinking** Suppose you want to solve the equation $-3m + 4 + 5m = -6$. What would you do as your first step?

55. **Writing** To solve $-\frac{1}{2}(3x - 5) = 7$, you can use the Distributive Property, or you can multiply each side of the equation by -2. Which method do you prefer? Explain why.

The perimeter of each rectangle is 64 in. Find the value of x.

56. 57.

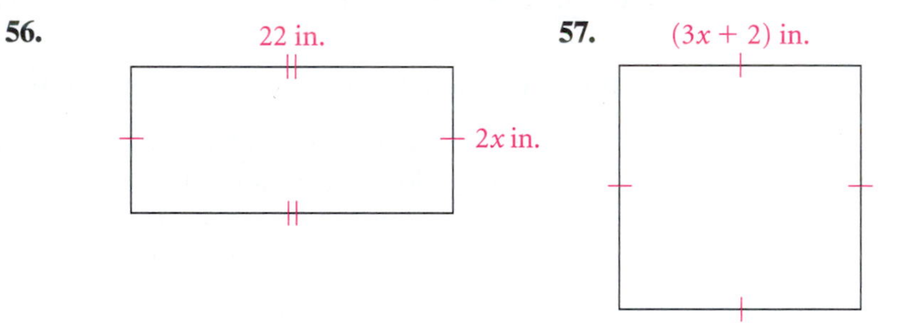

Use an equation to solve each problem.

58. John and two friends rent a canoe at a park. Each person must rent a life jacket. If the bill for the rental of the canoe and life jackets is $41, for how many hours did they rent the canoe?

59. The MacNeills rented a moving truck for $49.95 plus $.30 per mile. Before returning the truck, they filled the tank with gasoline, which cost $18.32. The total cost was $95.87. Find the number of miles the truck was driven.

60. Jane's cell phone plan is $40 per month plus $.15 per minute for each minute over 200 minutes of call time. If Jane's cell phone bill is $58.00, for how many extra calling minutes was she billed?

61. Write an expression with four terms that can be simplified to an expression with two terms.

Visit: PHSchool.com
Web Code: bae-0202

Find the value of x. (*Hint:* The sum of the measures of the angles of a triangle is 180°.)

62. **63.** **64.**

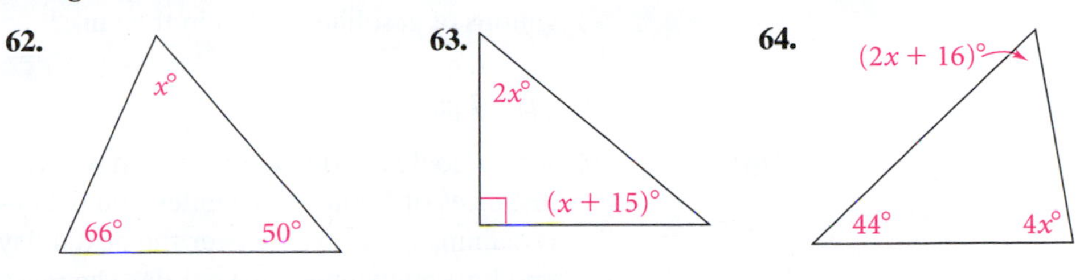

65. The equation $c = p + 0.07p$ relates the price of an item p with its cost c after 7% tax is added. A student has \$12.50. What is the cost of the most expensive item he can buy?

66. Nadia has \$70 in her bank account. Each week she deposits \$3 from her allowance and \$15 from babysitting. The equation $b = 70 + (15 + 3)w$ relates her bank balance b to weeks w. When will she have \$160 in her bank account?

C Challenge

For Exercises 67–69, use an equation to solve each problem.

67. You fill your car's gas tank when it is about $\frac{1}{2}$ empty. The next week, you fill the tank a second time when it is about $\frac{3}{4}$ empty. If you buy a total of $18\frac{1}{2}$ gal of gas on these two days, about how many gallons does the tank hold?

68. A work crew has two pumps, one new and one old. The new pump can fill a tank in 5 hours. The old pump can fill the same tank in 7 hours.

a. How much of a tank can be filled in 1 hour with the new pump? With the old pump?

b. Write an expression for the number of tanks the new pump can fill in t hours. (*Hint:* Write the rate at which the new pump fills tanks as a fraction and then multiply by t.)

c. Write an expression for the number of tanks the old pump can fill in t hours.

d. Write and solve an equation for the time it will take the pumps to fill one tank if the pumps are used together.

69. Mr. Fairbanks invested half his money in land, a tenth in stock, and a twentieth in bonds. He put the remaining \$35,000 in a savings account. What is the total amount of money that Mr. Fairbanks saved or invested?

Multiple Choice Practice

For California Standards Tutorials, visit PHSchool.com. Web Code: baq-9045

Alg1 2.0 **70.** Simplify the expression $-\frac{3}{4} - \left[-\left(-\frac{2}{5}\right)\right]$.

(A) $\frac{7}{20}$ (B) $-\frac{1}{4}$ (C) $-\frac{7}{20}$ (D) $-\frac{23}{20}$

Alg1 4.0 **71.** Solve $8n + 5 - 2n = 41$.

(A) $3\frac{1}{2}$ (B) $4\frac{1}{2}$ (C) 6 (D) $7\frac{2}{3}$

Alg1 5.0 **72.** If a number is increased by 3 and that number is doubled, the result is −8. What was the original number?

(A) −7
(B) −5.5
(C) 1
(D) 6

Alg1 5.0

73. The gas tank in Royston's car holds 12 gal of gasoline. The car averages 29 mi/gal. Royston filled up the tank and then drove 140 mi. About how many gallons of gasoline are left in the tank?

A 6 gal
B 7 gal
C 8 gal
D 9 gal

Alg1 5.0

74. Josie's goal is to run 40 miles each week. This week she has already run distances of 5.3 miles, 6.5 miles, and 6.2 miles. If she wants to spread out the remaining miles evenly over the next 4 days, which equation can you use to find how many miles (m) per day she must run?

A $5.3 + 6.5 + 6.2 + 40 = m$

B $40 - 5.2 - 6.5 - 6.2 = m$

C $5.3 + 6.5 + 6.2 + 4m = 40$

D $5.3 + 6.5 + 6.2 + m = \frac{40}{4}$

Alg1 5.0

75. A cell phone company charges $.35 for the first minute but only $.10 every minute after that. Which equation can you use to find how many minutes m Eric talked if the bill for the call was $5.45?

A $0.35 + 0.10(m - 1) = 5.45$
B $0.35 + 0.10m = 5.45$
C $0.10 + 0.35(m - 1) = 5.45$
D $0.10 + 0.35m = 5.45$

Mixed Review

GO for Help

Lesson 2-1

Solve each equation.

76. $2y + 4 = -6$
77. $3x - 15 = 33$
78. $-4n + 20 = 36$
79. $-8 - c = 11$
80. $3x + 5 = 12$
81. $-4y - 3 = 15$
82. $8m - 4 = 8$
83. $-p + 3 = 10$

84. One cell phone plan costs $39.95 per month. The first 500 minutes of usage are free. Each minute thereafter costs $.35. Find the number of minutes of usage over 500 minutes for a bill of $69.70.

Lesson 1-8

Mental Math Simplify each expression.

85. $14 \cdot 4 \cdot 25$
86. $16 + 28 + 34 + 72$
87. $-8 + 15 - 9 + 2$
88. $3 \cdot 3 \cdot 10$
89. $2 \cdot 8 \cdot 5$
90. $27 + 46 - 17 - 16$

Lessons 1-4 through 1-6

Simplify each expression.

91. $2 - 6$
92. $-9 \cdot (-3)$
93. $-9 + (-4)$
94. $16 \div (-4)$
95. $-7 + (-3)$
96. $-5 - (-3)$
97. $-5 \cdot 6$
98. $-25 \div (-5)$

Activity Lab: Modeling Equations

FOR USE WITH LESSON 2-3

> **5.0** Solve multi-step problems involving linear equations in one variable. ***Develop***
> **25.0** Use properties of the number system to justify each step of a procedure. ***Develop***

Models can help you understand how to solve equations that have variables on both sides.

EXAMPLE

Model and solve $3a - 2 = a + 4$.

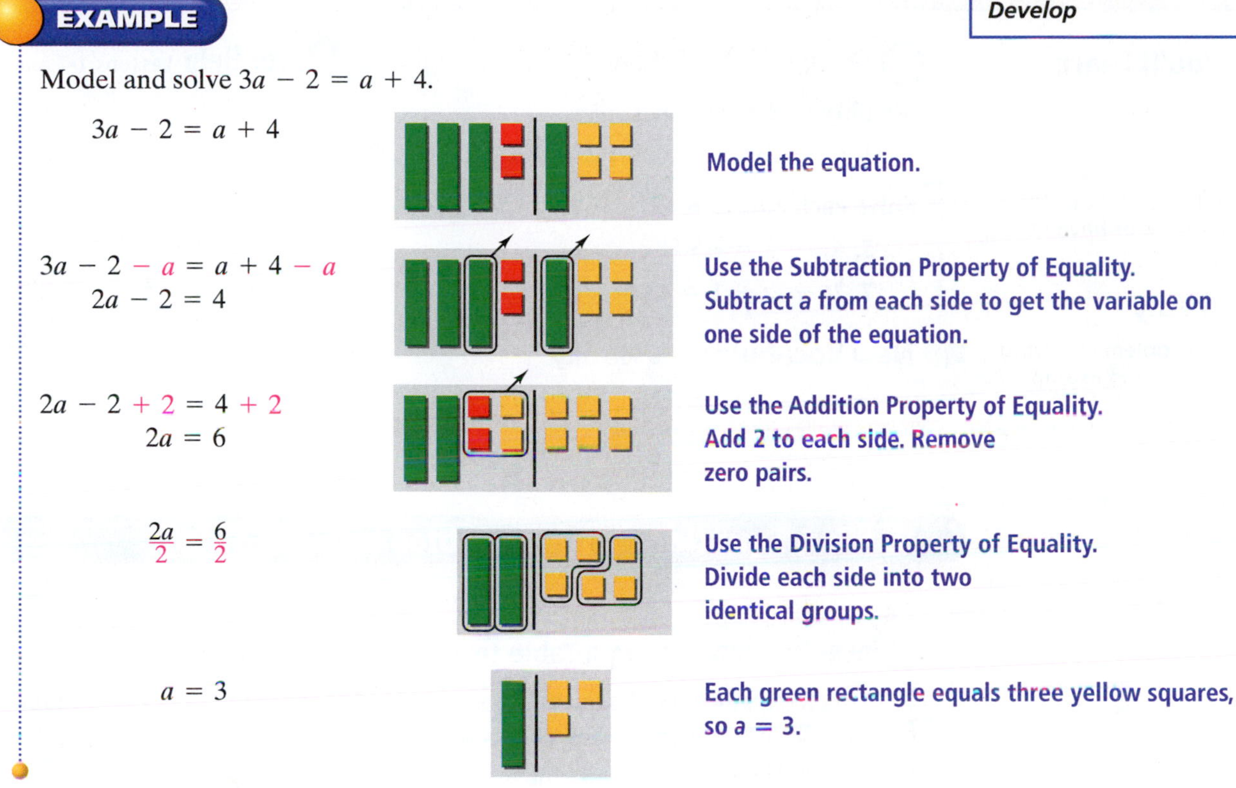

EXERCISES

Write an equation for each model. Use models to solve each equation.

1. 3.

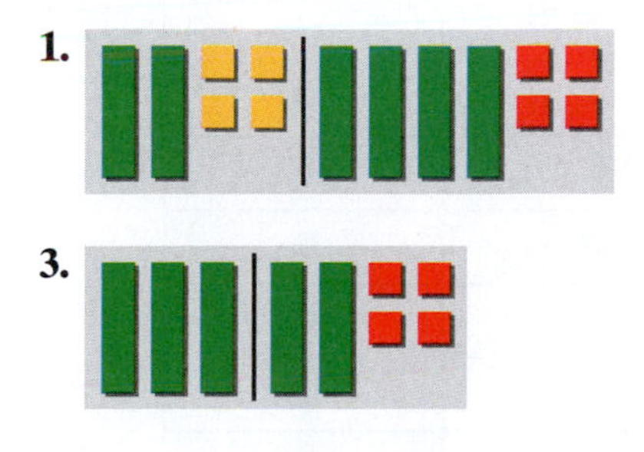

2. 4.

Use models to solve each equation.

5. $4x + 2 = 2x + 6$
6. $2y - 2 = 4y + 2$
7. $2a + 2 = a + 8$
8. $5b - 4 = 2b + 5$
9. $z - 8 = 2z - 1$
10. $4(p + 1) = 2p - 2$
11. $5n - 3 = 2(n + 3)$
12. $2(k + 1) = 5(k - 2)$

CALIFORNIA CHECK SYSTEM

2-3 Equations With Variables on Both Sides

California Content Standards

4.0 Simplify expressions before solving linear equations. ***Develop***

5.0 Solve multi-step problems, including word problems, involving linear equations in one variable and provide justification for each step. ***Develop***

25.3 Given a linear equation, determine whether the statement is true. ***Introduce***

What You'll Learn

- To solve equations with variables on both sides
- To identify equations that are identities or have no solution

. . . And Why

To solve a problem involving skate rentals, as in Example 2

Check Skills You'll Need

GO for Help Lessons 1-7 and 2-2

Simplify each expression.

1. $6x - 2x$ **2.** $2x - 6x$ **3.** $5x - 5x$ **4.** $-5x + 5x$

Solve each equation.

5. $4x + 3 = -5$ **6.** $-x + 7 = 12$

7. $2t - 8t + 1 = 43$ **8.** $0 = -7n + 4 - 5n$

New Vocabulary

- identity

Solving Equations With Variables on Both Sides

CA Standards Investigation — Using a Table to Solve an Equation

Costs for a key chain business are \$540 to get started plus \$3 per key chain. The cost of producing k key chains is $(540 + 3k)$ dollars. Key chains sell for \$7 each. The revenue for selling k key chains is $7k$ dollars. To make a profit, revenue must be greater than costs.

1. Copy and complete the following table.

Key Chains	Cost	Revenue
k	$540 + 3k$	$7k$
100	840	700
110	■	■
120	■	■
130	■	■
140	■	■
150	■	■

2. For 110 key chains, which is greater, the cost or the revenue?

3. When will the revenue be greater than the cost?

4. Use your table to estimate the solution of $540 + 3k = 7k$.

5. Explain how solving an equation can help you decide whether a business can make a profit or not.

To solve an equation that has variables on both sides, use the Addition or Subtraction Properties of Equality to get the variables on one side of the equation.

1 EXAMPLE Variables on Both Sides

Solve $6x + 3 = 8x - 21$.

$6x + 3 = 8x - 21$	
$6x + 3 - 6x = 8x - 21 - 6x$	Subtract $6x$ from each side.
$3 = 2x - 21$	Combine like terms.
$3 + 21 = 2x - 21 + 21$	Add 21 to each side.
$24 = 2x$	Simplify.
$\frac{24}{2} = \frac{2x}{2}$	Divide each side by 2.
$x = 12$	Simplify.

The value of x is 12.

CA Standards Check 1 Solve each equation.

a. $-6d = d + 4$

b. $2(c - 6) = 9c + 2$

c. $m - 5 = 3m$

d. $7k - 4 = 5k + 16$

2 EXAMPLE Application

You can buy used in-line skates from your friend for \$40, or you can rent some. Either way, you must rent safety equipment. How many hours must you skate for the cost of renting and buying skates to be the same?

Relate	cost of friend's skates	plus	safety equipment rental	equals	skates plus equipment rental
Define	Let h = the number of hours you must skate.				
Write	40	$+$	$1.5h$	$=$	$3.5h$

$40 + 1.5h = 3.5h$	
$40 + 1.5h - 1.5h = 3.5h - 1.5h$	Subtract $1.5h$ from each side.
$40 = 2h$	Combine like terms.
$\frac{40}{2} = \frac{2h}{2}$	Divide each side by 2.
$20 = h$	Simplify.

You must skate for 20 hours for the cost to be the same.

Check Is the solution reasonable? Buying skates and renting safety equipment for 20 hours costs $40 + 1.5(20) = 70$, or \$70. The cost of renting both skates and safety equipment for 20 hours is $3.5(20) = 70$, or \$70. The answer is correct.

CA Standards Check 2 A hairdresser is considering ordering a certain shampoo. Company A charges \$4 per 8-oz bottle plus a \$10 handling fee per order. Company B charges \$3 per 8-oz bottle plus a \$25 handling fee per order. How many bottles must the hairdresser buy to justify using Company B?

Special Cases: Identities and No Solutions

An equation has no solution if no value of the variable makes the equation true. The equation $2x = 2x + 1$ has no solution. An equation that is true for every value of the variable is an **identity.** The equation $2x = 2x$ is an identity.

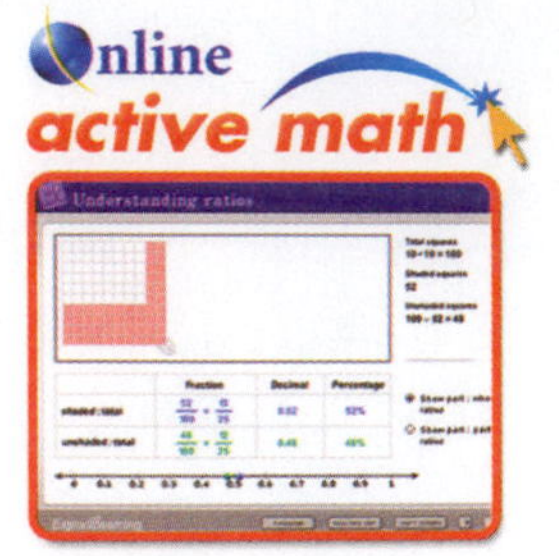

Online active math

For: Solving Equations Activity
Use: Interactive Textbook, 2-3

3 EXAMPLE Identities and Equations With No Solutions

a. Solve $10 - 8a = 2(5 - 4a)$.

$10 - 8a = 2(5 - 4a)$

$10 - 8a = 10 - 8a$ — Use the Distributive Property.

$10 - 8a + 8a = 10 - 8a + 8a$ — Add $8a$ to each side.

$10 = 10$ — Always true!

This equation is true for every value of a, so the equation is an identity.

b. Solve $6m - 5 = 7m + 7 - m$.

$6m - 5 = 7m + 7 - m$

$6m - 5 = 6m + 7$ — Combine like terms.

$6m - 5 - 6m = 6m + 7 - 6m$ — Subtract $6m$ from each side.

$-5 = 7$ — Not true for any value for m!

This equation has no solution.

CA Standards Check 3 Determine whether $9 + 5n = 5n - 1$ is an *identity* or whether it has *no solution*.

EXERCISES

For more exercises, see *Extra Skills and Word Problem Practice.*

Standards Practice

Alg1 4.0, 5.0, 25.3

A Practice by Example

Example 1 (page 85)

GO for Help

Solve each equation. Check your answer.

1. $6x - 2 = x + 13$

2. $5y - 3 = 2y + 12$

3. $4k - 3 = 3k + 4$

4. $5m + 3 = 3m + 9$

5. $8 - x = 2x - 1$

6. $2n - 5 = 8n + 7$

7. $3a + 4 = a + 18$

8. $6b + 14 = -7 - b$

9. $5a - 14 = -5 + 8a$

10. $3 + 4x = 3x + 6$

11. $30 - 7z = 10z - 4$

12. $8x - 3 = 7x + 2$

13. $-36 + 2w = -8w + w$

14. $4p - 10 = p + 3p - 2p$

Example 2 (page 85)

Write and solve an equation for each situation. Check your solution.

15. One phone company charges \$16.95 per month and \$.05 per minute for local calls. Another charges \$22.95 per month and \$.02 per minute for local calls. For what number of minutes of local calls per month is the cost the same?

16. One health club charges a \$44 sign-up fee and \$30 per month. Another health club charges a \$99 sign-up fee and \$25 per month. For what number of months is the cost the same?

Example 3 (page 86)

17. a. Use the equation $9 - 6x = 3(3 - 2x)$. Substitute four different values for x and simplify.

b. What kind of equation is $9 - 6x = 3(3 - 2x)$?

Determine whether each equation is an *identity* or whether it has *no solution*.

18. $14 - (2q + 5) = -2q + 9$

19. $6x + 1 = 6x - 8$

20. $-8x + 14 = -2(4x - 7)$

21. $y - 5 = -(5 - y)$

22. $a - 4a = 2a + 1 - 5a$

23. $9x + 3x - 10 = 3(3x + x)$

B Apply Your Skills

Solve each equation. If the equation is an identity, write *identity.* If it has no solution, write *no solution.*

24. $18x - 5 = 3(6x - 2)$

25. $9 + 5a = 2a + 9$

26. $3(x - 4) = 3x - 12$

27. $6x = 4(x + 5)$

28. $\frac{3}{5}k - \frac{1}{10}k = \frac{1}{2}k + 1$

29. $0 = 0.98b + 0.02b - b$

30. $5m - 2(m + 2) = -(2m + 15)$

31. $\frac{7}{8}w = \frac{4}{8}w + \frac{6}{8}w$

32. A toy company spends \$1500 per day for factory expenses plus \$8 to make each toy. Each toy sells for \$12. Which equation could be used to find the number of toys t the company has to sell in one day to equal its daily cost?

- (A) $1500 + 8t = 12$
- (B) $12 + 8t = 1500$
- (C) $1500 + 8t = 12t$
- (D) $8t = 12t + 1500$

33. A company manufactures tote bags. The company spends \$1200 each day for overhead expenses plus \$9 per tote bag for labor and materials. The tote bags sell for \$25 each. How many tote bags must the company sell each day to equal its daily costs for overhead, labor, and materials? Write an equation and solve.

Find the value of x.

Vertical angles are congruent, so their measures are equal.

34. **35.**

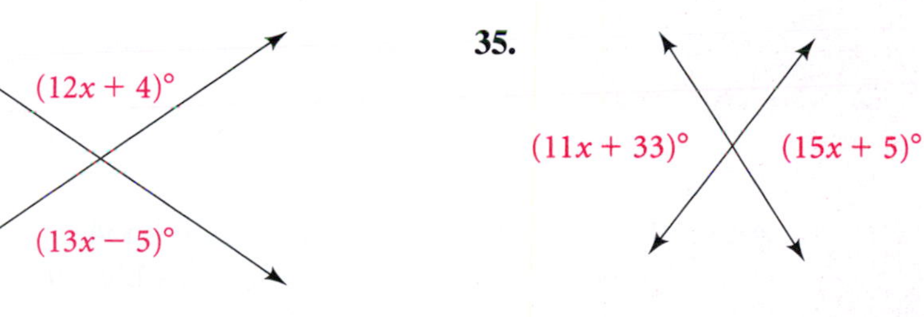

Error Analysis **Find the mistake in the solution of each equation. Explain the mistake and solve the equation correctly.**

36.

$2x = 11x + 45$

$2x - 11x = 11x - 11x + 45$

$9x = 45$

$\frac{9x}{9} = \frac{45}{9}$

$x = 5$

37.

$4.5 - y = 2(y - 5.7)$

$4.5 - y = 2y - 11.4$

$4.5 - y - y = 2y - y - 11.4$

$4.5 = y - 11.4$

$4.5 + 11.4 = y - 11.4 + 11.4$

$15.9 = y$

Homework Video Tutor

Visit: PHSchool.com
Web Code: bae-0203

38. Writing Is an equation that has 0 for a solution the same as an equation with no solution? Explain.

39. Don set up a table to solve $5(x - 3) = 4 - 3(x + 1)$.
   a. Does Don's table show a solution to the equation?
   b. Between which two values of x is the solution to the equation? How do you know?
   c. For what values of x is $4 - 3(x + 1)$ less than $5(x - 3)$?

	A	B	C
1	x	$5(x - 3)$	$4 - 3(x + 1)$
2	−5	−40	16
3	−3	−30	10
4	−1	−20	4
5	1	−10	−2
6	3	0	−8

C Challenge

Write an equation with a variable on each side such that you get the given solution.

40. $x = 0$
41. x is a positive number.
42. x is a negative number.
43. All values of x are solutions.
44. No values of x are solutions.
45. $x = 1$

46. Use the equations below to find the length of the bat.

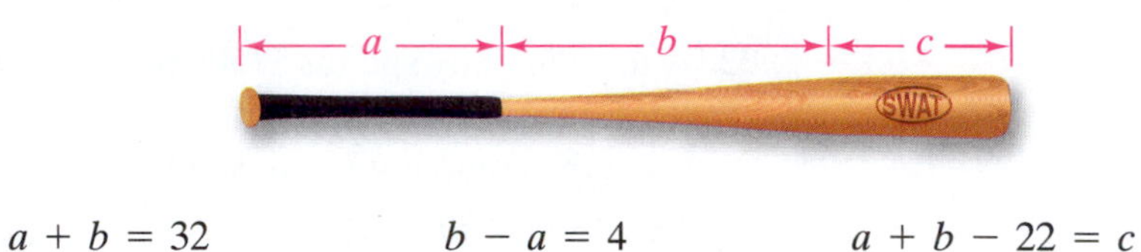

$a + b = 32$ $\qquad b - a = 4$ $\qquad a + b - 22 = c$

47. The perimeters of the rectangles below are equal. Find the length and width of each rectangle.

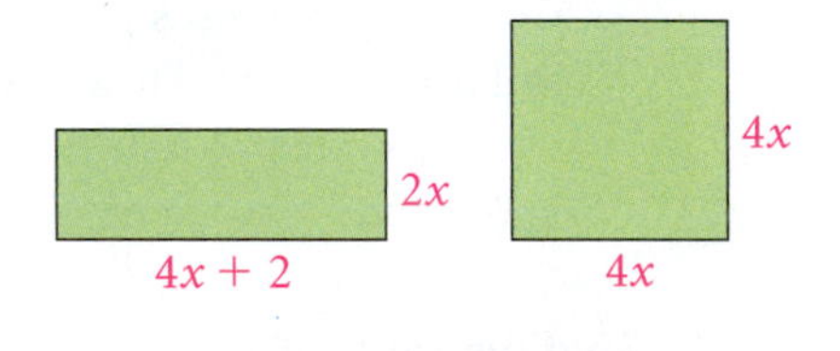

Multiple Choice Practice

For California Standards Tutorials, visit PHSchool.com. Web Code: baq-9045

Alg1 5.0 48. Ace Truck Rental charges \$54.00 a day plus 9¢ per mile. Roni's Truck Rental charges \$38.00 a day plus 13¢ per mile. For how many miles will the cost of renting a truck for one day at Ace equal the cost at Roni's?

(A) 40 mi (B) 170 mi (C) 400 mi (D) 418 mi

Alg1 4.0 49. Which equation is NOT equivalent to $3p - 2 = 6p + 4$?

(A) $3p = 6p + 6$
(B) $-6 = 3p$
(C) $3p = 6$
(D) $-3p - 2 = 4$

Alg1 5.0 50. A record store sells CDs for \$12.00 each. A music club offers 5 free CDs and charges \$15.00 for each additional CD. Which equation can you use to find the number of CDs x that would cost the same under both plans?

(A) $15x - 5 = 12x$
(B) $12x - 5 = 15x$
(C) $12x = 15(x - 5)$
(D) $12(x - 5) = 15x$

Alg1 5.0

51. Solve $2y = 3y - 20$.

Ⓐ -20 Ⓑ -4 Ⓒ 4 Ⓓ 20

Alg1 4.0, 5.0

52. Which of the following equations is NOT equivalent to the others?

Ⓐ $-2(y - 3) = -6y$

Ⓑ $-2y - 6 = -6y$

Ⓒ $y = -\frac{3}{2}$

Ⓓ $4y = -6$

Alg1 4.0, 5.0

53. Solve $2(y - 3) = 1.2 - y$.

Ⓐ -1.6 Ⓑ 1.4 Ⓒ 1.6 Ⓓ 2.4

Alg1 4.0, 5.0

54. Which of the following is NOT a subset of rational numbers?

Ⓐ $\{1, 2, 3, \ldots\}$

Ⓑ $\{-5, \sqrt{12}, 6.1\}$

Ⓒ $\{-1.3, \sqrt{25}, 8.4\}$

Ⓓ $\{-3, 0, \frac{2}{3}\}$

Mixed Review

GO for Help

Lesson 2-2

Solve each equation.

55. $9 = -4y + 6y - 5$

56. $-2(a - 3) = 14$

57. $0.5m + 2.8 = 3.64$

58. $\frac{1}{2}x + 4 = \frac{2}{3}$

59. $4.8 = 1.25(y - 17)$

60. $4\left(\frac{1}{4} + x\right) = 5$

Lesson 2-1

61. An art gallery owner is framing a painting. The width of the painting to be displayed is 30 in. He wants the width of the framed painting to be $38\frac{1}{2}$ in. How wide should each section of the frame be?

Lesson 1-3

Order the numbers in each group from least to greatest.

62. $-\frac{3}{5}, -\frac{5}{8}, -\frac{4}{5}$

63. 5.04, 5.009, 5.043

64. 8.1, 8.02, 8.3

65. $-100, 93, -87, 500$

66. $0.45, -1.24, 2.24, 1.23$

67. $9.7, -9.8, 8.6, 0.9$

Checkpoint Quiz 1

Lessons 2-1 through 2-3

Solve each equation.

1. $9 + \frac{d}{5} = 19$

2. $-x - 4 = -20$

3. $\frac{2k}{5} + \frac{3}{4} = 2$

4. $6.85 - 0.25t = 10.6$

5. $4n + 7 + 6n = 32$

6. $5(3 - d) = 2d + 1$

7. $8(h - 1) = 6h + 4 + 2h$

8. $43 = 8y - 11$

Write and solve an equation for each situation. Check your solution.

9. Peter was building a porch. Placing boards of equal length from end to end, Peter found that 4 boards were 3 ft too long for the porch length, while 3 boards were 5 ft too short. How long was each board?

10. You and a pilot friend decide to rent an airplane to do some sightseeing. One service charges \$100 plus \$80 per hour, while another charges \$250 plus \$70 per hour for the same airplane. At what number of hours is the cost the same?

Review Transforming Formulas

FOR USE WITH LESSON 2-4

5.0 Solve multi-step problems, including word problems, and provide justification for each step. ***Develop***

A **literal equation** is an equation involving two or more variables. Formulas are special types of literal equations. To transform a literal equation, you solve for one variable in terms of the others. This is helpful when you need to use a formula numerous times.

1 EXAMPLE Transforming Geometric Formulas

Solve the formula for the area of a triangle $A = \frac{1}{2}bh$ for height h. Then find the height of the triangle if the area is 48 in.^{2} and the base is 4 in.

Step 1 Solve for h.

$$A = \frac{1}{2}bh$$

$2A = 2\left(\frac{1}{2}\right)bh$ **Multiply each side by 2.**

$2A = bh$ **Simplify.**

$\frac{2A}{b} = \frac{bh}{b}$ **Divide each side by *b* to get *h* alone on one side of the equation.**

$\frac{2A}{b} = h$ **Simplify.**

Step 2 Evaluate $\frac{2A}{b} = h$ for $A = 48$ and $b = 4$.

$\frac{2(48)}{4} = h$ **Substitute 48 for *A* and 4 for *b*.**

$\frac{96}{4} = h$ **Simplify.**

$24 = h$

The height is 24 in.

Sometimes an equation will only have variables. Transforming this type of equation is no different from transforming equations with numbers. The goal is to get the variable you are solving for alone on one side of the equation.

2 EXAMPLE Transforming Equations With Only Variables

Solve $ab - d = c$ for b in terms of a, d, and c.

$ab - d + d = c + d$ **Add *d* to each side.**

$ab = c + d$ **Combine like terms.**

$\frac{ab}{a} = \frac{c + d}{a}$ **Divide each side by *a*, $a \neq 0$.**

$b = \frac{c + d}{a}$ **Simplify.**

3 EXAMPLE Transforming Formulas for Real-World Problems

The formula $C = \frac{5}{9}(F - 32)$ gives the Celsius temperature C in terms of the Fahrenheit temperature F. Transform the formula to find Fahrenheit temperature in terms of Celsius temperature. Then find the Fahrenheit temperature when the Celsius temperature is 30°.

Step 1 Solve for F.

$$C = \frac{5}{9}(F - 32)$$

$$\frac{9}{5} \cdot C = \frac{9}{5} \cdot \frac{5}{9}(F - 32)$$ **Multiply each side by $\frac{9}{5}$, the reciprocal of $\frac{5}{9}$.**

$$\frac{9}{5}C = F - 32$$ **Simplify.**

$$\frac{9}{5}C + 32 = F - 32 + 32$$ **Add 32 to each side.**

$$\frac{9}{5}C + 32 = F$$ **Simplify.**

Step 2 Find F when $C = 30$.

$$\frac{9}{5}(30) + 32 = F$$ **Substitute 30 for C.**

$$54 + 32 = F$$ **Find $\frac{9}{5}(30)$.**

$$86 = F$$

30°C is equivalent to 86°F.

EXERCISES

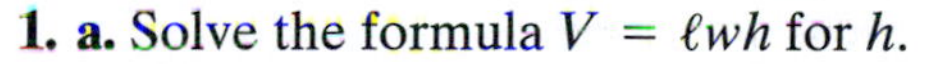

1. a. Solve the formula $V = \ell wh$ for h.
   b. Copy and complete the table to find the height for rectangular prisms with the given volumes, lengths, and widths.

V	54 in.^{3}	64 in.^{3}	72 in.^{3}	90 in.^{3}
ℓ	3 in.	4 in.	3 in.	18 in.
w	2 in.	4 in.	8 in.	2 in.
h	■	■	■	■

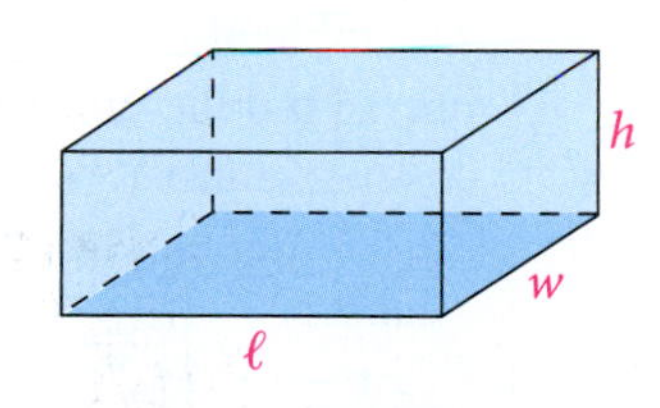

2. a. Bricklayers use the formula $N = 7LH$ to estimate the number of bricks N needed to build a wall of height H given a length L in feet. Transform the formula to find the height of a wall in terms of the length and the number of bricks.
   b. What is the height of a wall that is 30 feet long and requires 2135 bricks?

3. You can use the number of chirps a cricket makes in one minute to estimate the outside temperature F in Fahrenheit. Transform the formula $F = \frac{n}{4} + 37$ to find the number of chirps a cricket makes in a minute in terms of a given temperature. How many chirps can you expect if the temperature is 60°F?

2-4 Ratio and Proportion

California Content Standards

5.0 Solve multi-step problems, including word problems, involving linear equations in one variable and provide justification for each step. ***Develop***

15.0 Apply algebraic techniques to solve rate problems. ***Introduce***

25.0 Use properties of the number system to justify each step of a procedure. ***Develop***

What You'll Learn

- To find ratios and rates
- To solve proportions

. . . And Why

To use proportions in application problems involving nutrition, as in Example 5

Check Skills You'll Need

GO for Help Skills Handbook pages 598 and 601

Write each fraction in simplest form.

1. $\frac{49}{84}$
2. $\frac{24}{42}$
3. $\frac{135}{180}$

Simplify each product.

4. $\frac{35}{25} \times \frac{40}{14}$
5. $\frac{99}{144} \times \frac{96}{88}$
6. $\frac{21}{81} \times \frac{108}{56}$

New Vocabulary

- ratio
- rate
- unit rate
- unit analysis
- proportion
- extremes of a proportion
- means of a proportion
- cross products

Ratios and Rates

A **ratio** is a comparison of two numbers by division. The ratio of a to b is $a:b$ or $\frac{a}{b}$, where $b \neq 0$. If a and b represent quantities measured in different units, then the ratio of a to b is a **rate.**

A **unit rate** is a rate with a denominator of 1. An example of a unit rate is $\frac{40 \text{ miles}}{1 \text{ hour}}$. You can write this rate as 40 miles per hour or 40 mi/h.

Price of Apple Juice

Price	Volume
$ .72	16 oz
$1.20	32 oz
$1.60	64 oz

1 EXAMPLE Using Unit Rates

The table at the left gives prices for different sizes of the same brand of apple juice. Find the unit rate (cost per ounce) for each bottle. Which has the lowest cost per ounce?

cost → / ounces → $\frac{\$.72}{16 \text{ oz}} = \$.045/\text{oz}$ — Divide the numerator and denominator by 16.

cost → / ounces → $\frac{\$1.20}{32 \text{ oz}} = \$.0375/\text{oz}$ — Divide the numerator and denominator by 32.

cost → / ounces → $\frac{\$1.60}{64 \text{ oz}} = \$.025/\text{oz}$ — Divide the numerator and denominator by 64.

The unit rate for the 16-oz bottle is 4.5¢/oz, for the 32-oz bottle is 3.75¢/oz, and for the 64-oz bottle is 2.5¢/oz. The 64-oz bottle has the lowest cost per ounce.

CA Standards Check 1 Main Street Florist sells two dozen roses for $24.60. Fresh Flowers sells six roses for $7.50. Find the unit rate for each. Which florist has the lower cost per rose?

You can use formulas like distance = rate × time ($d = rt$) to write an equation to solve real-world problems. To write an equation, use a unit rate for r.

In 2005, Lance Armstrong won his seventh Tour de France with a record average speed of 41.65 km/h.

2 EXAMPLE Application

In 2004, Lance Armstrong won the Tour de France, completing the 3391-km course in about 83.6 hours. Find Lance's unit rate, which is his average speed. Write an equation that relates the distance he cycles d to the time t he cycles. Cycling at his average speed, about how long would it take Lance to cycle 185 km?

Step 1 Find Lance's unit rate.

$$\begin{array}{l} \textbf{distance} \rightarrow \\ \textbf{time} \rightarrow \end{array} \frac{3391 \text{ km}}{83.6 \text{ h}} \approx 40.6 \text{ kilometers per hour}$$

Step 2 Write an equation that includes the unit rate.

$d = rt$

$d = 40.6t$

Step 3 Use the equation to find t when $d = 185$.

$185 = 40.6t$

$\frac{185}{40.6} = \frac{40.6t}{40.6}$

$4.56 \approx t$

Traveling at his average speed, it would take Lance a little over $4\frac{1}{2}$ hours to cycle 185 km.

CA Standards Check **2** Suppose you walk 2 miles in 40 minutes.

a. Find the average walking speed. Write an equation that relates the distance d you walk to the time t you walk.

b. Use the equation to find how far you would walk in 75 min.

To change one unit of measure to another, you can use rates that equal 1. Since 60 min $=$ 1 h, both $\frac{60 \text{ min}}{1 \text{ h}}$ and $\frac{1 \text{ h}}{60 \text{ min}}$ equal 1. You can use $\frac{60 \text{ min}}{1 \text{ h}}$ as a *conversion factor* to change hours into minutes and $\frac{1 \text{ h}}{60 \text{ min}}$ to change minutes into hours.

When converting from one unit to another, as in hours to minutes or minutes to hours, you must decide which conversion factor will produce the appropriate unit. This process is called **unit analysis,** or *dimensional analysis*.

A cheetah can run the length of a football field in less than 3 seconds.

3 EXAMPLE Converting Rates

A cheetah ran 300 feet in 2.92 seconds. What was the cheetah's average speed in miles per hour?

You need to convert feet to miles and seconds to hours.

$\frac{300 \text{ ft}}{2.92 \text{ s}} \cdot \frac{1 \text{ mi}}{5280 \text{ ft}} \cdot \frac{60 \text{ s}}{1 \text{ min}} \cdot \frac{60 \text{ min}}{1 \text{ h}}$ **Use appropriate conversion factors.**

$= \frac{300 \cancel{\text{ft}}}{2.92 \cancel{\text{s}}} \cdot \frac{1 \text{ mi}}{5280 \cancel{\text{ft}}} \cdot \frac{60 \cancel{\text{s}}}{1 \cancel{\text{min}}} \cdot \frac{60 \cancel{\text{min}}}{1 \text{ h}}$ **Divide the common units.**

≈ 70 mi/h **Simplify.**

The cheetah's average speed was about 70 mi/h.

CA Standards Check **3** A sloth travels 0.15 miles per hour. Convert this speed to feet per minute.

Solving Proportions

A **proportion** is an equation that states that two ratios are equal.

$$\frac{a}{b} = \frac{c}{d} \text{ for } b \neq 0 \text{ and } d \neq 0$$

You read this proportion as "a is to b as c is to d." For this proportion a and d are the **extremes of the proportion,** and b and c are the **means of the proportion.** Another way you may see this proportion written is $a:b = c:d$.

Vocabulary Tip

Multiplication Property of Equality: For all numbers a, b, and c, if $a = b$, then $ac = bc$.

You can use the Multiplication Property of Equality to solve a proportion for a variable.

4 EXAMPLE Using the Multiplication Property of Equality

Solve $\frac{t}{9} = \frac{5}{6}$.

$\frac{t}{9} = \frac{5}{6}$

$\frac{t}{9} \cdot 18 = \frac{5}{6} \cdot 18$ — Multiply each side by the least common multiple of 9 and 6, which is 18.

$2t = 15$ — Simplify.

$\frac{2t}{2} = \frac{15}{2}$ — Divide each side by 2.

$t = 7.5$ — Simplify.

CA Standards Check 4 Solve each proportion.

a. $\frac{x}{8} = \frac{5}{6}$ b. $\frac{y}{12} = \frac{4}{7}$ c. $\frac{18}{50} = \frac{m}{15}$

You can use the Multiplication Property of Equality to prove an important property of proportions.

If $\frac{a}{b} = \frac{c}{d}$

then $\frac{a}{b} \cdot bd = \frac{c}{d} \cdot bd$ — Multiplication Property of Equality

$\frac{ab^{1}d}{_1b} = \frac{cbd^{1}}{_1d}$ — Divide the common factors.

and $ad = cb$ — Simplify.

or $ad = bc$ — Commutative Property of Multiplication

The products ad and bc are the **cross products** of the proportion $\frac{a}{b} = \frac{c}{d}$.

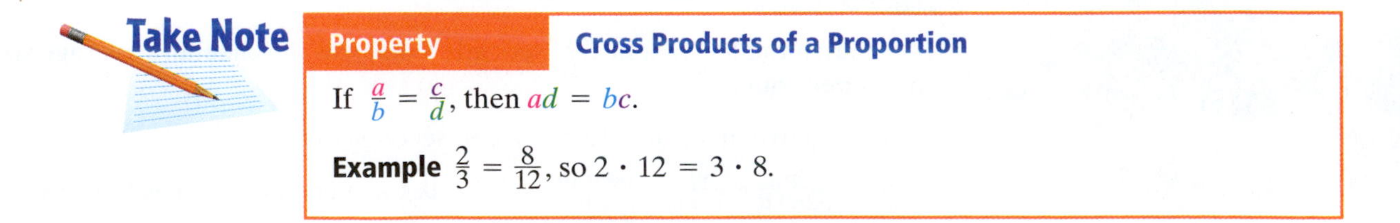

Property Cross Products of a Proportion

If $\frac{a}{b} = \frac{c}{d}$, then $ad = bc$.

Example $\frac{2}{3} = \frac{8}{12}$, so $2 \cdot 12 = 3 \cdot 8$.

Notice that for a proportion, the product of the extremes ad equals the product of the means bc. The Cross Products property is also called the means-extremes property of proportions.

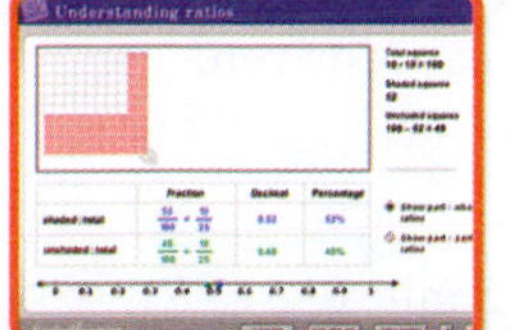

For: Proportion Activity
Use: Interactive Textbook, 2-4

5 EXAMPLE Using Cross Products

A box of cereal weighing 350 grams contains 21 grams of fat. Find the number of grams of fat in the recommended serving size of 50 grams.

$$\begin{array}{rll} \text{weight} \rightarrow \ \text{fat} \rightarrow \ \frac{350}{21} &= \frac{50}{x} & \\ 350(x) &= (50)(21) & \text{Write cross products.} \\ 350x &= 1050 & \text{Simplify.} \\ \frac{350x}{350} &= \frac{1050}{350} & \text{Divide each side by 350.} \\ x &= 3 & \text{Simplify.} \end{array}$$

A 50-gram serving has about 3 grams of fat.

CA Standards Check 5 Solve each proportion by using cross products.

a. $\frac{x}{4} = \frac{25}{12}$ **b.** $\frac{24}{5} = \frac{y}{7}$ **c.** $\frac{54}{d} = \frac{72}{64}$

In Example 6, the ratios that form the proportion have variable expressions with more than one term. To solve for the variable, you will use cross products and the Distributive Property.

6 EXAMPLE Solving Multi-Step Proportions

Solve the proportion $\frac{x+4}{5} = \frac{x-2}{7}$.

$$\begin{array}{rll} \frac{x+4}{5} &= \frac{x-2}{7} & \\ (x+4)(7) &= 5(x-2) & \text{Write cross products.} \\ 7x + 28 &= 5x - 10 & \text{Use the Distributive Property.} \\ 2x + 28 &= -10 & \text{Subtract } 5x \text{ from each side.} \\ 2x &= -38 & \text{Subtract 28 from each side.} \\ x &= -19 & \text{Divide each side by 2.} \end{array}$$

CA Standards Check 6 Solve each proportion.

a. $\frac{x+2}{14} = \frac{x}{10}$ **b.** $\frac{3}{w+6} = \frac{5}{w-4}$ **c.** $\frac{y-15}{y+4} = \frac{35}{7}$

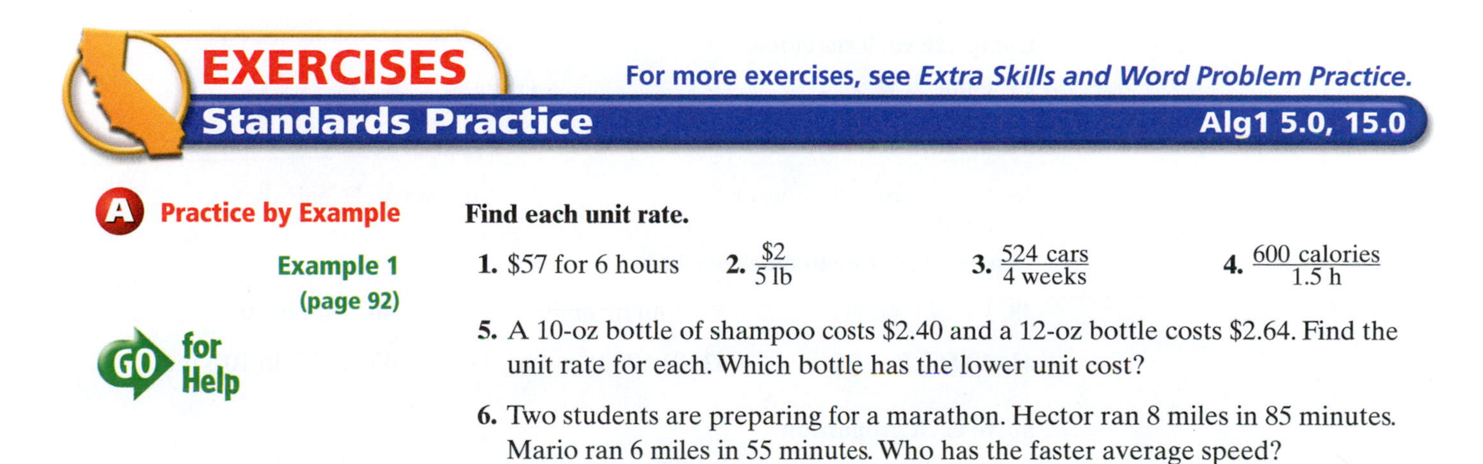

EXERCISES

Standards Practice

For more exercises, see *Extra Skills and Word Problem Practice*.

Alg1 5.0, 15.0

A Practice by Example

Example 1 (page 92)

GO for Help

Find each unit rate.

1. \$57 for 6 hours **2.** $\frac{\$2}{5 \text{ lb}}$ **3.** $\frac{524 \text{ cars}}{4 \text{ weeks}}$ **4.** $\frac{600 \text{ calories}}{1.5 \text{ h}}$

5. A 10-oz bottle of shampoo costs \$2.40 and a 12-oz bottle costs \$2.64. Find the unit rate for each. Which bottle has the lower unit cost?

6. Two students are preparing for a marathon. Hector ran 8 miles in 85 minutes. Mario ran 6 miles in 55 minutes. Who has the faster average speed?

Example 2 (page 93)

7. Mrs. Magdalino kept records on how much she spent on gasoline and the maintenance of her car. She found that it cost \$485 to drive 500 mi in a month.
   a. Find the cost per mile. Write an equation that relates the cost c for gasoline and maintenance of a car to the number of miles m the car is driven.
   b. Use the equation to find the cost for driving 1200 miles.
   c. About how many miles are driven for a cost of \$820?

8. You are riding your bicycle. It takes you 20 minutes to go 5 miles.
   a. Find your average speed. Write an equation that relates the distance d you cycle to the number of minutes m you cycle.
   b. How long would it take you to cycle 12 miles?

Example 3 (page 93)

Choose A or B for the correct conversion factor for each situation.

9. quarts to gallons
A. $\frac{1 \text{ gal}}{4 \text{ qt}}$ **B.** $\frac{4 \text{ qt}}{1 \text{ gal}}$

10. ounces to pounds
A. $\frac{1 \text{ lb}}{16 \text{ oz}}$ **B.** $\frac{16 \text{ oz}}{1 \text{ lb}}$

11. inches to yards
A. $\frac{36 \text{ in.}}{1 \text{ yd}}$ **B.** $\frac{1 \text{ yd}}{36 \text{ in.}}$

12. miles to feet
A. $\frac{5280 \text{ ft}}{1 \text{ mi}}$ **B.** $\frac{1 \text{ mi}}{5280 \text{ ft}}$

Complete each statement.

13. 8 h = ■ min **14.** 120 cm = ■ m **15.** 3 h = ■ s

Example 4 (page 94)

Solve each proportion.

16. $\frac{2}{8} = \frac{n}{20}$ **17.** $\frac{4}{6} = \frac{m}{9}$ **18.** $\frac{5}{6} = \frac{c}{9}$ **19.** $\frac{7}{5} = \frac{k}{18}$

20. $\frac{3}{4} = \frac{x}{10}$ **21.** $\frac{3}{8} = \frac{x}{30}$ **22.** $\frac{8}{d} = -\frac{12}{30}$ **23.** $\frac{5}{9} = \frac{8}{w}$

Example 5 (page 95)

24. A canary's heart beats 200 times in 12 seconds. Use a proportion to find how many times its heart beats in 42 seconds.

25. Suppose you traveled 66 kilometers in 1.25 hours. Moving at the same speed, how many kilometers would you cover in 2 hours?

Example 6 (page 95)

Solve each proportion.

26. $\frac{x + 3}{4} = \frac{7}{8}$ **27.** $\frac{a - 6}{5} = \frac{7}{12}$ **28.** $\frac{8}{9} = \frac{w - 2}{6}$

29. $\frac{1}{c + 5} = \frac{2}{3}$ **30.** $\frac{8}{b + 10} = \frac{4}{2b - 7}$ **31.** $\frac{k + 5}{10} = \frac{k - 12}{9}$

B Apply Your Skills

Complete each statement.

32. \$2/lb = ■ ¢/oz **33.** \$3/lb = ■ ¢/oz

34. 4¢/day = \$ ■/yr **35.** 5¢/day = \$ ■/yr

36. 5 cm/min = ■ m/week **37.** 1 qt/min = ■ gal/week

Express each rate in miles per hour.

38. 1 mi in 3 min **39.** 1 mi in 4 min **40.** 1 mi in 300 s

41. 10,560 ft in 2 h **42.** 21,120 ft in 4 h **43.** 270 ft in 10.8 min

Solve each proportion.

44. $\frac{m + 12}{9m} = \frac{5}{9}$ **45.** $\frac{p}{20} = \frac{p - 4}{5}$ **46.** $\frac{n + 12}{4} = \frac{n}{16}$

47. Human hair grows at a rate of about 2.45 mm per week. Find the unit rate (millimeters per day). Write an equation that relates the amount of growth g to number of days n. Use the equation to find about how much hair grows in 30 days.

48. According to the *Guinness Book of World Records*, the peregrine falcon has a record diving speed of 168 miles per hour. Write this speed in feet per second.

About $\frac{1}{12}$ of 13-year-olds in the United States spend more than 2 hours per night on homework.

Below are the survey results of 60 students. These results are representative of the 1250 students in the school. Use the table for Exercises 49–51.

Question	Number Answering Yes
Do you work on weekends?	31
Do you spend 2 or more hours per night on homework?	36
Do you buy lunch in the school cafeteria?	48

49. Predict the number of students in the school who work on weekends.

50. Predict the number of students in the school who spend 2 or more hours per night on homework.

51. Predict the number of students in the school who buy lunch in the school cafeteria.

52. **Writing** Write an explanation telling an absent classmate how to use cross products to solve a proportion. Include an example.

53. Your car averages 34 miles per gallon on the highway. If gas costs \$2.10 per gallon, how much does it cost in dollars per mile to drive your car on the highway?

(A) \$.06/mi (B) 16 mi/dollar (C) \$16/mi (D) 0.06 mi/dollar

54. Population density is a unit rate describing the number of individuals per unit of area. An example of population density is 5 people per square mile. Use the diagram below. Find the population densities of Mongolia, Bangladesh, and the United States. Round your answers to the nearest integer.

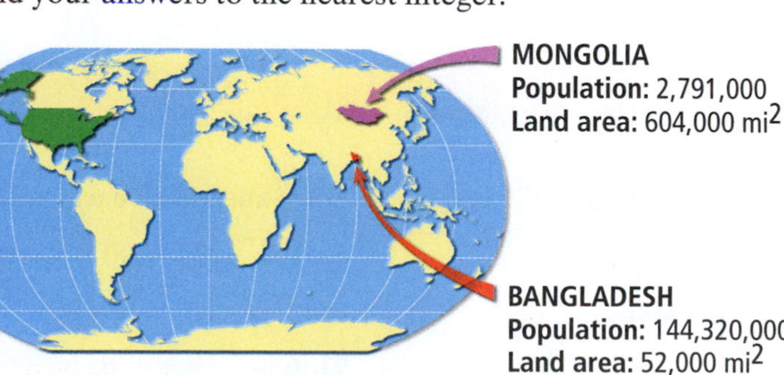

55. Estimate your walking rate in feet per second. Write this rate in miles per hour.

56. Bonnie and Tim do some yardwork for their neighbor. The ratio comparing the amount of time each one works is 7 : 4. The neighbor pays them \$88. If Bonnie worked more, how much should each of them receive?

Visit: PHSchool.com
Web Code: bae-0204

57. Transformers use coils of wire to increase or decrease voltage. The following proportion relates the number of turns of wire in the coils to the voltages. (*Note:* Each semicircle in the diagram represents a turn of wire.)

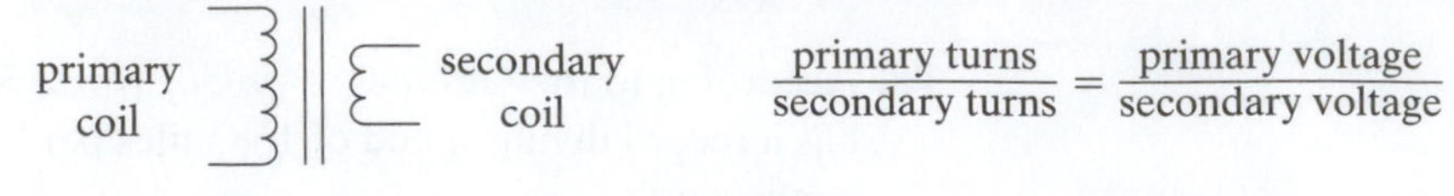

$$\frac{\text{primary turns}}{\text{secondary turns}} = \frac{\text{primary voltage}}{\text{secondary voltage}}$$

Suppose the primary-coil voltage is 120 volts. Use the proportion $\frac{5}{2} = \frac{120}{v}$ to find the secondary-coil voltage.

C Challenge

Solve each proportion.

58. $\frac{x^2 - 3}{5x + 2} = \frac{x}{5}$

59. $\frac{w^3 + 7}{w} = \frac{9w^2 + 7}{9}$

60. $\frac{m^2 - 8}{3m} = \frac{4m + 1}{12}$

61. Long-distance runners usually refer to their speed in terms of pace, a rate measured in minutes per mile rounded to the nearest hundredth.
   a. Naoko Takahashi of Japan won the gold medal in the marathon at the 2000 Olympic games. She set an Olympic record, completing the 26.2-mile race in 2:23:14 (2 hours, 23 minutes, 14 seconds). Find her pace.
   b. Tegla Loroupe of Kenya set the women's world record at the 1999 Berlin marathon. Her time was 2:20:43. Find her pace.

Multiple Choice Practice

For California Standards Tutorials, visit PHSchool.com. Web Code: baq-9045

Alg1 1.0

62. Which set of numbers is NOT closed under multiplication?
   A integers
   B real numbers
   C irrational numbers
   D rational numbers

Alg1 4.0

63. Simplify the algebraic expression $-a(2b - 3c) - 3a(b + c)$.
   A ab
   B $-5ab$
   C $ab - 6ac$
   D $-5ab - 6ac$

Alg1 5.0

64. Norman received $60 for working 8 hours. At this rate, how much would he receive for working 35 hours?
   A $7.50
   B $262.50
   C $480
   D $2100

Mixed Review

Lessons 2-1, 2-2

Solve and check each equation.

GO for Help

65. $15x + 30 = 90$

66. $34 = \frac{t}{4} + 5$

67. $-31 = 7h + 11$

68. $2b + 4.3 - b = 9.8$

69. $-\frac{3}{5}(c + 20) = 54$

70. $\frac{5v}{6} + \frac{7}{6} = \frac{1}{12}$

71. $6 = 7 - \frac{t}{2} + 8$

72. $9b + 8b - 13 = 106$

73. $2(p - 7.5) - 4 = 32$

Lesson 1-3

Decide whether each statement is *true* or *false*. If false, give a counterexample.

74. All positive integers are natural numbers.

75. A number cannot have a value equal to its square.

76. All integers are rational numbers.

GPS Guided Problem Solving

FOR USE WITH LESSON 2-4

5.0 Solve multi-step problems, including word problems, involving linear equations. ***Develop***
15.0 Apply algebraic techniques to solve rate problems. ***Develop***
25.0 Use properties of the number system to justify each step of a procedure. ***Develop***

Understanding Word Problems **Read through the problem below. Then follow along with what Rasia thinks as she solves the problem. Check your understanding with the exercise at the bottom of the page.**

Ian allows himself 5 hours to travel 255 miles. He travels 90 miles in the first 1.5 hours. Suppose Ian continues to travel at the same speed. How long a break can he take and still reach his destination in 8 hours?

What Rasia Thinks	What Rasia Writes
I need to read the problem carefully so that I can understand it. I'll write down the important information.	Ian travels 90 miles in 1.5 hours.
First, I will define a variable and write a proportion to find out how long it will take Ian to travel 255 miles at the same rate.	Let t = the time it takes Ian to travel 255 miles.
I will solve the proportion by using cross products. Then I will simplify and divide each side by 90.	$\frac{1.5}{90} = \frac{t}{255}$ $1.5(255) = 90(t)$ $382.5 = 90t$ $\frac{382.5}{90} = \frac{90t}{90}$ $4.25 = t$
Now I will subtract the time from allotted time of 5 hours to find how long a lunch break Ian can take.	$5 - 4.25 = 0.75$
I will write my answer in a sentence. Also, I need to remember to include the units.	Ian can take a break that is 0.75 hour, or 45 minutes, long.

GO

Video

Visit: P

Web C

EXERCISE

A seamstress needs to make 25 dresses by the end of a day. Her workday is 8 hours long, and she can make 6 dresses in 1.7 hours. If she continues to work at the same rate, how long a lunch break can she take and still make all 25 dresses?

A table can also help you understand relationships in distance-rate-time problems.

3 EXAMPLE Same-Direction Travel

High-speed trains that go from Boston to New York in less than 4 hours can reach a speed of 150 mi/h.

A train leaves a train station at 1 P.M. It travels at an average rate of 72 mi/h. A high-speed train leaves the same station an hour later. It travels at an average rate of 90 mi/h. The second train follows the same route as the first train on a parallel track. In how many hours will the second train catch up with the first train?

Define Let t = the time the first train travels.

Then $t - 1$ = the time the second train travels.

Relate

Train	Rate	Time	Distance Traveled
1	72	t	$72t$
2	90	$t - 1$	$90(t - 1)$

Write $72t = 90(t - 1)$ **The distances traveled by the trains are equal.**

Method 1 Solve by using a table.

Use a table to evaluate each side of the equation. Look for matching values.

Time	$72t$	$90(t - 1)$
1	$72(1) = 72$	$90(1 - 1) = 0$
2	$72(2) = 144$	$90(2 - 1) = 90$
3	$72(3) = 216$	$90(3 - 1) = 180$
4	$72(4) = 288$	$90(4 - 1) = 270$
5	$72(5) = 360$	$90(5 - 1) = 360$ ✓

The first train travels 360 miles in 5 hours. The second train travels 360 miles in 4 hours $(t - 1)$. The second train will catch up with the first train in 4 hours.

Method 2 Solve the equation.

$72t = 90t - 90$ **Use the Distributive Property to simplify $90(t - 1)$.**

$72t - 72t = 90t - 90 - 72t$ **Subtract $72t$ from each side.**

$0 = 18t - 90$ **Combine like terms.**

$0 + 90 = 18t - 90 + 90$ **Add 90 to each side.**

$90 = 18t$ **Simplify.**

$\frac{90}{18} = \frac{18t}{18}$ **Divide each side by 18.**

$t = 5$ **Simplify.**

$t - 1 = 4$ **Find the time the second train travels.**

The second train will catch up with the first train in 4 h.

CA Standards Check 3 A group of campers and one group leader left a campsite in a canoe. They traveled at an average rate of 10 km/h. Two hours later, the other group leader left the campsite in a motorboat. He traveled at an average rate of 22 km/h.

a. How long after the canoe left the campsite did the motorboat catch up with it?

b. How long did the motorboat travel?

For uniform motion problems that involve a round trip, it is important to remember that the distance going is equal to the distance returning.

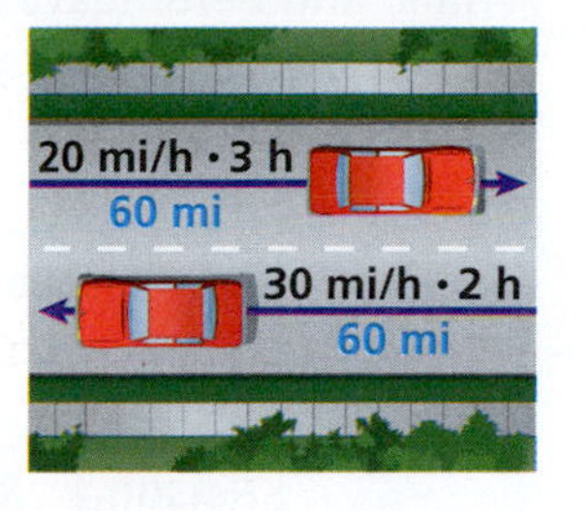

Since the distances are equal, the products of rate and time for traveling in both directions are equal. That is, $20 \cdot 3 = 30 \cdot 2$.

4 EXAMPLE Round-Trip Travel

Noya drives into the city to buy a software program at a computer store. Because of traffic, she averages only 15 mi/h. On her drive home she averages 35 mi/h. If the total travel time is 2 hours, how long does it take her to drive to the store?

Problem Solving Tip

The total travel time is for a round trip. If it takes t out of a 2-hour round trip to get to the store, then $2 - t$ is the time it will take for the drive home.

Define Let t = time of Noya's drive to the computer store.

$2 - t$ = the time of Noya's drive home.

Relate

Part of Noya's Travel	Rate	Time	Distance
To the computer store	15	t	$15t$
Return home	35	$2 - t$	$35(2 - t)$

Noya drives $15t$ miles to the computer store and $35(2 - t)$ miles back.

Write

$15t = 35(2 - t)$ The distances traveled to and from the store are equal.

$15t = 70 - 35t$ Use the Distributive Property.

$15t + 35t = 70 - 35t + 35t$ Add $35t$ to each side.

$50t = 70$ Combine like terms.

$\frac{50t}{50} = \frac{70}{50}$ Divide each side by 50.

$t = 1.4$ Simplify.

It took Noya 1.4 h to drive to the computer store.

CA Standards Check

4 On his way to work from home, your uncle averaged only 20 miles per hour. On his drive home, he averaged 40 miles per hour. If the total travel time was $1\frac{1}{2}$ hours, how long did it take him to drive to work?

For uniform motion problems involving two objects moving in opposite directions, you can write equations using the fact that the sum of their distances is the total distance.

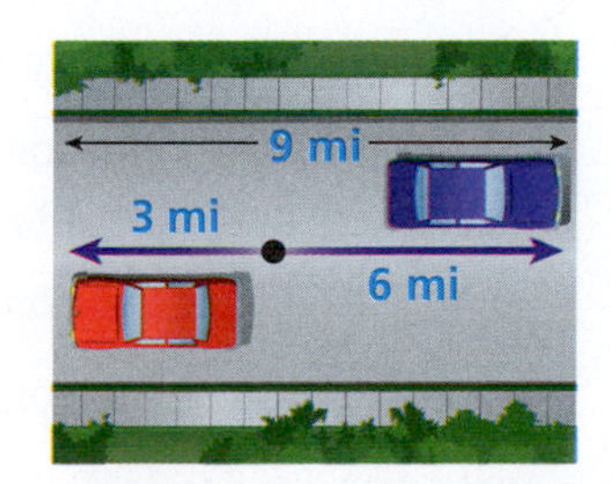

5 EXAMPLE Opposite-Direction Travel

Jane and Peter leave their home traveling in opposite directions on a straight road. Peter drives 15 mi/h faster than Jane. After 3 hours, they are 225 miles apart. Find Peter's rate and Jane's rate.

Define Let r = Jane's rate.
Then $r + 15$ = Peter's rate.

Relate

Person	Rate	Time	Distance
Jane	r	3	$3r$
Peter	$r + 15$	3	$3(r + 15)$

Jane's distance is $3r$. Peter's distance is $3(r + 15)$.

Write $3r + 3(r + 15) = 225$ — The sum of Jane's and Peter's distances is the total distance, 225 miles.

$3r + 3(r + 15) = 225$

$3r + 3r + 45 = 225$ — Use the Distributive Property.

$6r + 45 = 225$ — Combine like terms.

$6r + 45 - 45 = 225 - 45$ — Subtract 45 from each side.

$6r = 180$ — Simplify.

$\frac{6r}{6} = \frac{180}{6}$ — Divide each side by 6.

$r = 30$ — Simplify.

Jane's rate is 30 mi/h, and Peter's rate is 15 mi/h faster, which is 45 mi/h.

CA Standards Check 5 Sarah and John leave Perryville traveling in opposite directions on a straight road. Sarah drives 12 miles per hour faster than John. After 2 hours, they are 176 miles apart. Find Sarah's speed and John's speed.

EXERCISES

For more exercises, see *Extra Skills and Word Problem Practice*.

Standards Practice Alg1 4.0, 5.0, 15.0

A Practice by Example

Example 1 (page 100)

GO for Help

Find the width and length of each rectangle with the given conditions.

1. The length is 3 in. more than the width. The perimeter is 30 in.
2. The width is one half the length. The perimeter is 54 cm.
3. The length is 3 yd more than twice the width. The perimeter is 36 yd.

Example 2 (page 101)

Find the integers with the given sum.

4. The sum of three consecutive integers is 915.
5. The sum of two consecutive *even* integers is 118. (*Hint*: What must you add to an even integer to get the next greater even integer?)
6. The sum of two consecutive *even* integers is -298.
7. The sum of two consecutive *odd* integers is 56.

Example 3 (page 102)

For Exercises 8–11, use the following information. A moving van leaves a house traveling at an average rate of 40 mi/h. The family leaves the house $\frac{1}{2}$ hour later following the same route in a car. They travel at an average rate of 60 mi/h.

8. Define a variable for the time traveled by the moving van.

9. Write an expression for the time traveled by the car.

10. Copy and complete the table.

Vehicle	Rate	Time	Distance Traveled
Moving van	■	■	■
Car	■	■	■

11. Make a table comparing the distance traveled by the moving van and the car for each hour. How long will it take the car to catch up with the van?

Example 4 (page 103)

12. An airplane flies from New Orleans, Louisiana, to Atlanta, Georgia, at an average rate of 320 miles per hour. The airplane then returns at an average rate of 280 miles per hour. The total travel time is 3 hours.

a. Copy and complete the table.

Part of Flight	Rate	Time	Distance
To Atlanta	■	■	■
Return to New Orleans	■	■	■

b. Write and solve an equation to find the flying time from New Orleans to Atlanta.

Example 5 (page 104)

13. Two bicyclists ride in opposite directions. The speed of the first bicyclist is 5 miles per hour faster than the second. After 2 hours they are 70 miles apart. Find their rates.

B Apply Your Skills

14. The sum of three consecutive *odd* integers is -87. What are the integers?

15. Use the diagram below. Together, the kite and tail are 15 ft 6 in. long.

a. Write an expression for the length of the kite and tail together.
b. Write 15 ft 6 in. in terms of feet.
c. Write and solve an equation to find the length of the tail.

16. A bus traveling at an average rate of 30 miles per hour left the city at 11:45 A.M. A car following the bus at 45 miles per hour left the city at noon. At what time did the car catch up with the bus?

17. Ellen and Kate raced on their bicycles to the library after school. They both left school at 3:00 P.M. and bicycled along the same path. Ellen rode at a speed of 12 miles per hour and Kate rode at 9 miles per hour. Ellen got to the library 15 minutes before Kate. At what time did Ellen get to the library?

Visit: PHSchool.com
Web Code: bae-0205

18. **a.** Which of the following numbers is not the sum of three consecutive integers?

I. 51 **II.** 61 **III.** 72 **IV.** 81

b. **Critical Thinking** What common trait do the other numbers share?

19. At 1:30 P.M., Tom leaves in his boat from a dock and heads south. He travels at a rate of 25 miles per hour. Ten minutes later, Mary leaves the same dock in her speedboat and heads after Tom. If she travels at a rate of 30 miles per hour, when will she catch up with Tom?

20. Two airplanes depart from an airport traveling in opposite directions. The second airplane is 200 miles per hour faster than the first. After 2 hours they are 1100 miles apart. Find the speeds of the airplanes.

21. At 12:00 P.M. a truck leaves Centerville traveling 45 mi/h. One hour later a train leaves Centerville traveling 60 mi/h. They arrive in Smithfield at the same time.

a. Use the table to find when the train and truck arrive in Smithfield.

b. **Critical Thinking** What piece of information can you get from the table that you would NOT get by solving the equation $45t = 60(t - 1)$?

Time	Truck $45t$	Train $60(t - 1)$
1 P.M.	45 mi	0 mi
2 P.M.	90 mi	60 mi
3 P.M.	135 mi	120 mi
4 P.M.	180 mi	180 mi
5 P.M.	225 mi	240 mi

22. Three friends were born in consecutive years. The sum of their birth years is 5982. Find the year in which each person was born.

23. **Writing** Describe the steps you would use to solve consecutive integer problems.

24. Write a word problem that could be solved using the equation $35(t - 1) = 20t$.

25. **a.** Write and solve an equation to find three consecutive integers with a sum of 126. Let $n =$ the first integer.

b. **Critical Thinking** In part (a), could you solve the problem by letting $n =$ the middle integer, $n - 1 =$ the smallest integer, and $n + 1 =$ the largest integer?

26. A group of ten 6- and 12-volt batteries are wired in series as shown below. The sum of their voltages is 84 volts. How many of each type of battery are used?

Batteries in Series

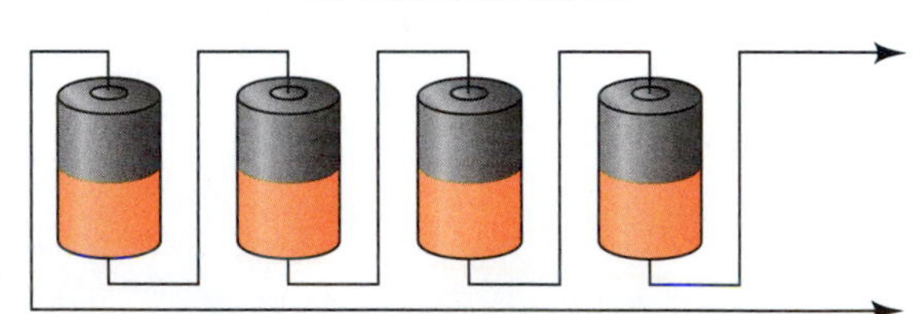

27. A triangle has a perimeter of 165 cm. The first side is 65 cm less than twice the second side. The third side is 10 cm less than the second side. Write and solve an equation to find the length of each side of the triangle.

28. At 9:00 A.M., your friends begin hiking at 2 mi/h. You begin from the same place at 9:25 A.M. You hike at 3 mi/h.

a. How long will you have hiked when you catch up with your friends?

b. At what time will you catch up with your friends?

29. Find five consecutive *odd* integers such that the sum of the first and the fifth is one less than three times the fourth.

Multiple Choice Practice

For California Standards Tutorials, visit PHSchool.com. Web Code: baq-9045

Alg1 4.0, 5.0

30. Solve $3n - 7 + 2n = 8n + 11$.

(A) -6 (B) $1\frac{1}{3}$ (C) $3\frac{3}{5}$ (D) 9

Alg1 4.0, 5.0

31. Which equation does NOT have -2 as its solution?

(A) $2x + 5 = 5x + 11$
(B) $7n + 9 = 3 - 9n$
(C) $3k + 6 - 4k = k + 10$
(D) $4 + 3q = 7q + 12$

Alg1 15.0

32. A truck traveling at an average rate of 45 miles per hour leaves a rest stop. Fifteen minutes later a car traveling at an average rate of 60 miles per hour leaves the same rest stop traveling the same route. How long will it take for the car to catch up with the truck?

(A) 15 minutes
(B) 45 minutes
(C) 1 hour 15 minutes
(D) 3 hours

Mixed Review

Lesson 2-3

GO for Help

Solve each equation. If the equation is an identity, write *identity.* If it has no solution, write *no solution.*

33. $2x = 7x + 10$

34. $2q + 4 = 4 - 2q$

35. $0.5t + 3.6 = 4.2 - 1.5t$

36. $2x + 5 + x = 2(3x + 3)$

37. $4 + x + 3x = 2(2x + 5)$

38. $8z + 2 = 2(z - 5) - z$

Lesson 2-2

39. Brendan earns \$8.25 per hour at his job. He also makes \$12.38 per hour for any number of hours over 40 that he works in one week. He worked 40 hours last week, plus some overtime, and made \$385.71. How many overtime hours did he work?

Checkpoint Quiz 2

Lessons 2-4 through 2-5

Solve each proportion.

1. $\frac{8}{k} = -\frac{12}{30}$

2. $\frac{3}{5} = \frac{y + 1}{9}$

3. $\frac{-8}{m} = \frac{7}{20}$

4. $\frac{12}{30} = \frac{16}{v}$

5. $\frac{5}{2 - x} = \frac{7}{10}$

6. $\frac{3 + x}{8} = \frac{7}{12}$

7. It takes you 12 min to bike 2.5 mi. If you continue traveling at the same rate, how long will it take you to bike 7 mi?

8. The length of a rectangle is 5 cm more than its width. The perimeter of the rectangle is 46 cm. What is the length of the rectangle?

9. The sum of three consecutive odd integers is 465. Find the integers.

10. Marcus and Beth leave college traveling in opposite directions on a straight road. Beth drives 13 mi/h faster than Marcus. After 4 hours, they are 452 miles apart. Find their rates.

Review: Proportions and Percents

For Use With Lesson 2-6

15.0 Apply algebraic techniques to solve percent problems. ***Develop***

To solve a percent problem such as "Find 38% of 320," you change the percent to a decimal and multiply.

$$38\% \text{ of } 320 \rightarrow 0.38 \cdot 320 = 121.6$$

For more involved percent problems, you can think of a percent as a ratio that compares a number to 100. You can solve problems involving percents using this proportion. Diagrams will help you visualize relationships.

$$\text{percent}\left\{\frac{n}{100} = \frac{\text{part}}{\text{whole}}\right.$$

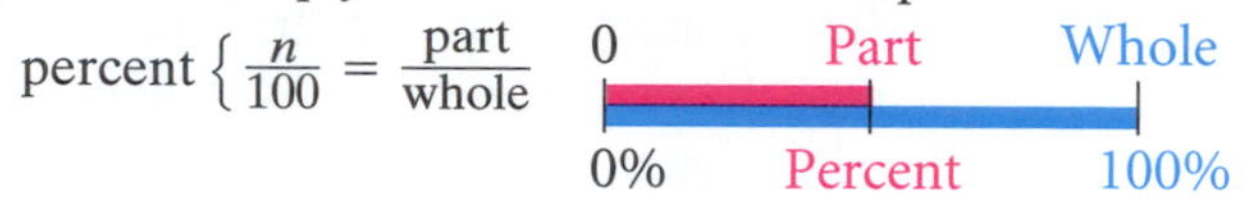

1 EXAMPLE

At Summerville High School there are 553 freshmen, which is 35% of the total number of students. How many students attend the high school?

Relate 35% of the total number of students is 553 students.

Define Let n = the total number of students.

0 — 553 — n
0% — 35% — 100%

Write $\frac{35}{100} = \frac{553}{n}$ ← **part** ← **whole**

$35n = 55{,}300$ **Find the cross products.**

$n = 1580$ **Divide each side by 35.**

There are a total of 1580 students at Summerville High School.

When you use proportions to solve real-world problems involving percents, first establish what is the part and what is the whole. In the next example, notice that the part is actually greater than the whole.

2 EXAMPLE

Band members had a fundraising goal of $2500 as they earned money to go to the state competition. The fundraiser was more successful than they expected, and they raised $3275. What percent of their goal did they raise?

Relate What percent of $2500 is $3275?

Define Let n = the percent.

0 — $2500 — $3275
0% — 100% — n%

Write $\frac{n}{100} = \frac{3275}{2500}$ ← **part** ← **whole**

$2500n = 327{,}500$ **Find the cross products.**

$n = 131$ **Divide each side by 2500.**

The band members raised 131% of their goal.

You can estimate some percents using fractions. These are some of the percent-fraction equivalents that you should remember.

$20\% = \frac{1}{5}$ $25\% = \frac{1}{4}$ $33.\overline{3}\% = \frac{1}{3}$ $50\% = \frac{1}{2}$ $66.\overline{6}\% = \frac{2}{3}$ $75\% = \frac{3}{4}$

You can also solve a percent problem by translating from words to an equation.

3 EXAMPLE

According to the United States Geological Survey, surface water accounts for 77.6% of our country's total daily water supply. The daily surface water supply is about 264 billion gallons. Estimate the total daily water supply.

Relate 77.6% of total daily water supply is 264 billion gallons

0 264 w
0% 77.6% 100%

Define Let w = the total water supply.

Write 77.6% $\cdot$ w = 264

$\frac{3}{4}w = 264$ **75% is close to 77.6%. Use $\frac{3}{4}$ to estimate.**

$\left(\frac{4}{3}\right)\frac{3}{4}w = \left(\frac{4}{3}\right)264$ **Multiply by $\frac{4}{3}$, the reciprocal of $\frac{3}{4}$.**

$w = 352$ **Simplify.**

The total daily water supply is about 352 billion gallons.

EXERCISES

Solve each problem.

1. What percent of 40 is 20?
2. What percent of 20 is 40?
3. 20% of what number is 40?
4. 40% of what number is 20?
5. 8% of 125 is what number?
6. What percent of 125 is 8?
7. 15% of what number is 24?
8. 120% of what number is 48?
9. Carlos worked 31.5 hours at a hospital as a volunteer. This represents 87.5% of his school's requirement for community service. How many hours does his school require for community service?
10. Suppose you work in an electronics store. You earn a 6% commission on every item that you sell. How much commission do you earn if you sell a $545 sound system?
11. Juan earns a 5.5% commission on his bicycle sales. In September, he earned $214.28 in commissions. What were his sales for the month?
12. Jane paid $1185 in sales tax on her new car. The car cost $15,800 before the tax was added. What percent was the sales tax rate?
13. The formula for simple interest is $I = prt$, where I is the interest, p is the principal, r is the interest rate per year, and t is the time in years.
    a. You invest $550 for three years. Find the amount of simple interest you earn with an annual interest rate of 4.5%.
    b. Suppose you invested $900 for two years. You earned $67.50 in simple interest. What was the annual rate of interest?
    c. You invest $812 with an annual interest rate of 6.5%. You earned $316.68 in simple interest. For how many years was the money invested?
14. Sneakers are on sale for 33% off. The original price of the sneakers is $56.
    a. Estimate the amount the sneakers have been marked down.
    b. Estimate the sale price of the sneakers.

2-6 Mixture Problems

California Content Standards

4.0 Simplify expressions before solving linear equations. ***Develop***
15.0 Apply algebraic techniques to solve percent mixture problems. ***Develop***
25.0 Use properties of the number system to justify each step of a procedure. ***Develop***

What You'll Learn

- To solve mixture problems

. . . And Why

To solve real-world problems involving consumer issues, as in Example 1

Check Skills You'll Need

GO for Help Review page 108

Write an equation for each problem and solve.

1. What is 20% of 20?
2. 8 is what percent of 20?
3. 18 is 90% of what number?
4. 27 is 90% of what number?
5. 12 is what percent of 80?
6. What is 60% of 65?

Solving Mixture Problems

Mixture problems involve combining two or more quantities. To solve mixture problems, it is helpful to organize the given and unknown quantities in a table.

1 EXAMPLE Solving Mixture Problems

For help with defining one variable in terms of another, go to Lesson 2-5, Example 1.

Raisins cost \$2 per pound and nuts cost \$5 per pound. How many pounds of each should you use to make a 30-lb mixture that costs \$4 per pound?

Define Let r = the number of pounds of raisins.

Then $30 - r$ = the number of pounds of nuts.

Relate

	Amount (lb)	Cost Per Pound	Cost (dollars)
Raisins	r	\$2	$2r$
Nuts	$30 - r$	\$5	$5(30 - r)$
Mixture	30	\$4	$4(30)$

Write $2r + 5(30 - r) = 4(30)$ — The cost of raisins plus the cost of nuts equals the cost of the mixture.

$2r + 150 - 5r = 120$ — Use the Distributive Property.

$-3r + 150 = 120$ — Combine like terms.

$-3r + 150 - 150 = 120 - 150$ — Subtract 150 from each side.

$-3r = -30$ — Simplify.

$\frac{-3r}{-3} = \frac{-30}{-3}$ — Divide each side by −3.

$r = 10$ — Simplify.

You should use 10 lb of raisins and 30 − 10, or 20, lb of nuts.

CA Standards Check **1** How much of each do you need to make a 50-lb mixture that costs \$3.50/lb?

Some mixture problems involve percents.

2 EXAMPLE Solving Percent Mixture Problems

A chemist has one solution that is 40% acid and another solution that is 80% acid. How many liters of each solution does the chemist need to make 300 liters of a solution that is 64% acid?

Problem Solving Tip

Amount of Solution × Percent of Acid = Amount of Acid

Define Let a = the number of liters of 40% acid solution.

Then $300 - a$ = the number of liters of 80% acid solution.

Relate

	Amount of Solution (L)	Percent Acid	Amount of Acid (L)
40% Solution	a	40%	$0.4a$
80% Solution	$300 - a$	80%	$0.8(300 - a)$
64% Solution	300	64%	$0.64(300)$

Write

$0.4a + 0.8(300 - a) = 0.64(300)$ The amount of acid in the 40% and 80% solutions equals the amount of acid in the mixture.

$0.4a + 240 - 0.8a = 192$ Use the Distributive Property.

$-0.4a + 240 = 192$ Combine like terms.

$-0.4a + 240 - 240 = 192 - 240$ Subtract 240 from each side.

$-0.4a = -48$ Simplify.

$\frac{-0.4a}{-0.4} = \frac{-48}{-0.4}$ Divide each side by -0.4.

$a = 120$ Simplify.

The chemist needs 120 L of 40% solution and 300 − 120, or 180, L of 80% solution.

Check 40% of 120 L is 48 L and 80% of 180 L is 144 L. The total amount of acid in the mixture is 48 + 144, or 192, L. This is equal to 64% of 300 L.

CA Standards Check 2 A chemist has a 10% acid solution and a 60% acid solution. How many liters of each solution does the chemist need to make 200 L of a solution that is 50% acid?

EXERCISES Standards Practice

For more exercises, see *Extra Skills and Word Problem Practice.*

Alg1 4.0, 15.0

A Practice by Example

Example 1 (page 110)

1. A coffee shop owner mixes two types of coffees to make a specialty blend. Alone, the coffees sell for $7.50 per pound and $10.00 per pound. How many pounds of each type of coffee should be used to make 15 pounds of a mixture that sells for $8.95 per pound? Copy and complete the table below.

	Amount (lb)	Cost Per Pound	Cost (dollars)
Coffee 1	c	■	■
Coffee 2	$15 - c$	■	■
Mixture	■	■	■

2. A store sells mixtures of peanuts and almonds for \$4.50 per pound. Peanuts sell for \$2.95 per pound, and almonds sell for \$5.95 per pound. How many pounds of each should be used to make 90 pounds of this mixture?

Example 2
(page 111)

3. A scientist wants to make a solution that is 30% acid using one solution that is 50% acid and another solution that is 20% acid. How many liters of each solution does the scientist need to make 75 liters of the mixture? Copy and complete the table below.

	Amount of Solution (L)	Percent Acid	Amount of Acid (L)
50% Solution	a	■	■
20% Solution	$75 - a$	■	■
30% Solution	■	■	■

4. A solution is 30% chlorine and another solution is 70% chlorine. How many liters of each solution should you use to make 150 liters of a solution that is 55% chlorine?

B Apply Your Skills

For Exercises 5–8, use the following information. A chemist needs a solution that is 75% acid but only has solutions that are 35% and 85% acid. If the chemist measures 120 mL of the 85% solution, how many milliliters of the 35% solution should she add to make a 75% solution?

5. Copy and complete the table below.

	Amount of Solution (mL)	Percent Acid	Amount of Acid (mL)
35% Solution	x	■	■
85% Solution	120	■	■
75% Solution	$120 + x$	■	■

6. Write an equation to represent the situation.

7. How many milliliters of the 35% solution should the chemist add?

8. **Reasoning** Is your answer reasonable? Explain.

9. A 20-pound mixture of banana chips and dried apricots costs \$6.89 per pound. The mixture contains 6 pounds of bananas chips that cost \$1.99 per pound. What is the cost per pound of the dried apricots?

10. Jessica plans to make a fruit juice blend using the two juices at the right. She wants to sell the mixture for an amount between \$1.40 and \$1.45 per liter. What are the minimum and maximum amounts of each juice Jessica can use to make 25 L of the blend?

11. Juan mixes 25 mL of a 15% acid solution with 60 mL of a 25% acid solution and 48 mL of a 50% acid solution. About what percent acid is the final solution?

Homework Video Tutor

Visit: PHSchool.com
Web Code: bae-0206

12. **Writing in Math** Can you make 50 mL of a 35% acid solution with 32 mL of a 45% solution and 18 mL of a 15% solution? Explain.

13. How much water should you add to 230 mL of a 20% salt solution to make the solution 15% salt? Round to the nearest milliliter.

Multiple Choice Practice

For California Standards Tutorials, visit PHSchool.com. Web Code: baq-9045

Alg1 5.0

14. Jared needs to solve the equation $\frac{2x - 3}{3} = 2$. What should he do first?

(A) Multiply each side of the equation by 2.
(B) Multiply each side of the equation by 3.
(C) Subtract 2 from each side of the equation.
(D) Cancel the 3 in the numerator and the 3 in the denominator.

Alg1 1.1

15. Which statement is NOT true?

(A) All irrational numbers are real numbers.
(B) All natural numbers are whole numbers.
(C) Even numbers are closed under addition.
(D) Prime numbers are closed under addition.

Alg1 15.0

16. A chemist uses an 80% acid solution and a 30% acid solution to make 200 liters of a 60% acid solution. How much of the 30% solution should be used?

(A) 60 L (B) 80 L (C) 100 L (D) 120 L

Mixed Review

Lesson 2-5

17. A jet leaves the airport at Charlotte, North Carolina, traveling at an average rate of 564 km/h. Another jet leaves the airport one half hour later traveling at 744 km/h in the same direction. Use an equation to find how long the second jet will take to overtake the first.

Lessons 1-7, 1-8

Name the property that each equation illustrates.

18. $-6g + 10 + g = -6g + 10 + 1g$

19. $-6g + 10 + 1g = -6g + 1g + 10$

20. $-6g + 1g + 10 = (-6 + 1)g + 10$

21. $-4s - 8 + 3(s + 5) = -4s - 8 + 3s + 15$

22. $-4s - 8 + 3s + 15 = -4s + 3s + (-8) + 15$

23. $-4s + 3s + (-8) + 15 = (-4 + 3)s + (-8) + 15$

Lesson 1-2

Simplify each expression.

24. $4 + 3 \cdot 5^2$ **25.** $-6 + 72 \div 12 - 1$ **26.** $2 - 4^3 \div 8 + 10$

27. $7(9 - 4) + 3$ **28.** $(6^2 - 2^3) - 9 \div 3$ **29.** $(56 - 4^2 \cdot 3) \div (-4)$

Test-Taking Strategies

Finding Needed Information

Some test questions ask you to find the missing information needed to solve a problem. For these questions, first figure out how you would solve the problem. Then look at the given information and decide what information you still need.

EXAMPLE

Luis bought two orders of French fries for $.99 each and a cheeseburger for $2.59. He also paid 7% tax on his order. What other information is needed to find the change Luis will receive from the cashier?

- (A) The total cost of the order
- (B) The amount of money he gave the cashier
- (C) The amount of money in his wallet
- (D) The total amount of tax he paid

To find the change Luis received, you need to know the total cost of his purchase, and subtract that from the amount he gives the cashier. Since the prices, number of items, and tax rate are given, you can find the total amount of his purchase. The needed information is the amount of money Luis gave the cashier, so B is the correct answer.

Multiple Choice Practice

1. Pam is buying T-shirts for her cousins. Each T-shirt costs $9.95. Her parents will cover half of the cost. What other information is needed to find the amount of money her parents have to pay for the T-shirts?

- (A) The ages of her cousins
- (B) The family's weekly budget
- (C) The number of cousins
- (D) The size of the T-shirts

2. Michael wants to estimate his monthly cellular phone expenses. He pays $50 per month, and he expects to use an average of 25 more minutes than he is allotted each month. What other information is needed to estimate his monthly cellular phone bill?

- (A) The cost of his cellular phone
- (B) The number of minutes he is allotted per month
- (C) The amount allotted in his budget for his cellular phone bill
- (D) The cost of each extra minute

3. Jose sold 20 bottles of water on Saturday and twice that amount on Sunday. He charges $1.50 per bottle. What additional information is needed to find the amount of profit he made?

- (A) The number of bottles sold on Saturday
- (B) The number of bottles sold on Sunday
- (C) The amount of money he paid for each bottle
- (D) The amount of money he charges for each bottle

Chapter 2 Review

Vocabulary Review

English and Spanish Audio Online

Addition Property of Equality (p. 68)
consecutive integers (p. 101)
cross products (p. 94)
Division Property of Equality (p. 68)
elements (p. 75)
equivalent equations (p. 68)
extremes of a proportion (p. 94)
identity (p. 86)
intersection (p. 75)
inverse operations (p. 68)
literal equation (p. 90)
means of a proportion (p. 94)
Multiplication Property of Equality (p. 68)
null set (p. 75)
proportion (p. 94)
rate (p. 92)
ratio (p. 92)
set (p. 75)
solution of an equation (p. 68)
subset (p. 75)
Subtraction Property of Equality (p. 68)
uniform motion (p. 101)
union (p. 75)
unit analysis (p. 93)
unit rate (p. 92)

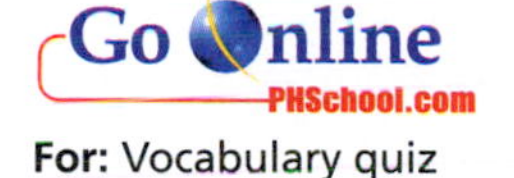

For: Vocabulary quiz
Web Code: baj-0251

Choose the correct item to complete each sentence.

1. Addition and subtraction are examples of (*inverse operations, extremes of a proportion*).
2. (*Consecutive integers, Solutions of equivalent equations*) have the same value.
3. To change one unit of measure to another you can use a (*proportion, rate*) that is equal to 1.
4. You can use (*cross products, unit analysis*) to solve a proportion that involves one variable.
5. A(n) (*literal equation, identity*) is an equation that is true for any value of the variable.
6. An object that moves at a constant rate is said to be in (*uniform motion, proportion*).

Skills and Concepts

Lesson 2-1

- To solve two-step equations (p. 69)
- To use deductive reasoning (p. 71)

Alg1 5.0, 25.0

A two-step equation is an equation that has two operations. You can use models to solve a two-step equation. To solve a two-step equation, first add or subtract. Then multiply or divide.

Solve each equation. Then check your solution.

7. $5x - 8 = 12$
8. $7t - 3 = 18$
9. $\frac{c}{5} - 4 = -3$
10. $-2q - 5 = -11$
11. $-3m + 8 = 2$
12. $11y + 9 = 130$

13. A state park charges admission of \$6 per person plus \$3 for parking. Jo paid \$27 when her car entered the park. Write and solve an equation to find the number of people in Jo's car. Be sure to explain what your variable represents.

Solve each equation. Justify each step.

14. $314 = -n + 576$
15. $-\frac{1}{4}w - 1 = 6$
16. $3h - 4 = 5$

Lesson 2-2

- To use the Distributive Property when combining like terms (p. 76)
- To use the Distributive Property when solving equations (p. 77)

Alg1 2.0, 4.0, 5.0

You can combine like terms and use the Distributive Property to simplify expressions and solve equations.

Solve each equation.

17. $b + 4b = -90$

18. $-x + 7x = 24$

19. $2(t + 5) = 9$

20. $-(3 - 10y) = 12$

21. $x - (4 - x) = 0$

22. $4n + 7 + 6n = 32$

23. $\frac{3y}{4} - \frac{y}{2} = 5$

24. $0.36p + 0.26 = 3.86$

25. The width of a rectangle is 6 cm less than the length. The perimeter is 72 cm. Write and solve an equation to find the dimensions of the rectangle.

Lesson 2-3

- To solve equations with variables on both sides (p. 84)
- To identify equations that are identities or have no solution (p. 86)

Alg1 4.0, 5.0, 25.3

You can use the properties of equality to solve an equation with variables on both sides. An equation has no solution if no value of the variable makes the equation true. An equation is an **identity** if every value of the variable makes the equation true.

Solve each equation.

26. $4n - 6n = 2n$

27. $4(5x - 2) - 6x = 5(2x + 4)$

28. $3(2t - 6) = 3t - 9$

29. $5(3 - d) = 2d + 1$

30. $12(h - 1) = 6h + 4 + 2h$

31. $-5v - 6 = 3v + 10$

Determine whether each equation is an *identity* or whether it has *no solution*.

32. $4h + 7 = 4h - 3$

33. $-6w + 12 = -2(3w - 4)$

34. $-5a - 7 + 4a = -(a - 7)$

35. $5 - (8f + 10) = -8f - 5$

Use an equation to solve each problem.

36. One online bookstore charges \$10 per book and \$8 for shipping. Another online bookstore charges \$12 per book and offers free shipping. For what number of books is the cost the same?

37. A cable company charges \$39.95 per month for basic cable service and \$8.95 per month for each premium channel. If Derek's monthly bill is \$66.80, how many premium channels does he receive?

Lesson 2-4

- To find ratios and rates (p. 92)
- To solve proportions (p. 94)

Alg1 5.0, 15.0, 25.0

A **ratio** is a comparison of two numbers by division. A **rate** is a ratio that compares quantities measured in different units. A **proportion** is a statement that two ratios are equal. You can solve a proportion involving a single variable by finding the **cross products.**

Write in miles per hour. Round to the nearest tenth where necessary.

38. 2.5 mi/min

39. 300 ft/min

40. 4 in./s

41. 130 ft in 12.5 s

Solve each proportion.

42. $\frac{4}{12} = \frac{c}{6}$

43. $\frac{t}{5} = \frac{23}{50}$

44. $\frac{-9}{m} = \frac{3}{2}$

45. $\frac{x}{8} = \frac{x - 5}{6}$

46. $\frac{12}{r} = \frac{4}{0.5r - 1}$

47. $\frac{d - 2}{d + 9} = \frac{3}{14}$

48. You are reading a book for your English class. It takes you 75 minutes to read 45 pages.

a. Find your average speed. Write an equation that relates the number of pages p you read to the number of minutes m you read.

b. The book you are reading has 195 pages. How long will it take you to read the book?

Lesson 2-5

- To define a variable in terms of another variable (p. 100)
- To model distance-rate-time problems (p. 101)

Alg1 4.0, 5.0, 15.0

Many types of real-world problems can be solved using equations. You can also use tables and diagrams to help organize information or solve the problem.

Write and solve an equation for each situation.

49. The Great Seto Bridge in Japan is about 7.6 mi long. How long would it take you to cross the bridge if you were walking at 4 mi/h?

50. The sum of three consecutive integers is 582. Find the three integers.

51. A supertanker leaves port traveling north at an average speed of 10 knots. Two hours later a cruise ship leaves the same port, heading south at an average speed of 18 knots. How many hours after the cruise ship sails will the two ships be 209 nautical miles apart? (1 knot = 1 nautical mile per hour)

52. Juan drives to work. Because of traffic conditions, he averages 22 miles per hour. He returns home at an average speed of 32 miles per hour. His total travel time is $2\frac{1}{4}$ hours.

Lesson 2-6

- To solve mixture problems (p. 110)

Alg1 4.0, 15.0, 25.0

One type of real-world problem involves mixtures. To solve mixture problems, you can use algebraic techniques and organize the data in tables.

53. A mixture of dried fruit and nuts sells for $4.30 per pound. Separately, the dried fruit sells for $2.50 per pound, and the nuts sell for $7.00 per pound. How much of each is needed to make 50 pounds of the mixture? Copy and complete the table below.

	Amount (lb)	Cost Per Pound	Cost (dollars)
Dried Fruit	■	■	■
Nuts	■	■	■
Mixture	■	■	■

54. Vanessa needs 100 mL of a 44% acid solution for a chemistry experiment. She has a 30% acid solution and a 65% acid solution. How many milliliters of each solution does she need to make the mixture?

Chapter 2 Test

For: Chapter Test
Web Code: baa-0252

Solve each equation. Then check.

1. $3w + 2 - w = -4$

2. $\frac{1}{4}(k - 1) = 10$

3. $6(y + 3) = 24$

4. $\frac{5n + 1}{8} = \frac{1}{2}$

5. If $2t + 3 = -9$, what is the value of $-3t - 7$?

6. Solve $2x - 4 = -7$. Justify each step.

Define a variable and write an equation to model each situation. Then solve.

7. Your chorus holds a car wash. They have \$25.00 for making change. At the end of the car wash, they have \$453.50. How much money did they make?

8. The rate to rent a certain truck is \$55 per day and \$0.20 per mile. Your family pays \$80 to rent this truck for one day. How many miles did your family drive?

9. Movie tickets for an adult and three children cost \$20. An adult's ticket costs \$2 more than a child's ticket. Find the cost of an adult's ticket.

Solve each proportion.

10. $\frac{3}{4} = \frac{c}{20}$

11. $\frac{8}{15} = \frac{4}{w}$

12. $\frac{w}{6} = \frac{6}{15}$

13. $\frac{5}{t} = \frac{25}{100}$

Solve. If the equation is an identity, write *identity*. If it has no solution, write *no solution*.

14. $9j + 3 = 3(3j + 1)$

15. $4v - 9 = 6v + 7$

16. $2(1 - 2y) = 4y + 18$

17. $4p - 5 + p = 7 + 5p + 2$

Write an equation and solve.

18. The sum of two consecutive *odd* integers is 56. Find the two odd integers.

19. The sum of four consecutive *even* integers is 308. Find the four integers.

20. The length of a rectangle is 8 cm more than twice the width. The perimeter of the rectangle is 34 cm. What is the length of the rectangle?

Complete each statement.

21. 14¢/oz = \$■/lb

22. 7 gal/wk = ■ qt/h

23. 35 mi/h = ■ ft/min

24. 120 ft/day = ■ in./min

25. A taxicab company charges a flat fee of \$1.85, plus an additional \$.40 per quarter-mile.
 a. Write a formula to find the total cost for each fare.
 b. Use this formula to find the cost for 1 person to travel 8 mi.

Define a variable and write an equation to model each situation. Then solve.

26. Jan is one year younger than her brother Bill and one year older than her sister Sue. The sum of the three children's ages is 57. How old is each child?

27. At noon, your family starts out from Louisville to go to Memphis driving at 40 mi/h. Your uncle leaves Memphis to come to Louisville two hours later. He is taking the same route and driving at 60 mi/h. The two cities are 380 miles apart. At what time do the cars meet?

28. John and William leave their home traveling in opposite directions on a straight road. John drives 20 miles per hour faster than William. After 4 hours they are 250 miles apart. Find their rates.

Solve each equation.

29. $-y - 3 = 8$

30. $15 = -z + 8$

31. $-q + 5 = 10$

32. $-a + 9 = 25$

33. One solution is 75% acid, and another solution is 15% acid. How many liters of each solution should you use to make 90 liters of 35% solution?

34. A coffee blend consists of two types of coffee that individually sell for \$8.50 and \$6.00 per pound. The blend sells for \$7.00 per pound. How many pounds of each type of coffee should be used to make 20 pounds of the mixture?

Standards Mastery

Cumulative Practice

Some questions ask you to determine which situation can be represented by a given equation. Read the question at the right. Then follow the tips to answer the sample question.

Mandy is selling historic photos to raise money for a class trip. She can order each photo for $2.75 and each frame for $4.25. Mandy plans to sell each photo with a frame for $10.00. Which equation best represents the total amount of money t Mandy will have for the class trip after selling n photos with frames?

(A) $t = 10 - 2.75 - 4.25n$
(B) $t = 10n - (2.75 + 4.25)$
(C) $t = 10 - (2.75 - 4.25)n$
(D) $t = [10 - (2.75 - 4.25)]n$

Tip 1
Analyze the situation. Mandy is buying items that cost $2.75 and $4.25, and then reselling them together for $10.00.

Tip 2
Make sure you know what each variable represents; t is the amount of money she makes after selling n framed photos.

Think It Through

Mandy's total cost is $2.75 + $4.25 per item. She then sells each item for $10. Mandy makes $10 – ($2.75 + $4.25) after selling one item, and [$10 – ($2.75 + $4.25)]$n$ after selling n items. Therefore, the correct answer is D.

Vocabulary Review

As you solve problems, you must understand the meanings of mathematical terms. Match each term with its mathematical meaning.

A. formula	**I.** the distance around the outside of a figure
B. reciprocal	**II.** any value that makes an equation true
C. perimeter	**III.** a math sentence that defines the relationship between quantities
D. solution	**IV.** the multiplicative inverse of a nonzero number

Read each question. Then write the letter of the correct answer on your paper.

1. Simplify the expression $2b - 3a + b + a$. **(Lesson 1-8)**

(A) -1
(B) ab
(C) $b - a$
(D) $3b - 2a$

2. Simplify the expression $64s - (8s - 1)$. **(Lesson 1-7)**

(A) $8s + 1$
(B) $8s - 1$
(C) $56s + 1$
(D) $56s - 1$

3. Simplify the expression $3(12x + 2) - 2(10x + 3)$. **(Lesson 1-7)**

(A) $16x$
(B) $16x + 5$
(C) $16x + 9$
(D) $16x + 12$

4. Erica is making feathered caps for her school play. Each cap must have 3 feathers. Which equation best represents the number of feathers f Erica needs to make c caps? **(Lesson 2-1)**

(A) $c = 3f$
(B) $f = 3c$
(C) $c = f + 3$
(D) $f = c + 3$

5. Sabrina bought a used car with 28,000 miles. If she drives 36 miles each day, which equation can be used to find the total number of miles m Sabrina will have on her car after she drives it for d days? **(Lesson 2-1)**

(A) $d = 36m + 28{,}000$
(B) $m = 36d + 28{,}000$
(C) $m + 36d = 28{,}000$
(D) $d = 28{,}000m + 36$

6. Travis sells black and white photos of cities across the country. Each photo's width is half the length. Which equation best represents the area a of a photo, given its length ℓ? **(Lesson 2-1)**

(A) $A = \frac{1}{2}\ell$
(B) $A = \frac{1}{2}\ell^2$
(C) $A = \frac{1}{4}\ell^2$
(D) $A = 2\ell^2$

Cumulative Practice (continued)

7. The perimeter of a rectangle is given by the equation $2w + 33 = 54$. What is w, the width of the rectangle? **(Lesson 2-1)**

Ⓐ 10.5　Ⓑ 42　Ⓒ 43.5　Ⓓ 174

8. The formula for the time that a traffic light remains yellow is $t = \frac{1}{8}s + 1$, where t represents the time in seconds, and s represents the speed limit in miles per hour (mph). If the light is yellow for 6 seconds, what is the speed limit in miles per hour (mph)? **(Lesson 2-1)**

Ⓐ 25 mph　Ⓑ 30 mph　Ⓒ 40 mph　Ⓓ 56 mph

9. Which expression represents the sum of 3 odd integers of which $2n + 1$ is the least integer? **(Lesson 2-5)**

Ⓐ $2n + 6$　Ⓑ $6n + 3$　Ⓒ $6n + 6$　Ⓓ $6n + 7$

10. Which property is shown by the equation $5 + (3 + 6) = 5 + (6 + 3)$? **(Lesson 1-8)**

Ⓐ Identity Property of Multiplication
Ⓑ Commutative Property of Addition
Ⓒ Identity Property of Addition
Ⓓ Commutative Property of Multiplication

11. Evaluate $2a^2$ for $a = 3$. **(Lesson 1-2)**

Ⓐ 6　Ⓑ 12　Ⓒ 18　Ⓓ 36

12. The rectangle and the triangle shown below have the same perimeter. What is the perimeter of the rectangle? **(Lesson 2-3)**

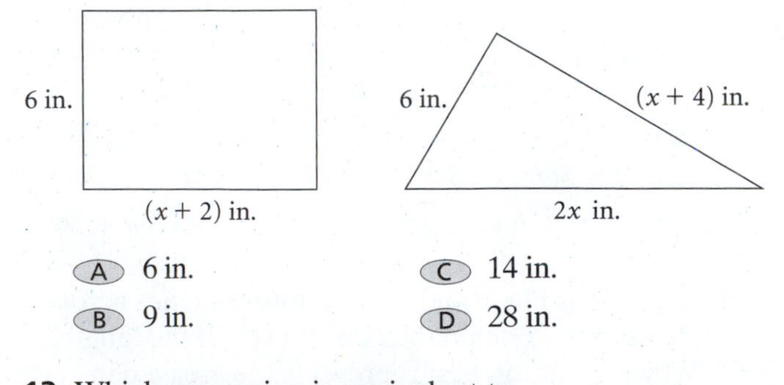

Ⓐ 6 in.　Ⓑ 9 in.　Ⓒ 14 in.　Ⓓ 28 in.

13. Which expression is equivalent to $-2(3x - 4) - (-2x + 1)$? **(Lesson 2-2)**

Ⓐ $-3x + 7$　Ⓑ $-3x - 7$　Ⓒ $-4x + 7$　Ⓓ $-4x - 7$

14. Tanya wants to buy a digital audio player that sells for \$149.99. She has \$64 in her bank account and is saving \$18 each week. How long will it take Tanya to save enough money to buy the player? **(Lesson 2-2)**

Ⓐ 3 weeks　Ⓑ 4 weeks　Ⓒ 5 weeks　Ⓓ 6 weeks

15. Sonia's friend simplified an expression, as shown below:

$$5^2 - 2^2 \cdot 12 \div 2 + 3$$

Step 1: $5^2 - 2^2 \cdot 6 + 3$

Step 2: $5^2 - 2^2 \cdot 9$

Step 3: $3^2 \cdot 9$

Step 4: $9 \cdot 9$

Step 5: 81

In which step did Sonia's friend make the first mistake? **(Lesson 1-2)**

Ⓐ Step 1, because exponents comes before division in the order of operations
Ⓑ Step 2, because addition comes before multiplication in the order of operations
Ⓒ Step 3, because exponents come before subtraction in the order of operations
Ⓓ Step 4, because multiplication comes before exponents in the order of operations

16. The perimeter of the triangle below is 22.6 in. What is the value of n? **(Lesson 2-2)**

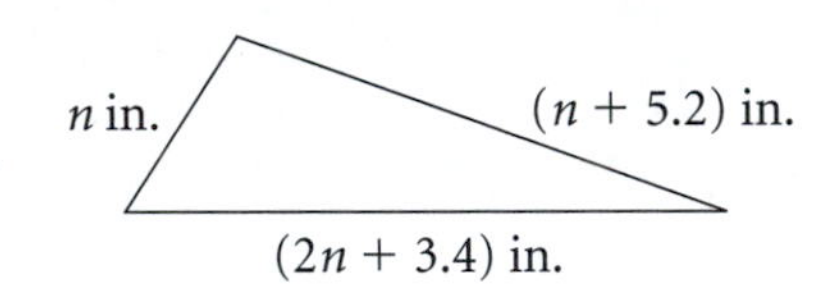

Ⓐ 3.5　Ⓑ 7.8　Ⓒ 4.6　Ⓓ 9.4

17. Which property is shown by the equation $5 \cdot (3 \cdot 4) = (5 \cdot 3) \cdot 4$? **(Lesson 1-8)**

Ⓐ Commutative Property of Multiplication
Ⓑ Associative Property of Multiplication
Ⓒ Commutative Property of Addition
Ⓓ Associative Property of Addition

18. Simplify the expression $6(4x - 1) - 3(8x + 2)$. **(Lesson 2-2)**

Ⓐ $48x$　Ⓑ -12　Ⓒ $48x - 12$　Ⓓ 0

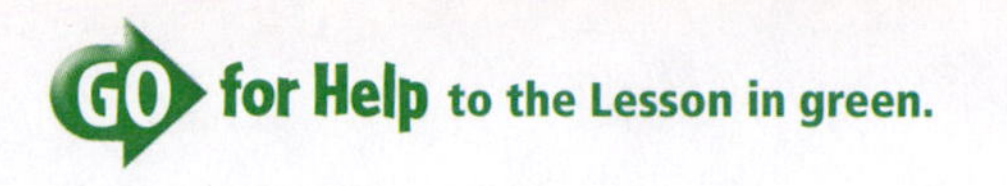

Standards Mastery

19. What was done to the first equation to get the second equation? **(Lesson 2-1)**

$$4x - 16 = 20$$
$$4x = 36$$

Ⓐ Added 20 to each side
Ⓑ Subtracted 16 from each side
Ⓒ Added 14 to each side
Ⓓ Added 16 to each side

20. Evaluate $|a| - |b|$ when $a = -15$ and $b = 8$. **(Lesson 1-3)**

Ⓐ -23 Ⓑ -7 Ⓒ 7 Ⓓ 23

21. What is the opposite of this product? **(Lesson 1-3)**

$$\left(\frac{2}{3}\right)(-5)(-6)\left(\frac{4}{5}\right)$$

Ⓐ -16 Ⓑ $\frac{5}{15}$ Ⓒ 16 Ⓓ $-\frac{120}{8}$

22. What is the reciprocal of this expression? **(Lesson 1-3)**

$$-\frac{7}{8} \div \frac{5}{9}$$

Ⓐ $\frac{40}{63}$ Ⓑ $\frac{63}{40}$ Ⓒ $-\frac{63}{40}$ Ⓓ $-\frac{40}{63}$

23. Which property guarantees the truth of this statement? **(Lesson 1-8)**

$$2(5 \cdot 8) = (2 \cdot 5) \cdot 8$$

Ⓐ Closure Property of Addition
Ⓑ Identity Property of Multiplication
Ⓒ Distributive Property
Ⓓ Associative Property of Multiplication

24. A chemist made 100 mL of a 16% acid solution by mixing a 10% acid solution with a 30% acid solution. How much of the 30% acid solution did the chemist use? **(Lesson 2-6)**

Ⓐ 30 mL Ⓒ 60 mL
Ⓑ 35 mL Ⓓ 70 mL

25. A 5% acid solution is added to 8 L of a 60% acid solution to make a 25% solution. How much of the 5% acid solution must be added? **(Lesson 2-6)**

Ⓐ 1.4 L Ⓒ 14 L
Ⓑ 11.2 L Ⓓ 56 L

26. Which operation should be done first to simplify this expression? **(Lesson 1-2)**

$$56(9 - 3 \div 4 \cdot 2)$$

Ⓐ $56 \cdot 9$ Ⓒ $9 - 3$
Ⓑ $3 \div 4$ Ⓓ $4 \cdot 2$

27. What is the solution of $3(3x + 2) + 5 = 5(3x - 8) + 9$? **(Lesson 2-3)**

Ⓐ $x = 1$ Ⓒ $x = 7$
Ⓑ $x = 2\frac{2}{3}$ Ⓓ $x = 3\frac{2}{3}$

28. In which step was the first error made? **(Lesson 1-8)**

$5a - 3(4a + 2)$
Step 1: $5a - (12a + 6)$
Step 2: $(5a - 12a) + 6$
Step 3: $(5 - 12)a - + 6$
Step 4: $-7a + 5$

Ⓐ Step 1 Ⓒ Step 3
Ⓑ Step 2 Ⓓ Step 4

Standards Reference Guide

California Content Standard	Item Number(s)
Alg1 1.0	10, 17, 23, 26
Alg1 2.0	11, 20–22
Alg1 4.0	1–3, 13, 16, 18
Alg1 5.0	4–9, 12, 14, 19, 27
Alg1 15.0	24, 25
Alg1 25.2	15, 32

For additional review and practice, see the *California Standards Review and Practice Workbook* or go online to use the

Visit: PHSchool.com, **Web Code:** baq-9045

Solving Inequalities

What You've Learned

California Content Standards

2.0 Understand and use such operations as taking the opposite and finding the reciprocal.

4.0 Simplify expressions before solving linear equations in one variable.

5.0 Solve multi-step problems, including word problems, involving linear equations in one variable and provide justification for each step.

Check Your Readiness

for Help to the Lesson in green.

Ordering Rational Numbers (Lesson 1-3)

Complete each statement with <, =, or >.

1. $-3 \blacksquare -5$ **2.** $7 \blacksquare \frac{14}{2}$ **3.** $-8 \blacksquare -8.4$ **4.** $-\frac{3}{2} \blacksquare -1$

Absolute Value (Lesson 1-3)

Simplify each expression.

5. $5 + |4 - 6|$ **6.** $|30 - 28| - 6$ **7.** $|-7 + 2| - 4$

Solving One-Step Equations (Review page 68)

Solve each equation. Check your solution.

8. $x - 4 = -2$ **9.** $b + 4 = 7$ **10.** $-\frac{3}{4}y = 9$ **11.** $\frac{m}{12} = 2.7$

12. $-8 + x = 15$ **13.** $n - 7 = 22.5$ **14.** $-\frac{12}{7}z = 48$ **15.** $\frac{5y}{4} = -15$

Solving Two-Step Equations (Lesson 2-1)

Solve each equation. Check your solution.

16. $-5 + \frac{b}{4} = 7$ **17.** $4.2m + 4 = 25$ **18.** $-12 = 6 + \frac{3}{4}x$ **19.** $6 = -z - 4$

20. $4m + 2.3 = 9.7$ **21.** $\frac{5}{8}t - 7 = -22$ **22.** $-4.7 = 3y + 1.3$ **23.** $12.2 = 5.3x - 3.7$

Solving Multi-Step Equations (Lesson 2-2)

Solve each equation. Check your solution.

24. $4t + 7 + 6t = -33$ **25.** $2a + 5 = 9a - 16$ **26.** $\frac{1}{3} + \frac{4y}{6} = \frac{2}{3}$

27. $6(y - 2) = 8 - 2y$ **28.** $n + 3(n - 2) = 10.4$ **29.** $\frac{1}{2}w + 3 = \frac{2}{3}w - 5$

▲ Wind turbines make electricity from wind. Large turbines range in size from 50 to 750 kilowatts. You can use a compound inequality to express this range.

What You'll Learn Next

California Content Standards

3.0 Solve equations and inequalities involving absolute values.

4.0 Simplify expressions before solving linear inequalities in one variable.

5.0 Solve multi-step problems, including word problems, involving linear inequalities in one variable and provide justification for each step.

25.3 Given a specific algebraic statement involving linear or absolute value expressions or equations or inequalities, determine whether the statement is true sometimes, always, or never.

New Vocabulary

English and Spanish Audio Online

- **compound inequality** (p. 151)
- **equivalent inequalities** (p. 131)
- **solution of an inequality** (p. 124)

Academic Vocabulary

- **define** (p. 158)
- **describe** (p. 158)
- **explain** (p. 158)

3-1 Inequalities and Their Graphs

California Content Standards

5.0 Solve multi-step problems, including word problems, involving linear inequalities in one variable and provide justification for each step. ***Develop***

What You'll Learn

- To identify solutions of inequalities
- To graph and write inequalities

. . . And Why

To write inequalities for speed limits and starting salaries, as in Example 5

Check Skills You'll Need

GO for Help Lesson 1-3

Graph the numbers on the same number line.

1. 4 **2.** -3 **3.** $\frac{9}{3}$ **4.** 0 **5.** 1.5

Complete each statement with <, =, or >.

6. $-3 \blacksquare -5$ **7.** $4.29 \blacksquare 4.8$ **8.** $(-3)(-4) \blacksquare 12$

9. $-1 - 2 \blacksquare 6 - 9$ **10.** $-\frac{3}{4} \blacksquare -\frac{4}{5}$ **11.** $\frac{1}{3} + \frac{1}{3} \blacksquare \frac{1}{2} + \frac{1}{2}$

New Vocabulary • solution of an inequality

Identifying Solutions of Inequalities

Vocabulary Tip

Less than and is less than have different meanings. For example, "x less than 3" means $3 - x$; "x is less than 3" means $x < 3$.

A **solution of an inequality** is any number that makes the inequality true. For example, the solutions of the inequality $x < 3$ are all numbers that are less than 3.

1 EXAMPLE Identifying Solutions by Mental Math

Is each number a solution of $x \le 7$?

a. 9 No, $9 \le 7$ is not true.

b. $\frac{14}{2}$ $\frac{14}{2} = 7$. Yes, $\frac{14}{2} \le 7$ is true.

CA Standards Check

1 Is each number a solution of $x \ge -4.1$?

a. -5 **b.** -4.1 **c.** 8 **d.** 0

You can determine whether a value is a solution of an inequality by evaluating an expression.

2 EXAMPLE Identifying Solutions by Evaluating

Is each number a solution of $2 - 5x > 13$?

a. 3

$2 - 5x > 13$

$2 - 5(3) > 13$ ← Substitute for x.

$2 - 15 > 13$ ← Simplify.

$-13 \not> 13$ ← Compare.

3 does not make the original inequality true, so 3 is not a solution.

b. -4

$2 - 5x > 13$

$2 - 5(-4) > 13$ ← Substitute for x.

$2 + 20 > 13$ ← Simplify.

$22 > 13$ ← Compare.

-4 does make the original inequality true, so -4 is a solution.

CA Standards Check 2 Is each number a solution of $6x - 3 > 10$?

a. 1 **b.** 2 **c.** 3 **d.** 4

Graphing and Writing Inequalities in One Variable

You can use a graph to indicate all of the solutions of an inequality.

Vocabulary Tip

You normally read $-1 \geq a$ as "-1 is greater than or equal to a." The inequality symbol also indicates that a is less than or equal to -1.

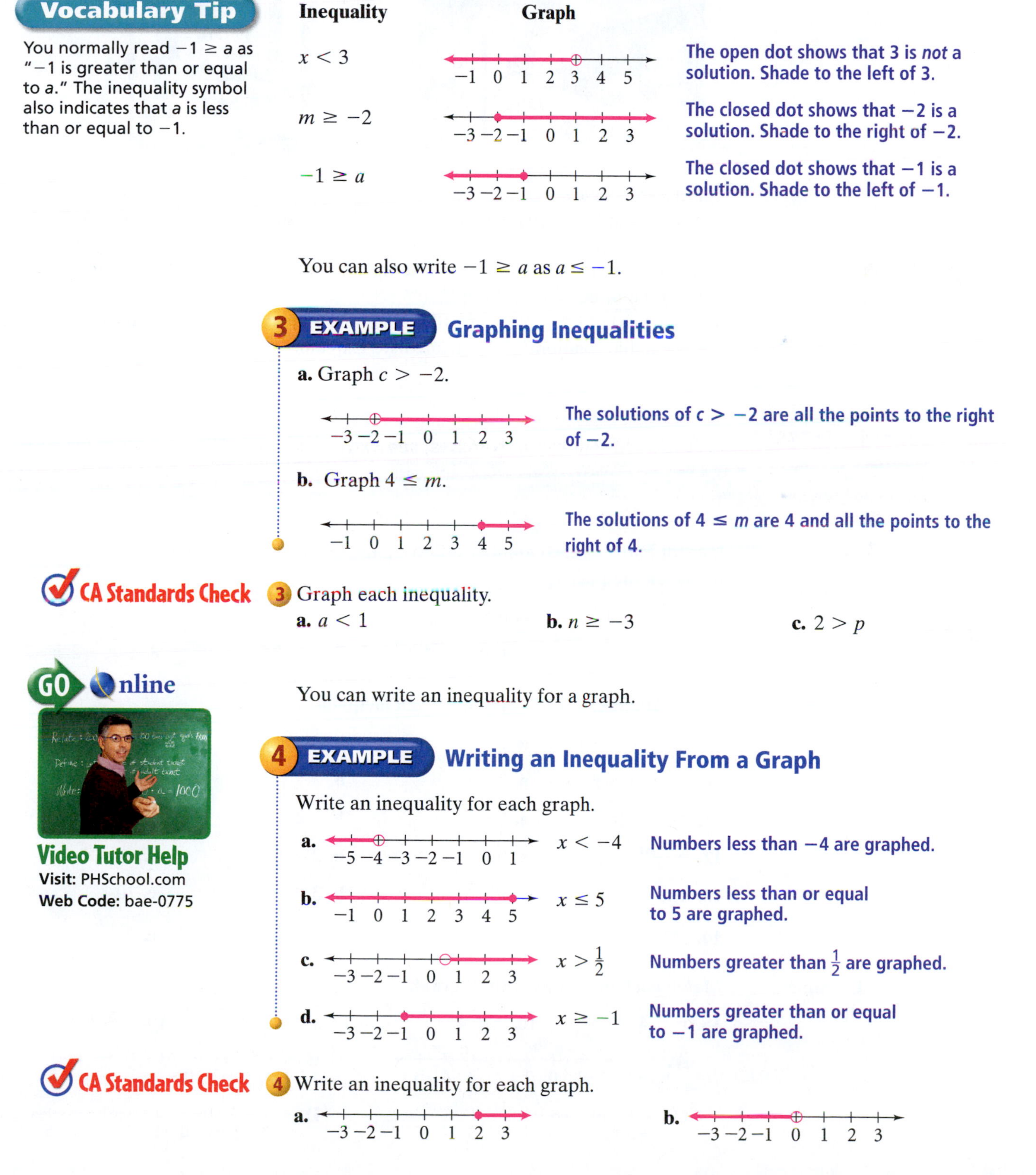

Inequality	Graph	
$x < 3$		The open dot shows that 3 is *not* a solution. Shade to the left of 3.
$m \geq -2$		The closed dot shows that -2 is a solution. Shade to the right of -2.
$-1 \geq a$		The closed dot shows that -1 is a solution. Shade to the left of -1.

You can also write $-1 \geq a$ as $a \leq -1$.

3 EXAMPLE Graphing Inequalities

a. Graph $c > -2$.

The solutions of $c > -2$ are all the points to the right of -2.

b. Graph $4 \leq m$.

The solutions of $4 \leq m$ are 4 and all the points to the right of 4.

CA Standards Check 3 Graph each inequality.

a. $a < 1$ **b.** $n \geq -3$ **c.** $2 > p$

GO Online

Video Tutor Help

Visit: PHSchool.com

Web Code: bae-0775

You can write an inequality for a graph.

4 EXAMPLE Writing an Inequality From a Graph

Write an inequality for each graph.

a. $x < -4$ Numbers less than -4 are graphed.

b. $x \leq 5$ Numbers less than or equal to 5 are graphed.

c. $x > \frac{1}{2}$ Numbers greater than $\frac{1}{2}$ are graphed.

d. $x \geq -1$ Numbers greater than or equal to -1 are graphed.

CA Standards Check 4 Write an inequality for each graph.

a.

b.

You can describe real-world situations using an inequality.

5 EXAMPLE Application

Define a variable and write an inequality for each situation.

a.

Let s = a legal speed.
The sign indicates that $s \leq 65$.

b.

Let p = pay per hour (in dollars).
The sign indicates that $p \geq 6.15$.

CA Standards Check 5 **a. Critical Thinking** In part (a) of Example 5, can the speed be *all* real numbers less than or equal to 65? Explain.

b. In part (b) of Example 5, are all real numbers greater than or equal to \$6.15 reasonable solutions of the inequality? Explain.

EXERCISES

Standards Practice

For more exercises, see *Extra Skills and Word Problem Practice.*

Alg1 5.0, 24.3, 25.1

A Practice by Example

GO for Help

Example 1 (page 124)

Mental Math Is each number following the inequality a solution of the given inequality?

1. $v \geq -5; 4$ **2.** $0.5 > c; 2$ **3.** $b < 4; -0.5$ **4.** $d \leq \frac{17}{3}; 5$

5. $g \leq \frac{12}{5}; 3$ **6.** $k < 0; -1$ **7.** $a > 3.2; 3$ **8.** $x \geq -2.5; -2.5$

Example 2 (page 124)

Is each number a solution of the given inequality?

9. $3x - 7 > -1$ **a.** 2 **b.** 0 **c.** 5

10. $4n - 3 \leq 5$ **a.** 2 **b.** 3 **c.** -1

11. $2y + 1 < -3$ **a.** 0 **b.** -2 **c.** 1

12. $\frac{4 - m}{m} \geq 5$ **a.** 0.5 **b.** 2 **c.** -4

13. $n(n - 3) < 54$ **a.** 9 **b.** 3 **c.** 10

14. $5(2q - 8) \geq 7$ **a.** -2 **b.** $\frac{9}{2}$ **c.** 6

Example 3 (page 125)

Match each inequality with its graph.

15. $x < 4$ **16.** $x \geq 4$ **17.** $x > 4$ **18.** $x \leq 4$

A.
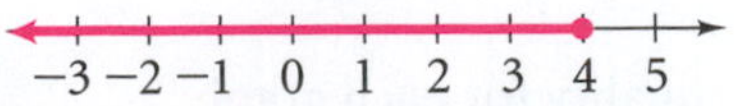

B.
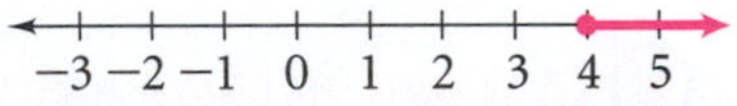

C.
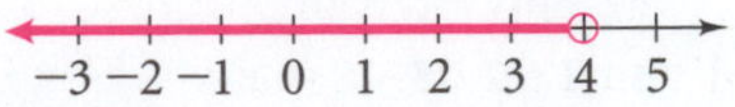

D.
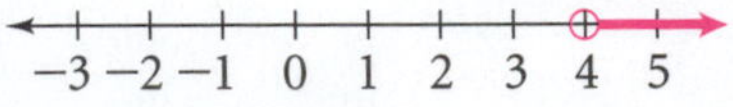

Graph each inequality.

19. $x > 1$ **20.** $s < -3$ **21.** $y \leq -4$ **22.** $t \geq -1$

23. $-2 < d$ **24.** $-\frac{3}{2} \leq b$ **25.** $7 \geq a$ **26.** $4.25 > c$

Example 4 (page 125)

Write an inequality for each graph.

27. −4 −3 −2 −1 0 1 2 3 4

29. −4 −3 −2 −1 0 1 2 3 4

31. −2 −1 0 1 2 3 4 5 6

28. **30.** **32.**

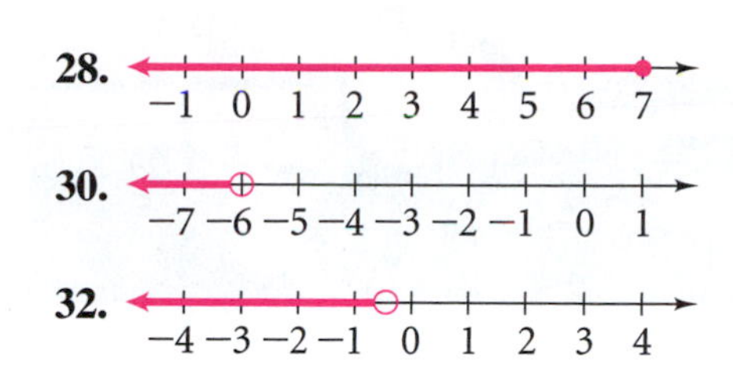

Example 5 (page 126)

Define a variable and write an inequality to model each situation.

33. A bus can seat at most 48 students.

34. In many states, you must be at least 16 years old to obtain a driver's license.

35. It is not safe to use a light bulb of more than 60 watts in this light fixture.

36. At least 350 students attended the band concert Friday night.

37. The Navy's flying squad, the Blue Angels, makes more than 75 appearances each year.

B Apply Your Skills

Write each inequality in words.

38. $n < 5$ **39.** $b > 0$ **40.** $7 \geq x$ **41.** $z \geq -5.6$

42. $4 > q$ **43.** $-1 \geq m$ **44.** $35 \geq w$ **45.** $g - 2 < 7$

46. $a \leq 3$ **47.** $6 + r > -2$ **48.** $8 \leq h$ **49.** $1.2 > k$

50. Writing Explain how you choose whether to draw an open or a closed dot when you graph an inequality.

51. Describe a situation that you can represent using the inequality $x \geq 18$.

52. Suppose your school plans a musical. Adult tickets are \$5 and student tickets are \$4. Let a represent the number of adult tickets and s represent the number of student tickets. Which inequality represents ticket sales of at least \$4000?

Ⓐ $4a + 5s < 4000$ Ⓒ $5a + 4s > 4000$

Ⓑ $5a + 4s \leq 4000$ Ⓓ $5a + 4s \geq 4000$

Rewrite each inequality so that the variable is on the left. Then graph the solutions.

53. $2 < x$ **54.** $-5 \geq b$ **55.** $0 \leq r$ **56.** $5 > a$

Graph each inequality from the given description.

57. t is nonnegative. **58.** x is positive.

59. k is no more than 3. **60.** r is at least 2.

61. s is at most 4. **62.** v is no less than 7.

Visit: PHSchool.com
Web Code: bae-0301

63. Writing Explain how you interpret the phrases "at least" and "at most" in an inequality that models a real-world situation.

Use the map below for Exercises 64–65.

There are at least 1700 flights in and out of Los Angeles International Airport each day.

64. You plan to go from New York City to Los Angeles. Let x be the distance in miles of any air-route between New York City and Los Angeles. The shortest route is a direct flight. Using the map, write a true statement about the mileage of any route from New York City to Los Angeles.

65. Your travel agent is making plans for you to go from Chicago to New Orleans. A direct flight costs too much. Option A consists of flights from Chicago to Dallas to New Orleans. Option B consists of flights from Chicago to Orlando to New Orleans. Write an inequality comparing the mileage of these two options.

For help with counterexamples, go to Lesson 1-3, Example 3.

66. Reasoning A student claims that the inequality $3x + 1 > 0$ is always true because multiplying a number by three and then adding one to it makes the number greater than zero. Use a counterexample to show why the student is not correct.

67. Critical Thinking Describe how you can display the solutions of the inequality $x \neq 3$ on a number line.

68. Critical Thinking Explain the difference between "4 greater than x" and "$4 > x$."

69. Critical Thinking Which is the correct graph of $-4 < -x$? Explain.

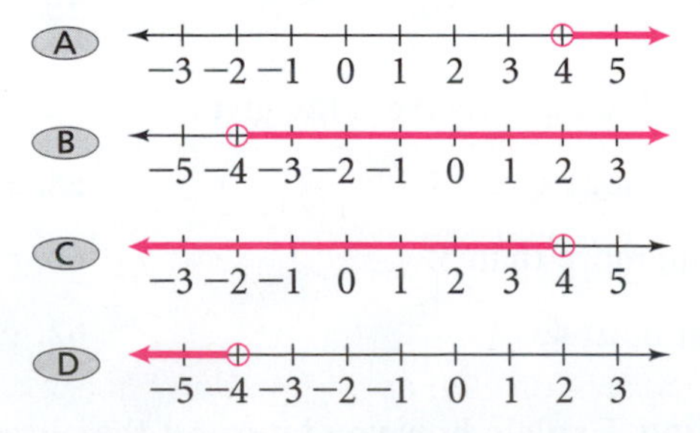

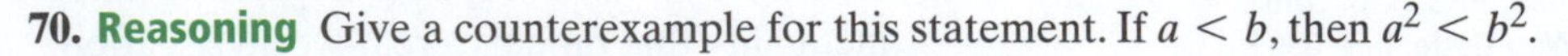

70. Reasoning Give a counterexample for this statement. If $a < b$, then $a^2 < b^2$.

Problem Solving Tip

In Exercise 71, make logical choices for values of *a* and *b*. Use positive and negative numbers as well as zero.

71. Reasoning Describe the numbers a and b for which the following statement is true. If $a < b$, then $a^2 = b^2$.

Graph on a number line.

72. all values of x such that $x > -2$ and $x \leq 2$

73. all values of x such that $x < -1$ or $x > 3$

Multiple Choice Practice

For California Standards Tutorials, visit PHSchool.com. Web Code: baq-9045

Alg1 1.0

74. What is the least whole number solution of $k \geq -5$?

Ⓐ -5 Ⓑ -4 Ⓒ 0 Ⓓ 1

Alg1 5.0

75. You must work at least 20 years in a company in order to receive full benefits upon retirement. Which inequality or graph does NOT describe this situation?

Ⓐ $y \geq 20$

Ⓑ $20 \leq y$

Ⓒ $y > 20$

Ⓓ 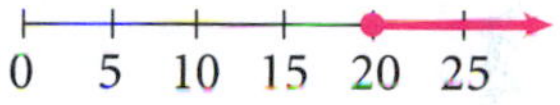

Alg1 24.3

76. Which value makes the inequality $x^2 \geq x$ false?

Ⓐ $-\frac{1}{4}$ Ⓑ 0 Ⓒ $\frac{1}{4}$ Ⓓ 1

Alg1 5.0

77. The local fire code requires that no more than 150 persons occupy a conference room. Which graph includes a number of people in violation of the fire code?

Ⓐ 

Ⓑ 

Ⓒ 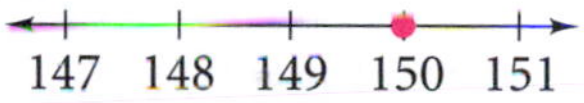

Ⓓ 

Alg1 1.0, 24.3

78. Give a counterexample to the statement "The set of whole numbers is closed under subtraction."

Ⓐ 6 and -2 are whole numbers, but $6 - (-2)$ is not a whole number.
Ⓑ -2 and 6 are whole numbers, but $-2 - 6$ is not a whole number.
Ⓒ 6 and 2 are whole numbers, but $6 - 2$ is not a whole number.
Ⓓ 2 and 6 are whole numbers, but $2 - 6$ is not a whole number.

Mixed Review

Lesson 2-6

79. Suppose you have 2% milk and 0.5% milk. How much of each should you mix to make a 12-oz glass of 1% milk?

GO for Help

Lesson 2-1

Solve each equation.

80. $5t - 2 = 14$ **81.** $4 = 3 - 8h$ **82.** $3w + 11 = -10$

83. $\frac{m}{4} + 6 = 15$ **84.** $-7y + 13 = -8$ **85.** $9 = 12 - \frac{c}{3}$

Lesson 1-8

Name the property that each equation demonstrates.

86. $3(2 \cdot 7) = (3 \cdot 2)7$ **87.** $5 \times 1 = 1 \times 5$ **88.** $3 + 4 = 4 + 3$

GO Online Lesson Quiz Visit: PHSchool.com, Web Code: baa-0301

3-2 Solving Inequalities Using Addition and Subtraction

California Content Standards

5.0 Solve multi-step problems, including word problems, involving linear inequalities in one variable and provide justification for each step. ***Develop***

What You'll Learn

- To use addition to solve inequalities
- To use subtraction to solve inequalities

. . . And Why

To solve a problem involving safe loads, as in Example 4

Check Skills You'll Need GO for Help Lesson 1-4 and Review page 68

Complete each statement with <, =, or >.

1. $-3 + 4 \blacksquare -5 + 4$ **2.** $-3 + 6 \blacksquare 4 + 6$ **3.** $-3.4 + 2 \blacksquare -3.45 + 2$

Solve each equation.

4. $x - 4 = 5$ **5.** $n - 3 = -5$ **6.** $t + 4 = -5$ **7.** $k + \frac{2}{3} = \frac{5}{6}$

New Vocabulary • equivalent inequalities

Using Addition to Solve Inequalities

Equivalent inequalities are inequalities with the same solutions. For example, $x < 3$ and $x + 4 < 7$ are equivalent inequalities. You can add the same value to each side of an inequality, just as you did with equations.

$x < 3$

$x + 4 < 7$

Take Note

Property **Addition Property of Inequality**

For every real number a, b, and c,

if $a > b$, then $a + c > b + c$; if $a < b$, then $a + c < b + c$.

Examples $3 > 1$, so $3 + 2 > 1 + 2$. $-5 < 4$, so $-5 + 2 < 4 + 2$.

This property is also true for $\geq$ and $\leq$.

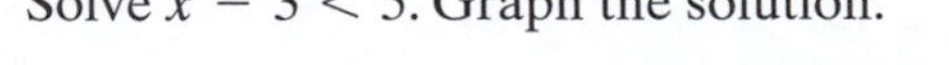

1 EXAMPLE Using the Addition Property of Inequality

Solve $x - 3 < 5$. Graph the solution.

$x - 3 + 3 < 5 + 3$ **Add 3 to each side.**

$x < 8$ **Simplify.**

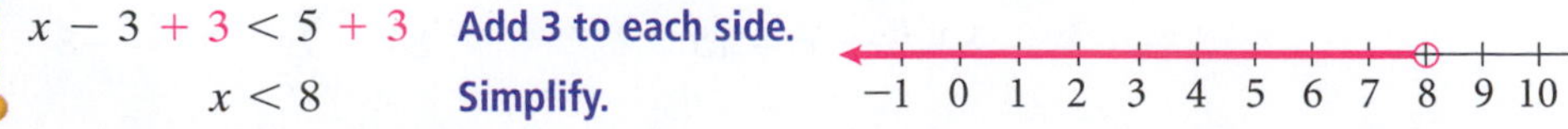

CA Standards Check **1** Solve $m - 6 > -4$. Graph your solution.

Vocabulary Tip

The word <u>infinite</u> indicates that the number of solutions is unlimited. The solutions cannot be listed.

An inequality has an infinite number of solutions, so it is not possible to check all the solutions. You can check your computations and the direction of the inequality symbol. The steps below show how to check that $x < 8$ describes the solutions to Example 1.

Step 1 Check the computation. See if 8 is the solution to the equation $x - 3 = 5$.

$x - 3 = 5$

$8 - 3 \stackrel{?}{=} 5$ **Substitute 8 for *x*.**

$5 = 5$ ✓

Step 2 Check the inequality symbol. Choose any number less than 8 and substitute it into $x - 3 < 5$. In this case, use 7.

$x - 3 < 5$

$7 - 3 < 5$ **Substitute 7 for *x*.**

$4 < 5$ ✓

Since the computation and the direction of the inequality symbol are correct, $x - 3 < 5$ and $x < 8$ are equivalent inequalities. So the solution of $x - 3 < 5$ is $x < 8$.

2 EXAMPLE Solving and Checking Solutions

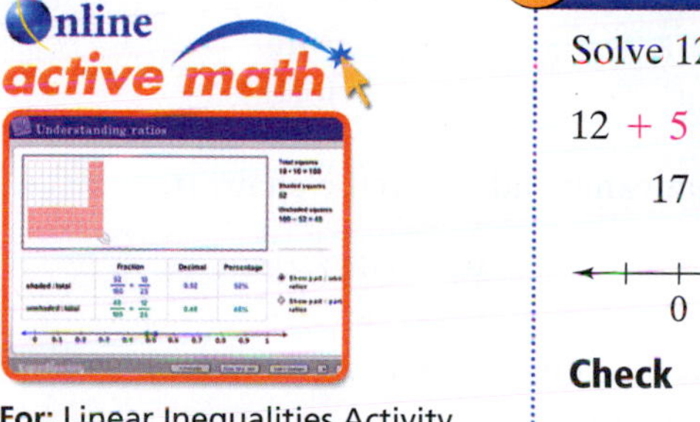

For: Linear Inequalities Activity
Use: Interactive Textbook, 3-2

Solve $12 \le x - 5$. Graph and check your solution.

$12 + 5 \le x - 5 + 5$ **Add 5 to each side.**

$17 \le x$ **Simplify.**

0 10 20

Check $12 = x - 5$ **Check the computation.**

$12 \stackrel{?}{=} 17 - 5$ **Substitute 17 for *x*.**

$12 = 12$ ✓

$12 \le x - 5$ **Check the direction of the inequality.**

$12 \le 18 - 5$ **Substitute 18 for *x*.**

$12 \le 13$ ✓

CA Standards Check **2** Solve $n - 7 \le -2$. Graph and check your solution.

Using Subtraction to Solve Inequalities

You can subtract the same number from each side of an inequality to make an equivalent inequality.

Property **Subtraction Property of Inequality**

For every real number a, b, and c,

if $a > b$, then $a - c > b - c$; if $a < b$, then $a - c < b - c$.

Examples $3 > -1$, so $3 - 2 > -1 - 2$ $-5 < 4$, so $-5 - 2 < 4 - 2$

This property is also true for $\ge$ and $\le$.

3 EXAMPLE Using the Subtraction Property of Inequality

Solve $y + 5 < -7$. Graph the solution.

$y + 5 - 5 < -7 - 5$ **Subtract 5 from each side.**

$y < -12$ **Simplify.**

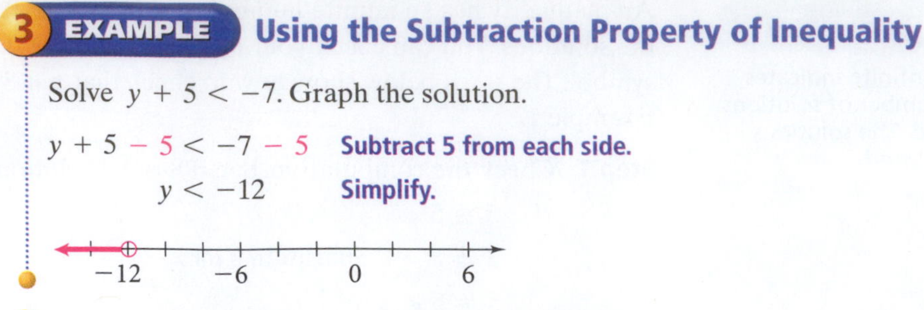

CA Standards Check **3** Solve $t + 3 \geq 8$. Graph and check your solution.

You can use inequalities to model real-world situations.

4 EXAMPLE Application

Vocabulary Tip

The *maximum* amount is greater than or equal to the possible amount.

The maximum safe load of a chairlift is 680 lb. A cyclist rides the chairlift with his bicycle. The cyclist weighs 124 lb, and the bicycle weighs 32 lb. Which inequality best describes how much additional weight w the chairlift could safely carry?

Ⓐ $124 + w \leq 680 + 32$ Ⓒ $124 + 32 + w \leq 680$

Ⓑ $32 + w \geq 680 + 124$ Ⓓ $124 + 32 + w \geq 680$

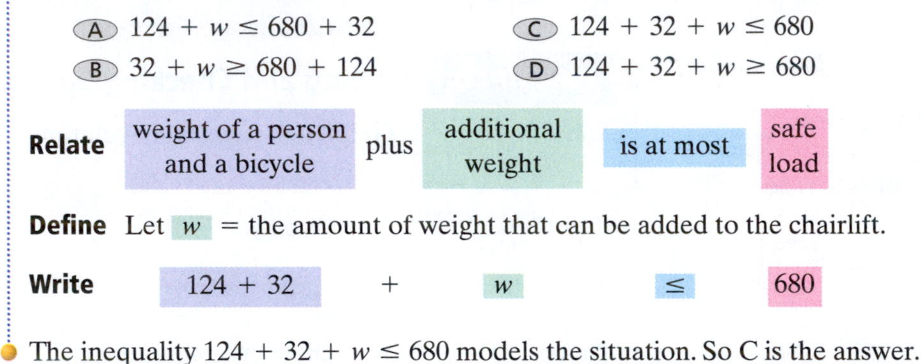

Relate	weight of a person and a bicycle	plus	additional weight	is at most	safe load
Define	Let w = the amount of weight that can be added to the chairlift.				
Write	$124 + 32$	$+$	w	$\leq$	680

The inequality $124 + 32 + w \leq 680$ models the situation. So C is the answer.

CA Standards Check **4** Your class brought 42 blankets on Monday and 65 blankets on Wednesday. Write an inequality to describe how many blankets the class must donate on Friday to make or exceed their goal of at least 160 blankets.

EXERCISES Standards Practice

For more exercises, see *Extra Skills and Word Problem Practice*.

Alg1 5.0, 24.3, 25.1

A Practice by Example

Examples 1, 2 (pages 130, 131)

GO for Help

State what number you would add to each side of the inequality to solve the inequality.

1. $d - 5 \geq -4$ **2.** $0 < c - 8$ **3.** $z - 4.3 \geq 1.6$

Solve each inequality. Graph and check your solution.

4. $x - 1 > 10$ **5.** $t - 3 < -2$ **6.** $-5 > b - 1$

7. $7 \leq d - 3$ **8.** $s - 2 \geq -6$ **9.** $r - 9 \leq 0$

10. $-4 \geq w - 2$ **11.** $-1 < -4 + d$ **12.** $y - \frac{1}{2} \leq -5$

13. $-\frac{2}{3} > q - 4$ **14.** $x - 2 \geq 0.5$ **15.** $3.2 > -1.3 + r$

16. $-3.4 > m - 1.8$ **17.** $b - \frac{3}{8} < \frac{1}{8}$ **18.** $n - 2\frac{1}{2} > \frac{1}{2}$

Example 3 (page 132)

State what number you would subtract from each side of the inequality to solve the inequality.

19. $w + 2 > -1$ **20.** $8 < \frac{5}{3} + r$ **21.** $5.7 \geq k + 3.1$

Solve each inequality. Graph and check your solution.

22. $w + 4 \leq 9$ **23.** $m + 5 > -3$ **24.** $1 < 8 + b$

25. $-2 \geq 4 + a$ **26.** $k + 3 \leq 4$ **27.** $3 > 4 + x$

28. $-5 < 1 + p$ **29.** $\frac{3}{5} + z \geq -\frac{2}{5}$ **30.** $7.5 + y < 13$

31. $\frac{1}{2} < m + 2$ **32.** $2.7 \geq a + 3$ **33.** $-2.9 < 4.1 + p$

34. $\frac{1}{4} \geq h + \frac{3}{4}$ **35.** $5.3 + d > 3.8$ **36.** $t + \frac{3}{8} < -\frac{1}{8}$

Example 4 (page 132)

37. Your brother has $2000 saved for a vacation. His airplane ticket is $637. Write and solve an inequality to find how much he can spend for everything else.

38. You have an allowance of $15.00 per week. You are in a bowling league that costs $6.50 each week, and you save at least $5.00 each week. Write and solve an inequality to show how much you have left to spend each week.

39. A school club is selling reflectors for Bicycle Safety Day. Each member is encouraged to sell at least 50 reflectors. You sell 17 on Monday and 12 on Tuesday. How many reflectors do you need to sell on Wednesday to meet your goal?

B Apply Your Skills

State what you must do to the first inequality in order to get the second.

40. $36 \leq -4 + y$; $40 \leq y$ **41.** $9 + b > 24$; $b > 15$ **42.** $m - \frac{1}{2} < \frac{3}{8}$; $m < \frac{7}{8}$

Solve each inequality.

43. $w - 3 + 1 \geq 9$ **44.** $\frac{1}{2} + c \leq 3\frac{1}{2}$ **45.** $y - 0.3 < 2.8$

46. $-6 > n - \frac{1}{5}$ **47.** $z + 4.1 < -5.6$ **48.** $-4.1 > y - 0.9$

49. $\frac{2}{3} + t - \frac{5}{6} > 0$ **50.** $5 \leq v - 4 - 7$ **51.** $3.6 + k \geq -4.5$

52. $6 + b - 7 < 5$ **53.** $m + 2.3 \leq -1.2$ **54.** $4 \geq k - \frac{3}{4}$

55. $h - \frac{1}{2} \geq -1$ **56.** $-7.7 \geq x - 2$ **57.** $-2 > 9 + 3 + w$

A gymnast's final score on a routine is the sum of the Difficulty Score and the Execution Score.

58. Your local bank offers free checking for accounts with a balance of at least $500. Suppose you have a balance of $516.46 and you write a check for $31.96. How much must you deposit to avoid being charged a service fee?

59. a. If $45 + 47 = t$, does $t = 45 + 47$?
b. If $45 + 47 < r$, is $r < 45 + 47$?
c. Critical Thinking Discuss the differences between these two examples.

60. Suppose your sister wants to qualify for a regional gymnastics competition. At today's competition she must score at least 57.0 points. She scored 13.8 on the vault, 14.9 on the balance beam, and 13.2 on the uneven parallel bars. The event that remains is the floor exercise.
a. Write and solve an inequality that models the information.
b. Explain what the solution means in terms of the original situation.
c. Write three scores your sister could make that would allow her to qualify for the regional gymnastics competition.

In 1971, a computer chip could hold 2300 transistors. In 2004, a chip could hold 410,000,000 transistors.

61. Suppose your computer has 512 megabytes (MB) of memory. You have used 360.8 MB of memory. What is the maximum amount of memory you can use for other programs and functions?

62. To earn an A in Ms. Orlando's math class, students must score a total of at least 135 points on the three tests. On the first two tests, Amy's scores were 47 and 48. What is the minimum score she must get on the third test to earn an A?

63. a. Use each of the inequality symbols $<$, $\leq$, $>$, and $\geq$ to write four addition or subtraction inequalities.

b. Solve each of the inequalities in part (a) and graph your solution.

64. a. Sam says that he can solve $z - 8.6 \geq 5.2$ by replacing z with 13, 14, and 15. When $z = 13$, the inequality is false. When $z = 14$ and $z = 15$, the inequality is true. So Sam says that the solution is $z \geq 14$. Is his reasoning correct? Justify your answer.

b. Writing Explain why substituting values into the inequality does not guarantee that your solution is correct.

Solve each inequality.

65. $4x + 4 - 3x \geq 5$

66. $-5n - 3 + 6n < 2$

67. $7t - (6t - 2) \leq -1$

68. $5k - 2(2k + 1) > 8$

69. $-6(a + 2) + 7a \leq 12$

70. $-2(a - 3) + 3(a + 2) < 4$

Visit: PHSchool.com
Web Code: bae-0302

Error Analysis Find and correct the student's mistake in the work below.

71.

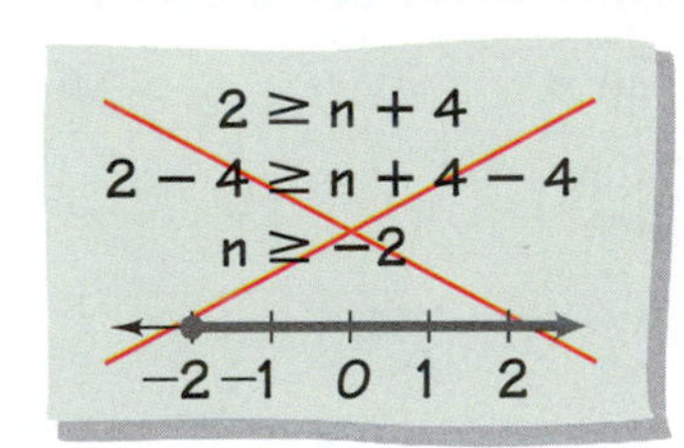

72.

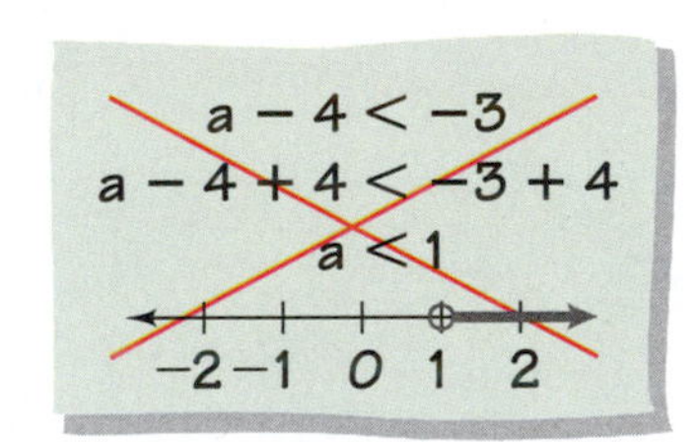

C Challenge

Math Reasoning Decide if each inequality is true for all real numbers. If the inequality is *not* true, give a counterexample.

73. $a - b < a + b$

74. If $a \geq b$, then $a + c \geq b + c$.

75. If $c > d$, then $a - c < a - d$.

76. If $a < b$, then $a < b + c$.

77. Find real numbers x, y, z, and w for which it is true that $x > y$ and $z > w$, but it is not true that $x - z > y - w$.

78. The Triangle Inequality Theorem states that the sum of the lengths of any two sides of a triangle is greater than the length of the third side. Following are inequalities for sides of the triangle shown.

$$a + b > c \qquad b + c > a \qquad a + c > b$$

a. Write an inequality using $c - b$ and a.

b. Write an inequality using $a - c$ and b.

c. Write an inequality using $b - a$ and c.

d. Writing Write a generalization about the length of the third side and the difference of the lengths of the other two sides.

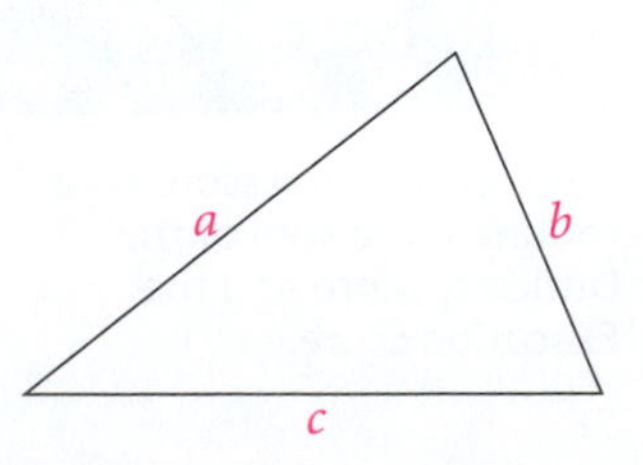

Multiple Choice Practice

For California Standards Tutorials, visit PHSchool.com. Web Code: baq-9045

Alg1 5.0

79. Solve $-12 + n > 20$.

(A) $n < 32$
(B) $n > 32$
(C) $n < 8$
(D) $n > 8$

Alg1 2.0

80. Which number is the reciprocal of 7?

(A) -7
(B) $\frac{7}{1}$
(C) $\frac{1}{7}$
(D) $-\frac{1}{7}$

Alg1 5.0

81. Which graph represents all real number solutions of $x + 4 \geq 8$?

(A) −1 0 1 2 3 4 5
(B) −5 −4 −3 −2 −1 0 1
(C) −1 0 1 2 3 4 5
(D) −3 −2 −1 0 1 2 3

Alg1 1.0, 25.3

82. Is the statement, "If a and b are whole numbers, then $b - a$ is also a whole number," *always*, *sometimes*, or *never* true?

(A) The statement is always true.
(B) The statement is sometimes true, when $a \geq b$.
(C) The statement is sometimes true, when $a \leq b$.
(D) The statement is never true.

Alg1 5.0

83. Hector is flying his plane. To avoid a storm, he climbs 5500 ft without going above his plane's maximum safe altitude of 35,000 ft. The inequality $a + 5500 \leq 35{,}000$ represents his original altitude a in feet. Which of the following could be the original altitude?

(A) 40,500 ft
(B) 30,000 ft
(C) 29,750 ft
(D) 27,750 ft

Mixed Review

GO for Help

Lesson 3-1

Define a variable and write an inequality to model each situation.

84. An octopus can be up to 10 ft long.

85. A hummingbird migrates more than 1850 mi.

86. Your average in algebra class must be 90 or greater for you to receive an A for the term.

87. You must read at least 25 pages this weekend.

Lesson 1-2

Simplify.

88. $9^2 + 17$

89. $4(5 - 3)^2 - 3^2$

90. $0.2(4.2 - 3.4) + 0.4$

91. $3 \cdot 2 + 5^2$

92. $3 + 7^2 - 4$

93. $4^3 + 3^2$

3-3 Solving Inequalities Using Multiplication and Division

California Content Standards

5.0 Solve multi-step problems, including word problems, involving linear inequalities in one variable and provide justification for each step. ***Develop***

What You'll Learn

- To use multiplication to solve inequalities
- To use division to solve inequalities

. . . And Why

To find how much food can be purchased for a food bank, as in Example 4

Check Skills You'll Need

GO for Help Review page 68 and Lesson 2-1

Solve each equation.

1. $8 = \frac{1}{2}t$ **2.** $14 = -21x$ **3.** $\frac{x}{6} = -1$

4. $5d = 32$ **5.** $\frac{2}{3}x = -12$ **6.** $0.5n = 9$

Write an inequality for each graph.

7. 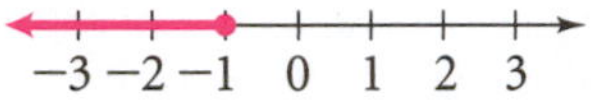

8. 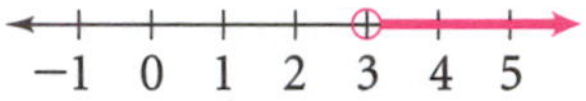

Using Multiplication to Solve Inequalities

CA Standards Investigation: Multiplying Each Side of an Inequality

Consider the inequality $4 > 1$.

1. Copy and complete each statement at the right by replacing each ■ with $<$, $>$, or $=$.
2. What happens to the inequality symbol when you multiply each side by a positive number?
3. What happens to the inequality symbol when you multiply each side by zero?
4. What happens to the inequality symbol when you multiply each side by a negative number?

$4 \cdot 3$ ■ $1 \cdot 3$
$4 \cdot 2$ ■ $1 \cdot 2$
$4 \cdot 1$ ■ $1 \cdot 1$
$4 \cdot 0$ ■ $1 \cdot 0$
$4 \cdot -1$ ■ $1 \cdot -1$
$4 \cdot -2$ ■ $1 \cdot -2$
$4 \cdot -3$ ■ $1 \cdot -3$

You can multiply each side of an inequality by the same number, just as you did with equations. When you multiply each side of an inequality by a positive number, the direction of the inequality symbol stays the same. When you multiply each side by a negative number, the direction of the inequality symbol reverses.

Take Note

Property **Multiplication Property of Inequality for $c > 0$**

For every real number a and b, and for $c > 0$,

if $a > b$, then $ac > bc$; if $a < b$, then $ac < bc$.

Examples $4 > -1$, so $4(5) > -1(5)$. $-6 < 3$, so $-6(5) < 3(5)$.

This property is also true for $\geq$ and $\leq$.

You can use the Multiplication Property of Inequality to solve inequalities that involve division.

1 EXAMPLE Multiplying by a Positive Number

Solve $\frac{x}{2} < -1$. Graph and check the solution.

$2\left(\frac{x}{2}\right) < 2(-1)$ Multiply each side by 2. Do not reverse the inequality symbol.

$x < -2$ Simplify each side.

−5 −4 −3 −2 −1 0 1 2 3 4 5

Check $\frac{x}{2} = -1$ Check the computation.

$\frac{-2}{2} \stackrel{?}{=} -1$ Substitute −2 for *x*.

$-1 = -1$ ✓ Simplify.

$\frac{x}{2} < -1$ Check the direction of the inequality.

$\frac{-3}{2} < -1$ ✓ Substitute −3 for *x*.

CA Standards Check 1 Solve each inequality. Graph and check your solution.

a. $\frac{b}{4} > \frac{1}{2}$ **b.** $\frac{d}{3} \geq \frac{5}{6}$ **c.** $\frac{4}{3}y \leq -8$

Take Note

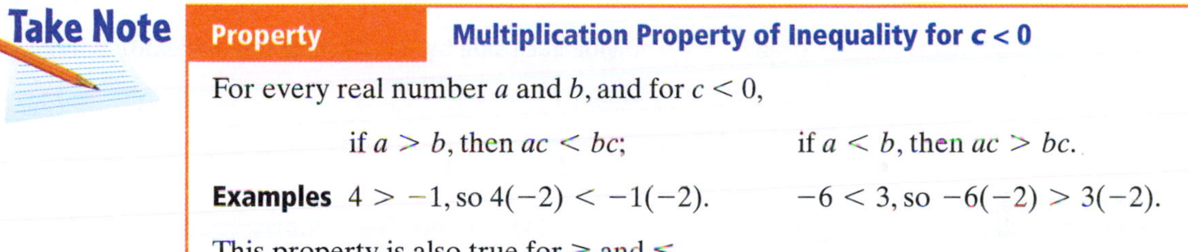

Property Multiplication Property of Inequality for $c < 0$

For every real number a and b, and for $c < 0$,

if $a > b$, then $ac < bc$; if $a < b$, then $ac > bc$.

Examples $4 > -1$, so $4(-2) < -1(-2)$. $-6 < 3$, so $-6(-2) > 3(-2)$.

This property is also true for $\geq$ and $\leq$.

2 EXAMPLE Multiplying by a Negative Number

Which graph shows the solution of $-\frac{2}{3}n \leq 2$?

Ⓐ −6 −5 −4 −3 −2 −1 0 1 2 3 4

Ⓑ −6 −5 −4 −3 −2 −1 0 1 2 3 4

Ⓒ −6 −5 −4 −3 −2 −1 0 1 2 3 4

Ⓓ −4 −3 −2 −1 0 1 2 3 4 5 6

$\left(-\frac{3}{2}\right)\left(-\frac{2}{3}n\right) \geq \left(-\frac{3}{2}\right)2$ Multiply each side by $-\frac{3}{2}$, the reciprocal of $-\frac{2}{3}$. Reverse the inequality symbol.

$n \geq -3$ Simplify.

B is the correct answer.

Study Tip

To check the graph in Choice B, use the endpoint, −3, to check for equality. Use another point, 0, to check the inequality.

$-\frac{2}{3}(-3) = 2$ ✓

$-\frac{2}{3}(0) \leq 2$ ✓

Since the points check, B is the correct answer.

CA Standards Check 2 Solve each inequality. Graph and check the solution.

a. $-\frac{k}{4} > -1$ **b.** $-t < \frac{1}{2}$ **c.** $6 \leq -\frac{3}{5}w$

Using Division to Solve Inequalities

Solving inequalities using division is similar to solving inequalities using multiplication. Remember that division by zero is undefined.

Take Note

Property **Division Property of Inequality**

For every real number a and b, and for $c > 0$,

if $a > b$, then $\frac{a}{c} > \frac{b}{c}$; if $a < b$, then $\frac{a}{c} < \frac{b}{c}$.

Examples $6 > 4$, so $\frac{6}{2} > \frac{4}{2}$. $2 < 8$, so $\frac{2}{2} < \frac{8}{2}$.

For every real number a and b, and for $c < 0$,

if $a > b$, then $\frac{a}{c} < \frac{b}{c}$; if $a < b$, then $\frac{a}{c} > \frac{b}{c}$.

Examples $6 > 4$, so $\frac{6}{-2} < \frac{4}{-2}$. $2 < 8$, so $\frac{2}{-2} > \frac{8}{-2}$.

This property also applies to $\geq$ and $\leq$.

3 EXAMPLE Dividing to Solve an Inequality

Solve $-5z \geq 25$. Graph the solution.

$\frac{-5}{-5}z \leq \frac{25}{-5}$ **Divide each side by −5. Reverse the inequality symbol.**

$z \leq -5$ **Simplify.**

−9 −8 −7 −6 −5 −4 −3 −2 −1 0 1

CA Standards Check 3 Solve the inequality. Graph and check your solution.

a. $-2t < -8$ **b.** $-3w \geq 12$ **c.** $0.6 > -0.2n$

There are times when you must think about which types of numbers are acceptable as solutions of inequalities that represent real-world situations.

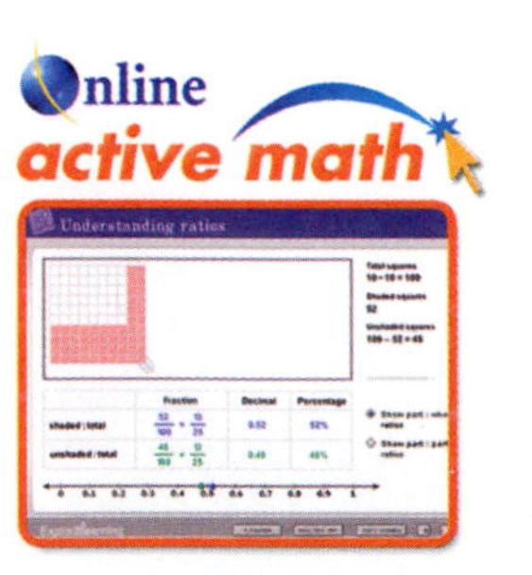

Online active math

For: Solving Inequalities Activity
Use: Interactive Textbook, 3-3

4 EXAMPLE Application

The student council votes to buy food for a local food bank. A case of 12 jars of spaghetti sauce costs \$13.75. What is the greatest number of cases of sauce the student council can buy if they use at most \$216 for this project?

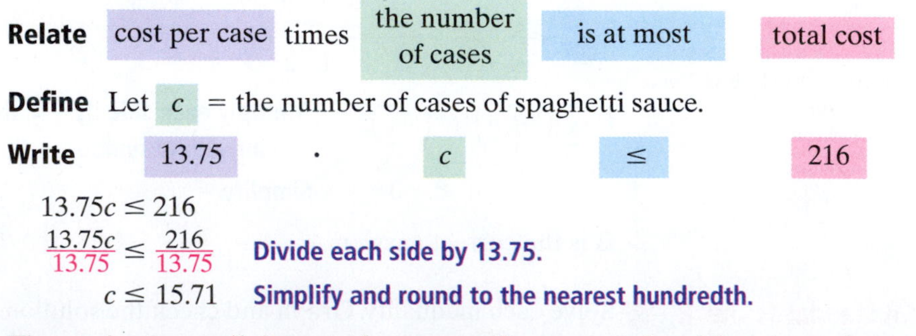

Relate cost per case times the number of cases is at most total cost

Define Let c = the number of cases of spaghetti sauce.

Write $13.75 \cdot c \leq 216$

$13.75c \leq 216$

$\frac{13.75c}{13.75} \leq \frac{216}{13.75}$ **Divide each side by 13.75.**

$c \leq 15.71$ **Simplify and round to the nearest hundredth.**

The student council does not have enough money to buy 16 cases, so they can buy at most 15 cases of sauce for the food bank.

CA Standards Check 4 Students in the school band are selling calendars. They earn \$.40 on each calendar they sell. Their goal is to earn more than \$327. Write and solve an inequality to find the fewest number of calendars they can sell and still reach their goal.

EXERCISES

For more exercises, see *Extra Skills and Word Problem Practice.*

Standards Practice

Alg1 5.0, 25.3

A Practice by Example

Examples 1, 2 (page 137)

GO for Help

Solve each inequality. Graph and check your solution.

1. $\frac{t}{4} \geq -1$ **2.** $\frac{s}{6} < 1$ **3.** $1 \leq -\frac{w}{2}$ **4.** $2 < -\frac{p}{4}$

5. $-2 < \frac{y}{2}$ **6.** $-\frac{v}{3} \geq 0.5$ **7.** $4 > \frac{2}{3}x$ **8.** $-5 \leq \frac{5}{2}k$

9. $0 < -\frac{7}{8}x$ **10.** $\frac{4}{3}y \geq 0$ **11.** $-\frac{5}{7}x > -5$ **12.** $6 \geq -\frac{3}{2}d$

13. $-\frac{4}{9} < \frac{2}{3}c$ **14.** $\frac{3}{4}b \geq -\frac{9}{8}$ **15.** $-\frac{5}{3}u > \frac{5}{6}$ **16.** $-\frac{5}{8} > -\frac{5}{6}n$

Example 3 (page 138)

17. $3t < -9$ **18.** $4m \geq 8$ **19.** $10 \leq -2w$ **20.** $-20 > -5c$

21. $-27 \geq 3z$ **22.** $-7b > 42$ **23.** $18d < -12$ **24.** $-3x \leq 16$

25. $-7 < 2q$ **26.** $16 > 3.2h$ **27.** $-1.5d < -6$ **28.** $3.6 \leq -0.8m$

Example 4 (page 138)

29. The science club charges \$4.50 per car at their car wash. Write and solve an inequality to find how many cars they have to wash to earn at least \$300.

30. Suppose you earn \$6.15 per hour working part time at a dry cleaner. Write and solve an inequality to find how many full hours you must work to earn at least \$100.

B Apply Your Skills

Write four solutions to each inequality.

31. $\frac{x}{2} \leq -1$ **32.** $\frac{r}{3} \geq -4$ **33.** $-1 \geq \frac{t}{3}$ **34.** $0.5 > \frac{1}{2}c$

35. $-\frac{3}{4}q > 4$ **36.** $1 < -\frac{5}{7}s$ **37.** $-4.5 \leq -0.9p$ **38.** $-2.7w \geq 28$

Tell what you must do to the first inequality in order to get the second.

39. $-\frac{c}{4} > 3$; $c < -12$ **40.** $\frac{n}{5} \leq -2$; $n \leq -10$

41. $5z > -25$; $z > -5$ **42.** $\frac{3}{4}b \leq 3$; $b \leq 4$

43. $-12 < 4a$; $-3 < a$ **44.** $-b \geq 3.4$; $b \leq -3.4$

Replace each ■ with the number that makes the inequalities equivalent.

45. ■$s > 14$; $s < -7$ **46.** ■$x \geq 25$; $x \leq -5$

47. $-8u \leq$ ■; $u \geq -0.5$ **48.** $-2a >$ ■; $a < -9$

49. $36 <$ ■r; $r < -3.6$ **50.** $-k \leq$ ■; $k \geq -7.5$

51. **Critical Thinking** If $x \geq y$ and $-x \geq -y$, what can you conclude about x and y?

Estimation **Estimate the solution of each inequality.**

52. $-2.099r < 4$ **53.** $3.87j > -24$ **54.** $20.95 \geq \frac{1}{2}p$ **55.** $-\frac{20}{39}s \leq -14$

Homework Video Tutor

Visit: PHSchool.com
Web Code: bae-0303

Depending on its size, an elevator at a construction site can have a maximum load from 900 lb to 20,000 lb.

56. An elevator can lift at most 4400 lb. A concrete block has a weight of 42 lb. What is the maximum number of concrete blocks that the elevator can lift?

57. Writing Explain how solving the equation $-\frac{x}{3} = 4$ is similar to and different from solving the inequality $-\frac{x}{3} > 4$.

58. Critical Thinking Write four different inequalities with $x > 3$ as their solution that you can solve using multiplication or division.

Solve each inequality.

59. $4d \leq -28$	**60.** $\frac{u}{7} > 5$	**61.** $2 < -8s$	**62.** $\frac{3}{2}k \geq -45$
63. $0.3y < 2.7$	**64.** $9.4 \leq -4t$	**65.** $-h \geq 4$	**66.** $\frac{5}{2}x > 5$
67. $24 < -\frac{8}{3}x$	**68.** $0 < -\frac{1}{6}b$	**69.** $\frac{5}{6} > -\frac{1}{3}p$	**70.** $-0.2m \geq 9.4$
71. $6 < -9g$	**72.** $4n \geq 9$	**73.** $-3.5 < -m$	**74.** $\frac{2}{5}z \geq -1$

75. Michael solved the inequality $-2 > \frac{y}{-3}$ and got $6 < y$. Erica solved the same inequality and got $y > 6$. Are they both correct? Explain.

76. A friend calls you and asks you to meet at a location 3 miles from your home in 20 minutes. You set off on your bicycle after the telephone call. Write and solve an inequality to find the average rate in miles per minute you could ride to be at your meeting place within 20 minutes.

77. a. Error Analysis Kia solved $-15q \leq 135$ by adding 15 to each side of the inequality. What mistake did she make?

b. Kia's solution was $q \leq 150$. She checked her work by substituting 150 for q in the original inequality. Why didn't her check let her know that she had made a mistake?

c. Find a number that satisfies Kia's solution but does not satisfy $-15q \leq 135$.

C Challenge

Math Reasoning If a, b, and c are real numbers, for which values of a is each statement true?

78. If $c < 0$, then $ac < a$.

79. If $b > c$, then $ab > ac$.

80. If $b > c$, then $a^2b > a^2c$.

81. If $b > c$, then $\frac{b}{a} < \frac{c}{a}$.

82. Suppose you have a plastic globe that you wish to put into a gift box. The circumference of the globe is 15 in. The edges of cube-shaped boxes are either 3 in., 4 in., 5 in., or 6 in. Write and solve an inequality to find the boxes that will hold the globe. (*Hint:* circumference = $\pi \cdot$ diameter)

83. The Sumaris' den floor measures 18 ft by 15 ft. They want to cover the floor with square tiles that are $\frac{9}{16}$ ft^2. Write and solve an inequality to find the least number of tiles they need to cover the floor.

Multiple Choice Practice

For California Standards Tutorials, visit PHSchool.com. Web Code: baq-9045

Alg1 5.0

84. Mr. Houston expects to pay \$16,800 in income taxes. This is no more than $\frac{1}{3}$ of his salary. Which inequality describes his earned income?

(A) $x > 50{,}400$
(B) $x \geq 50{,}400$
(C) $x < 50{,}400$
(D) $x \leq 50{,}400$

Alg1 5.0

85. Solve $\frac{2}{5}x = 16$.

(A) 8 (C) 80
(B) 40 (D) 32

Alg1 4.0

86. To solve $7x - (5x + 3) = 11$, which expression should result when you first simplify $7x - (5x + 3)$?

(A) $2x + 3$ (C) $-x$
(B) $2x - 3$ (D) -1

Alg1 2.0

87. Which number is the additive inverse of 5?

(A) -5 (B) 0 (C) $\frac{1}{5}$ (D) $-\frac{1}{5}$

Mixed Review

GO for Help

Lesson 3-2 **Solve each inequality.**

88. $x + 3 \leq -4$ **89.** $\frac{5}{8} > \frac{3}{4} + w$ **90.** $t - 3.4 \geq 5.8$ **91.** $0 < d - 4$

92. $3.2 \geq m + 7.1$ **93.** $y - 2 < 6$ **94.** $-3 > a - 4$ **95.** $k + 12 \leq 15$

Lesson 2-2 **Solve each equation.**

96. $3t + 5 - t = 9$ **97.** $-3(2n + 1) = 9$ **98.** $\frac{3x}{4} - \frac{1}{2} = \frac{1}{4}$

Lesson 1-8 **Name the property that each exercise illustrates.**

99. $(-7) + 7 = 0$ **100.** $-3\left(-\frac{1}{3}\right) = 1$ **101.** $2 + 0 = 2$

102. $1x = x$ **103.** $4(2 \cdot 5) = (4 \cdot 2)5$ **104.** $4(2 \cdot 5) = 4(5 \cdot 2)$

Checkpoint Quiz 1 — Lessons 3-1 through 3-3

Solve each inequality. Graph your solution.

1. $6 < c + 1$ **2.** $5x < -30$ **3.** $\frac{p}{3} \leq -2$

4. $y - 4 \geq -2$ **5.** $12 + g < 4$ **6.** $-3b \geq 15$

7. Determine whether each of the following is a solution of $x + 7 \leq 3$.

a. -4 **b.** 0 **c.** $-\frac{17}{4}$ **d.** -3.9

8. Determine whether each of the following is a solution of $-4x < -12$.

a. 3 **b.** 0 **c.** $\frac{7}{3}$ **d.** π

Write and solve an inequality that models each situation.

9. You plan to buy a bicycle that will cost at least \$180. You have saved \$38 and your parents have given you \$50. How much more money m do you need to save?

10. Your local garden shop has plants on sale for \$1.50 each. You are planning a vegetable garden. You have \$20 to spend on tomato plants. What is the greatest number of plants p you can buy?

Mathematical Reasoning

Conditional Statements

FOR USE WITH LESSON 3-3

24.2 Identify the hypothesis and conclusion in logical deduction. ***Introduce, Develop***

24.3 Use counterexamples to show that an assertion is false. ***Develop***

An *if–then* statement is called a **conditional.** Every conditional has two parts. The part following *if* is the **hypothesis,** and the part following *then* is the **conclusion.**

1 EXAMPLE

Identify the hypothesis and conclusion of the conditional statement "If an animal is a horse, then it has four legs."

The hypothesis is "an animal is a horse." The conclusion is "it has four legs."

The **converse** of a conditional switches the hypothesis and the conclusion. Sometimes converses of conditionals are not true. Recall that any example that proves a statement false is a counterexample. You need only one counterexample to prove that the statement is false.

2 EXAMPLE

Write the converse of the conditional statement "If an animal is a horse, then it has four legs." If the converse is false, give a counterexample.

The converse is "If it has four legs, then an animal is a horse." The converse is false because a cat has four legs, and a cat is not a horse.

EXERCISES

Identify the hypothesis and the conclusion for each conditional statement.

1. If it rains tomorrow, then the game will be cancelled.

2. If you are under 35 years old, then you cannot be president.

3. If an instrument is a trumpet, then it has valves.

Write the converse of each conditional statement. If the converse is false, give a counterexample.

4. If a number is divisible by 6, then it is divisible by 3.

5. If a number has an odd number of factors, then it is a perfect square.

6. If a number is a whole number, then it is an integer.

7. If x is positive, then $2x$ is positive.

8. If x is positive, then x^2 is positive.

9. If a and b are positive, then ab is positive.

10. If $x = 1$, then $x^2 = x$.

11. If $x < y$, then $x + 2 < y + 2$.

12. If $x^2 < 1$, then $x < 1$.

13. If x is negative, then $|x|$ is positive.

14. If $|a| < 1$, then $a < 1$.

3-4 Solving Multi-Step Inequalities

California Content Standards

4.0 Simplify expressions before solving linear inequalities. ***Master***

5.0 Solve multi-step problems, including word problems, involving linear inequalities in one variable and provide justification for each step. ***Master***

What You'll Learn

- To solve multi-step inequalities with variables on one side
- To solve multi-step inequalities with variables on both sides

. . . And Why

To find the measurements of a banner, as in Example 2

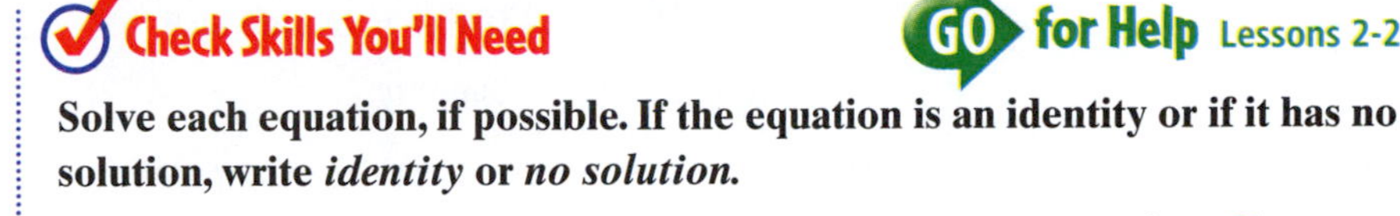

Check Skills You'll Need

GO for Help Lessons 2-2 and 2-3

Solve each equation, if possible. If the equation is an identity or if it has no solution, write *identity* or *no solution.*

1. $3(c + 4) = 6$

2. $3t + 6 = 3(t - 2)$

3. $5p + 9 = 2p - 1$

4. $7n + 4 - 5n = 2(n + 2)$

5. $\frac{1}{2}k - \frac{2}{3} + k = \frac{7}{6}$

6. $2t - 32 = 5t + 1$

Find the missing dimension of each rectangle.

7. perimeter = 110 cm

8. perimeter = 78 in.

Solving Inequalities With Variables on One Side

Sometimes you need to perform two or more steps to solve an inequality. Models can help you understand how to solve multi-step inequalities.

$2x - 3 < 1$ — **Model the inequality.**

$2x - 3 + 3 < 1 + 3$ — **Add 3 to each side.**

$2x < 4$ — **Simplify by removing the zero pairs.**

$\frac{2x}{2} < \frac{4}{2}$ — **Divide each side into two equal groups.**

$x < 2$ — **Each green rectangle is less than two yellow squares, so $x < 2$.**

To solve inequalities, you undo addition and subtraction first. Then undo multiplication and division.

1 EXAMPLE Using More Than One Step

Solve $7 + 6a > 19$. Check the solution.

$7 + 6a - 7 > 19 - 7$ **Subtract 7 from each side.**

$6a > 12$ **Simplify.**

$\frac{6a}{6} > \frac{12}{6}$ **Divide each side by 6.**

$a > 2$ **Simplify.**

Check $7 + 6a = 19$ **Check the computation.**

$7 + 6(2) \stackrel{?}{=} 19$ **Substitute 2 for a.**

$19 = 19$ ✓

$7 + 6a > 19$ **Check the direction of the inequality.**

$7 + 6(3) > 19$ **Substitute 3 for a.**

$25 > 19$ ✓

CA Standards Check 1 Solve each inequality. Check your solution.

a. $-3x - 4 \leq 14$ **b.** $5 < 7 - 2t$ **c.** $-8 < 5n - 23$

You can adapt formulas like the formula for the perimeter of a rectangle to write inequalities. You determine which inequality symbol to use from the situation.

2 EXAMPLE Application

A committee for the school band decides that the length of its banner should be 18 feet. A band member drew the diagram at the left. If no more than 48 feet of trim can be used, what are the possible widths of the banner?

Relate Since the border goes around the edges of a rectangular banner, you can adapt the perimeter formula $P = 2\ell + 2w$.

	twice the length	plus	twice the width	can be no more than	the length of trim
Write	$2(18)$	$+$	$2w$	$\leq$	48

$2(18) + 2w \leq 48$

$36 + 2w \leq 48$ **Simplify 2(18).**

$36 + 2w - 36 \leq 48 - 36$ **Subtract 36 from each side.**

$2w \leq 12$ **Simplify.**

$\frac{2w}{2} \leq \frac{12}{2}$ **Divide each side by 2.**

$w \leq 6$ **Simplify.**

The banner's width must be 6 feet or less.

CA Standards Check 2 To make a second banner, the committee decided to make the length 12 feet. They have 40 feet of a second type of trim. Write and solve an inequality to find the possible widths of the second banner.

3 EXAMPLE Using the Distributive Property

Solve $2(t + 2) - 3t \geq -1$.

$2t + 4 - 3t \geq -1$	Use the Distributive Property.
$-t + 4 \geq -1$	Combine like terms.
$-t + 4 - 4 \geq -1 - 4$	Subtract 4 from each side.
$-t \geq -5$	Simplify.
$\frac{-t}{-1} \leq \frac{-5}{-1}$	Divide each side by -1. Reverse the inequality symbol.
$t \leq 5$	Simplify.

CA Standards Check 3 Solve each inequality. Check your solution.

a. $4p + 2(p + 7) < 8$ **b.** $15 \leq 5 - 2(4m + 7)$ **c.** $8 > 3(5 - b) + 2$

Solving Inequalities With Variables on Both Sides

Many inequalities have variables on both sides of the inequality symbol. You need to gather the variable terms on one side and the constant terms on the other side.

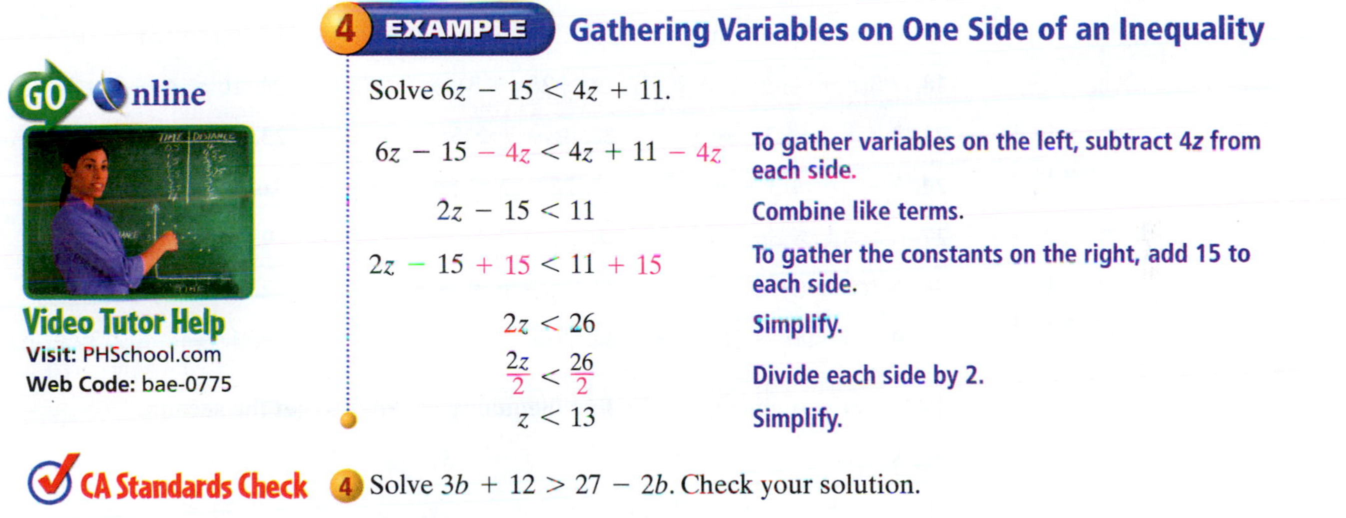

4 EXAMPLE Gathering Variables on One Side of an Inequality

GO Online

Video Tutor Help
Visit: PHSchool.com
Web Code: bae-0775

Solve $6z - 15 < 4z + 11$.

$6z - 15 - 4z < 4z + 11 - 4z$	To gather variables on the left, subtract 4*z* from each side.
$2z - 15 < 11$	Combine like terms.
$2z - 15 + 15 < 11 + 15$	To gather the constants on the right, add 15 to each side.
$2z < 26$	Simplify.
$\frac{2z}{2} < \frac{26}{2}$	Divide each side by 2.
$z < 13$	Simplify.

CA Standards Check 4 Solve $3b + 12 > 27 - 2b$. Check your solution.

5 EXAMPLE Multi-Step Inequalities

Solve $-3(4 - m) \geq 2(4m - 14)$.

$-12 + 3m \geq 8m - 28$	Use the Distributive Property.
$-12 + 3m - 8m \geq 8m - 28 - 8m$	Subtract 8*m* from each side.
$-12 - 5m \geq -28$	Combine like terms.
$-12 - 5m + 12 \geq -28 + 12$	Add 12 to each side.
$-5m \geq -16$	Simplify.
$\frac{-5m}{-5} \leq \frac{-16}{-5}$	Divide each side by -5. Reverse the inequality symbol.
$m \leq 3\frac{1}{5}$	Simplify.

CA Standards Check 5 Solve $-6(x - 4) \geq 7(2x - 3)$. Check your solution.

EXERCISES

For more exercises, see *Extra Skills and Word Problem Practice.*

Standards Practice

Alg1 4.0, 5.0

A Practice by Example

Example 1 (page 144)

GO for Help

Solve each inequality. Check your solution.

1. $4d + 7 \leq 23$
2. $5m - 3 > -18$
3. $-4x - 2 < 8$
4. $5 - 3n \geq -4$
5. $8 \leq -12 + 5q$
6. $5 \leq 11 + 3h$
7. $-7 \leq 5 - 4a$
8. $10 > 29 - 3b$
9. $5 - 9c > -13$

Example 2 (page 144)

Write and solve an inequality.

10. On a trip from Death Valley National Park to Redwood National Park, the Sampson family wants to travel at least 420 miles in 8 hours of driving. What must be their average rate of speed?

Example 3 (page 145)

11. You want to solve an inequality containing the expression $-3(2x - 3)$. The next line in your solution would rewrite this expression as __?__.

Solve each inequality.

12. $2(j - 4) \geq -6$
13. $-(6b - 2) > 0$
14. $-2(h + 2) < -14$
15. $-3 \leq 3(5x - 16)$
16. $25 > -(4y + 7)$
17. $4(w - 2) \leq 10$
18. $-3(c + 4) - 2 > 7$
19. $-2(r - 3) + 7 \geq 8$
20. $16 \leq 4 - 3(n - 13)$

Example 4 (page 145)

21. $3w + 2 < 2w + 5$
22. $3t + 7 \geq 5t + 9$
23. $4d + 7 \geq 1 + 5d$
24. $5 - 2n \leq 3 - n$
25. $2k - 3 \leq 5k + 9$
26. $3s + 16 > 6 + 4s$
27. $6p - 1 > 3p + 8$
28. $3x + 2 > -4x + 16$
29. $2 - 3m < 4 + 5m$

Example 5 (page 145)

30. $-3(v - 3) \geq 5 - 4v$
31. $3q + 6 \leq -5(q + 2)$
32. $3(2 + r) \geq 15 - 2r$
33. $9 + x < 7 - 2(x - 3)$
34. $2(m - 8) < -8 + 3m$
35. $2v - 4 \leq 2(3v - 6)$

B Apply Your Skills

Tell what you must do to the first inequality in order to get the second.

36. $8 - 4s > 16; -4s > 8$
37. $\frac{2}{3}g + 7 \geq 9; \frac{2}{3}g \geq 2$
38. $2y - 5 > 9 + y; y > 14$
39. $-8 > \frac{z}{-5} - 2; 30 < z$

40. **Writing** Suppose a friend is having difficulty solving $2.5(p - 4) > 3(p + 2)$. Explain how to solve the inequality, showing all necessary steps and identifying the properties you would use.

41. Mandela is starting a part-time word-processing business out of his home. He plans to charge \$15 per hour. The table at the right shows his expected monthly business expenses. Which inequality describes the number of hours h he must work in a month to make a profit of at least \$600?

Expense	Cost
Equipment rental	\$490
Materials	\$45
Business phone	\$65

Ⓐ $15h \geq 600$

Ⓑ $15h + 600 \geq 490 + 45 + 65$

Ⓒ $15h \geq 490 + 45 + 65 + 600$

Ⓓ $15h + 600 \leq 490 + 45 + 65$

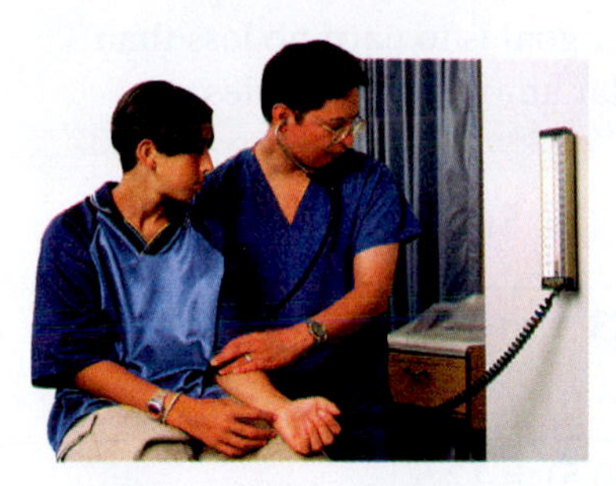

The normal systolic blood pressure for a 13-year-old is at most 116.5.

42. The sophomore class is planning a picnic. The cost of a permit to use a city park is \$250. To pay for the permit, there is a fee of \$.75 for each sophomore and \$1.25 for each guest who is not a sophomore. Two hundred sophomores plan to attend. Write and solve an inequality to find how many guests must attend for the sophomores to pay for the permit.

43. Systolic blood pressure is the higher number in a blood pressure reading. It is measured as your heart muscle contracts. The formula $P \leq \frac{1}{2}a + 110$ gives the normal systolic blood pressure P based on age a.

a. At age 20, does 120 represent a maximum or a minimum normal systolic pressure?

b. Find the normal systolic blood pressure for a 50-year-old person.

Match each inequality with its graph below.

44. $-2x - 2 > 4$ **45.** $2 - 2x > 4$ **46.** $2x + 2 > 4$

47. $2x + 2 > 4x$ **48.** $2x - 2 > 4$ **49.** $-2(x - 2) > 4$

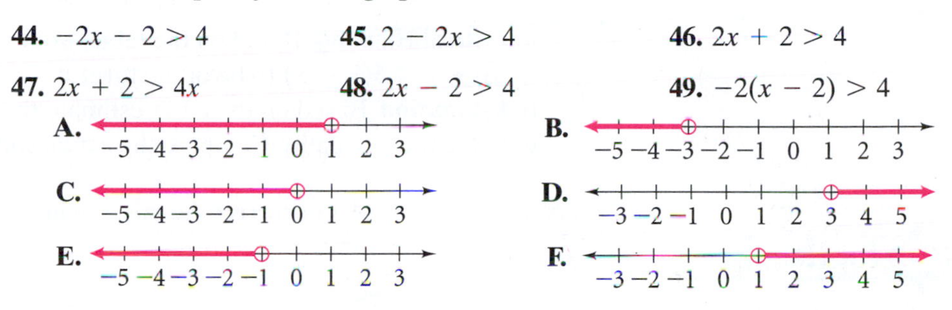

50. Write two different inequalities that you can solve by adding 5 and multiplying by −3. Solve each inequality.

Vocabulary Tip

Inequalities or equations that are always true are called identities.

Solve each inequality.

51. $\frac{4}{3}r - 3 < r + \frac{2}{3} - \frac{1}{3}r$

52. $4 - 2m \leq 5 - m + 1$

53. $-2(0.5 - 4s) \geq -3(4 - 3.5s)$

54. $\frac{1}{2}n - \frac{1}{8} \geq \frac{3}{4} + \frac{5}{6}n$

55. $-(8 - s) < 0$

56. $3.8 - k \leq 5.2 - 2k$

57. $10 > 3(2n - 1) - 5(4n + 3)$

58. $3(3r + 1) - (r + 4) \leq 13$

59. $2(3x + 7) > 4(7 - 2x)$

60. $4(a - 2) - 6a \leq -9$

61. $4(3m - 1) \geq 2(m + 3)$

62. $17 - (4k - 2) \geq 2(k + 3)$

63. $2n - 3(n + 3) \leq 14$

64. $5x - \frac{1}{2}(3x + 8) \leq -4 + 3x$

65. $5a - 2(a - 15) < 10$

66. $5c + 4(c - 1) \geq 2 + 5(2 + c)$

67. a. Solve $5t + 4 \leq 8t - 5$ by gathering the variable terms on the left side and the constant terms on the right side of the inequality.

b. Solve $5t + 4 \leq 8t - 5$ by gathering the constant terms on the left side and the variable terms on the right side of the inequality.

c. Compare the results of parts (a) and (b).

68. a. **Mental Math** Like equations, some inequalities are true for all values of the variable, and some inequalities are not true for any values of the variable. Determine whether each inequality is *always* true or *never* true.

i. $4s + 6 \geq 6 + 4s$ **ii.** $3r + 5 > 3r - 2$ **iii.** $4(n + 1) < 4n - 3$

b. **Critical Thinking** How can you tell whether an inequality is always true or never true without solving?

Visit: PHSchool.com
Web Code: bae-0304

69. Joleen is a sales associate in a clothing store. Each week she earns \$250 plus a commission equal to 3% of her sales. This week her goal is to earn no less than \$460. Write and solve an inequality to find the dollar amount of the sales she must have to reach her goal.

70. A student uses the table below to help solve $6x + 1 < 5(3 - x)$.

x	$6x + 1$	$<$	$5(3 - x)$
0	$6(0) + 1 = 1$	true	$5(3 - 0) = 15$
0.5	$6(0.5) + 1 = 4$	true	$5(3 - 0.5) = 12.5$
1	$6(1) + 1 = 7$	true	$5(3 - 1) = 10$
1.5	$6(1.5) + 1 = 10$	false	$5(3 - 1.5) = 7.5$

a. **Critical Thinking** Based on the table, would you expect the solution of $6x + 1 < 5(3 - x)$ to be of the form $x < n$ or $x > n$? Explain.
b. **Estimation** Based on the table, estimate the value of n.
c. Solve the inequality. Compare the actual solution to your estimated solution.

Error Analysis **Find and correct the mistake in each student's work.**

For a guide to solving Exercise 71, see p. 150.

71.

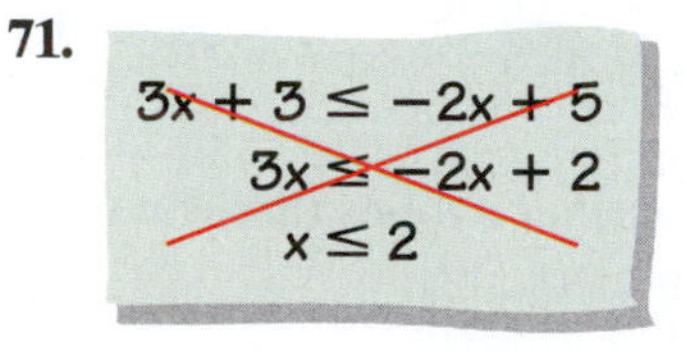

72.

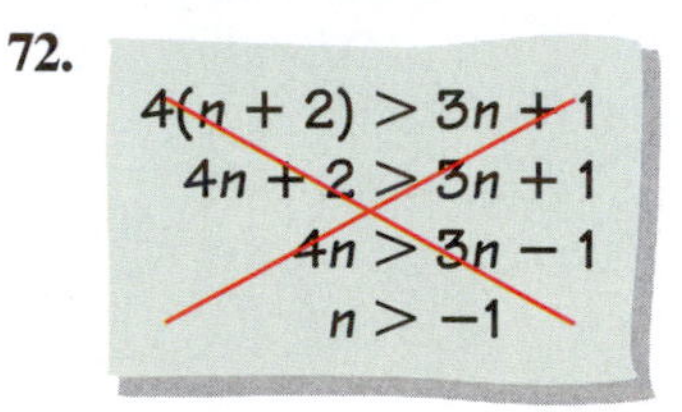

73. a. Solve $ax + b > c$ for x, where a is positive.
b. **Critical Thinking** Solve $ax + b > c$ for x, where a is negative.

74. The base of a triangle is 10 in. Its height is $(x + 4)$ in. Its area is no more than 56 in.^{2}. What are the possible integer values of x?

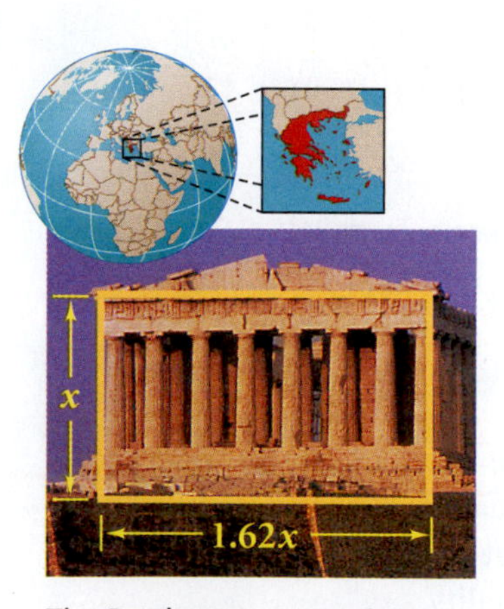

The Parthenon, an ancient Greek temple, has dimensions that form a golden rectangle.

75. The rectangle shown on the building at the left is a golden rectangle. Artists often use the golden rectangle because they consider it to be pleasing to the eye. The ratio of two sides of a golden rectangle is approximately 1 : 1.62. Suppose you are making a picture frame in the shape of a golden rectangle. You have a 46-in. length of wood to use for a frame. What are the dimensions of the largest frame you can make? Round to the nearest tenth of an inch.

76. **Critical Thinking** Find a value of a such that the number line below shows all the solutions of $ax + 4 \leq -12$.

−1 0 1 2 3 4 5 6 7 8 9

77. You can earn money by handing out flyers in the afternoon for \$6.50 an hour and by typing a newsletter in the evening for \$8 an hour. You have 20 hours available to work. What is the greatest number of hours you can spend handing out flyers and still make at least \$145?

78. The freight elevator of a building can safely carry a load of at most 4000 lb. A worker needs to move 50-lb boxes from the loading dock to the fourth floor of the building. The worker weighs 160 lb. The cart she uses weighs 95 lb.
a. What is the greatest number of boxes she can move in one trip?
b. How many trips must she make to deliver 310 boxes to the fourth floor?

Multiple Choice Practice

For California Standards Tutorials, visit PHSchool.com. Web Code: baq-9045

Alg1 5.0

79. Solve $2x - 8 > 4x + 2$.

(A) $x < -5$
(B) $x < 5$
(C) $x > -5$
(D) $x > 5$

Alg1 1.1

80. Which statement below is NOT true?

(A) The set of integers is *not* closed under division.
(B) The set of rational numbers is closed under division (except by 0).
(C) The set of odd whole numbers is closed under addition.
(D) The set of even whole numbers is closed under addition.

Alg1 15.0

81. How many liters of a 40% solution should be added to 6 L of a 20% solution to make a 25% solution?

(A) 1 L
(B) 2 L
(C) 3 L
(D) 4 L

Alg1 4.0

82. To solve $9x + 4 - 3x = 40$, which expression should result when you first simplify $9x + 4 - 3x$?

(A) $10x$
(B) -10
(C) $6x + 4$
(D) $-13x - 3$

Alg1 5.0

83. Great Gifts pays its supplier \$65 for each box of 12 bells. The owner wants to determine the least amount x he can charge his customers per bell in order to make at least a 50% profit per box. Which inequality should he use?

(A) $12x \geq 1.50(65)$
(B) $65x \geq 1.50(12)$
(C) $65x \leq 1.50(12)$
(D) $12x \leq 1.50(65)$

Mixed Review

GO for Help

Lesson 3-3

Solve each inequality.

84. $-9m \geq 36$

85. $-24 \leq 3y$

86. $\frac{x}{3} > -4$

87. $-\frac{t}{3} \leq 1$

88. $\frac{2}{3}b < 18$

89. $42 > -\frac{3}{7}w$

90. $56 < 42p$

91. $0.5d \geq 3.5$

92. $\frac{x}{5} > 10$

93. $-0.6s \leq 0.42$

Lesson 2-5

94. Your family leaves your town traveling at an average rate of 45 mi/h. Two hours later, your neighbor leaves your town along the same road at an average rate of 60 mi/h. How many hours will it take your neighbor to overtake you?

Lesson 1-6

Simplify each expression.

95. -4^2

96. $(-4)^2$

97. $(-2)^3(-3)$

98. -2^4

GPS Guided Problem Solving

FOR USE WITH PAGE 148, EXERCISE 71

25.2 Judge the validity of an argument according to whether the properties of the real number system have been applied correctly at each step. ***Develop***

Analyzing Errors **Read the exercise below and then follow along with what Gina thinks and writes. Check your understanding with the exercise at the bottom of the page.**

Error Analysis Find and correct the mistake in the student's work at the right.

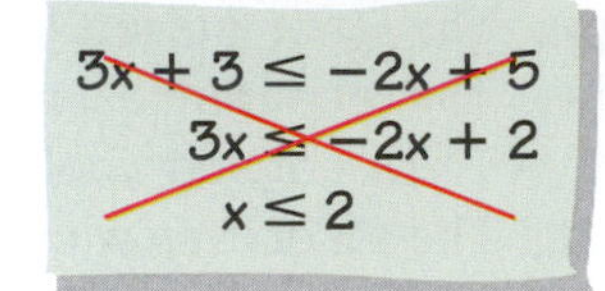

What Gina Thinks	What Gina Writes
I am going to solve the inequality and see where my work is different from the student's work.	$3x + 3 \le -2x + 5$
I'll subtract 3 from each side and then simplify.	$3x + 3 - 3 \le -2x + 5 - 3$ $3x \le -2x + 2$
Our work agrees. There is no mistake so far.	
I'll add $2x$ to each side so I can get the x's on the left. Then I'll divide each side by 5 to get x alone. My solution is different from the student's work!	$3x + 2x \le -2x + 2x + 2$ $5x \le 2$ $\frac{5x}{5} \le \frac{2}{5}$ $x \le \frac{2}{5}$
I think the student *subtracted* $2x$ from each side. That's the mistake, because $-2x - 2x$ equals $-4x$, not zero! If the student thought it was zero, the equation would have x on the left side and 2 on the right side. That's what is written: $x \le 2$.	
I'll write my answer in a sentence.	The student tried to subtract $2x$ from each side instead of adding it to each side.

EXERCISE

Find and correct the mistake in the work at the right.

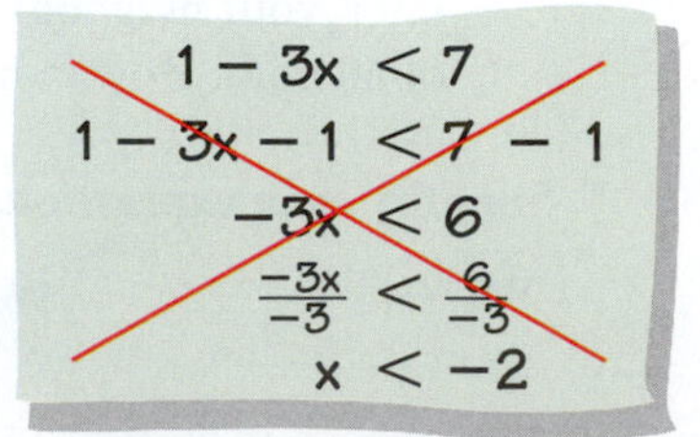

3-5 Compound Inequalities

California Content Standards

3.0 Solve equations and inequalities involving absolute values. ***Introduce***

What You'll Learn

- To solve and graph inequalities containing *and*
- To solve and graph inequalities containing *or*

. . . And Why

To solve a problem involving the chemistry of a swimming pool, as in Example 3

Lessons 1-2 and 3-1

Graph each pair of inequalities on one number line.

1. $c < 8; c \geq 10$ **2.** $t \geq -2; t \leq -5$ **3.** $m \leq 7; m > 12$

Use the given value of the variable to evaluate each expression.

4. $3n - 6; 4$ **5.** $7 - 2b; 5$

6. $\frac{12 + 13 + y}{3}; 17$ **7.** $\frac{2d - 3}{5}; 9$

New Vocabulary • compound inequality

Solving Compound Inequalities Containing *And*

Two inequalities that are joined by the word *and* or the word *or* form a **compound inequality.**

You can write the compound inequality $x \geq -5$ and $x \leq 7$ as $-5 \leq x \leq 7$.

$x \geq -5$
$x \leq 7$
−6 −5 −4 −3 −2 −1 0 1 2 3 4 5 6 7 8
$-5 \leq x \leq 7$

Vocabulary Tip

The word <u>inclusive</u> is related to the word <u>included</u>.

The graph above shows that a solution of $-5 \leq x \leq 7$ is in the overlap of the solutions of the inequality $x \geq -5$ and the inequality $x \leq 7$.

You can read $-5 \leq x \leq 7$ as "x is greater than or equal to -5 and less than or equal to 7." Another way to read it is "x is between -5 and 7, inclusive."

1 EXAMPLE Writing a Compound Inequality

Write a compound inequality that represents each situation. Graph the solutions.

a. all real numbers that are at least -2 and at most 4

$n \geq -2$ and $n \leq 4$

$-2 \leq n \leq 4$

−3 −2 −1 0 1 2 3 4 5

b. Today's temperatures will be above 32°F, but not as high as 40°F.

$32 < t$ and $t < 40$

$32 < t < 40$

30 31 32 33 34 35 36 37 38 39 40 41 42

CA Standards Check **1** Write a compound inequality that represents each situation. Graph your solution.

a. all real numbers greater than -2 but less than 9

b. The books were priced between \$3.50 and \$6.00, inclusive.

A solution of a compound inequality joined by *and* is any number that makes both inequalities true. One way you can solve a compound inequality is by writing two inequalities.

2 EXAMPLE Solving a Compound Inequality Containing *And*

Solve $-4 < r - 5 \leq -1$. Graph your solution.

Write the compound inequality as two inequalities joined by *and*.

$-4 < r - 5$	and	$r - 5 \leq -1$	
$-4 + 5 < r - 5 + 5$	|	$r - 5 + 5 \leq -1 + 5$	Solve each inequality.
$1 < r$	and	$r \leq 4$	Simplify.

$$1 < r \leq 4$$

−5 −4 −3 −2 −1 0 1 2 3 4 5

CA Standards Check 2 Solve each inequality. Graph your solution.

a. $-6 \leq 3x < 15$ b. $-3 < 2x - 1 < 7$ c. $7 < -3n + 1 \leq 13$

You could also solve an inequality like $-4 < r - 5 \leq -1$ by working on all three parts of the inequality at the same time. You work to get the variable alone between the inequality symbols.

3 EXAMPLE Application

The acidity of the water in a swimming pool is considered normal if the average of three pH readings is between 7.2 and 7.8, inclusive. The first two readings for a swimming pool are 7.4 and 7.9. What possible values for the third reading p will make the average pH normal?

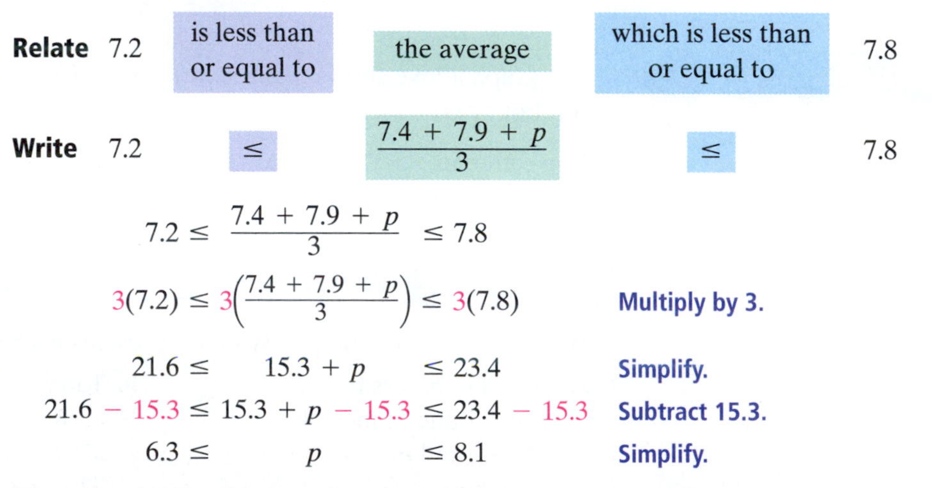

Relate	7.2	is less than or equal to	the average	which is less than or equal to	7.8
Write	7.2	$\leq$	$\frac{7.4 + 7.9 + p}{3}$	$\leq$	7.8

$$7.2 \leq \frac{7.4 + 7.9 + p}{3} \leq 7.8$$

$$3(7.2) \leq 3\left(\frac{7.4 + 7.9 + p}{3}\right) \leq 3(7.8) \quad \text{Multiply by 3.}$$

$$21.6 \leq 15.3 + p \leq 23.4 \quad \text{Simplify.}$$

$$21.6 - 15.3 \leq 15.3 + p - 15.3 \leq 23.4 - 15.3 \quad \text{Subtract 15.3.}$$

$$6.3 \leq p \leq 8.1 \quad \text{Simplify.}$$

The value for the third reading must be between 6.3 and 8.1, inclusive.

The lifeguard is checking the pH of swimming pool water. The pH of a substance is a measure of how acidic or basic it is. pH is measured on a scale from 0 to 14. Pure water is neutral, with a pH of 7.

CA Standards Check 3

a. Suppose the first two readings for the acidity of water in a swimming pool are 7.0 and 7.9. What possible values for the third reading will make the average pH normal?

b. **Critical Thinking** If two readings are 8.0 and 8.4, what possible values for the third reading will make the average pH normal? Are these third readings likely? Explain.

Solving Compound Inequalities Joined by *Or*

A solution of a compound inequality joined by *or* is any number that makes either inequality true.

4 EXAMPLE Writing Compound Inequalities

Write a compound inequality that represents each situation. Graph the solution.

a. all real numbers that are less than -3 or greater than 7

$x < -3$ or $x > 7$

$-4\ -3\ -2\ -1\ 0\ 1\ 2\ 3\ 4\ 5\ 6\ 7\ 8$

b. Discounted fares are available to children 12 and under or to adults at least 60 years of age.

$n \leq 12$ or $n \geq 60$; $n \geq 0$ because age cannot be negative.

$0\ 10\ 20\ 30\ 40\ 50\ 60\ 70$

CA Standards Check **4** Write an inequality that represents all real numbers that are at most -5 or at least 3. Graph your solution.

For a compound inequality joined by *or*, you must solve each of the two inequalities separately.

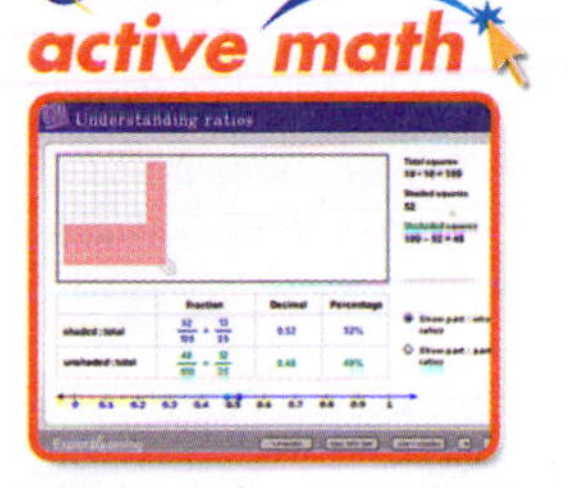

For: Compound Inequality Activity
Use: Interactive Textbook, 3-5

5 EXAMPLE Solving a Compound Inequality Containing *Or*

Solve the compound inequality $4v + 3 < -5$ or $-2v + 7 < 1$. Graph the solution.

$4v + 3 < -5$	or	$-2v + 7 < 1$
$4v + 3 - 3 < -5 - 3$		$-2v + 7 - 7 < 1 - 7$
$4v < -8$		$-2v < -6$
$\frac{4v}{4} < \frac{-8}{4}$		$\frac{-2v}{-2} > \frac{-6}{-2}$
$v < -2$	or	$v > 3$

$-5\ -4\ -3\ -2\ -1\ 0\ 1\ 2\ 3\ 4\ 5$

CA Standards Check **5** Solve the compound inequality $-2x + 7 > 3$ or $3x - 4 \geq 5$. Graph your solution.

EXERCISES

For more exercises, see *Extra Skills and Word Problem Practice.*

Standards Practice

Alg1 3.0

A Practice by Example

GO for Help Example 1 (page 151)

Write a compound inequality that represents each situation. Graph your solution.

1. all real numbers that are between -4 and 6
2. all real numbers that are at least 2 and at most 9
3. The circumference of a baseball is between 23 cm and 23.5 cm.
4. A tropical storm has wind speeds of at least 40 mi/h but no more than 74 mi/h.

Examples 2, 3 (page 152)

Solve each compound inequality. Graph your solution.

5. $-3 < j + 2 < 7$ **6.** $3 \leq w + 2 \leq 7$ **7.** $2 < 3n - 4 \leq 14$

8. $7 \leq 3 - 2p < 11$ **9.** $-2 < -3x + 7 < 4$ **10.** $1.5 < w + 3 \leq 6.5$

11. $-16 < -3x + 8 < -7$ **12.** $-1 < 4m + 7 \leq 11$ **13.** $-9 < -2s - 1 \leq -7$

14. $12 \leq \frac{14 + 17 + a}{3} \leq 16$ **15.** $\frac{1}{2} < \frac{3x - 1}{4} < 5$ **16.** $-2 \leq \frac{5 - x}{3} \leq 2$

Example 4 (page 153)

For each situation write and graph an inequality.

17. all real numbers n that are at most -3 or at least 5

18. all real numbers x that are less than 3 or greater than 7

19. all real numbers h less than 1 or greater than 3

20. all real numbers b less than 100 or greater than 300

Example 5 (page 153)

Solve each compound inequality. Graph your solution.

21. $3b - 1 < -7$ or $4b + 1 > 9$ **22.** $4 + k > 3$ or $6k < -30$

23. $3c + 4 \geq 13$ or $6c - 1 < 11$ **24.** $6 - a < 1$ or $3a \leq 12$

25. $7 - 3c \geq 1$ or $5c + 2 \geq 17$ **26.** $5y + 7 \leq -3$ or $3y - 2 \geq 13$

27. $2d + 5 \leq -1$ or $-2d + 5 \leq 5$ **28.** $5z - 3 > 7$ or $4z - 6 < -10$

B Apply Your Skills

Write a compound inequality that each graph could represent.

29. −4 −3 −2 −1 0 1 2 3 4

30. −4 −3 −2 −1 0 1 2 3 4

31. −4 −3 −2 −1 0 1 2 3 4

32. −4 −3 −2 −1 0 1 2 3 4

Solve each compound inequality.

33. $3q - 2 > 10$ or $3q - 2 \leq -10$ **34.** $3 - 2h > 17$ or $5h - 3 > 17$

35. $1 \leq 0.25t \leq 3.5$ **36.** $25r < 400$ or $100 < 4r$

37. $-20 \leq 3t - 2 < 1$ **38.** $\frac{3x + 1}{4} - 4 > 3$ or $\frac{3 - 2x}{5} > 3$

at rest

d in.

39. The force exerted on a spring is proportional to the distance the spring stretches from its relaxed position. Suppose you stretch a spring distance d in inches by applying force F in pounds. For a certain spring, $\frac{d}{F} = 0.8$. You apply forces between 25 and 40 pounds, inclusive. Which inequality describes the stretch of the spring?

A $25 \leq d \leq 40$ C $20 < d < 32$

B $31.25 \leq d \leq 40$ D $20 \leq d \leq 32$

40. Reasoning Describe the solutions of $3x - 8 < 7$ or $2x - 9 > 1$.

41. Writing Explain the difference between the words *and* and *or* in a compound inequality.

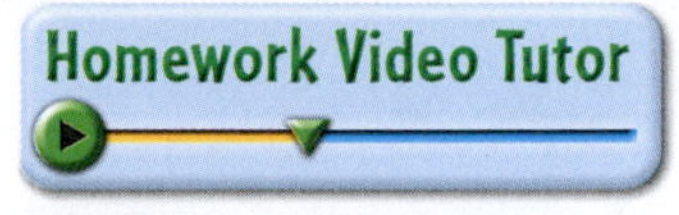

Visit: PHSchool.com
Web Code: bae-0305

The graph below shows the average monthly high and low temperatures for Detroit, Michigan, and Charlotte, North Carolina.

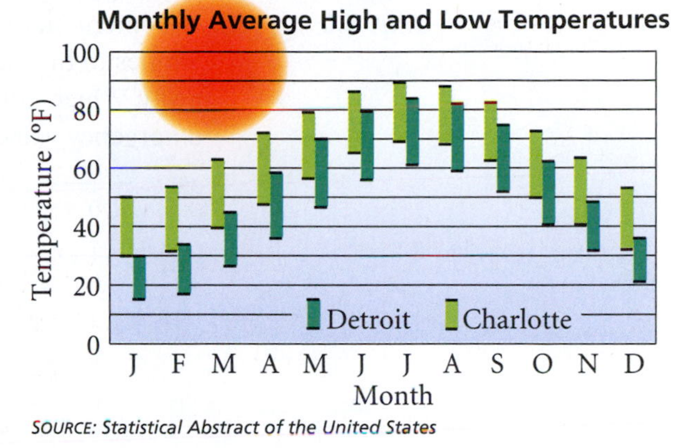

SOURCE: Statistical Abstract of the United States

42. Write a compound inequality for Charlotte's average temperature in June.

43. Write a compound inequality for Detroit's average temperature in January.

44. Write a compound inequality for the yearly temperature range for each city.

45. Describe a real-life situation that you could represent with $-2 < x < 8$.

C Challenge

46. In nursing school, students learn temperature ranges for bath water. Tepid water is approximately 80°F to 93°F, warm water is approximately 94°F to 98°F, and hot water is approximately 110°F to 115°F. Model these ranges on one number line. Label each interval.

Write a compound inequality that each graph could represent.

47. −4 −2 0 2 4

48. −2 0 2 4

49. When you exercise, your pulse rate rises. Recommended pulse rates vary with age and physical condition. For vigorous exercise, such as jogging, the inequality $0.7(220 - a) \leq R \leq 0.85(220 - a)$ gives a target range for pulse rate R (in beats per minute), based on age a (in years).

a. What is the target range for pulse rates for a person 35 years old? Round to the nearest whole number.

b. Your cousin's target pulse rate is in the range between 140 and 170 beats per minute. What is your cousin's age?

To estimate your pulse rate, count the number of beats you feel in 15 seconds at a pressure point. Multiply this number by 4.

50. Find three consecutive even integers whose sum is between 48 and 60.

51. Find three consecutive even integers such that one half of their sum is between 15 and 21.

Multiple Choice Practice

For California Standards Tutorials, visit PHSchool.com. Web Code: baq-9045

Alg1 4.0

52. Simplify $-6(2t - 8)$.

Ⓐ $-12t + 48$
Ⓑ $-6t + 48$
Ⓒ $-4t - 8$
Ⓓ $-12t - 48$

Alg1 5.0

53. Which equation has no solution?

Ⓐ $4\left(\frac{1}{2}x - 1\right) = \frac{1}{2}$
Ⓑ $5 - 6x = 2(1 - 3x)$
Ⓒ $6(2x - 3) = 2(6x - 9)$
Ⓓ $7(x + 8) - x = 0$

Alg1 1.0 **54.** Simplify $15 - 5 \times 2 + 4^2$.

Ⓐ 13 Ⓑ 21 Ⓒ 28 Ⓓ 36

Alg1 5.0 **55.** An emergency vehicle responding to a call about a heart-attack victim traveled 5 miles to the victim's home and then delivered him to the hospital 10 miles away. Which graph below represents the possible distances between the emergency vehicle and the hospital when the call was received?

Ⓐ 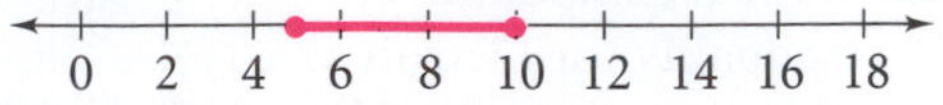

Ⓑ 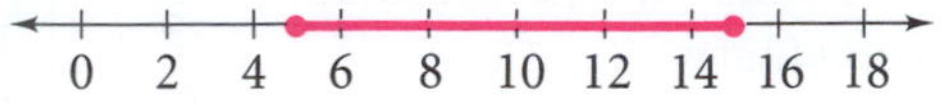

Ⓒ 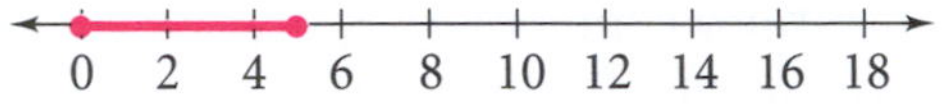

Ⓓ 

Alg1 1.0 **56.** Which set of numbers is NOT closed under subtraction?

Ⓐ integers Ⓒ whole numbers

Ⓑ real numbers Ⓓ rational numbers

Alg1 5.0 **57.** Which value is NOT a solution of either $-3x - 7 \geq 8$ or $-2x - 11 \leq -31$?

Ⓐ -6 Ⓑ 0 Ⓒ 10 Ⓓ 16

Mixed Review

GO for Help

Lesson 3-4 **Solve each inequality.**

58. $5 < 6b + 3$ **59.** $12n \leq 3n + 27$ **60.** $2 + 4r \geq 5(r - 1)$

Lesson 2-3 **Solve each equation. If necessary, write *identity* or *no solution*.**

61. $x - 3 = 5x + 1$ **62.** $4(w + 3) = 10w$ **63.** $8p - 4 = 4(2p - 1)$

Checkpoint Quiz 2 — Lessons 3-4 through 3-5

Solve each inequality. Graph the solution.

1. $8d + 2 < 5d - 7$ **2.** $2n + 1 \geq -3$ **3.** $-1 \leq 4m + 7 \leq 11$

4. $5s - 3 + 1 < 8$ **5.** $5(3p - 2) > 50$ **6.** $3 - x \geq 7$ or $2x - 3 > 5$

Write an inequality that represents each situation.

7. A cat weighs less than 8 pounds.

8. We expect today's temperature to be between 65°F and 75°F, inclusive.

9. The length of each side of a rectangular picture frame needs to be 15 in. You have only one 48-in. piece of wood to use for this frame. Write and solve an inequality that describes the possible widths for this frame.

10. Solve $-2x + 7 \leq 45$.

Mathematical Reasoning

Algebraic Proofs

For Use With Lesson 3-5

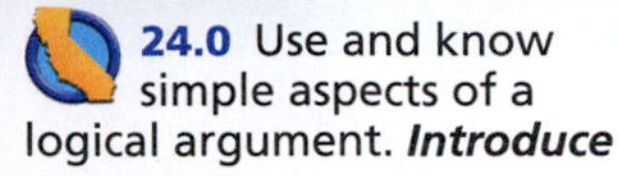

You can use the properties you have studied along with the four properties below to prove algebraic relationships.

Reflexive, Symmetric, and Transitive Properties of Equality

For every real number a, b, and c:

Reflexive Property: $a = a$ **Example:** $5x = 5x$

Symmetric Property: If $a = b$, then $b = a$. **Example:** If $15 = 3t$, then $3t = 15$.

Transitive Property: If $a = b$ and $b = c$, then $a = c$. **Example:** If $d = 3y$ and $3y = 6$, then $d = 6$.

Transitive Property of Inequality

For all real numbers a, b, and c, if $a < b$ and $b < c$, then $a < c$. **Example:** If $8x < 7$ and $7 < y^2$, then $8x < y^2$.

EXAMPLE

Prove each statement for all real numbers a, b, and c.

a. If $a = b$, then $ac = bc$.

$a = b$	Given
$ac = ac$	Reflexive Property
$ac = bc$	Substitute b for a.

b. If $c < 0$ and $a < b$, then $c < b - a$.

$c < 0$	Given
$a < b$	Given
$a - a < b - a$	Subtraction Property of Inequality
$a + (-a) < b - a$	Definition of subtraction
$0 < b - a$	Inverse Property of Addition
$c < b - a$	Transitive Property of Inequality

EXERCISES

Name the property that each exercise illustrates.

1. If $3.8 = z$, then $z = 3.8$.

2. If $x = \frac{1}{2}y$ and $\frac{1}{2}y = -2$, then $x = -2$.

3. $-r = -r$

4. If $k < m^2$ and $m^2 < 4$, then $k < 4$.

5. If $x = w^2$, then $w^2 = x$.

Supply the missing reasons to prove each statement.

6. $(a + b) + (-a) = b$

$(a + b) + (-a) = (b + a) + (-a)$	?
$= b + [a + (-a)]$	?
$= b + 0$	?
$= b$	?
$(a + b) + (-a) = b$	?

7. If $a < b$ and $c < d$, then $a + c < b + d$.

$a < b$	Given
$a + c < b + c$	?
$c < d$	Given
$b + c < b + d$	?
$a + c < b + d$	?

Vocabulary Builder

High-Use Academic Words

High-use academic words are words that you see often in textbooks and on tests. These words are not math vocabulary terms, but knowing them will help you to succeed in mathematics.

Words to Learn: Direction Words

Some words tell you what to do in a problem. You need to understand what these words are asking so that you give the correct answer.

Word	Meaning
Describe	To **write about a topic** so the reader can understand or visualize it
Explain	To **give the reasoning** for an answer
Define	To **give the meaning** of a word or expressions or to tell what a variable stands for in order to model a real-world situation

EXERCISES

1. Describe how you walk from your classroom to the cafeteria.

2. Explain why you participate in your favorite school activity.

3. Define the term *extracurricular*.

Describe each of the following.

4. the graph that represents the inequality $m + 4 \geq 9$

5. a real-world situation that can be modeled by the equation $3x - 2 = 5$

Explain why each statement is *true* or *false*.

6. All integers are positive.

7. All unit rates are ratios.

Define a variable and write an inequality to model each situation.

8. The elevator can hold no more than 14 people.

9. Miguel needs to earn at least 86 on his test to maintain his A average.

10. **Word Knowledge** Think about the word *identify*.

a. Choose the letter for how well you know the word.

A. I know its meaning.

B. I have seen it, but I do not know its meaning.

C. I don't know it.

b. **Research** Look up *identify* in a dictionary or online. Write any definition that might apply to its use in mathematics.

c. Write a sentence involving mathematics that uses the word *identify*.

3-6 Absolute Value Equations and Inequalities

California Content Standards

3.0 Solve equations and inequalities involving absolute values. ***Develop, Master***

What You'll Learn

- To solve equations that involve absolute value
- To solve inequalities that involve absolute value

. . . And Why

To find a range of acceptable measurements for parts of an engine, as in Example 4

Check Skills You'll Need

GO for Help Lessons 1-3 and 1-4

Simplify.

1. $|15|$ **2.** $|-3|$ **3.** $|18 - 12|$

4. $-|-7|$ **5.** $|12 - (-12)|$ **6.** $|-10 + 8|$

Complete each statement with $<$, $=$, or $>$.

7. $|3 - 7|$ ■ 4 **8.** $|-5| + 2$ ■ 6 **9.** $|7| - 1$ ■ 8

10. $\left|6 - 2\frac{1}{4}\right|$ ■ $3\frac{5}{8}$ **11.** $\left|-4\frac{2}{3}\right| + 2\frac{1}{3}$ ■ $2\frac{1}{2}$ **12.** $\left|-3\frac{1}{8} - 4\frac{1}{2}\right|$ ■ $7\frac{5}{8}$

Solving Absolute Value Equations

Recall that the absolute value of a number is its distance from zero on a number line. Since absolute value represents distance, it can never be negative.

Quick Review

$|3| = 3$

$|-3| = 3$

The graph of $|x| = 3$ is below.

3 units 3 units

−5 −4 −3 −2 −1 0 1 2 3 4 5

Find the numbers that are 3 units from 0.

The two solutions of the equation $|x| = 3$ are -3 and 3.

You can use the properties of equality to solve an absolute value equation.

1 EXAMPLE Solving an Absolute Value Equation

Solve $|x| + 5 = 11$.

$|x| + 5 - 5 = 11 - 5$ Subtract 5 from each side.

$|x| = 6$ Simplify.

$x = 6$ or $x = -6$ Definition of absolute value.

Check $|x| + 5 = 11$

$|6| + 5 \stackrel{?}{=} 11$ Substitute for x.

$6 + 5 = 11$ ✓

$|-6| + 5 \stackrel{?}{=} 11$

$6 + 5 = 11$ ✓

CA Standards Check 1 Solve each equation. Check your solution.

a. $|t| - 2 = -1$ **b.** $3|n| = 15$ **c.** $4 = 3|w| - 2$

d. Critical Thinking Is there a solution of $2|n| = -15$? Explain.

Some absolute value equations such as $|2p + 5| = 11$ have variable expressions within the absolute value symbols. The expression inside the absolute value symbols can be either positive or negative.

Take Note

Rule **Solving Absolute Value Equations**

To solve an equation in the form $|A| = b$, where A represents a variable expression and $b > 0$, solve $A = b$ and $A = -b$.

2 EXAMPLE Solving an Absolute Value Equation

Solve $|2p + 5| = 11$.

$2p + 5 = 11$	← Write two equations. →	$2p + 5 = -11$
$2p + 5 - 5 = 11 - 5$	← Subtract 5 from each side. →	$2p + 5 - 5 = -11 - 5$
$2p = 6$		$2p = -16$
$\frac{2p}{2} = \frac{6}{2}$	← Divide each side by 2. →	$\frac{2p}{2} = \frac{-16}{2}$
$p = 3$		$p = -8$

The value of p is 3 or -8.

CA Standards Check 2 Solve each equation. Check your solution.

a. $|c - 2| = 6$ **b.** $-5.5 = |t + 2|$ **c.** $|7d| = 14$

Solving Absolute Value Inequalities

You can write absolute value inequalities as compound inequalities.

The graphs below show two absolute value inequalities.

$|n - 1| < 3$

3 units 3 units

−3 −2 −1 0 1 2 3 4 5

$|n - 1| < 3$ represents all numbers whose distance from 1 is less than 3 units. So $-3 < n - 1 < 3$.

$|n - 1| > 3$

3 units 3 units

−3 −2 −1 0 1 2 3 4 5

$|n - 1| > 3$ represents all numbers whose distance from 1 is greater than 3 units. So $n - 1 < -3$ or $n - 1 > 3$.

Take Note

Rule **Solving Absolute Value Inequalities**

To solve an inequality in the form $|A| < b$, where A is a variable expression and $b > 0$, solve $-b < A < b$.

To solve an inequality in the form $|A| > b$, where A is a variable expression and $b > 0$, solve $A < -b$ or $A > b$.

Similar rules are true for $|A| \le b$ or $|A| \ge b$.

3 EXAMPLE Solving an Absolute Value Inequality

Solve $|v - 3| \geq 4$. Graph the solutions.

$v - 3 \leq -4$ or $v - 3 \geq 4$ **Write a compound inequality.**

$v - 3 + 3 \leq -4 + 3$ | $v - 3 + 3 \geq 4 + 3$ **Add 3.**

$v \leq -1$ or $v \geq 7$ **Simplify.**

−2 −1 0 1 2 3 4 5 6 7 8

CA Standards Check 3 Solve and graph $|w + 2| > 5$.

A manufacturer sets limits for how much an item can vary from its specifications. You can use an absolute value equation to model a quality-control situation.

4 EXAMPLE Application

Pistons of a car engine.

The ideal diameter of a piston for one type of car engine is 90.000 mm. The actual diameter can vary from the ideal by at most 0.008 mm. Find the range of acceptable diameters for the piston.

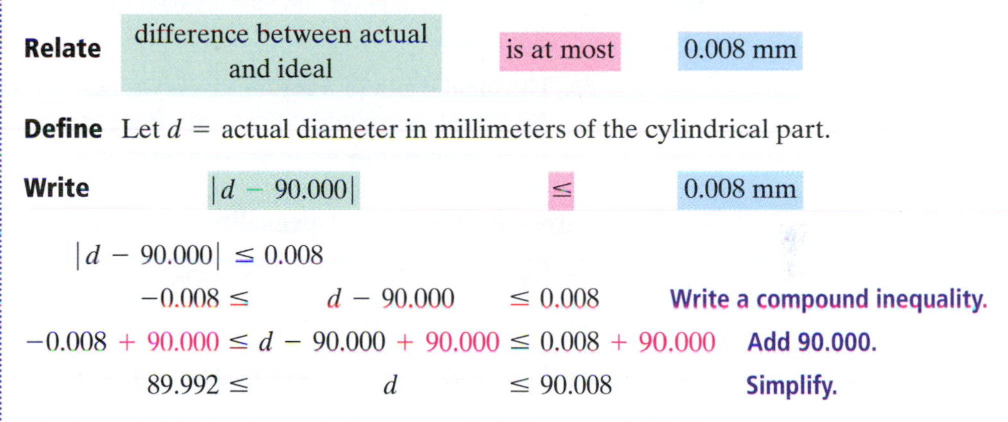

Relate difference between actual and ideal | is at most | 0.008 mm

Define Let d = actual diameter in millimeters of the cylindrical part.

Write $|d - 90.000|$ | $\leq$ | 0.008 mm

$|d - 90.000| \leq 0.008$

$-0.008 \leq d - 90.000 \leq 0.008$ **Write a compound inequality.**

$-0.008 + 90.000 \leq d - 90.000 + 90.000 \leq 0.008 + 90.000$ **Add 90.000.**

$89.992 \leq d \leq 90.008$ **Simplify.**

The actual diameter must be between 89.992 mm and 90.008 mm, inclusive.

CA Standards Check 4 The ideal weight of one type of model airplane engine is 33.86 ounces. The actual weight may vary from the ideal by at most 0.05 ounce. Find the range of acceptable weights for this engine.

EXERCISES

For more exercises, see *Extra Skills and Word Problem Practice.*

Standards Practice Alg1 3.0

A Practice by Example

Example 1 (page 159)

GO for Help

Solve each equation. If there is no solution, write *no solution*.

1. $|b| = 2$
2. $4 = |y|$
3. $|w| = \frac{1}{2}$
4. $|n| + 2 = 8$
5. $7 = |s| + 4$
6. $|x| - 10 = -3$
7. $4|d| = 20$
8. $-3|m| = -6$
9. $|y| + 3 = 3$
10. $12 = -4|k|$
11. $2|z| - 5 = 1$
12. $16 = 5|p| - 4$

Example 2 (page 160)

Solve each equation. If there is no solution, write *no solution*.

13. $|r - 8| = 5$ **14.** $|c + 2| = 6$ **15.** $2 = |g + 1|$

16. $3 = |m + 2|$ **17.** $|v - 2| = 7$ **18.** $-3|y - 3| = 9$

19. $2|d + 3| = 8$ **20.** $-2|7d| = -14$ **21.** $1.2|5p| = 3.6$

Example 3 (page 161)

22. Complete each statement with *less than* or *greater than*.

a. For $|x| < 5$, the graph includes all points whose distance is __?__ 5 units from 0.

b. For $|x| > 5$, the graph includes all points whose distance is __?__ 5 units from 0.

Solve each inequality. Graph your solution.

23. $|k| > 2.5$ **24.** $|w| < 2$ **25.** $|x + 3| < 5$

26. $|n + 8| \geq 3$ **27.** $|y - 2| \leq 1$ **28.** $|p - 4| \leq 3$

29. $|2c - 5| < 9$ **30.** $|2y - 3| \geq 7$ **31.** $|3t + 1| > 8$

32. $|4x + 1| > 11$ **33.** $|5t - 4| \geq 16$ **34.** $|3 - r| < 5$

Example 4 (page 161)

35. The ideal diameter of a gear for a certain type of clock is 12.24 mm. An actual diameter can vary by 0.06 mm. Find the range of acceptable diameters.

36. The ideal width of a certain conveyor belt for a manufacturing plant is 50 in. An actual conveyor belt can vary from the ideal by at most $\frac{7}{32}$ in. Find the acceptable widths for this conveyor belt.

B Apply Your Skills

Solve each equation or inequality.

37. $|2d| + 3 = 21$ **38.** $|-3n| - 2 = 7$ **39.** $|p| - \frac{2}{3} = \frac{5}{6}$

40. $|t| + 2.7 = 4.5$ **41.** $4|k + 1| = 16$ **42.** $-2|c - 4| = -8$

43. $|3d| \geq 6$ **44.** $|n| - 3 > 7$ **45.** $9 < |c + 7|$

46. $\frac{|v|}{-3} = -4.2$ **47.** $|6.5x| < 39$ **48.** $4|n| = 32$

49. $\left|\frac{1}{2}a\right| + 1 = 5$ **50.** $|a| + \frac{1}{2} = 3\frac{1}{2}$ **51.** $4 - 3|m + 2| > -14$

Write an absolute value inequality that represents each situation.

52. all numbers less than 3 units from 0

53. all numbers more than 7.5 units from 0

54. all numbers more than 2 units from 6

55. all numbers at least 3 units from –1

56. In a poll for the upcoming mayoral election, 42% of likely voters said they planned to vote for Lucy Jones. This poll has a margin of error of ± 3 percentage points. Use the inequality $|v - 42| \leq 3$ to find the least and greatest percent of voters v likely to vote for Lucy Jones according to this poll.

The United States produces over 2.5 billion pounds of dry pasta per year.

57. A manufacturer makes 16-ounce boxes of pasta. The manufacturer knows that not every box weighs exactly 16 ounces. The allowable difference is 0.05 ounce. Write and solve an absolute value inequality that represents this situation.

Visit: PHSchool.com
Web Code: bae-0306

58. A box of one brand of crackers should weigh 454 g. The quality-control inspector randomly selects boxes to weigh. The inspector sends back any box that is not within 5 g of the ideal weight.

a. Write an absolute value inequality for this situation.

b. What is the range of allowable weights for a box of crackers?

59. Acceptable diameters for one type of gear are from 6.25 mm to 6.29 mm. Write an absolute value inequality for the acceptable diameters for the gear.

60. Writing Explain why $|2c - 5| + 9 < 4$ has no solution.

61. Write an absolute value equation using the numbers 5, 3, −12. Then solve your equation.

62. Critical Thinking What are the solutions of $|w + 2| > -5$?

Error Analysis **Find and correct the student's mistake in the work below.**

63. **64.**

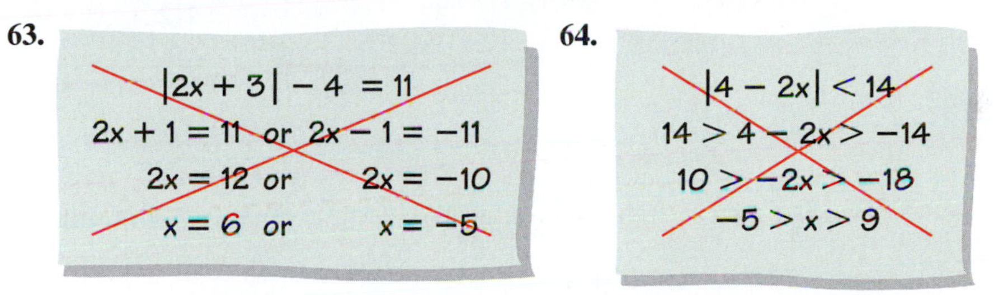

65. a. A meteorologist reported that the previous day's temperatures varied 14 degrees from the normal temperature of 25°F. What were the maximum and minimum temperatures possible on the previous day?

b. Write an absolute value equation for the temperature.

Challenge

Solve each equation. Check your solution.

66. $|x + 4| = 3x$ **67.** $|4x - 5| = 2x + 1$ **68.** $\frac{4}{3}|2x + 3| = 4x$

Replace the ■ with ≤, ≥, or =.

69. $|a + b|$ ■ $|a| + |b|$

70. $|a - b|$ ■ $|a| - |b|$

71. $|ab|$ ■ $|a| \cdot |b|$

72. $\left|\frac{a}{b}\right|$ ■ $\frac{|a|}{|b|}, b \neq 0$

Write an absolute value inequality that each graph could represent.

73. −6 −4 −2 0 2 4 6

74. −6 −4 −2 0 2 4 6

Multiple Choice Practice

For California Standards Tutorials, visit PHSchool.com. Web Code: baq-9045

Alg1 3.0

75. Which compound inequality has the same meaning as $|x + 4| < 8$?

(A) $-12 < x < 4$

(B) $x < -12$ or $x > 4$

(C) $-12 > x > 4$

(D) $x > -12$ or $x < 4$

Alg1 3.0

76. Which of the following values is a solution of $|2 - x| < 4$?

(A) −2 (B) −1 (C) 6 (D) 7

Online Lesson Quiz Visit: PHSchool.com, Web Code: baa-0306

Alg1 3.0

77. A delivery driver receives a bonus if he delivers pizza to a customer in 30 minutes plus or minus 5 minutes. Which inequality or equation represents the driver's allotted time to receive a bonus?

Ⓐ $|x - 30| < 5$ Ⓒ $|x - 30| > 5$

Ⓑ $|x - 30| = 5$ Ⓓ $|x - 30| \leq 5$

Alg1 5.0

78. Which are solutions of $3(x - 4) \leq 18$ and $2(x - 1) \geq 6$?

I. 9 II. 12 III. 15

Ⓐ I only Ⓑ II only Ⓒ I and III Ⓓ II and III

Alg1 3.0

79. Water is in a liquid state if its temperature t, in degrees Fahrenheit, satisfies the inequality $|t - 122| < 90$. Which graph represents the temperatures described by this inequality?

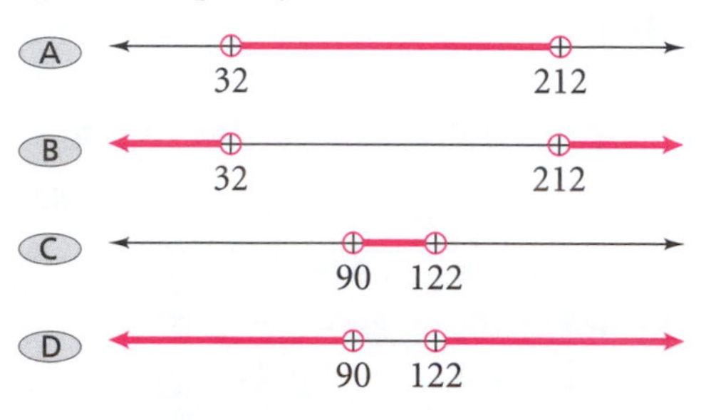

Alg1 3.0

80. The graphs below show the number of miles three people want to cycle per day.

Ramon: 5 10 15 20 25 30 35 40

Kathleen: 5 10 15 20 25 30 35 40

Allan: 5 10 15 20 25 30 35 40

Which inequality shows a trip length that would be acceptable to all three bikers?

Ⓐ $|x + 22.5| \leq 12.5$ Ⓒ $|x - 22.5| \leq 2.5$

Ⓑ $|x + 2.5| \leq 22.5$ Ⓓ $|x - 2.5| \leq 12.5$

Mixed Review

GO for Help

Lesson 3-5

Write a compound inequality to model each situation.

81. Elevation in North America is between the highest elevation of 20,320 ft above sea level at Mount McKinley, Alaska, and the lowest elevation of 282 ft below sea level at Death Valley, California.

82. Normal body temperature t is within 0.6 degrees of 36.6°C.

Lesson 2-2

Solve each equation.

83. $3t + 4t = -21$ **84.** $9(-2n + 3) = -27$ **85.** $k + 5 - 4k = -10$

86. $5x + 3 - 2x = -21$ **87.** $5.4m - 2.3 = -0.5$ **88.** $3(y - 4) = 9$

Lesson 1-3

Write each group of numbers from least to greatest.

89. $3, -2, 0, -2.5, \pi$ **90.** $\frac{15}{2}, -1.5, -\frac{4}{3}, 7, -2$

91. 0.001, 0.01, 0.009, 0.011 **92.** $-\pi, 2\pi, -2.5, -3, 3$

Mathematical Reasoning

Sometimes, Always, Never

FOR USE WITH LESSON 3-6

24.3 Use counter-examples to show that an assertion is false. ***Develop***
25.3 Given a specific algebraic statement, determine whether the statement is true sometimes, always, or never. ***Develop***

An equation or inequality is *sometimes* true, *always* true, or *never* true. To test the truth of an equation or inequality, you should try substituting different numerical values for the variables. Be sure to use a variety of numbers including 0, 1, fractions, and negative numbers.

EXAMPLE

Determine whether each statement is *sometimes, always,* or *never* true. Justify your reasoning.

a. $|x + y| = |x| + |y|$

Try the values $x = 3$ and $y = 5$.

$|3 + 5| \stackrel{?}{=} |3| + |5|$

$|8| \stackrel{?}{=} 3 + 5$

$8 = 8$ true ✓

Try the values $x = -3$ and $y = 5$.

$|-3 + 5| \stackrel{?}{=} |-3| + |5|$

$|2| \stackrel{?}{=} 3 + 5$

$2 \neq 8$ false ✗

The statement $|x + y| = |x| + |y|$ is *sometimes* true.

b. $|x| < x$

$|x| < x$, so the statement becomes $x < x$. A number cannot be less than itself. So the statement is *never* true.

EXERCISES

Determine whether each statement is *sometimes, always*, or *never* true. Justify your reasoning.

1. $x + x = x$

2. $x^2 = x$

3. $x + 1 = 1 + x$

4. $3(x + 2) = 3x + 2$

5. $|xy| = |x||y|$

6. $|x - y| = |x| - |y|$

7. $2 + x = x$

8. $2x = x$

9. $|x - 1| = 4$

10. $|x - 1| = -4$

11. $x^2 > 0$

12. $|x - y| < 0$

13. $xy + 1 \geq 1$

14. $|xy| + 1 \geq 1$

15. $\left|\frac{x}{2}\right| \leq |x|$

16. $|x - 1| \leq |x|$

Identifying True Statements

Some questions may ask you to determine which statement in a group of statements is true or not true. To answer the questions correctly, you must test each statement carefully.

EXAMPLE

The graph shows the number of hours Gloria worked over a seven-day period.

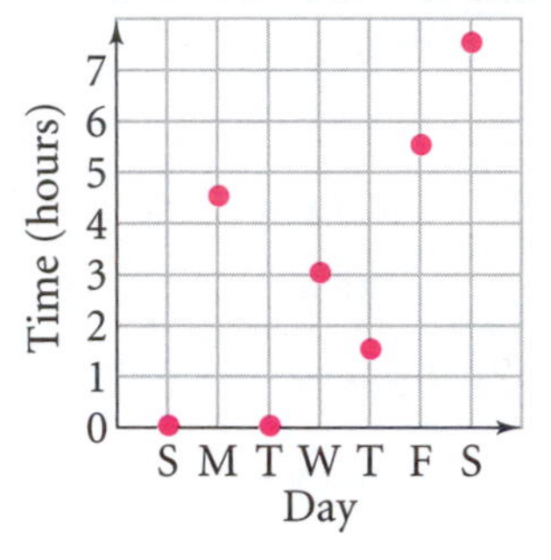

Based on the graph, which statement is NOT true?

(A) Gloria worked more than 21.5 hours over the course of the week.

(B) Gloria worked fewer hours on Wednesday than she did on Monday.

(C) Gloria worked more hours on Friday than she did on Monday, Tuesday, and Wednesday combined.

(D) Gloria averaged more than 3 hours per day over the seven days.

Read the values off the graph to test the statements.

A. Find the total number of hours Gloria worked.

Total hours $= 0 + 4.5 + 0 + 3 + 1.5 + 5.5 + 7.5 = 22$ ✓

Statement A is true.

B. Compare the number of hours Gloria worked on Monday and Wednesday.

$3 < 4.5$ ✓ Statement B is true.

C. Find the total hours Gloria worked on Monday, Tuesday, and Wednesday. Then compare with the hours she worked on Friday.

$4.5 + 0 + 3 = 7.5$, $5.5 > 7.5$ ✘ Statement C is false.

D. Divide the total hours by the number of days.

$\frac{22}{7} = 3\frac{1}{7} > 3$ ✓ Statement D is true.

Statement C is NOT true, so C is the correct answer.

Multiple Choice Practice

1. Based on the graph shown above, which statement is true?

(A) Gloria worked 3 hours more on Monday than she did on Wednesday.

(B) If Gloria earns \$7 per hour, she would have earned \$140.50 over the course of the week.

(C) Gloria worked all 7 days that week.

(D) Gloria worked a total of 13 hours on her two longest workdays.

Chapter 3 Review

Vocabulary Review

English and Spanish Audio Online

compound inequality (p. 151)
conclusion (p. 142)
conditional (p. 142)
converse (p. 142)
equivalent inequalities (p. 130)
hypothesis (p. 142)
solution of an inequality (p. 124)

Go Online
PHSchool.com
For: Vocabulary quiz
Web Code: baj-0351

Write the letter of the choice that correctly completes each sentence.

1. A solution of an inequality is any number that makes the inequality __?__.
   A. complete **B.** reversed **C.** true **D.** false
2. An inequality is equivalent to another inequality if the two inequalities have __?__.
   A. the same number of terms
   B. the same graphs
   C. real-number solutions
   D. no solutions
3. Compound inequalities are joined by __?__.
   A. either the word *and* or the word *or*
   B. the word *or*
   C. the word *and*
   D. equations
4. Write the expression "absolute value of x" as __?__.
   A. $[x]$ **B.** $-x$ **C.** $|x|$ **D.** $a = x$
5. A number's distance from 0 on a number line is the number's __?__.
   A. solution of an inequality
   B. compound form
   C. equivalent form
   D. absolute value

Skills and Concepts

Lesson 3-1

- To identify solutions of inequalities (p. 124)
- To graph and write inequalities (p. 125)

Alg1 5.0

A **solution of an inequality** is any number that makes the inequality true. A graph can indicate all the solutions of an inequality. A closed dot indicates that the number is a solution. An open dot indicates that the number is *not* a solution.

Graph each inequality.

6. $x > 3$
7. $m \leq -5$
8. $10 \geq p$
9. $r < 2.5$

Write an inequality for each graph.

Define a variable and write an inequality to model each situation.

14. At least 600 people attended a school play.
15. An elevator can carry at most 15 people.
16. The temperature was less than 32°F.

Lessons 3-2 and 3-3

- To use addition to solve inequalities (p. 130)
- To use subtraction to solve inequalities (p. 131)
- To use multiplication to solve inequalities (p. 136)
- To use division to solve inequalities (p. 138)

Alg1 5.0

To solve inequalities, you may need to find a simpler, equivalent inequality. **Equivalent inequalities** have the same solution. You can add, subtract, multiply, or divide both sides of an inequality by the same number to find a simpler equivalent inequality. Multiplying or dividing by a negative number causes the direction of the inequality symbol to be *reversed.*

Properties of Inequality

For all real numbers a, b, and c:

- If $a > b$, then $a + c > b + c$ and $a - c > b - c$.
- If $a < b$, then $a + c < b + c$ and $a - c < b - c$.
- If $a > b$ and $c > 0$, then $ac > bc$ and $\frac{a}{c} > \frac{b}{c}$.
- If $a < b$ and $c > 0$, then $ac < bc$ and $\frac{a}{c} < \frac{b}{c}$.
- If $a > b$ and $c < 0$, then $ac < bc$ and $\frac{a}{c} < \frac{b}{c}$.
- If $a < b$ and $c < 0$, then $ac > bc$ and $\frac{a}{c} > \frac{b}{c}$.

These properties are also true for inequalities involving $\leq$ and $\geq$.

Solve each inequality. Graph and check the solution.

17. $h + 3 > 2$ **18.** $t - 4 < -9$ **19.** $8m \geq -24$ **20.** $-6w \leq 12$

21. $q + 0.5 > -2$ **22.** $y - 8 > -22$ **23.** $-\frac{3}{5}n \geq -9$ **24.** $\frac{5}{8}d \geq \frac{5}{2}$

25. $0 \leq 2 + t$ **26.** $0 < 4c$ **27.** $-0.3 \geq u - 2.8$ **28.** $3 > -\frac{1}{3}p$

29. You have an allowance of \$12.00. You buy a discount movie ticket that costs at least \$3.50 and popcorn that costs \$2.75. Write and solve an inequality to find how much you have for other spending.

30. Suppose you earn \$7.25 per hour working part-time as a florist. Write and solve an inequality to find how many full hours you must work to earn at least \$200.

Lesson 3-4

- To solve multi-step inequalities with variables on one side (p. 143)
- To solve multi-step inequalities with variables on both sides (p. 145)

When you solve equations, sometimes you need to use more than one step. The same is true for inequalities. Many inequalities have variables on both sides of the inequality symbol. You need to gather the variable terms on one side of the inequality and the constant terms on the other side.

Solve each inequality. Check your solution.

31. $3n + 5 > -1$ **32.** $4k - 1 \leq -3$ **33.** $\frac{5}{8}b < 25$

34. $6(c - 1) \leq -18$ **35.** $3m > 5m + 12$ **36.** $t - 4t < -9$

37. $0.5x - 2 \geq -4x + 7$ **38.** $-\frac{6}{7}y - 6 \geq 42$ **39.** $4 + \frac{x}{2} > 2x$

40. Trenton sells electronics supplies. Each week he earns \$190 plus a commission equal to 4% of his sales. This week his goal is to earn no less than \$500. Write and solve an inequality to find the amount of sales he must have to reach his goal.

Lesson 3-5

- To solve and graph inequalities containing *and* (p. 151)
- To solve and graph inequalities containing *or* (p. 153)

Alg1 3.0

Two inequalities that are joined by the word *and* or the word *or* are called **compound inequalities.** A solution of a compound inequality joined by *and* makes both inequalities true. A solution of a compound inequality joined by *or* makes either inequality true. A number sentence with two inequality symbols, such as $a < x < b$ represents the compound inequality $a < x$ and $x < b$.

Graph each compound inequality.

41. $x > -3$ and $x < 2$ **42.** $m < -2$ or $m \geq 1$ **43.** $-3 \leq k < 4$

Solve each compound inequality and graph the solutions.

44. $-3 \leq z - 1 < 3$ **45.** $-2 \leq d + \frac{1}{2} < 4\frac{1}{2}$ **46.** $0 < -8b \leq 12$

47. $2t \leq -4$ or $7t \geq 49$ **48.** $-1 \leq a - 3 < 2$ **49.** $-2 \leq 3a - 8 < 4$

50. In Miami, Florida, July's average high temperature is 89°F. July's average low temperature is 75°F. Write a compound inequality to represent Miami's average temperature in July.

Lesson 3-6

- To solve equations that involve absolute value (p. 159)
- To solve inequalities that involve absolute value (p. 160)

Alg1 3.0

Recall that the absolute value of a number is its distance from 0 on a number line. Since absolute value represents distance, it can never be negative.

Solving Absolute Value Equations and Inequalities

- To solve an equation in the form $|A| = b$, where A represents a variable expression and $b > 0$, solve the equations $A = b$ or $A = -b$.
- To solve an inequality in the form $|A| < b$, where A represents a variable expression and $b > 0$, solve $-b < A < b$.
- To solve an inequality in the form $|A| > b$, where A represents a variable expression and $b > 0$, solve $A < -b$ or $A > b$.

Similar rules are true for $|A| \leq b$ and $|A| \geq b$.

Write an absolute value inequality that represents each set of numbers.

51. all numbers n that are more than 3 units from -2

52. all numbers n that are within 5 units of 12

Solve each equation or inequality.

53. $|y| = 5$ **54.** $|n + 2| \geq 4$ **55.** $|-5x| \leq 15$

56. $\left|\frac{1}{2}m\right| < 4.8$ **57.** $|2x - 7| - 1 > 0$ **58.** $|p + 3| = 9.5$

59. $|k - 8| = 0$ **60.** $|3x + 5| > -2$ **61.** $|6 - b| = -1$

62. $4|k + 5| > 8$ **63.** $4 + |r + 2| = 7$ **64.** $-2 + |3.6z| \geq -1.1$

65. The ideal diameter of a steel reinforcement rod is 2.8 cm. The actual diameter may vary from the ideal by at most 0.06 cm. Find the range of acceptable diameters for this steel rod.

66. The ideal length of a certain nail is 20 mm. The actual length can vary from the ideal by at most 0.4 mm. Find the range of acceptable lengths of the nail.

Chapter 3 Test

Go Online PHSchool.com For: Chapter Test Web Code: baa-0352

Determine whether each number is a solution of the given inequality.

1. $4z + 7 \geq 15$ **a.** -2 **b.** 2 **c.** 5

2. $-2g + 3 > 5$ **a.** -3 **b.** -1 **c.** 4

Define a variable and write an inequality to model each situation.

3. A student can take at most 7 classes.

4. The school track team needs at least 5 runners to compete at Saturday's meet.

5. Elephants can drink up to 40 gallons of water at a time.

6. Your cousin's early-morning paper route has more than 32 homes.

Write an inequality for each graph.

7. **8.** **9.** **10.**

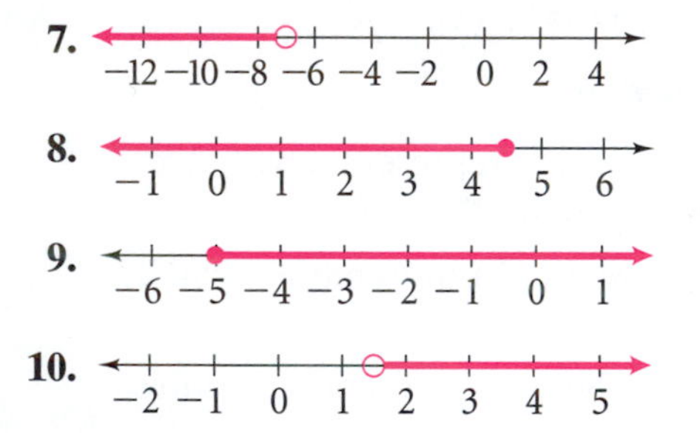

Solve each inequality. Graph the solution.

11. $z + 7 \leq 9$

12. $-16 \geq 4y$

13. $-\frac{1}{3}x < 2$

14. $8 - u > 4$

15. $-5 + 4t \leq 3$

16. $5w \geq -6w + 11$

17. $-\frac{7}{2}m < 14$

18. $6y - 7 < -2y + 13$

19. $|x - 5| \geq 3$

20. $|2h + 1| < 5$

21. $9 \leq 6 - b < 12$

22. $-10 < 4q < 12$

23. $4 + 3n \geq 1$ or $-5n > 25$

24. $10k < 75$ and $4 - k \leq 0$

Solve each inequality. Check your solution.

25. $3(d - 1) > -4$

26. $5(-2 + b) < 3b + 2$

27. $3(m + 3) + 4 \leq 15$

28. $0.5(x + 3) - 2.1 \geq -1$

Write a compound inequality that each graph could represent.

29. **30.**

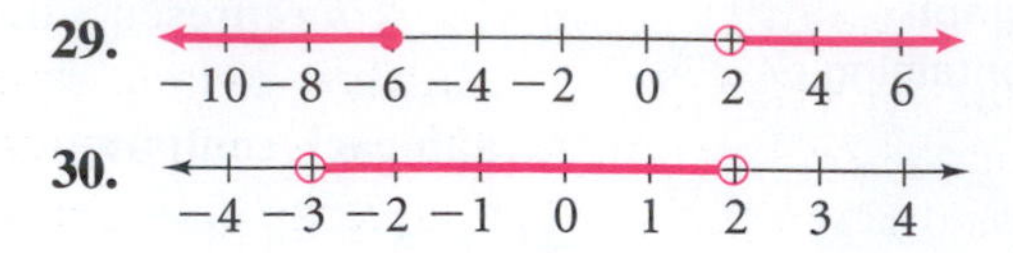

Solve each equation. Check your solution.

31. $|4k - 2| = 11$

32. $23 = |n + 10|$

33. $|3c + 1| - 4 = 13$

34. $4|5 - t| = 20$

35. **Writing** Explain why the solution to $ax - 1 < 3$ is not $x < \frac{4}{a}$. Use solutions of the inequality with different values of a to support your explanation.

36. Write an absolute value inequality that has 3 and -5 as two of its solutions.

37. The chart below shows the number of cans of food collected by a club during the first four weeks of a food drive.

Food Drive

Week	Number of Cans
1	702
2	470
3	492
4	547

The goal is to collect at least 3000 cans in 5 weeks. Write and solve an inequality to find how many cans should be collected during Week 5 to meet or exceed the goal.

38. A freight elevator can safely hold no more than 2000 pounds. An elevator operator must take 55-pound boxes to a storage area. If he weighs 165 pounds, how many boxes can he safely move at one time?

39. A manufacturer is cutting plastic sheets to make rectangles that are 11.125 in. by 7.625 in. Each rectangle's length and width must be within 0.005 in. of the desired size. Write and solve inequalities to find the acceptable range for the length ℓ and for the width w.

Standards Mastery

Cumulative Practice

Some questions ask you to determine which situation can be represented by a given equation. Read the question at the right. Then follow the tips to answer the sample question.

Juan has a wireless phone plan that costs $25 per month. He must also pay $.10 per minute for each minute over 500 minutes. Juan's phone bill was more than $30 last month. Which inequality best represents the number of minutes m Juan spent on the phone last month?

(A) $25 + 0.1m + 500 > 30$
(B) $25 + 0.1m - 500 < 30$
(C) $25 + 0.1(m + 500) < 30$
(D) $25 + 0.1(m - 500) > 30$

Tip 1
Make sure you know what the inequality should say. The bill is more than $30. You can eliminate answer choices that say the bill is less than $30.

Tip 2
Look at what Juan pays for. He only pays extra if he uses more than 500 minutes.

Think It Through

Juan's bill is greater than $30, so the answer must be either A or D. The number of minutes he pays extra for is $m - 500$, so the correct answer is D.

Vocabulary Review

As you solve problems, you must understand the meanings of mathematical terms. Choose the correct term to complete each sentence.

A. Two inequalities that are joined by the word *and* or the word *or* form a (*compound, connected*) inequality.

B. (*Equivalent, Similar*) inequalities are inequalities with the same solution.

C. Any number that makes an inequality true is a (*point, solution*) of the inequality.

D. A(n) (*open, closed*) dot on the graph of an inequality shows that the point is included in the solution set.

E. An algebraic (*expression, equation*) is a mathematical phrase that can include numbers, variables, and operation symbols.

Read each question. Then write the letter of the correct answer on your paper.

1. What is the solution of $2u + 5.2 \leq 9.4 + u$? **(Lesson 3-2)**

(A) $u \leq 146.0$
(B) $u \leq 48.9$
(C) $u \leq 14.6$
(D) $u \leq 4.2$

2. Which is a solution of $-x + 3 > 10$? **(Lesson 3-4)**

(A) -9
(B) -7
(C) 7
(D) 9

3. What is the solution of $-\frac{1}{9}a + 1 < 8$? **(Lesson 3-4)**

(A) $a > 7$
(B) $a < 7$
(C) $a > -63$
(D) $a < -63$

4. What is the solution of $6f + 1 > -14$? **(Lesson 3-4)**

(A) $f > -2.5$
(B) $f < -2.5$
(C) $f > 2.5$
(D) $f < 2.5$

5. Which equation is equivalent to $2(3x - 1) - 3(5x - 3) = 4$? **(Lesson 2-2)**

(A) $-3x - 5 = 4$
(B) $-9x - 4 = 4$
(C) $-9x - 11 = 4$
(D) $-9x + 7 = 4$

6. Leah saved $16,000 for a new car that costs $10,500, plus $1,200 each year for car insurance. If Leah buys the car, which inequality can be used to find the maximum number of years she can pay the insurance with her current savings? **(Lesson 3-4)**

(A) $10{,}500 + 1{,}200x \leq 16{,}000$
(B) $10{,}500 - 1{,}200x \leq 16{,}000$
(C) $16{,}000 + 1{,}200x \leq 10{,}500$
(D) $16{,}000 - 1{,}200x \leq 10{,}500$

Cumulative Practice (continued)

7. What is the solution of $|t - 6| < 5$? **(Lesson 3-6)**

   A $-7 < t < 3$ C $1 < t < 11$
   B $7 < t < -3$ D $-1 < t < -11$

8. What is the solution of $w - 4 \geq 18 + 3w$? **(Lesson 3-4)**

   A $w \leq 3.5$ C $w \leq -11$
   B $w \geq 3.5$ D $w \geq -11$

9. Which situation can be represented by the inequality $2y + 3 \leq x$? **(Lesson 3-4)**

   A Matt's age x is no more than 3 years greater than twice Annie's age y.
   B In a class, there are no more than 3 fewer tennis players x than twice the number of soccer players y.
   C The cost of a hardcover book x is at least \$3 more than twice the cost of the paperback book y.
   D A men's store sells at least 3 times more than twice as many button-down shirts y as pullover shirts x.

10. What is the solution of $8 - 2x > 24$? **(Lesson 3-4)**

   A $x < -8$ C $x < 8$
   B $x > -8$ D $x > 8$

11. What is the solution of $-4(s + 2) - 2s > 28$? **(Lesson 3-4)**

   A $s < -6$ C $s > -6$
   B $s < -\frac{26}{6}$ D $s > -\frac{26}{6}$

12. Chelsea's baby sister is 25 inches long. She is wearing pajamas that fit babies up to 32 inches long. Which inequality can be used to find the number of inches x the baby can grow and still fit into the pajamas? **(Lesson 3-2)**

   A $32 \leq 25 - x$ C $32 \geq 25 - x$
   B $32 \leq 25 + x$ D $32 \geq 25 + x$

13. Which graph represents the solutions to the inequality $3n < n + 4$? **(Lesson 3-4)**

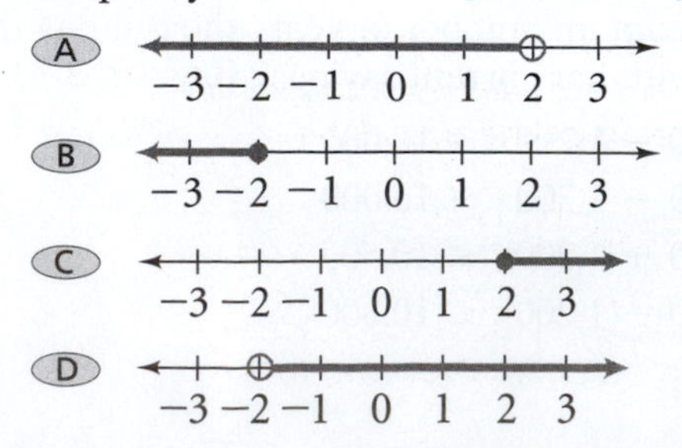

14. Simplify the expression $3(6x + 2) - 2(5x + 3)$. **(Lesson 1-7)**

   A $8x$ C $8x + 9$
   B $8x + 5$ D $8x + 12$

15. Which graph represents the solutions to the inequality $3(f + 2) > 2f + 4$? **(Lesson 3-4)**

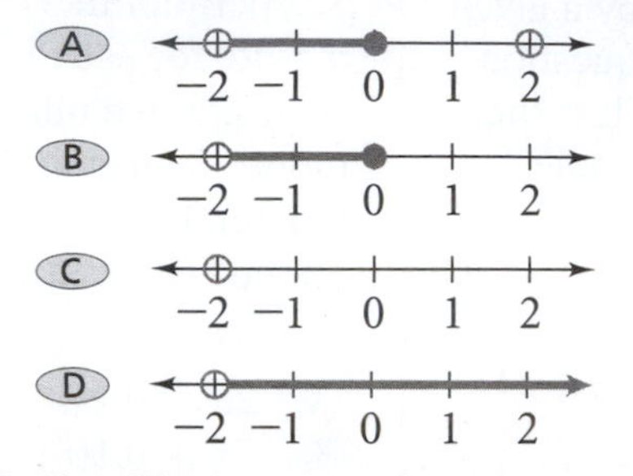

16. Simplify the expression $2b - a + b + 3a$. **(Lesson 1-8)**

   A 5 C $b + 4a$
   B $5ab$ D $3b + 2a$

17. Which property guarantees the truth of the statement $-2 \cdot (7 \cdot 4) = (-2 \cdot 7) \cdot 4$? **(Lesson 1-8)**

   A Closure Property of Addition
   B Identity Property of Multiplication
   C Distributive Property
   D Associative Property of Multiplication

18. Which operation should be done first to simplify the expression $12 + 6 \cdot 3 - [35 - 14 \div 7]$? **(Lesson 1-2)**

   A $12 + 6$ C $35 - 14$
   B $6 \cdot 3$ D $14 \div 7$

19. Which property is shown by the equation $8 \cdot (7 \cdot 9) = (7 \cdot 9) \cdot 8$? **(Lesson 1-8)**

   A Commutative Property of Multiplication
   B Associative Property of Multiplication
   C Commutative Property of Addition
   D Associative Property of Addition

20. Which inequality is equivalent to $6s - (2s - 1) < 6$? **(Lesson 3-4)**

   A $4s + 1 < 6$ C $3s + 1 < 6$
   B $4s - 1 < 6$ D $3s - 1 < 6$

21. What is the solution set of the inequality $|-2k - 3| < 7$? **(Lesson 3-6)**

   A $k < -5$ or $k > -2$ C $k > 5$ or $k < 2$
   B $2 > k > -5$ D $2 < k < 5$

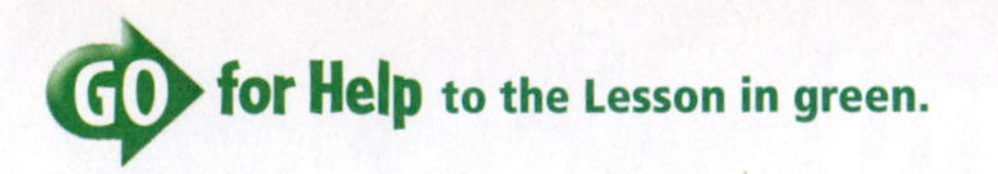

Standards Mastery

22. Which value of x is a counterexample to the statement "$|x - 3| + 2 \leq 2$ has no solutions"? **(Lesson 3-6)**

Ⓐ $x = 1$ Ⓒ $x = 3$

Ⓑ $x = 2$ Ⓓ $x = 6$

23. What is the solution set of the inequality $|n - 3| - 2 < 7$? **(Lesson 3-6)**

Ⓐ $n > 12$ or $n < -2$ Ⓒ $n > 12$ or $n < -6$

Ⓑ $-2 > n > 12$ Ⓓ $-6 < n < 12$

24. A 25% acid solution is added to 10 L of a 70% acid solution to make a 50% solution. How much of the 25% acid solution must be added? **(Lesson 2-6)**

Ⓐ 4 L Ⓑ 6 L Ⓒ 8 L Ⓓ 10 L

25. State whether $|x| + 16 \geq 16$ is *sometimes, always*, or *never* true. **(Lesson 3-6)**

Ⓐ always true

Ⓑ sometimes true, when $x \geq 0$

Ⓒ sometimes true, when $|x| \geq 1$

Ⓓ never true

26. Which value of a is a counterexample to the statement "If $5 \geq 3$, then $5a \geq 3a$"? **(Lesson 3-3)**

Ⓐ $a = 4$ Ⓒ $a = 0$

Ⓑ $a = 1$ Ⓓ $a = -2$

27. What is the solution of the equation $|3x - 6| = 9$? **(Lesson 3-6)**

Ⓐ $x = 1$ or $x = -5$

Ⓑ $x = 5$ or $x = -1$

Ⓒ $x = -5$ or $x = -1$

Ⓓ $x = 5$ or $x = 1$

28. State whether $|x - 5| + 4 < 3$ is *sometimes, always*, or *never* true. **(Lesson 3-6)**

Ⓐ always true

Ⓑ sometimes true, when $x < 4$

Ⓒ sometimes true, when $x < 4$ or $x > 6$

Ⓓ never true

29. Pablo can wash 6 cars in 40 minutes. At this rate, how many cars can Pablo wash in four hours? **(Lesson 2-4)**

Ⓐ 24 Ⓑ 36 Ⓒ 44 Ⓓ 60

30. Solve $|2x - 1| \geq 3$. **(Lesson 3-6)**

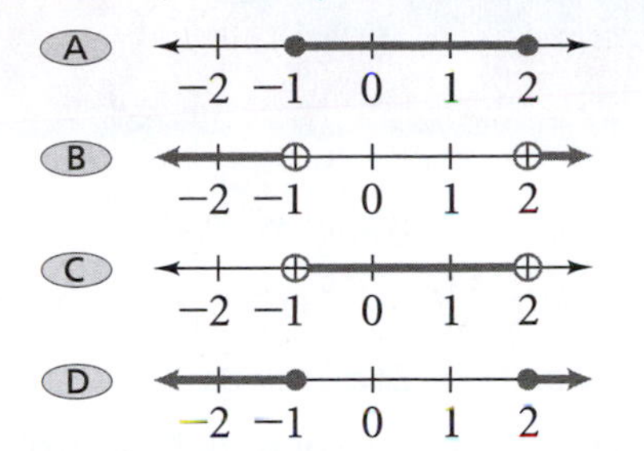

31. What is the solution of the equation $|5x - 9| = 12$? **(Lesson 3-6)**

Ⓐ $x = 21$ or $x = -3$ Ⓒ $x = 6$ or $x = 2.4$

Ⓑ $x = 4.2$ or $x = -0.6$ Ⓓ $x = 3$ or $x = -21$

32. State whether $|x + 4| + 3 > 2$ is *sometimes, always*, or *never* true. **(Lesson 3-6)**

Ⓐ always true

Ⓑ sometimes true, when $x < -4$

Ⓒ sometimes true, when $x > -5$

Ⓓ never true

Standards Reference Guide

California Content Standard	Item Number(s)
Alg1 1.0	17–19
Alg1 3.0	7, 21, 23, 27, 30, 31
Alg1 4.0	5, 14, 16, 20
Alg1 5.0	1–4, 6, 8–13, 15
Alg1 15.0	24, 29
Alg1 24.3	22, 26
Alg1 25.3	25, 28, 32

For additional review and practice, see the *California Standards Review and Practice Workbook* or go online to use the

California Standards Tutorials

Visit: PHSchool.com, **Web Code:** baq-9045

CALIFORNIA CHECK SYSTEM

CHAPTER 4 Graphs and Functions

What You've Learned

California Content Standards

3.0 Solve equations and inequalities involving absolute values.

5.0 Solve multi-step problems, including word problems, involving linear equations and linear inequalities in one variable and provide justification for each step.

15.0 Apply algebraic techniques to solve rate problems and percent mixture problems.

Check Your Readiness

GO for Help to the Lesson in green.

Writing Equations (Lesson 1-1)

Define a variable and write an equation to model each situation.

1. The total price is the number of pens times \$.59.
2. The tower is 200 feet taller than the house.
3. What is the perimeter of an equilateral triangle?

Evaluating Expressions (Lesson 1-2)

Evaluate each expression.

4. $3x - 2y$, for $x = -1$ and $y = 2$
5. $-w^2 + 3w$, for $w = -3$
6. $\frac{3 + k}{k}$, for $k = 3$
7. $h - (h^2 - 1) \div 2$, for $h = -1$

Using Cross Products (Lesson 2-4)

Solve the following proportions.

8. $\frac{4}{w} = \frac{5}{8}$
9. $\frac{c}{2.2} = \frac{3}{11}$
10. $\frac{4}{0.5} = \frac{36}{p}$
11. $-\frac{29}{2} = \frac{d}{4}$

Graphing Inequalities (Lesson 3-1)

Graph each inequality.

12. $c \leq -5$
13. $s > 2$
14. $v < 4$
15. $m \geq -1$

Solving Absolute Value Equations (Lesson 3-6)

Solve each equation. If there is no solution, write *no solution*.

16. $|r + 2| = 2$
17. $-3|d - 5| = -6$
18. $-3.2 = |8p|$

▲ Lake Tahoe is an excellent place for boating. Given a constant speed, the distance a paddleboat travels is a function of time.

What You'll Learn Next

California Content Standards

16.0 Understand the concepts of a relation and a function, determine whether a given relation defines a function, and give pertinent information about given relations and functions.

17.0 Determine the domain of independent variables and the range of dependent variables defined by a graph, a set of ordered pairs, or a symbolic expression.

18.0 Determine whether a relation defined by a graph, a set of ordered pairs, or a symbolic expression is a function and justify the conclusion.

New Vocabulary

English and Spanish Audio Online

- **constant of variation for direct variation** (p. 202)
- **constant of variation for indirect variation** (p. 209)
- **dependent variable** (p. 188)
- **direct variation** (p. 202)
- **domain** (p. 181)
- **function** (p. 181)
- **function notation** (p. 187)
- **independent variable** (p. 188)
- **inductive reasoning** (p. 215)
- **inverse variation** (p. 209)
- **range** (p. 181)
- **relation** (p. 181)
- **vertical-line test** (p. 183)

4-1 Graphing on the Coordinate Plane

California Content Standards

Prepares for Alg1 6.0 Graph a linear equation.

What You'll Learn

- To graph points on the coordinate plane

. . . And Why

To locate points on a plane, as in Example 1

Check Skills You'll Need

Graph each number on a number line.

1. 6 **2.** -5 **3.** 2.7 **4.** 0

Write the coordinate of each point on the number line below.

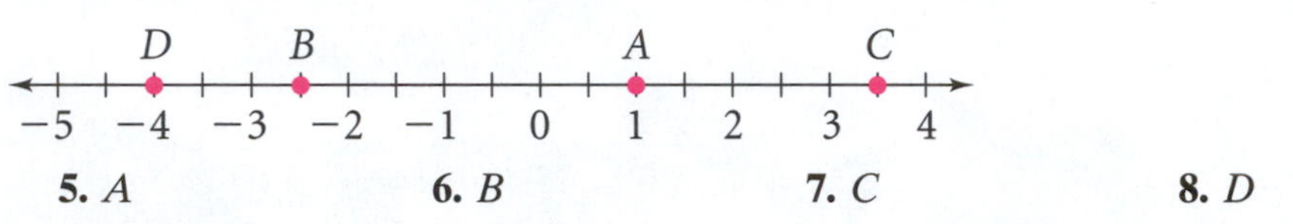

5. A **6.** B **7.** C **8.** D

New Vocabulary • coordinate plane • x-axis • y-axis • origin • quadrants • ordered pair • coordinates • x-coordinate • y-coordinate

Graphing Points on the Coordinate Plane

Two number lines that intersect at right angles form a **coordinate plane.** The horizontal axis is the **x-axis** and the vertical axis is the **y-axis.** The axes intersect at the **origin** and divide the coordinate plane into four sections called **quadrants.**

B (−2, 4) y-axis
Quadrant II Quadrant I
x-axis
origin
Quadrant III Quadrant IV

An **ordered pair** of numbers identifies the location of a point. These numbers are the **coordinates** of the point on the graph. Point B has coordinates $(-2, 4)$.

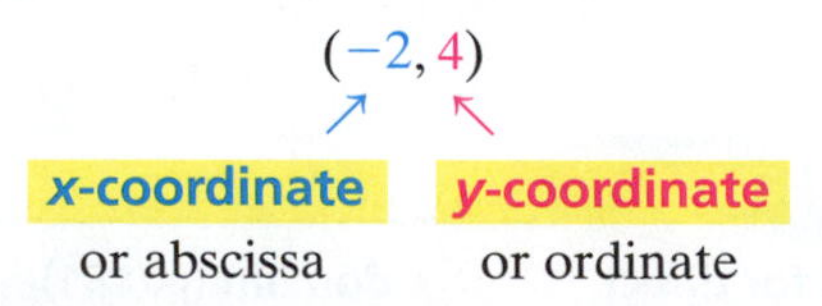

The x-coordinate tells you how far to move right (positive) or left (negative) from the origin. The y-coordinate tells you how far to move up (positive) or down (negative) from the origin.

1 EXAMPLE Identifying Coordinates

a. Name the coordinates of point Z in the graph below.

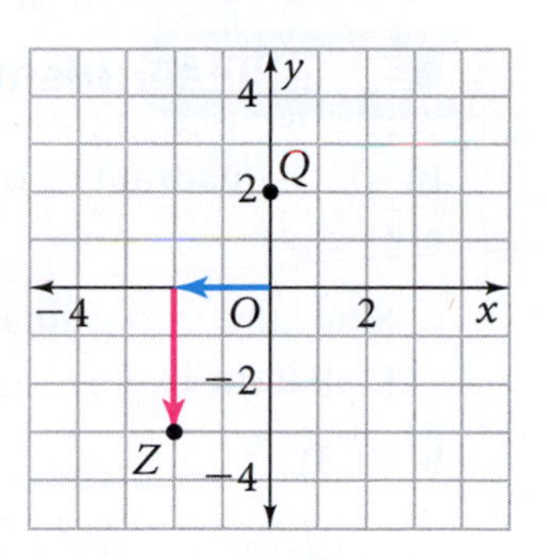

Move 2 units to the left of the origin. Then move 3 units down. The coordinates of Z are $(-2, -3)$.

b. Name the coordinates of point Q in the graph above.

Since Q is directly above the origin, the x-coordinate is 0. Move 2 units up from the origin. The coordinates of Q are $(0, 2)$.

CA Standards Check **1** Name the coordinates of each point in the graph below.

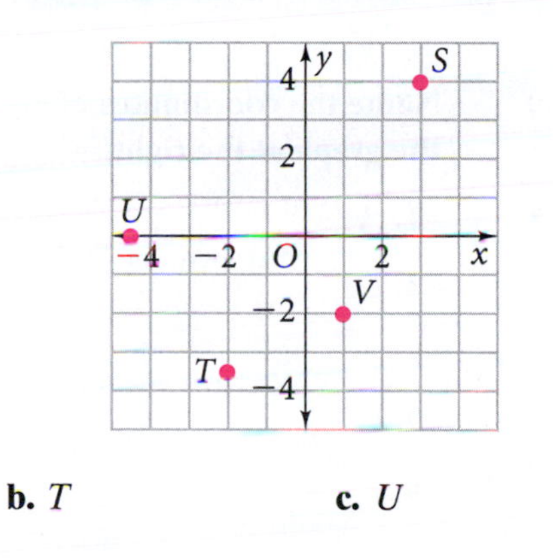

a. S **b.** T **c.** U **d.** V

To graph a point $P(x, y)$ on the coordinate plane, graph the ordered pair (x, y).

2 EXAMPLE Graphing Points

a. Graph the point $A\left(-2\frac{1}{2}, 3\right)$ on the coordinate plane.

Move $2\frac{1}{2}$ units to the left of the origin. Then move 3 units up.

b. Graph the point $B(3, 0)$ on the coordinate plane.

Since the y-coordinate is 0, point B is on the x-axis. Move 3 units to the right of the origin.

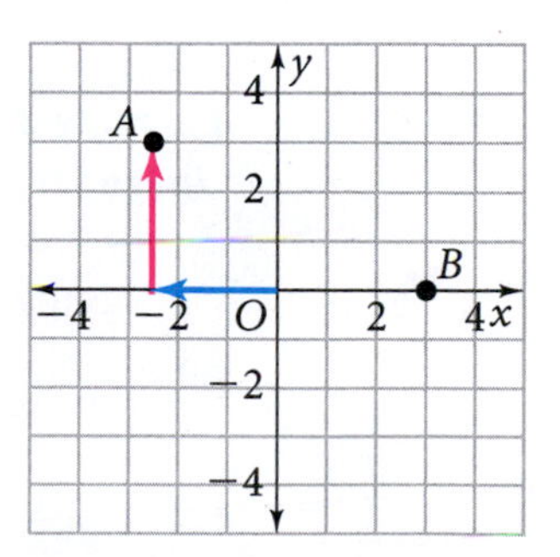

CA Standards Check **2** Graph the points on the same coordinate plane.

a. $C(2, 4)$ **b.** $D\left(-1\frac{1}{2}, -4\right)$ **c.** $E\left(3, -2\frac{1}{2}\right)$ **d.** $F(0, 3)$

You can determine which quadrant a point is in by graphing the point or by considering the signs of the x- and y-coordinates. A point that is on an axis is not considered to be in a quadrant.

3 EXAMPLE Identifying Quadrants

In which quadrant or on which axis would you find each point?

a. $(-1, 5)$

Since the x-coordinate is negative and the y-coordinate is positive, the point is in Quadrant II.

b. $(0, 3)$

Since the x-coordinate is 0, the point is on the y-axis.

CA Standards Check 3 In which quadrant or on which axis would you find each point?

a. $(-2, 0)$ **b.** $(4, -1)$ **c.** $(-3, -5)$ **d.** $(2.7, 3.6)$

EXERCISES

Standards Practice

For more exercises, see *Extra Skills and Word Problem Practice*.

Alg1 24.3, 25.3

A Practice by Example

Example 1 (page 177)

GO for Help

Name the coordinates of each point on the graph at the right.

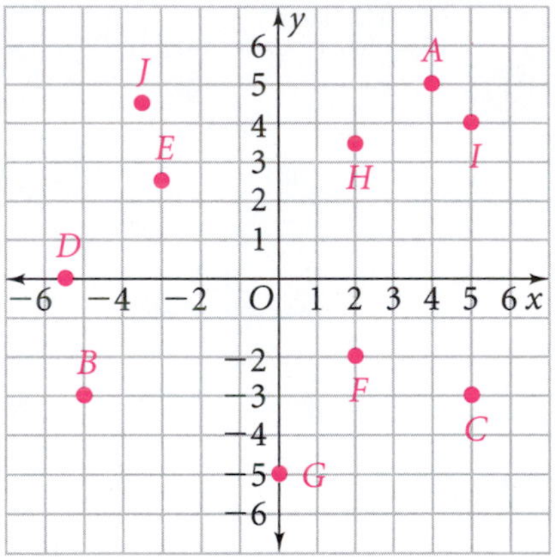

1. A **2.** B

3. C **4.** D

5. E **6.** F

7. G **8.** H

9. I **10.** J

Example 2 (page 177)

Graph the points on the same coordinate plane.

11. $(3, 0)$ **12.** $\left(-1\frac{1}{2}, 2\right)$

13. $(-2, -3)$ **14.** $\left(4, -2\frac{1}{2}\right)$

Example 3 (page 178)

In which quadrant or on which axis would you find each point?

15. $\left(-10\frac{1}{2}, 6\right)$ **16.** $(-12, 0)$ **17.** $(8, -18)$ **18.** $(0, 30)$

B Apply Your Skills

Mental Math Write the coordinates of each point.

19. the point 3 units to the left of the y-axis and 4 units above the x-axis

20. the point 5 units to the right of the y-axis and on the x-axis

21. the point 6 units to the right of the y-axis and 6 units below the x-axis

22. the point on the y-axis and 2 units above the x-axis

Visit: PHSchool.com
Web Code: bae-0401

Complete each statement.

23. If the x-coordinate and the y-coordinate of an ordered pair are positive, the ordered pair is in Quadrant __?__.

24. If the x-coordinate of an ordered pair is negative, and the y-coordinate is positive, the ordered pair is in Quadrant __?__.

25. If the x-coordinate of an ordered pair is 0, the ordered pair is on the __?__-axis.

Math Reasoning **Is each statement *always, sometimes,* or *never true*? If a statement is not always true, give a counterexample.**

26. If $x = y$, then (x, y) is in Quadrant I.

27. If (x, y) is in Quadrant II, then (y, x) is in Quadrant IV.

28. If $x + y = 0$, then (x, y) is in Quadrant II.

Name the coordinates of points *V, W, X, Y,* and *Z*.

29. **30.**

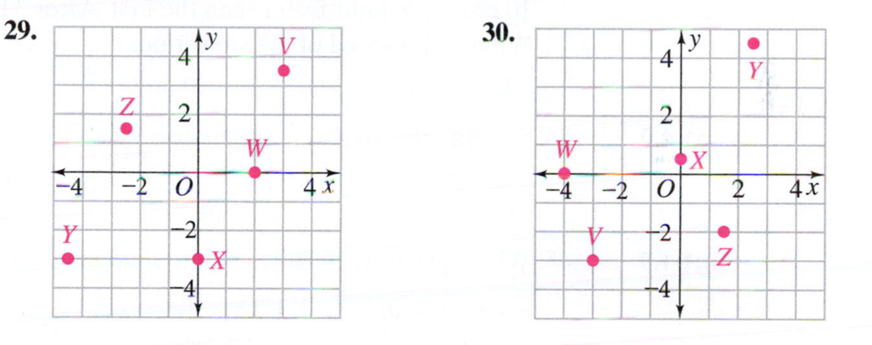

31. **Writing in Math** If $xy = 0$, what do you know about the location of point (x, y) on the coordinate plane? Explain.

Write the coordinates of three points that satisfy each condition.

32. The x-coordinate is the opposite of the y-coordinate.

33. The x-coordinate and the y-coordinate have the same absolute value.

Graph and connect the points in the order given. Connect the last point to the first. Name the figure.

34. $(4, 4), (-1, 1), (2, -4), (7, -1)$

35. $(-3, 0), (0, 5), (3, 0), (0, -5)$

36. $(-2, 1), (2, 4), (5, 0)$

37. $(5, -3), (2, -7), (-6, -1), (-3, 3)$

38. Find the perimeter and area of a rectangle whose vertices have coordinates $(4, 1), (-3, 1), (-3, -2)$, and $(4, -2)$.

39. Find the area of a triangle whose vertices have coordinates $(-1, 2), (-1, -1)$, and $(-6, 2)$.

40. Points with the coordinates $(0, 3), (2, 5), (4, 3)$, and $(2, 1)$ lie on a circle with center $(2, 3)$. Find another circle with center $(2, 3)$, such that there are at least eight points on the circle with integers for the x- and y-coordinates. What are the coordinates of the eight points?

Multiple Choice Practice

For California Standards Tutorials, visit PHSchool.com. Web Code: baq-9045

Alg1 6.0

41. In which quadrant on the coordinate plane does the point (–3, –1) lie?

A I   B II   C III   D IV

Alg1 5.0

42. Leah saved \$16,000 for a car that costs 10,500, plus \$1200 each year for insurance. If Leah buys the car, which inequality can be used to find the maximum number of years she can pay the insurance with her current savings?

A $10{,}500 + 1200x \leq 16{,}000$
B $10{,}500 - 1200x \leq 16{,}000$
C $16{,}000 + 1200x \leq 10{,}500$
D $16{,}000 - 1200x \leq 10{,}500$

Alg1 3.0

43. The solutions of which inequality are $x > 9$ or $x < -1$?

A $|x + 4| < 5$
B $|x + 4| > 5$
C $|x - 4| < 5$
D $|x - 4| > 5$

Alg1 15.0

44. Two boats leave a ramp traveling in opposite directions. The second boat is 10 miles per hour faster than the first. After 3 hours they are 150 miles apart. What is the speed of the slower boat?

A 10 mi/h   B 20 mi/h   C 30 mi/h   D 40 mi/h

Alg1 4.0

45. Simplify the algebraic expression $5(5x - 3) - 2(3x + 1)$.

A $5x - 13$
B $5x - 17$
C $19x - 13$
D $19x - 17$

Alg1 1.0

46. Which property is shown by the following equation?

$-1 + (1 + 0) = (-1 + 1) + 0$

A Inverse Property of Addition
B Identity Property of Addition
C Commutative Property of Addition
D Associative Property of Addition

Mixed Review

GO for Help

Lessons 3-6

47. The ideal weight of a nickel is 0.176 ounce. To check that there are 40 nickels in a roll, a bank weighs the roll and allows for an error of 0.015 ounce in the total weight.

a. Write an absolute value inequality to represent the acceptable weights of a roll of 40 nickels if the wrapper weighs 0.05 ounce.

b. Find the range of acceptable weights.

Lessons 3-4

Solve each inequality.

48. $5x + 2 < 37$

49. $x + 4 > 2x - 4$

50. $8x + 4 - 3x \geq 3x$

51. $7 > -4x - 9$

52. $7(x + 1) \leq 6(x - 1)$

53. $-2 + 5x < 8 - 10x$

Lessons 2-6

Determine the amount of each of the two solutions that must be mixed to make 250 mL of a 40% acid solution. Round to the nearest milliliter.

54. 25% acid, 80% acid

55. 30% acid, 60% acid

56. 15% acid, 75% acid

57. 10% acid, 45% acid

4-2 Relations and Functions

California Content Standards

16.0 Understand the concepts of a relation and a function, determine whether a given relation defines a function, and give pertinent information about given relations and functions. ***Introduce***

17.0 Determine the domain of independent variables and the range of dependent variables defined by a graph or a set of ordered pairs. ***Introduce***

18.0 Determine whether a relation defined by a graph or a set of ordered pairs is a function. ***Introduce, Develop***

What You'll Learn

- To identify functions

... And Why

To determine whether a relation is a function, as in Examples 2 and 3

Check Skills You'll Need

GO for Help Lesson 4-1

Graph each point on a coordinate plane.

1. (2, −4) **2.** (0, 3) **3.** (−1, −2) **4.** (−3, 0)

New Vocabulary

- relation
- domain
- range
- function
- vertical-line test

Identifying Functions

Adult giraffes have heights from 4.25 m to 5.5 m, or about 14 ft to 18 ft.

A **relation** is a set of ordered pairs. The (age, height) ordered pairs below form a relation.

Giraffe Heights

Age (years)	18	16	20	14
Height (meters)	4.0	4.5	5.5	5.0

You can list the set of ordered pairs in a relation using braces.

$$\{(18, 4.0), (16, 4.5), (20, 5.5), (14, 5.0)\}$$

You can also represent a relation using a graph or a *mapping diagram.*

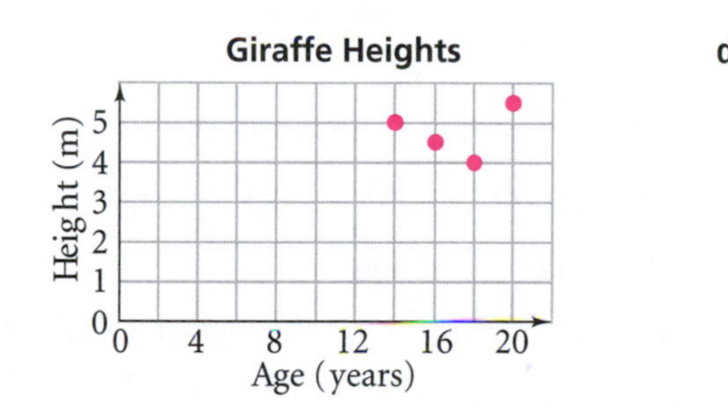

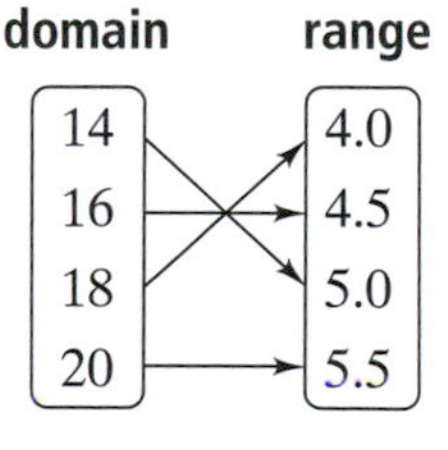

The **domain** of a relation is the set of the first coordinates. The **range** of a relation is the set of second coordinates. The domain of the data above is {14, 16, 18, 20}. The range is {4.0, 4.5, 5.0, 5.5}.

A relation that assigns to each value in the domain exactly one value in the range is called a **function.**

1 EXAMPLE Identifying a Function Given a Table

Find the domain and range of the relation. Is the relation a function?

Running Times

Distance (meters)	100	800	400	200
Time (seconds)	10	107	45	20

domain: {100, 200, 400, 800}
range: {10, 20, 45, 107}

List the values in order. Do not repeat values.

Each value in the domain corresponds to exactly one value in the range.
Yes, the relation is a function.

CA Standards Check 1 Find the domain and range of each relation. Is each relation a function?

a.

x	y
−2	3
3	−1
5	0
−4	3

b.

x	y
−3	−5
6	7
−3	4
8	−2

To make a mapping diagram, list the domain values and the range values in order. Draw arrows from the domain values to their range values.

2 EXAMPLE Using a Mapping Diagram

Find the domain and range of each relation. Use a mapping diagram to determine whether each relation is a function.

a. {(11, −2), (12, −1), (13, −2), (20, 7)}

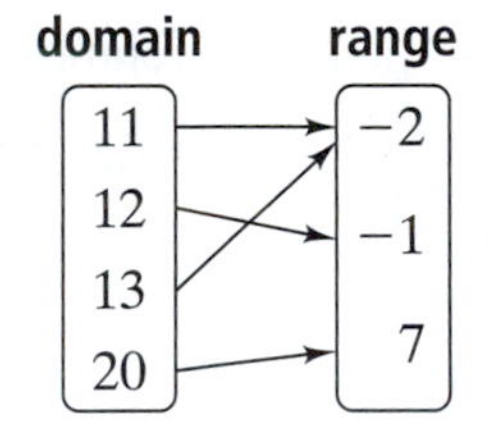

There is no value in the domain that corresponds, or maps, to more than one value of the range.

The relation is a function.

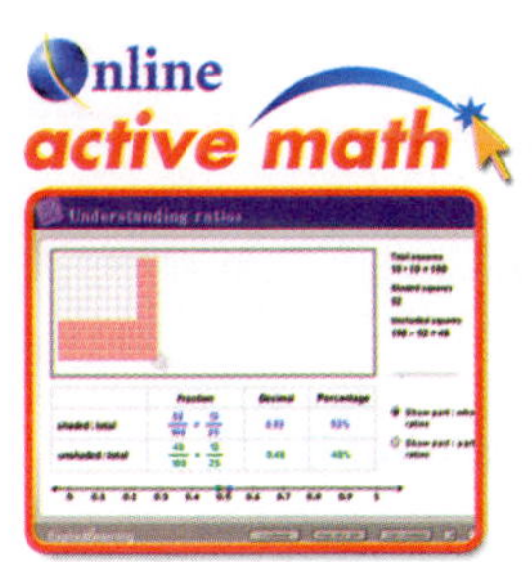

For: Function Activity
Use: Interactive Textbook, 4-2

b. {(−2, −1), (−1, 0), (6, 3), (−2, 1)}

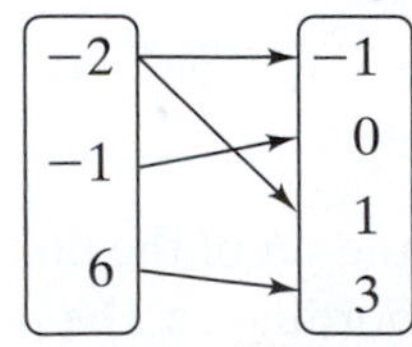

The domain value −2 corresponds to two range values, −1 and 1.

The relation is not a function.

CA Standards Check 2 Find the domain and range of each relation. Use a mapping diagram to determine whether each relation is a function.

a. {(3, −2), (8, 1), (9, 2), (3, 3), (−4, 0)} **b.** {(6.5, 0), (7, −1), (6, 2), (2, 6), (5, −1)}

Another way you can tell whether a relation is a function is to analyze the graph of the relation using the **vertical-line test.** If any vertical line passes through more than one point of the graph, then for some value of x there is more than one value of y. Therefore, the relation is not a function.

3 EXAMPLE Using the Vertical-Line Test

Find the domain and range of each relation. Use the vertical-line test to determine whether each relation is a function.

a. $\{(3, 0), (-2, 1), (0, -1), (-3, 2), (3, 2)\}$

domain: $\{-3, -2, 0, 3\}$

range: $\{-1, 0, 1, 2\}$

Step 1 Graph the ordered pairs on a coordinate plane.

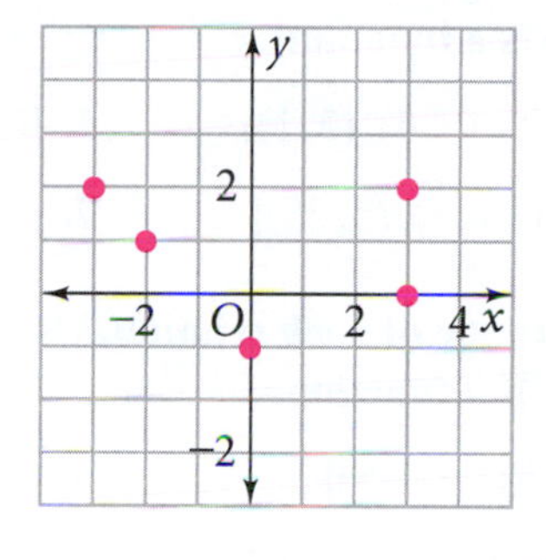

Step 2 Pass a pencil across the graph.

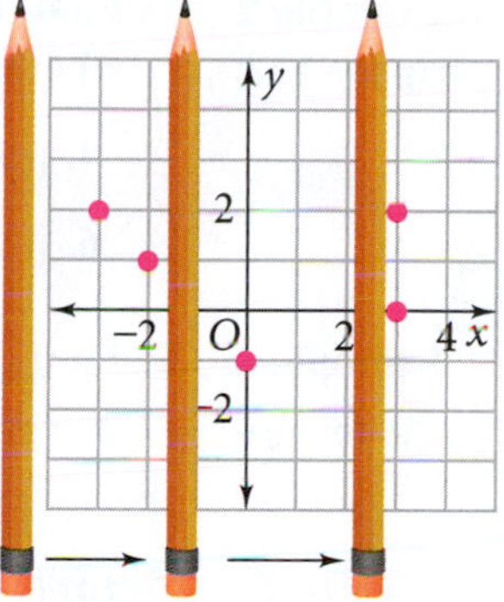

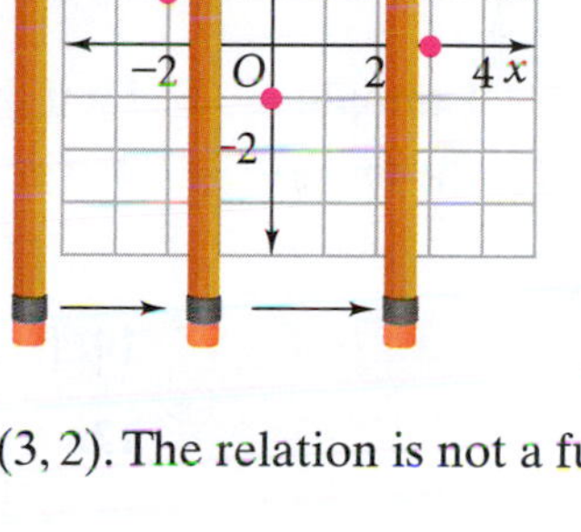

A vertical line passes through (3, 0) and (3, 2). The relation is not a function.

b.

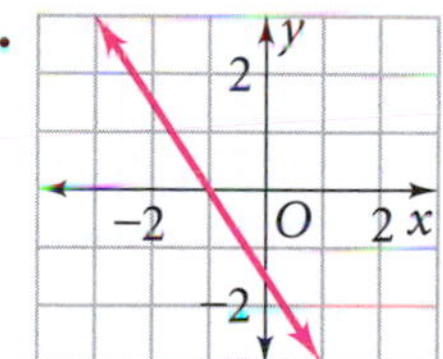

domain: set of all real numbers
range: set of all real numbers

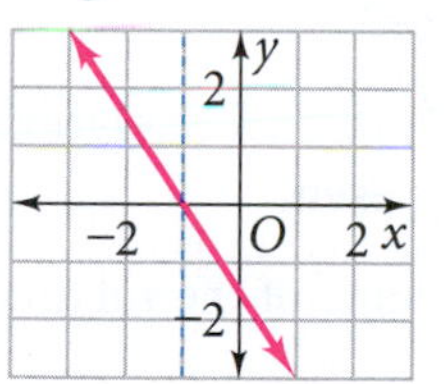

No vertical line intersects the graph at more than one point. The relation is a function.

c.

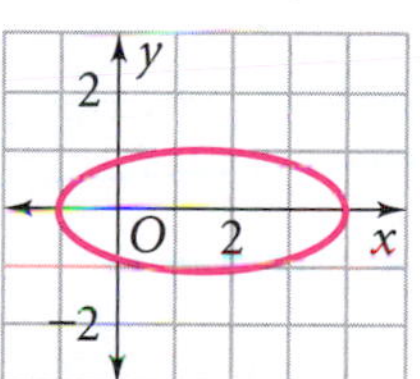

domain: $\{x: -1 \leq x \leq 4\}$
range: $\{y: -1 \leq y \leq 1\}$

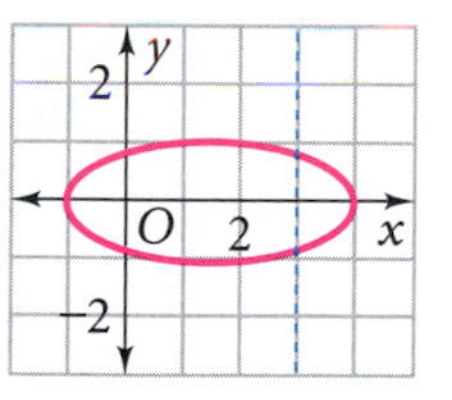

A vertical line intersects the graph at more than one point. The relation is not a function.

For help with set notation, go to the Activity Lab on page 75.

CA Standards Check

3 Find the domain and range of each relation. Use the vertical-line test to determine whether each relation is a function.

a. $\{(0, 2), (1, -1), (-1, 4), (0, -3), (2, 1)\}$

b.

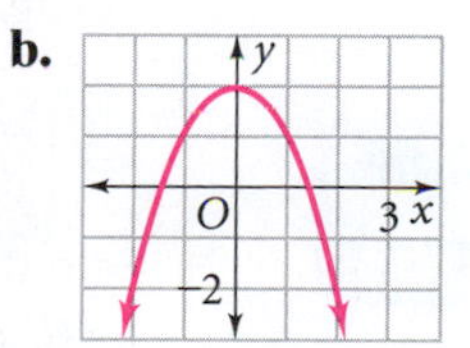

EXERCISES
Standards Practice

For more exercises, see *Extra Skills and Word Problem Practice*.

Alg1 16.0, 17.0, 18.0

A Practice by Example

Example 1 (page 182)

Find the domain and range of each relation. Is each relation a function?

1.

x	y
1	−3
6	−2
9	−1
1	3

2.

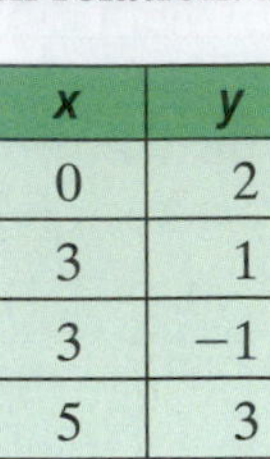

x	y
0	2
3	1
3	−1
5	3

3.

x	y
−4	−4
−1	−4
0	−4
3	−4

Example 2 (page 182)

Find the domain and range of each relation. Use a mapping diagram to determine whether each relation is a function.

4. $\{(3, 7), (3, 8), (3, -2), (3, 4), (3, 1)\}$

5. $\{(6, -7), (5, -8), (1, 4), (5, 5)\}$

6. $\{(0.04, 0.2), (0.2, 1), (1, 5), (5, 25)\}$

7. $\{(4, 2), (1, 1), (0, 0), (1, -1), (4, -2)\}$

Example 3 (page 183)

Find the domain and range of each relation. Use the vertical-line test to determine whether each relation is a function.

8. $\{(2, 5), (3, -5), (4, 5), (5, -5)\}$

9. $\{(5, 0), (0, 5), (5, 1), (1, 5)\}$

10. $\{(3, -1), (-2, 3), (-1, -5), (3, 2)\}$

11. $\{(-2, 9), (3, 9), (-0.5, 9), (4, 9)\}$

12.

13.

14.

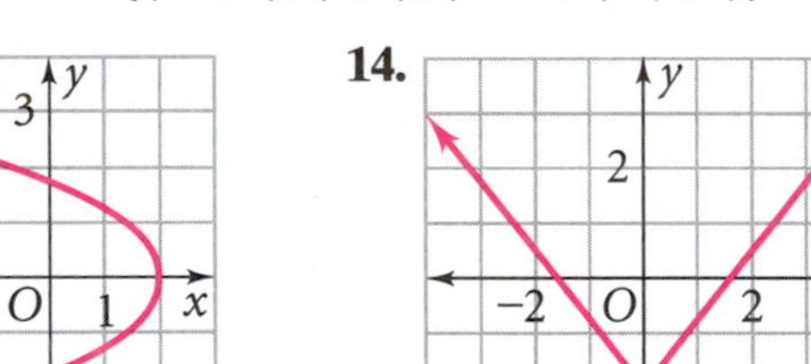

B Apply Your Skills

15. Error Analysis A student thinks that the relation $\{(2, 1), (3, -2), (4, 5), (5, -2)\}$ is not a function because two values in the domain have the same range value. What is the student's error?

16. Make a data table that represents a relation that is *not* a function. Describe what your data might represent.

17. a. Find the domain and range of the relation between grams of fat and number of calories.

Calories Per Serving of Some Common Foods

Food	Grams of Fat	Number of Calories	Food	Grams of Fat	Number of Calories
Whole Milk	8	150	Eggs	6	80
Chicken	4	90	Ham	19	245
Corn	1	70	Broccoli	1	45
Ground Beef	10	185	Cheese	9	115

b. Make a graph of the relation.

c. Is the relation a function? Explain.

Homework Video Tutor

Visit: PHSchool.com
Web Code: bae-0402

Find the domain and range of each function. Use the vertical-line test to determine whether each relation is a function.

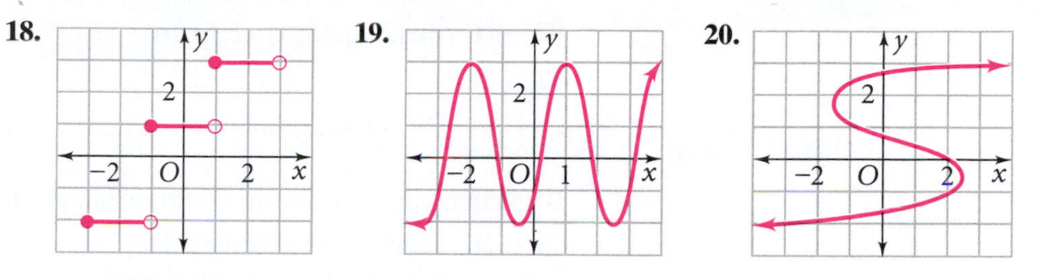

Iguanas

Age (years)	Length (inches)
2	30
4	37
3	31
5	45
4	40

21. Use the data in the table at the left. Is an iguana's length a function of its age? Explain.

For Exercises 22–25 assume that each variable has a different value. Determine whether each relation is a function.

22. $\{(a, b), (b, a), (c, c), (e, d)\}$

23. $\{(b, b), (c, d), (d, c), (c, a)\}$

24. $\{(c, e), (c, d), (c, b)\}$

25. $\{(a, b), (b, c), (c, d), (d, e)\}$

Math Reasoning **Is each statement *always*, *sometimes*, or *never* true? Explain.**

26. A relation is a function.

27. A function is a relation.

28. If the graph of a relation intersects the x-axis exactly twice, then the relation is *not* a function.

29. If the graph of a relation intersects the y-axis exactly twice, then the relation is *not* a function.

C Challenge

30. **Critical Thinking** Can the graph of a function be a horizontal line? A vertical line? Explain why or why not.

31. **Critical Thinking** If a relation is a function, can the number of domain values be less than the number of range values? Explain why or why not.

32. How many different mappings exist between two domain values $\{x_1, x_2\}$ and two range values $\{y_1, y_2\}$? Justify your answer with mapping diagrams.

Multiple Choice Practice

For California Standards Tutorials, visit PHSchool.com. Web Code: baq-9045

Alg1 16.0, 17.0

33. Which of the following statements is true about the relation below?

Mount Rushmore Temperatures (°F)

At Base of Mountain	At Top of Mountain
80	72
65	58
93	84
98	91
74	69

(A) The domain is {65, 74, 80, 93, 98}.

(B) The range is {58, 69, 72, 84, 91}.

(C) The relation is a function.

(D) All of the statements are true.

Alg1 18.0

34. Which ordered pair could be removed from the relation below to change it into a function?

$\{(2,3), (3,2), (2,5), (5,4), (1,6), (6,-1), (25,31)\}$

Ⓐ $(2,5)$ Ⓑ $(25,31)$ Ⓒ $(6,-1)$ Ⓓ $(3,2)$

Alg1 24.2, 24.3

35. Which statement about the following sentence is false?

If a statement has only one counterexample, then the statement is false.

Ⓐ The conclusion is, "a statement has only one counterexample."
Ⓑ The hypothesis is, "the statement is true."
Ⓒ The sentence is false; you need more than one counterexample to prove that a statement is false.
Ⓓ All the statements are false.

Mixed Review

GO for Help

Lesson 3-3

Solve each inequality.

36. $\frac{j}{3} \leq -4$ **37.** $\frac{r}{2} > 7$ **38.** $5 \geq -\frac{m}{6}$ **39.** $-1 > -\frac{s}{8}$

40. $4b < -16$ **41.** $2c \leq 10$ **42.** $27 \geq -9w$ **43.** $-24 > -3h$

Lesson 3-1

Is each number a solution of $-4x + 5 \geq 9$?

44. 4 **45.** 0 **46.** -1 **47.** -2

Lesson 2-5

48. Two taxis travel in opposite directions. The speed of the first taxi is 10 miles per hour faster than the second. After 3 hours, they are 150 miles apart. Find their rates.

Checkpoint Quiz 1

Lessons 4-1 through 4-2

For Exercises 1–7, use the graph at the right. Name the point with the given coordinates.

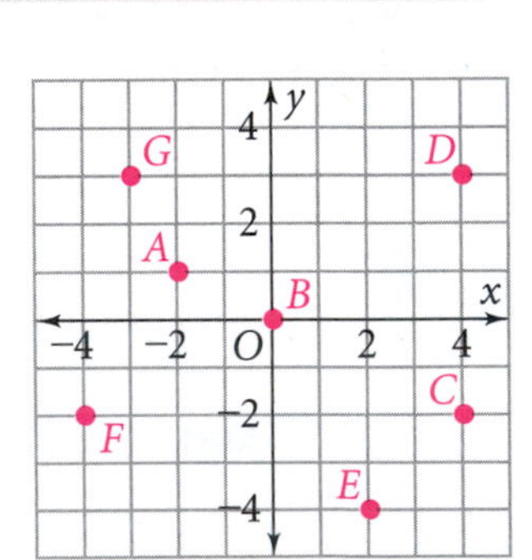

1. $(4, -2)$ **2.** $(4, 3)$

3. $(2, -4)$ **4.** $(-2, 1)$

Name the coordinates of each point.

5. B **6.** F **7.** G

Determine whether each relation is a function.

8.

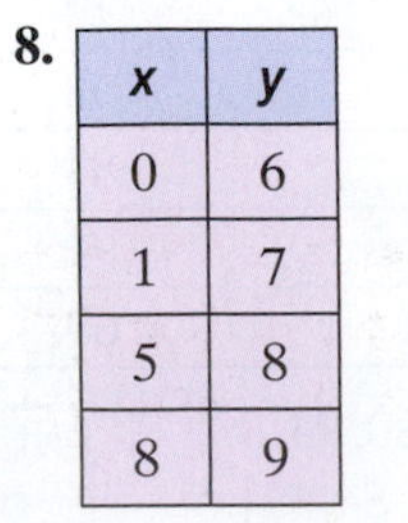

x	y
0	6
1	7
5	8
8	9

9.

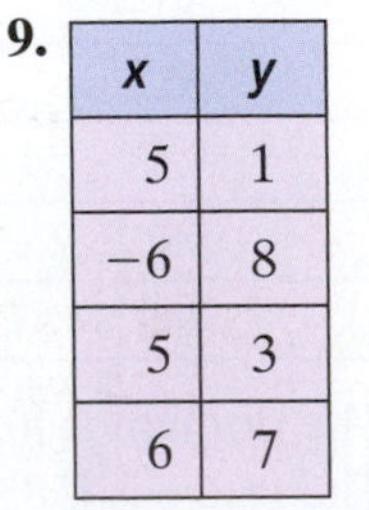

x	y
5	1
−6	8
5	3
6	7

10.

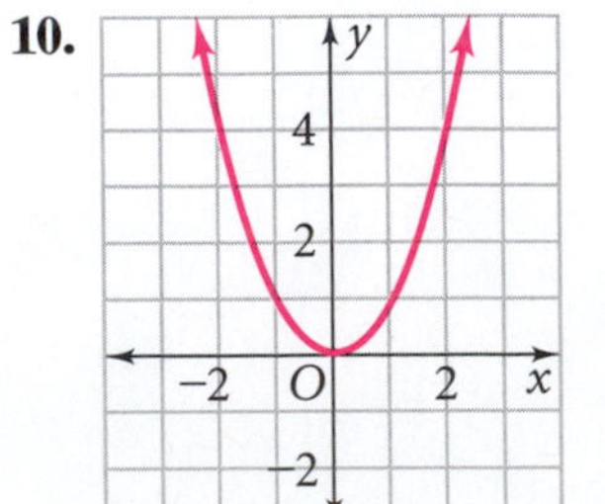

Function Rules, Tables, and Graphs

California Content Standards

16.0 Understand the concepts of a relation and a function, determine whether a given relation defines a function, and give pertinent information about given relations and functions. ***Develop***

17.0 Determine the domain of independent variables and the range of dependent variables defined by a graph or a symbolic expression. ***Develop***

18.0 Determine whether a relation defined by a symbolic expression is a function and justify the conclusion. ***Master***

What You'll Learn

- To model functions using rules, tables, and graphs
- To identify symbolic expressions as functions

. . . And Why

To find the cost of making CDs, as in Example 3

Check Skills You'll Need

GO for Help Lesson 4-2

Determine whether each relation is a function.

1.

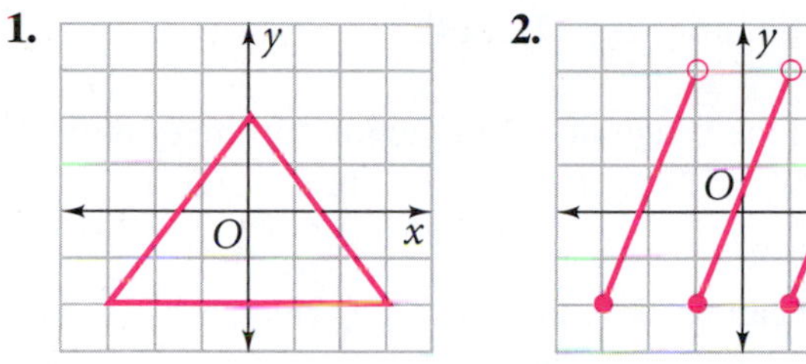

2.

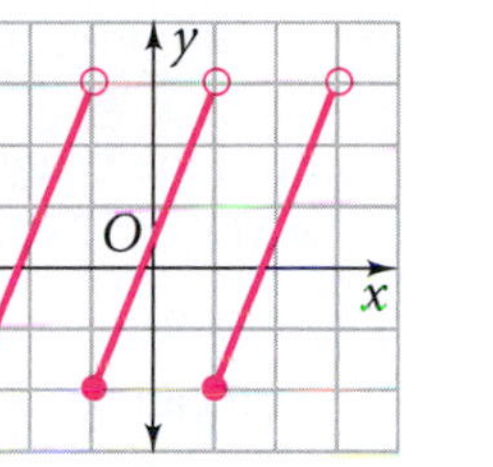

3.

New Vocabulary

- function rule
- function notation
- independent variable
- dependent variable

Function Rules to Tables and Graphs

Words and Notations Used With a Function

Domain	Range
input	output
x	$f(x)$
x	y

A **function rule** is an equation that describes a function. You can think of a function rule as an input-output machine.

If you know the input values, you can use a function rule to find the output values. The output values depend on the input values.

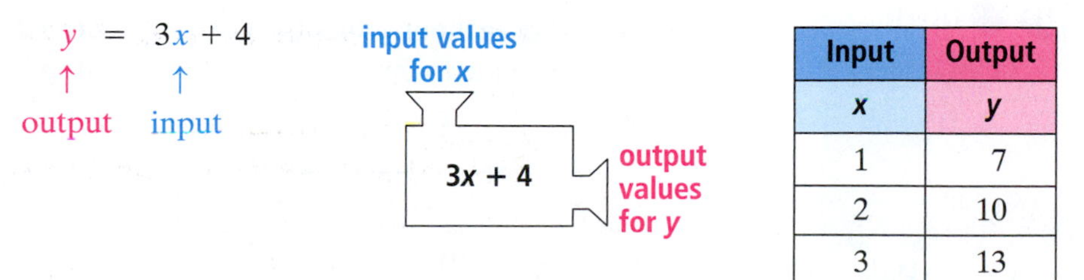

Input	Output
x	**y**
1	7
2	10
3	13

Another way to write the function $y = 3x + 4$ is $f(x) = 3x + 4$. A function is in **function notation** when you use $f(x)$ to indicate the outputs. You read $f(x)$ as "f of x" or "f is a function of x." The notations $g(x)$ and $h(x)$ also indicate functions of x.

1 EXAMPLE Evaluating a Function Rule

Study Tip

You can think of the notation $f(6)$ as "Replace x with 6 to find the value of the function when $x = 6$."

a. Evaluate $f(x) = -3x - 10$ for $x = 6$.

$f(x) = -3x - 10$

$f(6) = -3(6) - 10$ Substitute 6 for x.

$f(6) = -18 - 10$ Simplify.

$f(6) = -28$

b. Evaluate the function rule $f(a) = -3a + 5$ to find the range of the function for the domain $\{-3, 1, 4\}$.

$f(a) = -3a + 5$	$f(a) = -3a + 5$	$f(a) = -3a + 5$
$f(-3) = -3(-3) + 5$	$f(1) = -3(1) + 5$	$f(4) = -3(4) + 5$
$f(-3) = 14$	$f(1) = 2$	$f(4) = -7$

The range is $\{-7, 2, 14\}$.

CA Standards Check **1** Find the range of each function for the domain $\{-2, 0, 5\}$.

a. $f(x) = 2x + 1$ **b.** $y = -x + 2$ **c.** $g(t) = t^2 - 4$

You can model functions using rules, tables, and graphs. A function rule shows how the variables are related. A table identifies specific input and output values of the function. A graph gives a visual picture of the function.

The inputs are values of the **independent variable**. The outputs are the corresponding values of the **dependent variable**.

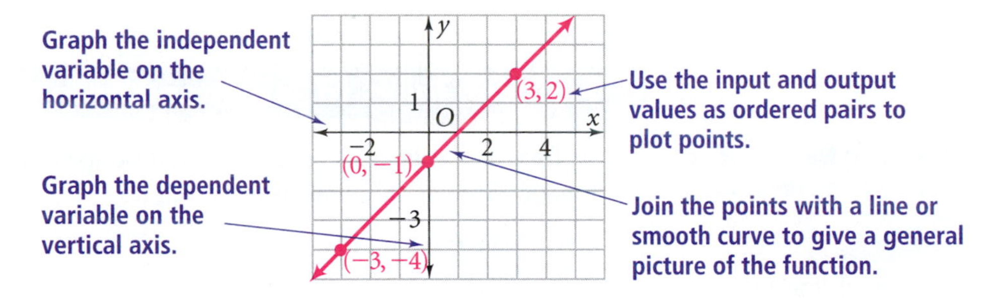

2 EXAMPLE Three Views of a Function

Model the function rule $y = -\frac{1}{2}x + 1$ using a table of values and a graph.

Step 1 Choose input values for x. Evaluate to find y.

Step 2 Plot points for the ordered pairs.

Step 3 Connect the points.

x	$y = -\frac{1}{2}x + 1$	(x, y)
−4	$y = -\frac{1}{2}(-4) + 1 = 3$	(−4, 3)
0	$y = -\frac{1}{2}(0) + 1 = 1$	(0, 1)
2	$y = -\frac{1}{2}(2) + 1 = 0$	(2, 0)

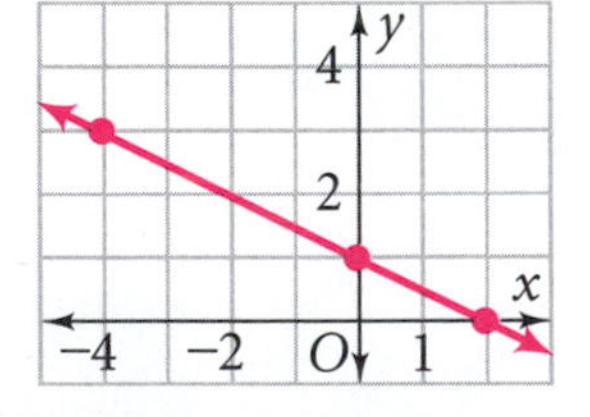

GO Online

Video Tutor Help

Visit: PHSchool.com

Web Code: bae-0775

CA Standards Check **2** Model the rule $f(x) = 3x + 4$ with a table of values and a graph.

When you draw a graph for a real-world situation, choose appropriate intervals for the units on the axes. Be sure the intervals are equal. Also, if the data are positive numbers, use only the first quadrant.

3 EXAMPLE Application

Suppose your group recorded a CD. Now you want to copy and sell it. One company charges \$250 for making a master CD and designing the art for the cover. There is also a cost of \$3 to burn each CD. The total cost $P(c)$ depends on the number of CDs c burned. Use the function rule $P(c) = 250 + 3c$ to make a table of values and a graph.

c	$P(c) = 250 + 3c$	$(c, P(c))$
100	$250 + 3(100) = 550$	(100, 550)
200	$250 + 3(200) = 850$	(200, 850)
300	$250 + 3(300) = 1150$	(300, 1150)
500	$250 + 3(500) = 1750$	(500, 1750)

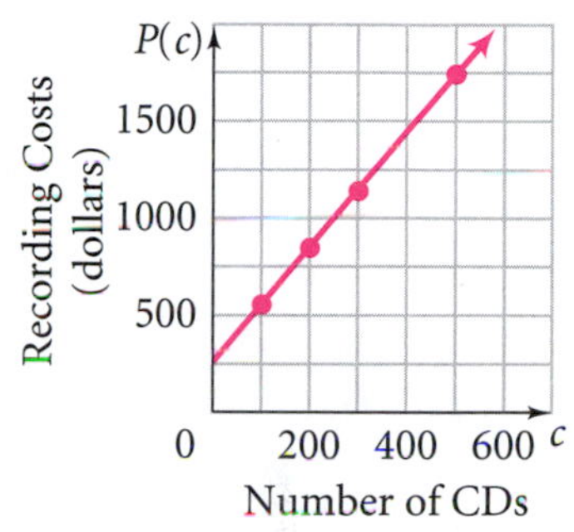

CA Standards Check 3 **a.** Another company charges \$300 for making a master and designing the art. It charges \$2.50 for burning each CD. Use the function rule $P(c) = 300 + 2.5c$. Make a table of values and a graph.

b. Your band decides to use the second company. You plan on making between 100 and 300 CDs. Find a reasonable range for this situation.

Some functions have graphs that are not straight lines. You can graph a function as long as you know its rule. After you have graphed the ordered pairs that you have calculated from a rule, join the points with a smooth line or curve.

4 EXAMPLE Graphing Functions

Graph the function $y = |x| + 1$. Then find the domain and range.

Make a table of values.

x	$f(x) = \lvert x \rvert + 1$	$(x, f(x))$
−3	$\lvert -3 \rvert + 1 = 4$	(−3, 4)
−1	$\lvert -1 \rvert + 1 = 2$	(−1, 2)
0	$\lvert 0 \rvert + 1 = 1$	(0, 1)
1	$\lvert 1 \rvert + 1 = 2$	(1, 2)
3	$\lvert 3 \rvert + 1 = 4$	(3, 4)

Then graph the data.

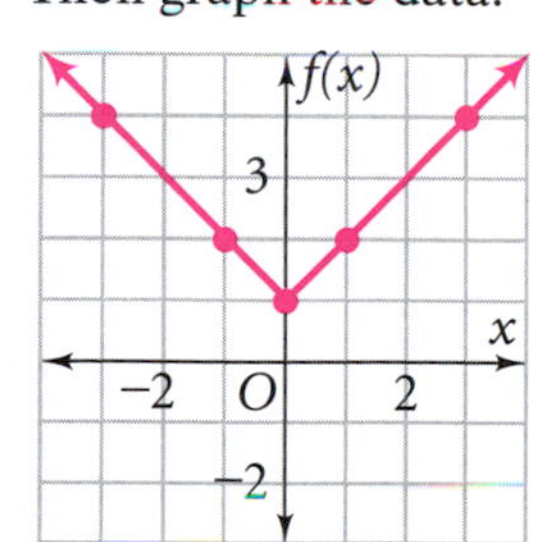

domain: set of all real numbers

range: $\{y: y \geq 1\}$. **Use the letter y to describe the range.**

CA Standards Check 4 Make a table of values and graph each function. Then find the domain and range.

a. $f(x) = |x| - 1$ **b.** $y = x^2 - 1$

Identifying Symbolic Expressions as Functions

You can determine whether a relation is a function by analyzing its symbolic expression. The relation must assign exactly one range to each domain value. To find the domain of a function defined by a symbolic expression, determine for which numbers the rule is not meaningful. For example, a rule is not meaningful when its denominator equals zero, since dividing by zero is undefined.

5 EXAMPLE Identifying Functions

Find the domain of each relation. Determine whether each relation is a function.

a. $y = 3x - 2$

Multiplication and subtraction are defined for all real numbers, so the domain is the set of real numbers. For every real number x, the value of $3x - 2$ is a unique real number, so the relation is a function.

b. $y = \frac{1}{3 + x}$

The relation is undefined when $3 + x = 0$, or $x = -3$. So the domain is $\{x: x \neq -3\}$. The value of $\frac{1}{3 + x}$ is a unique real number for every number in the domain, so the relation is a function.

c. $x = y^2$

The value of y^2 is always positive or equal to 0, so the domain is $\{x: x \geq 0\}$. The relation assigns two y-values, 1 and -1, to $x = 1$, so it is not a function.

CA Standards Check **5** Find the domain of each relation. Determine whether each relation is a function.

a. $y = -2x + 1$ **b.** $y = \frac{1}{x - 5}$ **c.** $x = |y|$

EXERCISES

For more exercises, see *Extra Skills and Word Problem Practice.*

Standards Practice

Alg1 16.0, 17.0, 18.0

A Practice by Example

Example 1 (page 188)

Find the range of each function for the domain {−4, 1, 3}.

1. $y = x + 7$ **2.** $f(x) = 11x - 1$ **3.** $g(x) = x^2$ **4.** $h(x) = -4x$

5. $y = 15 - x$ **6.** $f(n) = n^2 + 2$ **7.** $g(t) = \frac{1}{4}t$ **8.** $h(a) = -3a + 5$

Example 2 (page 188)

GO for Help

Model each rule with a table of values and a graph.

9. $f(x) = -3x$ **10.** $g(x) = -3x + 1$ **11.** $f(x) = -3x - 2$

12. $y = 2x - 7$ **13.** $f(x) = 8 - x$ **14.** $y = 5 + 4x$

15. $h(x) = \frac{1}{4}x$ **16.** $y = 4x$ **17.** $y = x + 4$

Example 3 (page 189)

18. Juan charges $3.50 per hour for baby-sitting.

a. Write a rule to describe how the amount of money M earned is a function of the number of hours h spent baby-sitting.

b. Make a table of values.

c. Graph the values and join the points with a line.

d. **Estimation** Use the graph to estimate how long it will take Juan to earn $15.

19. The figure at the right is a regular pentagon. The function $P(\ell) = 5\ell$ describes the perimeter of a regular pentagon with side length ℓ.
   a. Make a table of values for $\ell = 1, 2, 3,$ and 4.
   b. Graph the function.

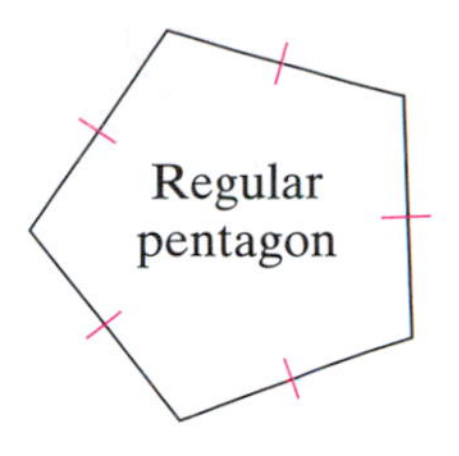

Example 4 (page 189)

Graph each function. Then find the domain and range.

20. $y = |x|$
21. $y = |x| + 2$
22. $g(x) = x^2$
23. $f(x) = x^2 - 1$
24. $f(x) = |x| + 3$
25. $y = x^2 + 3$
26. $y = |x| - 4$
27. $g(x) = -x^2 - 1$
28. $h(x) = -x^2 + 2$

Example 5 (page 190)

Find the domain of each relation. Determine whether each relation is a function.

29. $y = 5x$
30. $y = -x + 2$
31. $x = |y| - 2$
32. $y = \frac{1}{x}$
33. $y = \frac{1}{x - 3}$
34. $y = \frac{4x}{x - 1}$
35. $y = x^2$
36. $x = y^2 + 3$
37. $x = 2|y|$

B Apply Your Skills

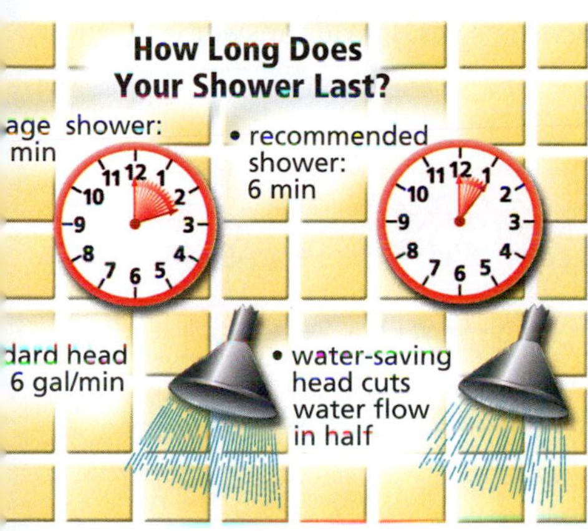

Opinion Research Corp.

38. The equation $w = 6m$ models the gallons of water w used by a standard shower head for a shower that takes m minutes. The function $w = 3m$ models the water-saving shower head.
   a. Suppose you take a 6-minute shower using a water-saving shower head. How much water do you save compared to an average shower with a standard shower head?
   b. Graph both functions on the same coordinate plane.
   c. How much water did you use during your last shower?
   d. How did you find your answer?

39. a. Find the domain of $x = -y^2$.
   b. **Writing** Determine whether or not the relation $x = -y^2$ is a function. Explain.

Find the range of each function for the domain {−2, 0, 3.5}.

40. $f(x) = 3x + 1$
41. $g(x) = 3x - 5$
42. $f(s) = -3s + 4$
43. $g(v) = |v| - 5$
44. $h(n) = 12 - n$
45. $g(w) = 5(w - 2)$

46. a. Make a table for the perimeters of the rectangles formed by each set of blue tiles.

Fig. 1 Fig. 2 Fig. 3 Fig. 4

   b. The perimeter $P(t)$ is a function of the number of tiles t. Write a rule for the data in your table and graph the function.

Graph each function. Then find the domain and range.

47. $f(x) = \frac{3}{4}x + 7$
48. $y = x^2 - 4x + 4$
49. $y = |2x|$
50. $y = x + \frac{1}{2}$
51. $f(x) = 7 - 5x$
52. $f(x) = \left|\frac{1}{2}x\right|$
53. $f(x) = \left|\frac{1}{2}x\right| + 1$
54. $y = 1 - x^2$
55. $f(x) = -5x^2$

Visit: PHSchool.com
Web Code: bae-0403

56. **a.** Graph each function on the same coordinate plane.

i. $f(x) = |x| + 2$ **ii.** $f(x) = |x| + 4$ **iii.** $f(x) = |x| - 3$

b. **Critical Thinking** In the function $y = |x| + b$, how does changing the value of b change the graph of the function?

57. **a.** Graph each function on the same coordinate plane.

i. $f(x) = |2x|$ **ii.** $f(x) = |0.5x|$ **iii.** $f(x) = |3x|$

b. **Critical Thinking** In the function $y = |ax|$, how does changing the value of a change the graph of the function?

C Challenge

58. The function $s(x)$, sometimes called the signum function, is defined as

$$s(x) = \begin{cases} 1 \text{ if } x > 0 \\ 0 \text{ if } x = 0 \\ -1 \text{ if } x < 0 \end{cases}$$

For example, $s(17) = 1$, $s(0) = 0$, and $s(-32) = -1$.

a. Evaluate $s(3.77)$, $s(0.003)$, $s(-1.5)$, and $s(-2300)$.

b. The domain of the function is all real numbers. What is the range?

c. Make a table of values and graph the function.

d. **Make a Conjecture** Do you think $s(a + b) = s(a) + s(b)$? First, test some values of a and b. If your answer is *yes*, justify your answer. If your answer is *no*, give a counterexample.

Multiple Choice Practice

For California Standards Tutorials, visit PHSchool.com. Web Code: baq-9045

Alg1 16.0

59. Which of the following is NOT represented by the function $f(x) = 2x - 1$?

Ⓐ $\{(1, 1), (2, 3), (3, 5), (4, 7)\}$

Ⓑ

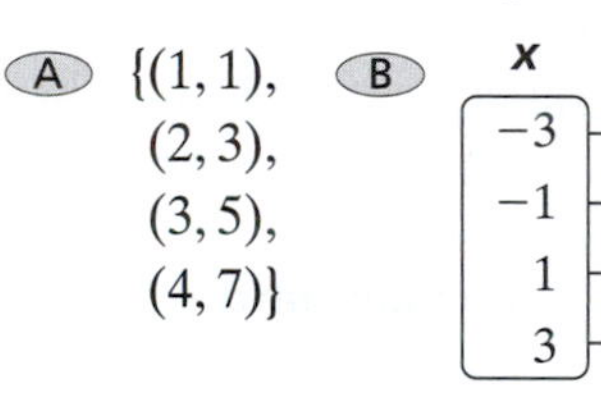

Ⓒ

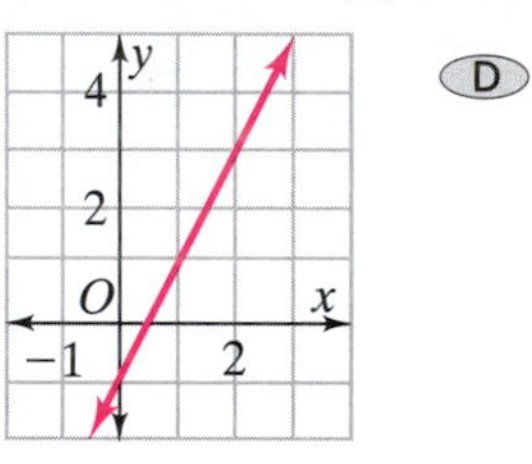

Ⓓ

x	f(x)
−5	−2
−1	0
3	2
7	4

Alg1 17.0

60. Which of the following functions has a domain that includes 0?

Ⓐ $f(x) = \sqrt{x - 5}$ Ⓑ $f(x) = \frac{5}{\sqrt{x}}$ Ⓒ $f(x) = \frac{1}{5 - x}$ Ⓓ $f(x) = \frac{1}{x}$

Mixed Review

GO for Help

Lesson 4-2 **Find the domain and range of each relation.**

61. $\{(2, 7), (1, 3), (-4, 6), (-1, 0), (0, -5)\}$

62. $\{(3, 1), (5, 6), (-2, 1), (-5, 6), (4, -1)\}$

63. $\{(-3.5, 8), (0.4, 3), (6.9, 0), (-7, 1.1)\}$

64. $\{(1, 1), (1, 2), (1, 3), (1, 4), (1, 5)\}$

Lesson 3-5 **For each situation write and graph an inequality.**

65. all real numbers a that are less than -3 or greater than 5

66. all real numbers b that are at most 0 or at least 4

67. all real numbers c that are less than -6 or greater than -2

Vocabulary Builder

Relation and Function

The words *relation* and *function* have an everyday meaning in addition to a mathematical meaning. Understanding their everyday meanings may help you distinguish between relations and functions in mathematics.

A *relation* is a connection or significant association between two or more things.

A *function* is a relation in which one thing is dependent on another.

In both the mathematical and everyday meanings, a function is a particular type of relation.

EXAMPLE

Determine whether the relationship between each pair of entities is best described as a *relation* or a *function*. Explain.

a. Rhonda, Rhonda's sibling

Relation; Rhonda and her sibling are related because they have the same parents, but neither depends on the other.

b. the size of a balloon, the amount of air inside the balloon

Function; the size of a balloon depends on the amount of air inside it.

EXERCISES

Determine whether the relationship between each pair of entities is best described as a *relation* or a *function*. Explain.

1. the thickness of a dictionary, the number of pages in a dictionary

2. domain: {1, 2, 3, 4, 5}, range: {0}

3. a car, the car's license plate number

4. domain: {0}, range: {1, 2, 3, 4, 5}

5. the amount of energy you have one day, the amount of sleep you got the night before

Complete each sentence.

6. __?__ is a function of nutrition.

7. The amount of sunlight outside is a function of __?__.

8. __?__ is a function of the number of goals.

9. The weight of your hiking backpack is a function of __?__.

Is each mathematical object *sometimes*, *always*, or *never* a function? Explain.

10. the graph of a line

11. a scatter plot of 20 data points

12. the graph of a circle

13. an absolute value graph

4-4 Writing a Function Rule

California Content Standards

16.0 Give pertinent information about given relations and functions. ***Develop***

What You'll Learn

- To write a function rule given a table or a real-world situation

. . . And Why

To write a function rule for finding profit, as in Example 3

Check Skills You'll Need

GO for Help Lesson 4-3

Model each rule with a table of values.

1. $f(x) = 5x - 1$ **2.** $y = -3x + 4$ **3.** $g(t) = 0.2t - 7$

4. $y = 4x + 1$ **5.** $f(x) = 6 - x$ **6.** $c(d) = d + 0.9$

Evaluate each function rule for $n = 2$.

7. $A(n) = 2n - 1$ **8.** $f(n) = -3 + n - 1$ **9.** $g(n) = 6 - n$

Writing Function Rules

You can write a rule for a function by analyzing a table of values. Look for a pattern relating the independent and dependent variables.

1 EXAMPLE Writing a Rule From a Table

Write a function rule for each table.

a.

x	f(x)
1	5
2	6
3	7
4	8

Ask yourself, "What can I do to 1 to get 5, to 2 to get 6, . . . ?"

You add 4 to each x-value to get the $f(x)$ value.

Relate $f(x)$ equals x plus 4

Write $f(x)$ $=$ x $+$ 4

A rule for the function is $f(x) = x + 4$.

b.

x	y
1	1
3	9
6	36
9	81

Ask yourself, "What can I do to 3 to get 9, to 6 to get 36, . . . ?"

You multiply each x-value times itself to get the $f(x)$ value.

Relate y equals x times itself

Write y $=$ x^2

A rule for the function is $y = x^2$.

CA Standards Check

1 Write a function rule for each table.

a.

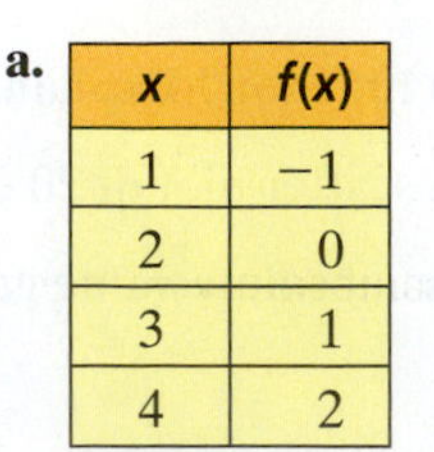

x	f(x)
1	−1
2	0
3	1
4	2

b.

x	y
1	2
2	4
3	6
4	8

c.

x	y
1	3
2	4
3	5
4	6

The Museum of Science in Boston, Massachusetts, had an exhibit called The Walk Through Computer™ 2000.

2 EXAMPLE Application

The exhibit at the left is a scale model of a desktop computer. It is about 20 times the size of a desktop computer of typical size.

a. Write a function rule to describe this relationship.

Relate larger size is 20 times typical size

Define Let n = length of typical computer.

Let $L(n)$ = length of larger size shown in museum exhibit.

Write $L(n) = 20 \cdot n$

The function rule $L(n) = 20n$ describes the relationship between the size of the computer in the exhibit and a typical computer.

b. A space bar on a computer of typical size is $4\frac{3}{8}$ in long. About how long is the space bar in the exhibit?

$L(n) = 20 \cdot n$

$L(n) = 20 \cdot 4\frac{3}{8}$ **Substitute $4\frac{3}{8}$ for n.**

$L(n) = 87\frac{1}{2}$ **Simplify.**

The space bar in the exhibit is about $87\frac{1}{2}$ in. long.

CA Standards Check 2 **a.** A carpenter buys finishing nails by the pound. Each pound of nails costs \$1.19. Write a function rule to describe this relationship.
b. How much do 12 lb of finishing nails cost?

When you write a function, the dependent variable is defined in terms of the independent variable. In Example 3 below, profit depends on the number of lawns mowed, so profit is a function of the number of lawns mowed.

3 EXAMPLE Application

Problem Solving Tip

If you need to find a pattern or write an equation, setting up a table can help you get organized.

Suppose you borrow money from a relative to buy a lawn mower that costs \$245. You charge \$18 to mow a lawn. Write a rule to describe your profit $P(n)$ as a function of the number of lawns mowed n. Which equation best describes the situation?

(A) $P(n) = 18n$

(B) $P(n) = 18 + 245$

(C) $P(n) = 18n - 245$

(D) $P(n) = 245 + 18n$

Relate total profit is \$18 times lawns mowed minus cost of mower

Write $P(n) = 18 \cdot n - 245$

The function rule $P(n) = 18n - 245$ describes your profit as a function of the number of lawns mowed. So C is the correct answer.

CA Standards Check 3 Suppose you buy a word-processing software package for \$199. You charge \$15 per hour for word processing. Write a rule to describe your profit as a function of the number of hours you work.

EXERCISES

Standards Practice

For more exercises, see *Extra Skills and Word Problem Practice.*

Alg1 16.0, 25.3

A Practice by Example

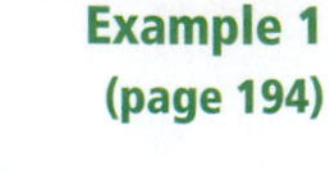

Example 1 (page 194)

GO for Help

Match each table with its rule.

1. $y = 4x$

2. $y = x - 4$

3. $y = -4 - x$

A.

x	y
-2	-6
-1	-5
0	-4
1	-3

B.

x	y
-1	-4
-2	-8
-3	-12
-4	-16

C.

x	y
-1	-3
0	-4
1	-5
2	-6

Write a function rule for each table.

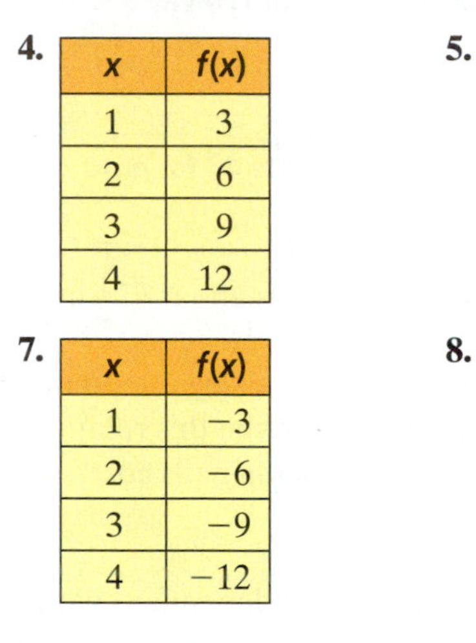

4.

x	$f(x)$
1	3
2	6
3	9
4	12

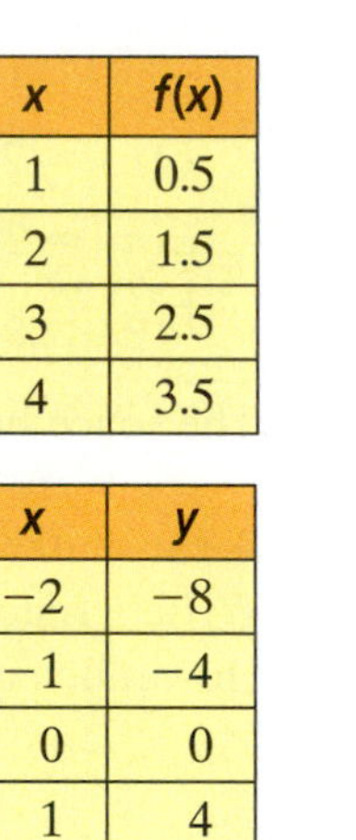

5.

x	$f(x)$
1	0.5
2	1.5
3	2.5
4	3.5

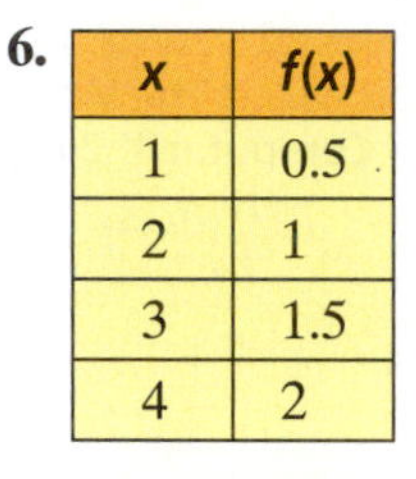

6.

x	$f(x)$
1	0.5
2	1
3	1.5
4	2

7.

x	$f(x)$
1	-3
2	-6
3	-9
4	-12

8.

x	y
-2	-8
-1	-4
0	0
1	4

9.

x	y
-8	64
-4	16
0	0
4	16
8	64

Example 2 (page 195)

Write a function rule for each situation.

10. the total cost $t(c)$ of c ounces of cinnamon if each ounce costs \$.79

11. the total distance $d(n)$ traveled after n hours at a constant speed of 45 miles per hour

12. the height $f(h)$ of an object in feet when you know the height h in inches

13. a worker's earnings $e(n)$ for n hours when the worker's hourly wage is \$6.37

14. the area $A(n)$ of a square when you know the length n of a side

15. the volume $V(n)$ of a cube when you know the length n of a side

16. the area $A(r)$ of a circle with radius r

Example 3 (page 195)

17. At a supermarket salad bar, the price of a salad depends on its weight. Salad costs \$.19 per ounce.

a. Write a rule to describe the function.

b. How much would an 8-ounce salad cost?

18. In 2006, the price of mailing a letter was \$.39 for the first ounce or part of an ounce and \$.24 for each ounce or part of an ounce after the first ounce.

a. Write a rule to describe the function.

b. How much did mailing a 4-ounce letter cost?

B Apply Your Skills

Write a function rule for each table.

19.

Distance (km)	Distance (m)
0.5	500
1.0	1000
1.5	1500
2.0	2000

20.

Inches	Centimeters
1	2.54
2	5.08
3	7.62
4	10.16

Buy additional books at our regular low Club price of $10.00 per book. To become a Book Express member, just buy 2 additional books within the first year. You may resign your membership at any time.

Use the advertisement at the left for Exercises 21–22.

21. a. Write a rule to find the total cost $C(a)$ for all the books a person buys through Book Express. Let a represent the number of additional books bought (after the first 6 books).

b. Suppose a person buys 9 books in all. Find the total cost.

c. Evaluate the function for $a = 6$. What does the output represent?

22. A bookstore sells the same books for an average price of $6 each.

a. Write a function rule to model the total cost $C(b)$ of books bought at the bookstore. Let b represent the number of books bought.

b. Evaluate your function for $b = 12$. What does the output represent?

c. You plan to buy 12 books. What is your average cost per book as a member of Book Express?

d. Is it less expensive to buy 12 books through the club or at the bookstore? Explain.

23. Use the table at the right.

a. Identify the dependent and independent variables.

b. Write a function rule that models the data in the table.

c. How many gallons of water would you use for 7 loads of laundry?

d. Critical Thinking In one month, you used 442 gallons of water for laundry. How many loads did you wash?

Water Used for Laundry

1 load	34 gallons
2 loads	68 gallons
3 loads	102 gallons
4 loads	136 gallons

24. Writing What advantage(s) can you see of having a function rule instead of a table of values for a function?

25. Write a function rule that models a real-world situation. Evaluate your function for an input value and explain what the output represents.

26. Math Reasoning The graph of $f(x) = \frac{1}{2}x$ is shown at the right. Which statement about the function is always true?

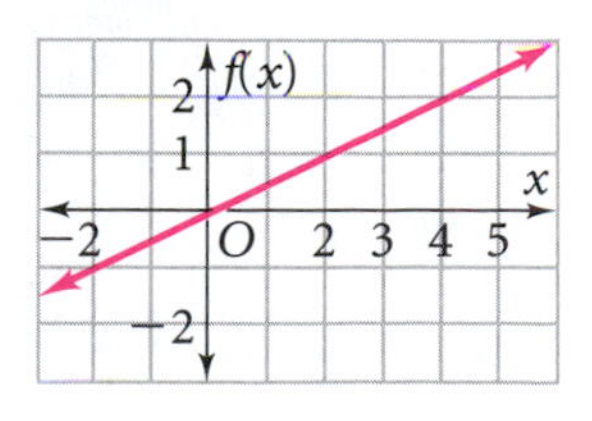

Ⓐ The value of y is always less than the value of x.

Ⓑ When the value of x is positive, the value of y is negative.

Ⓒ As the value of x increases, the value of y increases.

Ⓓ The value of y is always different from the value of x.

Visit: PHSchool.com
Web Code: bae-0404

Make a table of values for each graph. Use the table to write a function rule.

27. 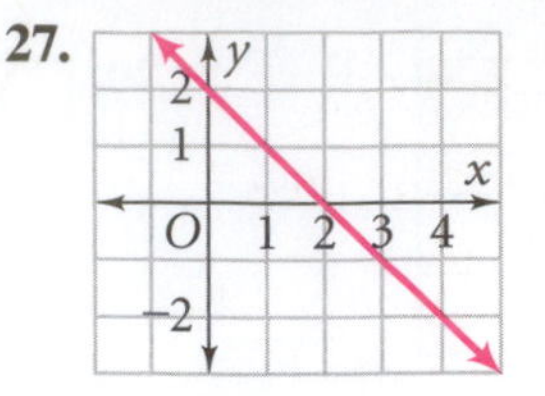

28. 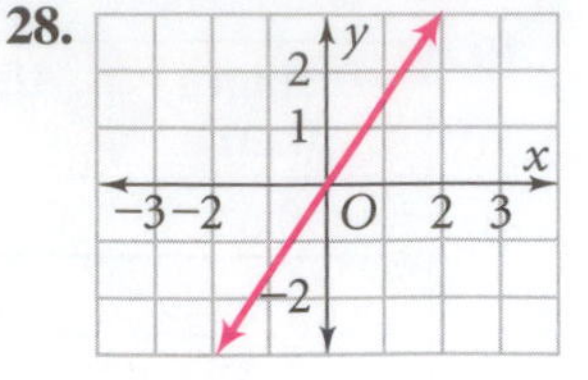

29. 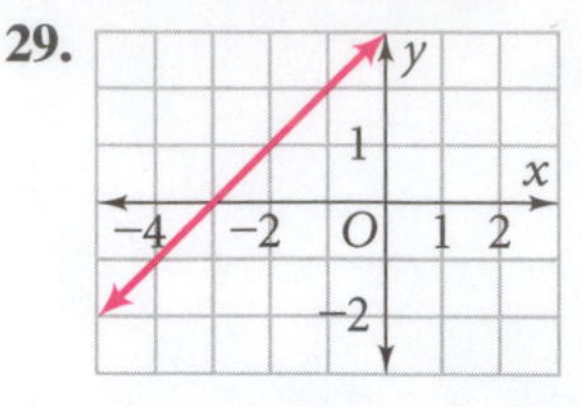

For a guide to solving Exercise 30, see p. 200.

30. You go to dinner and decide to leave a 15% tip for the server. You had \$45 when you came to the restaurant.

a. Make a table that shows how much money you would have left after buying a \$12, an \$18, a \$24, and a \$28 meal.

b. Write a function that relates the cost of the meal c to the amount of money you have left $A(c)$.

c. Graph the function.

31. a. Make a table for the area of the largest shaded triangle in each figure.

b. Write a function rule that relates the height of each figure h to the area of the triangle $A(h)$.

c. Graph the function.

Fig. 1 Fig. 2 Fig. 3

Challenge

Write a function rule for each table.

32. 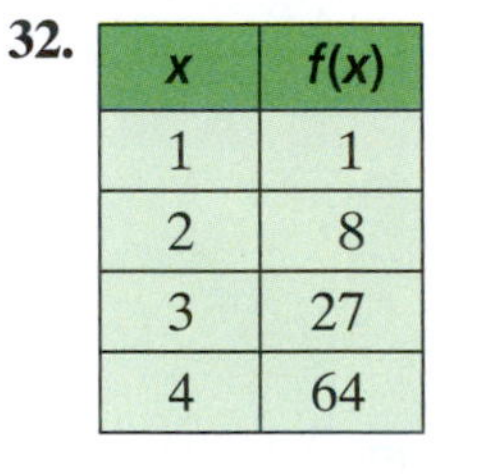

x	$f(x)$
1	1
2	8
3	27
4	64

33.

x	$f(x)$
−1	1
−2	8
−3	27
−4	64

34.

x	$f(x)$
−1	0
−2	7
−3	26
−4	63

35. A truck rental company charges \$44 per day for renting a medium-sized truck. There is also a charge of \$.38 per mile.

a. Write a function rule $c(m)$ to model the cost of renting a truck for a day and driving m miles.

b. Evaluate your function rule for $m = 70$ and $m = 120$.

c. You return the truck to the rental company and pay \$58.44 (excluding tax). How far did you drive?

d. Suppose you need to rent a truck for two days. You plan to drive 150 miles each day. How much will this cost?

The pickles found in burgers are made by soaking cucumbers in 10% brine concentration for several days and then storing them in vinegar.

36. The table at the right shows the relationship between the amount of pickling salt added to a gallon of water and the brine concentration, which is the percent of salt by weight.

a. Write a function rule to describe the relationship between salt volume and brine concentration.

b. Write a function rule to describe the relationship between salt weight and brine concentration.

Brine Strength

Salt Volume (cup)	Salt Weight (oz)	Brine Concentration (percent salt)
$\frac{1}{3}$	3.3	2.31
$\frac{1}{2}$	4.95	3.465
$\frac{2}{3}$	6.6	4.62
$\frac{3}{4}$	7.425	5.1975
1	9.9	6.93

Multiple Choice Practice

For California Standards Tutorials, visit PHSchool.com. Web Code: baq-9045

Alg1 16.0

37. Which is the graph of the function rule $f(x) = \frac{1}{2}x - 2$?

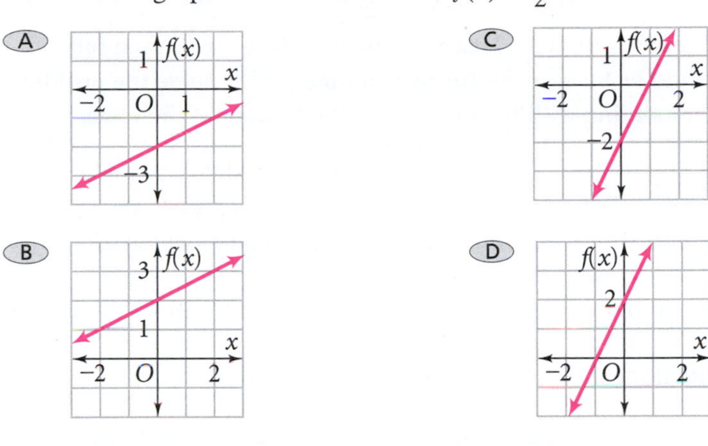

Alg1 18.0

38. For the graph $y = |x| + 1$, which of the following statements is true?

(A) The graph represents a function whose range is all real numbers.

(B) The graph represents a function that assigns to each member of the domain exactly one member in the range.

(C) The graph does not represent a function.

(D) The graph represents neither a function nor a relation.

Mixed Review

GO for Help

Lesson 4-3

Model each rule with a table of values and a graph.

39. $f(x) = x - 3$ **40.** $y = 5 - x$ **41.** $g(x) = -x + 3$

42. $f(x) = 2x - 3$ **43.** $y = |2x| - 3$ **44.** $y = 2x^2 - 3$

Find the range of each function for the domain $\{-1, 0.5, 3.7\}$.

45. $f(x) = x - 6$ **46.** $g(x) = -4x + 1$ **47.** $y = |x| - 1$

48. $s(t) = 5t^2$ **49.** $f(x) = 6x + 1$ **50.** $y = -3(x + 4)$

Lesson 2-4

51. The figure at the right shows how much juice you can get from some fruits.

a. What is the minimum number of oranges needed to make a cup of orange juice? What is the maximum number of oranges needed? (*Hint:* 16 tablespoons = 1 cup)

b. Suppose you buy a bag of 6 lemons and a bag of 5 limes. What is the most juice you can expect to get from these bags of fruit?

How Much Juice Is in an Average Fruit?

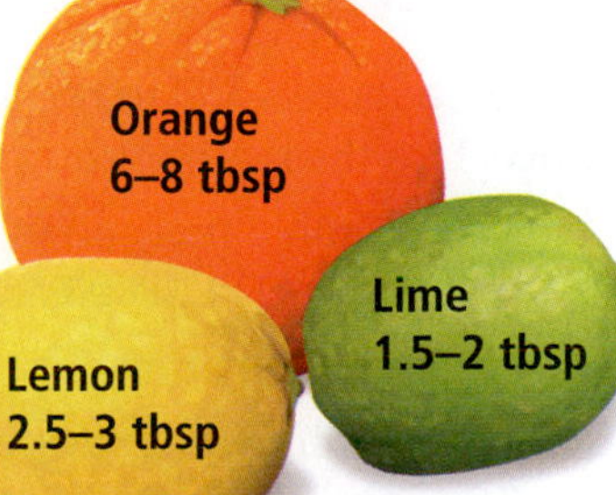

GPS Guided Problem Solving

For Use With Page 198, Exercise 30

16.0 Give pertinent information about given relations and functions. *Develop*

Understanding Math Problems **Read the exercise below and then follow along with Raymond as he uses the four-corner method to solve the problem. Check your understanding with the exercise at the bottom of the page.**

You go to dinner and decide to leave a 15% tip for the server. You had $45 when you came to the restaurant.

a. Make a table that shows how much money you would have left after buying a $12, an $18, a $24, and a $28 meal.

b. Write a function that relates the cost of the meal c to the amount of money you have left $A(c)$.

c. Graph the function.

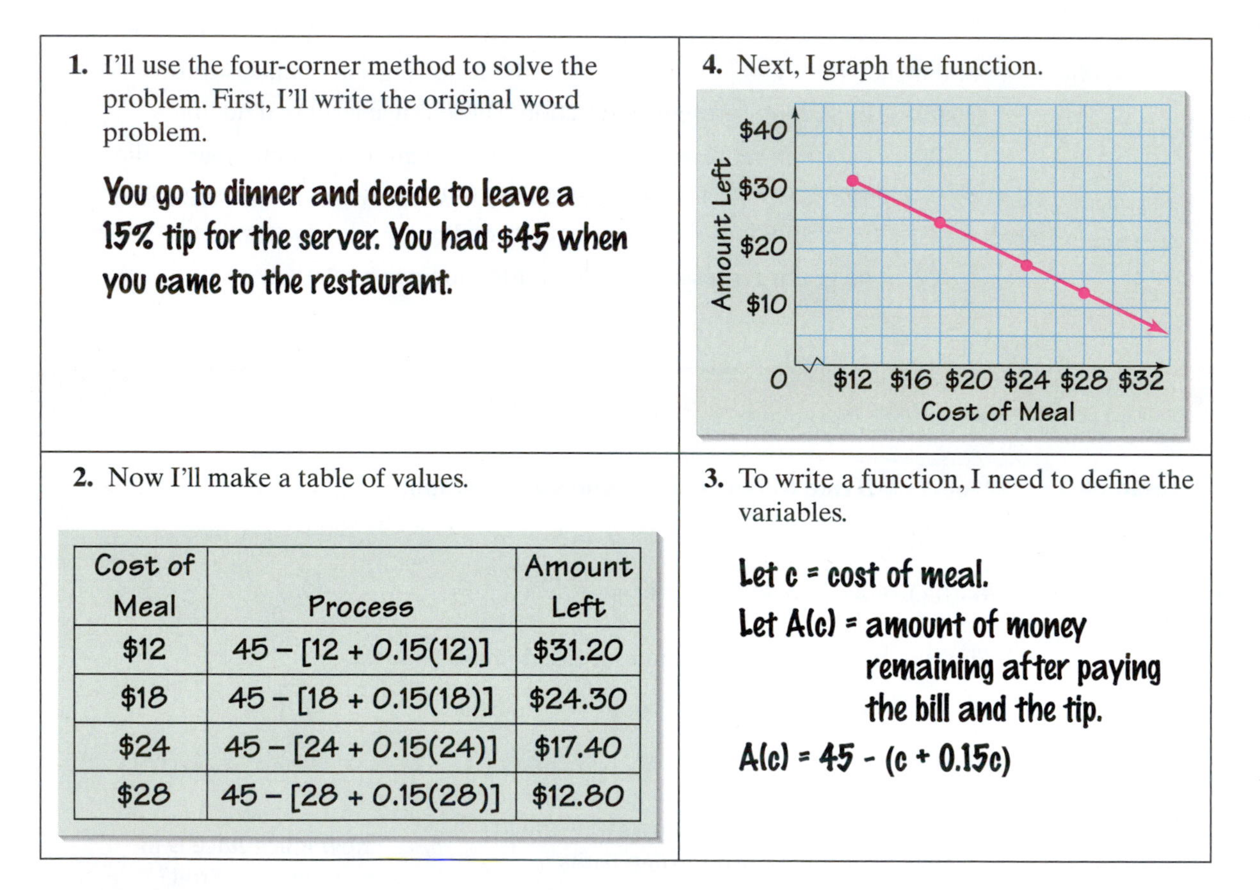

1. I'll use the four-corner method to solve the problem. First, I'll write the original word problem.

You go to dinner and decide to leave a 15% tip for the server. You had $45 when you came to the restaurant.

2. Now I'll make a table of values.

Cost of Meal	Process	Amount Left
$12	45 – [12 + 0.15(12)]	$31.20
$18	45 – [18 + 0.15(18)]	$24.30
$24	45 – [24 + 0.15(24)]	$17.40
$28	45 – [28 + 0.15(28)]	$12.80

3. To write a function, I need to define the variables.

Let c = cost of meal.

Let A(c) = amount of money remaining after paying the bill and the tip.

$A(c) = 45 - (c + 0.15c)$

4. Next, I graph the function.

EXERCISE

Suppose it costs $50 to register your car, and you pay 7% tax on the purchase price. Use the method shown above to organize your work.

a. Make a table that shows the total registry and tax costs for cars that cost $6000, $8000, $10,000, and $12,000.

b. Graph the function.

c. Write a function to describe the situation.

4-5 Direct Variation

California Content Standards

15.0 Apply algebraic techniques to solve rate problems. ***Develop***
16.0 Give pertinent information about given functions. ***Develop***

What You'll Learn

- To write an equation of a direct variation
- To use ratios and proportions with direct variations

. . . And Why

To write a direct variation relating to weather, as in Example 3

Check Skills You'll Need

GO for Help Lesson 2-4

Solve each proportion.

1. $\frac{5}{8} = \frac{x}{12}$ **2.** $\frac{4}{9} = \frac{n}{45}$ **3.** $\frac{25}{15} = \frac{y}{3}$

4. $\frac{7}{n} = \frac{35}{50}$ **5.** $\frac{8}{d} = \frac{20}{36}$ **6.** $\frac{14}{18} = \frac{63}{n}$

New Vocabulary • direct variation • constant of variation for direct variation

Writing the Equation of a Direct Variation

CA Standards Investigation Direct Variation

As you watch a movie, 24 individual pictures, or frames, flash on the screen each second. Here are three ways you can model the relationship between the number of frames $f(s)$ and the number of seconds s.

Table

s number of seconds	$f(s)$ number of frames
1	24
2	48
3	72
4	96
5	120

Graph

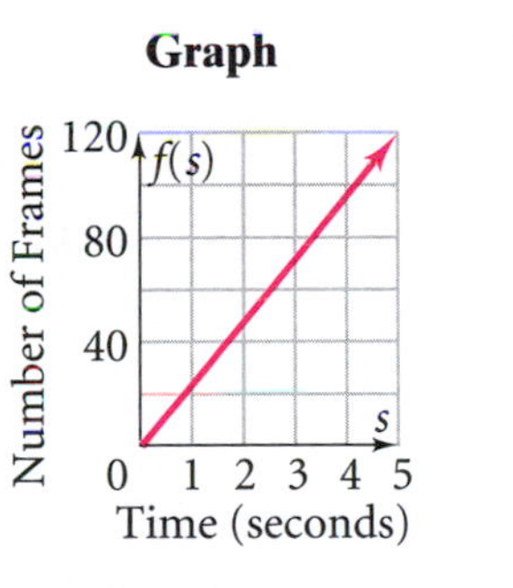

Function Rule

$f(s) = 24s$

1. As the number of seconds doubles, what happens to the number of frames?

2. Find the ratio $\frac{\text{number of frames}}{\text{number of seconds}}$ for each pair of data in the table.

3. For every increase of 1 second on the horizontal axis of the graph, what is the increase on the vertical axis?

4. What do you notice about your answers to Questions 2 and 3 and the coefficient of s in the function rule?

5. a. What number of frames corresponds to $s = 0$?
b. What is the ordered pair on the graph for the seconds and number of frames when $s = 0$?

The table in the investigation shows the number of frames of a movie that are projected over various lengths of time. The ratio $\frac{\text{number of frames}}{\text{time}} = 24$, which is constant. The number of frames is proportional to the time and 24 is the constant of variation.

Definition **Direct Variation**

A function in the form $y = kx$, where $k \neq 0$, is a **direct variation.** The **constant of variation for direct variation** k is the coefficient of x. The variables y and x are said to vary directly with each other.

Vocabulary Tip

Constant means *remaining the same.* Constant of variation means changing at the *same* rate.

For $y = kx$, y is a function of x. If $x = 0$, then $y = 0$, so the graph of a direct variation is a line that passes through (0, 0). To tell whether an equation represents a direct variation, solve for y. If the equation can be written in the form $y = kx$, where $k \neq 0$, it represents a direct variation.

1 EXAMPLE Is an Equation a Direct Variation?

Is each equation a direct variation? If it is, find the constant of variation.

a. $5x + 2y = 0$

$2y = -5x$ Subtract $5x$ from each side.

$y = -\frac{5}{2}x$ Divide each side by 2.

The equation has the form $y = kx$, so the equation is a direct variation. The constant of variation is $-\frac{5}{2}$.

b. $5x + 2y = 9$

$2y = 9 - 5x$ Subtract $5x$ from each side.

$y = \frac{9}{2} - \frac{5}{2}x$ Divide each side by 2.

The equation cannot be written in the form $y = kx$. It is not a direct variation.

CA Standards Check 1 Is each equation a direct variation? If it is, find the constant of variation.

a. $7y = 2x$ **b.** $3y + 4x = 8$ **c.** $y - 7.5x = 0$

To write an equation for a direct variation, you first find the constant of variation k using a point, other than the origin, that lies on the graph of the equation. Then use the value of k to write an equation.

Video Tutor Help
Visit: PHSchool.com
Web Code: bae-0775

2 EXAMPLE Writing an Equation Given a Point

Write an equation of the direct variation that includes the point (4, −3).

$y = kx$ Start with the function form of a direct variation.

$-3 = k(4)$ Substitute 4 for x and −3 for y.

$-\frac{3}{4} = k$ Divide each side by 4 to solve for k.

$y = -\frac{3}{4}x$ Write an equation. Substitute $-\frac{3}{4}$ for k in $y = kx$.

An equation of the direct variation is $y = -\frac{3}{4}x$.

CA Standards Check 2 Write an equation of the direct variation that includes the point (−3, −6).

Lightning can reach a maximum speed of about 1.4×10^8 m/s.

You can use a direct variation to describe a real-world situation in which the dependent variable varies directly with the independent variable.

3 EXAMPLE Application

Your distance from lightning varies directly with the time it takes you to hear thunder. If you hear thunder 10 seconds after you see lightning, you are about 2 miles from the lightning. Write an equation for the relationship between time and distance.

Relate The distance varies directly with the time. When $x = 10, y = 2$.

Define Let x = the number of seconds between your seeing lightning and your hearing thunder.

Let y = your distance in miles from the lightning.

Write

$y = kx$ — Use the general form of a direct variation.

$2 = k(10)$ — Substitute 10 for x and 2 for y.

$\frac{1}{5} = k$ — Divide each side by 10 to solve for k.

$y = \frac{1}{5}x$ — Write an equation. Substitute $\frac{1}{5}$ for k in $y = kx$.

The equation $y = \frac{1}{5}x$ relates the time x in seconds it takes you to hear the thunder to the distance y in miles you are from the lightning.

CA Standards Check

3. A recipe for a dozen corn muffins calls for 1 cup of flour. The number of muffins varies directly with the amount of flour you use. Write a direct variation for the relationship between the number of cups of flour and the number of muffins.

Proportions and Equations of Direct Variations

You can rewrite a direct variation $y = kx$ as $\frac{y}{x} = k$. When two sets of data vary directly, the ratio $\frac{y}{x}$ is the constant of variation. It is the same for each data pair.

Online active math

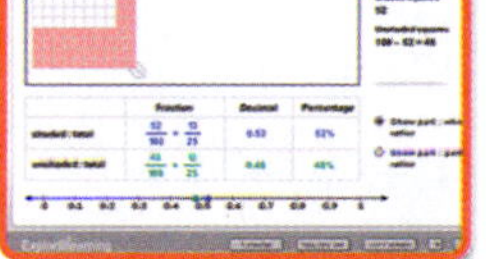

For: Direct Variation Activity
Use: Interactive Textbook, 4-5

4 EXAMPLE Direct Variations and Tables

For each table, use the ratio $\frac{y}{x}$ to tell whether y varies directly with x. If it does, write an equation for the direct variation.

a.

x	y	$\frac{y}{x}$
−3	2.25	$\frac{2.25}{-3} = -0.75$
1	−0.75	$\frac{-0.75}{1} = -0.75$
4	−3	$\frac{-3}{4} = -0.75$
6	−4.5	$\frac{-4.5}{6} = -0.75$

Yes, the constant of variation is −0.75. The equation is $y = -0.75x$.

b.

x	y	$\frac{y}{x}$
2	−1	$\frac{-1}{2} = -0.5$
4	1	$\frac{1}{4} = 0.25$
6	3	$\frac{3}{6} = 0.5$
9	4.5	$\frac{4.5}{9} = 0.5$

No, the ratio $\frac{y}{x}$ is not the same for all pairs of data.

4 For the data in each table, tell whether y varies directly with x. If it does, write an equation for the direct variation.

a.

x	y
−2	3.2
1	2.4
4	1.6

b.

x	y
4	6
8	12
10	15

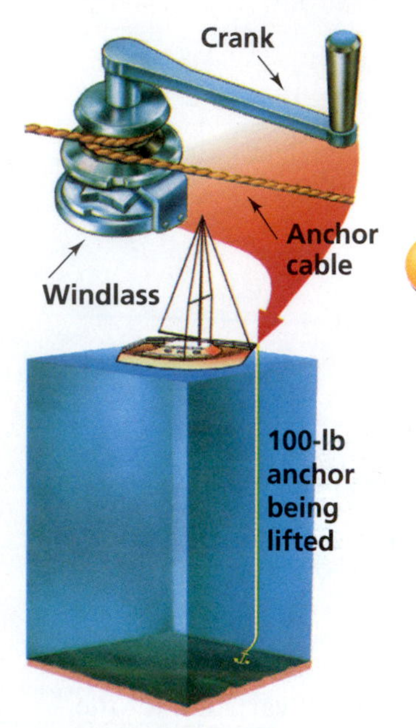

A windlass is a winch turned by a crank. It is used in a water well and to raise an anchor on a boat.

In a direct variation, the ratio $\frac{y}{x}$ is the same for all pairs of data where $x \neq 0$. So the proportion $\frac{y_1}{x_1} = \frac{y_2}{x_2}$ is true for the ordered pairs (x_1, y_1) and (x_2, y_2), where neither x_1 nor x_2 are zero. You can rewrite a proportion as an equation of direct variation.

5 EXAMPLE Application

The force you must apply to lift an object is proportional to the object's weight. You would need to apply 0.625 lb of force to a windlass to lift a 28-lb weight. How much force would you need to lift 100 lb?

Relate $\frac{\text{force}}{\text{weight}} = \frac{0.625}{28}$, which is about 0.0223.

Define Let n = the force you need to lift 100 lb.

Write Let w = the weight and f = the force.

$f = 0.0223w$ — Write an equation.

$f = 0.0223(100)$ — Substitute 100 for w.

$f = 2.23$ — Simplify.

You need about 2.2 lb of force to lift 100 lb.

CA Standards Check 5 Suppose a second windlass requires 0.5 lb of force to lift an object that weighs 32 lb. How much force would you need to lift 160 lb?

EXERCISES

Standards Practice

For more exercises, see *Extra Skills and Word Problem Practice.*

Alg1 15.0, 16.0

A Practice by Example

Example 1 (page 202)

GO for Help

Is each equation a direct variation? If it is, find the constant of variation.

1. $2y = 5x + 1$ **2.** $8x + 9y = 10$ **3.** $-12x = 6y$

4. $y + 8 = -x$ **5.** $5x - 6y = 0$ **6.** $-4 + 7x + 4 = 3y$

7. $-x = 10y$ **8.** $0.7x - 1.4y = 0$ **9.** $\frac{1}{2}x + \frac{1}{3}y = 0$

Example 2 (page 202)

Write an equation of the direct variation that includes the given point.

10. $(1, 5)$ **11.** $(5, 1)$ **12.** $(-8, 10)$ **13.** $(-5, -9)$

14. $(-2, 3)$ **15.** $(-6, 1)$ **16.** $(3, -4)$ **17.** $(6, -8)$

18. $(-6, 8)$ **19.** $(-5, -10)$ **20.** $(12, -8)$ **21.** $(35, 7)$

Example 3 (page 203)

Define the variables. Then write a direct variation to model each relationship.

22. The perimeter of a regular octagon varies directly with the length of one side of the octagon.

23. When you have a job that pays an hourly wage, the amount you earn varies directly with the number of hours you work. Suppose you earn \$7.10/hour working at the library.

Example 4 (page 203)

For the data in each table, tell whether y varies directly with x. If it does, write an equation for the direct variation.

24.

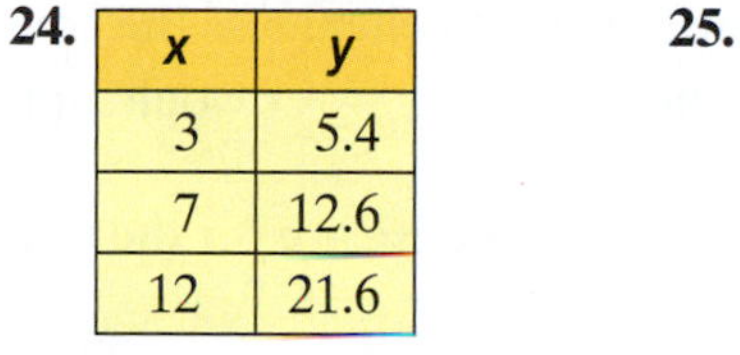

x	y
3	5.4
7	12.6
12	21.6

25.

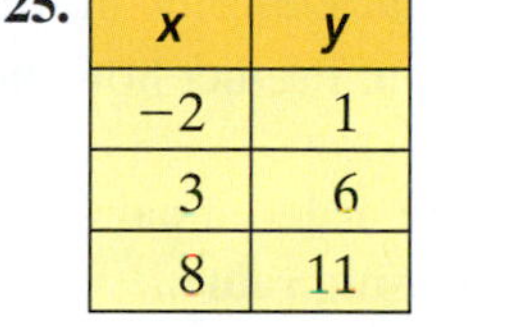

x	y
−2	1
3	6
8	11

26.

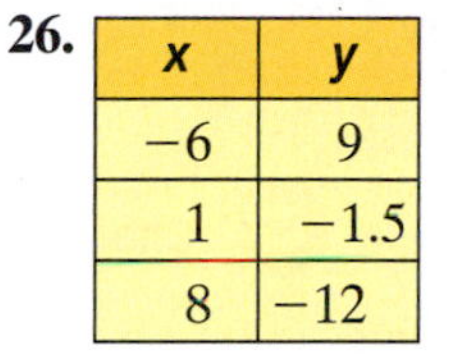

x	y
−6	9
1	−1.5
8	−12

Example 5 (page 204)

27. The force you apply to a lever is proportional to the weight you can lift. Suppose you can lift a 50-lb weight by applying 20 lb of force to a certain lever.
    a. What is the ratio of force to weight for the lever?
    b. Write an equation and find the force you need to lift a friend weighing 130 lb.

28. A bicyclist traveled at a constant speed during a timed practice period. Write an equation and find the distance the cyclist traveled in 30 min.

A Bicyclist's Practices

Elapsed Time	Distance
10 min	3 mi
25 min	7.5 mi

B Apply Your Skills

Write an equation of the direct variation that includes the given point.

29. $\left(3, \frac{1}{2}\right)$
30. $\left(\frac{1}{4}, -5\right)$
31. $\left(\frac{-5}{6}, \frac{6}{5}\right)$
32. $(1.2, 7.2)$
33. $(0.5, 4.5)$
34. $\left(-2, \frac{1}{16}\right)$
35. $(5.2, -1.5)$
36. $\left(-\frac{8}{3}, -\frac{9}{8}\right)$

37. **a. Writing** How can you tell whether two sets of data vary directly?
    b. How can you tell if a line is the graph of a direct variation?

Critical Thinking **Is each statement true or false? Explain.**

38. The graph of a direct variation may pass through $(-2, 4)$.

39. The graph of a direct variation may pass through $(0, 3)$.

40. If you triple an x-value of a direct variation, the y-value also triples.

Graph the direct variation that includes the given point. Write an equation of the line.

41. $(2, 5)$
42. $(-2, 5)$
43. $(2, -5)$
44. $(-2, -5)$

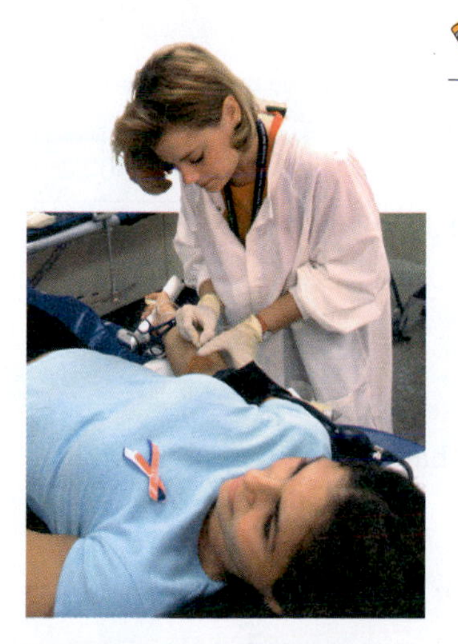

Since blood volume is proportional to body weight, a weight of 110 pounds has been determined to be the minimum for giving blood safely.

45. The amount of blood in a person's body varies directly with body weight. A person who weighs 160 lb has about 5 qt of blood.
    a. Find the constant of variation.
    b. Write an equation relating quarts of blood to weight.
    c. Estimate the number of quarts of blood in your body.

Homework Video Tutor

Visit: PHSchool.com
Web Code: bae-0405

46. Ohm's Law $V = I \times R$ relates the voltage, current, and resistance of a circuit. V is the voltage measured in volts. I is the current measured in amperes. R is the resistance measured in ohms.

a. Find the voltage of a circuit that has a current of 24 amperes and resistance of 2 ohms.

b. Find the resistance of a circuit that has a current of 24 amperes and a voltage of 18 volts.

47. Graph each direct variation on the same coordinate plane.

i. $y = x$ **ii.** $y = 2x$ **iii.** $y = 3x$ **iv.** $y = 4x$

a. Describe how the graphs change as the constant of variation increases.

b. Predict how the graph of $y = \frac{1}{2}x$ would appear.

C Challenge

The ordered pairs in each exercise are for the same direct variation. Find each missing value.

48. $(3, 4)$ and $(9, y)$

49. $(-1, 2)$ and $(4, y)$

50. $(-5, 3)$ and $(x, -4.8)$

51. $(1, y)$ and $\left(\frac{3}{2}, -9\right)$

52. $(2, 5)$ and $(x, 12.5)$

53. $(-2, 5)$ and $(x, -5)$

Problem Solving Tip

For Exercise 54, start with the relationship of miles and gallons: $\frac{m}{g} = 24$.

54. A car gets 24 miles per gallon. The number g of gallons of gas used varies directly with the number of miles m traveled.

a. Suppose the price of gas is \$3.12 per gallon. Write a function relating the cost c for g gallons of gas. Is this a direct variation?

b. Write a direct variation relating the cost of gas to the miles traveled.

Multiple Choice Practice

For California Standards Tutorials, visit PHSchool.com. Web Code: baq-9045

Alg1 15.0

55. On Thursday, Kevin sold 32 cups of lemonade and made \$40. If he made \$135 on Friday, how many cups of lemonade did he sell?

(A) 108 (B) 125 (C) 145 (D) 167

Alg1 7.0

56. The table at the right shows how much money was in Elisa's savings account after working a given number of weeks. Which equation represents the relationship between the number of weeks w Elisa has worked and the amount of money m in her savings account?

Week	Balance
1	\$300
2	\$375
3	\$450
4	\$525

(A) $m = 75w$ (C) $m = 75w + 225$

(B) $m = w + 75$ (D) $m = 75w + 300$

Alg1 25.3

57. Which expression will always produce an integer that is 1 less than a multiple of 10 when n is an integer?

(A) $1 - 10n$ (C) $n - 10 + 1$

(B) $10n - 1$ (D) $n + 10 - 1$

Alg1 5.0

58. Suppose you hire an electrician to install several electrical outlets. The electrician charges \$68 for materials plus \$40 per hour (or fraction of an hour). How much will the electrician charge you if the job takes $2\frac{1}{4}$ hours?

(A) \$148 (B) \$158 (C) \$188 (D) \$208

Mixed Review

Lesson 4-4 **Write a function rule for each table.**

59.

Number of People	Total Bill
1	\$3.00
2	\$6.00
3	\$9.00
4	\$12.00

60.

Amount Earned	Amount Spent
\$15	\$5
\$30	\$10
\$45	\$15
\$60	\$20

61.

Number of Days	Supplies Remaining
0	12 lb
2	10 lb
4	8 lb
6	6 lb

62.

Weight on Earth (lb)	Weight on Moon (lb)
96	16
123	20.5
144	24
171	28.5

Lessons 3-2, 3-3 **Solve each inequality.**

63. $r + 6 > -12$ **64.** $5 + c \leq 3.2$ **65.** $7m < -21$ **66.** $a - 4.5 \geq 12.1$

67. $\frac{n}{4} < -20$ **68.** $3t \geq 9.12$ **69.** $\frac{v}{-5} \leq \frac{1}{2}$ **70.** $b + 4\frac{2}{3} > 5\frac{1}{6}$

Lesson 1-6

71. Shipping For the ships that pass through the Panama Canal, the average toll is \$45,000 per ship. The canal authority earned about \$700 million in the year 2000. About how many ships passed through the canal that year? Round to the nearest hundred.

Checkpoint Quiz 2 — Lessons 4-3 through 4-5

Model each rule with a table of values and a graph. If the rule describes a direct variation, state the constant of variation.

1. $y = 4x + 1$ **2.** $y = \frac{1}{2}x$ **3.** $f(x) = -3x$ **4.** $y = -3x + 2$

Write a function rule for each situation.

5. the total cost $t(p)$ of p pounds of potatoes at \$.79 per pound

6. the total distance $d(n)$ traveled in n hours at a constant speed of 60 mi/h

Write an equation for the direct variation that includes the given point.

7. $(7, -2)$ **8.** $(-3, -6)$ **9.** $(-4, -5)$

10. a. The distance a wheel moves forward varies directly with the number of rotations. Suppose the distance d the wheel moves is 56 ft when the number of rotations n is 8. Find the constant of variation and write a direct variation equation to model this situation.

b. Use the direct variation you wrote for part (a) to find the distance the wheel moves in 20 rotations.

4-6 Inverse Variation

California Content Standards

15.0 Apply algebraic techniques to solve rate problems and work problems. ***Develop***
16.0 Give pertinent information about given functions. ***Master***

What You'll Learn

- To solve inverse variations
- To compare direct and inverse variation

. . . And Why

To balance weights on a fulcrum, as in Example 3

Check Skills You'll Need

GO for Help Lesson 4-5

Suppose y varies directly with x. Find each constant of variation.

1. $y = 5x$ **2.** $y = -7x$ **3.** $3y = x$ **4.** $0.25y = x$

Write an equation of the direct variation that includes the given point.

5. $(2, 4)$ **6.** $(3, 1.5)$ **7.** $(-4, 1)$ **8.** $(-5, -2)$

New Vocabulary

- inverse variation
- constant of variation for inverse variation

Solving Inverse Variations

CA Standards Investigation Inverse Variation

There are more than 1500 Habitat for Humanity affiliates in the United States. With volunteer labor, they have built more than 30,000 houses since 1978.
SOURCE: Habitat for Humanity

Suppose you are part of a volunteer crew constructing affordable housing. Building a house requires a total of 160 workdays. For example, a crew of 20 people can complete a house in 8 days.

1. How long should it take a crew of 40 people?

2. Copy and complete the table.

Crew size (x)	Construction Days (y)	Total Workdays
2	80	160
5	■	160
8	■	■
■	16	■
20	8	160
40	■	■

3. Graph the (x, y) data in the table above.

4. Describe what happens to construction time as the crew size increases.

In the table, the total number of workdays remains the same. The number of construction days decreases as the number of people on the crew increases. The relationship of construction days and crew size is an inverse variation.

Take Note

Definition — **Inverse Variation**

An equation in the form $xy = k$ or $y = \frac{k}{x}$, where $k \neq 0$, is an **inverse variation.**

The **constant of variation for inverse variation** is k, the product $x \cdot y$ for an ordered pair (x, y).

Inverse variations have graphs with the same general shape. You can see from the graph at the right how the constant of variation k affects the graph of $xy = k$.

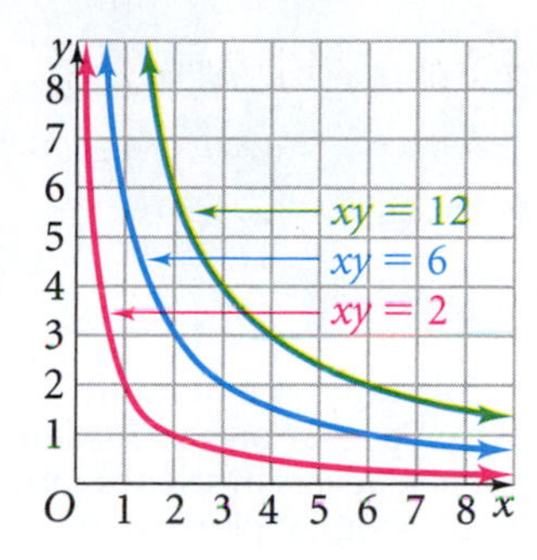

If you know the values of x and y for one point on the graph of an inverse variation, you can use the point to find the constant of variation k and the equation of the inverse variation.

1 EXAMPLE Writing an Equation Given a Point

Vocabulary Tip

There are several ways to describe an inverse variation:
- *y* varies inversely with *x*.
- *y* varies inversely as *x*.
- *y* is inversely proportional to *x*.

Suppose y varies inversely with x and $y = 7$ when $x = 5$. Write an equation for the inverse variation.

$xy = k$	**Use the general form of an inverse variation.**
$5(7) = k$	**Substitute 5 for x and 7 for y.**
$35 = k$	**Multiply to solve for k.**
$xy = 35$	**Write an equation. Substitute 35 for k in $xy = k$.**

The equation of the inverse variation is $xy = 35$, or $y = \frac{35}{x}$.

CA Standards Check 1 Suppose y varies inversely with x and $y = 9$ when $x = 2$. Write an equation for the inverse variation.

Suppose (x_1, y_1) and (x_2, y_2) are two ordered pairs of an inverse variation. Each ordered pair of an inverse variation has the same product k, that is $x_1 \cdot y_1 = k$ and $x_2 \cdot y_2 = k$. So $x_1 \cdot y_1 = x_2 \cdot y_2$.

2 EXAMPLE Finding the Missing Coordinate

The points (3, 8) and (2, y) are two points on the graph of an inverse variation. Find the missing value.

$x_1 \cdot y_1 = x_2 \cdot y_2$	**Use the equation $x_1 \cdot y_1 = x_2 \cdot y_2$, since you know coordinates but not the constant of variation.**
$3(8) = 2(y_2)$	**Substitute 3 for x_1, 8 for y_1, and 2 for x_2.**
$24 = 2(y_2)$	**Simplify.**
$12 = y_2$	**Solve for y_2.**

The missing value is 12. The point (2, 12) is on the graph of the inverse variation that includes the point (3, 8).

CA Standards Check 2 Each pair of points is on the graph of an inverse variation. Find the missing value.

a. $(3, y)$ and $(5, 9)$ **b.** $(75, 0.2)$ and $(x, 3)$

Application

A fulcrum is the point at which a lever pivots. Students can use levers in science labs to investigate physical properties.

The weight needed to balance a lever varies inversely with the distance from the fulcrum to the weight. Where should Julio, who weighs 150 lb, sit to balance the lever?

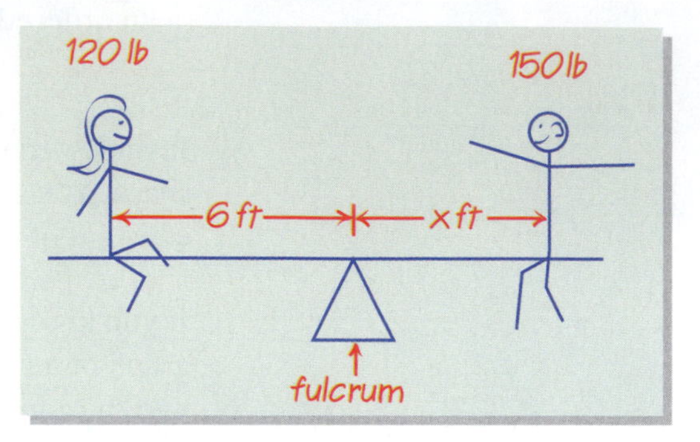

Relate A weight of 120 lb is 6 ft from the fulcrum. A weight of 150 lb is x ft from the fulcrum.
Weight and distance vary inversely.

Define Let $\text{weight}_1 = 120$ lb.
Let $\text{weight}_2 = 150$ lb.
Let $\text{distance}_1 = 6$ ft.
Let $\text{distance}_2 = x$ ft.

Write $\text{weight}_1 \cdot \text{distance}_1 = \text{weight}_2 \cdot \text{distance}_2$

$$120 \cdot 6 = 150 \cdot x \quad \text{Substitute.}$$
$$720 = 150x \quad \text{Simplify.}$$
$$\frac{720}{150} = x \quad \text{Solve for } x.$$
$$4.8 = x \quad \text{Simplify.}$$

Julio should sit 4.8 feet from the fulcrum to balance the lever.

CA Standards Check 3

a. A 100-lb weight is placed 4 ft from a fulcrum. How far from the fulcrum should a 75-lb weight be placed to balance the lever?

b. An 80-lb weight is placed 9 ft from a fulcrum. What weight should you put 6 ft from the fulcrum to balance the lever?

Comparing Direct and Inverse Variation

Recall that a direct variation is an equation in the form $y = kx$. This summary will help you recognize and use direct and inverse variations.

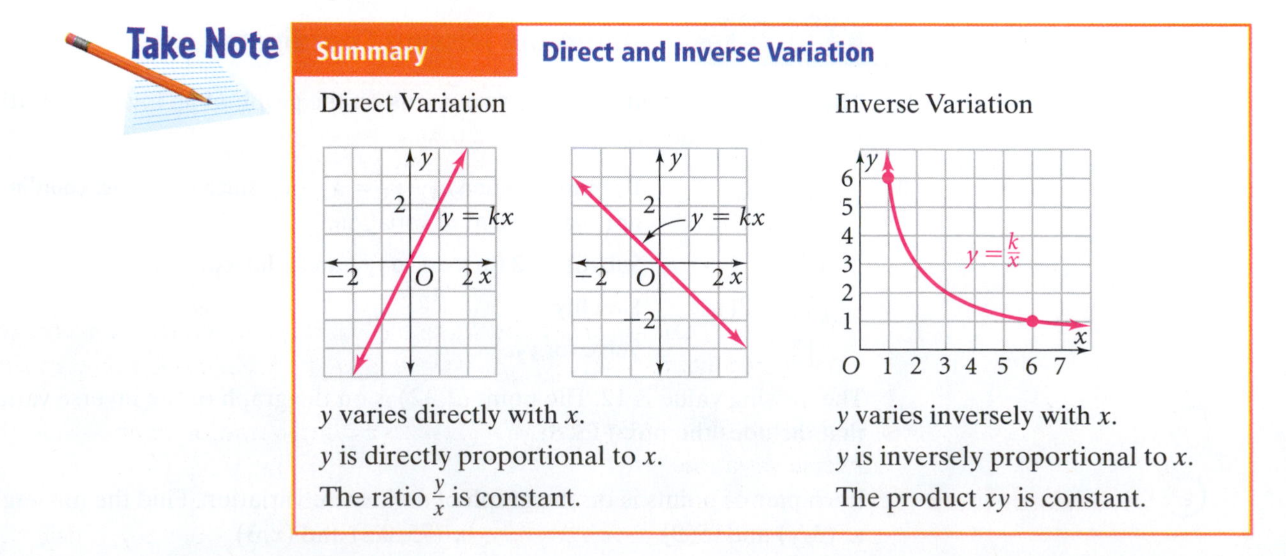

4 EXAMPLE Determining Direct or Inverse Variation

Do the data in each table represent a *direct variation* or an *inverse variation*? For each table, write an equation to model the data.

a.

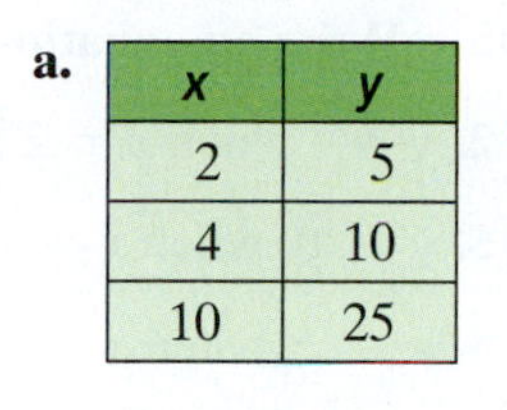

x	y
2	5
4	10
10	25

The values of y seem to vary directly with the values of x. Check each ratio $\frac{y}{x}$.

$\begin{matrix} y \rightarrow \\ x \rightarrow \end{matrix} \frac{5}{2} = 2.5 \qquad \frac{10}{4} = 2.5 \qquad \frac{25}{10} = 2.5$

The ratio $\frac{y}{x}$ is the same for all pairs of data. So this is a direct variation, and $k = 2.5$.

The equation is $y = 2.5x$.

b.

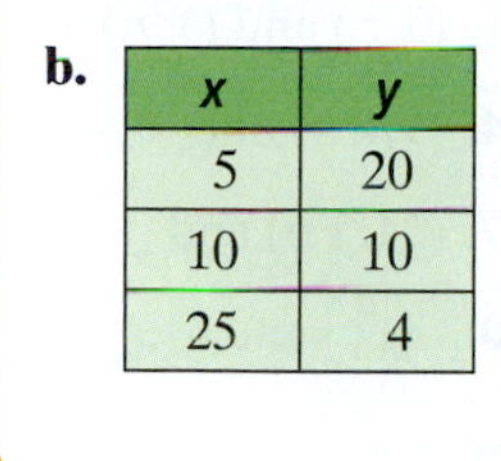

x	y
5	20
10	10
25	4

The values of y seem to vary inversely with the values of x. Check each product xy.

xy: $5(20) = 100 \qquad 10(10) = 100 \qquad 25(4) = 100$

The product xy is the same for all pairs of data. So this is an inverse variation, and $k = 100$.

The equation is $xy = 100$.

CA Standards Check 4 Determine whether the data in each table represent a direct variation or an inverse variation. Write an equation to model the data in each table.

a.

x	y
3	12
6	6
9	4

b.

x	y
3	12
5	20
8	32

Many real-world situations involve variation. You can look for a constant ratio or a constant product to determine whether the relationship is a direct variation or an inverse variation.

5 EXAMPLE Application

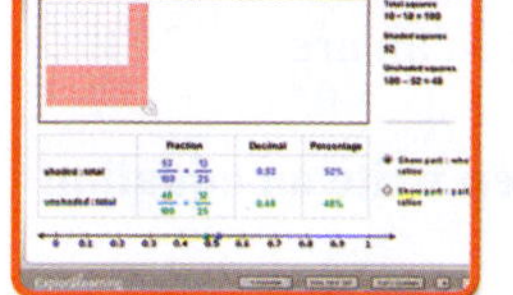

For: Variation Activity
Use: Interactive Textbook, 4-6

Explain whether each situation represents a direct variation or an inverse variation.

a. The cost of \$20 worth of gasoline is split among several people.

The cost per person times the number of people equals the total cost of the gasoline. Since the total cost is a constant product of \$20, this is an inverse variation.

b. You buy several markers for 70¢ each.

The cost per marker times the number of markers equals the total cost of the markers. Since the ratio $\frac{\text{cost}}{\text{marker}}$ is constant at 70¢ each, this is a direct variation.

CA Standards Check 5 Explain whether each situation represents a direct variation or an inverse variation.

a. You are in a discount store. All sweaters are on sale for \$15 each.

b. You walk 5 miles each day. Your speed and time vary from day to day.

EXERCISES

For more exercises, see *Extra Skills and Word Problem Practice.*

Standards Practice

Alg1 15.0, 16.0

A Practice by Example

Example 1 (page 209)

GO for Help

Suppose y varies inversely with x. Write an equation for the inverse variation.

1. $y = 6$ when $x = 3$

2. $y = 1$ when $x = 2$

3. $y = 7$ when $x = 8$

4. $y = 3$ when $x = 0.5$

5. $y = 10$ when $x = 2.4$

6. $y = 3.5$ when $x = 2.2$

7. $y = 6$ when $x = \frac{1}{3}$

8. $y = \frac{1}{16}$ when $x = 8$

9. $y = \frac{1}{10}$ when $x = \frac{3}{5}$

Example 2 (page 209)

Each pair of points is on the graph of an inverse variation. Find the missing value.

10. $(6, 12)$ and $(9, y)$

11. $(3, 5)$ and $(1, n)$

12. $(x, 11)$ and $(1, 66)$

13. $(x, 55)$ and $(5, 77)$

14. $(9.4, b)$ and $(6, 4.7)$

15. $(50, 13)$ and $(t, 5)$

16. $(4, 3.6)$ and $(1.2, g)$

17. $(24, 1.6)$ and $(c, 0.4)$

18. $(500, 25)$ and $(4, n)$

19. $\left(\frac{1}{2}, 24\right)$ and $(6, y)$

20. $\left(x, \frac{1}{2}\right)$ and $\left(\frac{1}{3}, \frac{1}{4}\right)$

21. $\left(\frac{1}{2}, 5\right)$ and $\left(b, \frac{1}{8}\right)$

Example 3 (page 210)

22. Suppose you take $2\frac{1}{2}$ h to drive from your house to a lake at 48 mi/h. How long will your return trip take at 40 mi/h?

23. Suppose a camper takes 2 h to ride around a reservoir at 10 mi/h at the beginning of the summer. By the end of the summer, she can ride around the reservoir in $1\frac{1}{2}$ h. What is her rate at the end of the summer?

Example 4 (page 211)

Do the data in each table represent a direct variation or an inverse variation? Write an equation to model the data in each table.

24.

x	y
2	1
5	2.5
8	4

25.

x	y
4	15
6	10
10	6

26.

x	y
3	24
9	8
12	6

Example 5 (page 211)

Explain whether each situation represents a direct variation or an inverse variation.

27. You buy some chicken for \$1.79/lb.

28. An 8-slice pizza is shared equally by a group of friends.

29. You find the length and width of several rectangles. Each has an area of 24 ft^2.

B Apply Your Skills

Find the constant of variation k for each inverse variation. Then write an equation for the inverse variation.

30. $y = 8$ when $x = 4$

31. $r = 3.3$ when $t = \frac{1}{3}$

32. $x = \frac{1}{2}$ when $y = 5$

33. $a = 25$ when $b = 0.04$

34. $p = 10.4$ when $q = 1.5$

35. $x = 5$ when $y = 75$

Does each formula represent a direct or an inverse variation? Explain.

36. the perimeter of an equilateral triangle: $P = 3s$

37. the time t to travel 150 mi at r mi/h: $t = \frac{150}{r}$

38. the circumference of a circle with radius r: $C = 2\pi r$

Visit: PHSchool.com
Web Code: bae-0406

39. Each of two rectangular lots is one quarter acre in size. One lot measures 99 ft by 110 ft. The other lot is 90 ft wide. What is the second lot's length?

40. Suppose 4 people can paint a house if they work 3 days each. How long would it take a crew of 5 people to paint the house?

Do the data in each table represent a direct or an inverse variation? Write an equation to model the data. Then complete the table.

41.

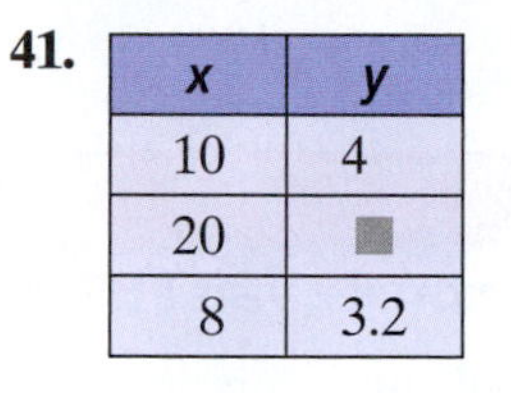

x	y
10	4
20	■
8	3.2

42.

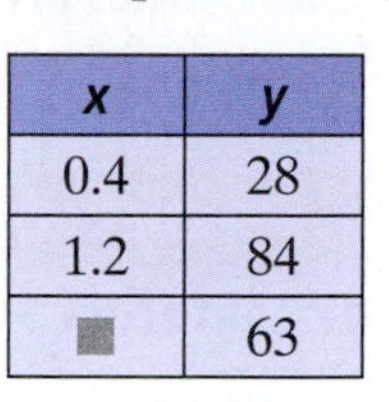

x	y
0.4	28
1.2	84
■	63

43.

x	y
1.6	30
4.8	10
■	96

44. Math Reasoning According to the First Law of Air Travel, for each situation below, will the distance to your gate be *greater* or *less* for this trip than for your last trip?

a. You have more luggage.
b. You have less time to make your flight.
c. You have less luggage.

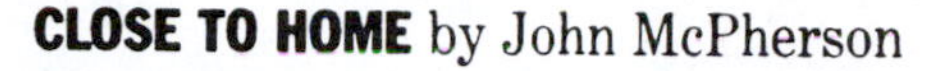
CLOSE TO HOME by John McPherson

The First Law of Air Travel
The distance to your connecting gate is directly proportional to the amount of luggage you are carrying and inversely proportional to the amount of time you have.

45. a. Suppose you want to earn \$80. How long will it take you if you are paid \$5/h; \$8/h; \$10/h; \$20/h?
b. What are the two variable quantities in part (a)?
c. Write an equation to represent this situation.

46. Write and graph a direct variation and an inverse variation that have the same constant of variation.

47. Boyle's Law states that volume V varies inversely with pressure P for any gas at a constant temperature in an enclosed space. Suppose a gas at constant temperature occupies 15.3 liters at a pressure of 40 millimeters of mercury. Write an equation that models this situation.

48. Critical Thinking The graphs p and q represent a direct variation and an inverse variation. Write an equation for each graph.

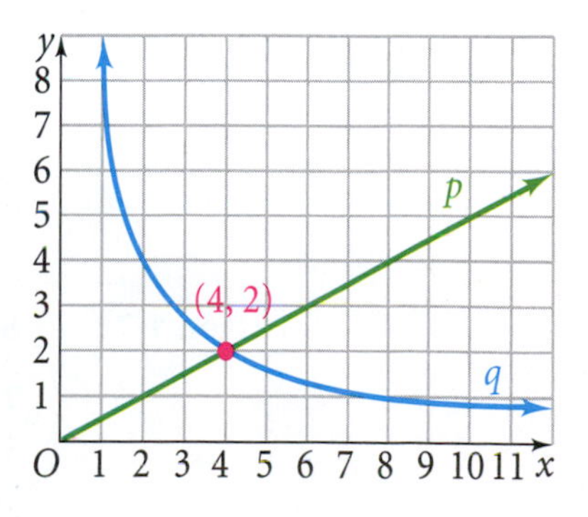

49. Writing Explain how the variable y changes in each situation.

a. y varies directly with x. The value of x is doubled.
b. y varies inversely with x. The value of x is doubled.

50. The intensity of a sound s varies inversely with the square of the distance d from the sound. This can be modeled by the equation $sd^2 = k$. If you move half the distance closer to the source of a sound, by what factor will the intensity of the sound increase? Explain your reasoning.

51. Write an equation to model each situation.
   a. y varies inversely with the fourth power of x.
   b. y varies inversely with the fourth power of x and directly with z.

Multiple Choice Practice

For California Standards Tutorials, visit PHSchool.com. Web Code: baq-9045

Alg1 15.0

52. Oscar's coach told him to drink a cup of water for every 4 laps he runs around the track. How many cups of water should Oscar drink if he runs 14 laps?

(A) 3.5 (B) 7.5 (C) 10 (D) 56

Alg1 5.0

53. Lou is ordering books online for \$4.99 each, plus \$2.95 per order for shipping. He has a coupon for 25% off the cost of the books, but the coupon does NOT apply to shipping. Which equation models the total cost c of ordering b books?

(A) $c = 4.99b + 2.95 - 0.25$
(B) $c = 0.25(4.99b + 2.95)$
(C) $c = 4.99b + 2.95 - 0.25(4.99b)$
(D) $c = 0.25(4.99b) + 2.95$

Alg1 16.0

54. What is the function rule for the table at the right?

(A) $f(x) = x - 5$
(B) $f(x) = -5x - 4$
(C) $f(x) = 5x - 1$
(D) $f(x) = -5x + 1$

x	$f(x)$
0	1
1	−4
2	−9
3	−14
4	−19

Alg1 3.0

55. What is the solution set of the inequality $|x + 4| < 8$?

(A) $-12 < x < 4$
(B) $-12 > x > 4$
(C) $x < -12$ or $x > 4$
(D) $x > -12$ or $x < 4$

Alg1 4.0

56. Solve $28 - 3b < 5b + 4$.

(A) $b < 3$ (B) $b > 4$ (C) $b > 3$ (D) $b < 4$

Mixed Review

GO for Help

Lesson 4-5

Write an equation of the direct variation that includes the given point.

57. $(1, 6)$ 58. $(-2, 8)$ 59. $(10, -1)$
60. $(-5, -4)$ 61. $(7, 11)$ 62. $(-28, 4)$

Lesson 4-1

Graph the points on the same coordinate plane.

63. $(3, -2)$ 64. $\left(-4, -1\frac{1}{2}\right)$ 65. $\left(2\frac{1}{2}, 0\right)$ 66. $(-2, 3.5)$

In which quadrant or on which axis would you find each point?

67. $(-6, 4.5)$ 68. $(0, -8)$ 69. $(7.2, 3.5)$ 70. $(-12, -0.9)$

Lesson 1-7

Simplify each expression.

71. $-(x + 1)$ 72. $6(8 - p)$ 73. $(4n + 7)(1.5)$
74. $5k + 11k$ 75. $0.25(24 - 16t)$ 76. $99m - 36m$

4-7

Inductive and Deductive Reasoning

California Content Standards

24.1 Explain the difference between inductive and deductive reasoning and identify and provide examples of each. *Develop, Master*

What You'll Learn

- To use inductive reasoning in continuing number patterns
- To distinguish between inductive and deductive reasoning

... And Why

To predict the next numbers in a pattern, as in Example 1

Check Skills You'll Need

GO for Help Lessons 1-5 and 1-6

Subtract.

1. $8 - (-6)$ **2.** $-7 - 10$ **3.** $1.5 - 3.4$

Simplify each expression.

4. $-2(5)$ **5.** $4(-8)$ **6.** $-3(-7)$

7. 6^2 **8.** -4^3 **9.** $(-3)^4$

New Vocabulary

- inductive reasoning
- conjecture

Inductive Reasoning and Number Patterns

Suppose you are visiting a city for the first time and notice that the first three streets you pass are A Street, B Street, and C Street. You would probably conclude that the next street would be D Street. You would be basing your conclusion on inductive reasoning.

Inductive reasoning is making conclusions based on patterns you observe. A conclusion you reach by inductive reasoning is a **conjecture**.

1 EXAMPLE Extending Number Patterns

Use inductive reasoning to describe each pattern. Then find the next two numbers.

a. 2, 5, 8, 11, . . .

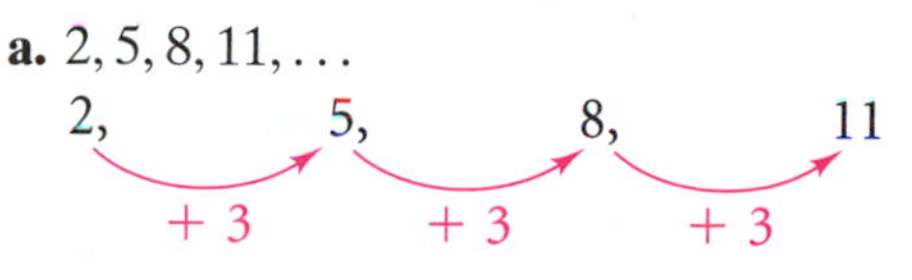

The pattern is "add 3 to the previous number." To find the next two numbers, you add 3 to each previous number: $11 + 3 = 14$, and $14 + 3 = 17$.

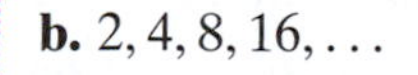

b. 2, 4, 8, 16, . . .

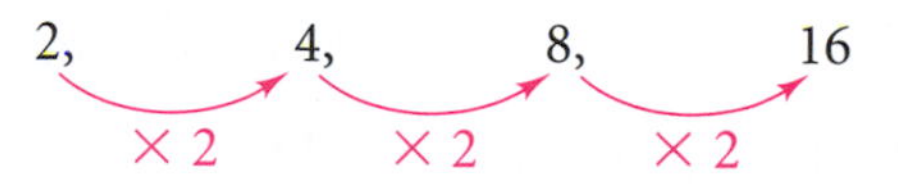

The pattern is "multiply the previous number by 2." To find the next two numbers, you multiply each previous number by 2: $16 \times 2 = 32$, and $32 \times 2 = 64$.

Vocabulary Tip

You read ". . . " at the end of a number pattern as "and so on."

CA Standards Check

1 Use inductive reasoning to describe each pattern. Then find the next two numbers in each pattern.

a. 3, 9, 27, 81, . . . **b.** 9, 15, 21, 27, . . . **c.** 2, −4, 8, −16, . . .

You can use inductive reasoning to write a function rule that describes a pattern.

2 EXAMPLE Writing a Function Rule to Describe a Pattern

Vocabulary Tip

The set of natural numbers is {1, 2, 3,. . .}. Natural numbers are also called counting numbers.

Look at the pattern of sums below. Write a function rule that gives the sum of the first n positive odd integers, where n is a natural number. Then predict the sum of the first 20 positive odd integers.

$1 = 1 = 1^2$

$1 + 3 = 4 = 2^2$

$1 + 3 = 5 = 9 = 3^2$

$1 + 3 + 5 + 7 = 16 = 4^2$

Each sum is the square of the number of addends in the expression.

Let n = a natural number.

Let $A(n)$ = the sum of the first n positive odd integers.

$A(n) = 1 + 3 + 5 + 7 + \ldots + n = n^2$

The sum of the first 20 positive odd integers is 20^2, or 400.

CA Standards Check 2 Look at the pattern of sums below. Write a function rule that gives the sum of the first n positive even integers, where n is a natural number. Then predict the sum of the first 30 positive even integers.

$2 = 2 = 1(2)$

$2 + 4 = 6 = 2(3)$

$2 + 4 + 6 = 12 = 3(4)$

$2 + 4 + 6 + 8 = 20 = 4(5)$

Inductive Reasoning and Deductive Reasoning

Recall that with deductive reasoning, you make conclusions based on given facts. In comparison, inductive reasoning involves making a conjecture based on an observed pattern.

3 EXAMPLE Determining Inductive or Deductive Reasoning

Explain whether each situation represents inductive reasoning or deductive reasoning.

a. At a football game, you notice that all the students from the opposing school are wearing red and blue. You conclude that their school colors are red and blue.

Since the conclusion is based on the observation that the students from the opposing school are wearing red and blue, this is inductive reasoning.

b. You solve the equation $x - 5 = 2$ by adding 5 to each side. You conclude that the value of x is 7.

When you add 2 to each side, you are applying the Addition Property of Equality. Since your answer is based on a property, this is deductive reasoning.

CA Standards Check 3 You conclude a person is at least 16 years old because he or she has a driver's license, and you know the legal driving age is 16 years. Explain whether this situation represents inductive reasoning or deductive reasoning.

EXERCISES

For more exercises, see *Extra Skills and Word Problem Practice.*

Standards Practice

Alg1 24.1

A Practice by Example

Example 1 (page 215)

GO for Help

Use inductive reasoning to describe each pattern. Then find the next two numbers in each pattern.

1. $4, 6, 8, 10, \ldots$

2. $4, 6, 9, 13\frac{1}{2}, \ldots$

3. $4, 6, 9, 13, \ldots$

4. $3, 3.04, 3.08, 3.12, \ldots$

5. $3, 3.3, 3.63, 3.993, \ldots$

6. $3, 1, -1, -3, \ldots$

7. $1.1, 2.2, 3.3, 4.4, \ldots$

8. $0.001, 0.01, 0.1, 1, \ldots$

9. $2, 8, 32, 128, \ldots$

10. $1, \frac{1}{4}, \frac{1}{9}, \frac{1}{16}, \ldots$

11. $9, -5, -19, -33, \ldots$

12. $1.5, 7.5, 37.5, 187.5, \ldots$

Example 2 (page 216)

Look at the pattern of sums below. Write a function rule that gives the sum of the first *n* numbers in each pattern, where *n* is a natural number. Then predict the sum for *n* = 10.

13.
$$\frac{1}{2} = \frac{1}{2} = 1 - \frac{1}{2}$$
$$\frac{1}{2} + \left(\frac{1}{2}\right)^2 = \frac{3}{4} = 1 - \left(\frac{1}{2}\right)^2$$
$$\frac{1}{2} + \left(\frac{1}{2}\right)^2 + \left(\frac{1}{2}\right)^3 = \frac{7}{8} = 1 - \left(\frac{1}{2}\right)^3$$
$$\frac{1}{2} + \left(\frac{1}{2}\right)^2 + \left(\frac{1}{2}\right)^3 + \left(\frac{1}{2}\right)^4 = \frac{15}{16} = 1 - \left(\frac{1}{2}\right)^4$$

14.
$$1 = 1 = \frac{1(2)}{2}$$
$$1 + 2 = 3 = \frac{2(3)}{2}$$
$$1 + 2 + 3 = 6 = \frac{3(4)}{2}$$
$$1 + 2 + 3 + 4 = 10 = \frac{4(5)}{2}$$

Example 3 (page 216)

Math Reasoning **Explain whether each situation represents inductive reasoning or deductive reasoning.**

15. A number pattern contains numbers that keep increasing in value by 3. You find the next number in the pattern by adding 3 to the previous number.

16. A judge finds the defendant in a case to be innocent because the crime was committed at the same time a witness saw the defendant at a grocery store.

17. The measures of two angles of a triangle are 30° and 55°. Since there are 180° in a triangle, you conclude that the measure of the third angle is 180° − 85°, or 95°.

18. After hearing the doorbell ring on many occasions, a child concludes that when the doorbell rings, there is someone at the door.

19. A graph shows time spent on homework versus grade level. Based on the linear distribution of the data points, you conclude that the higher the grade level, the more time students spend on homework.

B Apply Your Skills

Find the next two numbers in each pattern.

20. $20, 14, 8, 2, \ldots$

21. $2, 2\frac{1}{4}, 2\frac{1}{2}, 2\frac{3}{4}, 3, \ldots$

22. $2, 5, 10, 17, \ldots$

23. $12, 4, 1\frac{1}{3}, \frac{4}{9}, \ldots$

24. $0, 3, 8, 15, 24, \ldots$

25. $-5, 4, 13, 22, \ldots$

26. $40, 20, 10, 5, \ldots$

27. $7, 7\frac{1}{4}, 7\frac{1}{2}, 7\frac{3}{4}, \ldots$

28. $12, -4, \frac{4}{3}, -\frac{4}{9}, \ldots$

Homework Video Tutor

Visit: PHSchool.com
Web Code: bae-0407

29. a. Writing Explain the difference between inductive and deductive reasoning.
b. Give an example of inductive reasoning and of deductive reasoning.

In Santa Monica, Line 3 of the Big Blue Bus runs about every 15 minutes on weekday mornings.

30. Buses on your route run every 7 minutes from 6:30 A.M. to 10:00 A.M. You get to the bus stop at 7:56 A.M. How long will you have to wait for a bus?

31. Write a function rule for a number pattern that has -30 as the eighth number.

For Exercises 32 and 33, write the first five numbers in each pattern. Explain what the fifth number means in the context of the situation.

32. A baby's birth weight is 7 lb 4 oz. The baby gains 5 oz each week.

33. The balance of a car loan starts at $4500 and decreases $150 each month.

34. Use the number pattern 1, 2, 4, . . .

a. Find the difference between consecutive numbers in the pattern. Use inductive reasoning to predict the next number in the pattern.

b. Find the quotient of consecutive numbers in the pattern. Use inductive reasoning to predict the next number in the pattern.

c. **Critical Thinking** Explain why having more than three numbers in a pattern can help you make a conjecture that is more likely to be correct.

35. The first five rows of Pascal's Triangle are at the right.

a. Predict the numbers in the sixth row.

b. Find the sum of the numbers in each of the first five rows. Predict the sum of the numbers in the sixth row.

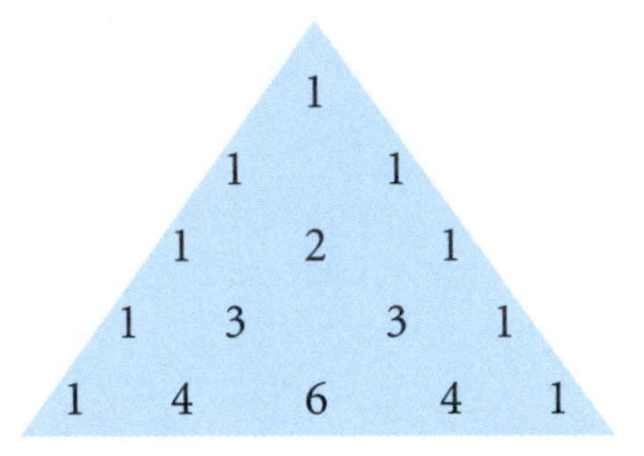

36. a. Verify the equations below. Use inductive reasoning to write a function rule that gives the sum for $2^1 + 2^2 + 2^3 + \ldots + 2^n$ for any natural number n.

$2^1 = 2^2 - 2$

$2^1 + 2^2 = 2^3 - 2$

$2^1 + 2^2 + 2^3 = 2^4 - 2$

$2^1 + 2^2 + 2^3 + 2^4 = 2^5 - 2$

b. **Math Reasoning** Are the equations above sufficient to prove that your function rule is correct? Explain.

37. There are 52 white keys on a piano. Each key produces a different frequency, or number of vibrations per second, when it is struck.

a. **Reasoning** Is this relation a function? Explain.

b. **Writing** Describe the patterns in the table.

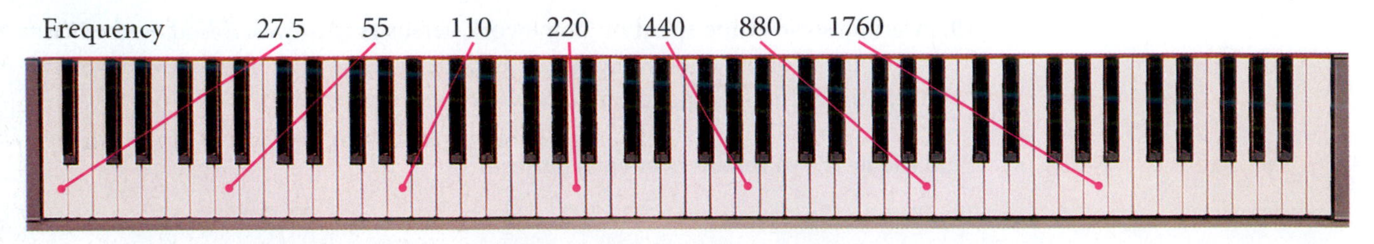

38. The Fibonacci pattern is 1, 1, 2, 3, 5, 8, 13, . . . After the first two numbers, each number is the sum of the preceding two numbers.

a. What is the next number in the pattern?

b. What is the eleventh number in the pattern?

c. Choose two other numbers to start a Fibonacci-like pattern. Write the first seven numbers in your pattern.

Challenge **Find the next expression in each pattern.**

39. $4, x + 4, 2x + 4, 3x + 4, \ldots$

40. $a + b + c, 4a + 3b + c, 7a + 5b + c, \ldots$

41. a. Draw the next figure in the pattern.

b. Reasoning What is the color of the 20th figure? Explain.

c. How many sides does the 28th figure have? Explain.

Multiple Choice Practice

For California Standards Tutorials, visit PHSchool.com. Web Code: baq-9045

Alg1 24.1

42. Sherri is working on a puzzle. To solve the puzzle, she must continue the pattern 24, 12, 6, 3, . . . What is the 7th number in the pattern?

(A) 0 (B) 0.25 (C) 0.375 (D) 1.5

Alg1 16.0

43. Marta started to work at a company in the year 2005. Her yearly salary was \$26,500. At the beginning of the next year she received a \$2,880 raise. Assume that she receives the same raise each year. Which function represents Marta's salary $f(n)$ for n years after 2005?

(A) $f(n) = 26{,}500 + 2880n$

(B) $f(n) = 26{,}500n + 2880$

(C) $f(n) = (26{,}500 + 2880)n$

(D) $f(n) = 26{,}500 + 2880^n$

Alg1 2.0

44. What is the solution of the equation $-\frac{3}{4}r = 1$?

(A) $-\frac{4}{3}$ (B) $-\frac{3}{4}$ (C) $\frac{3}{4}$ (D) $\frac{4}{3}$

Alg1 4.0

45. Solve $-5n + 16 \le -7n$.

(A) $n \le -8$ (B) $n \ge -8$ (C) $n \le 8$ (D) $n \ge 8$

Mixed Review

GO for Help

Lesson 4-6

Suppose y varies inversely with x. Write an equation for the inverse variation.

46. $y = 4$ when $x = 5$

47. $y = 1.2$ when $x = 8$

48. $y = \frac{1}{2}$ when $x = 24$

49. $y = 7$ when $x = 6.1$

Lesson 4-5

Write an equation of the direct variation that includes the given point.

50. $(4, -5)$

51. $(0.5, 12)$

52. $(-1, 14)$

53. $(10, 1.4)$

54. $(1.1, -3.1)$

55. $(11, -3.1)$

56. $(2, -3)$

57. $\left(\frac{1}{2}, \frac{1}{3}\right)$

Lesson 4-3

Find the range of each function for the domain $\{-2, 1, 5\}$.

58. $f(x) = -4x$

59. $g(x) = 1 - 4x$

60. $y = 3x + 4$

61. $y = 2|x|$

62. $h(x) = |2x|$

63. $f(x) = \frac{3}{4}x - 5$

Test-Taking Strategies

Using a Variable

You can solve many problems by using a variable to represent an unknown quantity. Try to let the variable be the quantity that you are looking for. Then use the variable to write an equation or inequality.

EXAMPLE

A brand of cereal comes in two sizes. The 12-oz size costs $4.35. At that rate, how much should the 20-oz box cost?

(A) $2.61 (B) $5.15 (C) $7.25 (D) $12.35

The problem is asking for the cost of a 20-oz box. Let the variable x be the cost of the 20-oz box. Write and solve a proportion to answer the question.

$\frac{12}{20} = \frac{4.35}{x}$ **Write a proportion.**

$12x = 20(4.35)$ **Find the cross products.**

$12x = 87.00$ **Simplify.**

$x = 7.25$ **Divide each side by 12.**

The 20-oz box should cost about $7.25, so C is the correct answer.

Multiple Choice Practice

1. One house painter charges an initial fee of $25, plus $15 per hour. A second painter charges $25 per hour. Find out how many hours a job takes for the charge of the second painter to be the same as the charge of the first painter.

(A) 2.5 (B) 2 (C) 1.5 (D) 1

2. On her vacation, Mary exchanges 150 U.S. dollars for Mexican pesos. The exchange rate that day is about 10.7 Mexico pesos for 1 dollar. Approximately how many pesos will Mary receive?

(A) 1605 (B) 1510 (C) 161 (D) 0.07

3. The table below shows the number of hours a clerk works per week and the amount of money she earns before taxes.

Hours Worked	Dollars Earned
12	$99.00
17	$140.25
21	$173.25
32	$264.00

How much money does the clerk earn if she works for 34 hours per week?

(A) $275.00 (B) $280.50 (C) $305.25 (D) $354.75

Chapter 4 Review

Vocabulary Review

English and Spanish Audio Online

conjecture (p. 215)
constant of variation for direct variation (p. 202)
constant of variation for inverse variation (p. 209)
coordinate plane (p. 176)
coordinates (p. 176)
dependent variable (p. 188)
direct variation (p. 202)
domain (p. 181)
function (p. 181)
function notation (p. 187)
function rule (p. 187)
independent variable (p. 188)
inductive reasoning (p. 215)
inverse variation (p. 209)
ordered pair (p. 176)
origin (p. 176)
quadrants (p. 176)
range (p. 181)
relation (p. 181)
vertical-line test (p. 183)
x-axis (p. 176)
x-coordinate (p. 176)
y-axis (p. 176)
y-coordinate (p. 176)

Match the vocabulary term in the column on the left with the most specific description in the column on the right.

1. direct variation
2. inductive reasoning
3. independent variable
4. function
5. range
6. conjecture

A. x-coordinate
B. y-coordinate
C. a function that can be expressed in the form $y = kx$, where $k \neq 0$
D. drawing conclusions based on observed patterns
E. a relation with exactly one value of the dependent variable for each value of the independent variable
F. a conclusion based on inductive reasoning

For: Vocabulary quiz
Web Code: baj-0451

Skills and Concepts

Lesson 4-1

- To graph points on the coordinate plane (p. 176)

Prepares for Alg1 6.0

A **coordinate plane** is formed by the intersection of two number lines. The ***x*-axis** and the ***y*-axis** divide the coordinate plane into four **quadrants**. An **ordered pair** gives the coordinates of a point. The ***x*-coordinate** shows how far to move left or right from the origin. The ***y*-coordinate** shows how far to move up or down from the origin.

Write the coordinates of each point.

7. R **8.** S **9.** T **10.** U

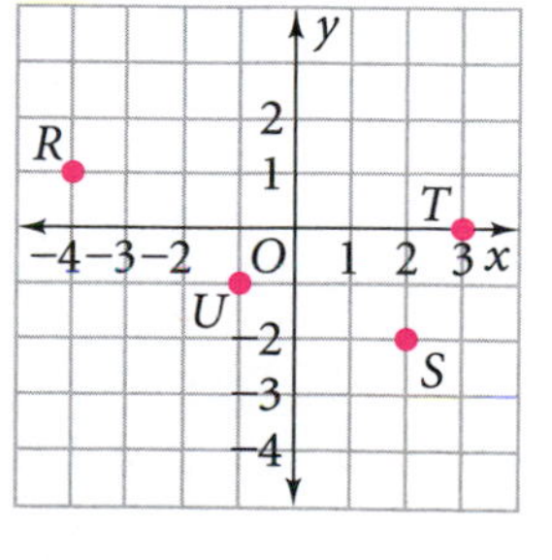

Graph each point on the coordinate plane.

11. $J(-6, 4)$ **12.** $K(0, -8)$ **13.** $L(7, 4)$

In which quadrant or on which axis would you find each point?

14. $(-4, 6)$ **15.** $(2\frac{1}{2}, -5)$ **16.** $(0, 3.5)$ **17.** $(-1\frac{1}{4}, -9)$

Lesson 4-2

- To identify functions (p. 181)

Alg1 16.0, 17.0, 18.0

A **relation** is a set of ordered pairs. The **domain** of a relation is the set of the first coordinates. The **range** of a relation is the set of second coordinates. A **function** is a relation that assigns exactly one value in the range to each value in the domain.

Find the domain and range of each relation. Is each relation a function?

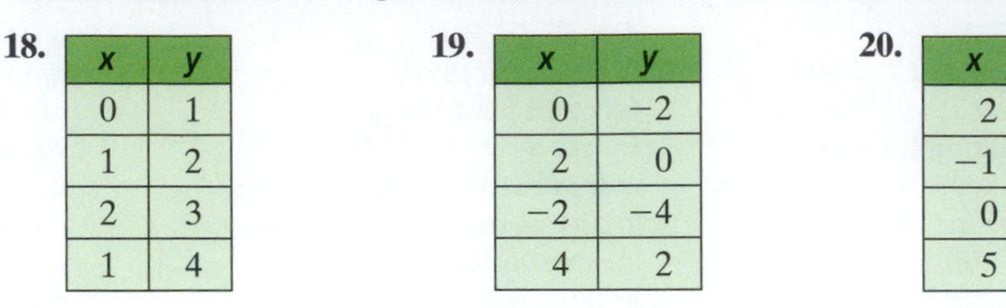

18.

x	y
0	1
1	2
2	3
1	4

19.

x	y
0	−2
2	0
−2	−4
4	2

20.

x	y
2	−3
−1	−3
0	−3
5	−3

Find the domain and range of each relation. Use a mapping diagram to determine whether the relation is a function.

21. $\{(-1, 0), (1, 0), (3, 0), (5, 0)\}$

22. $\{(3, -1), (6, 2), (4, -5), (9, 3)\}$

23. Use the vertical-line test to determine if the graph at the right is a function.

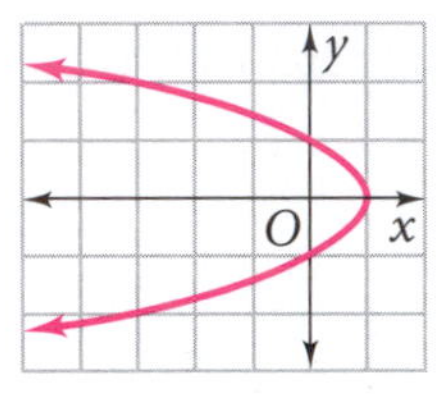

24. Writing When is a relation also a function?

Lessons 4-3 and 4-4

- To model functions using rules, tables, and graphs (p. 187)
- To identify symbolic expressions as functions (p. 190)
- To write a function rule given a table or a real-world situation (p. 194)

Alg1 16.0, 17.0, 18.0

A **function rule** is an equation that describes a function. A function is in **function notation** when it uses $f(x)$ for the outputs. When you graph data, put the **independent variable** on the horizontal axis and the **dependent variable** on the vertical axis.

Find the range of each function when the domain is $\{-4, 0, 1, 5\}$.

25. $y = 4x - 7$ **26.** $m = 0.5n + 3$ **27.** $p = q^2 + 1$ **28.** $w = 5 - 3z$

Model each rule with a table of values and a graph.

29. $f(x) = x^2 - 3$ **30.** $f(x) = -\frac{1}{2}x - 3$ **31.** $y = |x| - 7$ **32.** $y = 2x + 1$

Write a function rule for each table of values.

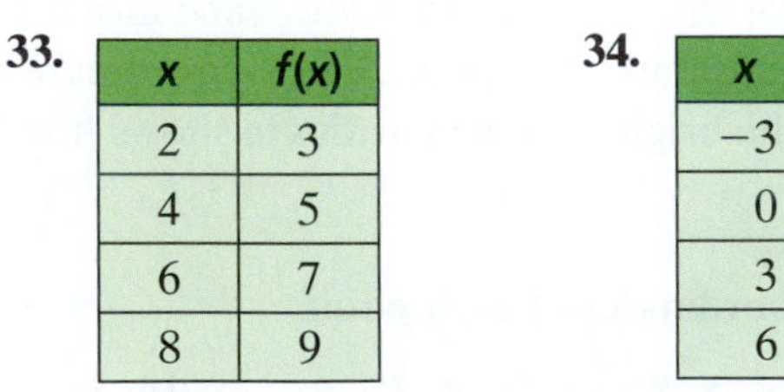

33.

x	f(x)
2	3
4	5
6	7
8	9

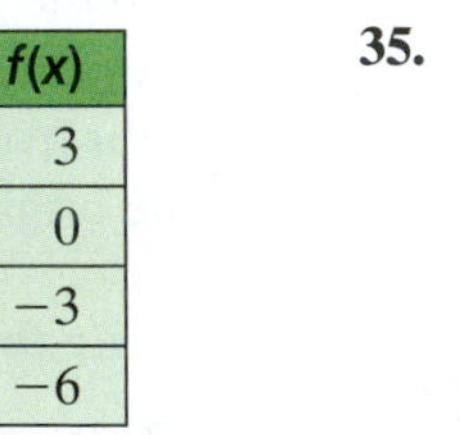

34.

x	f(x)
−3	3
0	0
3	−3
6	−6

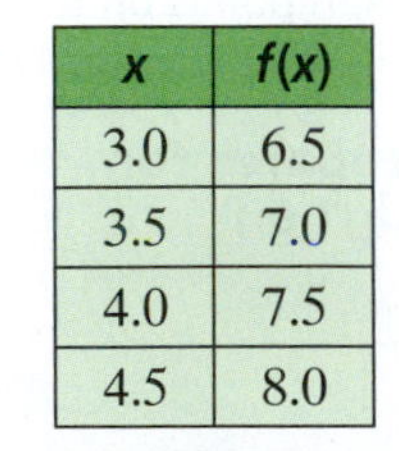

35.

x	f(x)
3.0	6.5
3.5	7.0
4.0	7.5
4.5	8.0

36. The table at the right compares inches of snow to the corresponding amounts of rain.
a. Write a function rule that models the data.
b. How many inches of rain correspond to 6 inches of snow?

Precipitation

Snow (in.)	Rain (in.)
3	0.3
5	0.5
10	1.0
7.5	0.75

37. What is the domain of the function $f(x) = \frac{1}{x + 10}$?

Lessons 4-5 and 4-6

- To write an equation of a direct variation (p. 201)
- To use ratios and proportions with direct variations (p. 203)
- To solve inverse variations (p. 208)
- To compare direct and inverse variation (p. 210)

Alg1 15.0, 16.0

A function is a **direct variation** if it has the form $y = kx$, where $k \neq 0$. The coefficient k is the **constant of variation.** When two quantities are related in such a way that their product is a nonzero constant, they form an **inverse variation.** An inverse variation can be written $xy = k$, where k is the **constant of variation.**

Is each equation a direct variation? If it is, find the constant of variation.

38. $f(x) = -3x$ **39.** $y = x - 3$ **40.** $y = 2x + 5$

Write an equation of the direct variation that includes the given point.

41. $(5, 1)$ **42.** $(-2, -2)$ **43.** $(-2, 6)$

Suppose y varies inversely with x. Write an equation for each inverse variation.

44. $x = 6$ when $y = 1$ **45.** $x = 90$ when $y = 0.1$ **46.** $x = 88$ when $y = 0.05$

Each pair of points is on the graph of an inverse variation. Find the missing value.

47. $(9, x)$ and $(3, 12)$ **48.** $(4, 2.65)$ and $(y, 4.24)$ **49.** $(r, 100)$ and $(75, 25)$

Do the data in each table represent a direct variation or an inverse variation? Write an equation to model the data in each table.

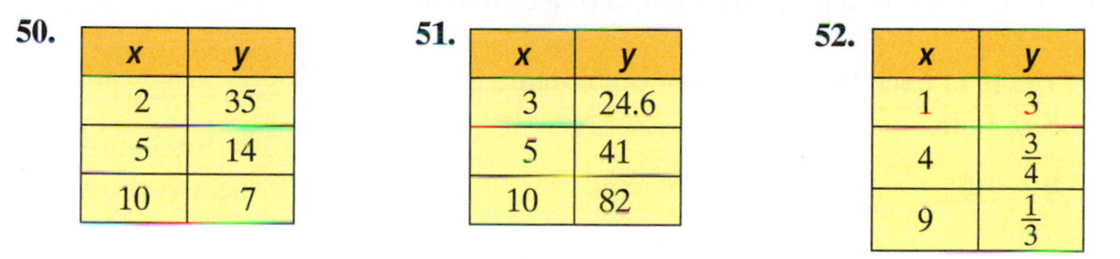

50.

x	y
2	35
5	14
10	7

51.

x	y
3	24.6
5	41
10	82

52.

x	y
1	3
4	$\frac{3}{4}$
9	$\frac{1}{3}$

Lesson 4-7

- To use inductive reasoning in continuing number patterns (p. 215)
- To distinguish between inductive and deductive reasoning (p. 216)

Alg1 24.1

Inductive reasoning is the process of making conclusions or **conjectures** based on patterns you observe.

Use inductive reasoning to describe each pattern. Then find the next three numbers in each pattern.

53. 99, 90, 81, 72, . . . **54.** 5, 8, 11, 14, . . . **55.** 12, 23, 34, 45, . . .

56. Look at the pattern of sums below. Write a function rule that gives the sum of the first n numbers in the pattern, where n is a natural number. Then predict the sum for $n = 20$.

$$\frac{1}{1 \cdot 2} = \frac{1}{2}$$

$$\frac{1}{1 \cdot 2} + \frac{1}{2 \cdot 3} = \frac{2}{3}$$

$$\frac{1}{1 \cdot 2} + \frac{1}{2 \cdot 3} + \frac{1}{3 \cdot 4} = \frac{3}{4}$$

$$\frac{1}{1 \cdot 2} + \frac{1}{2 \cdot 3} + \frac{1}{3 \cdot 4} + \frac{1}{4 \cdot 5} = \frac{4}{5}$$

57. You notice a large number of people carrying umbrellas and conclude that the weather forecast calls for rain. Explain whether this situation represents inductive reasoning or deductive reasoning.

Chapter 4 Test

Go Online PHSchool.com For: Chapter Test Web Code: baa-0452

Name the coordinates of each point on the graph at the right.

1. F 2. L

3. G 4. M

5. H 6. N

Determine whether each relation is a function. If the relation is a function, state the domain and range.

7.

x	y
-2	5
8	6
3	12
5	6

8.

x	y
9	6
3	8
4	9.5
9	2

9. **Writing** Explain how to use the vertical-line test to determine whether a graph is a graph of a function.

Find the range of each function when the domain is $\{-3, -1.5, 0, 1, 4\}$.

10. $r = 4t^2 + 5$ 11. $m = -3n - 2$

Model each rule with a table of values and a graph.

12. $f(x) = 1.5x - 3$ 13. $f(x) = -x^2 + 4$

Write a function rule to describe each statement.

14. the cost in dollars of printing dollar bills when it costs 3.8¢ to print a dollar bill

15. the amount of money you earn mowing lawns at \$15 per lawn

16. the profit you make selling flowers at \$1.50 each when each flower costs you \$.80

Write a function rule for each table of values.

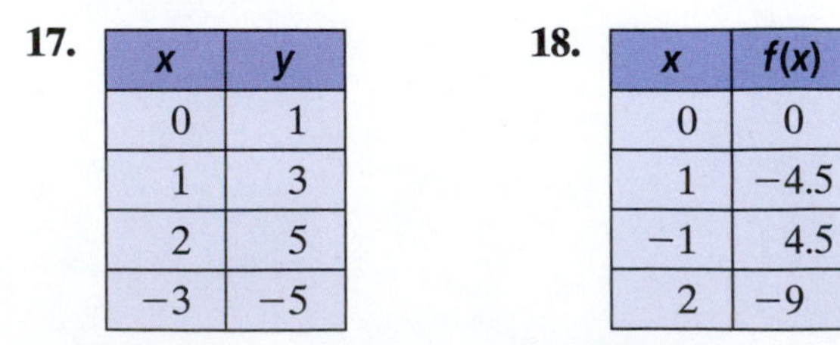

17.

x	y
0	1
1	3
2	5
-3	-5

18.

x	$f(x)$
0	0
1	-4.5
-1	4.5
2	-9

19. Describe a situation that could be modeled by the equation $y = 5x$.

20. The price of a turkey depends on its weight. Suppose turkeys sell for \$.59 per lb.
   a. Write a rule to describe the function.
   b. What is the price of a 14-lb turkey?
   c. If you had \$10 to buy a turkey, how big a turkey could you buy?

Write an equation of the direct variation that includes the given point.

21. $(2, 2)$ 22. $(-8, -4)$ 23. $(3, -1)$ 24. $(-5, 3)$

Determine whether each of the following graphs shows a direct variation. Write an equation for each direct variation.

25. 26.

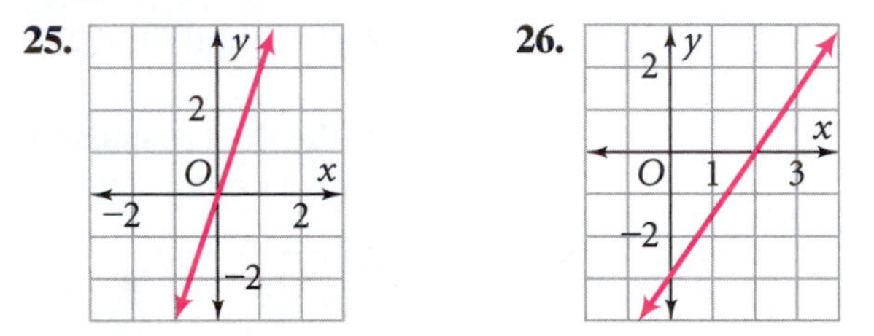

27. The total amount of water dripping from a leaky faucet varies directly with time. If water drips at the rate of 5 mL/min, how much water drips in 30 min?

Use inductive reasoning to find the next three numbers in each pattern.

28. $-55, -50, -45, -40, \ldots$ 29. $1.7, 2.7, 3.7, 4.7, \ldots$

Find the constant of variation k for each inverse variation.

30. $y = 5$ when $x = 6$ 31. $y = 78$ when $x = 0.1$

32. Write a function rule for the cost of catfish shown in the table below.

Weight (lb)	1	2	3	4	5
Cost (dollars)	3	6	9	12	15

33. You solve the inequality $-4w > 24$ by dividing each side by -4. You conclude that $w < -6$. Explain whether this situation represents inductive reasoning or deductive reasoning.

Standards Mastery

Cumulative Practice

Some questions ask you to determine whether a relation defined by a graph is a function. Read the question at the right. Then follow the tips to answer the sample question.

Tip 1
Use the vertical-line test to eliminate choices. If a vertical line intersects a graph in more than one point, the graph does not represent a function.

Which of the relations graphed below is a function?

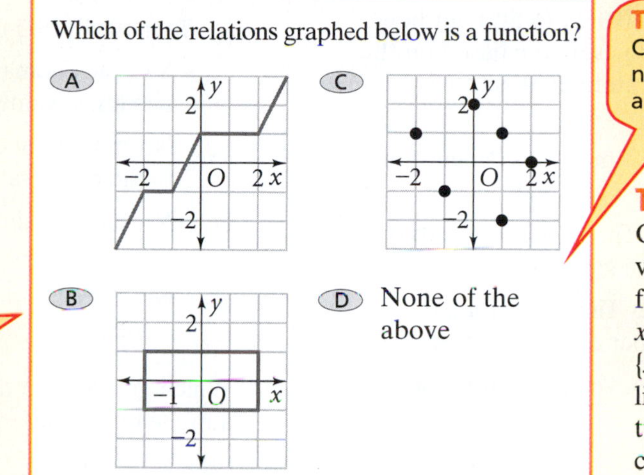

Tip 2
Consider the possibility that none of the graphs may be a function.

Think It Through
Graph A passes the vertical-line test. Graph B fails the test at every x-value in the domain $\{x: -2 \leq x \leq 2\}$. A vertical line intersects graph C at two points when x is 1. The correct answer is A.

Vocabulary Review

As you solve problems, you must understand the meanings of mathematical terms. Match each term with its mathematical meaning.

A. consecutive integers
B. direct variation
C. function
D. inductive reasoning
E. function rule

I. an equation that can be used to find a range value given a domain value
II. making conclusions based on patterns
III. a function in the form $y = kx$ where k is a constant and $k \neq 0$
IV. integers that differ by one
V. a relation where each value in the domain corresponds to exactly one value in the range

Read each question. Then write the letter of the correct answer on your paper.

1. Annie earns \$7 for each hour of baby-sitting. How much does she earn for 6 hours of baby-sitting? **(Lesson 4-5)**

   A \$13 B \$21 C \$42 D \$49

2. The score on Mr. Meyer's history test varies directly with the number of correct answers. A student with 14 correct answers receives a score of 84. What score would the student receive for 15 correct answers? **(Lesson 4-5)**

   A 85 B 87 C 90 D 99

3. The width of Ben's family room is 3 feet less than the length. If the perimeter of the family room is 70 feet, which equation can be used to find the length ℓ of the family room? **(Lesson 2-1)**

   A $70 = \ell - 3$
   B $70 = 2\ell - 3$
   C $70 = 2(\ell - 3)$
   D $70 = 2(2\ell - 3)$

4. The sum of two consecutive odd integers is 24. Which equation can be used to find the first integer n? **(Lesson 2-5)**

   A $n + 1 = 24$
   B $n + 2 = 24$
   C $2n + 1 = 24$
   D $2n + 2 = 24$

5. The price of a quart of cream is no more than twice the price of a pint of cream. If a quart of cream costs \$2.98, which inequality best describes the price p of a pint of cream? **(Lesson 3-3)**

   A $2.98 \geq 2p$
   B $2.98 \leq 2p$
   C $2(2.98) \geq p$
   D $2(2.98) \leq p$

Cumulative Practice (continued)

6. Rose can calculate her phone bill using the equation $b = 0.1m + 12$. Which is the dependent variable? **(Lesson 4-3)**

Ⓐ b Ⓑ 0.1 Ⓒ m Ⓓ 12

7. Tim uses the function $g = 0.05m$ to find out how much money he needs for gasoline g based on the miles he travels m. Which statement is true? **(Lesson 4-3)**

Ⓐ The number of miles Tim travels depends on how much he needs for gasoline.

Ⓑ The number of miles Tim travels depends on the price of a gallon of gasoline.

Ⓒ The amount of money Tim needs for gasoline depends on the number of miles he travels.

Ⓓ The amount of money Tim needs for gasoline depends on 0.05.

8. Max wrote a number pattern in which each number in the pattern is 1 less than twice the previous number. What is the 5th number in the pattern if the first number is 2? **(Lesson 4-7)**

Ⓐ 9 Ⓑ 17 Ⓒ 25 Ⓓ 33

9. Which expression can be used to find the first n numbers in the pattern below? **(Lesson 4-7)**

$$4, 11, 18, 25, \ldots$$

Ⓐ $n + 4$ Ⓒ $n + 7$

Ⓑ $4n + 7$ Ⓓ $7n - 3$

10. Which of the graphs below is a function? **(Lesson 4-2)**

Ⓐ Ⓒ

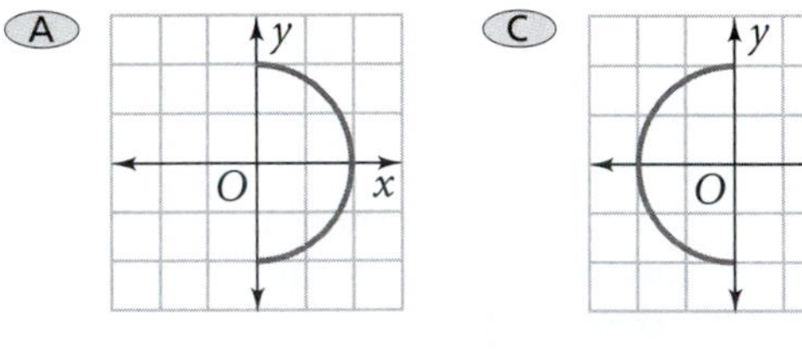

Ⓑ

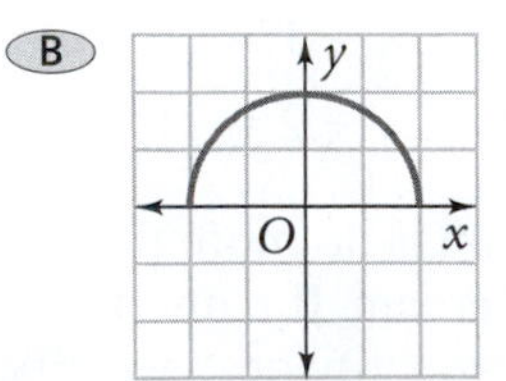

Ⓓ None of the above

11. Which equation below is NOT a function? **(Lesson 4-3)**

Ⓐ $y = x + 3$ Ⓒ $x = 3$

Ⓑ $y = 3$ Ⓓ $y = |x| + 3$

12. Which value of x would NOT make the relation $\{(0, 3), (2, 4), (x, 5), (6, 1)\}$ a function? **(Lesson 4-2)**

Ⓐ 2 Ⓑ 3 Ⓒ 4 Ⓓ 5

13. Is the following relation a function? **(Lesson 4-2)**

$\{(-2, 1), (0, 4), (3, 1), (3, 5), (-6, 0), (4, 1)\}$

Ⓐ Yes; each domain value corresponds to exactly one range value.

Ⓑ No; more than one domain value corresponds to the range value of 1.

Ⓒ No; the domain value 3 corresponds to more than one range value.

Ⓓ No; there are more domain values than range values.

14. Which graph has a domain of $\{x: -2 \le x \le 2\}$ and a range of $\{y: y \ge -1\}$? **(Lesson 4-3)**

Ⓐ Ⓒ Ⓑ

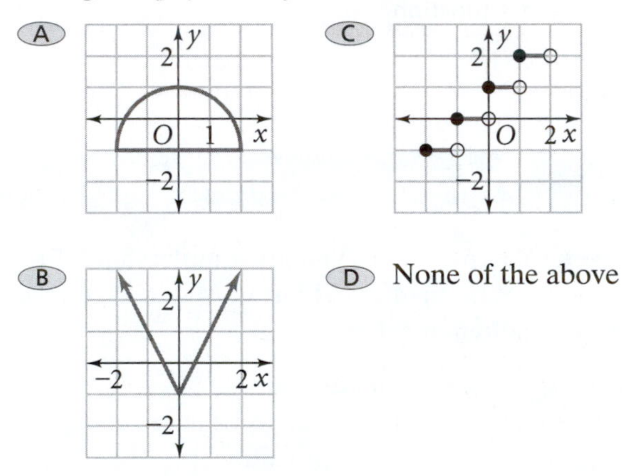

Ⓓ None of the above

15. What are the domain and range of the relation $\{(1, 2), (5, 3), (6, 4), (0, 8), (1, 0)\}$? **(Lesson 4-2)**

Ⓐ domain: $\{0, 2, 3, 4, 8\}$; range: $\{0, 1, 5, 6\}$

Ⓑ domain: $\{0, 1, 1, 5, 6\}$; range: $\{0, 2, 3, 4, 8\}$

Ⓒ domain: $\{0, 1, 5, 6\}$; range: $\{0, 2, 3, 4, 8\}$

Ⓓ domain and range: $\{0, 1, 2, 3, 4, 5, 6, 8\}$

16. Which function below has a domain of $\{x: x \ge -4\}$? **(Lesson 4-3)**

Ⓐ $f(x) = \sqrt{x + 4}$ Ⓒ $f(x) = \frac{1}{x + 4}$

Ⓑ $f(x) = x^2 + 16$ Ⓓ $f(x) = x + 4$

17. Mark gets paid \$.40 per mile to drive to work. How many miles did Mark drive if he received \$48.00? **(Lesson 4-5)**

Ⓐ 12 Ⓒ 120

Ⓑ 16 Ⓓ 160

Standards Mastery

18. Which is an example of inductive reasoning? **(Lesson 4-7)**

(A) You justify that $3(b + 2)$ simplifies to $3b + 6$ by using the Distributive Property.

(B) You know that to become president of the United States, you must be a natural-born citizen. You conclude that President Abraham Lincoln was born in the U.S.

(C) In order to graduate from a particular college, you must pass a swim test. Danielle graduates from the college. You conclude that she knows how to swim.

(D) You conclude that the next number in the pattern $1, -2, 3, -4, \ldots$ is 5.

19. Which is an example of deductive reasoning? **(Lesson 4-7)**

(A) Gas prices have increased every week for the past 5 weeks. You conclude that gas prices will increase next week.

(B) You conclude that since the side lengths of a triangle do not satisfy the Pythagorean Theorem, the triangle is not a right triangle.

(C) A doctor makes a diagnosis after studying a patient's symptoms.

(D) You predict a point on a graph based on the pattern of the data points.

20. Which statement is NOT true about the graph below? **(Lesson 4-3)**

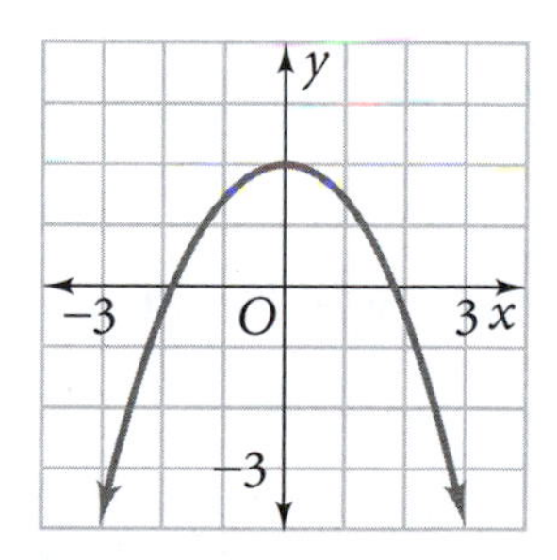

(A) The domain of the relation is $\{x: -3 \leq x \leq 3\}$.

(B) The range of the relation is $\{y: y \leq 2\}$.

(C) The graph passes the vertical-line test.

(D) The relation is a function.

21. What is the greatest value in the range of $y = x^2 - 7$ for the domain $\{-2, -1, 0, 1\}$? **(Lesson 4-3)**

(A) -8 (B) -7 (C) -6 (D) -3

22. William drove for 5 hours at an average speed of 54 mi/h. For the first two hours, he drove 45 mi/h. What was his average speed for the last three hours? **(Lesson 2-5)**

(A) 40 mi/h (C) 60 mi/h
(B) 50 mi/h (D) 65 mi/h

23. Rhonda mixes some 35% acid solution with some 70% acid solution to make 100 mL of a 42% acid solution. How much of the 35% acid solution did she use? **(Lesson 2-6)**

(A) 20 mL (C) 60 mL
(B) 40 mL (D) 80 mL

24. Which relation is a function? **(Lesson 4-2)**

(A) $\{(-2, 4), (4, 7), (-2, -3), (0, 10)\}$

(B) $\{(5, -6), (-3, 9), (-1, 2), (0, 4)\}$

(C) $\{(1, 2), (2, 3), (4, 1), (1, 5)\}$

(D) $\{(-3, 3), (-2, 2), (-1, 1), (-3, 0)\}$

Standards Reference Guide

California Content Standard	Item Number(s)
Alg1 5.0	3–5
Alg1 15.0	1, 2, 17, 22, 23
Alg1 16.0	6, 7, 20
Alg1 17.0	14–16, 21
Alg1 18.0	10–13, 24
Alg1 24.1	8, 9, 18, 19

For additional review and practice, see the *California Standards Review and Practice Workbook* or go online to use the

For: PHSchool.com, **Web Code:** baq-9045

Linear Equations and Their Graphs

What You've Learned

California Content Standards

5.0 Solve multi-step problems, including word problems, involving linear equations in one variable and provide justification for each step.

16.0 Understand the concepts of a relation and a function and give pertinent information about given relations and functions.

18.0 Determine whether a relation defined by a graph, a set of ordered pairs, or a symbolic expression is a function and justify the conclusion.

Check Your Readiness

GO for Help to the Lesson in green.

Adding and Subtracting Real Numbers (Lessons 1-4 and 1-5)

Simplify each expression.

1. $-5 + 7$ **2.** $2 - (-3)$ **3.** $-\frac{3}{4} + \frac{5}{6}$

4. $11 + (-4)$ **5.** $|1 - 8|$ **6.** $|-2 - 4|$

Solving Equations (Lesson 2-3)

Solve each equation. Check your solution.

7. $3x + 4x = 8 - x$ **8.** $12 - 3d = d$ **9.** $6x - 8 = 7 + x$

Transforming Equations (Review page 90)

Solve each equation for y.

10. $2y - x = 4$ **11.** $3x = y + 2$ **12.** $-2y - 2x = 4$

Identifying Coordinates (Lesson 4-1)

Name the coordinates of each point on the graph at the right.

13. A **14.** B

15. C **16.** D

17. E **18.** F

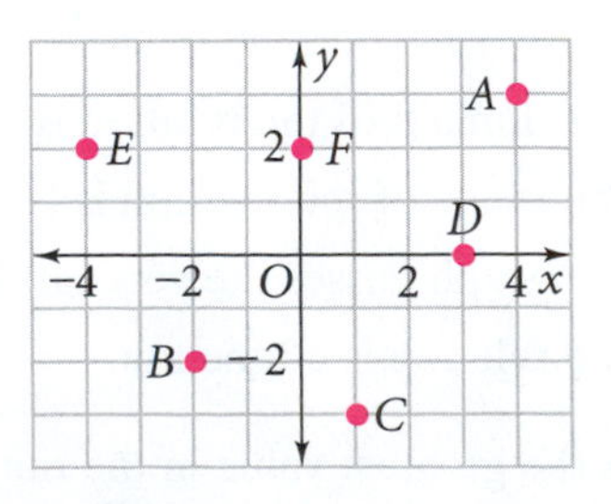

Graphing Functions (Lesson 4-3)

Make a table of values and graph each function.

19. $y = -\frac{2}{3}x$ **20.** $y = 2x + 1$ **21.** $y = x - 5$

What You'll Learn Next

California Content Standards

6.0 Graph a linear equation and compute the *x*- and *y*-intercepts.

7.0 Verify that a point lies on a line, given an equation of the line. Derive linear equations by using the point-slope formula.

8.0 Understand the concepts of parallel lines and perpendicular lines and how those slopes are related. Find the equation of a line perpendicular to a given line that passes through a given point.

▲ A glass pyramid covers the entrance to the Louvre Museum in Paris, France. Architects use slopes of parallel lines when designing buildings.

New Vocabulary

English and Spanish Audio Online

- **linear equation** (p. 239)
- **linear function** (p. 239)
- **linear parent function** (p. 239)
- **negative reciprocal** (p. 260)
- **parallel lines** (p. 259)
- **parent function** (p. 239)
- **perpendicular lines** (p. 260)
- **point-slope form** (p. 252)
- **rate of change** (p. 230)
- **slope** (p. 232)
- **slope-intercept form** (p. 240)
- **standard form** (p. 246)
- ***x*-intercept** (p. 246)
- ***y*-intercept** (p. 239)

5-1 Rate of Change and Slope

California Content Standards

6.0 Graph a linear equation and compute the *x*- and *y*-intercepts. ***Introduce***
7.0 Derive linear equations by using the point-slope formula. ***Introduce***
8.0 Understand the concepts of parallel lines and perpendicular lines and how those slopes are related. ***Introduce***

What You'll Learn

- To find rates of change from tables and graphs
- To find slope

. . . And Why

To find the rate of change of an airplane's altitude, as in Example 2

Check Skills You'll Need

GO for Help Lessons 4-3 and 1-5

Evaluate each function rule for $x = -5$.

1. $y = 7 - x$ **2.** $y = 2x + 5$ **3.** $y = -\frac{2}{5}x + 3$

Write in simplest form.

4. $\frac{7 - 3}{3 - 1}$ **5.** $\frac{3 - 5}{6 - 0}$ **6.** $\frac{8 - (-4)}{3 - 7}$

7. $\frac{-1 - 2}{0 - 5}$ **8.** $\frac{-6 - (-4)}{-2 - 6}$ **9.** $\frac{0 - 1}{1 - 0}$

New Vocabulary • rate of change • slope

Finding Rates of Change

CA Standards Investigation Exploring Rate of Change

The diagram at the right shows the side view of a ski lift.

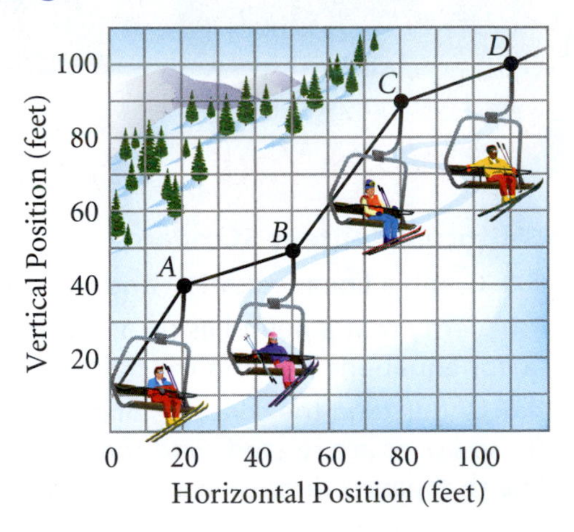

1. What is the vertical change from *A* to *B*? From *B* to *C*? From *C* to *D*?

2. What is the horizontal change from *A* to *B*? From *B* to *C*? From *D* to *D*?

3. Find the ratio of the vertical change to the horizontal change for each section of the ski lift.

4. Which section is the steepest? How does the ratio for that section compare to the ratios of the other sections?

Vocabulary Tip

A rate is a comparison of two quantities measured in different units.

In the graph above, $\overline{AB}$ and $\overline{BC}$ have different rates of change.

Rate of change allows you to see the relationship between two quantities that are changing. If one quantity depends on the other, then the following is true.

$$\text{rate of change} = \frac{\text{change in the dependent variable}}{\text{change in the independent variable}}$$

Cost of Renting a Computer	
Number of Days	Rental Charge
1	\$60
2	\$75
3	\$90
4	\$105
5	\$120

1 EXAMPLE Finding Rate of Change Using a Table

For the data at the left, is the rate of change for each pair of consecutive days the same? What does the rate of change represent?

$$\text{rate of change} = \frac{\text{change in cost}}{\text{change in number of days}}$$ **Cost depends on the number of days.**

$$\frac{75-60}{2-1} = \frac{15}{1} \qquad \frac{90-75}{3-2} = \frac{15}{1}$$

$$\frac{105-90}{4-3} = \frac{15}{1} \qquad \frac{120-105}{5-4} = \frac{15}{1}$$

The rate of change for each consecutive pair of days is $\frac{15}{1}$. The rate of change is the same for all the data. It costs \$15 for each day a computer is rented after the first day.

CA Standards Check **1** **a.** Find the rate of change using Days 5 and 2.

b. **Critical Thinking** Does finding the rate of change for just one pair of days mean that the rate of change is the same for all the data? Explain.

The graphs of all the ordered pairs (number of days, cost) in Example 1 lie on a line as shown at the right. So, the data are linear.

You can use a graph to find a rate of change. Recall that the independent variable is plotted on the horizontal axis and the dependent variable is plotted on the vertical axis.

Cost (dollars) 0 20 40 60 80 100 120; Days 1 2 3 4 5

$$\text{rate of change} = \frac{\text{vertical change}}{\text{horizontal change}} = \frac{\text{change in the dependent variable}}{\text{change in the independent variable}}$$

2 EXAMPLE Finding Rate of Change Using a Graph

The graph shows the altitude of an airplane as it comes in for a landing. Find the rate of change. Explain what this rate of change means.

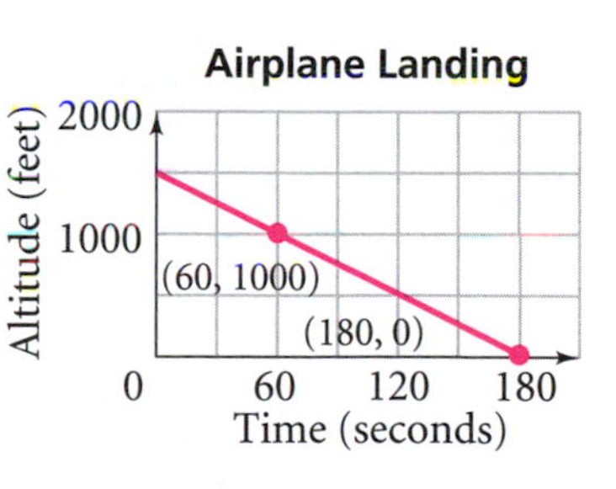

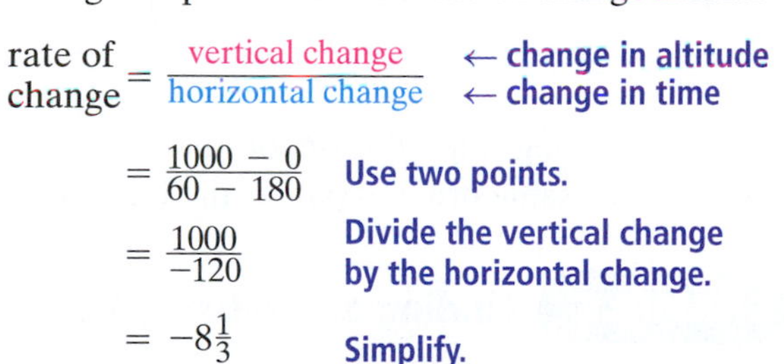

$$\text{rate of change} = \frac{\text{vertical change}}{\text{horizontal change}}$$ **← change in altitude** / **← change in time**

$$= \frac{1000-0}{60-180}$$ **Use two points.**

$$= \frac{1000}{-120}$$ **Divide the vertical change by the horizontal change.**

$$= -8\tfrac{1}{3}$$ **Simplify.**

The rate of change is $-8\frac{1}{3}$. The airplane descends $8\frac{1}{3}$ feet each second.

CA Standards Check **2** Find the rate of change of the data in the graph. The graph shows the distance traveled by an automobile over time.

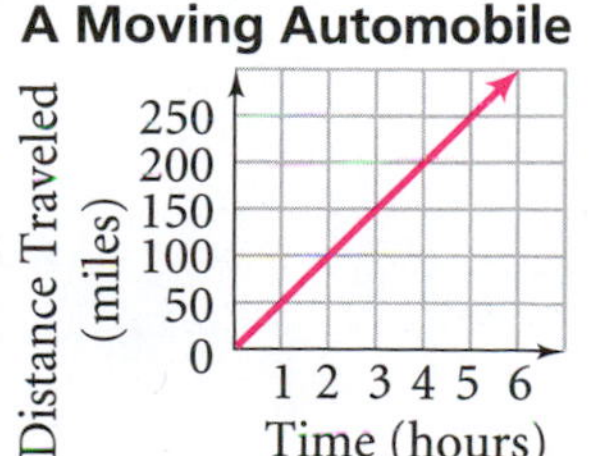

The grade of a road is the ratio of rise to run expressed as a percent. For example, a road with 100% grade is at a 45° angle with level ground.

Finding Slope

The slope of a line is its rate of change.

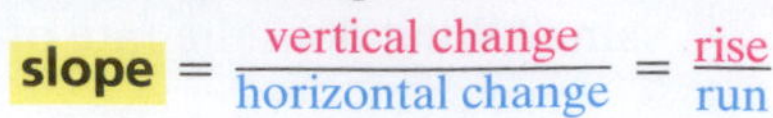

$$\textbf{slope} = \frac{\text{vertical change}}{\text{horizontal change}} = \frac{\text{rise}}{\text{run}}$$

3 EXAMPLE Finding Slope Using a Graph

Find the slope of the line.

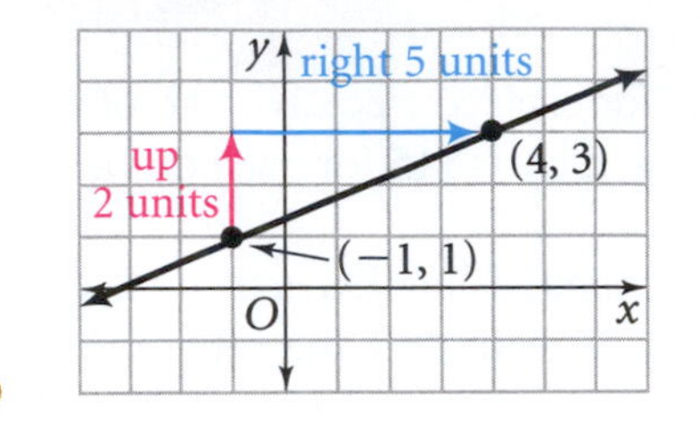

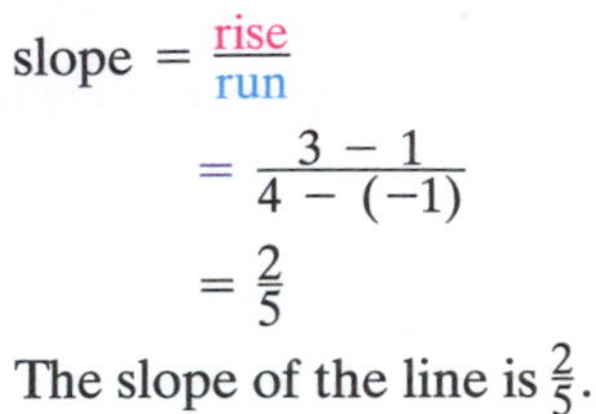

$$\text{slope} = \frac{\text{rise}}{\text{run}}$$
$$= \frac{3 - 1}{4 - (-1)}$$
$$= \frac{2}{5}$$

The slope of the line is $\frac{2}{5}$.

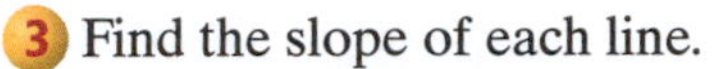

CA Standards Check 3 Find the slope of each line.

a.

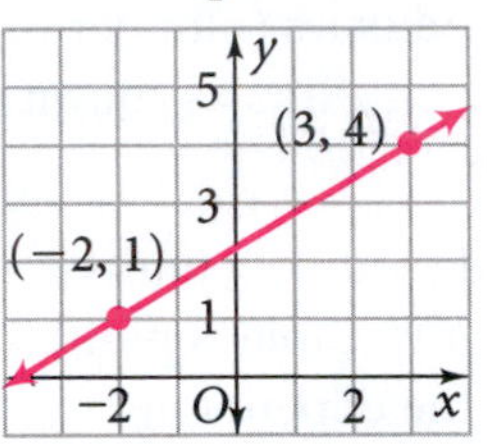

b.

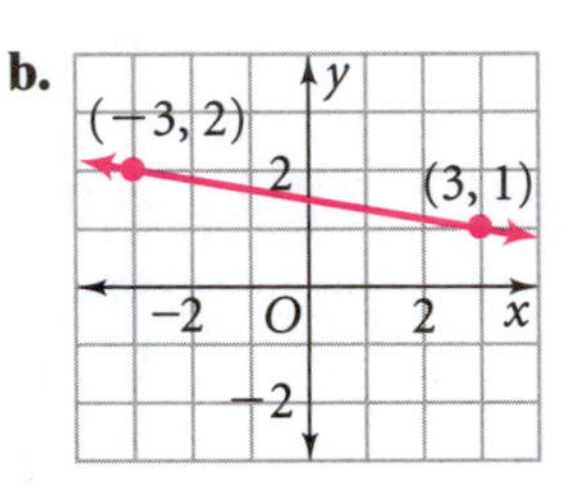

You can use any two points on a line to find its slope. You use subscripts to distinguish between two points. In the diagram, (x_1, y_1) are the coordinates of P, and (x_2, y_2) are the coordinates of Q. To find the slope of $\overleftrightarrow{PQ}$, you can use the following formula.

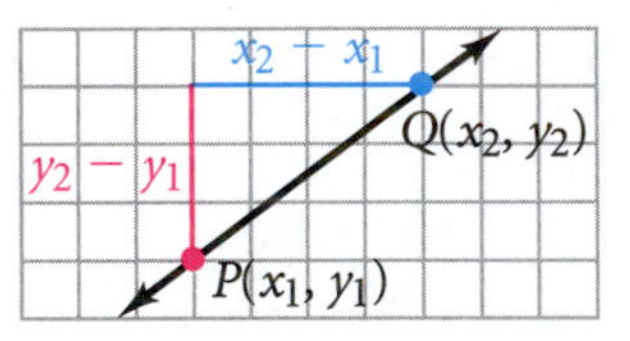

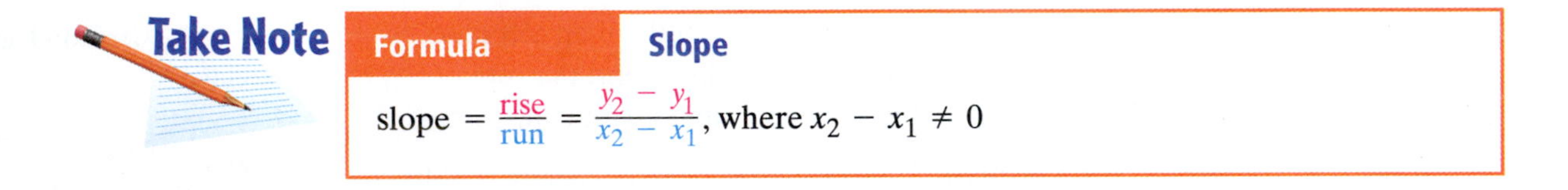

Take Note

Formula **Slope**

$$\text{slope} = \frac{\text{rise}}{\text{run}} = \frac{y_2 - y_1}{x_2 - x_1}, \text{ where } x_2 - x_1 \neq 0$$

When calculating slope, the x-coordinate you use first in the denominator must belong to the same ordered pair as the y-coordinate you use first in the numerator.

Study Tip

To set up the subtraction in the slope formula, think of moving from the coordinates of B to the coordinates of A.

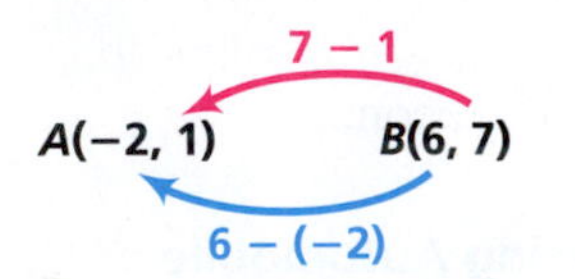

4 EXAMPLE Finding Slope Using Points

Find the slope of the line through $A(-2, 1)$ and $B(6, 7)$.

$$\text{slope} = \frac{y_2 - y_1}{x_2 - x_1}$$ Substitute (6, 7) for (x_2, y_2) and $(-2, 1)$ for (x_1, y_1).

$$= \frac{7 - 1}{6 - (-2)}$$

$$= \frac{6}{8}$$ Simplify.

The slope of $\overleftrightarrow{AB}$ is $\frac{6}{8}$ or $\frac{3}{4}$.

CA Standards Check 4 Find the slope of the line through $C(2, 5)$ and $D(4, 7)$.

You can also analyze the graphs of horizontal and vertical lines. The next example shows why the slope of a horizontal line is 0, and the slope of a vertical line is undefined.

5 EXAMPLE Horizontal and Vertical Lines

Video Tutor Help
Visit: PHSchool.com
Web Code: bae-0775

Find the slope of each line.

a.

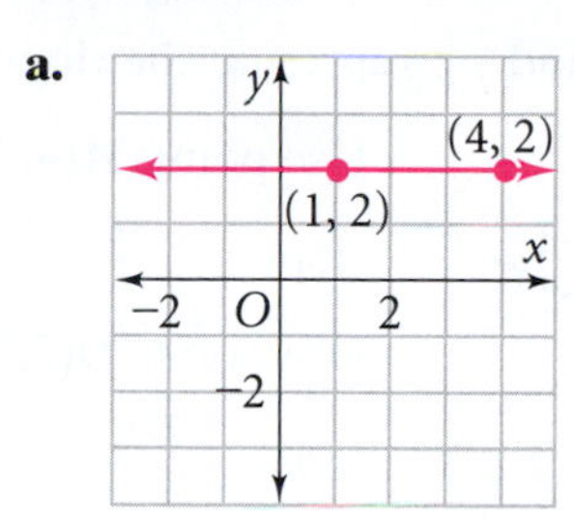

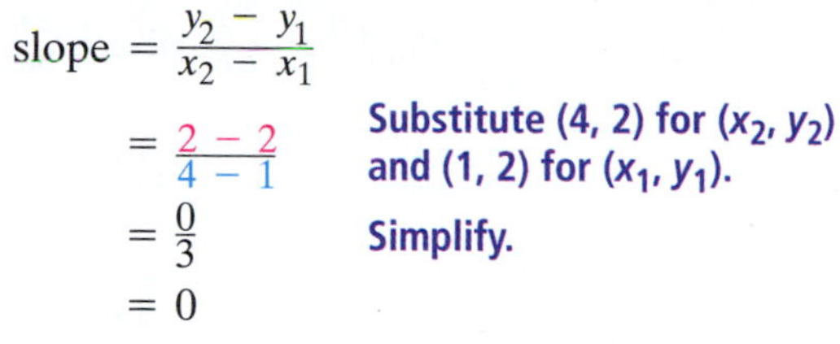

$$\text{slope} = \frac{y_2 - y_1}{x_2 - x_1}$$

$= \frac{2 - 2}{4 - 1}$ — Substitute (4, 2) for (x_2, y_2) and (1, 2) for (x_1, y_1).

$= \frac{0}{3}$ — Simplify.

$= 0$

The slope of the horizontal line is 0.

b.

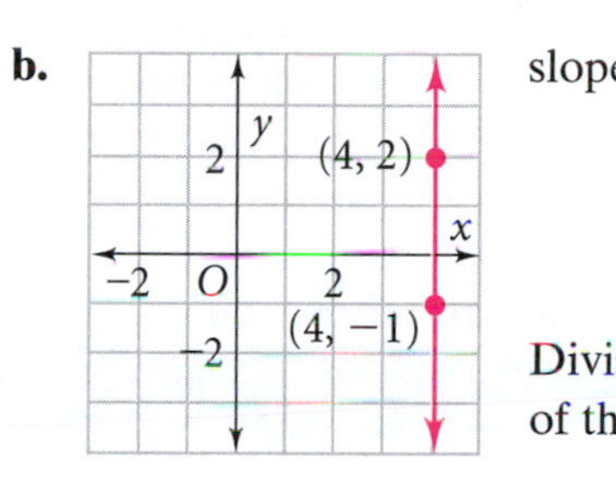

$$\text{slope} = \frac{y_2 - y_1}{x_2 - x_1}$$

$= \frac{2 - (-1)}{4 - 4}$ — Substitute (4, 2) for (x_2, y_2) and (4, −1) for (x_1, y_1).

$= \frac{3}{0}$ — Simplify.

Division by zero is undefined. So, the slope of the vertical line is undefined.

CA Standards Check 5 Find the slope of each line.

a.

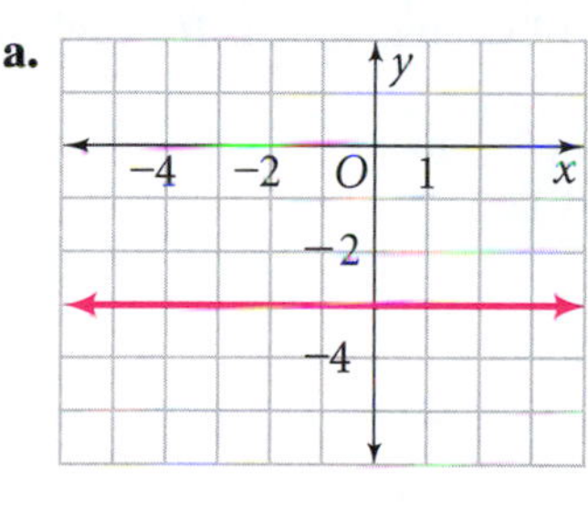

b.

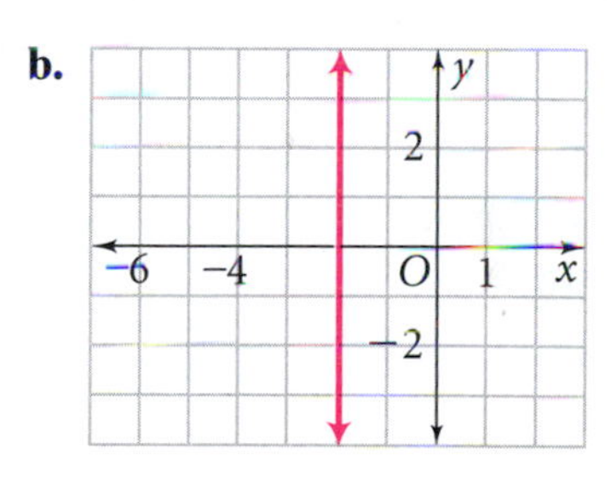

The following summarizes what you have learned about slope.

Summary **Slopes of Lines**

A line with positive slope slants upward from left to right.

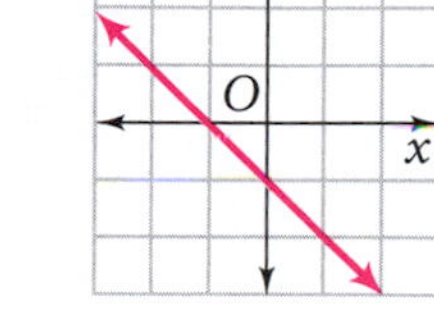

A line with negative slope slants downward from left to right.

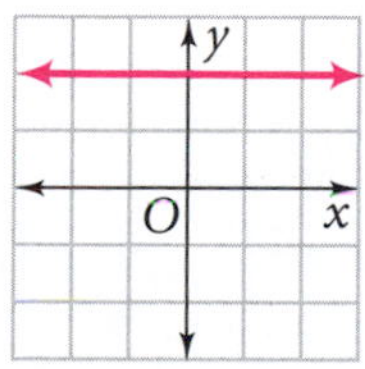

A line with a slope of 0 is horizontal.

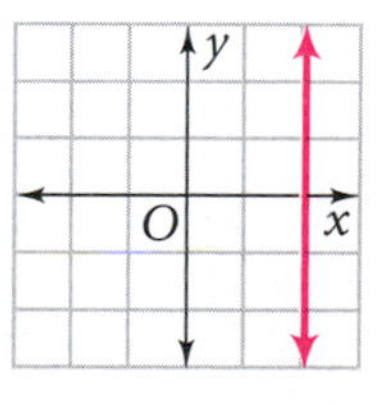

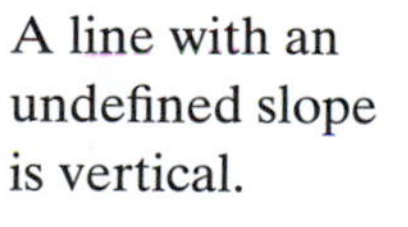

A line with an undefined slope is vertical.

Mathematical Reasoning

24.0 Derive linear equations by using the point-slope formula. *Develop*

Understanding the Slope of a Line

You can use similar triangles to show that the slope of a line is the same no matter which two points you use to calculate it. In the graph below, $\triangle ABC \sim \triangle DEF$. Recall that, in similar triangles, the ratios of the lengths of corresponding sides are equal. So $\frac{AB}{BC} = \frac{DE}{EF}$, where $\frac{AB}{BC}$ and $\frac{DE}{EF}$ represent the slope of the line.

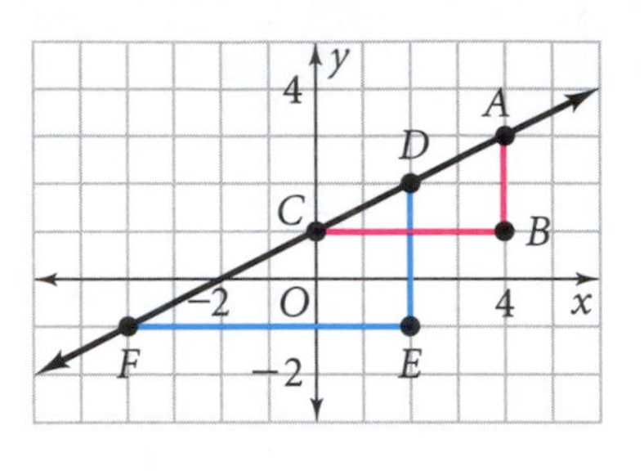

Use points $A(4, 3)$ and $C(0, 1)$.

$$\text{slope} = \frac{AB}{BC} = \frac{3-1}{4-0} = \frac{2}{4} \text{ or } \frac{1}{2}$$

Use points $D(2, 2)$ and $F(-4, -1)$.

$$\text{slope} = \frac{DE}{EF} = \frac{2-(-1)}{2-(-4)} = \frac{3}{6} \text{ or } \frac{1}{2}$$

So the slope of the line is the same regardless of which two points you use.

EXERCISES

For more exercises, see *Extra Skills and Word Problem Practice.*

Standards Practice

Alg1 6.0, 7.0, 8.0, 24.3

A Practice by Example

Examples 1, 2 (page 231)

The rate of change is constant in each table and graph. Find the rate of change. Explain what the rate of change means for each situation.

1.

Time (hours)	Temperature (°F)
1	−2
4	7
7	16
10	25
13	34

2.

People	Cost (dollars)
2	7.90
3	11.85
4	15.80
5	19.75
6	23.70

3.

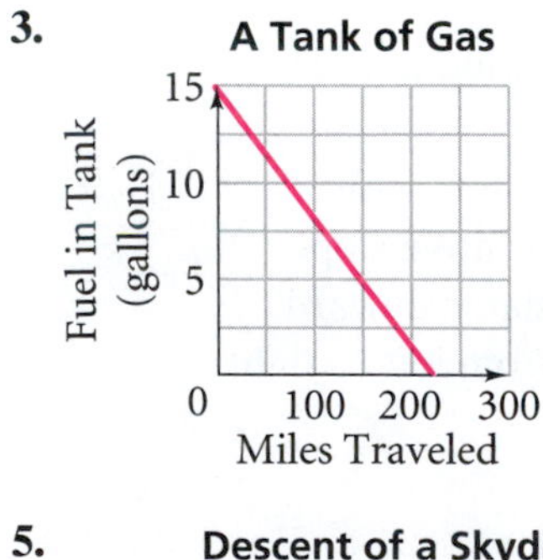
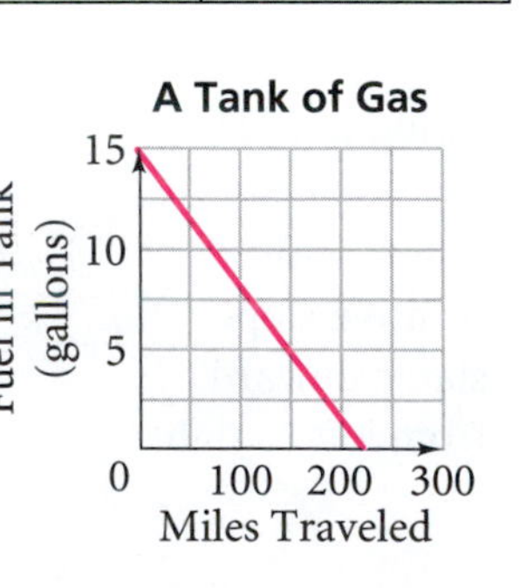

4.

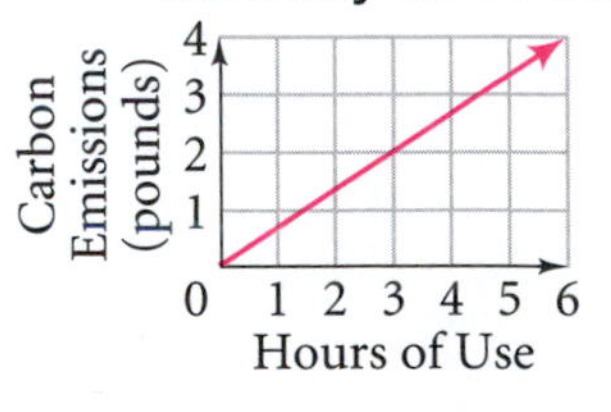

5.

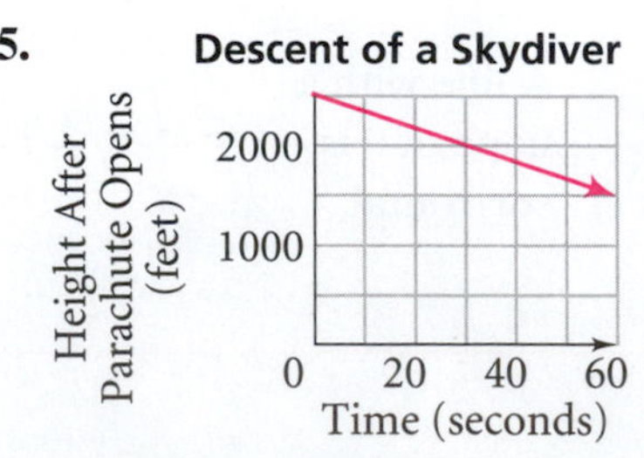

6.

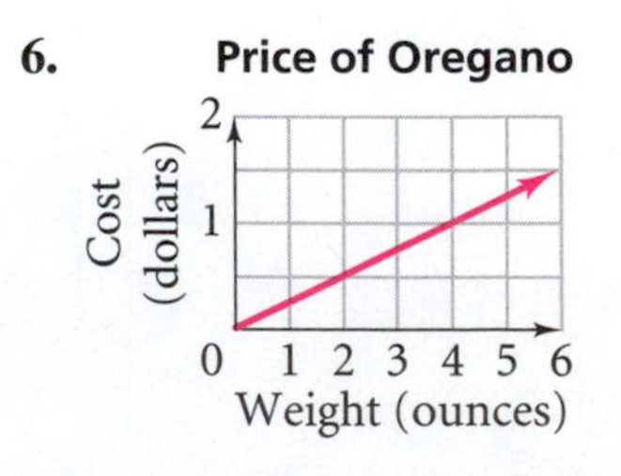

Example 3 (page 232)

Find the slope of each line.

7.

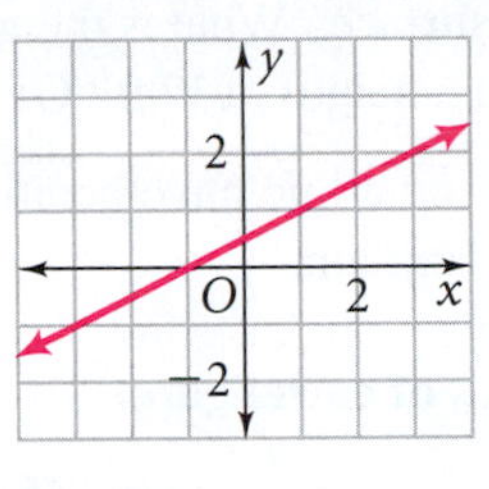

8.

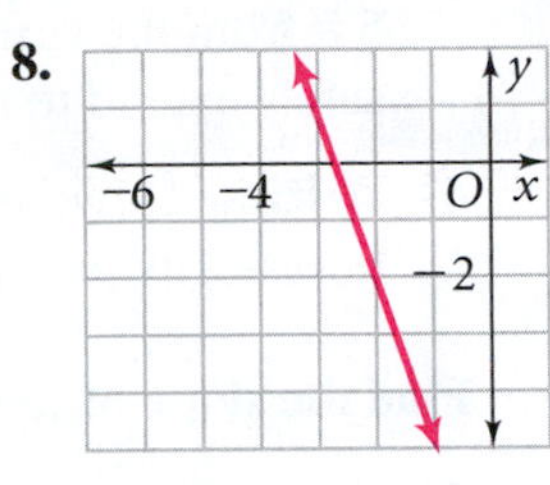

9.

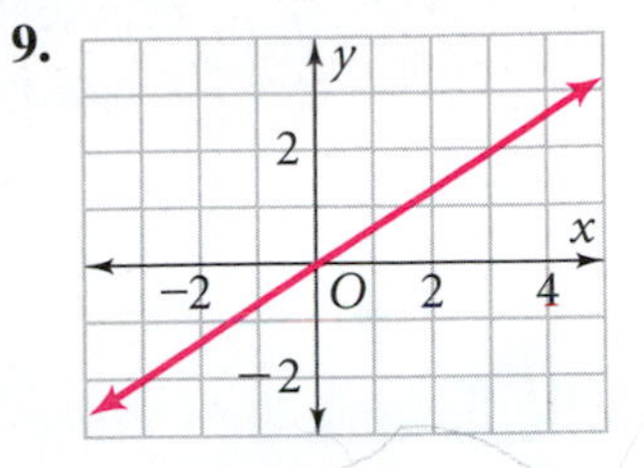

Example 4 (page 232)

Find the slope of the line that passes through each pair of points.

10. (3, 2), (5, 6)
11. (5, 6), (3, 2)
12. (4, 8), (8, 11)
13. (−4, 4), (2, −5)
14. (−2, 1), (1, −2)
15. (−3, 1), (3, −5)
16. (−8, 0), (1, 5)
17. (0, 0), (3, 5)
18. (−4, −5), (−9, 1)
19. (5, 0), (0, 2)
20. (−7, 1), (7, 8)
21. (0, −1), (1, −6)

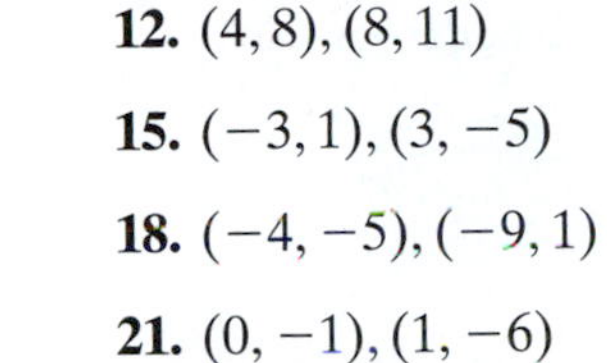

Example 5 (page 233)

State whether the slope is zero or undefined.

22. **23.**

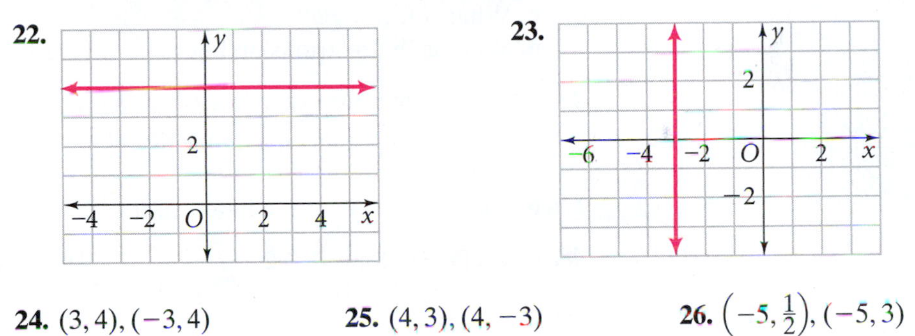

24. (3, 4), (−3, 4)
25. (4, 3), (4, −3)
26. $\left(-5, \frac{1}{2}\right), (-5, 3)$

B Apply Your Skills

Find the rate of change for each situation.

27. A baby is 18 in. long at birth and 27 in. long at ten months.

28. The cost of group museum tickets is $48 for four people and $78 for ten people.

29. You drive 30 mi in one hour and 120 mi in four hours.

Find the slope of the line passing through each pair of points.

30. (−7, 1), (7, 8)
31. $\left(4, 1\frac{2}{3}\right), \left(-2, \frac{2}{3}\right)$
32. (0, 3.5), (−4, 2.5)
33. $\left(\frac{1}{2}, 8\right), (1, -2)$
34. $\left(-5, \frac{1}{2}\right), (-5, 3)$
35. (0.5, 6.25), (3, −1.25)

Through the given point, draw the line with the given slope.

36. $K(3, 5)$ slope −2
37. $M(5, 2)$ slope $-\frac{1}{2}$
38. $Q(-2, 3)$ slope $\frac{3}{5}$
39. $R(2, -3)$ slope $-\frac{4}{3}$

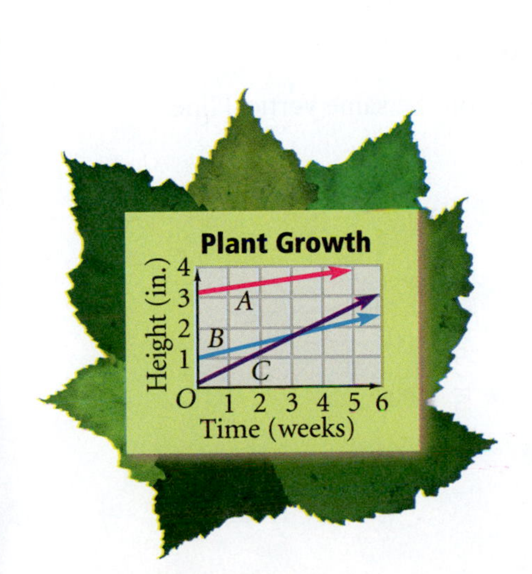

40. a. Which line in the graph at the left is the steepest?
b. During the 6-week period, which plant had the greatest rate of change? The least rate of change? How do you know?

41. a. Find the slope of the line through $A(4, -3)$ and $B(1, -5)$ using A for (x_2, y_2) and B for (x_1, y_1).
b. Find the slope of the line in part (a) using B for (x_2, y_2) and A for (x_1, y_1).
c. Critical Thinking Explain why it does not matter which point you use for (x_2, y_2) and which point you use for (x_1, y_1) when you calculate a slope.

42. An extension ladder has a label that says, "Do not place base of ladder less than 5 ft from the vertical surface." What is the greatest slope possible if the ladder can safely extend to reach a height of 12 ft? Of 18 ft?

43. **Writing** If two points on a line have positive coordinates, is the slope necessarily positive? Explain.

Homework Video Tutor

Visit: PHSchool.com
Web Code: bae-0501

Find the slope of the sides of each figure.

44.
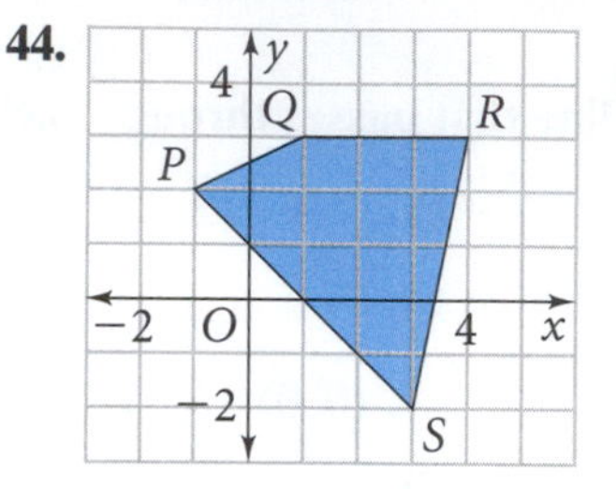

45.
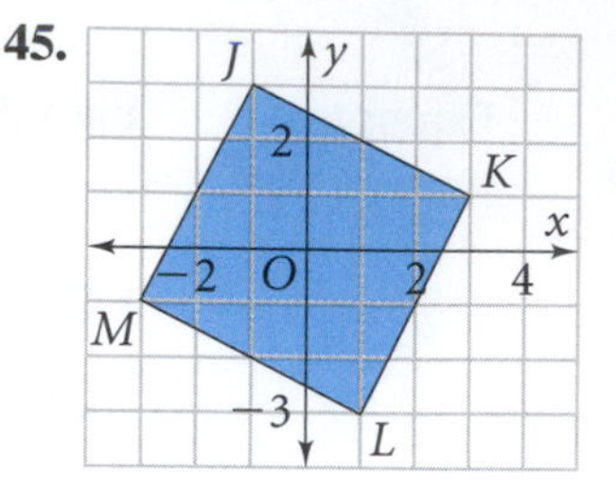

46. **a.** Graph the direct variation $y = -\frac{2}{3}x$.
b. What is the constant of variation?
c. What is the slope?
d. What is the relationship between the constant of variation and the slope?

47. **a.** Name two points on a line with a slope of $\frac{3}{4}$.
b. Name two points on a line with a slope of $-\frac{1}{2}$.

Each pair of points lies on a line with the given slope. Find x or y.

48. $(2, 4), (x, 8)$; slope $= -2$

49. $(2, 4), (x, 8)$; slope $= -\frac{1}{2}$

50. $(4, 3), (x, 7)$; slope $= 2$

51. $(x, 3), (2, 8)$; slope $= -\frac{5}{2}$

52. $(-4, y), (2, 4y)$; slope $= 6$

53. $(3, 5), (x, 2)$; undefined slope

For a guide to solving Exercise 54, see p. 238.

Math Reasoning **In Exercises 54–60, tell whether each statement is *true* or *false*. If false, give a counterexample.**

54. A rate of change must be either positive or zero.

55. All horizontal lines have the same slope.

56. A line with slope 1 always passes through the origin.

57. Two lines may have the same slope.

58. The slope of a line that passes through Quadrant III must be negative.

59. A line with slope 0 never passes through point $(0, 0)$.

60. Two points with the same x-coordinate are always on the same vertical line.

The rental cost of a carousel varies depending on whether the horses are 2 or 3 abreast.

61. The graph shows how much it costs to rent carousel equipment.
a. Estimate the slope of the line. What does that number mean?
b. Customers pay $2 for a ride. What is the average number of customers needed to cover the rental costs?

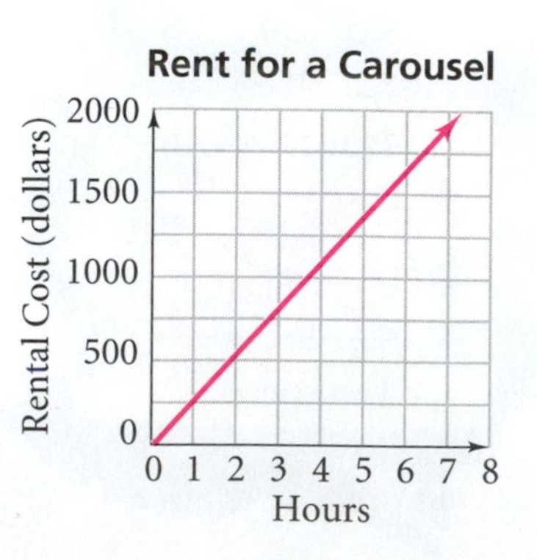

62. **Error Analysis** A friend says the slope of a line passing through $(1, 7)$ and $(3, 9)$ is equal to the ratio $\frac{1 - 3}{7 - 9}$. What is your friend's error?

Challenge

Find the slope of the line passing through each pair of points.

63. $(a, -b), (-a, -b)$ **64.** $(-m, n), (3m, -n)$ **65.** $(2a, b), (c, 2d)$

Do the points in each set lie on the same line? Explain your answer.

66. $A(1, 3), B(4, 2), C(-2, 4)$

67. $G(3, 5), H(-1, 3), I(7, 7)$

68. $D(-2, 3), E(0, -1), F(2, 1)$

69. $P(4, 2), Q(-3, 2), R(2, 5)$

70. $G(1, -2), H(-1, -5), I(5, 4)$

71. $S(-3, 4), T(0, 2), X(-3, 0)$

Multiple Choice Practice

For California Standards Tutorials, visit PHSchool.com. Web Code: baq-9045

Alg1 7.0

72. The line shown on the graph contains the points $(-3, -2)$ and $(2, 2)$. What is the slope of the line?

Ⓐ $\frac{1}{4}$ Ⓒ $\frac{5}{4}$

Ⓑ $\frac{4}{5}$ Ⓓ 4

Alg1 16.0

73. Which ordered pair could be removed from the relation below to change it into a function?

$\{(2, 3), (3, 2), (2, 5), (5, 4), (1, 6), (6, -1), (25, 31)\}$

Ⓐ $(2, 5)$ Ⓑ $(25, 31)$ Ⓒ $(6, -1)$ Ⓓ $(3, 2)$

Alg1 18.0

74. For the graph of $y = |x| + 1$, which of the following statements is true?

Ⓐ The graph represents a function whose range is all real numbers.

Ⓑ The graph represents a function that assigns to each member of the domain exactly one member of the range.

Ⓒ The graph does not represent a function.

Ⓓ The graph represents neither a function nor a relation.

Mixed Review

GO for Help

Lesson 4-4

Write a function rule for each situation.

75. the total cost of renting a movie for n days if it costs \$3.50/day

76. the total profit if supplies and wages cost \$232, and each item q sells for \$4.95

Lesson 3-6

Solve each equation. If there is no solution, write *no solution*.

77. $|c| + 4 = -3$ **78.** $-7|m| = -28$ **79.** $5|j| - 6 = 19$

Lesson 2-2

Solve.

80. $x + 3 + 2x = -6$ **81.** $3(2t + 5) = -9$ **82.** $9 = y + 2(4y - 5)$

83. $4n - 7(n - 9) = 42$ **84.** $2(7 - q) - 4 = 0$ **85.** $\frac{2}{5}(p + 10) = 0$

GPS Guided Problem Solving

FOR USE WITH PAGE 236, EXERCISE 54

24.3 Use counterexamples to show that an assertion is false and recognize that a single counterexample is sufficient to refute an assertion. *Develop*

Understanding Math Problems **Read through the problem below. Then follow along with what Vera thinks as she solves the problem. Check your understanding with the exercises at the bottom of the page.**

Tell whether the statement is *true* or *false*. If false, give a counterexample.

A rate of change must be either positive or zero.

What Vera Thinks	What Vera Writes
First, I will determine whether or not a rate of change can be positive.	Yes, the rate of change for (1, 2) and (3, 4) is positive. $\frac{4-2}{3-1} = \frac{2}{2}$, or 1
Then I will determine whether or not a rate of change can be zero.	Yes, the rate of change for (1, 2) and (4, 2) is zero. $\frac{2-2}{4-1} = \frac{0}{3}$, or 0
Can a rate of change be something other than positive or zero? Yes, a rate of change can be negative or undefined. I only need to give one counterexample to prove that the statement is false.	The rate of change for (2, 3) and (4, −1) is neither positive nor zero. $\frac{-1-3}{4-2} = \frac{-4}{2}$, or −2
I will write my answer in a sentence.	The statement is false. The rate of change for (2, 3) and (4, −1) is negative.

EXERCISES

Tell whether each statement is *true* or *false*. If false, give a counterexample.

1. A line always passes through three quadrants.
2. A vertical line always crosses the y-axis.
3. You can use any two points on a line to determine its slope.

5-2 Slope-Intercept Form

California Content Standards

6.0 Graph a linear equation. ***Develop***

7.0 Verify that a point lies on a line, given an equation of the line. ***Develop***

What You'll Learn

- To write linear equations in slope-intercept form
- To graph linear equations

. . . And Why

To use a graph to relate total cost to number of items purchased, as in Example 5

GO for Help Lessons 1-2 and 1-6

Evaluate each expression.

1. $6a + 3$ for $a = 2$

2. $-2x - 5$ for $x = 3$

3. $\frac{1}{4}x + 2$ for $x = 16$

4. $0.2x + 2$ for $x = 15$

5. $8 - 5n$ for $n = 3$

6. $-4p + 9$ for $p = 2$

New Vocabulary • linear function • parent function • linear parent function • linear equation • *y*-intercept • slope-intercept form

Writing Linear Equations

Vocabulary Tip

The word <u>linear</u> contains the word "line."

In Lesson 4-5, you studied direct variations such as $y = 3x$. The graph of a direct variation is a straight line. All direct variations are linear functions. A **linear function** is a function that graphs a line. Direct variations are only part of the family of linear functions. For example, $y = -\frac{1}{2}x + 1$ is a linear function but not a direct variation because it does not go through (0, 0).

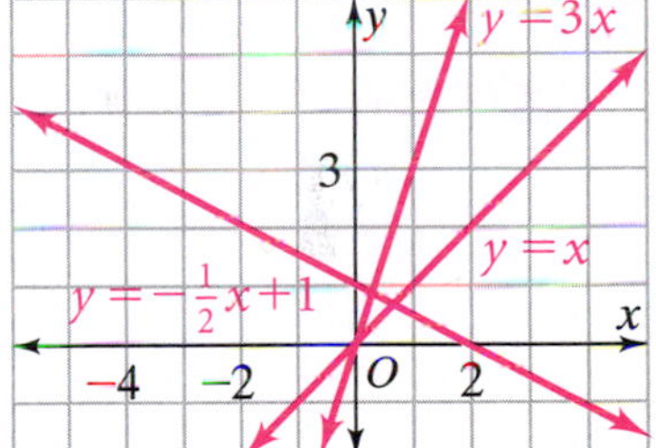

A **parent function** is the simplest equation of a function. The equation $y = x$ or $f(x) = x$ is the **linear parent function.**

A **linear equation** is an equation that models a linear function. In a linear equation, the variable cannot be raised to a power other than 1. So $y = 2x$ is the equation of a linear function, but $y = x^2$ or $y = 2^x$ are not.

The equation of a line gives important information about its graph. Consider the table and graph of $y = -2x + 1$.

x	−2x + 1	y
0	−2(0) + 1	1
1	−2(1) + 1	−1
2	−2(2) + 1	−3

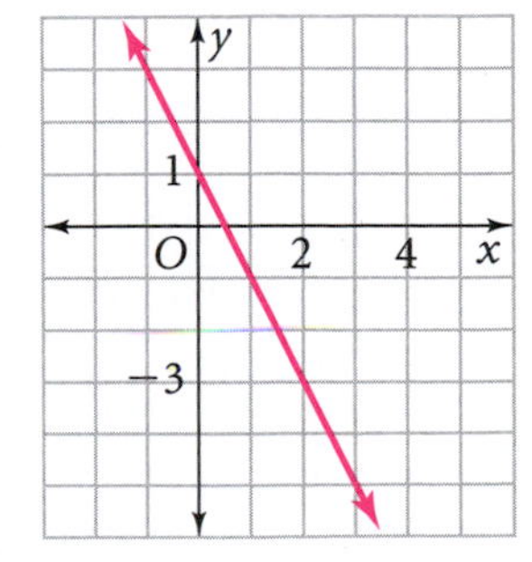

Two points on the line are (0, 1) and (2, −3). The slope is $\frac{1 - (-3)}{0 - 2} = -\frac{4}{2}$ or −2. The ***y*-intercept** is the *y*-coordinate of the point where a line crosses the *y*-axis. Since $y = -2x + 1$ crosses the *y*-axis at (0, 1), the *y*-intercept is 1.

If you know the slope of a line and its *y*-intercept, you can write the equation of the line. The letter *m* refers to the *slope.*

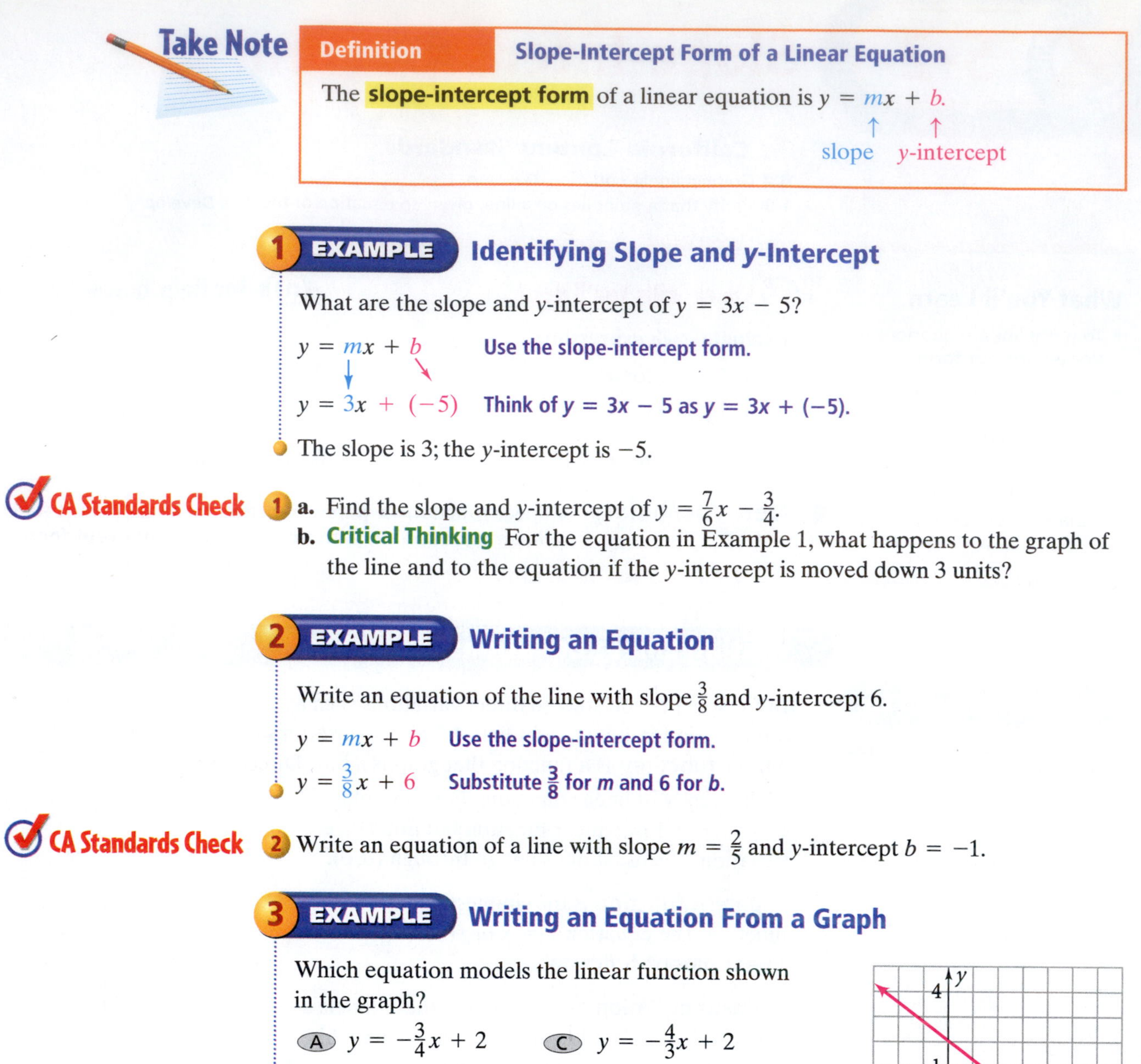

Take Note

Definition — **Slope-Intercept Form of a Linear Equation**

The **slope-intercept form** of a linear equation is $y = mx + b$.

m ↑ slope b ↑ y-intercept

1 EXAMPLE Identifying Slope and y-Intercept

What are the slope and y-intercept of $y = 3x - 5$?

$y = mx + b$ **Use the slope-intercept form.**

$y = 3x + (-5)$ **Think of $y = 3x - 5$ as $y = 3x + (-5)$.**

The slope is 3; the y-intercept is -5.

CA Standards Check 1
a. Find the slope and y-intercept of $y = \frac{7}{6}x - \frac{3}{4}$.
b. Critical Thinking For the equation in Example 1, what happens to the graph of the line and to the equation if the y-intercept is moved down 3 units?

2 EXAMPLE Writing an Equation

Write an equation of the line with slope $\frac{3}{8}$ and y-intercept 6.

$y = mx + b$ **Use the slope-intercept form.**

$y = \frac{3}{8}x + 6$ **Substitute $\frac{3}{8}$ for m and 6 for b.**

CA Standards Check 2 Write an equation of a line with slope $m = \frac{2}{5}$ and y-intercept $b = -1$.

3 EXAMPLE Writing an Equation From a Graph

Which equation models the linear function shown in the graph?

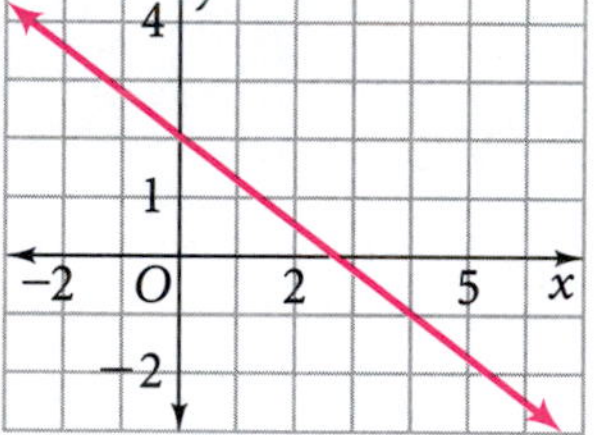

Ⓐ $y = -\frac{3}{4}x + 2$ Ⓒ $y = -\frac{4}{3}x + 2$

Ⓑ $y = 2x - \frac{4}{3}x$ Ⓓ $y = 2x - \frac{3}{4}$

Find the slope. Two points on the line are $(0, 2)$ and $(4, -1)$.

$$\text{slope} = \frac{-1 - 2}{4 - 0} = -\frac{3}{4}$$

The y-intercept is 2. Write an equation in slope-intercept form.

$y = mx + b$

$y = -\frac{3}{4}x + 2$ **Substitute $-\frac{3}{4}$ for m and 2 for b.**

The equation is $y = -\frac{3}{4}x + 2$. So the answer is A.

Online active math

For: Slope-Intercept Activity
Use: Interactive Textbook, 5-2

CA Standards Check 3
a. Write the equation of the line using the points $(0, 1)$ and $(2, 2)$.
b. Critical Thinking Does the equation of the line change if you use $(-2, 0)$ instead of $(2, 2)$? Explain.

Verifying Solutions and Graphing Linear Equations

Each point on the graph of an equation is an ordered pair that makes the equation true. To verify that a point lies on a line, substitute its coordinates for x and y in the equation. If doing so gives a true statement, then the point lies on the line.

4 EXAMPLE Verifying Points on a Line

a. Determine whether $(3, -5)$ lies on the graph of $y = -3x + 4$.

$$y = -3x + 4$$

$-5 \overset{?}{=} -3(3) + 4$ **Substitute 3 for x and −5 for y.**

$-5 \overset{?}{=} -9 + 4$ **Multiply.**

$-5 = -5$ ✓ **Add.**

$(3, -5)$ is a solution.

b. Determine whether $(8, 4)$ lies on the graph of $3y = 2x - 1$.

$$3y = 2x - 1$$

$3(4) \overset{?}{=} 2(8) - 1$ **Substitute 8 for x and 4 for y.**

$12 \overset{?}{=} 16 - 1$ **Multiply.**

$12 \neq 15$ ✗ **Subtract.**

$(8, 4)$ is *not* a solution.

CA Standards Check 4 **a.** Determine whether $(1, 6)$ lies on the graph of $y = 4x - 2$.
b. Determine whether $(5, -7)$ lies on the graph of $3y + 5x = 4$.

The graph of a linear equation is a line that indicates all the solutions of the equation. You can use the slope and y-intercept to graph a line.

5 EXAMPLE Graphing Equations

You buy vegetables at a farmer's market for \$2 per pound. The equation $y = 2x$ represents the situation where x is the number of pounds and y is the total cost of your purchase. Graph the equation.

In the United States, tomatoes cost an average of \$1.22 per pound.

Step 1
The y-intercept is 0. So plot a point at $(0, 0)$.

Step 2
The slope is 2, or $\frac{2}{1}$. Use the slope to plot a second point.

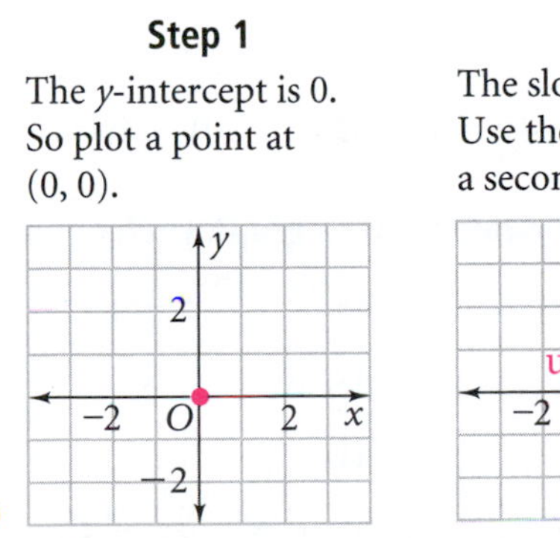

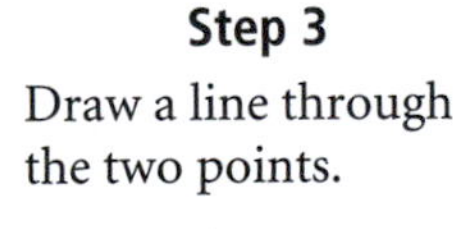

Step 3
Draw a line through the two points.

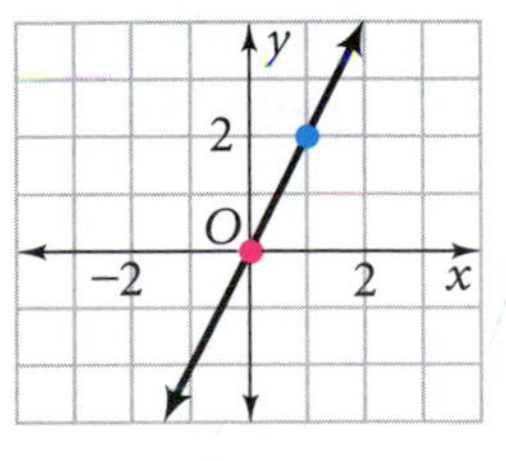

CA Standards Check 5 You buy various snacks for \$1.50 per bag. You save \$2 using your store rewards card. The equation $y = \frac{3}{2}x - 2$ represents the situation, where x is the number of bags and y is the total cost of your purchase. Graph the equation.

EXERCISES

Standards Practice

For more exercises, see *Extra Skills and Word Problem Practice*.

Alg1 6.0, 7.0

A Practice by Example

Example 1 (page 240)

GO for Help

Find the slope and *y*-intercept of each equation.

1. $y = -2x + 1$ **2.** $y = -\frac{1}{2}x + 2$ **3.** $y = x - \frac{5}{4}$

4. $y = 5x + 8$ **5.** $y = \frac{2}{3}x + 1$ **6.** $y = -4x$

7. $y = -x - 7$ **8.** $y = -0.7x - 9$ **9.** $y = -\frac{3}{4}x - 5$

Example 2 (page 240)

Write an equation of a line with the given slope and *y*-intercept.

10. $m = \frac{2}{9}, b = 3$ **11.** $m = 3, b = \frac{2}{9}$ **12.** $m = \frac{9}{2}, b = 3$

13. $m = 0, b = 1$ **14.** $m = -1, b = -6$ **15.** $m = -\frac{2}{3}, b = 5$

16. $m = 0.3, b = 4$ **17.** $m = 0.4, b = 0.6$ **18.** $m = -7, b = \frac{1}{3}$

19. $m = -\frac{1}{5}, b = -\frac{2}{5}$ **20.** $m = -\frac{1}{4}, b = \frac{5}{4}$ **21.** $m = \frac{8}{3}, b = \frac{2}{3}$

Example 3 (page 240)

Write the slope-intercept form of the equation for each line.

22. **23.** 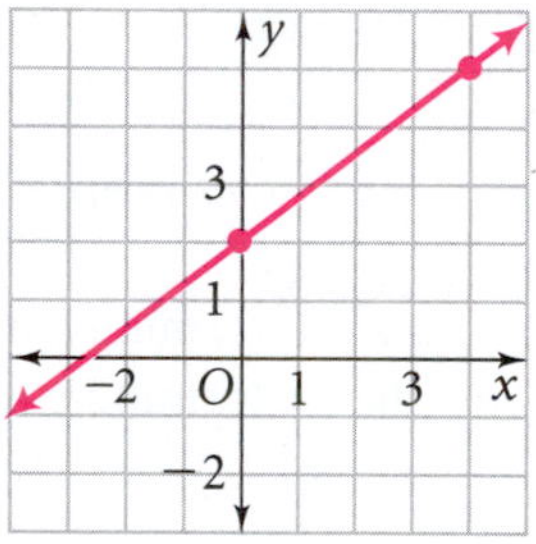 **24.**

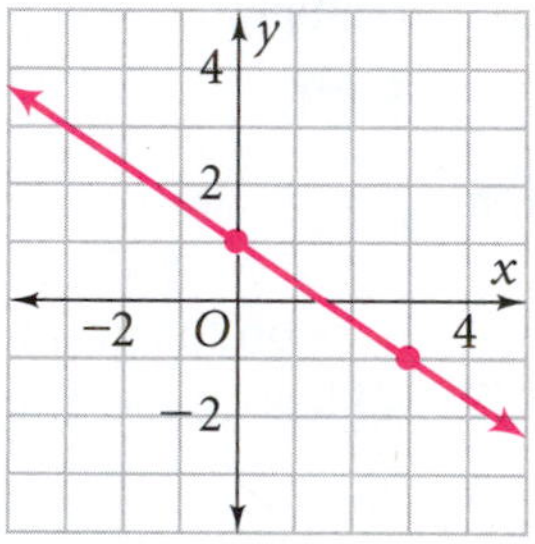

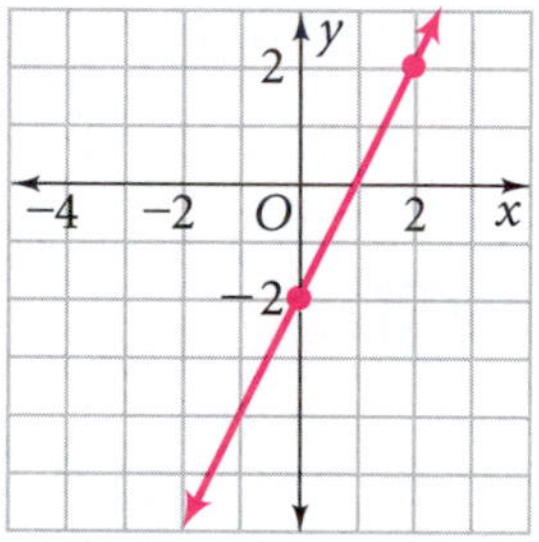

25. 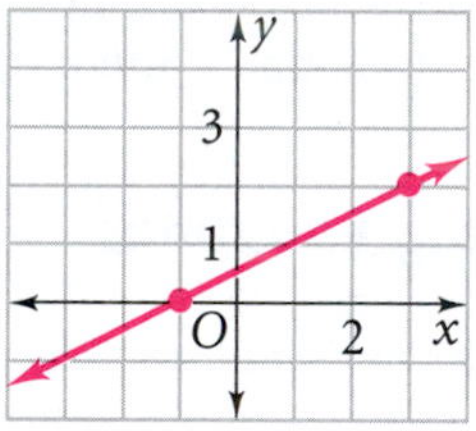 **26.** 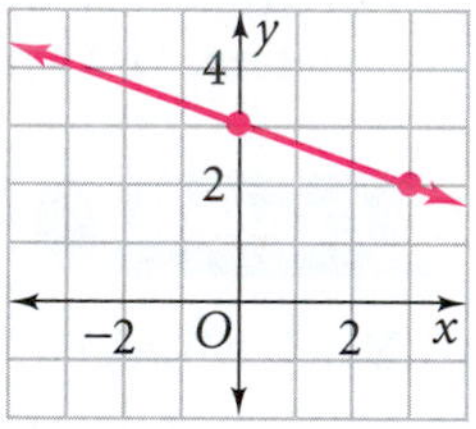 **27.**

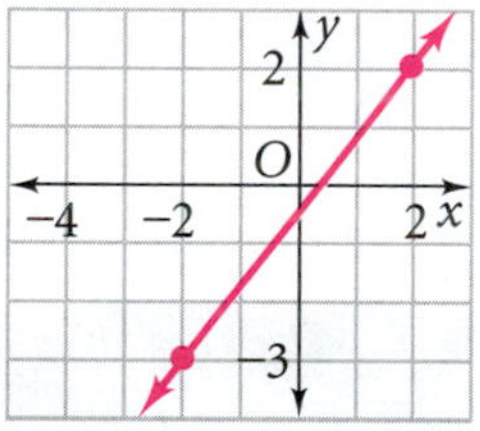

Example 4 (page 241)

Determine whether the ordered pair lies on the graph of the given equation.

28. $(-3, 4); y = -2x + 1$ **29.** $(2, 9); y = 6x - 3$ **30.** $(4, 3); 2x - 5y = -7$

31. $(-5, 6); -8x + 4y = 10$ **32.** $(-1, 0); -4y = 2x + 3$ **33.** $(0, -2); 6y = x - 3$

Example 5 (page 241)

Use the slope and *y*-intercept to graph each equation.

34. $y = \frac{1}{2}x + 4$ **35.** $y = \frac{2}{3}x - 1$ **36.** $y = -5x + 2$

37. $y = 2x + 5$ **38.** $y = x + 4$ **39.** $y = -x + 2$

40. $y = 4x - 3$ **41.** $y = -\frac{3}{2}x$ **42.** $y = \frac{2}{5}x - 3$

43. $y = -\frac{2}{3}x + 2$ **44.** $y = -\frac{4}{5}x + 4$ **45.** $y = -0.5x + 2$

46. You buy magnets online for \$2 each. Shipping costs \$5. The equation $y = 2x + 5$ represents the situation, where x is the number of magnets and y is the total cost of your purchase. Graph the equation.

B Apply Your Skills

Find the slope and y-intercept of each equation.

47. $y - 2 = -3x$ **48.** $y + \frac{1}{2}x = 0$ **49.** $y - 9x = \frac{1}{2}$

50. $y = 3x - 9$ **51.** $2y - 6 = 3x$ **52.** $-2y = 6(5 - 3x)$

53. $y - d = cx$ **54.** $y = (2 - a)x + a$ **55.** $2y + 4n = -6x$

Use the slope and y-intercept to graph each equation.

56. $y = 7 - 3x$ **57.** $2y + 4x = 0$ **58.** $3y + 6 = -2x$

59. $y + 2 = 5x - 4$ **60.** $4x + 3y = 2x - 1$ **61.** $-2(3x - 4) + y = 0$

62. Error Analysis Fred drew the graph at the right for the equation $y = -2x + 1$. What error did he make?

63. a. A candle begins burning at time $t = 0$. Its original height is 12 in. After 30 min the height of the candle is 8 in. Draw a graph showing the change in the height of the candle.

b. Write an equation that relates the height of the candle to the time it has been burning.

c. How many minutes after the candle is lit will it burn out?

Error Analysis Find and correct the student's mistake in the work below. Verify whether the point lies on the graph of the given line.

64. **65.**

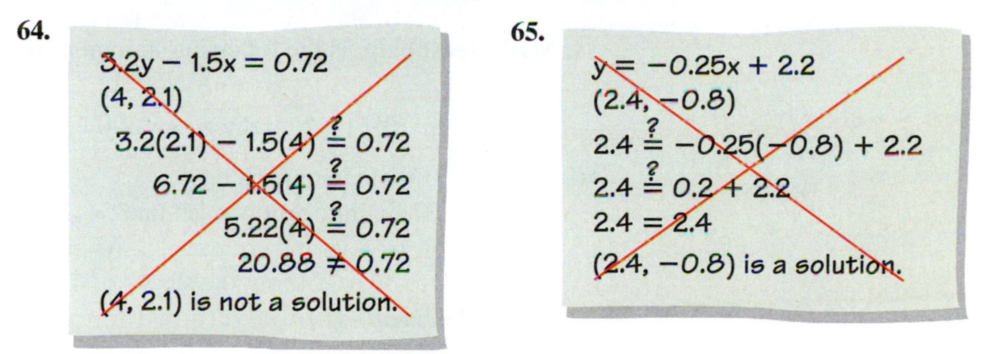

Determine whether the ordered pair lies on the graph of the given equation.

66. $(-4, 2); y = -\frac{3}{4}x + 1$ **67.** $(-6, 5); y = -\frac{1}{2}x + 2$ **68.** $(0, -1); y = x - \frac{5}{4}$

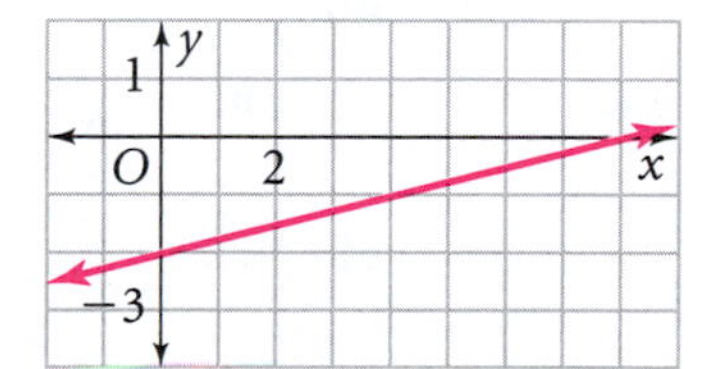

69. At the left is the graph of $y = \frac{1}{4}x - 2$. If the slope is doubled and the y-intercept stays the same, which of the graphs below represents the new linear function?

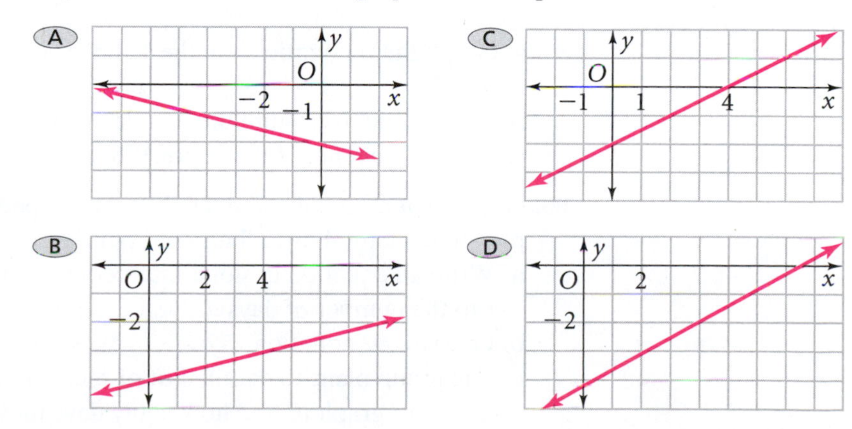

Visit: PHSchool.com
Web Code: bae-0502

The basic annual expense for cat owners is about $120.

70. When the Bryants leave town for a vacation, they put their cat in a kennel. The kennel charges $15 for a first-day flea bath and $5 per day. The equation $t = 15 + 5d$ relates the total charge t to the number of days d.

a. Rewrite the equation in slope-intercept form.

b. Graph the equation.

c. **Reasoning** Explain why the line you graph should lie only in Quadrant I.

71. **Writing** Explain the steps you would use to graph $y = \frac{3}{4}x + 5$.

72. **Critical Thinking** Which graphed line has the greater slope? Explain.

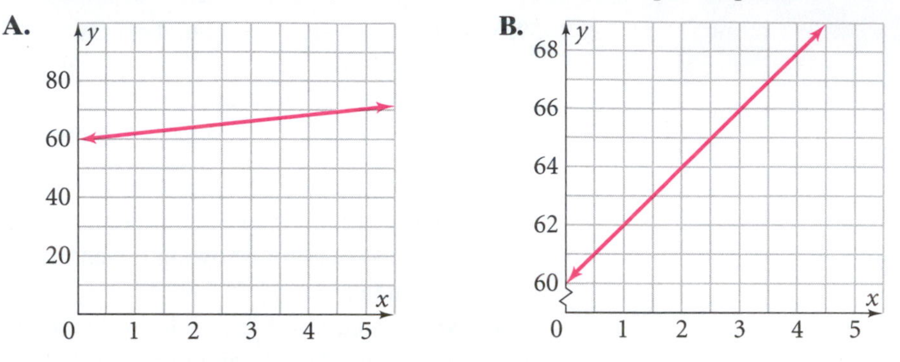

Given two points on a line, write the equation of the line in slope-intercept form.

73. (3, 5), (5, 9)

74. (5, –13), (2, –1)

75. (–4, 10), (6, 5)

76. (8, 7), (–12, 2)

77. (–7, 4), (11, –14)

78. (–1, –9), (2, 0)

79. **Math Reasoning** Is the following statement *sometimes*, *always*, or *never* true? Explain.

The point $(0, b)$ lies on the graph of the equation $y = mx + b$.

80. **a.** What is the slope of each line?

b. What is the y-intercept of each line?

c. The lines in the graph are parallel. What appears to be true about the slopes of parallel lines?

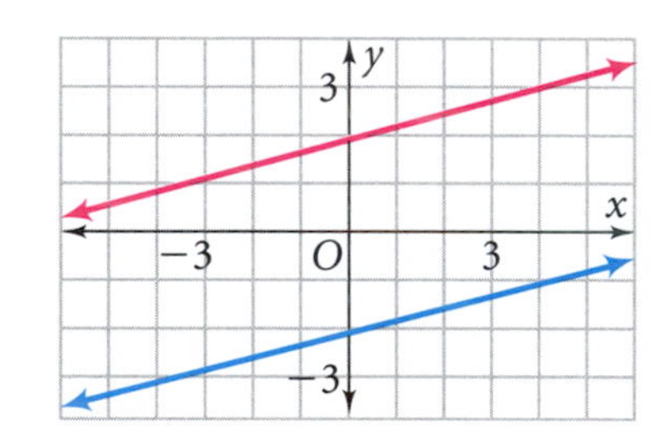

81. Write a linear equation. Identify the slope and y-intercept. Then graph your equation.

Challenge

Find the value of a such that the graph of the equation has the given slope.

82. $y = 2ax + 4; m = -1$

83. $y = -\frac{1}{2}ax - 5; m = \frac{5}{2}$

84. $y = \frac{3}{4}ax + 3; m = \frac{9}{16}$

85. **a.** Graph these equations on the same grid.

$y = 3$ $\quad$ $y = -3$ $\quad$ $x = 2$ $\quad$ $x = -2$

b. What geometric figure did you draw? Justify your answer.

c. Draw a diagonal of the figure. What is the equation of this line? Explain.

86. A group of mountain climbers begin an expedition with 265 lb of food. They plan to eat a total of 15 lb of food per day.

a. Write an equation in slope-intercept form relating the remaining food supply r to the number of days d.

b. Graph your equation.

c. The group plans to eat the last of their food the day their expedition ends. Use your graph to find how many days they expect the expedition to last.

Multiple Choice Practice

For California Standards Tutorials, visit PHSchool.com. Web Code: baq-9045

Alg1 7.0

87. Which point lies on the line represented by the equation $2x + 3y = -6$?

(A) $(2, -2)$ (B) $(-1, 2)$ (C) $(0, 2)$ (D) $(-3, 0)$

Alg1 3.0

88. What is the solution for the equation $|2x - 5| = 9$?

(A) $-7, 2$ (B) -2 or 7 (C) $-3, 5$ (D) -1 or 4

Alg1 6.0

89. Which equation represents a line that has a slope of –3 and a y-intercept of 6?

(A) $y = 3x - 6$

(B) $y = 6x - 3$

(C) $y = -3x + 6$

(D) $y = -6x + 3$

Alg1 6.0

90. Brian knows the coordinates of point P on a line. What additional information does he need to find the slope of the line?

(A) The length of the line

(B) The direction of the line

(C) The coordinates of another point on the line

(D) The distance between point P and another point on the line

Mixed Review

GO for Help

Lesson 2-2

Solve each equation.

91. $5(x + 1) = 8$ **92.** $-33 = 6h + 7 + 2h$ **93.** $-2(3 - k) = 15$

94. $17 = 4t - 2t + 1$ **95.** $4(n + 1) - 3 = 16$ **96.** $40 = 8p + 5 - p$

Lesson 3-4

Solve each inequality.

97. $1 + 5x + 1 > x + 9$ **98.** $7x + 3 < 2x + 28$ **99.** $4x + 4 > 2 + 2x$

100. $4x + 3 \leq 2x - 7$ **101.** $-x + 5 < 3x - 1$ **102.** $2x > 7x - 3 - 4x$

Checkpoint Quiz 1

Lessons 5-1 through 5-2

Find the slope of the line passing through each pair of points.

1. $(-1, 3), (6, -2)$ **2.** $(4, 5), (0, 2)$ **3.** $(-2, -3), (-1, -7)$ **4.** $(4, -4), (-5, 5)$

5. One year, people charged \$534 billion on the two most-used types of credit cards. Four years later, people charged \$1.021 trillion on these same two types of credit cards. What was the rate of change?

Graph each equation.

6. $y = 4x - 1$ **7.** $y = -\frac{2}{5}x + 6$ **8.** $y = -\frac{5}{3}x - 10$ **9.** $y = -0.75x$

10. Writing How are the graphs of $y = 3x + 5$, $y = \frac{2}{3}x + 5$, and $y = \frac{3}{5}x + 5$ alike? How are they different?

5-3 Standard Form

California Content Standards

6.0 Graph a linear equation and compute the x- and y-intercepts. ***Develop***

What You'll Learn

- To graph equations using intercepts
- To write equations in standard form

. . . And Why

To use an equation to model a real-world situation that involves exercise, as in Example 5

Check Skills You'll Need

GO for Help Review page 90 and Lesson 2-2

Solve each equation for y.

1. $3x + y = 5$ **2.** $y - 2x = 10$ **3.** $x - y = 6$

4. $20x + 4y = 8$ **5.** $9y + 3x = 1$ **6.** $5y - 2x = 4$

Clear each equation of decimals.

7. $6.25x + 8.5 = 7.75$ **8.** $0.4 = 0.2x - 5$ **9.** $0.9 - 0.222x = 1$

New Vocabulary • standard form of a linear equation • x-intercept

Graphing Equations Using Intercepts

CA Standards Investigation **Intercepts**

1. Graph the equation $3y - 2x = 12$ by making a table of values.
2. What is the y-intercept?
3. What is the value of x when the line crosses the x-axis?
4. In the equation $3y - 2x = 12$, what is the value of y when $x = 0$? What is the value of x when $y = 0$?
5. Using your answers to 2, 3, and 4, explain how you can make a graph of $3y - 2x = 12$ without making a table.

The slope-intercept form is just one form of a linear equation. Another form is standard form, which is 0useful in making quick graphs.

Definition **Standard Form of a Linear Equation**

The **standard form of a linear equation** is $Ax + By = C$, where A, B, and C are real numbers, and A and B are not both zero.

You can use the x- and y-intercepts to make a graph. The **x-intercept** is the x-coordinate of the point where a line crosses the x-axis. To graph a linear equation in standard form, you can find the x-intercept by substituting 0 for y and solving for x. Similarly, to find the y-intercept, substitute 0 for x and solve for y.

1 EXAMPLE Finding x- and y-Intercepts

Find the x- and y-intercepts of $3x + 4y = 8$.

Step 1 To find the x-intercept, substitute 0 for y and solve for x.

$$3x + 4y = 8$$
$$3x + 4(0) = 8$$
$$3x = 8$$
$$x = \frac{8}{3}$$

The x-intercept is $\frac{8}{3}$.

Step 2 To find the y-intercept, substitute 0 for x and solve for y.

$$3x + 4y = 8$$
$$3(0) + 4y = 8$$
$$4y = 8$$
$$y = 2$$

The y-intercept is 2.

CA Standards Check 1 Find the x- and y-intercepts of $4x - 9y = -12$.

If the x- and y-intercepts are integers, you can use them to make a quick graph.

2 EXAMPLE Graphing Lines Using Intercepts

Graph $2x + 3y = 12$ using intercepts.

Step 1 Find the intercepts.

$$2x + 3y = 12$$
$$2x + 3(0) = 12 \quad \text{Substitute 0 for } y.$$
$$2x = 12 \quad \text{Solve for } x.$$
$$x = 6$$
$$2(0) + 3y = 12 \quad \text{Substitute 0 for } x.$$
$$3y = 12 \quad \text{Solve for } y.$$
$$y = 4$$

Step 2 Plot (0, 4) and (6, 0).
Draw a line through the points.

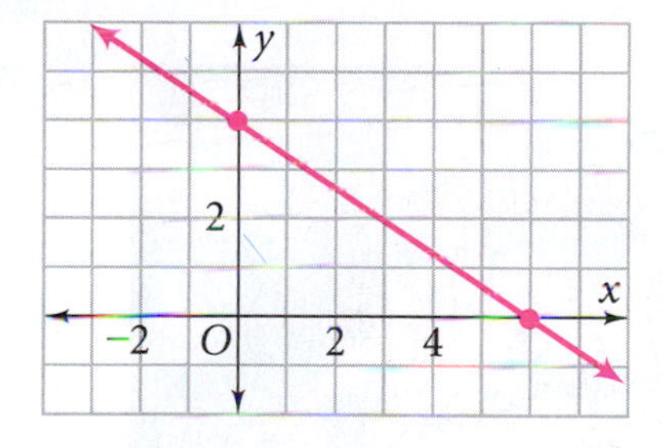

CA Standards Check 2 Graph $5x + 2y = -10$ using the x- and y-intercepts.

In the standard form of an equation $Ax + By = C$, either A or B, but not both, may be zero. If A or B is zero, the line is either horizontal or vertical.

3 EXAMPLE Graphing Horizontal and Vertical Lines

a. Graph $y = -3$.

$0x + 1y = -3$ ← Write in standard form.
For all values of x, $y = -3$.

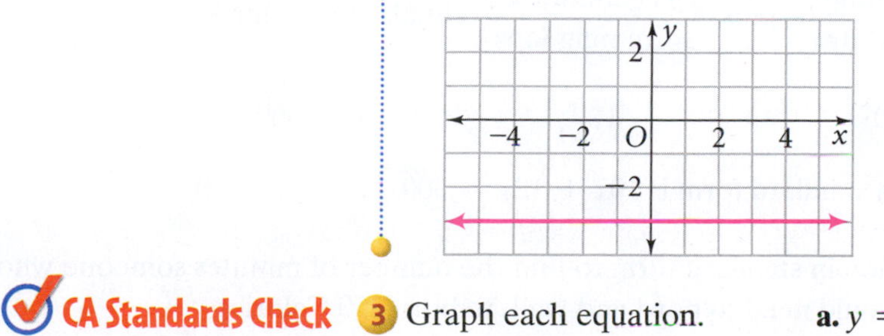

b. Graph $x = 2$.

$1x + 0y = 2$ ← Write in standard form.
For all values of y, $x = 2$.

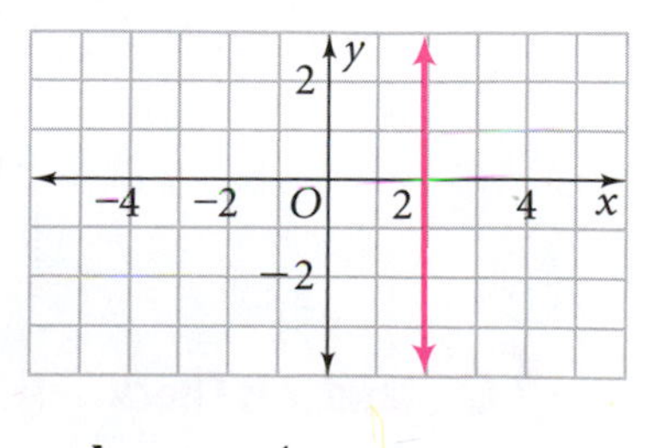

CA Standards Check 3 Graph each equation. **a.** $y = 5$ **b.** $x = -4$

Writing Equations in Standard Form

You can change an equation from slope-intercept form to standard form. If the equation contains fractions or decimals, multiply to write the equation using integers.

4 EXAMPLE Transforming to Standard Form

Write $y = \frac{3}{4}x + 2$ in standard form using integers.

$y = \frac{3}{4}x + 2$

$4y = 4\left(\frac{3}{4}x + 2\right)$ **Multiply each side by 4.**

$4y = 3x + 8$ **Use the Distributive Property.**

$-3x + 4y = 8$ **Subtract 3*x* from each side.**

The standard form of $y = \frac{3}{4}x + 2$ is $-3x + 4y = 8$.

CA Standards Check 4 Write $y = -\frac{2}{5}x + 1$ in standard form using integers.

You can write equations for real-world situations using standard form.

5 EXAMPLE Application

Write an equation in standard form to find the number of minutes someone who weighs 150 lb would need to bicycle and swim laps in order to burn 300 Calories. Use the data below.

Activity by a 150-lb Person	Calories Burned per Minute
Bicycling	10
Bowling	4
Hiking	7
Running 5.2 mi/h	11
Swimming, laps	12
Walking 3.5 mi/h	5

Doctors recommend 30 minutes of exercise each day.

Define Let x = the minutes spent bicycling.

Let y = the minutes spent swimming laps.

Relate 10 · minutes bicycling plus 12 · minutes swimming laps equals 300 calories

Write $10x + 12y = 300$

The equation in standard form is $10x + 12y = 300$.

CA Standards Check 5 Write an equation in standard form to find the number of minutes someone who weighs 150 lb would need to bowl and walk to burn 250 Calories.

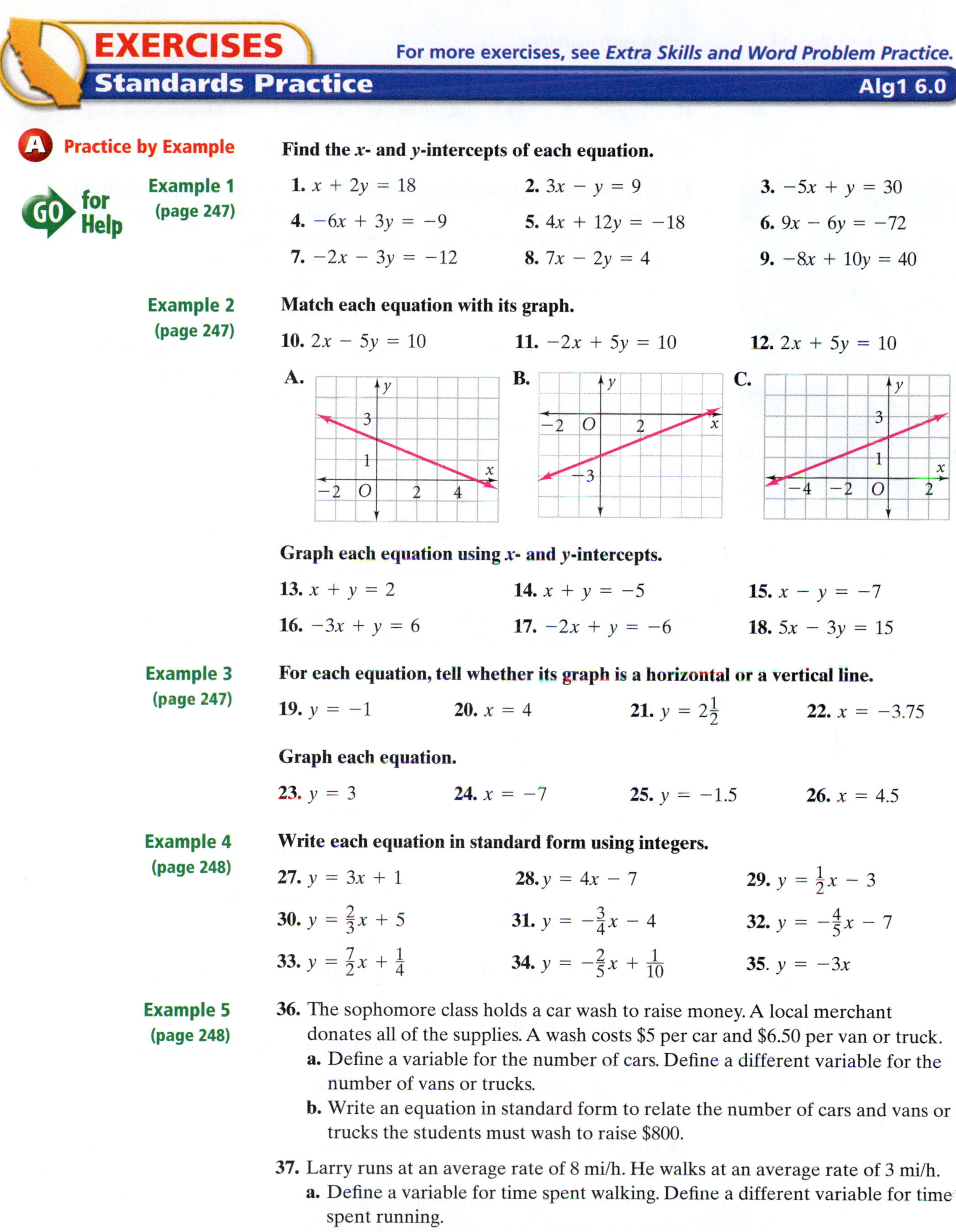

EXERCISES

Standards Practice

For more exercises, see *Extra Skills and Word Problem Practice.*

Alg1 6.0

A Practice by Example

GO for Help

Example 1 (page 247)

Find the x- and y-intercepts of each equation.

1. $x + 2y = 18$ **2.** $3x - y = 9$ **3.** $-5x + y = 30$

4. $-6x + 3y = -9$ **5.** $4x + 12y = -18$ **6.** $9x - 6y = -72$

7. $-2x - 3y = -12$ **8.** $7x - 2y = 4$ **9.** $-8x + 10y = 40$

Example 2 (page 247)

Match each equation with its graph.

10. $2x - 5y = 10$ **11.** $-2x + 5y = 10$ **12.** $2x + 5y = 10$

A. **B.** **C.**

Graph each equation using x- and y-intercepts.

13. $x + y = 2$ **14.** $x + y = -5$ **15.** $x - y = -7$

16. $-3x + y = 6$ **17.** $-2x + y = -6$ **18.** $5x - 3y = 15$

Example 3 (page 247)

For each equation, tell whether its graph is a horizontal or a vertical line.

19. $y = -1$ **20.** $x = 4$ **21.** $y = 2\frac{1}{2}$ **22.** $x = -3.75$

Graph each equation.

23. $y = 3$ **24.** $x = -7$ **25.** $y = -1.5$ **26.** $x = 4.5$

Example 4 (page 248)

Write each equation in standard form using integers.

27. $y = 3x + 1$ **28.** $y = 4x - 7$ **29.** $y = \frac{1}{2}x - 3$

30. $y = \frac{2}{3}x + 5$ **31.** $y = -\frac{3}{4}x - 4$ **32.** $y = -\frac{4}{5}x - 7$

33. $y = \frac{7}{2}x + \frac{1}{4}$ **34.** $y = -\frac{2}{5}x + \frac{1}{10}$ **35.** $y = -3x$

Example 5 (page 248)

36. The sophomore class holds a car wash to raise money. A local merchant donates all of the supplies. A wash costs \$5 per car and \$6.50 per van or truck.

a. Define a variable for the number of cars. Define a different variable for the number of vans or trucks.

b. Write an equation in standard form to relate the number of cars and vans or trucks the students must wash to raise \$800.

37. Larry runs at an average rate of 8 mi/h. He walks at an average rate of 3 mi/h.

a. Define a variable for time spent walking. Define a different variable for time spent running.

b. Write an equation in standard form to relate the times he could spend running and walking if he travels a distance of 15 mi.

B Apply Your Skills

Graph each equation.

38. $-3x + 2y = -6$ **39.** $x + y = 1$ **40.** $2x - 3y = 18$

41. $y - x = -4$ **42.** $y = 2x + 5$ **43.** $y = -3x - 1$

44. $2 - y = x - 6$ **45.** $9 + y = 8 - x$ **46.** $6x = y$

A peanut contains about 0.24 gram of protein.

47. Suppose you are preparing a snack mix. You want the total protein from peanuts and granola to equal 28 grams. Peanuts have 7 grams of protein per ounce, and granola has 3 grams of protein per ounce.
- **a.** Write an equation for the protein content of your mix.
- **b.** Graph your equation. Use your graph to find how many ounces of granola you should use if you use 1 ounce of peanuts.

48. You are sent to the store to buy sliced meat for a party. You are told to get roast beef and turkey, and you are given \$30. Roast beef is \$4.29/lb and turkey is \$3.99/lb. Write an equation in standard form to relate the pounds of each kind of meat you could buy at the store with \$30.

Write each equation in slope-intercept form. Make a sketch of the graph. Include the *x*- and *y*-intercepts.

49. $8x - 10y = -100$ **50.** $-6x + 7y = 21$ **51.** $12x + 15y = -45$

52. $-5x + 9y = -15$ **53.** $16x + 11y = -88$ **54.** $3x - 27y = 18$

55. Writing Two of the forms of a linear equation are slope-intercept form and standard form. Explain when each is more useful.

56. Critical Thinking The definition of standard form states that A and B can't both be zero. Explain why.

57. Error Analysis A student says that the equation $3x + 2y = 6$ is a standard form of the equation $y = \frac{3}{2}x + 3$. What is the student's error?

Write an equation for each line on the graph.

58. a **59.** b **60.** c **61.** d

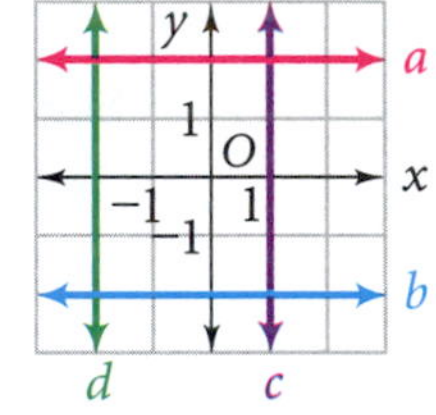

62. a. Suppose your school is having a talent show to raise money for new music supplies. You estimate that 200 students and 150 adults will attend. You estimate \$200 in expenses. Write an equation to find what ticket prices you should set to raise \$1000.
- **b.** Graph your equation. Choose three possible prices you could set for students' and adults' tickets. Which is the best choice? Explain.

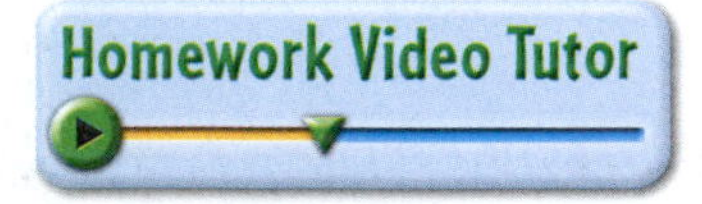

Visit: PHSchool.com
Web Code: bae-0503

C Challenge

63. Write an equation of a line that has the same slope as the line $3x - 5y = 7$ and the same y-intercept as the line $2y - 9x = 8$.

64. Graph each of the four lines below on the same graph. What figure do the four lines appear to form?

$-2x + 3y = 10$ $3x + 2y = -2$ $-2x + 3y = -3$ $3x + 2y = 11$

65. a. Graph $2x + 3y = 6$ and $2x + 3y = 18$.
- **b.** What is the slope of each line?
- **c.** How are the x- and y-intercepts of the two lines related?

Multiple Choice Practice

For California Standards Tutorials, visit PHSchool.com. Web Code: baq-9045

Alg1 6.0 **66.** What is the y-intercept of the line represented by the equation $4x + 6y = 3$?

Ⓐ $\frac{1}{2}$ Ⓑ $\frac{2}{3}$ Ⓒ 2 Ⓓ 3

Alg1 6.0 **67.** Christina recorded the height of her tomato plant for 3 weeks. She graphed a line to model her data. If Christina's plant grew about 2 inches each week, which graph could model her data?

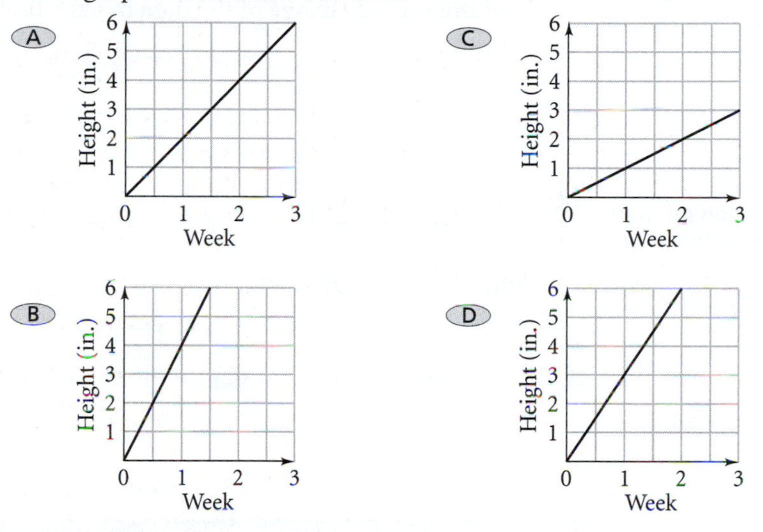

Alg1 16.0 **68.** Andy can use the function $c = 900n + 200$ to find the cost c of ordering n new computers for his business. What is the dependent variable?

Ⓐ c Ⓑ 900 Ⓒ n Ⓓ 200

Mixed Review

Lesson 5-2 **Determine whether the ordered pair is a solution of the equation.**

69. $(2, -3);\ y = -x - 1$ **70.** $(6, -1);\ y = 2x - 15$ **71.** $(-5, -7);\ y = -3x - 8$

Write the slope-intercept form of the equation for each line.

72. **73.**

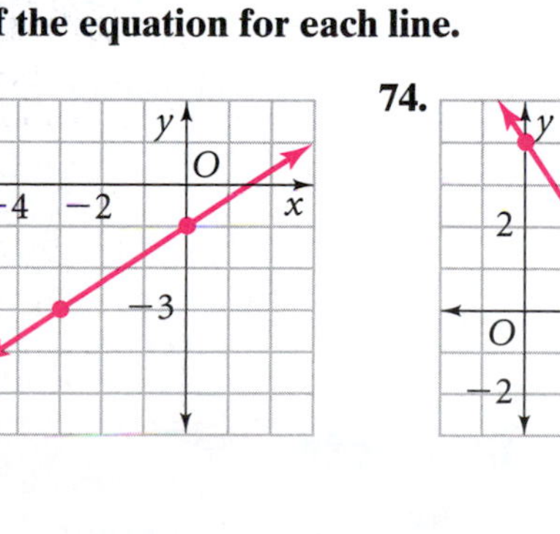

74.

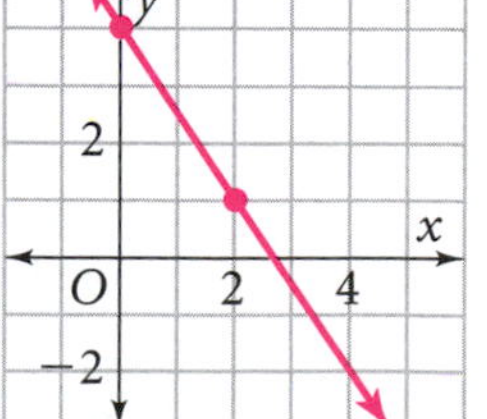

Lesson 2-4 **Solve each proportion.**

75. $\frac{a}{5} = \frac{12}{15}$ **76.** $\frac{2}{8} = \frac{w}{9}$ **77.** $\frac{x + 2}{4} = \frac{3}{8}$ **78.** $\frac{14}{4m} = \frac{16}{5m + 9}$

Point-Slope Form and Writing Linear Equations

California Content Standards

6.0 Graph a linear equation. ***Develop***

7.0 Derive linear equations by using the point-slope formula. ***Develop***

What You'll Learn

- To graph and write linear equations using point-slope form
- To write a linear equation using data

. . . And Why

To write an equation relating altitude and the boiling point of water, as in Example 5

Check Skills You'll Need

GO for Help Lessons 5-1 and 1-7

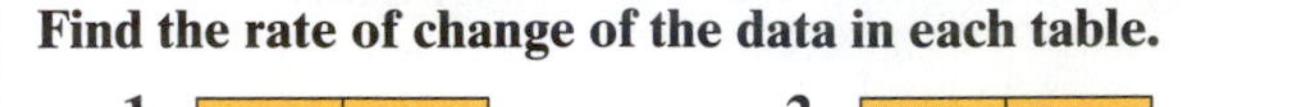

Find the rate of change of the data in each table.

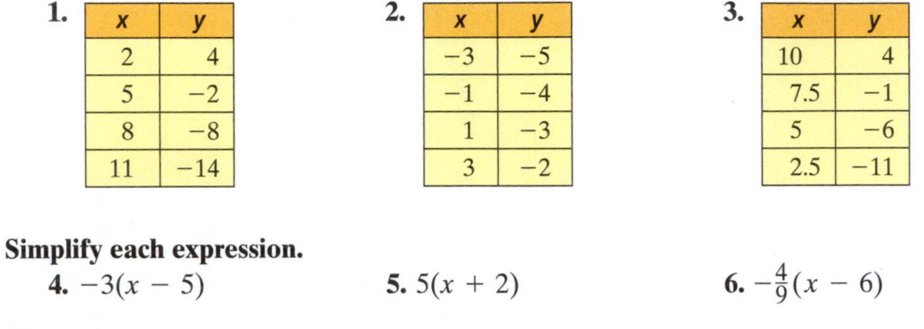

1.

x	y
2	4
5	−2
8	−8
11	−14

2.

x	y
−3	−5
−1	−4
1	−3
3	−2

3.

x	y
10	4
7.5	−1
5	−6
2.5	−11

Simplify each expression.

4. $-3(x - 5)$ **5.** $5(x + 2)$ **6.** $-\frac{4}{9}(x - 6)$

New Vocabulary • point-slope form

Using Point-Slope Form

You can use the definition of slope to find another form of a linear equation called the point-slope form.

$$\frac{y_2 - y_1}{x_2 - x_1} = m$$ Use the definition of slope.

Suppose you know that a line passes through the point (3, 4) and has slope 2.

$$\frac{y - 4}{x - 3} = 2$$ Substitute (3, 4) for (x_1, y_1) and substitute (x, y) for (x_2, y_2). Substitute 2 for m.

$$\frac{y - 4}{x - 3}(x - 3) = 2(x - 3)$$ Multiply each side by $x - 3$.

$$y - 4 = 2(x - 3)$$ Simplify the left side of the equation.

The equation $y - 4 = 2(x - 3)$ is in point-slope form.

$$y - 4 = 2(x - 3)$$

y-coordinate (4) slope (2) x-coordinate (3)

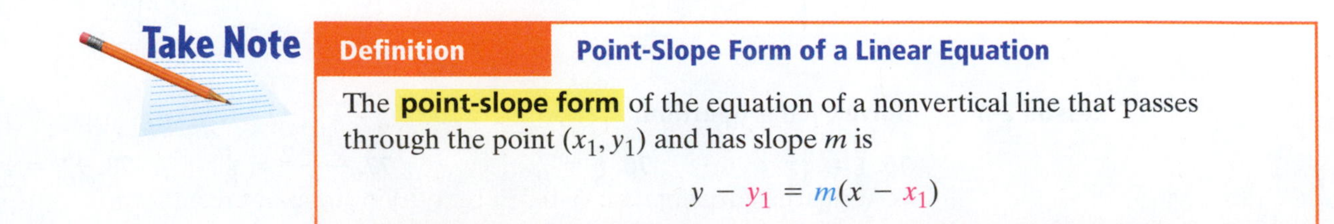

Take Note

Definition **Point-Slope Form of a Linear Equation**

The **point-slope form** of the equation of a nonvertical line that passes through the point (x_1, y_1) and has slope m is

$$y - y_1 = m(x - x_1)$$

1 EXAMPLE Graphing Using Point-Slope Form

Graph the equation $y - 5 = \frac{1}{2}(x - 2)$.

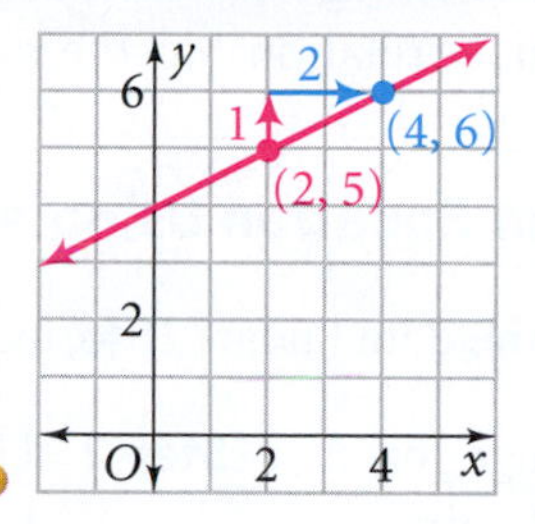

The equation shows that the line passes through (2, 5) and has a slope $\frac{1}{2}$.

Start at (2, 5). Using the slope, go up 1 unit and right 2 units to (4, 6). Draw a line through the two points.

CA Standards Check **1** Graph the equation $y - 5 = -\frac{2}{3}(x + 2)$.

2 EXAMPLE Writing an Equation in Point-Slope Form

Write the equation of the line that has slope -3 that passes through the point $(-1, 7)$.

$y - y_1 = m(x - x_1)$ **Use the point-slope form.**

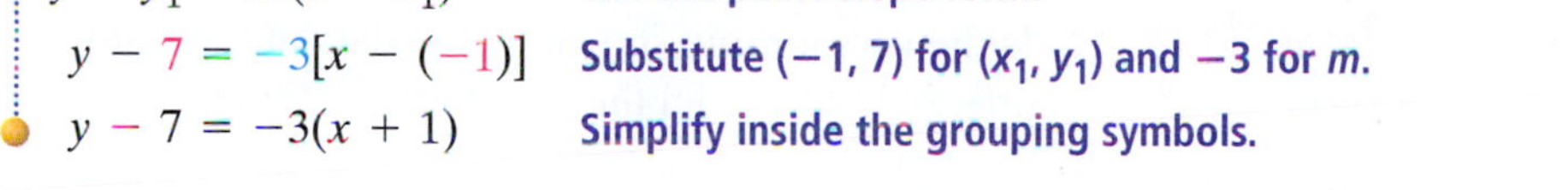

$y - 7 = -3[x - (-1)]$ **Substitute $(-1, 7)$ for (x_1, y_1) and -3 for m.**

$y - 7 = -3(x + 1)$ **Simplify inside the grouping symbols.**

CA Standards Check **2** Write the equation of the line that has slope $\frac{2}{5}$ that passes through the point $(10, -8)$.

If you know two points on a line, first use them to find the slope. Then you can write an equation using either point.

3 EXAMPLE Using Two Points to Write an Equation

Online active math

For: Point-Slope Activity
Use: Interactive Textbook, 5-4

Write equations for the line in point-slope form and in slope-intercept form.

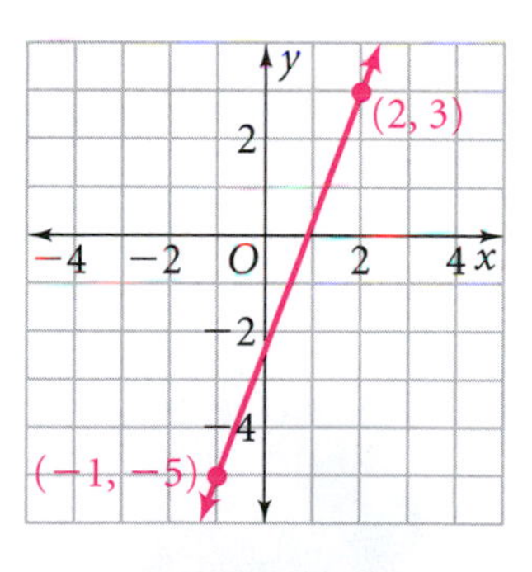

Step 1 Find the slope.

$$\frac{y_2 - y_1}{x_2 - x_1} = m$$

$$\frac{-5 - 3}{-1 - 2} = \frac{8}{3}$$

The slope is $\frac{8}{3}$.

Step 2 Use either point to write the equation in point-slope form. Use (2, 3).

$$y - y_1 = m(x - x_1)$$

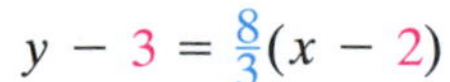

$$y - 3 = \frac{8}{3}(x - 2)$$

Step 3 Rewrite the equation from Step 2 in slope-intercept form.

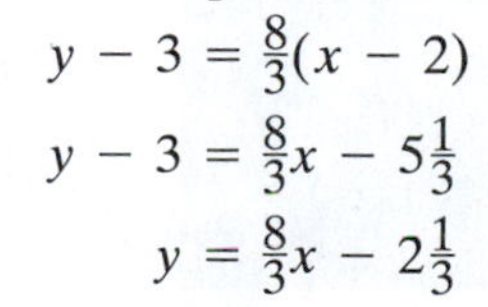

$$y - 3 = \frac{8}{3}(x - 2)$$

$$y - 3 = \frac{8}{3}x - 5\frac{1}{3}$$

$$y = \frac{8}{3}x - 2\frac{1}{3}$$

CA Standards Check **3** **a.** Write an equation for the line in Example 3 in point-slope form using the point $(-1, -5)$.

b. Write the equation you found in part (a) in slope-intercept form.

Writing Linear Equations Using Data

You can write a linear equation to model data in tables. Two sets of data have a linear relationship if the rate of change between consecutive pairs of data is the same. For data that have a linear relationship, the rate of change is the slope.

4 EXAMPLE Writing an Equation Using a Table

Is the relationship shown by the data linear? If so, model the data with an equation.

Step 1 Find the rate of change for consecutive ordered pairs.

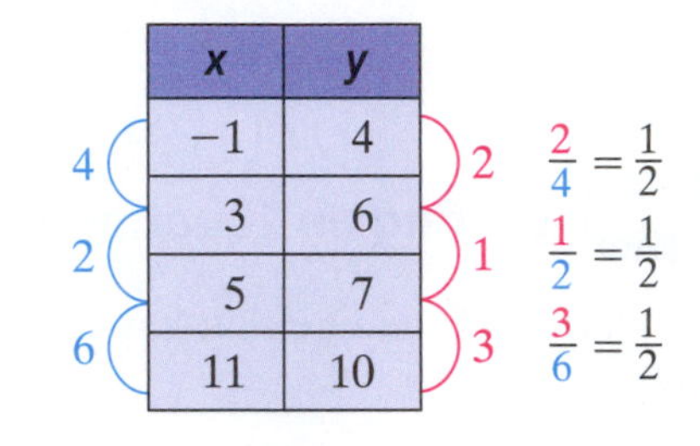

x	y
−1	4
3	6
5	7
11	10

$\frac{2}{4} = \frac{1}{2}$ $\quad \frac{1}{2} = \frac{1}{2}$ $\quad \frac{3}{6} = \frac{1}{2}$

Step 2 Use the slope and a point to write an equation.

$y - y_1 = m(x - x_1)$

Substitute (5, 7) for (x_1, y_1) and $\frac{1}{2}$ for m.

$y - 7 = \frac{1}{2}(x - 5)$

CA Standards Check 4 Is the relationship shown by the data at the right linear? If so, model the data with an equation.

x	y
−11	−7
−1	−3
4	−1
19	5

5 EXAMPLE Application

Is the relationship shown by the data linear? If so, model the data with an equation.

Boiling Point of Water

Altitude (1000 ft)	Temperature (°F)
8	197.6
4.5	203.9
3	206.6
2.5	207.5

(Changes in altitude: −3.5, −1.5, −0.5; changes in temperature: 6.3, 2.7, 0.9)

At 5280 feet above sea level, it takes 17 minutes to hard-boil an egg. To cook the same egg at sea level takes more than 40% longer.

Step 1 Find the rates of change for consecutive ordered pairs.

$\frac{6.3}{-3.5} = -1.8$ $\qquad \frac{2.7}{-1.5} = -1.8$ $\qquad \frac{0.9}{-0.5} = -1.8$

The relationship is linear. The rate of change is −1.8 degrees Fahrenheit per 1000 ft of altitude.

Step 2 Use the slope and a point to write an equation.

$y - y_1 = m(x - x_1)$ **Use the point-slope form.**

$y - 206.6 = -1.8(x - 3)$ **Substitute (3, 206.6) for (x_1, y_1) and −1.8 for m.**

The equation $y - 206.6 = -1.8(x - 3)$ relates altitude in thousands of feet x to the boiling point temperature in degrees Fahrenheit.

CA Standards Check 5 Is the relationship shown by the data in the table linear? If it is, model the data with an equation.

Working Outdoors

Temperature	Calories Burned per Day
68°F	3030
62°F	3130
56°F	3230
50°F	3330

In Example 5 you could rewrite $y - 206.6 = -1.8(x - 3)$ as $y = -1.8x + 212$. The y-intercept of 212°F is the boiling point of water at sea level.

Take Note

Summary **Linear Equations**

Slope-Intercept Form	Standard Form	Point-Slope Form
$y = mx + b$	$Ax + By = C$	$(y - y_1) = m(x - x_1)$
m is the slope and b is the y-intercept.	A and B are not both 0.	(x_1, y_1) lies on the graph of the equation, and m is the slope.
Examples		
$y = -\frac{2}{3}x + \frac{5}{3}$	$2x + 3y = 5$	$y - 1 = -\frac{2}{3}(x - 1)$

GO for Help

For more help with the three forms of a linear equation, see page 258.

EXERCISES

For more exercises, see *Extra Skills and Word Problem Practice.*

Standards Practice

Alg1 6.0, 7.0

A Practice by Example

Graph each equation.

Example 1 (page 253)

1. $y - 2 = (x - 3)$ **2.** $y - 2 = 2(x - 3)$ **3.** $y - 2 = -\frac{3}{2}(x - 3)$

4. $y + 5 = -(x - 2)$ **5.** $y + 1 = \frac{2}{3}(x + 4)$ **6.** $y - 1 = -3(x + 2)$

7. $y + 3 = -2(x - 1)$ **8.** $y - 4 = (x - 5)$ **9.** $y - 2 = 3(x + 2)$

GO for Help

Example 2 (page 253)

Write an equation in point-slope form for the line through the given point that has the given slope.

10. $(3, -4); m = 6$ **11.** $(4, 2); m = -\frac{5}{3}$ **12.** $(0, 2); m = \frac{4}{5}$

13. $(-2, -7); m = -\frac{3}{2}$ **14.** $(4, 0); m = 1$ **15.** $(5, -8); m = -3$

16. $(-5, 2); m = 0$ **17.** $(1, -8); m = -\frac{1}{5}$ **18.** $(-6, 1); m = \frac{2}{3}$

Example 3 (page 253)

A line passes through the given points. Write an equation for the line in point-slope form. Then rewrite the equation in slope-intercept form.

19. $(-1, 0), (1, 2)$ **20.** $(3, 5), (0, 0)$ **21.** $(4, -2), (9, -8)$

22. $(6, -4), (-3, 5)$ **23.** $(-1, -5), (-7, -6)$ **24.** $(-3, -4), (3, -2)$

25. $(2, 7), (1, -4)$ **26.** $(-2, 6), (5, 1)$ **27.** $(3, -8), (-2, 5)$

28. $\left(1, \frac{1}{2}\right), (3, 2)$ **29.** $\left(\frac{1}{2}, 2\right), \left(-\frac{3}{2}, 4\right)$ **30.** $(0.2, 1.1), (7, 3)$

Example 4 (page 254)

Is the relationship shown by the data linear? If so, model the data with an equation.

31.

x	y
−4	9
2	−3
5	−9
9	−17

32.

x	y
−10	−5
−2	19
5	40
11	58

33.

x	y
3	1
6	4
9	13
15	49

Example 5 (page 254)

34.

Speed Over Posted Speed Limit (mi/h)	Fine ($)
10	75
12	95
15	125
19	165

35.

Volume (gal)	Weight (lb)
0	0
2	16
4	33
6	50

B Apply Your Skills

Write an equation of each line in point-slope form.

36.

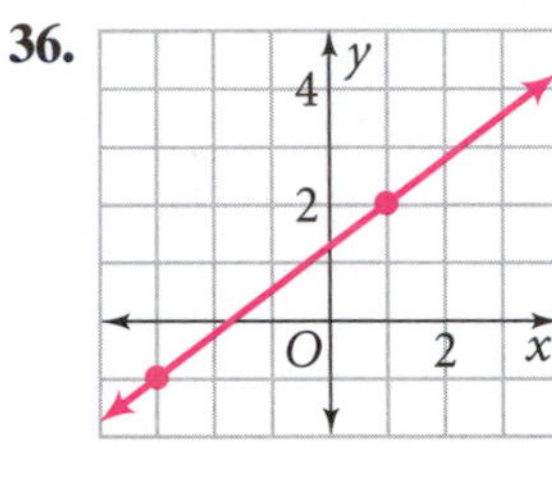

37.

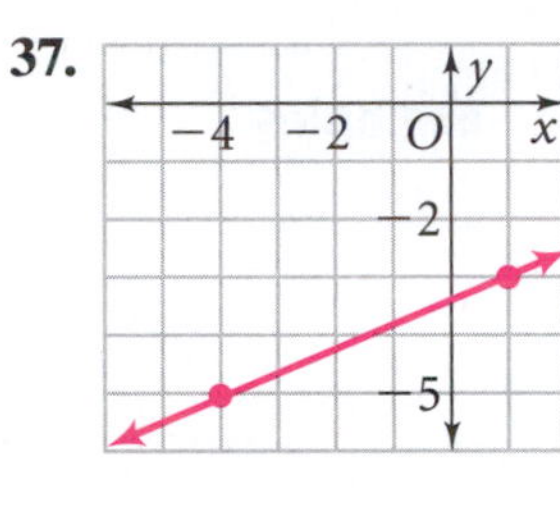

38.

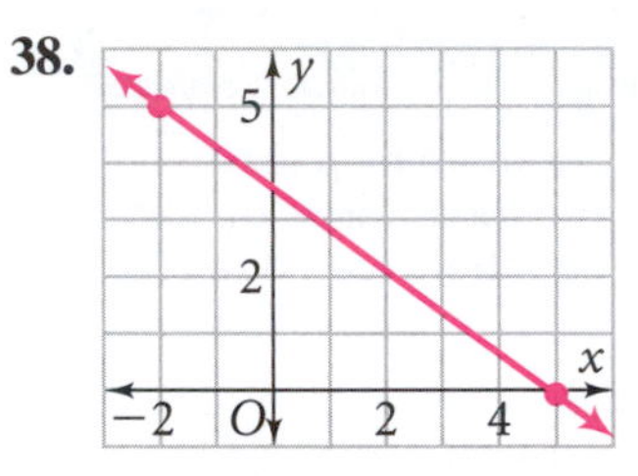

Write one equation of the line through the given points in point-slope form and one in standard form using integers.

39. $(1, 4), (-1, 1)$ **40.** $(6, -3), (-2, -3)$ **41.** $(0, 0), (-1, -2)$

42. $(0, 2), (-4, 2)$ **43.** $(-6, 6), (3, 3)$ **44.** $(2, 3), (-1, 5)$

45. $(5, -3), (3, 4)$ **46.** $(2, 2), (-1, 7)$ **47.** $(-7, 1), (5, -1)$

48. $(-8, 4), (-4, -2)$ **49.** $(2, 4), (-3, -6)$ **50.** $(5, 3), (4, 5)$

51. $(0, 1), (-3, 0)$ **52.** $(-2, 4), (0, -5)$ **53.** $(6, 2), (1, -1)$

54. At the surface of the ocean, pressure is 1 atmosphere. At 66 ft below sea level, the pressure is 3 atmospheres. The relationship of pressure and depth is linear.
a. Write an equation for the data.
b. Predict the pressure at 100 ft below sea level.

55. Worldwide carbon monoxide emissions are decreasing about 2.6 million metric tons each year. In 1991, carbon monoxide emissions were 79 million metric tons. Use a linear equation to model the relationship between carbon monoxide emissions and time. Let $x = 91$ correspond to 1991.

56. a. Write an equation in point-slope form that contains the point $(-4, -6)$. Explain your steps.
b. How many equations could you write in part (a)? Explain.

57. Critical Thinking How would the graph of $y - 12 = 8(x - 2)$ change if all of the subtraction signs were changed to addition signs?

58. Reasoning Is $y - 5 = 2(x - 1)$ an equation of a line through $(4, 11)$? Explain.

59. Use the graph at the right.
   a. Write an equation to model the data.
   b. What is the speed of sound at 15°C?
   c. Predict the speed of sound at 60°C.

Effect of Air Temperature on Speed of Sound

C Challenge

Write an equation in slope-intercept form of each line described below.

60. The line contains the point $(-3, -5)$ and has the same slope as $y + 2 = 7(x + 3)$.

61. The line contains the point $(1, 3)$ and has the same y-intercept as $y - 5 = 2(x - 1)$.

62. The line contains the point $(2, -2)$ and has the same x-intercept as $y + 9 = 3(x - 4)$.

Homework Video Tutor

Visit: PHSchool.com
Web Code: bae-0504

63. The table shows data that you can model using a linear function.
   a. Find the value of y when $x = 6$.
   b. Find the value of y when $x = 120$.
   c. Find the value of x when $y = 11$.
   d. Find the value of x when $y = 50$.

x	y
4	14
8	15.5
12	17
16	18.5

Multiple Choice Practice

For California Standards Tutorials, visit PHSchool.com. Web Code: baq-9045

Alg1 7.0

64. A line has a slope of -3 and passes through the point $(1, -5)$. What is the equation for the line?

   (A) $y = -3x - 2$
   (B) $y = -3x + 16$
   (C) $2y = -3x - 14$
   (D) $y = -3x + 8$

Alg1 7.0

65. When $y - 1 = -\frac{4}{5}(x - 3)$ is written in standard form using positive integers, what is the smallest possible coefficient of x?

   (A) -4
   (B) $-\frac{4}{5}$
   (C) 4
   (D) 5

Alg1 6.0

66. Which pair of numbers are reciprocals?

   (A) $-8, 8$
   (B) $\frac{7}{5}, \frac{5}{7}$
   (C) $\frac{1}{2}, -\frac{1}{2}$
   (D) $\frac{3}{4}, -\frac{4}{3}$

Mixed Review

GO for Help

Lesson 5-3

Graph each line.

67. $6x + 7y = 14$
68. $-2x + 9y = -9$
69. $5x - 4y = 24$
70. $3x - 8y = 4$
71. $5x + 18y = 6$
72. $-7x + 4y = -21$

Lesson 4-7

Use inductive reasoning to find the next two numbers in each pattern.

73. $-12, -7, -2, \ldots$
74. $\frac{1}{2}, \frac{5}{6}, \frac{7}{6}, \ldots$
75. $2.45, 2.52, 2.59, \ldots$
76. $-3.2, -3.25, -3.3, \ldots$
77. $18, 36, 72, \ldots$
78. $-9, -3, 1, \ldots$

GO Online Lesson Quiz Visit: PHSchool.com, Web Code: baa-0504

Vocabulary Builder

Understanding Vocabulary

There are three forms of a linear equation that you have studied in this chapter:

- slope-intercept form
- standard form
- point-slope form

To understand and remember these forms, it may help you to connect the common meaning of the words with their specialized meanings in mathematics.

Word	Common Meaning	Mathematical Meaning
Slope	An inclined surface (for example, the slope of a hill)	The rate of change that gives the steepness of a line: $\text{slope} = \frac{\text{vertical change}}{\text{horizontal change}} = \frac{\text{rise}}{\text{run}}$
Intercept	To cut off from a path (for example, to intercept a football)	The values of the points at which a line intersects (or cuts) the x-axis or y-axis
Standard	Generally accepted	A general form of an equation
Point	A dot or speck (noun)	A fixed location on a coordinate plane; every point has a unique x-value and y-value

Slope-intercept form, standard form, and point-slope form all give clues about the lines they will graph.

- Slope-intercept form tells the slope of the line and its y-intercept.

  Example $y = 3x - 1$ The graph of this equation has a slope of 3 and a y-intercept of -1.

- Standard form is the general form for linear equations. You can model many real-world situations using the standard form. Also, it is easy to find the x- and y-intercepts of the graph of an equation in this form.

  Example $5x - 2y = 100$ The graph of this equation intersects the y-axis at $\frac{100}{-2} = -50$ and intersects the x-axis at $\frac{100}{5} = 20$.

- Point-slope form tells a point on the line and the slope of the line.

  Example $y - 2 = 3(x - 5)$ The graph of this equation passes through the point (5, 2), and its slope is 3.

EXERCISES

For each situation, which form of a linear equation is easiest to write?

1. A submarine started at sea level and submerged at a steady rate of 8 feet per minute.

2. A plant growing at a steady rate measured 2 in. on day 5 and 13 in. on day 21.

Find the common meaning and the mathematical meaning of each word.

3. function **4.** relation **5.** range **6.** domain

7. variable **8.** base **9.** element **10.** term

Parallel and Perpendicular Lines

California Content Standards

7.0 Derive linear equations by using the point-slope formula. ***Master***

8.0 Understand the concepts of parallel lines and perpendicular lines and how those slopes are related. Find the equation of a line perpendicular to a given line that passes through a given point. ***Develop, Master***

What You'll Learn

- To determine whether lines are parallel
- To determine whether lines are perpendicular

. . . And Why

To use parallel and perpendicular lines to plan a bike path, as in Example 4

Check Skills You'll Need

GO for Help Lessons 1-6 and 5-2

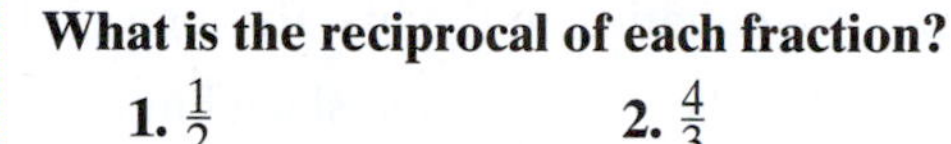

What is the reciprocal of each fraction?

1. $\frac{1}{2}$ **2.** $\frac{4}{3}$ **3.** $-\frac{2}{5}$ **4.** $-\frac{7}{5}$

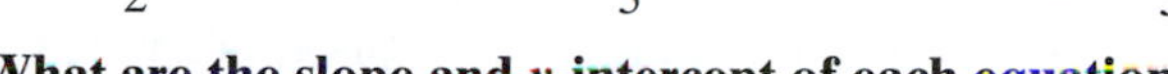

What are the slope and *y*-intercept of each equation?

5. $y = \frac{5}{3}x + 4$ **6.** $y = \frac{5}{3}x - 8$ **7.** $y = 6x$ **8.** $y = 6x + 2$

New Vocabulary

- parallel lines
- perpendicular lines
- negative reciprocal

Parallel Lines

In the graph at the right, the red and blue lines are parallel. **Parallel lines** are lines in the same plane that never intersect. The equation of the red line is $y = \frac{1}{2}x + \frac{3}{2}$. The equation of the blue line is $y = \frac{1}{2}x - 1$. You can use slope-intercept form to determine whether the lines are parallel.

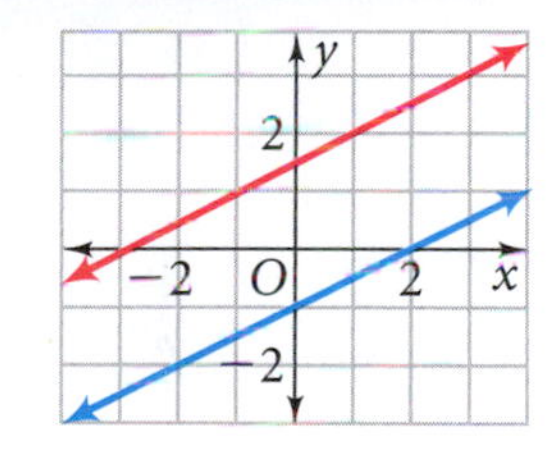

Property **Slopes of Parallel Lines**

Nonvertical lines are parallel if they have the same slope and different *y*-intercepts. *Any* two vertical lines are parallel.

Example The equations $y = \frac{2}{3}x + 1$ and $y = \frac{2}{3}x - 3$ have the same slope, $\frac{2}{3}$, and different *y*-intercepts. The graphs of the two equations are parallel.

1 EXAMPLE Determining Whether Lines Are Parallel

The lanes for competitive swimming are parallel.

Are the graphs of $y = -\frac{1}{3}x + 5$ and $2x + 6y = 12$ parallel? Explain.

Write $2x + 6y = 12$ in slope-intercept form. Then compare with $y = -\frac{1}{3}x + 5$.

$6y = -2x + 12$ **Subtract 2*x* from each side.**

$\frac{6y}{6} = \frac{-2x + 12}{6}$ **Divide each side by 6.**

$y = -\frac{1}{3}x + 2$ **Simplify.**

The lines are parallel. They have the same slope, $-\frac{1}{3}$, and different *y*-intercepts.

CA Standards Check **1** Are the graphs of $-6x + 8y = -24$ and $y = \frac{3}{4}x - 7$ parallel? Explain.

Video Tutor Help
Visit: PHSchool.com
Web Code: bae-0775

To write the equation of a line parallel to a given line, you use the slope of the given line and the point-slope form of a linear equation.

2 EXAMPLE Writing Equations of Parallel Lines

Write an equation for the line that contains (5, 1) and is parallel to $y = \frac{3}{5}x - 4$.

Step 1 Identify the slope of the given line.

$$y = \frac{3}{5}x - 4$$

↑ slope (the slope is $\frac{3}{5}$)

Step 2 Write the equation of the line through (5, 1) using slope-intercept form.

$y - y_1 = m(x - x_1)$ **point-slope form**

$y - 1 = \frac{3}{5}(x - 5)$ **Substitute (5, 1) for (x_1, y_1) and $\frac{3}{5}$ for m.**

$y - 1 = \frac{3}{5}x - \frac{3}{5}(5)$ **Use the Distributive Property.**

$y - 1 = \frac{3}{5}x - 3$ **Simplify.**

$y = \frac{3}{5}x - 2$ **Add 1 to each side.**

CA Standards Check 2 Write an equation for the line that contains (2, −6) and is parallel to $y = 3x + 9$.

Perpendicular Lines

The lines at the right are perpendicular. **Perpendicular lines** are lines that intersect to form right angles. The equation of the red line is $y = -\frac{1}{4}x - 1$. The equation of the blue line is $y = 4x + 2$.

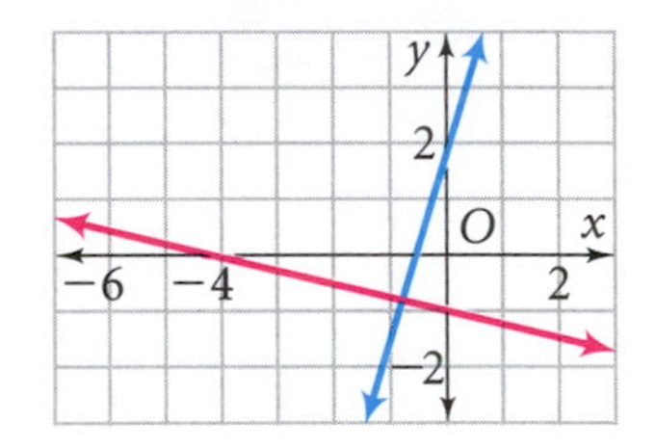

Property **Slopes of Perpendicular Lines**

Two lines are perpendicular if the product of their slopes is −1. A vertical and a horizontal line are also perpendicular.

Example The slope of $y = -\frac{1}{4}x - 1$ is $-\frac{1}{4}$. The slope of $y = 4x + 2$ is 4. Since $-\frac{1}{4} \cdot 4 = -1$, the graphs of the two equations are perpendicular.

The product of two numbers is −1 if one number is the **negative reciprocal** of the other. Here is how to find the negative reciprocal of a number.

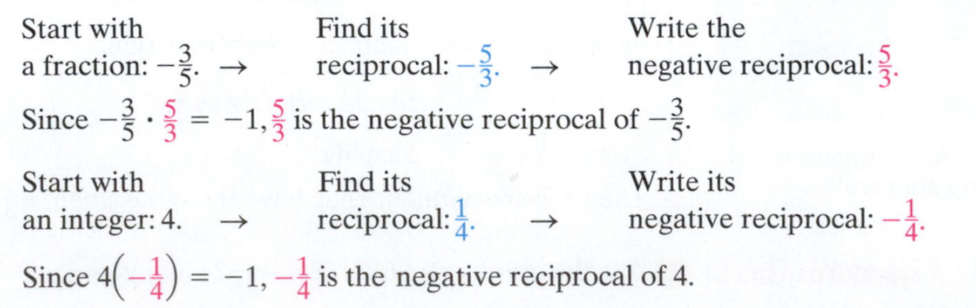

Start with a fraction: $-\frac{3}{5}$. → Find its reciprocal: $-\frac{5}{3}$. → Write the negative reciprocal: $\frac{5}{3}$.

Since $-\frac{3}{5} \cdot \frac{5}{3} = -1$, $\frac{5}{3}$ is the negative reciprocal of $-\frac{3}{5}$.

Start with an integer: 4. → Find its reciprocal: $\frac{1}{4}$. → Write its negative reciprocal: $-\frac{1}{4}$.

Since $4\left(-\frac{1}{4}\right) = -1$, $-\frac{1}{4}$ is the negative reciprocal of 4.

You can use the negative reciprocal of the slope of a given line to write an equation of a line perpendicular to that line.

3 EXAMPLE Writing Equations for Perpendicular Lines

Find the equation of the line that contains $(0, -2)$ and is perpendicular to $y = 5x + 3$.

Study Tip

After finding the slopes of the perpendicular lines, multiply the two slopes as a check.

$5(-\frac{1}{5}) = -1$

Step 1 Identify the slope of the given line.

$y = 5x + 3$

↑ slope

Step 2 Find the negative reciprocal of the slope.

The negative reciprocal of 5 is $-\frac{1}{5}$.

Step 3 Use the slope-intercept form to write an equation.

$y = mx + b$

$y = -\frac{1}{5}x + (-2)$ — **Substitute $-\frac{1}{5}$ for m, and -2 for b.**

$y = -\frac{1}{5}x - 2$ — **Simplify.**

The equation is $y = -\frac{1}{5}x - 2$.

CA Standards Check 3 Write an equation of the line that contains $(1, 8)$ and is perpendicular to $y = \frac{3}{4}x + 1$.

You can use equations of parallel and perpendicular lines to solve some real-world problems.

4 EXAMPLE Application

A jogging path for a new city park will connect the park entrance to Park Road. The path will be perpendicular to Park Road. Write an equation for the line representing the bike path.

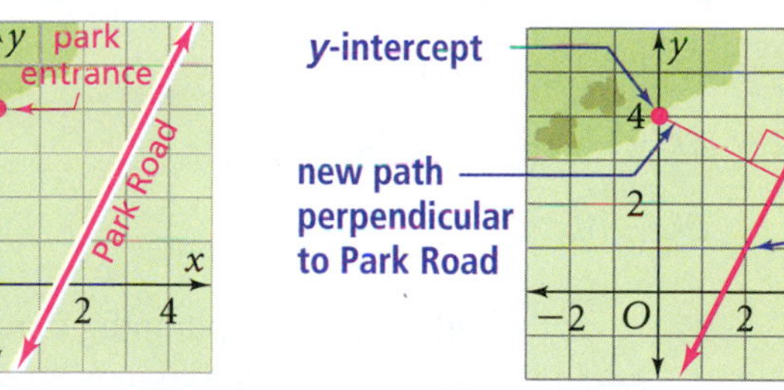

Beverly Gardens Park in Beverly Hills is a 1.9-mile-long linear park with a gravel jogging path.

Step 1 Find the slope m of Park Road.

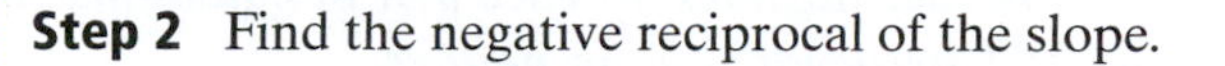

$m = \frac{y_2 - y_1}{x_2 - x_1} = \frac{5 - 1}{4 - 2} = \frac{4}{2} = 2$ — **Points (2, 1) and (4, 5) are on Park Road.**

Step 2 Find the negative reciprocal of the slope.

The negative reciprocal of 2 is $-\frac{1}{2}$. So the slope of the bike path is $-\frac{1}{2}$. The y-intercept is 4.

The equation for the bike path is $y = -\frac{1}{2}x + 4$.

CA Standards Check 4 A second jogging path is planned. It will be parallel to Park Road and will also contain the park entrance. Write an equation for the line representing this jogging path.

EXERCISES

For more exercises, see *Extra Skills and Word Problem Practice.*

Standards Practice

Alg1 7.0, 8.0

A Practice by Example

Example 1 (page 259)

GO for Help

Find the slope of a line parallel to the graph of each equation.

1. $y = \frac{1}{2}x + 2.3$

2. $y = -\frac{2}{3}x - 1$

3. $y = x$

4. $y = 6$

5. $3x + 4y = 12$

6. $7x - y = 5$

Are the graphs of the lines in each pair parallel? Explain.

7. $y = 4x + 12$
$-4x + 3y = 21$

8. $y = -\frac{3}{2}x + 2$
$3x + 2y = 8$

9. $y = \frac{1}{3}x + 3$
$x - 3y = 6$

10. $y = -\frac{1}{2}x + \frac{3}{2}$
$5x - 10y = 15$

11. $y = -3x$
$21x + 7y = 14$

12. $y = \frac{3}{4}x - 2$
$-3x + 4y = 8$

Example 2 (page 260)

Write an equation for the line that is parallel to the given line and that passes through the given point.

13. $y = 6x - 2; (0, 0)$

14. $y = -3x; (3, 0)$

15. $y = -2x + 3; (-3, 5)$

16. $y = -\frac{7}{2}x + 6; (-4, -6)$

17. $y = 0.5x - 8; (8, -5)$

18. $y = -\frac{2}{3}x + 12; (5, -3)$

Example 3 (page 261)

Find the slope of a line perpendicular to the graph of each equation.

19. $y = 2x$

20. $y = -3x$

21. $y = \frac{7}{5}x - 2$

22. $y = -\frac{x}{5} - 7$

23. $2x + 3y = 5$

24. $y = -8$

Write an equation for the line that is perpendicular to the given line and that passes through the given point.

25. $y = 2x + 7; (0, 0)$

26. $y = x - 3; (4, 6)$

27. $y = -\frac{1}{3}x + 2; (4, 2)$

28. $3x + 5y = 7; (-1, 2)$

29. $-10x + 8y = 3; (15, 12)$

30. $4x - 2y = 9; (8, -2)$

Example 4 (page 261)

31. A city's civil engineer is planning a new parking garage and a new street. The new street will go from the entrance of the parking garage to Handel St. It will be perpendicular to Handel St. What is the equation of the line representing the new street?

B Apply Your Skills

Tell whether the lines for each pair of equations are *parallel, perpendicular,* or *neither.*

32. $y = 4x + \frac{3}{4}, y = -\frac{1}{4}x + 4$

33. $y = \frac{2}{3}x - 6, y = \frac{2}{3}x + 6$

34. $y = -x + 5, y = x + 5$

35. $y = 5x, y = -5x + 7$

36. $y = \frac{x}{3} - 4, y = \frac{1}{3}x + 2$

37. $x = 2, y = 9$

38. $2x + y = 2, 2x + y = 5$

39. $3x - 5y = 3, -5x + 3y = 8$

40. Write an equation for a line parallel to the graph of $4x - y = 1$.

Visit: PHSchool.com
Web Code: bae-0505

Find the equation for each line.

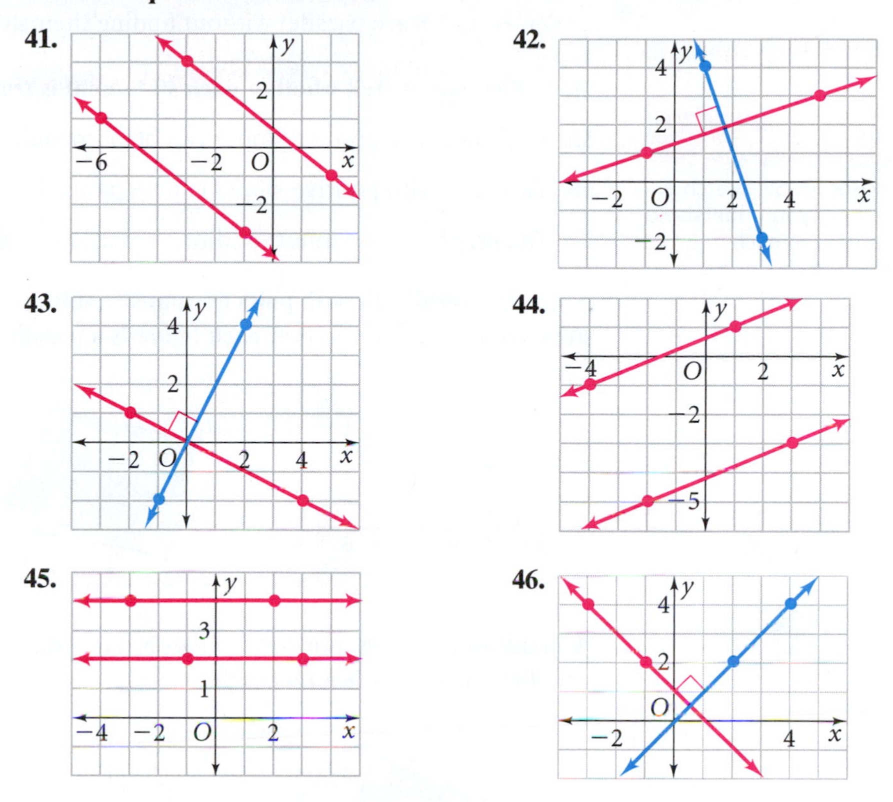

Use the map below for Exercises 47–49.

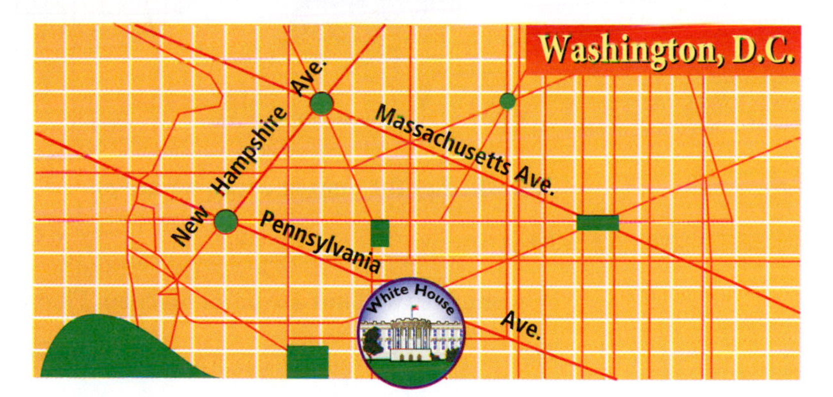

47. What is the slope of New Hampshire Avenue?

48. Show that the parts of Pennsylvania Avenue and Massachusetts Avenue near New Hampshire Avenue are parallel.

49. Show that New Hampshire Avenue is not perpendicular to Pennsylvania Avenue.

50. Which pair of equations graph as perpendicular lines?

Ⓐ $y = 4x + \frac{1}{2}$, $y = -4x + 3$
Ⓑ $y = \frac{2}{3}x + 1$, $y = 3x - 1$
Ⓒ $y = -\frac{3}{5}x - 9$, $y = \frac{5}{3}x + 8$
Ⓓ $y = -\frac{3}{5}x - 9$, $y = \frac{3}{5}x + 4$

51. Are the graphs of $2x + 7y = 6$ and $7y = 2x + 6$ parallel? Explain.

52. Are the graphs of $8x + 3y = 6$ and $8x - 3y = 6$ perpendicular? Explain.

53. Writing Are all horizontal lines parallel? Explain.

54. **Critical Thinking** Explain how you can tell that the graphs of $7x - 3y = 5$ and $7x - 3y = 8$ are parallel without finding their slopes.

Math Reasoning **Tell whether each statement is *true* or *false*. Explain your choice.**

Problem Solving Tip

For Exercises 55–57, sketch a graph to help you understand the statement in each exercise.

55. Two lines with positive slopes can be perpendicular.

56. Two lines with positive slopes can be parallel.

57. The graphs of two different direct variations can be parallel.

A quadrilateral with both pairs of opposite sides parallel is a parallelogram. Use slopes to determine whether each figure is a parallelogram.

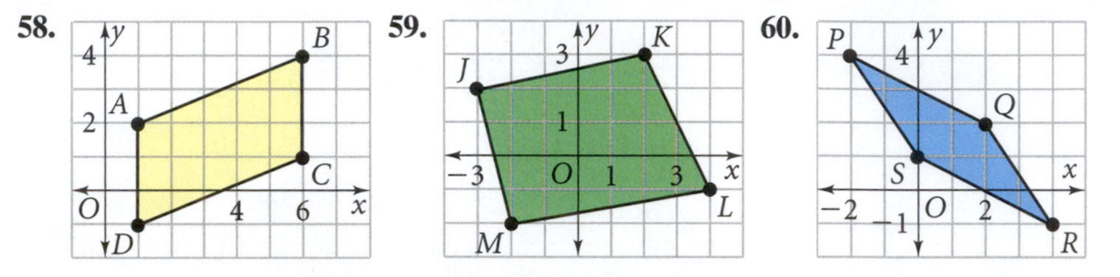

A quadrilateral with four right angles is a rectangle. Use slopes to determine whether each figure is a rectangle.

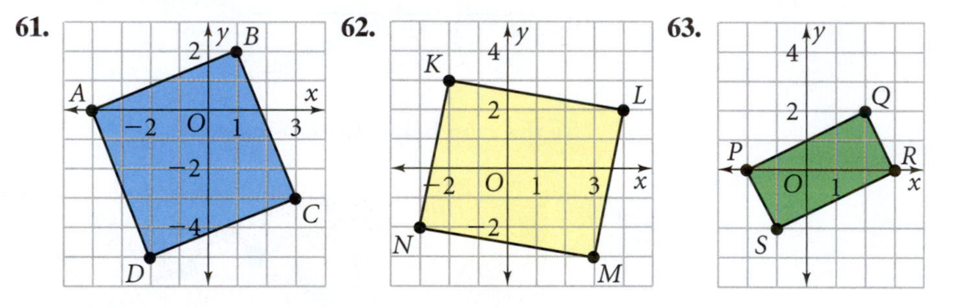

Tell whether the lines in each pair are *parallel*, *perpendicular*, or *neither*.

64. $ax - by = 5; -ax + by = 2$

65. $ax + by = 8; bx - ay = 1$

Assume the two lines are perpendicular. Find an equation for each line.

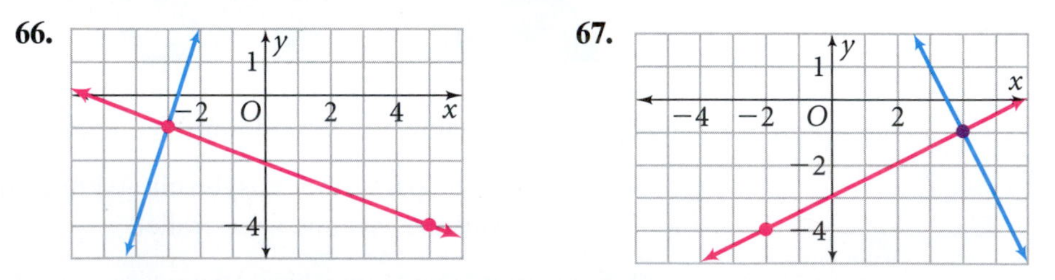

68. For what value of k are the graphs of $3x + 12y = 8$ and $6y = kx - 5$ parallel? Perpendicular?

69. A quadrilateral with two pairs of parallel sides and with diagonals that are perpendicular is a rhombus. Quadrilateral $ABCD$ has vertices $A(-2, 2)$, $B(1, 6)$, $C(6, 6)$, and $D(3, 2)$. Show that $ABCD$ is a rhombus.

70. A triangle with two sides that are perpendicular to each other is a right triangle. Triangle PQR has vertices $P(3, 3)$, $Q(2, -2)$, and $R(0, 1)$. Determine whether PQR is a right triangle. Explain.

Multiple Choice Practice

For California Standards Tutorials, visit PHSchool.com. Web Code: baq-9045

Alg1 8.0

71. Which equation represents a line that is parallel to $y = -2x + 1$?

(A) $y = -2x - 1$ (B) $y = -\frac{1}{2}x + 1$ (C) $y = 2x - 1$ (D) $y = \frac{1}{2}x + 1$

Alg1 6.0

72. Which line has a slope of 2 and a y-intercept of -1?

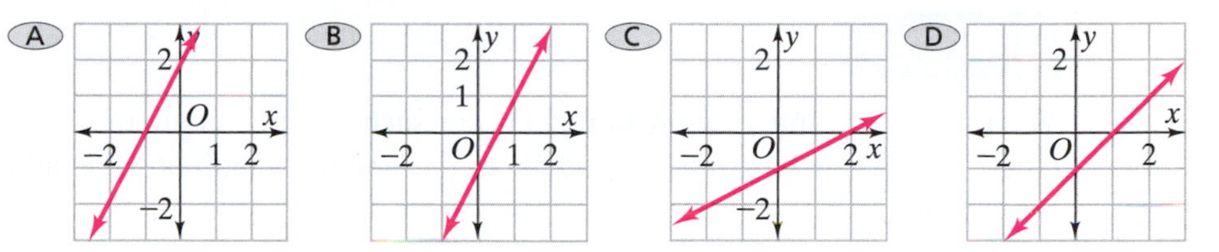

Alg1 7.0

73. Which equation represents a line that contains the points $(-3, 4)$ and $(1, -4)$?

(A) $y = -\frac{1}{2}x + 4$ (B) $y = 2x - 4$ (C) $y = -2x - 2$ (D) $y = \frac{1}{2}x + 3$

Mixed Review

Lesson 5-1

Find the slope of each line.

GO for Help

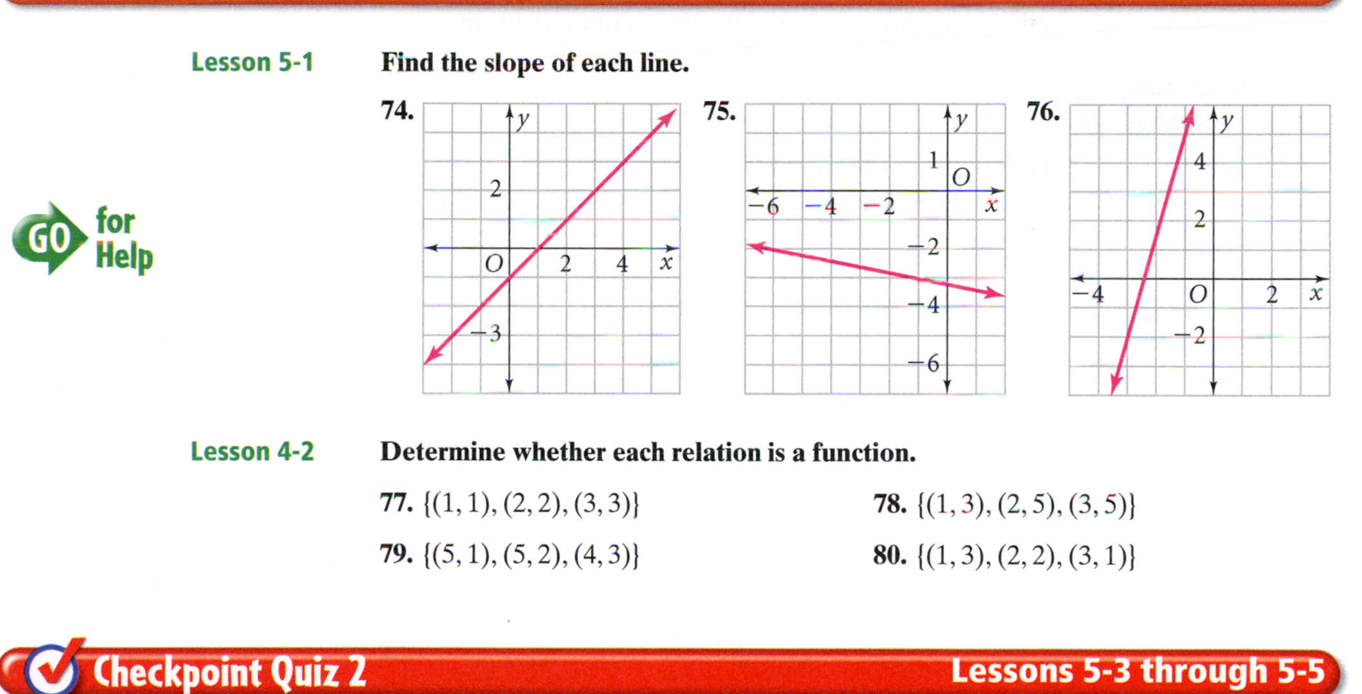

Lesson 4-2

Determine whether each relation is a function.

77. $\{(1, 1), (2, 2), (3, 3)\}$

78. $\{(1, 3), (2, 5), (3, 5)\}$

79. $\{(5, 1), (5, 2), (4, 3)\}$

80. $\{(1, 3), (2, 2), (3, 1)\}$

Checkpoint Quiz 2 — Lessons 5-3 through 5-5

1. Write an equation for the line through $(3, 4)$ that has a slope of $-\frac{1}{4}$.

Find the x- and y-intercepts of each equation. Then write an equation of the line that is parallel to the given line and that passes through the given point.

2. $x + y = 3; (5, 4)$

3. $3x + 2y = 1; (-2, 6)$

Write an equation of the line that is perpendicular to the given line and that passes through the given point.

4. $y = -4x + 2; (0, 2)$

5. $y = \frac{2}{3}x + 6; (-6, 2)$

Test-Taking Strategies

Drawing a Diagram

For some problems, it may help to draw a diagram of the given information if one is not provided.

1 EXAMPLE

The points R, S, and T lie on a line in order such that the length of $\overline{ST}$ is twice the length of $\overline{RS}$. The length of $\overline{RT}$ is 5 cm more than the length of $\overline{ST}$. Find the length of $\overline{RS}$ and $\overline{ST}$.

Draw $\overline{RT}$. Since $\overline{ST}$ is twice as long as $\overline{RS}$, let $RS = x$ and $ST = 2x$. Since the length of $\overline{RT}$ is 5 cm more than the length of $\overline{ST}$, let $RT = 5 + 2x$.

You can see from your diagram that $2x + x = 5 + 2x$. Solve this equation, and you find that $x = 5$. The length of $\overline{RS}$ is 5 cm and the length of $\overline{ST}$ is 10 cm.

2 EXAMPLE

The points $A(-8, 1)$, $B(-2, 7)$ and $C(4, -11)$ are the vertices of a triangle. Is Triangle ABC a right triangle?

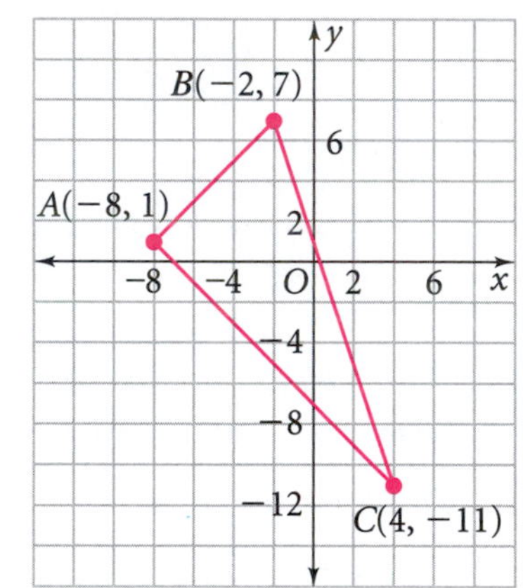

Two lines form a right angle if the product of their slopes is -1.

When you draw a diagram, you can see that the right angle cannot be at point C. You need to see if the product of the slopes of $\overline{AC}$ and $\overline{AB}$ or of $\overline{BC}$ and $\overline{AB}$ is -1. The slope of $\overline{AB}$ is 1, and the slope of $\overline{AC}$ is -1. The product of 1 and -1 is -1. So Triangle ABC is a right triangle.

Multiple Choice Practice

1. The points $L(4, 0)$, $M(10, 0)$, and $N(7, 5)$ form $\triangle LMN$. What is the sum of the slopes of the three sides of the triangle?

   (A) $-\frac{6}{5}$ (B) 0 (C) $\frac{10}{3}$ (D) 6

2. Three towns A, B, and C lie on a straight road in that order. The distance from B to C is 6 miles more than twice the distance from A to B. The distance from A to C is 2 miles more than four times the distance from A to B. What is the distance from A to B?

   (A) 2 (B) 4 (C) 6 (D) 8

Chapter 5 Review

Vocabulary Review

English and Spanish Audio Online

Choose the vocabulary term that correctly completes the sentence.

1. Two lines are __?__ if the product of their slopes is -1.
2. Two lines in the same plane that never intersect are __?__.
3. The equation $y - 2 = 3(x - 5)$ is written in __?__ form.
4. The ratio of the vertical change to the horizontal change is called the __?__.
5. The y-coordinate of the point at which the graph of a line crosses the vertical axis is called the __?__.

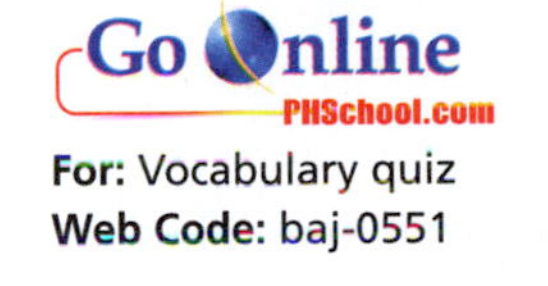

For: Vocabulary quiz
Web Code: baj-0551

Skills and Concepts

Lesson 5-1

- To find rates of change from tables and graphs (p. 230)
- To find slope (p. 232)

Alg1 6.0, 7.0, 8.0

Rate of change is the relationship between two quantities that are changing.

$$\text{rate of change} = \frac{\text{change in the dependent variable}}{\text{change in the independent variable}}$$

Slope is the ratio of the vertical change to the horizontal change.

$$\text{slope} = \frac{\text{vertical change}}{\text{horizontal change}} = \frac{\text{rise}}{\text{run}}$$

Find the rate of change for each situation.

6. A kitten grows from 5 oz at birth to 3 lb 5 oz at 6 months. (*Hint:* 1 lb = 16 oz)
7. A plant measures 0.5 in. at the end of Week 1 and 14 in. at the end of Week 5.

Find each rate of change. Explain what *rate of change* means in each situation.

8. 9. 10.

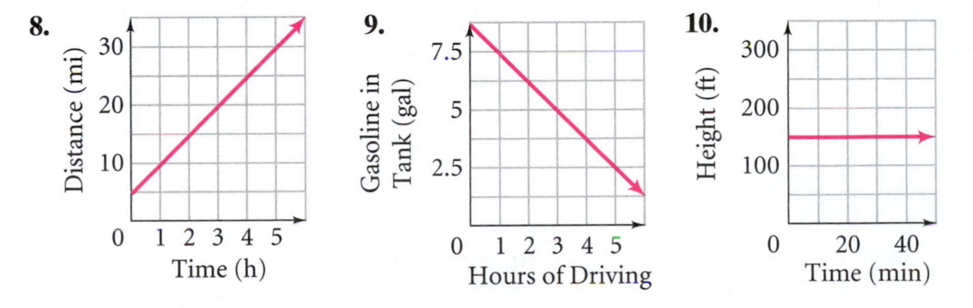

Find the slope of the line that passes through each pair of points.

11. $(3, -2)$ and $(-5, -4)$
12. $(4.5, -1)$ and $(4.5, 2.6)$
13. $(2, 5)$ and $(-5, -2)$

Lesson 5-2

- To write linear equations in slope-intercept form (p. 239)
- To graph linear equations (p. 241)

Alg1 6.0, 7.0

The graph of a **linear equation** is a line. The ***x*-intercept** of a line is the *x*-coordinate of the point where the line crosses the *x*-axis, and the ***y*-intercept** is the *y*-coordinate of the point where the line crosses the *y*-axis.

The **slope-intercept form of a linear equation** is $y = mx + b$, where m is the slope and b is the *y*-intercept.

Write an equation of a line with the given slope and *y*-intercept. Then graph the equation.

14. $m = 0, b = -3$ **15.** $m = -7, b = \frac{1}{2}$ **16.** $m = \frac{2}{5}, b = 0$

Write the slope-intercept form of the equation for each line.

17.

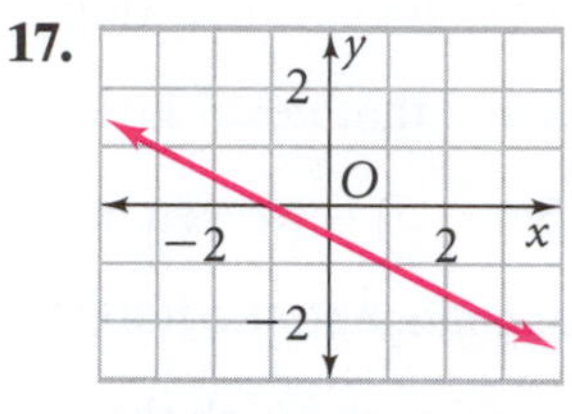

18.

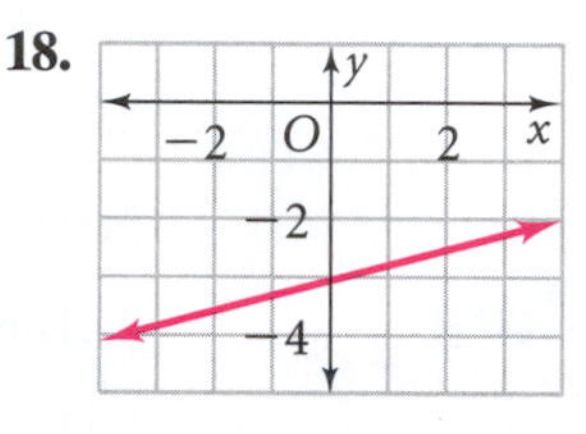

Determine whether the ordered pair lies on the graph of the given equation.

19. $(3, -10); y = -5x - 2$ **20.** $(8, 13); y = \frac{3}{4}x + 7$

21. $(9, 0.5); x - 2y = 8$ **22.** $(-1, -3); -6x + 3y = -4$

23. $(-2, 0); 4y = -8x + 3$ **24.** $(0, -4); -\frac{1}{2}y = x + 2$

Lesson 5-3

- To graph equations using intercepts (p. 246)
- To write equations in standard form (p. 248)

Alg1 6.0

The **standard form of a linear equation** is $Ax + By = C$, where A, B, and C are real numbers, and A and B are not both zero.

Find the *x*- and *y*-intercepts. Then graph each equation.

25. $5x + 2y = 10$ **26.** $6.5x - 4y = 52$ **27.** $x + 3y = -1$

Write each equation in standard form.

28. $y = \frac{3}{5}x + 7$ **29.** $y = -\frac{1}{3}x + 2$ **30.** $y = \frac{4}{3}x - 5$

Match each equation with its graph.

31. $2x - 3y = 6$ **32.** $2x + 3y = 6$ **33.** $2x + 3y = -6$

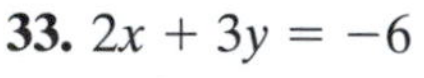

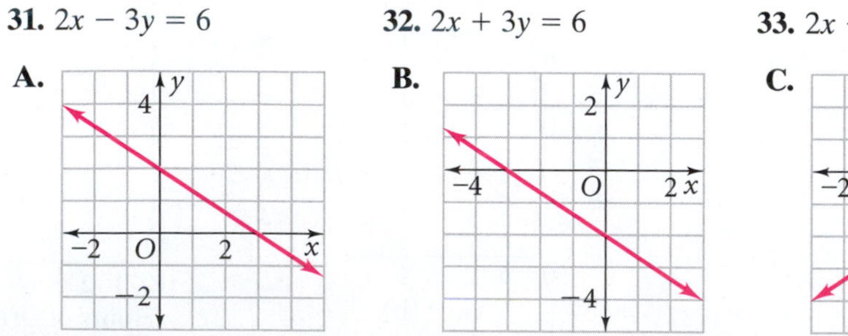

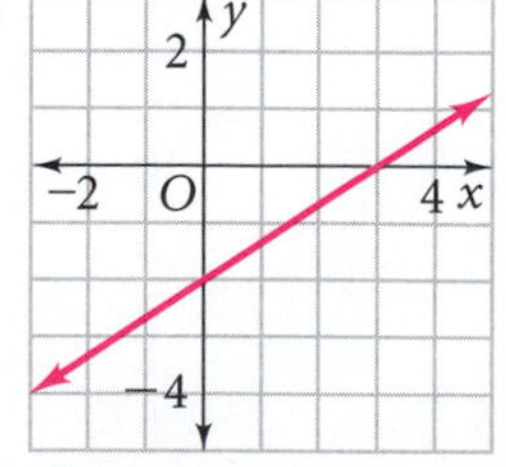

For each equation, tell whether its graph is a horizontal or a vertical line.

34. $y = -0.5$ **35.** $x = \frac{3}{8}$ **36.** $y = |-4|$

Lesson 5-4

- To graph and write linear equations using point-slope form (p. 252)
- To write a linear equation using data (p. 254)

Alg1 6.0, 7.0

The **point-slope form of a linear equation** is $y - y_1 = m(x - x_1)$, which passes through the point (x_1, y_1) and has slope m.

Use point-slope form to write an equation of a line that passes through the point (1, −2) with slope *m*.

37. $m = 2$ **38.** $m = \frac{3}{4}$ **39.** $m = -3$ **40.** $m = 0$

Use the point-slope form to write an equation of a line through the given points.

41. $(4, 3), (-2, 1)$ **42.** $(5, -4), (0, 2)$ **43.** $(-1, 0), (-3, -1)$

Are the data linear? If so, model the data with an equation.

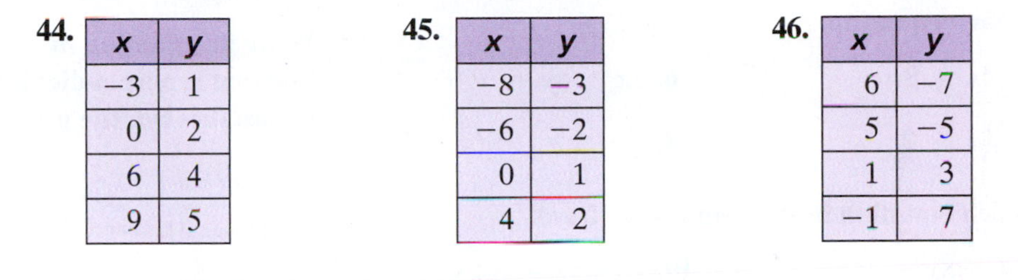

44.

x	y
−3	1
0	2
6	4
9	5

45.

x	y
−8	−3
−6	−2
0	1
4	2

46.

x	y
6	−7
5	−5
1	3
−1	7

Lesson 5-5

- To determine whether lines are parallel (p. 259)
- To determine whether lines are perpendicular (p. 260)

Alg1 7.0, 8.0

Parallel lines are lines in the same plane that never intersect. Nonvertical lines are parallel if they have the same slope. Two lines are **perpendicular lines** if they intersect to form right angles and the product of their slopes is −1.

Are the graphs of the lines in each pair parallel? Explain.

47. $y = -3x - 8$
$6x + 2y = -10$

48. $y = -\frac{2}{5}x - 1$
$2x + 5y = 20$

49. $y = \frac{3}{4}x - 2$
$-4x + 3y = -12$

Are the graphs of the lines in each pair perpendicular?

50. $y = -\frac{1}{3}x - 5$
$y = 3x + 6$

51. $y = -\frac{5}{4}x + 3$
$4x + 5y = -15$

52. $y = \frac{2}{3}x - 4$
$3x + 2y = 4$

Write an equation for each of the following conditions.

53. parallel to $y = 5x - 2$, through $(2, -1)$

54. perpendicular to $y = -3x + 7$, through $(3, 5)$

55. parallel to $y = 9x$, through $(0, -5)$

56. perpendicular to $y = 8x - 1$, through $(4, 10)$

Find the equation for each line.

57.

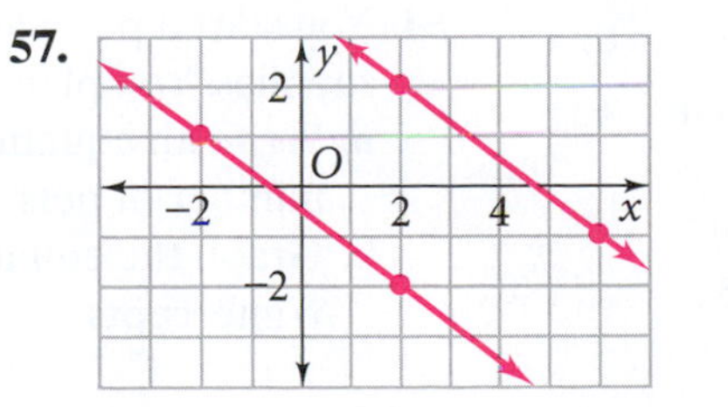

58.

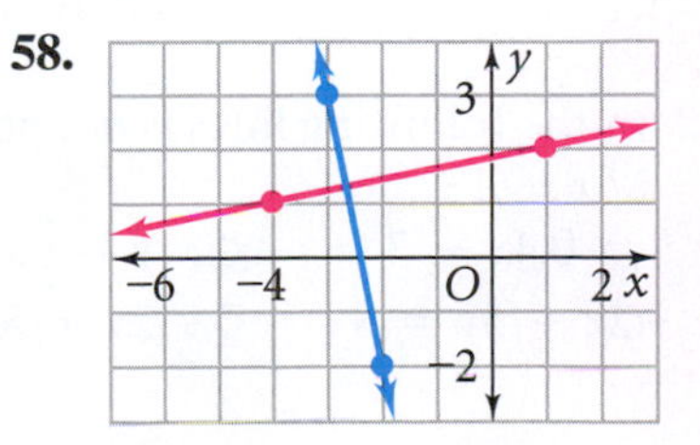

Chapter 5 Test

Go Online PHSchool.com For: Chapter Test Web Code: baa-0552

Tell whether each statement is *true* or *false*. Explain.

1. A rate of change must be positive.
2. The rate of change for a vertical line is 0.

Find the slope of the line that passes through each pair of points.

3. (4, 3), (3, 8)
4. (−2, 1), (6, −1)

Graph each equation.

5. $x - 4y = 8$
6. $2x + 4y = -4$
7. $y = \frac{1}{3}x + 2$
8. $y - 1 = -3(x - 3)$

Write each equation in slope-intercept form.

9. $-7y = 8x - 3$
10. $x - 3y = -18$
11. $5x + 4y = 100$
12. $9x = 2y + 13$

Find the *x*- and *y*-intercepts of each line.

13. $3x + 4y = -24$
14. $-6x + 2y = -8$
15. $-5x + 10y = 60$
16. $x + y = 1$

Write an equation in point-slope form for the line with the given slope and through the given point.

17. $(-2, -7); m = \frac{8}{3}$
18. $(4, -8); m = 3$
19. $(0, 3); m = -\frac{1}{2}$
20. $(9, 0); m = -5$
21. $(0, 4); m = 3$
22. $(-2, 0); m = -4$
23. $(5, -3); m = \frac{3}{4}$
24. $(-1, -9); m = -\frac{2}{3}$
25. $(-6, 4); m = -\frac{3}{5}$
26. $(7, 11); m = \frac{1}{2}$

Write an equation in point-slope form for the line through the given points.

27. (4, 9), (−2, −6)
28. (−1, 0), (3, 10)
29. (5, −8), (−9, −8)
30. (0, 7), (1, 5)

31. Which of the following lines is *not* perpendicular to $y = -2.5x + 13$?
 (A) $y = 0.4x - 7$
 (B) $-2x + 5y = 8$
 (C) $y = \frac{2}{5}x + 4$
 (D) $2y = 5x + 1.5$

Write an equation in slope-intercept form for a line that is parallel to the given line and that passes through the given point.

32. $y = 5x; (2, -1)$
33. $y = 5; (-3, 6)$
34. $y = 5x + 1; (2, -3)$
35. $y = -x - 9; (0, 5)$
36. $2x + 3y = 9; (-1, 4)$
37. $y = -\frac{1}{2}x; (3, -4)$
38. $y = -2x + 3; (-2, -1)$
39. $y = \frac{2}{3}x + 7; (-1, 2)$

Write an equation in slope-intercept form for a line that is perpendicular to the given line and that passes through the given point.

40. $(4, 0); y = -2x$
41. $(0, 2); x = -7$
42. $(-10, 3); y = -2x - 8$
43. $(12, 8); y = -3x - 9$
44. $(-1, 7); y = -\frac{1}{4}x + 6$
45. $(4, -9); -x + 2y = 10$
46. $(2, 1); -2x + 3y = -12$
47. $(-2, 3); y = -5x + 1$

48. Write the slope-intercept form of the equation for each line below.

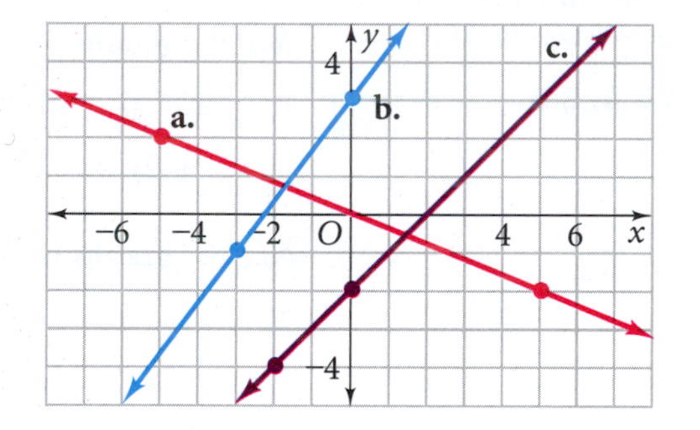

Determine whether the ordered pair lies on the graph of the given equation.

49. $(-2, 1); y = -3x - 5$
50. $(-1, -4); y = 8x + 2$
51. $(6, 3); y = -\frac{5}{6}x + 4$
52. $(4, -7); -4x - y = -9$

53. Write the equation of a line parallel to $y = 0.5x - 10$.

54. You start a pet-washing service. You spend \$30 on supplies. You plan to charge \$5 to wash each pet.
 a. Write an equation to relate your profit *y* to the number of pets *x* you wash.
 b. Graph the equation. What are the *x*- and *y*-intercepts?

Standards Mastery

Cumulative Practice

Some questions ask you to interpret a graph. Read the question at the right. Then follow the tips to answer the sample question.

The graph of a line is shown below.

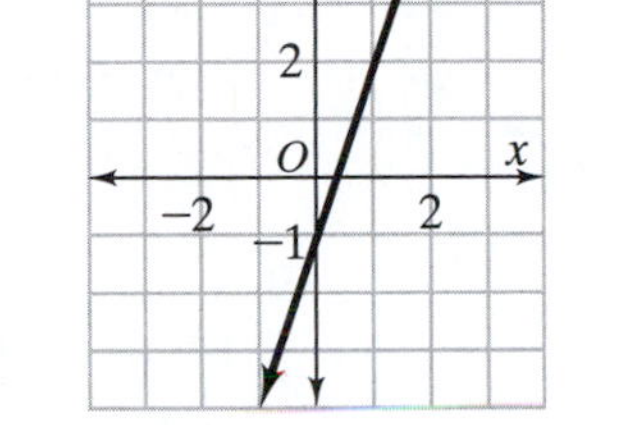

Which equation best represents the graph of the line?

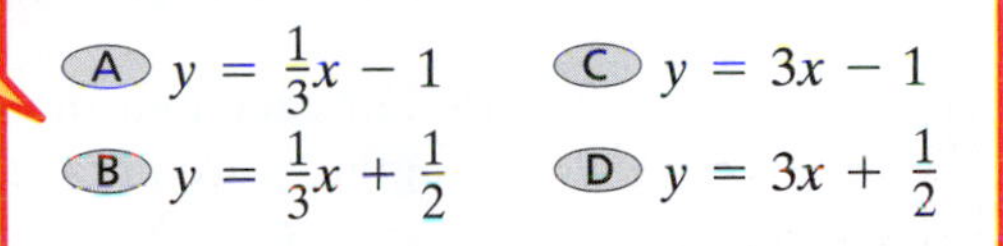

Ⓐ $y = \frac{1}{3}x - 1$ Ⓒ $y = 3x - 1$

Ⓑ $y = \frac{1}{3}x + \frac{1}{2}$ Ⓓ $y = 3x + \frac{1}{2}$

Tip 1
Think about what information you need to write the equation of a line. You can use slope, intercepts, or points on the line.

Tip 2
Look at the answer choices. The equations are written in slope-intercept form.

Think It Through

Since the answer choices are written in slope-intercept form, find the slope and y-intercept. The y-intercept is -1. To get from the point $(0, -1)$ to $(1, 2)$, you move 3 units up and 1 to the right. The slope is $\frac{3}{1} = 3$. The equation is $y = 3x - 1$. The correct answer is C.

Vocabulary Review

As you solve problems, you must understand the meanings of mathematical terms. Choose the correct term to complete each sentence.

A. The (*slope, y-intercept*) of a line is determined by $\frac{\text{rise}}{\text{run}}$.

B. The (*x-intercept, y-intercept*) is where a line crosses the x-axis.

C. The (*slope, y-intercept*) of a line defines a rate of change.

D. (*Parallel, Perpendicular*) lines have the same slope.

Read each question. Then write the letter of the correct answer on your paper.

1. The graph shows Jillian's distance from her house as she walks home from school. At what rate does Jillian walk? **(Lesson 5-1)**

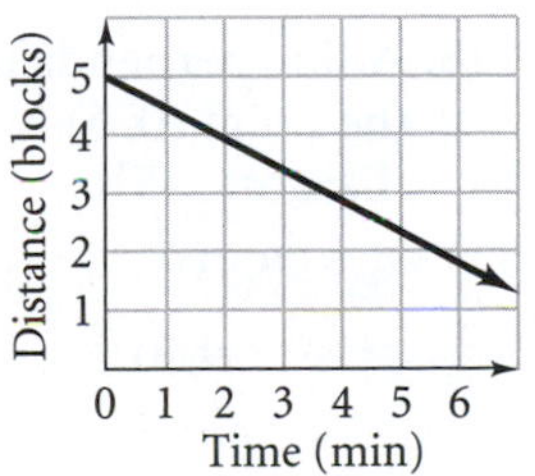

Ⓐ 1 block per minute

Ⓑ 1 minute per block

Ⓒ 2 blocks per minute

Ⓓ $\frac{1}{2}$ block per minute

2. Which is the equation of a line with slope 3? **(Lesson 5-2)**

Ⓐ $y = 3x - 4$ Ⓒ $y = 4x - 3$

Ⓑ $x = -3y + 5$ Ⓓ $y = -3x - 5$

3. What is the slope of the line shown in the graph at the right? **(Lesson 5-2)**

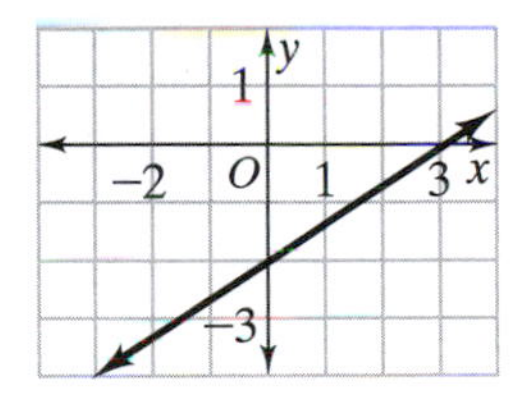

Ⓐ -2 Ⓒ $\frac{2}{3}$

Ⓑ $\frac{3}{2}$ Ⓓ 3

4. Trisha drew a diagram with 3 squares as shown at the right. Which expression represents the perimeter of the largest square? **(Lesson 2-5)**

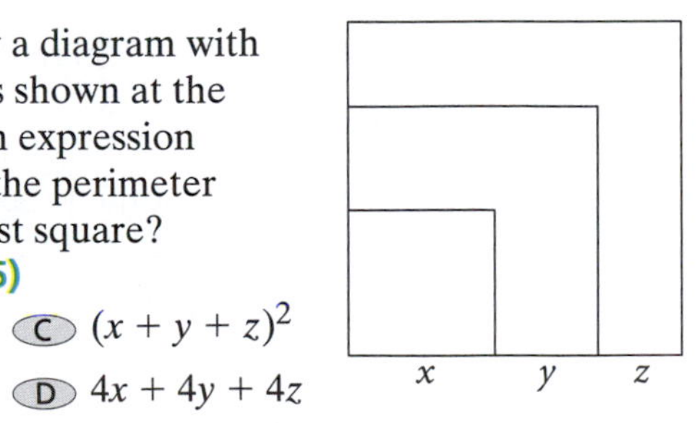

Ⓐ z^2 Ⓒ $(x + y + z)^2$

Ⓑ $4z$ Ⓓ $4x + 4y + 4z$

5. The length of Darren's family room is 3 times the width. If the width of Darren's family room is x, which expression best represents the area? **(Lesson 2-5)**

Ⓐ $3x^2$ Ⓒ $x^2 + 9$

Ⓑ $9x^2$ Ⓓ $(x + 3)^2$

6. Which expression could represent the sum of 3 consecutive even integers? (Lesson 2-5)

Ⓐ $n + 3$
Ⓑ $3n + 3$
Ⓒ $3n + 6$
Ⓓ $6n + 6$

7. Look at the graph at the right. If the y-intercept increases by 2 and the slope stays the same, what will the x-intercept be? (Lesson 5-2)

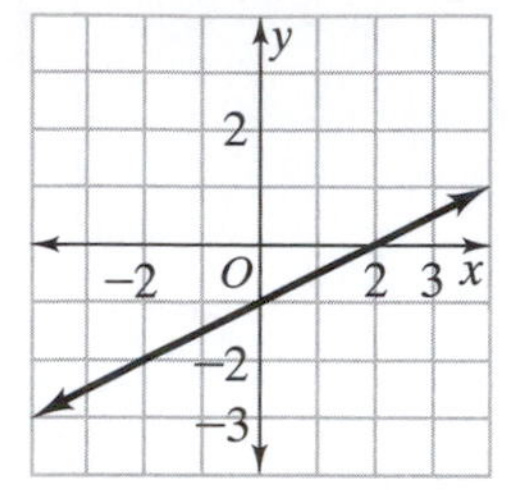

Ⓐ −3
Ⓑ −2
Ⓒ 1
Ⓓ 4

8. Which equation represents a line that is steeper than the line represented by $y = \frac{3}{4}x - 1$? (Lesson 5-2)

Ⓐ $y = -\frac{3}{4}x - 2$
Ⓑ $y = \frac{4}{3}x - 2$
Ⓒ $y = \frac{2}{3}x - 1$
Ⓓ $y = \frac{3}{4}x + 2$

9. There is \$65 in Hilo's class fund. The class is having a car wash to raise money for a trip. Hilo made the graph below to model the amount of money they will have if they charge \$4 for each car washed.

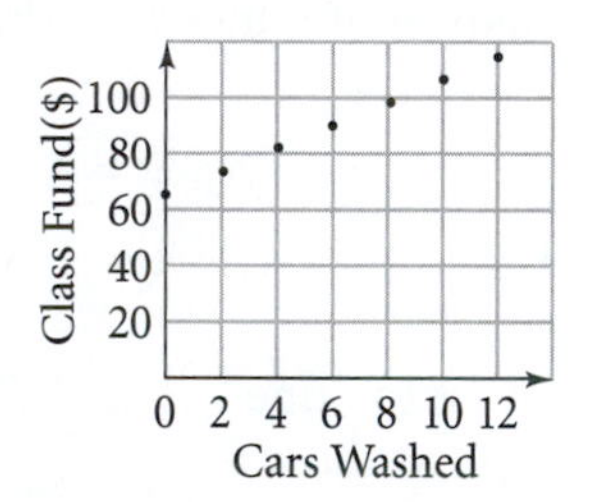

How would the graph change if they charged \$5 for each car washed? (Lesson 5-2)

Ⓐ The y-intercept would increase.
Ⓑ The slope would increase.
Ⓒ The y-intercept would decrease.
Ⓓ The slope would decrease.

10. What is the second step of the process? (Lesson 2-2)

Step 1. $4(3x + 6) - 1 = -13$
Step 2.
Step 3. $12x + 23 = -13$
Step 4. $12x = -36$
Step 5. $x = -3$

Ⓐ $4(3x + 5) = -13$
Ⓑ $12x + 6 - 1 = -13$
Ⓒ $12x + 24 - 1 = -13$
Ⓓ $(7x + 10) - 1 = -13$

11. What are the x- and y-intercepts of the equation $6x - 3y = 36$? (Lesson 5-3)

Ⓐ $x = -12$ and $y = 6$
Ⓑ $x = 6$ and $y = 12$
Ⓒ $x = 12$ and $y = -6$
Ⓓ $x = 6$ and $y = -12$

12. What is the equation of a line through point (2, 3) with a slope of $-\frac{5}{7}$? (Lesson 5-4)

Ⓐ $5x + 7y = 11$
Ⓑ $5x + 7y = 31$
Ⓒ $5x - 7y = -11$
Ⓓ $5x - 7y = 31$

13. What part of the statement below is the conclusion? (Activity Lab 3-3b)

If $4x + 2y = 9$, then $12x + 6y = 27$.

Ⓐ $8x + 4y = 18$
Ⓑ $4x + 2y = 9$
Ⓒ $16x + 8y = 36$
Ⓓ $12x + 6y = 27$

14. For each pair of equations, determine whether the graphs are parallel or perpendicular lines. (Lesson 5-5)

(1) $2x + 3y = 9$ and $4x + 6y = 27$
(2) $2x + 3y = 9$ and $3x - 2y = 27$

Ⓐ (1) is parallel; (2) is perpendicular.
Ⓑ (1) is parallel; (2) is parallel.
Ⓒ (1) is perpendicular; (2) is perpendicular.
Ⓓ (1) is perpendicular; (2) is parallel.

15. What is the equation of a line through point (2, 1) and perpendicular to $y = \frac{2}{3}x + 3$? (Lesson 5-5)

Ⓐ $2x - 3y = 1$
Ⓑ $3x + 2y = 8$
Ⓒ $3x + 2y = -4$
Ⓓ $3x + 2y = 7$

16. Suppose you earn \$74.25 for working 9 hours. How much will you earn for working 15 hours? (Lesson 2-4)

Ⓐ \$120
Ⓑ \$123.75
Ⓒ \$124.50
Ⓓ \$127.25

17. Which is NOT a solution of $5x - 4 < 12$? (Lesson 3-4)

Ⓐ −2 Ⓑ 0 Ⓒ 3 Ⓓ 4

18. A line perpendicular to $y = 3x - 2$ passes through the point (0, 6). Which other point lies on the line? (Lesson 5-5)

Ⓐ (9, 3)
Ⓑ (−9, 3)
Ⓒ (9, −3)
Ⓓ (−9, −3)

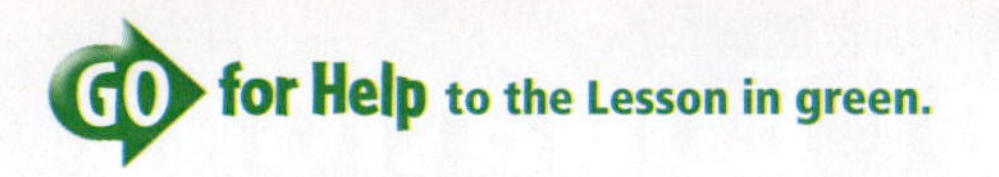

Standards Mastery

19. Which of the following is the solution of $6(4x - 3) = -54$? **(Lesson 2-2)**

Ⓐ -3 Ⓑ -1.5 Ⓒ 1.5 Ⓓ 3

20. Find $f(-2)$ when $f(x) = -3x + 4$. **(Lesson 4-2)**

Ⓐ -10 Ⓑ -2 Ⓒ 2 Ⓓ 10

21. Josie found the slope of the line shown below.

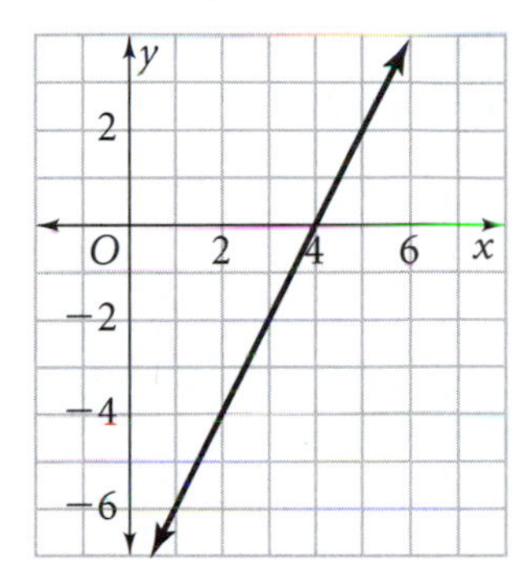

She used the points $(1, -6)$ and $(5, 2)$ and wrote $\frac{2-(-6)}{1-5} = \frac{8}{-4} = -2$ to find the slope. Which of the following describes her error? **(Lesson 5-1)**

Ⓐ She reversed x_1 and x_2 in the denominator.
Ⓑ She subtracted instead of added.
Ⓒ She used an x-value in the numerator.
Ⓓ She did not simplify the negative signs correctly.

22. Which equation represents a line that passes through $(2, -1)$ and $(3, 4)$? **(Lesson 5-4)**

Ⓐ $y = 5x - 11$ Ⓒ $y = \frac{1}{5}x + \frac{17}{5}$
Ⓑ $y = 5x + 7$ Ⓓ $y = 3x - 5$

23. Which equation represents a line that passes through $(2, -1)$ and that is perpendicular to the line $y = \frac{2}{5}x - \frac{7}{8}$? **(Lesson 5-5)**

Ⓐ $y = -\frac{5}{2}x - \frac{11}{2}$ Ⓒ $y = \frac{2}{5}x - \frac{19}{5}$
Ⓑ $y = -\frac{5}{2}x + 4$ Ⓓ $y = \frac{5}{2}x - 8$

24. Which of the following equations has a graph that contains the ordered pairs $(-3, 4)$ and $(1, -4)$? **(Lesson 5-4)**

Ⓐ $x + 2y = 8$ Ⓒ $2x + y = -2$
Ⓑ $2x - y = 4$ Ⓓ $x - 2y = -6$

25. Which expression is equivalent to $3(5x - 2) - 4(x + 3)$? **(Lesson 2-2)**

Ⓐ $19x + 6$ Ⓒ $11x - 18$
Ⓑ $4x - 12$ Ⓓ $12x + 10$

26. What is the range of the following relation?
$\{(0, 3), (1, 5), (2, 3), (3, 1), (4, 0), (5, 6)\}$ **(Lesson 4-2)**

Ⓐ $\{0, 1, 2, 3, 4, 5\}$ Ⓒ $\{0, 1, 3, 5, 6\}$
Ⓑ $\{0, 1, 3, 3, 5, 6\}$ Ⓓ $\{0, 1, 2, 3, 4, 5, 6\}$

27. What is the domain of the function $f(x) = x^2 - 4$? **(Lesson 4-2)**

Ⓐ $\{x: x \geq 0\}$ Ⓒ $\{-2, 2\}$
Ⓑ $\{x: x \geq -4\}$ Ⓓ all real numbers

28. What part of the statement below is the hypothesis?
If $-2x - 5 < 7$, then $-2x < 12$. **(Activity Lab 3-3b)**

Ⓐ $-2x - 5 < 7$ Ⓒ $x > -6$
Ⓑ $-2x < 12$ Ⓓ $x < -6$

Standards Reference Guide

California Content Standard	Item Number(s)
Alg1 4.0	10, 19, 25
Alg1 5.0	4–6, 16, 17
Alg1 6.0	1–3, 7–9, 11, 21
Alg1 7.0	12, 22, 24
Alg1 8.0	14, 15, 18, 23
Alg1 17.0	20, 26, 27
Alg1 24.2	13, 28

For additional review and practice, see the *California Standards Review and Practice Workbook* or go online to use the

For: PHSchool.com, **Web Code:** baq-9045

CALIFORNIA CHECK SYSTEM

CHAPTER 6

Systems of Equations and Inequalities

What You've Learned

California Content Standards

5.0 Solve multi-step problems, including word problems, involving linear equations and linear inequalities in one variable and provide justification for each step.

6.0 Graph a linear equation and compute the x- and y-intercepts.

7.0 Verify that a point lies on a line, given an equation of the line.

GO for Help to the Lesson in green.

Solving Equations (Lesson 2-3)

Solve each equation. If the equation is an identity, write *identity*. If it has no solution, write *no solution*.

1. $3(2 - 2x) = -6(x - 1)$ **2.** $3m + 1 = -m + 5$ **3.** $4x - 1 = 3(x + 1) + x$

4. $\frac{1}{2}(6x - 4) = 4 + x$ **5.** $5x = 2 - (x - 7)$ **6.** $x + 5 = x - 5$

Solving for a Variable (Review page 90)

Solve for y in terms of x.

7. $3x - 2y = -2$ **8.** $10 = x + 5y$ **9.** $2y = -2x - 8$

Writing Compound Inequalities (Lesson 3-5)

Write an inequality that represents each situation. Graph the solutions.

10. all real numbers that are between -10 and 3

11. Discounts are given to children under 12 and seniors over 60.

Writing a Function Rule (Lesson 4-4)

12. For every \$35 ticket, the box office charges a fee of \$4.50.
- **a.** Write a function rule that relates the total cost $C(t)$ to t, the number of tickets.
- **b.** What is the total cost for 3 tickets?
- **c.** How many tickets were purchased if the total cost was \$237?

Graphing Linear Equations (Lessons 5-2, 5-3, and 5-4)

Graph each line.

13. $2x + 4y = -8$ **14.** $y = -\frac{2}{3}x + 3$ **15.** $2x = y - 4$

▲ Farmers must keep track of their expenses and their income from selling produce at farmers' markets. In Lesson 6-4, you will solve systems of equations to find the point at which income equals expenses.

What You'll Learn Next

California Content Standards

6.0 Sketch the region defined by linear inequalities.

9.0 Solve a system of two linear equations in two variables algebraically and interpret the answer graphically. Solve a system of two linear inequalities in two variables and sketch the solution sets.

15.0 Apply algebraic techniques to solve rate problems and percent mixture problems.

New Vocabulary

English and Spanish Audio Online

- **elimination method** (p. 287)
- **infinitely many solutions** (p. 278)
- **linear inequality** (p. 303)
- **no solution** (p. 278)
- **solution of a system** (p. 276)
- **solution of a system of linear inequalities** (p. 309)
- **solution set** (p. 309)
- **substitution method** (p. 282)
- **system of linear equations** (p. 276)
- **system of linear inequalities** (p. 309)

Academic Vocabulary

- **eliminate** (p. 317)
- **substitute** (p. 317)

CALIFORNIA CHECK SYSTEM

6-1 Solving Systems by Graphing

California Content Standards

9.0 Solve a system of two linear equations in two variables and interpret the answer graphically. ***Introduce***

What You'll Learn

- To solve systems by graphing
- To analyze special types of systems

. . . And Why

To use graphs to compare growth of plants, as in Example 2

Check Skills You'll Need

GO for Help Lessons 2-3 and 5-2

Solve each equation.

1. $2n + 3 = 5n - 2$ **2.** $8 - 4z = 2z - 13$ **3.** $8q - 12 = 3q + 23$

Graph each pair of equations on the same coordinate plane.

4. $y = 3x - 6$
$y = -x + 2$

5. $y = 6x + 1$
$y = 6x - 4$

6. $y = 2x - 5$
$6x - 3y = 15$

New Vocabulary

- system of linear equations
- solution of a system of linear equations
- no solution
- infinitely many solutions

Solving Systems by Graphing

Two or more linear equations together form a **system of linear equations.** One way to solve a system of linear equations is by graphing each equation. Look for any point common to all the lines. Any ordered pair in a system that makes *all* the equations true is a **solution of the system of linear equations.**

1 EXAMPLE Solving a System of Equations

Solve by graphing. $y = 2x - 3$
$y = x - 1$

Graph both equations on the same coordinate plane.

$y = 2x - 3$ **The slope is 2. The *y*-intercept is −3.**

$y = x - 1$ **The slope is 1. The *y*-intercept is −1.**

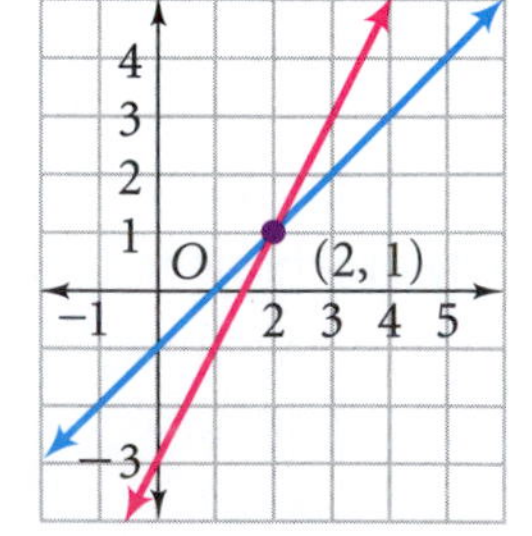

Find the point of intersection.

The lines intersect at (2, 1), so (2, 1) is the solution of the system.

Check See if (2, 1) makes both equations true.

$y = 2x - 3$ | $y = x - 1$

$1 \stackrel{?}{=} 2(2) - 3$ ← **Substitute (2, 1) for (*x*, *y*).** → $1 \stackrel{?}{=} 2 - 1$

$1 \stackrel{?}{=} 4 - 3$ | $1 = 1$ ✓

$1 = 1$ ✓

CA Standards Check **1** Solve by graphing. Check your solution.

a. $y = x + 5$
$y = -4x$

b. $y = -\frac{1}{2}x + 2$
$y = -3x - 3$

2 EXAMPLE Application

GO for Help

For help writing a function, go to Lesson 4-4, Example 2.

Suppose you are testing two fertilizers on bamboo plants A and B, which are growing under identical conditions. Plant A is 6 cm tall and growing at a rate of 4 cm/day. Plant B is 10 cm tall and growing at a rate of 2 cm/day. Which system of equations models the height of each plant $H(d)$ as a function of days d?

(A) $H(d) = 6d + 4$
$H(d) = 10d + 2$

(B) $H(d) = 6d + 4$
$H(d) = 2d + 10$

(C) $H(d) = 4d + 6$
$H(d) = 10d + 2$

(D) $H(d) = 4d + 6$
$H(d) = 2d + 10$

Relate	plant height	is	initial height	plus	daily growth
Write	Plant A: $H(d)$	$=$	6	$+$	$4d$
	Plant B: $H(d)$	$=$	10	$+$	$2d$

The system is $H(d) = 4d + 6$
$H(d) = 2d + 10.$

So, D is the correct answer.

CA Standards Check **2** You are testing two fertilizers on bamboo plants C and D. Plant C is 5 cm tall and growing at a rate of 3 cm/day. Plant D is 1 cm tall and growing at a rate of 4 cm/day. Write a system of equations that models the height $H(d)$ of each plant as a function of days d.

Under ideal conditions, some bamboo shoots can grow 2 feet per day.

3 EXAMPLE Interpreting Solutions

The system below models the heights of the bamboo plants in Example 2. Find the solution of the system by graphing. What does the solution mean in terms of the original situation?

Part 1 Find the solution by graphing.

$H(d) = 4d + 6$ The slope is 4. The y-intercept is 6.
$H(d) = 2d + 10$ The slope is 2. The y-intercept is 10.

Graph the equations.

$H(d) = 4d + 6$

$H(d) = 2d + 10$

The lines intersect at (2, 14).

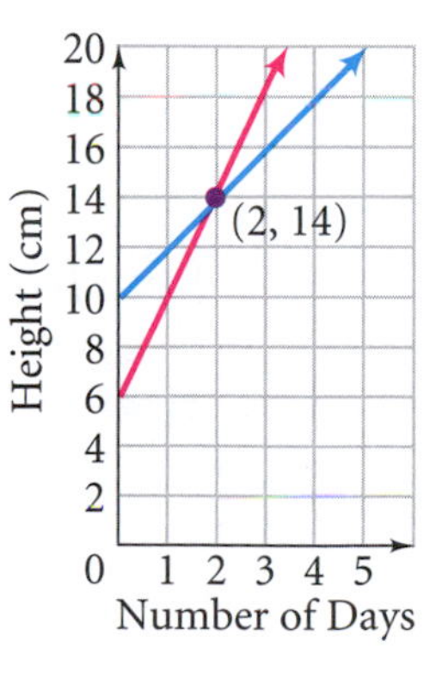

Part 2 Interpret the solution.

After 2 days, both plants will be the same height, 14 cm tall.

CA Standards Check **3** Two friends are walking around a quarter-mile track. One person has completed six laps before the second one starts. The system below models the distance $d(t)$ in miles each walker covers as a function of time t in hours.

$d(t) = 3t + 1.5 \qquad d(t) = 4t$

a. Find the solution of the system by graphing. Use units of 0.5 on your graph.
b. What does the solution mean in terms of the original situation?

Analyzing Special Types of Systems

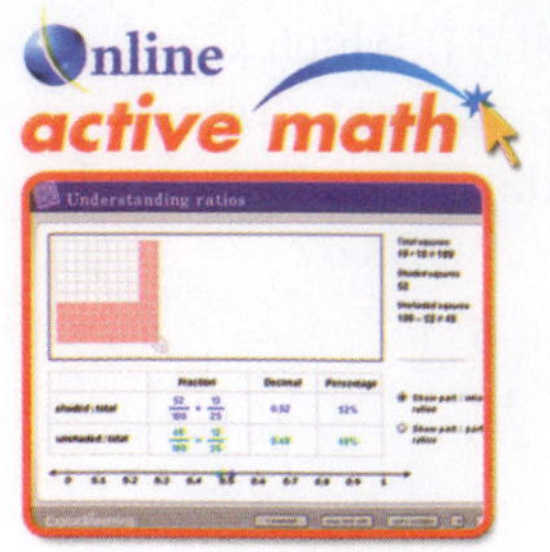

For: Linear System Activity
Use: Interactive Textbook, 6-1

When two lines are parallel, there are no points of intersection. So a system of linear equations has **no solution** when the graphs of the equations are parallel lines.

4 EXAMPLE Systems With No Solution

Solve by graphing. $y = -2x + 1$
$y = -2x - 1$

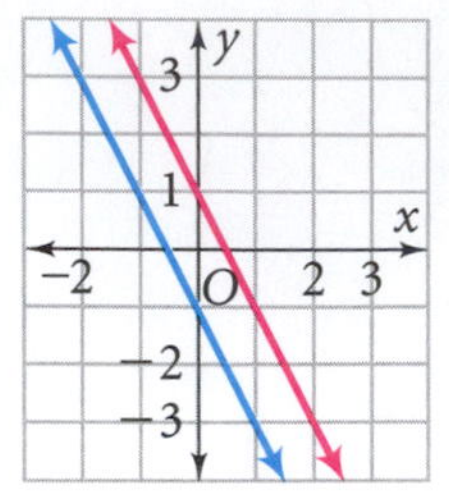

Graph both equations on the same coordinate plane.

$y = -2x + 1$ **The slope is −2. The *y*-intercept is 1.**
$y = -2x - 1$ **The slope is −2. The *y*-intercept is −1.**

The lines are parallel. There is no solution.

4 **Critical Thinking** Without graphing, how can you tell if a system has no solution? Give an example.

A system of linear equations has **infinitely many solutions** when the graphs of the equations are the same line. The coordinates of the points on the common line are all solutions of the system.

5 EXAMPLE Systems With Infinitely Many Solutions

Solve by graphing. $2x + 4y = 8$
$y = -\frac{1}{2}x + 2$

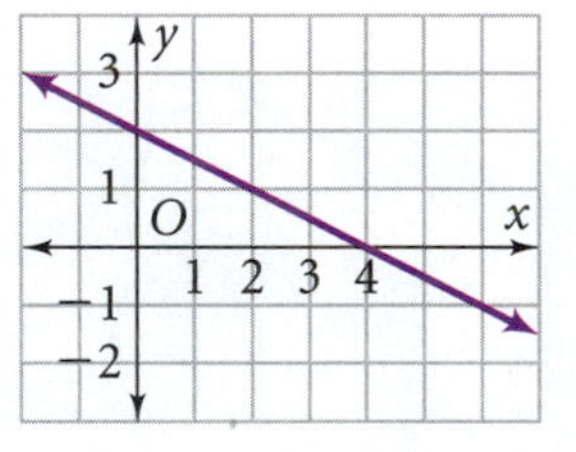

Graph both equations on the same coordinate plane.

$2x + 4y = 8$ **The *y*-intercept is 2. The *x*-intercept is 4.**
$y = -\frac{1}{2}x + 2$ **The slope is $-\frac{1}{2}$. The *y*-intercept is 2.**

The graphs are the same line. The solutions are an infinite number of ordered pairs (x, y) such that $y = -\frac{1}{2}x + 2$.

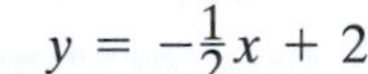

5 Solve by graphing. $y = \frac{1}{5}x + 9$
$5y = x + 45$

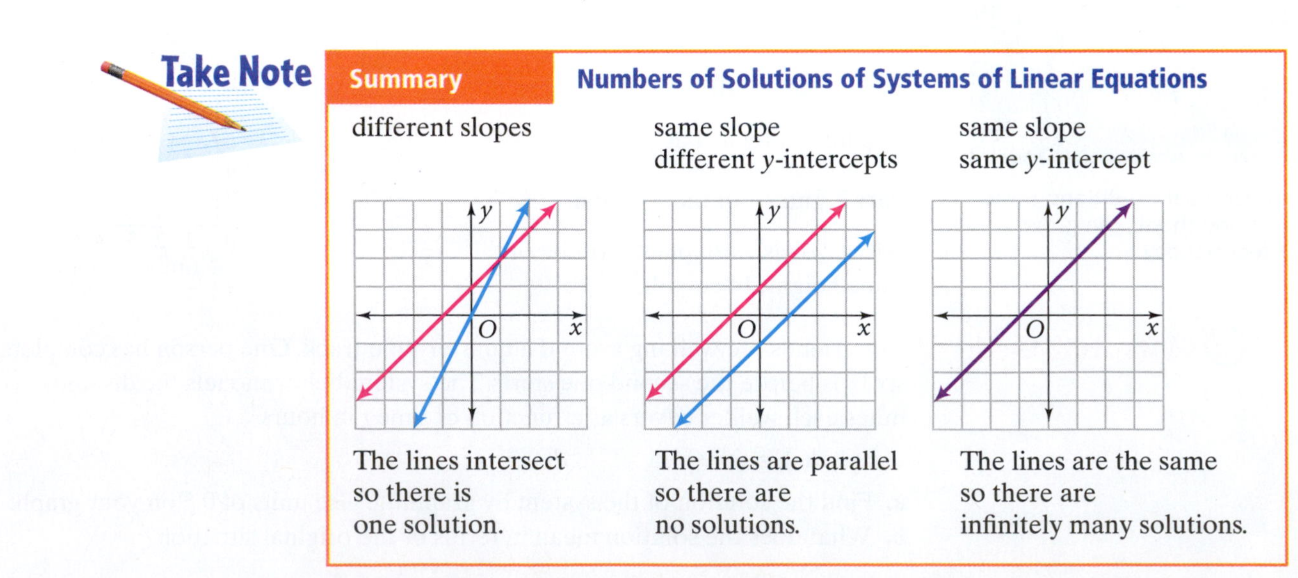

EXERCISES

Standards Practice

For more exercises, see *Extra Skills and Word Problem Practice.*

Alg1 9.0, 25.3

A Practice by Example

Example 1 (page 276)

GO for Help

Is $(-1, 5)$ a solution of each system? Explain.

1. $x + y = 4$
$x = -1$

2. $y = -x + 4$
$y = -\frac{1}{5}x$

3. $y = 5$
$x = y - 6$

4. $y = 2x + 7$
$y = x + 6$

Solve by graphing. Check your solution.

5. $y = x + 2$
$y = -2x + 2$

6. $y = x$
$y = 5x$

7. $y = 1$
$y = x$

8. $y = x + 4$
$y = 4x + 1$

9. $y = -\frac{1}{3}x + 1$
$y = \frac{1}{3}x - 3$

10. $y = \frac{1}{2}x + 1$
$y = -3x + 8$

11. $3x + 4y = 12$
$2x + 4y = 8$

12. $y = \frac{1}{2}x + 2$
$y = -x + 5$

Examples 2, 3 (page 277)

13. Suppose you have \$20 in your bank account. You start saving \$5 each week. Your friend has \$5 in his account and is saving \$10 each week. Assume that neither you nor your friend makes any withdrawals.
  a. After how many weeks will you and your friend have the same amount of money in your accounts?
  b. How much money will each of you have?

14. Suppose you have \$55 in your bank account. You start saving \$10 each week. Your friend has \$20 in her account and is saving \$15 each week. When will you and your friend have the same amount of money in your accounts?

Examples 4, 5 (page 278)

Graph each system. Tell whether the system has *no solution* or *infinitely many solutions.*

15. $y = -2x + 1$
$y = -2x - 3$

16. $x + 2y = 10$
$2x + 4y = 10$

17. $y = 3x + 4$
$-12x + 4y = 16$

18. $y = 2x + 6$
$4x - 2y = 8$

B Apply Your Skills

Without graphing, decide whether each system has *one solution, no solution,* or *infinitely many solutions.* Explain.

19. $y = 2x$
$y = 2x - 5$

20. $x + y = 4$
$2x + 2y = 8$

21. $y = -3x + 1$
$y = 3x + 7$

22. $3x - 5y = 0$
$y = \frac{3}{5}x$

23. Which graph shows the solution of the system below?
$y = -5x + 4$
$y = \frac{3}{4}x - 3$

A.

B.

24. A communications company offers a variety of calling card options. Card A has a 30¢ connection fee and then costs 2¢ per minute. Card B has a 10¢ connection fee and then costs 6¢ per minute. Find the length of the call that would cost the same with both cards.

100 m

0 m

73 m

25. Jim and Tony are on opposing teams in a soccer match. They are running after the same ball. Jim's path is the line $y = 3x$. Tony's path is the line $y = -2x + 100$. Solve by graphing to find the coordinates of the ball.

Write a system of two linear equations with the given characteristics.

26. One solution; perpendicular lines

27. No solution; one equation is $y = 2x + 5$.

28. Infinitely many solutions; the graph of one equation has a y-intercept of 3.

Solve by graphing. Check your solution.

29. $y = 4x + 12$
$y = -2x + 24$

30. $y = 3x - 5$
$y = 2x + 10$

31. $y = x + 18$
$y = -\frac{1}{2}x + 36$

32. $y = 4x + 80$
$y = \frac{1}{2}x + 10$

33. Below is a retelling of one of Aesop's fables. Read it and use the story to answer the questions below.

One day, the tortoise challenged the hare to a race. The hare laughed while bragging about how fast a runner he was. On the day of the race, the hare was so confident that he took a nap during the race. When he awoke, he ran as hard as he could, but he could not beat the slow-but-sure tortoise across the finish line.

a. The graph at the right shows the race of the tortoise and the hare. Which label should be on each axis?

b. **Writing** Which color indicates the tortoise? Which indicates the hare? Explain your answers.

c. What does the point of intersection mean?

34. Use the table to find the solution of the following system.

$y = -4x + 11$
$y = 3x - 3$

	A	B	C
1	x	$y = -4x + 11$	$y = 3x - 3$
2	−1	15	−6
3	0	11	−3
4	1	7	0
5	2	3	3
6	3	−1	6

35. Suppose you and your friends form a band. You want to record a demo. Studio A rents for \$100 plus \$50/hour. Studio B rents for \$50 plus \$75/hour.

a. Write a system that models the situation and solve by graphing.

b. Explain what the solution of the system means in terms of renting a studio.

Visit: PHSchool.com
Web Code: bae-0601

Challenge

36. a. **Critical Thinking** For what values of w and v does the system have exactly one solution? $y = -5x + w$, $y = -5x + v$

b. For what values of w and v does the system have no solution?

c. For what values of w and v does the system have infinitely many solutions?

37. a. **Math Reasoning** If $g \geq h$, the system at the right has no solution *always, sometimes,* or *never?* $y = gx + 3$, $y = hx + 7$

b. If $g \leq h$, the system has infinitely many solutions *always, sometimes,* or *never?*

38. The slope of the line joining point P to the origin is $\frac{2}{9}$. The slope of the line joining point P to $(-4, 3)$ is 1. Find the coordinates of point P.

Multiple Choice Practice

For California Standards Tutorials, visit PHSchool.com. Web Code: baq-9045

Alg1 9.0

39. The graphs of the linear equations $y = 3x + 2$ and $y = \frac{2}{3}x - \frac{8}{3}$ are shown at the right. What is the solution to $3x + 2 = \frac{2}{3}x - \frac{8}{3}$?

Ⓐ -4 Ⓑ -2 Ⓒ 2 Ⓓ 4

Alg1 6.0

40. Which equation represents a line that is parallel to $y = -\frac{8}{5}x + 4$?

Ⓐ $y = \frac{8}{5}x + 4$ Ⓑ $y = \frac{5}{8}x - 3$ Ⓒ $y = -\frac{8}{5}x - 2$ Ⓓ $y = -\frac{5}{8}x + 4$

Alg1 5.0

41. Max is ordering books from an online store. Each book costs \$4.99, and he has a coupon for 25% off the cost of the books. The shipping fee is \$2.95. Which equation can be used to find the cost c of b books?

Ⓐ $c = 4.99b + 2.95 - 0.25$

Ⓑ $c = 4.99b + 2.95 - 0.25(4.99b)$

Ⓒ $c = 0.25(4.99b + 2.95)$

Ⓓ $c = 0.25(4.99b) + 2.95$

Alg1 4.0

42. Which equation is equivalent to $6(1 - 5x) = 4 - 2(2 - x)$?

Ⓐ $-28x = 6$ Ⓑ $32x = 6$ Ⓒ $28x = 14$ Ⓓ $32x = 14$

Mixed Review

GO for Help

Lesson 3-6 **Solve each equation or inequality.**

43. $3|4 + x| = 24$

44. $5 > |x + 3|$

45. $6 = |x - 2| + 5$

Lesson 2-4 **Solve each proportion.**

46. $\frac{3}{x - 16} = \frac{9}{x}$

47. $\frac{c - 30}{c} = \frac{2}{7}$

48. $\frac{h}{4} = \frac{15 + h}{16}$

49. $\frac{3}{a + 2} = \frac{5}{a + 6}$

50. $\frac{2x}{6} = \frac{2 + x}{9}$

51. $\frac{6}{7} = \frac{2m}{24 + m}$

CALIFORNIA CHECK SYSTEM

6-2 Solving Systems Using Substitution

California Content Standards

9.0 Solve a system of two linear equations in two variables algebraically. ***Develop***

What You'll Learn

- To solve systems using substitution

. . . And Why

To solve problems involving transportation, as in Example 3

Check Skills You'll Need

GO for Help Lessons 2-3 and 6-1

Solve each equation.

1. $m - 6 = 4m + 8$ **2.** $4n = 9 - 2n$ **3.** $\frac{1}{3}t + 5 = 10$

For each system, is the ordered pair a solution of both equations?

4. $(5, 1)$ $\begin{aligned} y &= -x + 4 \\ y &= x - 6 \end{aligned}$

5. $(2, 2.4)$ $\begin{aligned} 4x + 5y &= 20 \\ 2x + 6y &= 10 \end{aligned}$

New Vocabulary • substitution method

Using Substitution

Vocabulary Tip

Substitution means one value or expression is used in place of another.

You can solve a system of equations by graphing when the solution contains integers. Another method for solving systems of equations is the **substitution method.** By replacing one variable with an equivalent expression containing the other variable, you can make a one-variable equation that you can solve using methods shown in Chapter 2.

1 EXAMPLE Using Substitution

Solve using substitution. $\begin{aligned} y &= -4x + 8 \\ y &= x + 7 \end{aligned}$

Step 1 Write an equation containing only one variable, and solve it.

$y = -4x + 8$	**Start with one equation.**
$x + 7 = -4x + 8$	**Substitute $x + 7$ for y.**
$5x + 7 = 8$	**Add $4x$ to each side.**
$5x = 1$	**Subtract 7 from each side.**
$x = 0.2$	**Divide each side by 5.**

Step 2 Solve for the other variable in either equation.

$y = 0.2 + 7$	**Substitute 0.2 for x in $y = x + 7$.**
$y = 7.2$	**Simplify.**

Since $x = 0.2$ and $y = 7.2$, the solution is $(0.2, 7.2)$.

Check

$7.2 \stackrel{?}{=} -4(0.2) + 8$	**Since $y = x + 7$ was used in Step 2, see if $(0.2, 7.2)$ solves $y = -4x + 8$.**
$7.2 = 7.2$ ✓	**Simplify.**

CA Standards Check **1** Solve using substitution. Check your solution. $\begin{aligned} y &= 2x \\ 7x - y &= 15 \end{aligned}$

To use the substitution method, you must have an equation that has already been solved for one of the variables.

2 EXAMPLE Using Substitution and the Distributive Property

Solve using the substitution method. $3y + 2x = 4$
$-6x + y = -7$

Step 1 Solve the second equation for y because it has a coefficient of 1.

$-6x + y = -7$

$y = 6x - 7$ — **Add $6x$ to each side.**

Step 2 Write an equation containing only one variable and solve.

$3y + 2x = 4$ — **Start with the other equation.**

$3(6x - 7) + 2x = 4$ — **Substitute $6x - 7$ for y. Use parentheses.**

$18x - 21 + 2x = 4$ — **Use the Distributive Property.**

$20x = 25$ — **Combine like terms and add 21 to each side.**

$x = 1.25$ — **Divide each side by 20.**

Step 3 Solve for the other variable in either equation.

$-6(1.25) + y = -7$ — **Substitute 1.25 for x in $-6x + y = -7$.**

$-7.5 + y = -7$ — **Simplify.**

$y = 0.5$ — **Add 7.5 to each side.**

Since $x = 1.25$ and $y = 0.5$, the solution is $(1.25, 0.5)$.

CA Standards Check 2 Solve using substitution. Check your solution. $6y + 8x = 28$
$3 = 2x - y$

3 EXAMPLE Application

Your school must transport 193 people to a competition. There are eight drivers available and two types of vehicles. The school buses seat 51 people each, and the minivans seat 8 people each. How many buses and minivans will be needed?

Let b = number of school buses.
Let m = number of minivans.

Number of drivers: $b + m = 8$
Number of people: $51b + 8m = 193$

Step 1 $b + m = 8$ — **Solve the first equation for m.**

$m = -b + 8$ — **Subtract b from each side.**

Step 2 $51b + 8(-b + 8) = 193$ — **Substitute $-b + 8$ for m in the second equation.**

$51b - 8b + 64 = 193$ — **Solve for b.**

$43b + 64 = 193$

$43b = 129$

$b = 3$

Step 3 $(3) + m = 8$ — **Substitute 3 for b in $b + m = 8$.**

$m = 5$

Three school buses and five minivans will be needed to transport 193 people.

According to the U.S. Department of Transportation, every year about 460,000 public school buses transport 24 million students to and from school.

CA Standards Check 3 A softball team played 149 games. The team won 8 more than two times the number of games they lost. How many games did they lose?

EXERCISES

Standards Practice

For more exercises, see *Extra Skills and Word Problem Practice.*

Alg1 9.0

A Practice by Example

Example 1 (page 282)

GO for Help

Mental Math Match each system with its solution at the right.

1. $y = x + 1$
   $y = 2x - 1$

2. $y = \frac{1}{2}x + 4$
   $2y + 2x = 2$

3. $2y = x + 3$
   $x = y$

4. $x - y = 1$
   $x = \frac{1}{2}y + 2$

A. $(3, 2)$
B. $(3, 3)$
C. $(-2, 3)$
D. $(2, 3)$

Solve each system using substitution. Check your solution.

5. $y = 4x - 8$
   $y = 2x + 10$

6. $C(n) = -3n - 6$
   $C(n) = n - 4$

7. $m = 5p + 8$
   $m = -10p + 3$

8. $y = -4x + 12\frac{1}{2}$
   $y = \frac{1}{4}x + 4$

9. $h = 6g - 4$
   $h = -2g + 28$

10. $a = \frac{2}{5}b - 3$
    $a = 2b - 18$

Example 2 (page 283)

11. $y = x - 2$
    $2x + 2y = 4$

12. $c = 3d - 27$
    $4d + 10c = 120$

13. $3x - 6y = 30$
    $y = -6x + 34$

14. $m = 4n + 11$
    $-6n + 8m = 36$

15. $7x - 8y = 112$
    $y = -2x + 9$

16. $t = 0.2s + 10$
    $4s + 5t = 35$

Example 3 (page 283)

17. The length of a rectangle is 5 cm more than twice the width. The perimeter of the rectangle is 34 cm. Find the dimensions of the rectangle.

18. Suppose you have \$28.00 in your bank account and start saving \$18.25 every week. Your friend has \$161.00 in his account and is withdrawing \$15 every week. When will your account balances be the same?

B Apply Your Skills

Solve each system by substitution. Check your solution.

19. $a - 1.2b = -3$
    $0.2b + 0.6a = 12$

20. $0.5x + 0.25y = 36$
    $y + 18 = 16x$

21. $y = 0.8x + 7.2$
    $20x + 32y = 48$

Growers in the United States plant about 2.5 million acres of sunflowers every year.

22. A farmer grows only sunflowers and flax on his 240-acre farm. This year he wants to plant 80 more acres of sunflowers than of flax. How many acres of each crop does the farmer need to plant?

23. Suppose you are thinking about buying one of two cars. Car A will cost \$17,655. You can expect to pay an average of \$1230 per year for fuel, maintenance, and repairs. Car B will cost about \$15,900. Fuel, maintenance, and repairs for it will average about \$1425 per year. After how many years are the total costs for the cars the same?

24. You have 28 coins that are all nickels n and dimes d. The value of the coins is \$2.05. Which system of equations can be used to find the number of nickels and the number of dimes?

    (A) $n + d = 28$
    $10n + 5d = 2.05$

    (B) $10n + 5d = 205$
    $n + d = 28$

    (C) $n + d = 205$
    $n + d = 28$

    (D) $n + d = 28$
    $5n + 10d = 205$

Visit: PHSchool.com
Web Code: bae-0602

Estimation **Graph each system to estimate the solution. Then use substitution to find the exact solution of the system.**

25. $y = 2x + 3$
$y = 0.5x - 2$

26. $y = -x + 4$
$y = 2x + 6$

27. $y = 0.7x + 3$
$y = -1.5x - 7$

28. **a.** Solve each system below using substitution.

$y = 0.5x + 4$
$-x + 2y = 8$

$6x - 2y = 10$
$y = 3x + 1$

b. Solve each system by graphing.

c. **Critical Thinking** Make a general statement about the solutions you get when solving by graphing and when solving by substitution.

Error Analysis **Two students solved the system at the right. Explain their mistakes and solve the system correctly.**

$x + y = 0$
$5x + 2y = -3$

29. **30.**

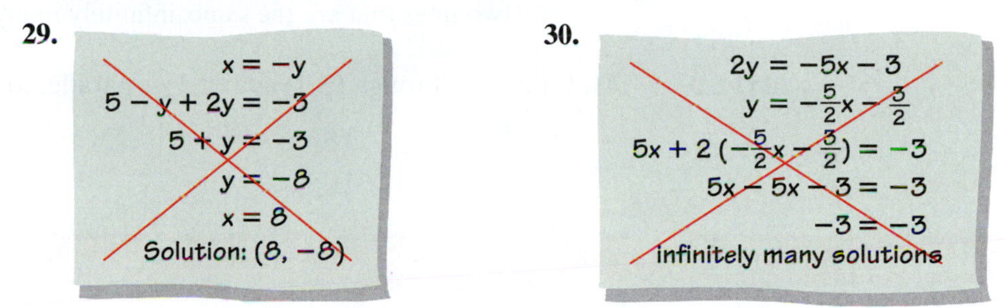

Solve each system using substitution.

31. $y = 2x$
$6x - y = 8$

32. $y = 3x + 1$
$x = 3y + 1$

33. $x - 3y = 14$
$x - 2 = 0$

34. $2x + 2y = 5$
$y = \frac{1}{4}x$

35. $4x + y = -2$
$-2x - 3y = 1$

36. $3x + 5y = 2$
$x + 4y = -4$

Challenge

37. There are 1170 students in a school. The ratio of girls to boys is 23 : 22. The system below describes relationships between the number of girls and the number of boys.

$g + b = 1170$ $\quad \frac{g}{b} = \frac{23}{22}$

a. Solve the proportion for g.

b. Solve the system.

c. How many more girls are there than boys?

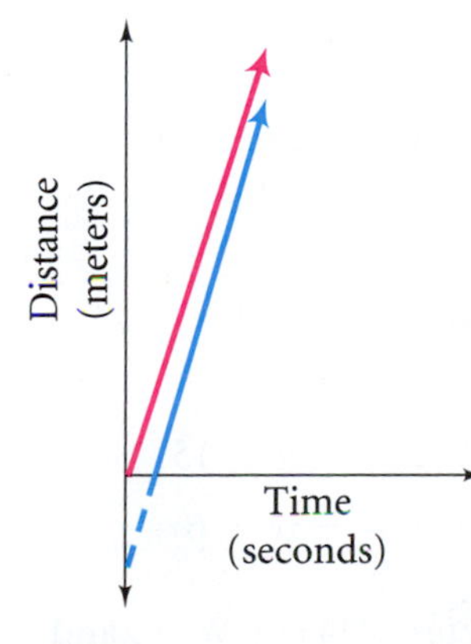

38. The graph at the left represents the start of a 100-meter race between Joetta and Gail. The red line and blue line represent Joetta's and Gail's time and distance. Joetta averages 8.8 m/s. Gail averages 9 m/s but starts 0.2 s after Joetta. At time 0.2 s, Gail's distance is 0 m. You can use point-slope form to write an equation that relates Gail's time t to her distance d.

$y - y_1 = m(x - x_1)$
$d - 0 = 9(t - 0.2)$
$d = 9t - 1.8$

Since Joetta starts at $t = 0$, the equation $d = 8.8t$ relates her time and distance.

a. Solve the system using substitution.

b. Will Gail overtake Joetta before the finish line?

Multiple Choice Practice

For California Standards Tutorials, visit PHSchool.com. Web Code: baq-9045

Alg1 9.0

39. What is the solution to the system of equations? $3x + y = 3$
$-2x - 4y = -22$

(A) $(-1, 0)$ (B) $(-1, 6)$ (C) $(1, 1)$ (D) $(6, -1)$

Alg1 9.0

40. Which best describes the graph and solution to this system of equations?

$y = 2x + 3$
$x + 2y = 1$

(A) two lines intersecting at $(0, 3)$; one solution
(B) two parallel lines; no solution
(C) two lines intersecting at $(-1, 1)$; one solution
(D) two lines that are the same; infinitely many solutions

Alg1 8.0

41. If the line through $(2, 1)$ and $(a, 3)$ is parallel to $6y - x = -10$, what is a?

(A) 5 (B) 7 (C) -1 (D) 14

Mixed Review

GO for Help

Lesson 6-1

Solve each system by graphing.

42. $y = x - 2$
$y = \frac{1}{2}x + 4$

43. $y = -2x + 5$
$y = -x + 3$

44. $y = \frac{3}{4}x - 1$
$y = \frac{1}{4}x + 1$

Lesson 4-3

Graph each function.

45. $y = 3x - 2$

46. $f(x) = x + 1$

47. $f(x) = -2x$

48. $y = |x| + 5$

49. $y = -2|x|$

50. $y = |x + 3| - 1$

Checkpoint Quiz 1

Lessons 6-1 through 6-2

Solve each system by graphing.

1. $y = 3x - 4$
$y = -2x + 1$

2. $y = \frac{4}{3}x - 2$
$y = \frac{2}{3}x$

3. $y = \frac{1}{4}x - 1$
$y = -2x - 10$

Solve each system using substitution.

4. $y = 3x - 14$
$y = x - 10$

5. $y = 2x + 5$
$y = 6x + 1$

6. $x = y + 7$
$y = 8 + 2x$

7. $3x + 4y = 12$
$y = -2x + 10$

8. $4x + 9y = 24$
$y = -\frac{1}{3}x + 2$

9. $5x + 2y = 15$
$y = -3x + 6$

10. A rectangle is 3 times longer than it is wide. The perimeter is 44 cm. Write and solve a system of equations to find the dimensions of the rectangle.

CALIFORNIA CHECK SYSTEM

6-3 Solving Systems Using Elimination

California Content Standards

9.0 Solve a system of two linear equations in two variables algebraically. ***Develop***

What You'll Learn

- To solve systems by adding or subtracting
- To multiply first when solving systems

. . . And Why

To analyze a ticket-sales situation, as in Example 2

Check Skills You'll Need

Solve each system using substitution.

1. $y = 4x - 3$
   $y = 2x + 13$
2. $y + 5x = 4$
   $y = 7x - 20$
3. $y = -2x + 2$
   $3x - 17 = 2y$

New Vocabulary

- elimination method

Adding or Subtracting to Solve Systems

Vocabulary Tip

Addition Property of Equality
If $a = b$,
then $a + c = b + c$.
Subtraction Property of Equality
If $a = b$,
then $a - c = b - c$.

The Addition and Subtraction Properties of Equality can be extended to state,

If $a = b$ and $c = d$, then $a + c = b + d$. If $a = b$ and $c = d$, then $a - c = b - d$.

You can use the properties of equality to solve a system by the **elimination method.** You can add or subtract equations to eliminate a variable.

1 EXAMPLE Adding Equations

Solve by elimination. $5x - 6y = -32$
$3x + 6y = 48$

Step 1 Eliminate y because the sum of the coefficients of y is zero.

$$\begin{aligned} 5x - 6y &= -32 \\ 3x + 6y &= 48 && \text{Add the two equations.} \\ \hline 8x + 0 &= 16 && \text{Addition Property of Equality} \\ x &= 2 && \text{Solve for } x. \end{aligned}$$

Step 2 Solve for the eliminated variable y using either of the original equations.

$$\begin{aligned} 3x + 6y &= 48 && \text{Choose the second equation.} \\ 3(2) + 6y &= 48 && \text{Substitute 2 for } x. \\ 6 + 6y &= 48 && \text{Simplify. Then solve for } y. \\ y &= 7 \end{aligned}$$

Since $x = 2$ and $y = 7$, the solution is (2, 7).

Check $5(2) - 6(7) \stackrel{?}{=} -32$ See if (2, 7) solves $5x - 6y = -32$.
$10 - 42 \stackrel{?}{=} -32$
$-32 = -32$ ✓

CA Standards Check 1 Solve by elimination. $6x - 3y = 3$
$-6x + 5y = 3$

There are 188 basketball teams in 26 conferences in the National Wheelchair Basketball Association.

2 EXAMPLE Application

Suppose your community center sells a total of 292 tickets for a basketball game. An adult ticket costs \$3. A student ticket costs \$1. The sponsors collect \$470 in ticket sales. Write and solve a system to find the number of each type of ticket sold.

Define Let a = number of adult tickets.
Let s = number of student tickets.

Relate total number of tickets — total amount of sales

Write $a + s = 292$ — $3a + 1s = 470$

Solve by elimination.

Step 1 Eliminate s because the difference of the coefficients of s is zero.

$$\begin{aligned} a + s &= 292 \\ 3a + s &= 470 \end{aligned}$$ Subtract the two equations.

$$-2a + 0 = -178$$ Subtraction Property of Equality

$$a = 89$$ Solve for a.

Step 2 Solve for the eliminated variable using either of the original equations.

$$a + s = 292$$ Choose the first equation.

$$89 + s = 292$$ Substitute 89 for a.

$$s = 203$$ Solve for s.

There were 89 adult tickets sold and 203 student tickets sold.

Check Is the solution reasonable? The answers 89 and 203 are close to 90 and 200. The total number of tickets is about $90 + 200 = 290$, close to 292. The total sales is about $\$3(90) + \$1(200)$ or \$470. The solution is reasonable.

CA Standards Check 2 Your class sells a total of 64 tickets to a play. A student ticket costs \$1, and an adult ticket costs \$2.50. Your class collects \$109 in total ticket sales. How many adult tickets did you sell? How many student tickets did you sell?

Multiplying First to Solve Systems

From Examples 1 and 2 you can see that to eliminate a variable its coefficients must have a sum or difference of zero. Sometimes you may need to multiply one or both of the equations by a nonzero number first.

3 EXAMPLE Multiplying One Equation

Solve by the elimination method. $2x + 5y = -22$
$10x + 3y = 22$

Step 1 Eliminate one variable.

Start with the given system.

$$\begin{aligned} 2x + 5y &= -22 \\ 10x + 3y &= 22 \end{aligned}$$

To prepare for eliminating x, multiply the first equation by 5.

$$\begin{aligned} &5(2x + 5y = -22) \\ &10x + 3y = 22 \end{aligned}$$

Subtract the equations to eliminate x.

$$\begin{aligned} 10x + 25y &= -110 \\ 10x + 3y &= 22 \\ \hline 0 + 22y &= -132 \end{aligned}$$

Step 2 Solve for y.

$$22y = -132$$
$$y = -6$$

Step 3 Solve for the eliminated variable using either of the original equations.

$2x + 5y = -22$ **Choose the first equation.**

$2x + 5(-6) = -22$ **Substitute −6 for *y*.**

$2x - 30 = -22$ **Solve for *x*.**

$2x = 8$

$x = 4$

The solution is $(4, -6)$.

CA Standards Check **3** Solve by elimination. $-2x + 15y = -32$
$7x - 5y = 17$

To solve real-world problems, you can also use the elimination method.

4 EXAMPLE Application

Suppose your class sells gift wrap for $4 per package and greeting cards for $10 per package. Your class sells 205 packages in all and receives a total of $1084. Find the number of each type of package sold.

Define Let w = number of packages of gift wrap sold.
Let c = number of packages of greeting cards sold.

Relate total number of packages total amount of sales

Write $w + c = 205$ $4w + 10c = 1084$

Problem Solving Tip

You can also eliminate w by multiplying the first equation by −4 and adding the two equations.

Step 1 Eliminate one variable.

Start with the given system.		To prepare for eliminating *w*, multiply the first equation by 4.		Subtract the equations to eliminate *w*.
$w + c = 205$	→	$4(w + c = 205)$	→	$4w + 4c = 820$
$4w + 10c = 1084$	→	$4w + 10c = 1084$	→	$4w + 10c = 1084$
				$0 - 6c = -264$

Step 2 Solve for c.

$$-6c = -264$$
$$c = 44$$

Step 3 Solve for the eliminated variable using either of the original equations.

$w + c = 205$ **Use the first equation.**

$w + 44 = 205$ **Substitute 44 for *c*.**

$w = 161$ **Solve for *w*.**

The class sold 161 packages of gift wrap and 44 packages of greeting cards.

CA Standards Check **4** Suppose another class sells a different brand of gift wrap, which costs $2 per package, and cards, which cost $5 per package. The class sells 220 packages in all and earns a total of $695. Find the number of each type of package sold.

Video Tutor Help
Visit: PHSchool.com
Web Code: bae-0775

To eliminate a variable, you may need to multiply both equations in a system by a nonzero number. Multiply each equation by values such that when you write equivalent equations, you can then add or subtract to eliminate a variable.

Multiplying Both Equations

Solve by elimination. $\begin{aligned} 4x + 2y &= 14 \\ 7x - 3y &= -8 \end{aligned}$

Step 1 Eliminate one variable.

Start with the given system.		To prepare for eliminating y, multiply one equation by 3 and the other equation by 2.		Add the equations to eliminate y.
$4x + 2y = 14$	$\rightarrow$	$3(4x + 2y = 14)$	$\rightarrow$	$12x + 6y = 42$
$7x - 3y = -8$	$\rightarrow$	$2(7x - 3y = -8)$	$\rightarrow$	$14x - 6y = -16$
				$26x + 0 = 26$

Step 2 Solve for x.

$$\begin{aligned} 26x &= 26 \\ x &= 1 \end{aligned}$$

Step 3 Solve for the eliminated variable y using either of the original equations.

$$\begin{aligned} 4x + 2y &= 14 && \text{Use the first equation.} \\ 4(1) + 2y &= 14 && \text{Substitute 1 for } x. \\ 2y &= 10 \\ y &= 5 \end{aligned}$$

The solution is $(1, 5)$.

CA Standards Check 5 Solve by elimination. $\begin{aligned} 15x + 3y &= 9 \\ 10x + 7y &= -4 \end{aligned}$

A flowchart like the one below can help you to decide how to eliminate a variable.

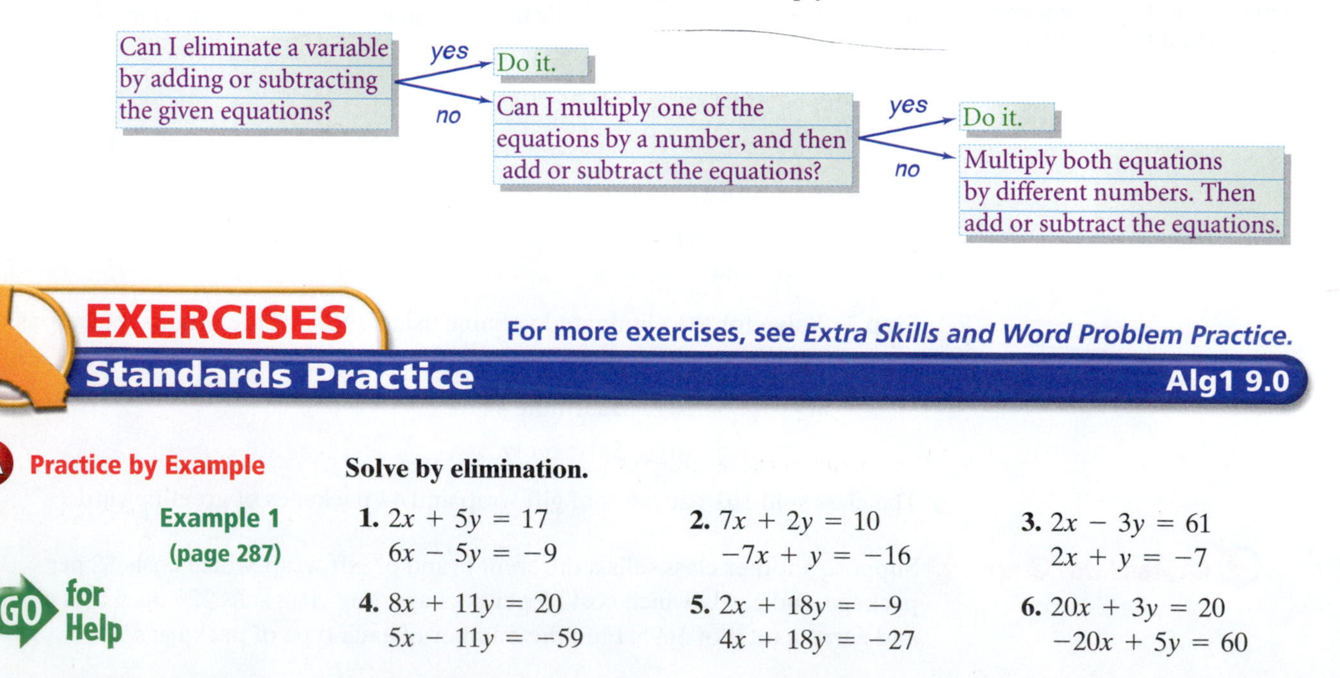

EXERCISES

For more exercises, see *Extra Skills and Word Problem Practice*.

Standards Practice

Alg1 9.0

A Practice by Example

Solve by elimination.

Example 1 (page 287)

GO for Help

1. $\begin{aligned} 2x + 5y &= 17 \\ 6x - 5y &= -9 \end{aligned}$
2. $\begin{aligned} 7x + 2y &= 10 \\ -7x + y &= -16 \end{aligned}$
3. $\begin{aligned} 2x - 3y &= 61 \\ 2x + y &= -7 \end{aligned}$
4. $\begin{aligned} 8x + 11y &= 20 \\ 5x - 11y &= -59 \end{aligned}$
5. $\begin{aligned} 2x + 18y &= -9 \\ 4x + 18y &= -27 \end{aligned}$
6. $\begin{aligned} 20x + 3y &= 20 \\ -20x + 5y &= 60 \end{aligned}$

Example 2 (page 288)

7. The sum of two numbers is 20. Their difference is 4.
   a. Write a system of equations that describes this situation.
   b. Solve by elimination to find the two numbers.

8. Your school sold 456 tickets for a school play. An adult ticket cost \$3.50. A student ticket cost \$1. Total ticket sales equaled \$1131. Let a equal the number of adult tickets sold, and let s equal the number of student tickets sold.
   a. Write a system of equations that relates the number of adult and student tickets sold to the total number of tickets sold and to the total ticket sales.
   b. Solve by elimination to find the number of each type of ticket sold.

Example 3 (page 288)

Solve by elimination.

9. $3x - 10y = -25$
   $4x + 40y = 20$

10. $7x + 15y = 32$
    $x - 3y = 20$

11. $x - 8y = 18$
    $-16x + 16y = -8$

12. $24x + 2y = 52$
    $6x - 3y = -36$

13. $88x - 5y = 39$
    $-8x + 3y = -1$

14. $2x + 4y = 8$
    $5x + y = -7$

Example 4 (page 289)

15. A photo studio offers several different packages. Let w equal the cost of a wallet-sized portrait, and let ℓ equal the cost of an 8×10 portrait.

   a. Write a system of equations that relates the cost of wallet-sized portraits and 8×10 portraits to the cost of the basic and deluxe packages.
   b. Find the cost of each type of portrait.

16. Two groups of students order burritos and tacos at a local restaurant. One order of 3 burritos and 4 tacos costs \$11.33. The other order of 9 burritos and 5 tacos costs \$23.56.
    a. Write a system of equations that describes this situation.
    b. Solve by elimination to find the cost of a burrito and the cost of a taco.

Example 5 (page 290)

Solve by elimination.

17. $3x + 2y = -9$
    $-10x + 5y = -5$

18. $4x + 5y = 15$
    $6x - 4y = 11$

19. $3x - 2y = 10$
    $2x + 3y = -2$

20. $-2x + 5y = 20$
    $3x - 7y = -26$

21. $10x + 8y = 2$
    $8x + 6y = 1$

22. $9x + 5y = 34$
    $8x - 2y = -2$

B Apply Your Skills

Solve each system using any method. Tell why you chose the method you used.

23. $y = 2x$
    $y = x - 1$

24. $7x + 8y = 25$
    $9x + 10y = 35$

25. $x = 12y - 14$
    $3y + 2x = 26$

26. $-20x + 7y = 137$
    $4x + 5y = 43$

27. $5y = x$
    $2x - 3y = 7$

28. $y = x + 2$
    $y = -2x + 3$

29. A weekend at the Beach Bay Hotel includes 2 nights and 4 meals. A week includes 7 nights and 10 meals. Let n = the cost of 1 night and m = the cost of 1 meal. Use the sign at the left to find the cost of 1 night and the cost of 1 meal.

30. a. A company sells brass and steel machine parts. One shipment contains 3 brass and 10 steel parts and costs \$48. A second shipment contains 7 brass and 4 steel parts and costs \$54. Find the cost of each type of machine part.

b. How much would a shipment containing 10 brass and 13 steel machine parts cost?

31. Error Analysis Rosa is solving a system by elimination. Her work is shown below. What error did she make?

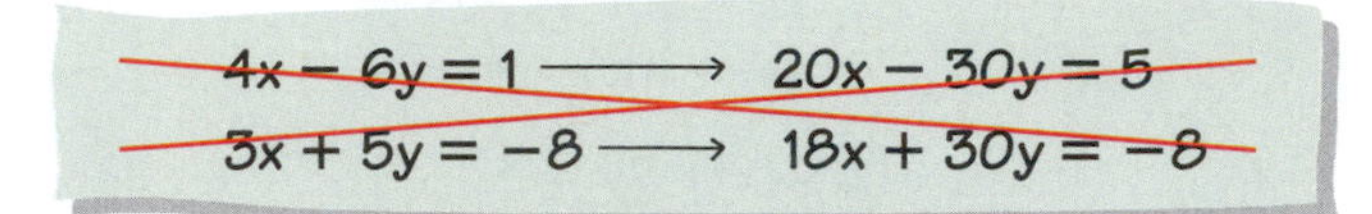

32. Write a system that can be solved by elimination. Solve your system.

Solve by elimination.

33. $\frac{1}{2}x + y = -1$
$16x - \frac{1}{2}y = 163$

34. $\frac{1}{4}x - 6y = -70$
$5x + \frac{3}{4}y = 49$

35. $-0.2x + 4y = -1$
$x + 0.5y = -15.5$

36. $y = 0.5x + 2$
$1.5x + y = 42$

37. $\frac{1}{4}x + \frac{33}{2} = y$
$y - 12 = -2x$

38. $\frac{2}{3}x - y = 70$
$\frac{1}{3}x - \frac{2}{3}y = 43$

39. Critical Thinking Find a value of n such that the x-value of the solution of the system at the right is 4.

$5x - 10y = 50$
$nx + 10y = 6$

Visit: PHSchool.com
Web Code: bae-0603

40. Writing Explain how to solve a system using elimination. Give examples of when you use addition, subtraction, and multiplication.

41. Two batteries produce a total voltage of 4.5 volts ($B_1 + B_2 = 4.5$). The difference in their voltages is 1.5 volts ($B_1 - B_2 = 1.5$). Find the voltages of the two batteries.

C Challenge

Solve by elimination.

42. $\frac{6}{x} - \frac{4}{y} = -4$
$\frac{3}{x} + \frac{8}{y} = 3$

43. $ax + y = c$
$ax + by = c$

44. $x + y + z = 41$
$x - y + z = 15$
$3x - z = 4$

45. Suppose your band wants to sell CDs and cassette tapes of your music. You use a production company that offers two different production packages.

	CDs	Tapes	Mastering	Artwork	Total Cost
Package #1	300	400	✓	✓	\$2080
Package #2	500	600	✓	✓	\$3120

Both packages charge \$100 to master your original recording and \$240 to create artwork. Find the average production cost of each CD and tape.

Vocabulary Tip

Density is the ratio of mass to volume.

Since $d = \frac{m}{v}$, $m = dv$.

46. A ring is made out of gold and copper. Gold has a density of 19.3 g/cm^3. Copper has a density of 9 g/cm^3. Mass m, density d, and volume v are related by the formula $m = dv$. The ring has a volume of 4.2 cm^3, and a mass of 52.22 g.

Let a = volume of gold. mass of gold $= dv = 19.3a$

Let c = volume of copper. mass of copper $= dv = 9c$

a. Solve the following system by elimination to find out how many grams of gold are in the ring.

$$a + c = 4.2$$
$$19.3a + 9c = 52.22$$

b. What is the percent of gold by mass?

Multiple Choice Practice

For California Standards Tutorials, visit PHSchool.com. Web Code: baq-9045

Alg1 9.0

47. Gabriel is considering taking one of the two jobs shown in the advertisement. Which system of equations can he use to find how much he must sell s in either job to receive the same pay p?

Sales Position
Salesperson Wanted
Knowledge of Cellular Phones
On-Site Sales
\$150/week + 20% commission

CAREER OPPORTUNITY
Sell stereo equipment in National Electronics Retail Chain!
\$200/week + 10% commission

Ⓐ $150 = 20s$, $200 = 10s$

Ⓑ $p = 20s + 150$, $p = 10s + 200$

Ⓒ $p = 0.2s + 150$, $p = 0.1s + 200$

Ⓓ $(150 + 0.2)s = p$, $(200 + 0.1)s = p$

Alg1 6.0

48. Where is the y-intercept on the graph of the line represented by the equation $5x + 15y = 30$?

Ⓐ $y = 2$ Ⓑ $y = 5$ Ⓒ $y = 6$ Ⓓ $y = 15$

Alg1 8.0

49. Which pair of equations graph as parallel lines?

Ⓐ $y = 3(x - 1)$, $2x + y = 7$

Ⓑ $y = 1 - \frac{2}{5}x$, $-2y = -5x$

Ⓒ $y = 3x + 6$, $\frac{2}{3} + \frac{1}{3}x = \frac{1}{9}y$

Ⓓ $7x = y$, $x = 7y$

Mixed Review

GO for Help

Lesson 6-2

Solve using substitution. Give the solutions in alphabetical order.

50. $y = 4x + 2$, $y = 6x - 10$

51. $p = q - 5$, $3p + q = 1$

52. $w + a = 4$, $w + 2a = 13$

Lesson 4-2

Determine whether each relation is a function.

53. $\{(2,3), (1,6), (0,-1), (1,-1), (3,3)\}$

54. $\{(-3,1), (0,2), (1,3), (3,4)\}$

55. $\{(0,4), (1,4), (2,4), (5,4)\}$

56. $\{(2,0), (0,0), (2,2), (0,2)\}$

Lesson 3-4

Solve each inequality.

57. $7a + 4 > 2a + 1$

58. $3(m - 1) \le 11 - 4m$

59. $-h - 34 < h + 16$

60. $3y + 4(y - 2) \le 18 + 3y$

61. $-9p - 5 > -4(2p + 3)$

62. $20 - z \ge 11(4 + z)$

6-4 Applications of Linear Systems

California Content Standards

9.0 Solve a system of two linear equations in two variables algebraically and interpret the answer graphically. ***Develop***

15.0 Apply algebraic techniques to solve rate and percent mixture problems. ***Develop***

What You'll Learn

- To write systems of linear equations

. . . And Why

To find average wind speed during an airplane flight, as in Example 3

Check Skills You'll Need

1. Two trains run on parallel tracks. The first train leaves a city $\frac{1}{2}$ hour before the second train. The first train travels at 55 mi/h. The second train travels at 65 mi/h. How long does the second train take to pass the first train?
2. Carl drives to the beach at an average speed of 50 mi/h. He returns home on the same road at an average speed of 55 mi/h. The trip home takes 30 min less. What is the distance from his home to the beach?

Writing Systems of Linear Equations

You must choose a method for solving systems before you solve a word problem.

Take Note

Summary — **Methods for Solving Systems of Linear Equations**

Graphing	Use graphing for solving systems that are easily graphed. If the point of intersection does not have integers for coordinates, find the exact solution by using one of the methods below.
Substitution	Use substitution for solving systems when one variable has a coefficient of 1 or −1.
Elimination	Use elimination for solving any system.

You can also solve the mixture problem in Example 1 using one variable, as you learned in Lesson 2-6.

1 EXAMPLE Application

A metalworker has some ingots of metal alloy that are 20% copper and others that are 60% copper. How many kilograms of each type of ingot should the metalworker combine to create 80 kg of a 52% copper alloy?

Define Let g = the mass of the 20% alloy.
Let h = the mass of the 60% alloy.

Relate mass of alloys — mass of copper

Write $g + h = 80$ — $0.2g + 0.6h = 0.52(80)$

Solve using substitution.

Step 1 Choose one of the equations and solve for a variable.

$g + h = 80$ — **Solve for *g*.**

$g = 80 - h$ — **Subtract *h* from each side.**

Step 2 Find h.

$$0.2g + 0.6h = 0.52(80)$$
$$0.2(80 - h) + 0.6h = 0.52(80) \quad \text{Substitute } 80 - h \text{ for } g\text{. Use parentheses.}$$
$$16 - 0.2h + 0.6h = 0.52(80) \quad \text{Use the Distributive Property.}$$
$$16 + 0.4h = 41.6 \quad \text{Simplify. Then solve for } h\text{.}$$
$$0.4h = 25.6$$
$$h = 64$$

Step 3 Find g. Substitute 64 for h in either equation.

$$g = 80 - 64$$
$$g = 16$$

You need 16 kg of 20% copper alloy and 64 kg of 60% copper alloy.

CA Standards Check **1** Suppose you combine ingots of 25% copper alloy and 50% copper alloy to create 40 kg of 45% copper alloy. How many kilograms of each do you need?

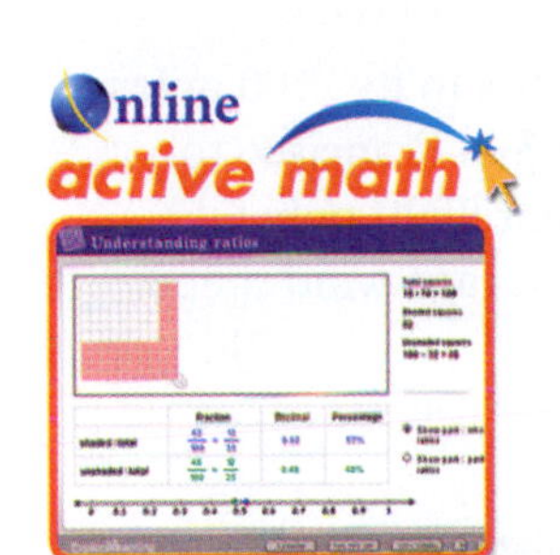

For: Linear System Activity
Use: Interactive Textbook, 6-4

In the business world the *break-even point* is the point at which income equals expenses. The graph at the right shows the break-even point for one business.

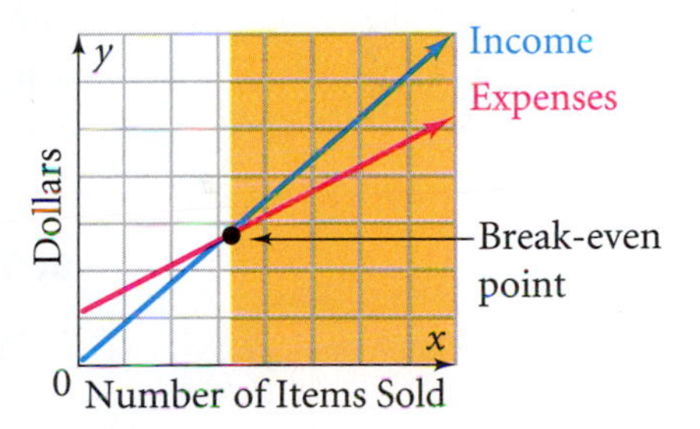

☐ Lose money ☐ Make money

The y-values on the red line represent dollars spent on expenses. The y-values on the blue line represent dollars received as income. So y represents expenses and income.

2 EXAMPLE Finding a Break-Even Point

Suppose a club publishes a newsletter. Expenses are \$.90 for printing and mailing each copy, plus \$600 total for research and writing. The price of the newsletter is \$1.50 per copy. How many copies of the newsletter must the club sell to break even?

Define Let x = the number of copies.
Let y = the amount of dollars of expenses or income.

Relate Expenses are printing costs plus research and writing. Income is price times copies sold.

Write $y = 0.9x + 600$ $\qquad$ $y = 1.5x$

Use substitution since it is easy to substitute for y with these equations.

$$y = 0.9x + 600 \quad \text{Start with one equation.}$$
$$1.5x = 0.9x + 600 \quad \text{Substitute } 1.5x \text{ for } y\text{.}$$
$$0.6x = 600 \quad \text{Solve for } x\text{.}$$
$$x = 1000$$

To break even, the club must sell 1000 copies.

CA Standards Check **2** Suppose another club publishes a newsletter. Expenses are \$.35 for printing and mailing each copy, plus \$770 total for research and writing. The newsletter costs \$.55 per copy. How many copies of the newsletter must the club sell to break even?

In Lesson 2-5, you modeled rate-time-distance problems using one variable. You can also model rate-time-distance problems using two variables. The steady west-to-east winds across the United States act as tail winds for planes traveling from west to east. The tail winds increase a plane's groundspeed. For planes traveling east to west, the head winds decrease a plane's groundspeed.

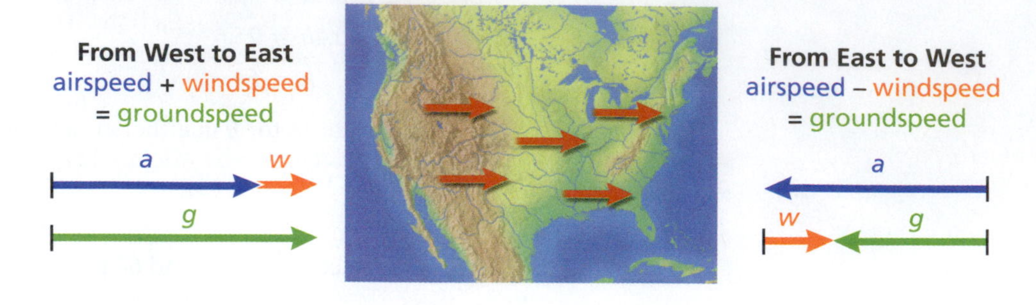

3 EXAMPLE Application

Suppose you fly from Miami to San Francisco. It takes 6.5 hours to fly 2600 miles against a head wind. At the same time, your friend flies from San Francisco to Miami. Her plane travels at the same average airspeed, but her flight only takes 5.2 hours. Find the average airspeed of the planes. Find the average wind speed.

Define Let A = the airspeed. Let W = the wind speed.

Relate

with tail wind	with head wind
(rate)(time) = distance	(rate)(time) = distance
$(A + W)$(time) = distance	$(A - W)$(time) = distance

Write $(A + W)5.2 = 2600$ $\quad$ $(A - W)6.5 = 2600$

Step 1 Divide to get the variables of each equation with coefficients of 1 or -1.

$(A + W)5.2 = 2600 \rightarrow A + W = 500$ **Divide each side by 5.2.**

$(A - W)6.5 = 2600 \rightarrow A - W = 400$ **Divide each side by 6.5.**

Step 2 Eliminate W.

$$A + W = 500$$
$$\underline{A - W = 400}$$
$$2A + 0 = 900$$

Add the equations to eliminate W.

Step 3 Solve for A.

$A = 450$ **Divide each side by 2.**

Step 4 Solve for W using either of the original equations.

$A + W = 500$ **Use the first equation.**

$450 + W = 500$ **Substitute 450 for A.**

$W = 50$ **Solve for W.**

The average airspeed of the planes is 450 mi/h. The average wind speed is 50 mi/h.

CA Standards Check **3** A plane takes about 4.5 hours to fly 1800 miles from Chicago to Sacramento. At the same time, another plane flies from Chicago to Sacramento. This plane travels with the same average airspeed, but the flight to Chicago takes 3.75 hours. Find the average airspeed of the planes. Find the average wind speed.

EXERCISES

Standards Practice

For more exercises, see *Extra Skills and Word Problem Practice*.

Alg1 9.0, 15.0

A Practice by Example

Example 1 (page 294)

1. Tyrel and Dalia bought some pens and pencils. Tyrel bought 4 pens and 5 pencils, which cost him \$6.71. Dalia bought 5 pens and 3 pencils, which cost her \$7.12. Let a equal the price of a pen. Let b equal the price of a pencil.
   a. Write an equation that relates the number of pens and pencils Tyrel bought to the amount he paid for them.
   b. Write an equation that relates the number of pens and pencils Dalia bought to the amount she paid for them.
   c. Solve the system you wrote for parts (a) and (b) to find the price of a pen and the price of a pencil.

2. Suppose you have just enough money, in coins, to pay for a loaf of bread priced at \$1.95. You have 12 coins, all quarters and dimes. Let q equal the number of quarters and d equal the number of dimes. Which system models the given information?
   (A) $q + d = 12$; $q + d = 1.95$
   (B) $10q + 25d = 12$; $q + d = 1.95$
   (C) $25q + 10d = 195$; $q + 12 = d$
   (D) $q + d = 12$; $25q + 10d = 195$

3. Suppose you want to combine two types of fruit drink to create 24 kilograms of a drink that will be 5% sugar by weight. Fruit drink A is 4% sugar by weight, and fruit drink B is 8% sugar by weight.
   a. Copy and complete the table below.

	Fruit Drink A 4% Sugar	Fruit Drink B 8% Sugar	Mixed Fruit Drink 5% Sugar
Fruit Drink (kg)	■	■	■
Sugar (kg)	■	■	■

   b. Write a system of equations that relates the amounts of fruit drink A and fruit drink B to the total amount of drink needed and to the total amount of sugar needed.
   c. Solve the system to find how much of each type of fruit drink you need to use.

4. You have \$22 in your bank account and deposit \$11.50 each week. At the same time your cousin has \$218 but is withdrawing \$13 each week.
   a. When will your accounts have the same balance?
   b. How much money will each of you have after 12 weeks?

Example 2 (page 295)

5. Suppose you invest \$10,410 in equipment to manufacture a new board game. Each game costs \$2.65 to manufacture and sells for \$20. How many games must you make and sell before your business breaks even?

6. Several students decide to start a T-shirt company. After initial expenses of \$280, they purchase each T-shirt wholesale for \$3.99. They sell each T-shirt for \$10.99. How many must they sell to break even?

Example 3 (page 296)

7. A family is canoeing downstream (with the current). Their speed relative to the banks of the river averages 2.75 mi/h. During the return trip, they paddle upstream (against the current), averaging 1.5 mi/h relative to the riverbank.

a. Write an equation for the rate of the canoe downstream.
b. Write an equation for the rate of the canoe upstream.
c. Solve the system to find the family's paddling speed in still water.
d. Find the speed of the current of the river.

8. John flies from Atlanta, Georgia, to San Francisco, California. It takes 5.6 hours to travel 2100 miles against the head wind. At the same time, Debby flies from San Francisco to Atlanta. Her plane travels with the same average airspeed but, with a tail wind, her flight takes only 4.8 hours.
a. Write a system of equations that relates time, airspeed, and wind speed to distance for each traveler.
b. Solve the system to find the airspeed.
c. Find the wind speed.

B Apply Your Skills

Without solving, what method would you choose to solve each system: *graphing*, *substitution*, or *elimination*? Explain your reasoning.

9. $4s - 3t = 8$
$t = -2s - 1$

10. $y = 3x - 1$
$y = 4x$

11. $3m - 4n = 1$
$3m - 2n = -1$

12. $y = -2x$
$y = -\frac{1}{2}x + 3$

13. $2x - y = 4$
$x + 3y = 16$

14. $u = 4v$
$3u - 2v = 7$

15. A piece of glass with an initial temperature of 99°C is cooled at a rate of 3.5 degrees Celsius per minute (°C/min). At the same time, a piece of copper with an initial temperature of 0°C is heated at a rate of 2.5°C/min. Let m = the number of minutes, and t = the temperature in degrees Celsius after m minutes.
a. Write a system of equations that relates the temperature t of each material to the time m. Solve the system.
b. **Writing** Explain what the solution means in this situation.

16. The perimeter of the rectangle is 34 cm. The perimeter of the triangle is 30 cm. Find the values of m and n.

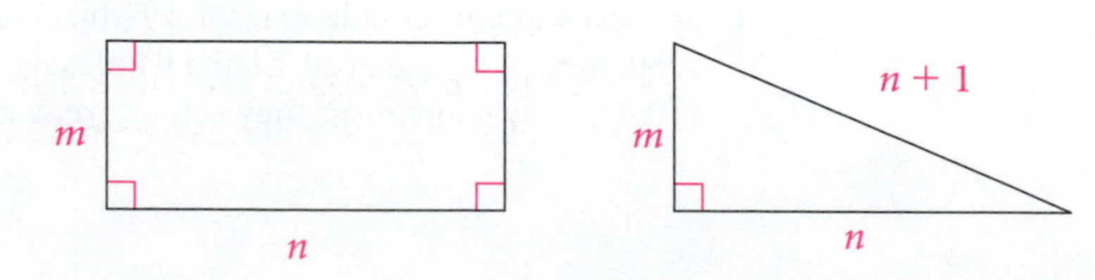

Visit: PHSchool.com
Web Code: bae-0604

17. Write a problem for the total of two types of coins. Then solve the problem.

For a guide to solving Exercise 18, see p. 301.

18. A garden supply store sells two types of lawn mowers. Total sales of mowers for the year were \$8379.70. The total number of mowers sold was 30. The small mower costs \$249.99. The large mower costs \$329.99. Find the number sold of each type of mower.

19. Suppose you want to combine two solutions to make 100 milliliters of 34% acid solution. Solution A is 25% acid and solution B is 40% acid.

a. Copy and complete the table below.

	Solution A 25% Acid	Solution B 40% Acid	Mixture 34% Acid
Solution (mL)	■	■	■
Acid (mL)	■	■	■

b. Write and solve a system of equations to find out how much of each solution you need to use.

The recommended maximum speed of an ultralight aircraft like the one pictured above is about 50 mi/h.

20. Suppose you are flying an ultralight aircraft like the one pictured at the left. You fly to a nearby town, 18 miles away. With a tail wind, the trip takes $\frac{1}{3}$ hour. Your return flight with a head wind takes $\frac{3}{5}$ hour.

a. Find the average airspeed of the ultralight aircraft.

b. Find the average wind speed.

21. Suppose the ratio of girls to boys in your school is 19 : 17. There are 1908 students altogether.

a. Solve the proportion $\frac{g}{b} = \frac{19}{17}$ for g.

b. Write and solve the system of equations to find the total number of boys b and girls g.

22. Suppose you are trying to decide whether to buy ski equipment. Typically, it costs you \$60 a day to rent ski equipment and buy a lift ticket. You can buy ski equipment for about \$400. A lift ticket alone costs \$35 for one day.

a. Find the break-even point.

b. **Critical Thinking** If you expect to ski five days a year, should you buy the ski equipment? Explain.

23. Find the values of x and y.

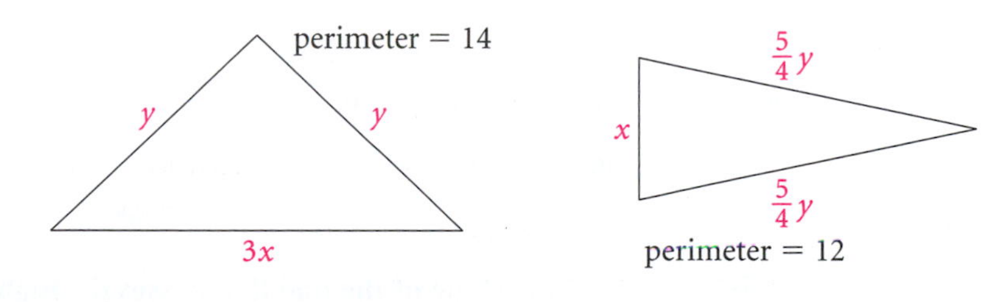

24. You can represent the value of any two-digit number with the expression $10a + b$, where a is the tens' place digit and b is the ones' place digit. If a is 5 and b is 7, then the value of the number is $10(5) + 7$, or 57.
Use a system of equations to find the two-digit number described below.

- The ones' place digit is one more than twice the tens' place digit.
- The value of the number is two more than five times the ones' place digit.

25. An artist sells original hand-painted greeting cards. He makes \$2.50 profit on a small card and \$4.00 profit on a large card. He generally sells 5 large cards for every 2 small cards. He wants a profit of \$10,000 from large and small cards this year.

a. Find the quantity of each card the artist needs to sell to reach his goal.

b. The artist can create a card every 12 minutes. How many hours will he need to make enough to reach his profit target if he sells them all?

c. What is the artist's hourly rate of pay?

Multiple Choice Practice

For California Standards Tutorials, visit PHSchool.com. Web Code: baq-9045

Alg1 9.0

26. Craig has 4 more nickels than dimes. If he has \$.80, which system of equations can he use to find the number of nickels n and the number of dimes d he has?

Ⓐ $n = d + 4$
$0.1d + 0.5n = 0.8$

Ⓑ $d = n + 4$
$0.1d + 0.5n = 0.8$

Ⓒ $n = d + 4$
$0.1d + 0.05n = 0.8$

Ⓓ $d = n + 4$
$0.1d + 0.05n = 0.8$

Alg1 6.0

27. Which is the equation of a line with an x-intercept of -2 and a y-intercept of 3?

Ⓐ $y = \frac{3}{2}x - 2$

Ⓑ $y = \frac{3}{2}x + 3$

Ⓒ $y = -\frac{2}{3}x - 2$

Ⓓ $y = -\frac{2}{3}x + 3$

Alg1 6.0

28. Which is the solution to the system of equations shown in the graph at the right?

Ⓐ $(5, -3)$

Ⓑ $(-3, -5)$

Ⓒ $(2, 0)$

Ⓓ $(0, -2)$

Alg1 4.0

29. Simplify the expression $13(2x - 3) + \frac{1}{2}(16 - 6x)$.

Ⓐ $14x - 31$

Ⓑ $23x - 31$

Ⓒ $29x - 47$

Ⓓ $29x + 31$

Mixed Review

GO for Help

Lesson 6-3 **Solve by elimination.**

30. $2x + 5y = 13$
$3x - 5y = 7$

31. $4x + 2y = -10$
$-2x + 3y = 33$

32. $7x + 6y = 30$
$9x - 8y = 15$

Lesson 5-1 **Find the slope of the line that passes through each pair of points.**

33. $(2, 4), (6, 10)$

34. $(-3, 1), (10, 14)$

35. $(8, -11), (5, -12)$

36. $(1.2, 7), (4.6, 0.2)$

37. $\left(5, -\frac{1}{2}\right), \left(-6, 3\frac{1}{2}\right)$

38. $(8, 0), (8, 5)$

Lesson 3-5 **Solve each inequality and graph the solutions.**

39. $6 < y < 10$

40. $-8 < n \leq 3$

41. $2 < k + 1 < 7$

42. $4 \leq 4p \leq 16$

43. $-13 < 3c + 2 \leq 17$

44. $21 > 5w - 4 > 1$

GPS Guided Problem Solving

For Use With Page 299, Exercise 18

9.0 Solve a system of two linear equations in two variables algebraically. *Develop*

Understanding Word Problems **Read the exercise below and then follow along with what Bill thinks and writes. Check your understanding by solving the exercise at the bottom of the page.**

A garden supply store sells two types of lawn mowers. Total sales of mowers for the year were \$8379.70. The total number of mowers sold was 30. The small mowers cost \$249.99. The large mowers cost \$329.99. Find the number of each type of mower sold.

What Bill Thinks	What Bill Writes
I'll read the problem and write down the important information.	Total sales = \$8379.70 Total number of mowers = 30 Small mowers cost \$249.99. Large mowers cost \$329.99.
Where should I start? Well, it's always helpful to write sentences based on the information I'm given. Total sales include the sales for both the small mowers and the large mowers.	Total sales = sales from small mowers + sales from large mowers
Total number of mowers is the number of small mowers *plus* the number of large mowers.	Total number of mowers = number of small mowers + number of large mowers
Now I'll define some variables. The problem asks for the number of small mowers and the number of large mowers. I'll use 2 variables.	Number of small mowers = s Number of large mowers = w
Now I can write 2 equations.	Total sales: $8379.70 = 249.99s + 329.99w$ Total number: $30 = s + w$
Since the first equation has large numbers, it's probably easier to rewrite the second equation and substitute into the first equation. I'll then solve for w and s.	$s = 30 - w$ $8379.70 = (249.99)(30 - w) + 329.99w$ $8379.70 = 7499.70 + 80w$ $880 = 80w$ $11 = w;\ s = 30 - 11 = 19$
I'll write my answer in a sentence.	The store sold 19 small mowers and 11 large mowers.

EXERCISE

A nursery sells small apple trees for \$19.99 and large apple trees for \$35.99. Total sales for the year were \$1907.27. The total number of apple trees sold was 73. Find the number of each type of apple tree sold.

6-5 Linear Inequalities

California Content Standards

6.0 Sketch the region defined by linear inequalities. *Master*

What You'll Learn

- To graph linear inequalities
- To write and use linear inequalities when modeling real-world situations

. . . And Why

To analyze possible purchases within a budget, as in Example 3

Check Skills You'll Need

Lessons 3-1 and 5-2

Describe each statement as *always, sometimes,* or *never* true.

1. $-3 > -2$ **2.** $8 \leq 8$ **3.** $4n \geq n$

Write each equation in slope-intercept form.

4. $2x - 3y = 9$ **5.** $y + 3x = 6$ **6.** $4y - 3x = 1$

New Vocabulary • linear inequality • solutions of an inequality

Graphing Linear Inequalities

CA Standards Investigation — Graphing Inequalities

1. Graph $y = x + 4$ on a coordinate plane.
2. Test three points that lie above the graph of $y = x + 4$. Substitute the coordinates of each of the points for (x, y) in the inequality $y > x + 4$. If the results are true statements, mark the points on your graph.
3. Test three points that lie below the graph of $y = x + 4$. Substitute the coordinates of each of the points for (x, y) in the inequality $y > x + 4$. If the results are true statements, mark the points on your graph.
4. **Critical Thinking** To graph $y > x + 4$, would you choose points above or below $y = x + 4$?
5. Determine whether you would graph points above or below the graph of $y = x - 2$ to graph the inequality $y < x - 2$.

Just as you have used inequalities to describe graphs on a number line, you can use inequalities to describe regions of a coordinate plane.

To review graphing inequalities in one variable, see p. 125.

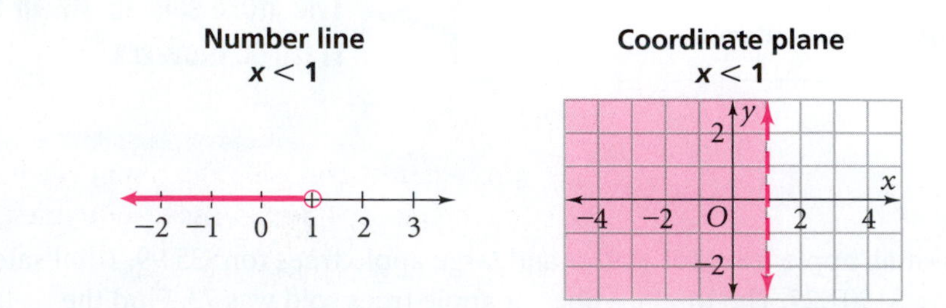

A **linear inequality** describes a region of the coordinate plane that has a boundary line. The **solutions of an inequality** are the coordinates of the points that make the inequality true.

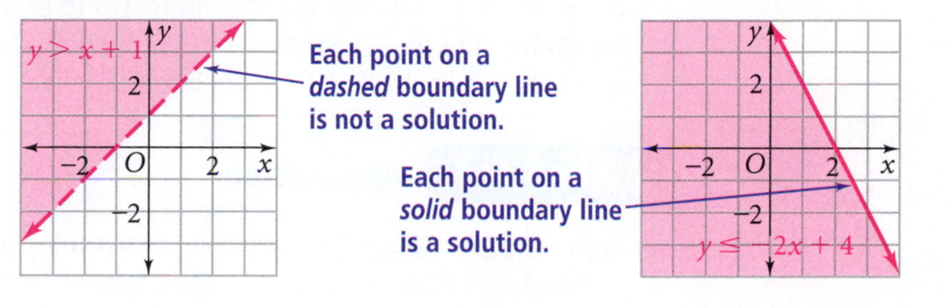

As you can see in the graphs above, you can tell from an inequality whether to shade above or below the boundary line. For an inequality written in the form of $y <$ or $y \leq$, shade below the boundary line. For an inequality written in the form of $y >$ or $y \geq$, shade above the boundary line.

1 EXAMPLE Graphing an Inequality

For: Linear Inequality Activity
Use: Interactive Textbook, 6-5

Graph $y < 2x + 3$.

First graph the boundary line $y = 2x + 3$.

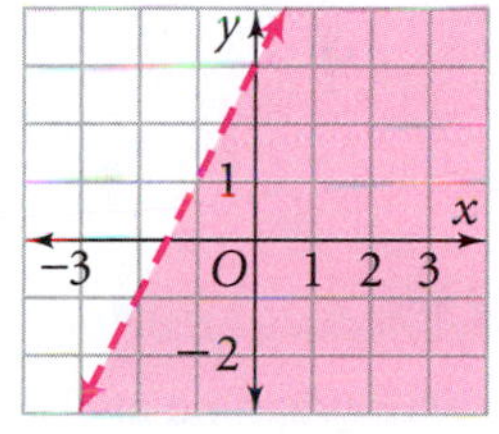

The coordinates of points on the boundary line do not make the inequality true. So, use a dashed line.

Shade below the boundary line.

Check The point (0, 0) is in the region of the graph of the inequality. See if (0, 0) satisfies the inequality.

$y < 2x + 3$

$0 < 2(0) + 3$ Substitute (0, 0) for (x, y).

$0 < 3$ ✓

CA Standards Check 1 Graph $y \geq 3x - 1$.

In order to tell whether you shade above or below a boundary line, it may be helpful to write the inequality in slope-intercept form.

2 EXAMPLE Rewriting to Graph an Inequality

Graph $3x - 5y \leq 10$.

Solve $3x - 5y \leq 10$ for y.

$3x - 5y \leq 10$

$-5y \leq -3x + 10$ Subtract $3x$ from each side.

$y \geq \frac{3}{5}x - 2$ Divide each side by -5. Reverse the inequality symbol.

Graph $y = \frac{3}{5}x - 2$.

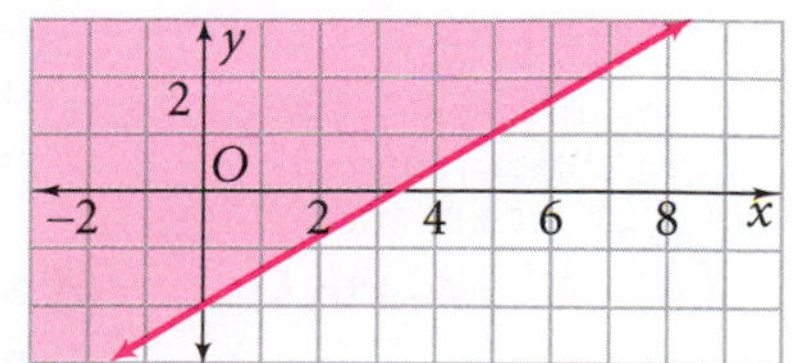

The coordinates of points on the boundary line make the inequality true. So, use a solid line.

Since $y \geq \frac{3}{5}x - 2$, shade above the line.

CA Standards Check 2 Graph $6x + 8y \geq 12$.

Modeling Real-World Situations

Many situations are modeled by inequalities that have a boundary line of the form $Ax + By = C$. You can use the intercepts to graph the boundary line of the inequality. Choose a test point not on the boundary line to determine whether the solutions are above or below the boundary line.

3 EXAMPLE Application

Suppose your budget for a party allows you to spend no more than \$12 on peanuts and cashews. Peanuts cost \$2/lb and cashews cost \$4/lb. Find three possible combinations of peanuts and cashews you can buy.

Relate	cost of peanuts	plus	cost of cashews	is less than or equal to	total budget
Define	Let x = the number of pounds of peanuts.				
	Let y = the number of pounds of cashews.				
Write	$2x$	$+$	$4y$	$\leq$	12

For help with graphing an equation using intercepts, go to Lesson 5-3, Example 2.

Graph $2x + 4y = 12$ by graphing the intercepts, $(6, 0)$ and $(0, 3)$.

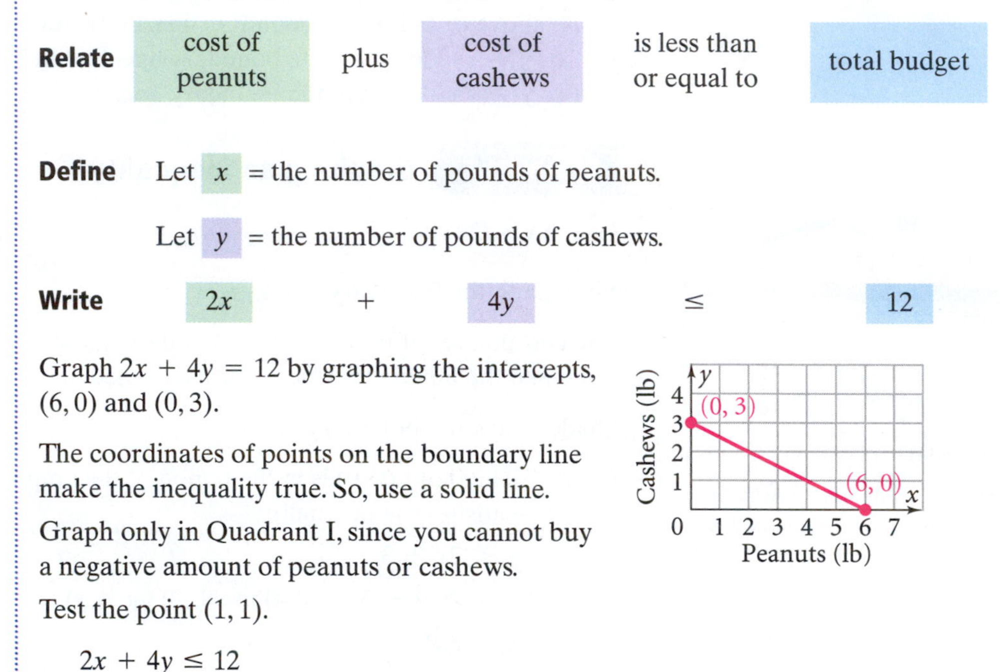

The coordinates of points on the boundary line make the inequality true. So, use a solid line.

Graph only in Quadrant I, since you cannot buy a negative amount of peanuts or cashews.

Test the point $(1, 1)$.

$$2x + 4y \leq 12$$

$2(1) + 4(1) \leq 12$ **Substitute (1, 1) for (x, y).**

$6 \leq 12$ **Since the inequality is true, (1, 1) is a solution.**

Shade the region containing $(1, 1)$. The graph below shows all the possible solutions of the problem.

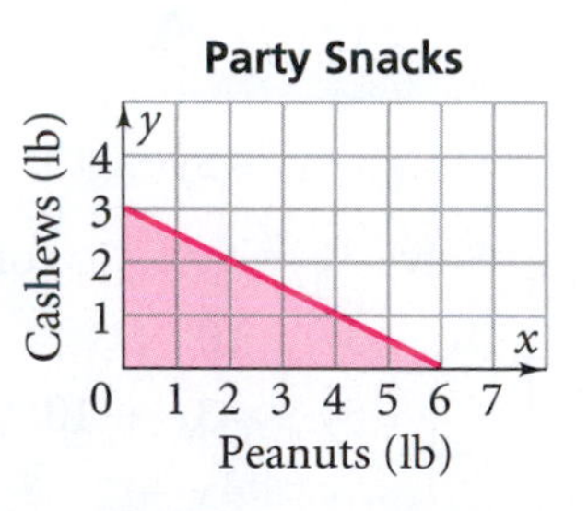

Since the boundary line is included in the graph, the intercepts are also solutions of the inequality. The solution $(2, 2)$ means that if you buy 2 lb of peanuts, you can buy 2 lb of cashews. Three solutions are $(2, 2)$, $(3, 1)$, and $(1, 2)$.

CA Standards Check 3 Suppose you plan to spend no more than \$24 on meat for a cookout. At your local market, hamburger costs \$3.00/lb and chicken wings cost \$2.40/lb. Find three possible combinations of hamburger and chicken wings you can buy.

EXERCISES

For more exercises, see *Extra Skills and Word Problem Practice.*

Standards Practice

Alg1 6.0

A Practice by Example

Example 1 (page 303)

Determine whether point P is a solution of the linear inequality.

1. $y \leq -2x + 1; P(2, 2)$ **2.** $x < 2; P(1, 0)$ **3.** $y \geq 3x - 2; P(0, 0)$

4. $y > x - 1; P(0, 1)$ **5.** $y \geq -\frac{2}{5}x + 4; P(0, 0)$ **6.** $y > \frac{5}{3}x - 4; P(0, 1)$

Choose the linear inequality that describes each graph.

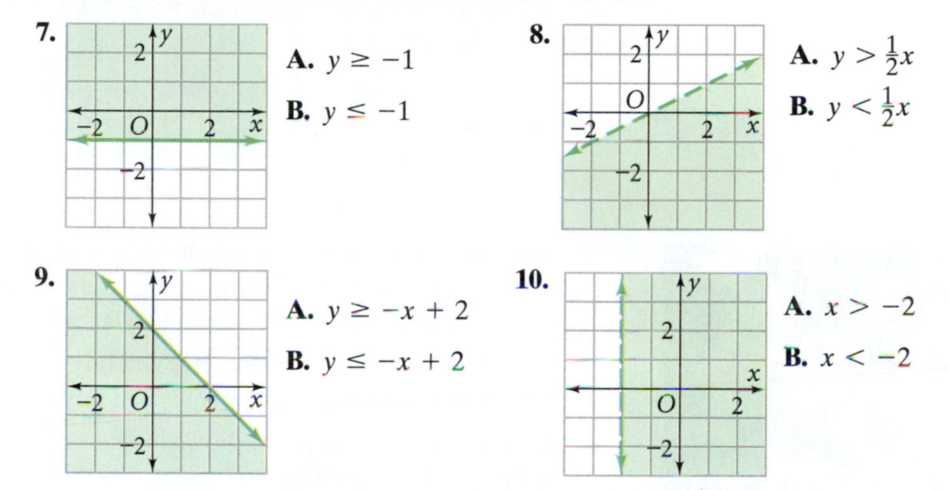

7. **A.** $y \geq -1$ **B.** $y \leq -1$

8. **A.** $y > \frac{1}{2}x$ **B.** $y < \frac{1}{2}x$

9. **A.** $y \geq -x + 2$ **B.** $y \leq -x + 2$

10. **A.** $x > -2$ **B.** $x < -2$

Graph each linear inequality.

11. $y \leq \frac{1}{4}x - 1$ **12.** $y \geq \frac{1}{4}x - 1$ **13.** $y < -4x - 1$ **14.** $y \geq 4x - 1$

15. $y < 5x - 5$ **16.** $y \leq \frac{2}{5}x - 3$ **17.** $y \leq -3x$ **18.** $y \geq -\frac{1}{2}x$

Example 2 (page 303)

Write each linear inequality in slope-intercept form. Then graph the inequality.

19. $2x - 3y \geq 7$ **20.** $5x - 3y \leq 6$ **21.** $4x - 6y \geq 16$ **22.** $-4y - 6x > 8$

Example 3 (page 304)

23. Gold crepe paper costs $5 per roll, and blue crepe paper costs $3 per roll. Your budget allows you to spend at most $48 for crepe paper. How many rolls of gold and blue crepe paper can you buy without exceeding your budget?

Let x = the number of rolls of blue crepe paper.
Let y = the number of rolls of gold crepe paper.

a. Write a linear inequality that describes the situation.
b. Graph the linear inequality.
c. Write three possible solutions to the problem.
d. **Critical Thinking** The point $(-2, 5)$ is a solution of the inequality. Is it a solution of the problem? Explain.

At least 16 million backpacks are sold in the United States each year.

24. A company makes nylon and canvas backpacks. The profit on a nylon backpack is $3 and the profit on a canvas backpack is $10. How many backpacks must the company sell to make a profit of more than $250?
a. Write a linear inequality that describes the situation.
b. Graph the linear inequality.
c. Write three possible solutions to the problem.
d. **Critical Thinking** Which values are reasonable for the domain and for the range? Explain.

B Apply Your Skills

Graph each linear inequality.

25. $y \leq \frac{2}{5}x + 2$ **26.** $y \geq -\frac{2}{5}x + 2$ **27.** $4x - 5y \leq 10$ **28.** $4x + 5y \leq 10$

29. $4y < 6x + 2$ **30.** $2x + 3y \leq 6$ **31.** $4x - 4y \leq 8$ **32.** $y - 2x < 2$

33. Writing Explain how you can tell from a linear inequality whether you will shade above or below the graph of the boundary line.

Write the linear inequality shown in each graph.

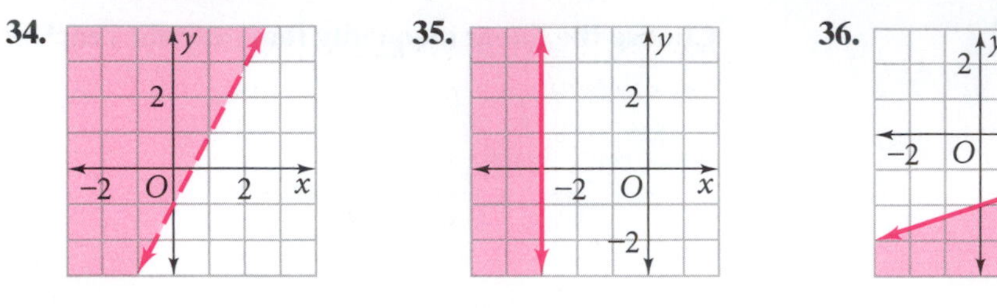

In 2005, there were about 13,600 licensed radio stations in the United States.

37. Suppose you work at a local radio station. You are in charge of a \$180 budget for new tapes and CDs. Record companies will give you 21 promotional (free) CDs. You can buy tapes for \$8 and CDs for \$12.

Let x = the number of CDs you buy.
Let y = the number of tapes you buy.

a. Write an inequality that shows the number of tapes and CDs you can buy.
b. Graph the inequality.
c. Is (8, 9) a solution of the inequality? Explain what the solution means.
d. If you buy only tapes and you buy as many as possible, how many new recordings will the station get?

Write the linear inequality described. Then graph the inequality.

38. x is positive. **39.** y is negative.

40. y is not negative. **41.** x is less than y.

42. Error Analysis Jan's graph of the inequality $4x + 6y > 12$ is shown below. What is wrong with the graph?

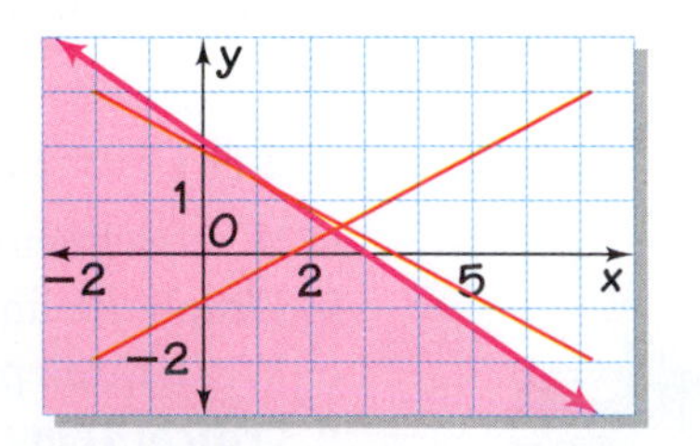

43. Alexis and Noah are playing a game in which players earn points by forming words using game pieces with letters on them. Words are worth either 5 points or 8 points. The first player to earn at least 100 points wins the game.

a. Write and graph an inequality that represents the number of 5-point and 8-point words needed to win the game.
b. Noah has formed ten 5-point words and four 8-point words. Based on your graph, does he have enough points to win the game? Explain.
c. Write three possible solutions to the problem.

44. **Critical Thinking** Write an inequality that describes the entire part of the coordinate plane *not* included in the solution of $y \geq x + 2$.

For Exercise 45, draw a diagram of a possible garden.

45. You want to fence a rectangular area of your yard for a garden. You plan to use no more than 50 ft of fencing.
   a. Write and graph a linear inequality that describes this situation.
   b. **Open-Ended** What are two possible sizes for a square garden?
   c. Can you make the garden 12 ft by 15 ft? Justify your answer.

C Challenge

For Exercises 46–47, write the inequality that has the solution described.

46. The points (0, –3) and (8, 5) lie on the boundary line, but neither point is a solution. The point (1, 1) is not a solution.

47. The points (7, 12) and (–3, –8) lie on the boundary line, and each point is a solution. The point (1, 1) is also a solution.

48. a. Write and graph an inequality in the form $Ax + By > C$, where A, B, and C are all positive.
   b. Write and graph an inequality in the form $Ax + By < C$, where A, B, and C are all positive.
   c. **Reasoning** Both inequalities are in standard form. Make a conjecture about the inequality symbol and the region shaded.
   d. Would your conjecture in part (c) be different if B were negative?

Visit: PHSchool.com
Web Code: bae-0605

49. a. Is the point (4, 5) a solution of the inequality $y > x - 1$?
   b. Is the point (4, 5) a solution of the inequality $y < 3x$?
   c. Find one other point that is a solution of both inequalities.
   d. Draw a graph that shows all the points that are solutions of both inequalities.

Multiple Choice Practice

For California Standards Tutorials, visit PHSchool.com. Web Code: baq-9045

Alg1 6.0

50. Carol is buying asparagus and bananas at the grocery store. Asparagus costs \$3.00 per pound and bananas cost \$.50 per pound. Which inequality represents the number of pounds of asparagus a and the number of pounds of bananas b Carol can buy with \$20.00?

   (A) $3a + 0.5b < 20$
   (B) $3a + 0.5b > 20$
   (C) $3a + 0.5b \leq 20$
   (D) $3a + 0.5b \geq 20$

Alg1 7.0

51. Which could be the equation of a line that contains the points (1, 3) and (6, 2)?

   (A) $y = -\frac{1}{5}x + b$ (B) $y = -\frac{1}{2}x + b$ (C) $y = 2x + b$ (D) $y = 5x + b$

Alg1 9.0

52. Which substitution should you use to solve the system of equations at the right?

$$5y + x = 5$$
$$\tfrac{11}{5}x = 11 + y$$

   (A) $5\left(\frac{11}{5}x - 11\right) + x = 5$
   (B) $\frac{11}{5}x = 11 + \left(\frac{11}{5}x - 11\right)$
   (C) $5\left(1 - \frac{1}{5}x\right) + x = 5$
   (D) $\frac{11}{5}(5 + 5y) = 11 + y$

Alg1 3.0

53. Which of the following is NOT a solution of the inequality $12 + 5|b - 1| < 34.5$?

   (A) -3 (B) 0 (C) 5 (D) 6

Mixed Review

Lesson 6-4

For Exercises 54–55, define the variables and write a system of equations for each situation. Solve by any method.

GO for Help

54. Suppose you invest $12,000 in equipment to manufacture a new board game. Each game costs $2.50 to manufacture and sells for $18. How many games must you make and sell for your business to break even?

55. Suppose you are canoeing along a river with a steady current. Your average speed upstream is 2.5 mi/h. On the return trip you paddle with the current, and your average speed is 4 mi/h. Find the average speed of the current and your average speed if you were paddling in still water.

Lesson 4-7

Find the next two numbers in each pattern.

56. $-8, 4, -2, \ldots$

57. $4, 11, 18, \ldots$

58. $2, 6, 18, \ldots$

59. $11, 5, -1, \ldots$

Lesson 2-4

Solve each proportion.

60. $\frac{3}{4} = \frac{m}{16}$

61. $\frac{6}{7} = \frac{24}{g}$

62. $\frac{4}{w} = \frac{8}{22}$

63. $\frac{9}{10} = \frac{15}{a}$

64. $\frac{x + 1}{3} = \frac{2}{9}$

65. $\frac{n - 2}{5} = \frac{6}{15}$

66. $\frac{8}{r + 1} = \frac{4}{7}$

67. $\frac{9}{x + 3} = \frac{18}{19}$

Checkpoint Quiz 2 — Lessons 6-3 through 6-5

For Exercises 1–5, solve each system using elimination.

1. $2x + 5y = 2$
$3x - 5y = 53$

2. $-8x - 3y = 69$
$8x + 7y = -65$

3. $4x + 2y = 34$
$10x - 4y = -5$

4. $11x - 13y = 89$
$-11x + 13y = 107$

5. $3x + 6y = 42$
$-7x + 8y = -109$

6. You have a total of 21 coins, all nickels and dimes. The total value is $1.70. Write and solve a system of equations to find the number of dimes d and the number of nickels n that you have.

7. Suppose you start an ice cream business. You buy a freezer for $200. It costs you $.35 to make each single-scoop ice cream cone. You sell each cone for $1.20. Write and solve a system of equations to find the break-even point for your business.

8. To go to a campsite 12 miles away, you paddle a canoe against the current of a river for 4 hours. During your return trip you paddle with the current, and you travel the same distance in 3 hours. Write and solve a system of equations to find your paddling speed in still water. Find the speed of the current of the river.

Graph each inequality.

9. $y \geq 2x - 4$

10. $3x + 4y < 18$

Systems of Linear Inequalities

California Content Standards

9.0 Solve a system of two linear inequalities in two variables and sketch the solution sets. *Master*

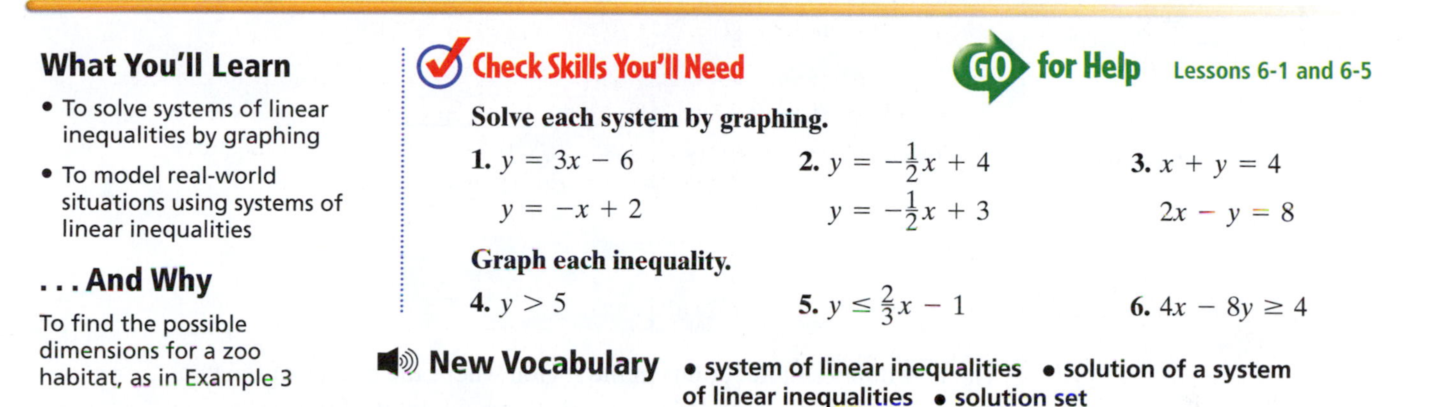

What You'll Learn

- To solve systems of linear inequalities by graphing
- To model real-world situations using systems of linear inequalities

. . . And Why

To find the possible dimensions for a zoo habitat, as in Example 3

Check Skills You'll Need

GO for Help Lessons 6-1 and 6-5

Solve each system by graphing.

1. $y = 3x - 6$
$y = -x + 2$

2. $y = -\frac{1}{2}x + 4$
$y = -\frac{1}{2}x + 3$

3. $x + y = 4$
$2x - y = 8$

Graph each inequality.

4. $y > 5$

5. $y \leq \frac{2}{3}x - 1$

6. $4x - 8y \geq 4$

New Vocabulary • system of linear inequalities • solution of a system of linear inequalities • solution set

Solving Systems of Linear Inequalities by Graphing

Two or more linear inequalities together form a **system of linear inequalities.** The system below describes the lavender-shaded region of the graph. Notice that there are two boundary lines.

System of Linear Inequalities

$x \geq 3$
$y < -2$

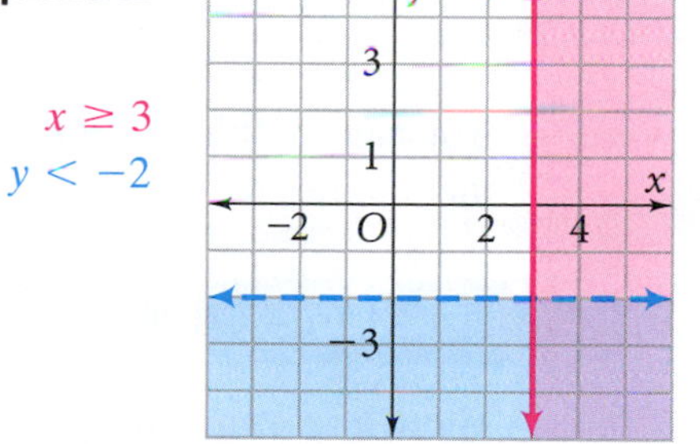

You can describe all the points of a quadrant with a system of linear inequalities.

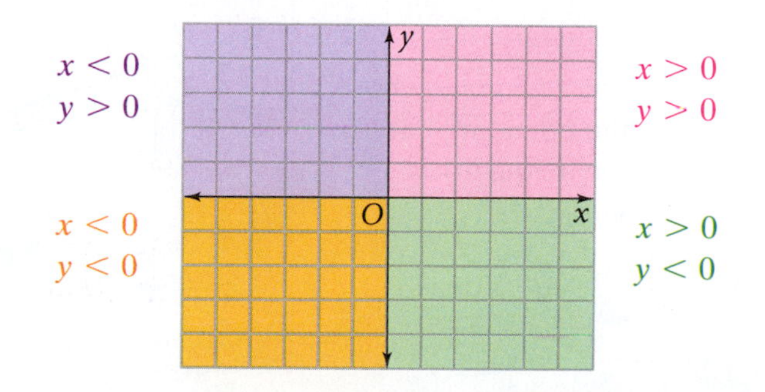

$x < 0$, $y > 0$

$x > 0$, $y > 0$

$x < 0$, $y < 0$

$x > 0$, $y < 0$

A **solution of a system of linear inequalities** makes each inequality in the system true. The graph of a system shows the **solution set,** or the set of all solutions.

1 EXAMPLE Graphing a System of Inequalities

Online active math

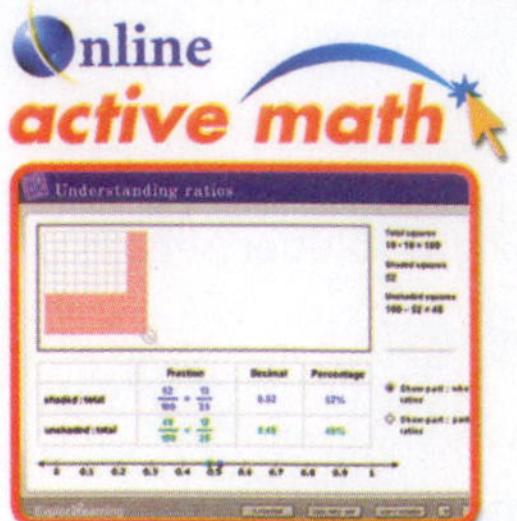

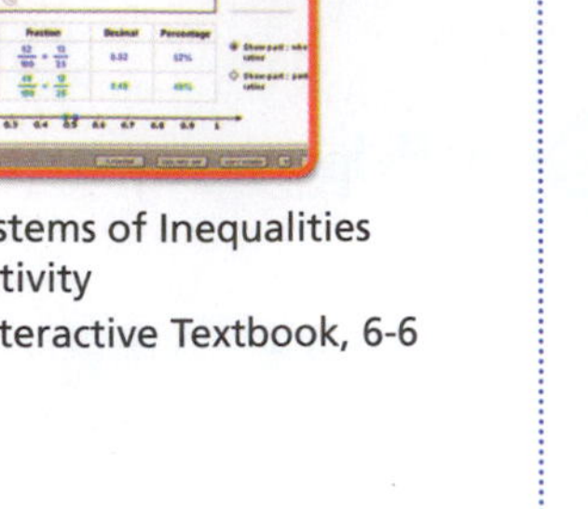

For: Systems of Inequalities Activity
Use: Interactive Textbook, 6-6

Solve by graphing. $y > 2x - 5$
$3x + 4y < 12$

Graph $y > 2x - 5$ and $3x + 4y < 12$.

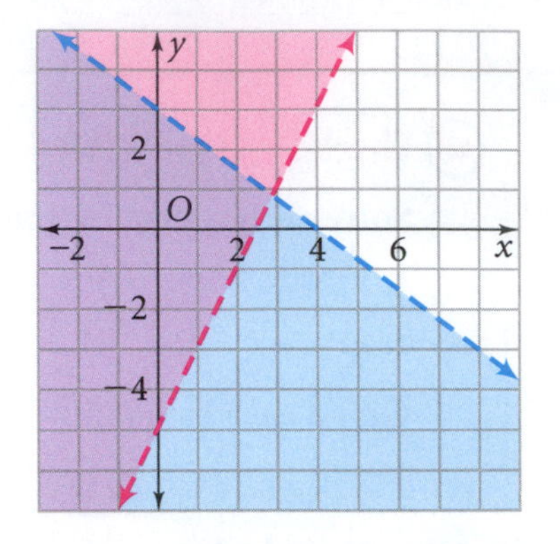

The coordinates of the points in the region where the graphs of the two inequalities overlap (shaded in lavender) are solutions of the system.

Check The point (0, 0) is in the region graphed by both inequalities. See if (0, 0) satisfies both inequalities.

$y > 2x - 5$		$3x + 4y < 12$
$0 > 2(0) - 5$	⟵ **Substitute (0, 0) for (x, y).** ⟶	$3(0) + 4(0) < 12$
$0 > -5$ ✓		$0 < 12$ ✓

CA Standards Check 1 Solve by graphing. $y \geq -x + 2$
$2x + 4y < 4$

You can combine your knowledge of linear equations with your knowledge of inequalities to describe a graph using a system of inequalities.

2 EXAMPLE Writing a System of Inequalities From a Graph

GO Online
Video Tutor Help
Visit: PHSchool.com
Web Code: bae-0775

Write a system of linear inequalities from each shaded region below.

red region

boundary: $y = x - 2$

The region lies above the boundary line, so the inequality is $y > x - 2$.

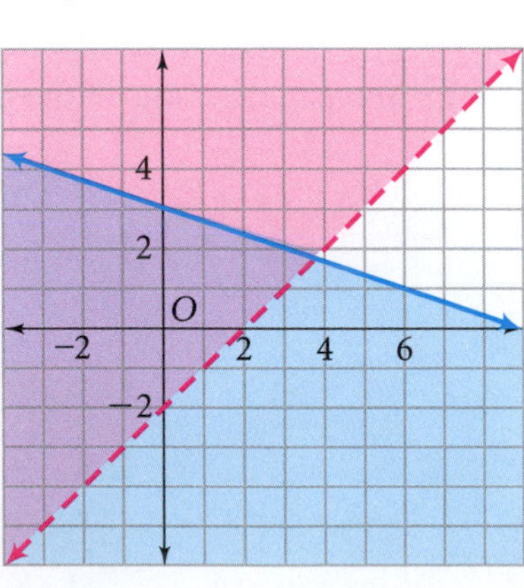

blue region

boundary: $y = -\frac{1}{3}x + 3$

The region includes the boundary line and the points lying below the boundary line, so the inequality is $y \leq -\frac{1}{3}x + 3$.

system for the lavender region: $y > x - 2$
$y \leq -\frac{1}{3}x + 3$

2 Write a system of inequalities for the lavender region in each of the following graphs.

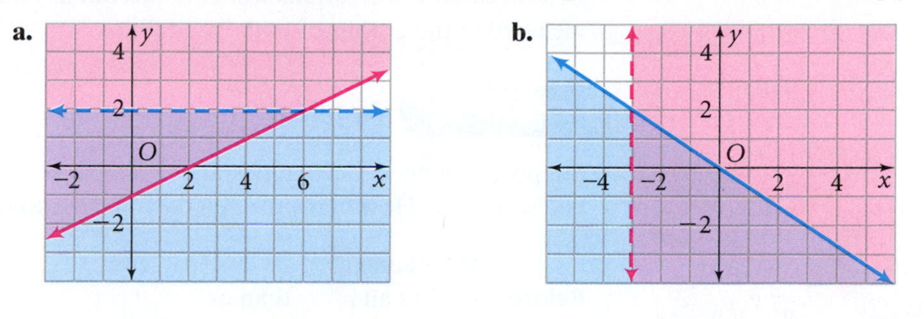

Writing and Using Systems of Linear Inequalities

You can model some real-world situations by graphing linear inequalities. When you graph real-world situations, you often need to plan how you will scale each axis. Use the values for the x- and y-intercepts to determine your scale.

3 EXAMPLE Application

A zookeeper wants to fence a rectangular habitat for goats. The length of the habitat should be at least 80 ft, and the distance around it should be no more than 310 ft. What are the possible dimensions of the habitat?

It is recommended that each goat in a habitat have at least 15 square feet of bedded area.

Relate	the length	is at least	80 ft	the perimeter	is no more than	310 ft

Define Let x = width of the habitat.
Let y = length of the habitat.

Write	y	$\geq$	80	$2x + 2y$	$\leq$	310

Solve by graphing. $y \geq 80$
$2x + 2y \leq 310.$

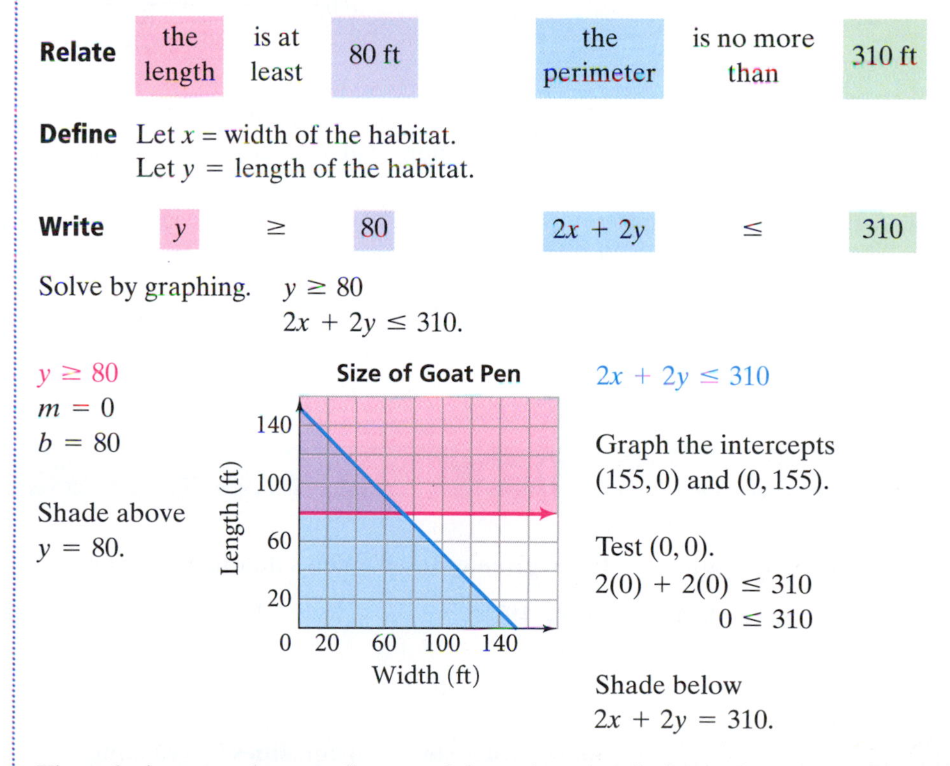

$y \geq 80$
$m = 0$
$b = 80$

Shade above $y = 80$.

$2x + 2y \leq 310$

Graph the intercepts (155, 0) and (0, 155).

Test (0, 0).
$2(0) + 2(0) \leq 310$
$0 \leq 310$

Shade below $2x + 2y = 310$.

The solutions are the coordinates of the points that lie in the lavender region and on the parts of the two lines that border the lavender region.

CA Standards Check

3 Suppose you want to fence a rectangular garden plot. You want the length of the garden to be at least 50 ft and the perimeter to be no more than 140 ft. Solve by graphing to show all of the possible dimensions of the garden.

Some real-world situations have a domain and range that include only integers. In such cases, the solutions will be some, but not all, of the points in the region included in the graphs of both inequalities.

In 1932, you would have needed a 3¢ stamp to mail a letter. To mail the same letter in 2007 would cost 39¢.

4 EXAMPLE Application

Suppose you need $2.40 in postage to mail a package. You have 9 stamps, some 24¢ and some 39¢. How many of each do you need to mail the package?

Relate	the number of 24¢ and 39¢ stamps	is less than or equal to	9	the value of 24¢ and 39¢ stamps	is at least	240¢

Define Let a = the number of 24¢ stamps. Let b = the number of 39¢ stamps.

Write	$a + b$	$\leq$	9	$24a + 39b$	$\geq$	240

Solve by graphing.

$a + b \leq 9$

$24a + 39b \geq 240$

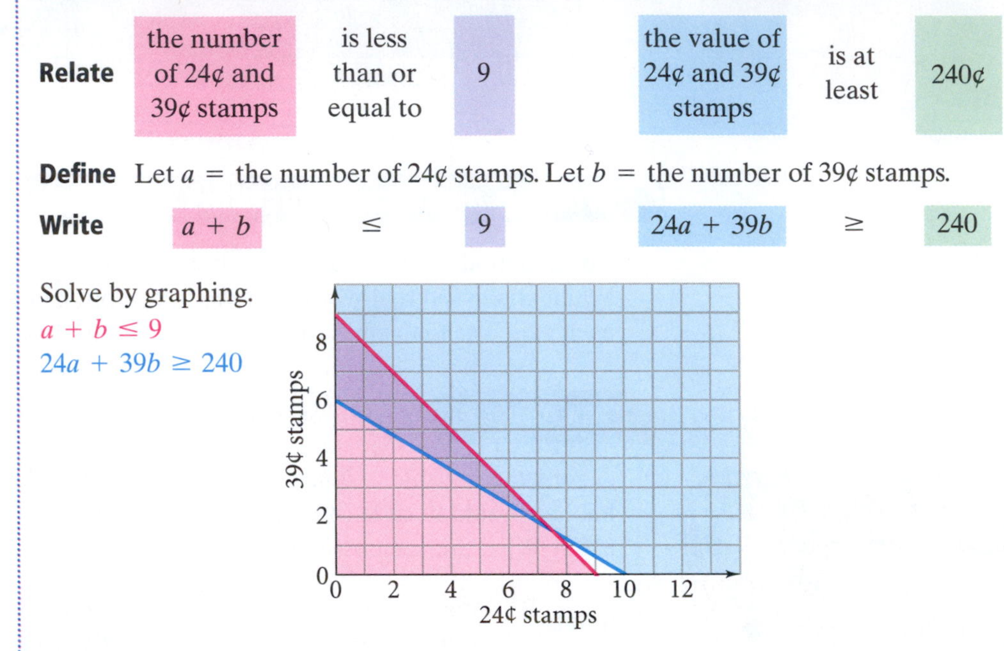

The solutions are all of the coordinates of points that are nonnegative integers lying in the region shaded lavender and on its boundary lines.

CA Standards Check 4 **a.** Give two solutions from the graph in Example 4.

b. Does either solution give you the exact postage needed to mail the package?

c. **Critical Thinking** Why are the solutions to the problem only nonnegative integers?

EXERCISES

Standards Practice

For more exercises, see *Extra Skills and Word Problem Practice.*

Alg1 9.0

A Practice by Example

Example 1 (page 310)

GO for Help

Is the given ordered pair a solution of the system of inequalities?

1. (1, 19)
$y \leq 7x - 13$
$y > 3x + 6$

2. (4, 10)
$9x - y \geq 23$
$5x + 0.2y \geq 20$

3. (−2, 40)
$y > -13x + 29$
$y \leq 9x + 11$

Solve each system of inequalities by graphing.

4. $y < 2x + 4$
$-3x - 2y \geq 6$

5. $y < 2x + 4$
$2x - y \leq 4$

6. $y > 2x + 4$
$2x - y \leq 4$

7. $y > \frac{1}{4}x$
$y \leq -x + 4$

8. $y < 2x - 3$
$y > 5$

9. $y \leq -\frac{1}{3}x + 7$
$y \geq -x + 1$

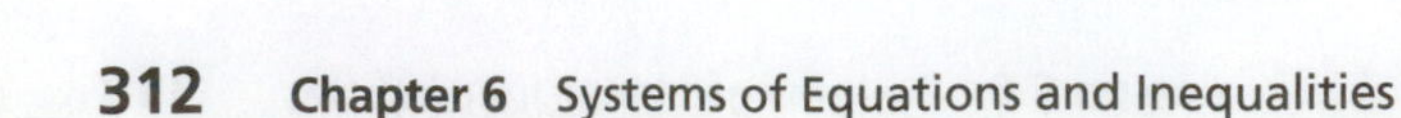

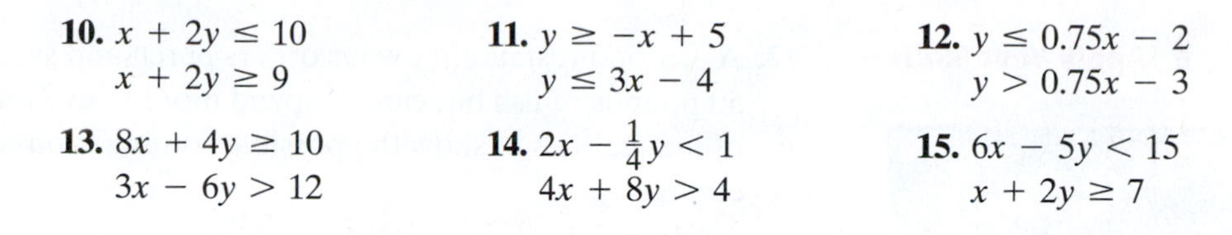

10. $x + 2y \leq 10$
$x + 2y \geq 9$

11. $y \geq -x + 5$
$y \leq 3x - 4$

12. $y \leq 0.75x - 2$
$y > 0.75x - 3$

13. $8x + 4y \geq 10$
$3x - 6y > 12$

14. $2x - \frac{1}{4}y < 1$
$4x + 8y > 4$

15. $6x - 5y < 15$
$x + 2y \geq 7$

Example 2 (page 310)

Write a system of inequalities for each graph.

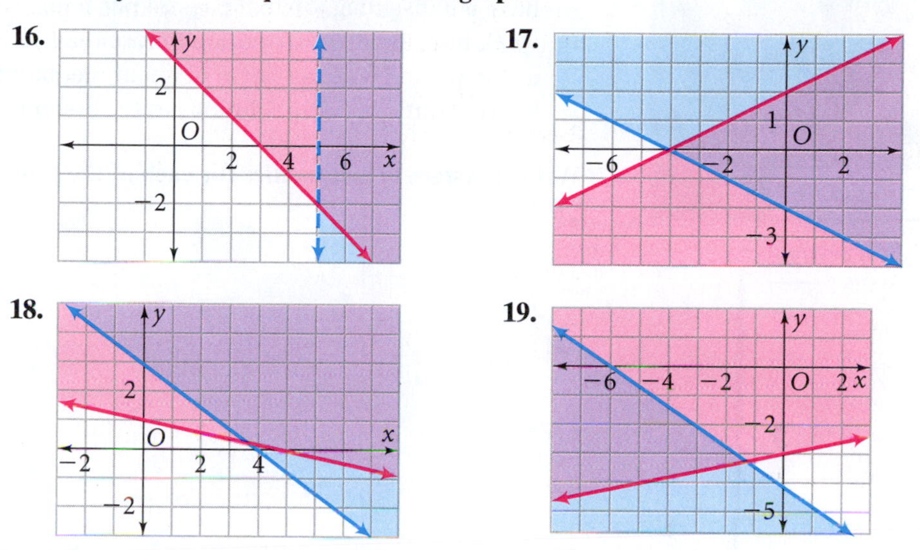

Example 3 (page 311)

20. Suppose you buy flour and cornmeal in bulk to make flour tortillas and corn tortillas. Flour costs \$1.50/lb. Cornmeal costs \$2.50/lb. You want to spend less than \$9.50 on flour and cornmeal, and you need at least 4 lb altogether.

a. Write a system of inequalities that describes this situation.

b. Graph the solution set of the system.

21. Suppose you want to fence a rectangular area for your dog. You will use the house as one of the four sides. Since the house is 40 ft wide, the length ℓ needs to be no more than 40 ft. You plan to use at least 150 ft of fencing. Graph the following system to find possible dimensions for the rectangle.

$$\ell \leq 40$$
$$\ell + 2w \geq 150$$

Example 4 (page 312)

22. Suppose you receive a \$50 gift certificate to the Cityside Music and Books store. All CDs at the store cost \$9.99, and all books cost \$5.99. You want to buy some books and at least one CD.

a. Write a system of inequalities for x books and y CDs that describes this situation.

b. Graph the solution set of the system.

c. What purchase does the ordered pair (2, 6) represent? Is it a solution to your system? Explain.

d. Find a solution in which you spend almost all of the gift certificate.

B Apply Your Skills

23. A seafood restaurant owner orders perch and salmon. He wants to buy at least 50 pounds of fish but cannot spend more than $180. Write and graph a system of inequalities to show the possible combinations of perch and salmon he could buy.

24. Suppose you have a job in an ice cream shop that pays $6 per hour. You also have a babysitting job that pays $4 per hour. You want to earn at least $60 per week but would like to work no more than 12 hours per week.

a. Graph and write a system of linear inequalities that describes this situation.

b. Give three possible solutions to the system.

Write a system of inequalities for each of the following graphs.

25. **27.**

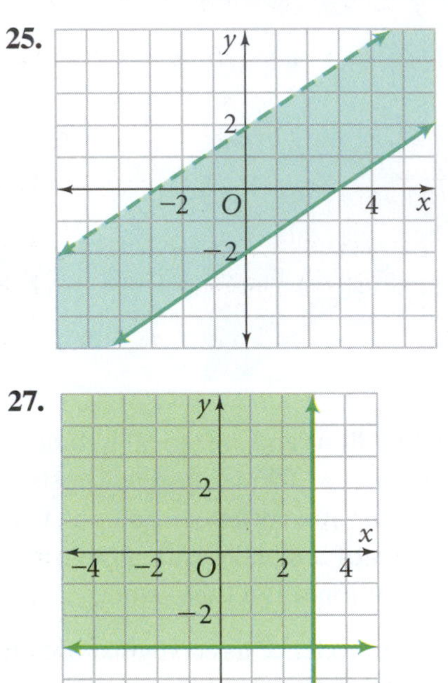

26.

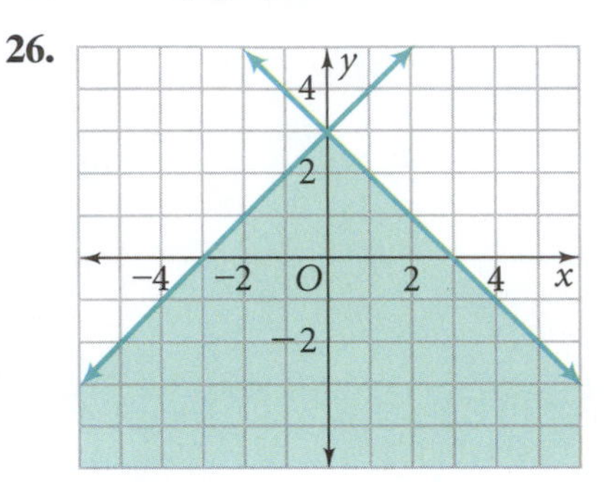

28.

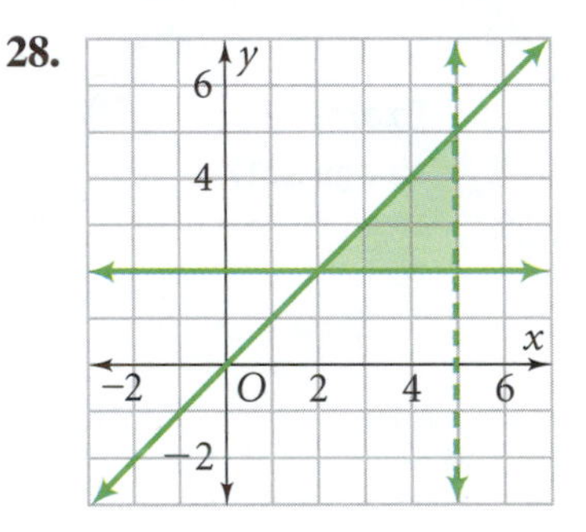

Write a system of linear inequalities with the given characteristics.

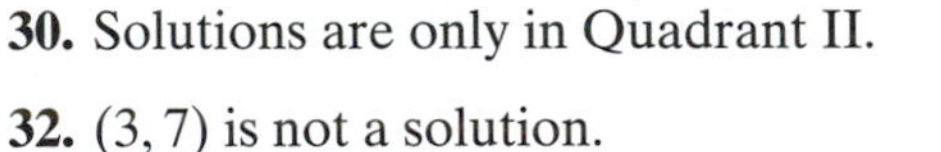

29. $(0, 0)$ is a solution.

30. Solutions are only in Quadrant II.

31. There is no solution.

32. $(3, 7)$ is not a solution.

33. Solutions are only in Quadrant IV.

34. Which region represents the solution to the system?

$y \geq \frac{1}{2}x + 1$

$4x + 2y \leq 8$

(A) I (C) II

(B) III (D) IV

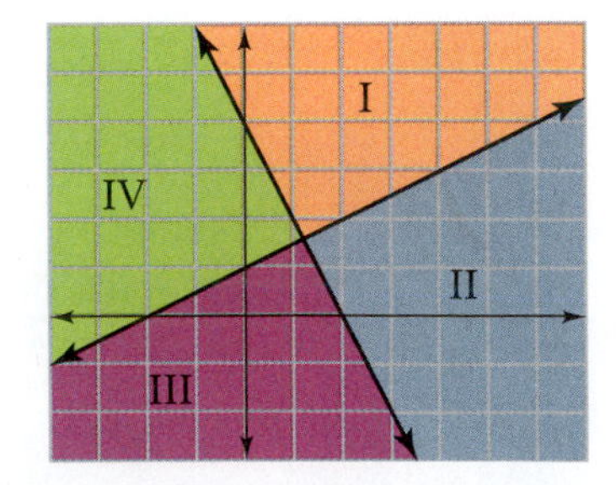

35. a. A clothing store has a going-out-of-business sale. They are selling pants for $10.99 and shirts for $4.99. You can spend as much as $45 and want to buy at least one pair of pants. Write and graph a system of inequalities that describes this situation.

b. Suppose you need to buy at least three pairs of pants. From your graph, find all the ordered pairs that are possible solutions.

Visit: PHSchool.com
Web Code: bae-0606

36. **a.** Graph each inequality. $y > 4x + 1$
$y < 4x - 2$

b. Writing Will the boundary lines $y = 4x + 1$ and $y = 4x - 2$ ever intersect? Explain.

c. Will the shaded regions you drew in part (a) overlap?

d. Does the system of inequalities have any solutions?

37. **a.** Graph the system of inequalities. $y > 3x - 5$
$y < 3x + 4$

b. Will the boundary lines $y = 3x - 5$ and $y = 3x + 4$ ever intersect? Explain.

c. Describe the shape of the overlapping region.

38. Write a system of four inequalities that describes a rectangle. Graph the system.

39. The following system of inequalities describes a right isosceles triangle.
$x > 0$
$y > 0$
$y < mx + 4$

a. Find m.

b. Find the area of the triangle.

GO for Help

For help with area, see Skills Handbook page 604.

The solution region of each system of linear inequalities below forms a figure. (a) Describe the shape. (b) Find the vertices. (c) Find the area.

40. $y \geq \frac{1}{2}x + 1$
$y \leq 2$
$x \geq -4$

41. $x \geq 1$
$x \leq 5$
$y \geq -1$
$y \leq 3$

42. $x \geq 0$
$x \leq 2$
$y \geq -4$
$y \leq -x + 2$

43. $x \geq 2$
$y \geq -3$
$x + y \leq 4$

44. A jeweler plans to produce a ring made of silver and gold. The price of gold is approximately \$10/g. The price of silver is approximately \$.15/g. She considers the following in deciding how much gold and silver to use in the ring.

- The total mass must be more than 10 g but less than 20 g.
- The ring must contain at least 3 g of gold.
- The total cost of the gold and silver must be less than \$60.

Let s = the mass of silver in grams and d = the mass of gold in grams.

a. Write and graph the four inequalities that describe this situation.

b. For one solution (s, d), find the mass of the ring and the cost of the gold and silver.

45. Solve $|y| \geq x$. (*Hint:* Write two inequalities; then graph them.)

Write a system of linear inequalities with the given characteristics.

46. (2, 5) and (5, 2) are not solutions; (5, 5) is a solution.

47. (−3, 2) and (3, 2) are not solutions; (−2, 6) is a solution.

48. A drum maker sells two sizes of frame drums like the ones at the left. A 14-in. drum sells for \$180 and an 18-in. drum sells for \$240. He is trying to decide how many drums to build and considers the following:

- He wants to produce and sell at least \$2700 worth of drums.
- He has materials to make no more than 17 drums.
- He plans to make more 14-in. drums than 18-in. drums.
- He wants to make at least four 18-in. drums.

a. Write and graph the four inequalities that describe this situation.

b. Give one possible solution to the system.

Multiple Choice Practice

For California Standards Tutorials, visit PHSchool.com. Web Code: baq-9045

Alg1 9.0

49. Last year, Brooke earned $12,000, and her federal tax was 8 times her state tax. She paid a total of $1,665 in taxes. Which system of equations can be used to find the amount of federal tax f and the amount of state tax s Brooke paid?

(A) $f = 8s$, $f + s = 1665$

(B) $f + s = 1665$, $f + 8s = 12{,}000$

(C) $f + s = 12{,}000$, $f + 8s = 1665$

(D) $f = 1664 - s$, $f = 12{,}000 - 8s$

Alg1 6.0

50. The equation $y = 1.25x + 6$ represents the hourly pay y for a person who has been working at Jake's Landscaping for x years. What will be the hourly pay for a person who begins working next week?

(A) $1.25

(B) $4.75

(C) $6.00

(D) $7.25

Alg1 17.0

51. For which function is the x-value always less than the corresponding y-value?

(A) $y = x^2$ (B) $y = -x^2$ (C) $y = x^2 - 1$ (D) $y = x^2 + 1$

Alg1 8.0

52. The equation of line m is $y + \frac{1}{2}x = -3$. The equation of line n is $3y - 5 = 6x + 16$. Which statement about the two lines is true?

(A) They are parallel.

(B) They are perpendicular.

(C) Their slopes are undefined.

(D) Their slopes are 0.

Mixed Review

GO for Help

Lesson 6-5

Graph each linear inequality.

53. $y > x - 5$ **54.** $y \leq -2x + 4$ **55.** $y > -3$

56. $y + x \leq 7$ **57.** $3y - x \geq 6$ **58.** $4y + 2x < 8$

Lesson 5-5

Find the slope of a line parallel to the graph of each equation.

59. $5x - 2y = 8$ **60.** $y - 17 = -3x$ **61.** $0.5y - 10 + 4x = 0$

Find the slope of a line perpendicular to the graph of each equation.

62. $y = 4x$ **63.** $y = 5x - 7$ **64.** $y = \frac{3}{8}x + 19$

65. $y = -\frac{9}{10}x - 3$ **66.** $6y + 13x = 22$ **67.** $-4x - 15y = 74$

Lesson 4-4

Write a function rule for each table.

68.

x	f(x)
1	7
2	14
3	21
4	28
5	35

69.

x	f(x)
1	7
2	8
3	9
4	10
5	11

70.

x	f(x)
−2	4
−1	1
0	0
1	1
2	4

Vocabulary Builder

Understanding Vocabulary

You have explored several algebraic methods for solving a system of two linear equations.

- substitution method
- elimination method

To understand and remember these methods, it may help you to connect the common meanings of the words with their specialized meanings in mathematics.

Word	Common Meaning	Mathematical Meaning
Substitute	To put or use in the place of another	To put an equivalent expression in place of a variable in another equation
Eliminate	To remove; to get rid of	To get rid of a variable by adding or subtracting equations

EXERCISES

Determine whether each situation is an example of *substitution* or *elimination*.

1. To evaluate $3n^2$ for $n = 5$, you replace n with 5.
2. The person with the least number of votes leaves the competition.
3. You know that the answer to a multiple-choice question is positive. You conclude that Choice D is not the correct answer because it is a negative number.
4. Another math teacher fills in for your teacher.
5. To determine whether the point (2, 3) is a solution of $y = -x + 4$, you check whether the statement $3 = -2 + 4$ is true.

Copy and complete the table below. Use a dictionary to look up the common meanings of words, if necesssary.

	Word	Common Meaning	Mathematical Meaning
6.	?	Free from influence	An independent variable is not affected by any other factors.
7.	Irrational	Lacking reason or understanding	?
8.	Dependent	?	A dependent variable depends on the value of the independent variable.
9.	Parallel	Comparable; having the same tendency	?
10.	Identity	?	?

Test-Taking Strategies

Finding Multiple Correct Answers

In questions with multiple correct answers, you have to determine the truth of a number of statements. As you test each statement, mark it as true or false. Then choose the option with all those that are true.

EXAMPLE

Which point or points are a solution of the system of inequalities? $y > x$
$y < 3x - 4$

I. $(1, 2)$ **II.** $(3, 4)$ **III.** $(3, 7)$

Ⓐ I only Ⓑ I and II Ⓒ I and III Ⓓ II only

Method 1 Graph the system of inequalities. Then plot each point. If the point is in the lavender region, it is a solution of the system. Only the point $(3, 4)$ is in the lavender region. The correct answer is D.

Method 2 Test whether each point satisfies both inequalities. The y-coordinate is greater than the x-coordinate for each point, so all the points satisfy the inequality $y > x$. Test each point in the second inequality.

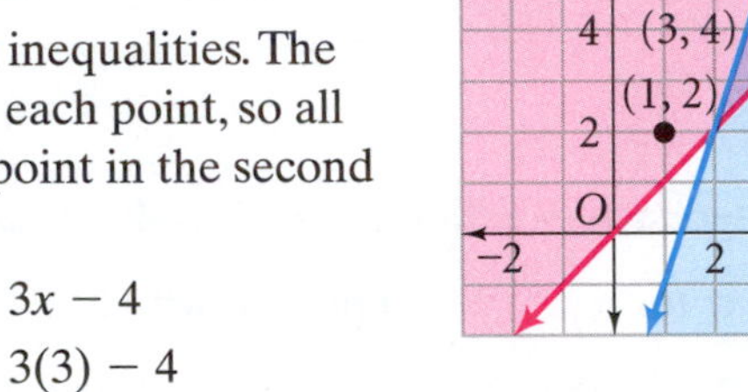

$y < 3x - 4$	$y < 3x - 4$	$y < 3x - 4$
$2 < 3(1) - 4$	$4 < 3(3) - 4$	$7 < 3(3) - 4$
$2 < -1$ ✗	$4 < 5$ ✓	$7 < 5$ ✗

The only point that makes both inequalities true is $(3, 4)$. The correct answer is D.

Multiple Choice Practice

1. Which point or points are a solution to the system of inequalities? $y > 4x - 2$
$x \leq \frac{1}{2}y$

I. $(0, 0)$ **II.** $(2, 3)$ **III.** $(-1, -4)$

Ⓐ I only Ⓑ II only Ⓒ III only Ⓓ I and III

2. Which system or systems of inequalities contain the point $(6, -2)$ as a solution?

I. $-4 \geq y - x$
$x \leq 5$

II. $y \leq \frac{1}{3}x - 1$
$y \geq -5x + 5$

III. $y - 1 < 5x$
$-2 \geq 3x - y$

Ⓐ I only Ⓑ I and II Ⓒ I, II, and III Ⓓ II only

3. Louis is selling lemonade for $.25 per cup. He bought the lemonade mix for $8.40 and the cups for $.05 each. Which statement(s) must be true?

I. His break-even point is 42 cups.
II. When he sells 20 cups, his income will be $13.40.
III. His income is greater than his expenses when he sells 20 cups.

Ⓐ I and II only Ⓑ I and III only Ⓒ I only Ⓓ III only

Chapter 6 Review

Vocabulary Review

English and Spanish Audio Online

elimination method (p. 287)
infinitely many solutions (p. 278)
linear inequality (p. 303)
no solution (p. 278)
solution of a system of linear equations (p. 276)
solution of a system of linear inequalities (p. 309)
solution set (p. 309)
solutions of an inequality (p. 303)
substitution method (p. 282)
system of linear equations (p. 276)
system of linear inequalities (p. 309)

Go Online PHSchool.com
For: Vocabulary quiz
Web Code: baj-0651

Choose the vocabulary term that correctly completes each sentence.

1. ___?___ is a method for solving a system of linear equations in which you multiply one or both equations by a nonzero number to get a variable term with coefficients that have a sum or difference of zero.

2. Any ordered pair that makes all equations in a system of equations true is a(n) ___?___.

3. A(n) ___?___ is formed by two or more linear inequalities.

4. Each point whose coordinates make an inequality true is a(n) ___?___.

5. ___?___ is a method for solving a system of linear equations in which at least one equation must first be solved for a single variable.

Skills and Concepts

Lesson 6-1

- To solve systems by graphing (p. 276)
- To analyze special types of systems (p. 278)

Alg1 9.0

Two or more linear equations form a **system of linear equations.** You can solve a system of linear equations by graphing. A point where all the lines intersect is a **solution of the system of linear equations.**

6. Which graph shows the solution of the following system? $y = x - 1$, $y = -x + 3$

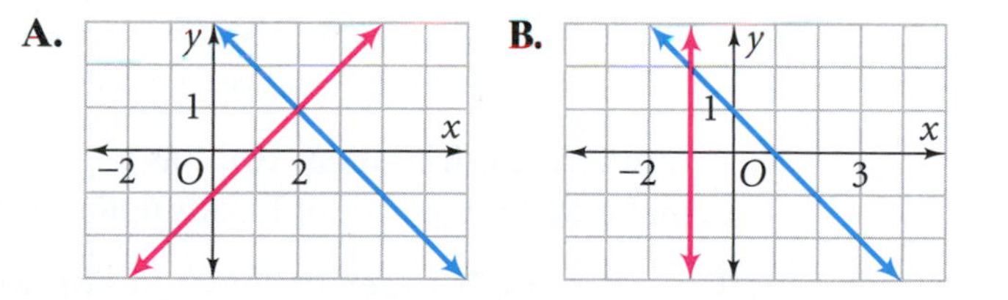

7. Is (2, 5) a solution of the following system? Explain. $y = 2x + 1$, $2x - y = 8$

8. How many solutions does the following system have? Explain. $y = -\frac{1}{2}x + 2$, $3x + 6y = 12$

9. Critical Thinking What kinds of systems would be hard to solve by graphing?

Solve each system by graphing.

10. $y = 3x - 1$
$y = -x + 3$

11. $x - y = -3$
$3x + y = -1$

12. $-x + 2y = -2$
$y = \frac{1}{2}x + 3$

Lesson 6-2

- To solve systems using substitution (p. 282)

Alg1 9.0

You can also solve a system of linear equations using the **substitution method.** By replacing one variable with an equivalent expression containing the other variable, you create a one-variable equation to solve.

Solve each system using substitution.

13. $y = 3x + 11$
$y = -2x + 1$

14. $4x - y = -12$
$-6x + 5y = -3$

15. $8x = -2y - 10$
$2x = 4y$

16. $y = 5x - 8$
$5y = 2x + 6$

17. Writing Explain how you determine if a system has no solution or infinitely many solutions when you solve a system using substitution.

18. There are 24 questions on a test. Each question is worth either 4 points or 5 points. The total is 100 points.

a. Write a system of equations to find the number of each type of question.
b. Solve the system by substitution.
c. How many questions of each type are on the test?

Lesson 6-3

- To solve systems by adding or subtracting (p. 287)
- To multiply first when solving systems (p. 288)

Alg1 9.0

You can solve a system of linear equations using the **elimination method.** You add or subtract the equations to eliminate one variable. You can multiply one or both of the equations by a nonzero number before adding or subtracting.

Solve each system using elimination. Check your solution.

19. $y = -3x + 5$
$y = -4x - 1$

20. $2x - 3y = 5$
$x + 2y = -1$

21. $x + y = 10$
$x - y = 2$

22. $x + 4y = 12$
$2x - 3y = 6$

23. A farmer raises chickens and cows. There are 34 animals in all. The farmer counts 110 legs on these animals. Write and solve a system of equations to find the number of each type of animal the farmer has.

Lesson 6-4

- To write systems of linear equations (p. 294)

Alg1 9.0, 15.0

You can use systems of linear equations to solve word problems. First, define variables. Then model the situation with a system of linear equations.

24. A furniture finish contains twice as much turpentine as linseed oil. If you plan to make 16 fluid ounces of furniture finish, how much turpentine do you need?

25. The difference between the measures of two complementary angles is 36°. Find both angle measures. (*Hint*: Two angles are complementary if the sum of their measures is 90°.)

26. The perimeter of a rectangle is 114 feet. Its length is three more than twice its width. Find the dimensions of the rectangle.

27. Marcella bought 3 packages of balloons and 4 packages of favors for $14.63. Rupert bought 2 packages of balloons and 5 packages of favors for $16.03. Find the price of a package of balloons.

28. An airplane flew for 6 hours with a 22-km/h tail wind. The return flight against the same wind took 8 hours. Find the speed of the plane in still air.

Lesson 6-5

- To graph linear inequalities (p. 302)
- To use linear inequalities when modeling real-world situations (p. 304)

Alg1 6.0

A **linear inequality** describes a region of the coordinate plane. The **solutions of the inequality** are the coordinates of the points that make the inequality true.

Graph each linear inequality.

29. $y < -3x + 8$ **30.** $y \geq 2x - 1$ **31.** $y \leq 0.5x + 6$ **32.** $y > -\frac{1}{4}x - 2$

Write the linear inequality shown in each graph.

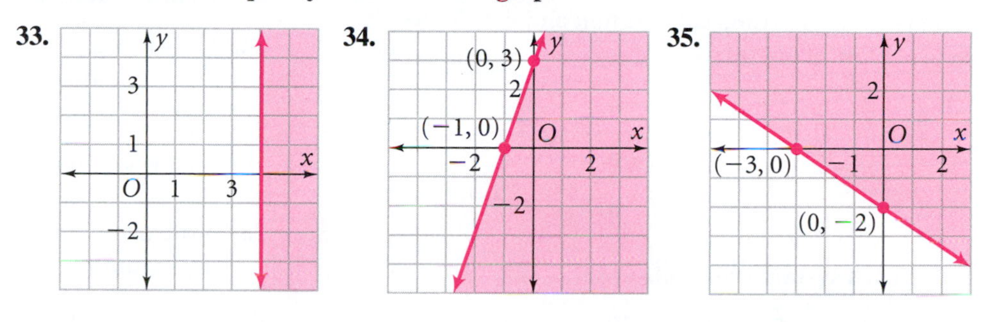

Lesson 6-6

- To solve systems of linear inequalities by graphing (p. 309)
- To model real-world situations using systems of linear inequalities (p. 311)

Two or more linear inequalities form a **system of linear inequalities.** To find the **solution set** of a system of linear inequalities, graph each linear inequality. The solution region is where all the inequalities are true.

Solve each system of linear inequalities by graphing.

36. $y \geq -4x + 1$, $y \leq \frac{5}{2}x - \frac{9}{2}$

37. $x - y < 10$, $x + y \leq 8$

38. $y \leq x - 3$, $y > x - 7$

39. $y < 5x$, $y \geq 0$

Write the system of inequalities shown in each graph.

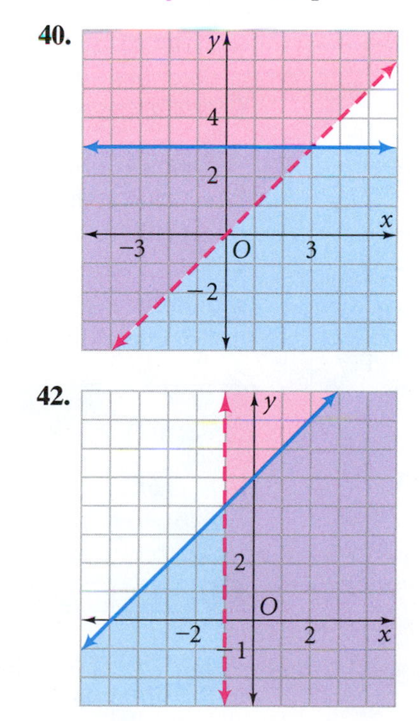

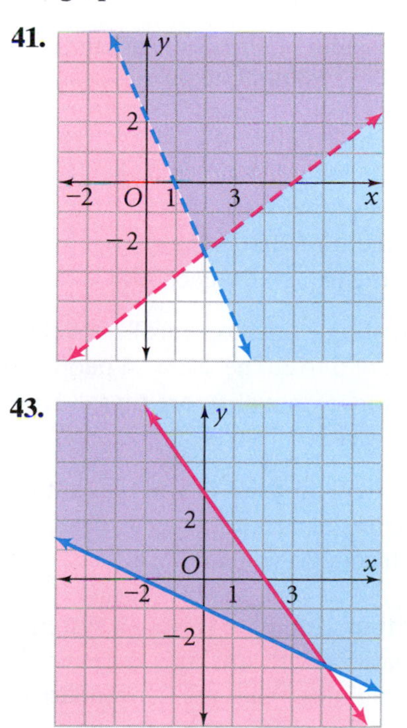

Chapter 6 Test

Go Online PHSchool.com For: Chapter Test Web Code: baa-0652

Solve each system by graphing.

1. $y = 3x - 7$
$y = -x + 1$

2. $4x + 3y = 12$
$2x - 5y = -20$

Critical Thinking **Suppose you try to solve systems of linear equations using substitution and get the results below. How many solutions does each system have?**

3. $x = 8$

4. $5 = y$

5. $-7 = 4$

6. $x = -1$

7. $2 = y$

8. $9 = 9$

Solve each system using substitution.

9. $y = 4x - 7$
$y = 2x + 9$

10. $y = -2x - 1$
$y = 3x - 16$

11. $8x + 2y = -2$
$y = -5x + 1$

12. $y + 6 = 2x$
$4x - 10y = 4$

Solve each system using elimination.

13. $4x + y = 8$
$-3x - y = 0$

14. $2x + 5y = 20$
$3x - 10y = 37$

15. $x + y = 10$
$-x - 2y = -14$

16. $3x + 2y = -19$
$x - 12y = 19$

Write a system of equations to model each situation. Solve by any method.

17. Your local cable company offers two plans: basic service with one movie channel for $35 per month or basic service with two movie channels for $45 per month. What is the charge for the basic service and the charge for each movie channel?

18. A writing workshop enrolls novelists and poets in a ratio of 5 to 3. There are 24 people at the workshop. How many novelists are there? How many poets are there?

19. You have 15 coins in your pocket that are either quarters or nickels. They total $2.75. How many of each coin do you have?

20. Writing Compare solving a system of linear equations with solving a system of linear inequalities. What are the similarities? What are the differences?

21. Which point is *not* a solution of $y < 3x - 1$?

Ⓐ $(2, -4)$ Ⓑ $(5, 7)$ Ⓒ $(0, -1)$ Ⓓ $(-2, -9)$

Solve each system by graphing.

22. $y > 4x - 1$
$y \leq -x + 4$

23. $y \geq 3x + 5$
$y > x - 2$

24. $x > -3$
$-3x + y \geq 6$

25. $2x - y \leq 2$
$y \geq 4$

26. Write a system of two linear equations. Solve by any method.

27. Leo held a garage sale. He priced all the items at a dime or a quarter. His sales totaled less than $5.

a. Write a linear inequality that describes the situation. Graph the linear inequality.

b. What is the maximum possible number of items that could have been sold for a dime?

c. What is the maximum possible number of items that could have been sold for a quarter?

28. Mrs. Paulson bought chicken wire to enclose a rectangular garden. She is restricted to a width of no more than 30 ft. She would like to use at most 180 ft of chicken wire.

a. Write a system of linear inequalities that describes this situation.

b. Graph the system to show all possible solutions.

29. A chemist needs to mix a solution containing 30% insecticide with a solution containing 50% insecticide to make 200 L of a solution that is 42% insecticide. How much of each solution should she use?

a. Complete the table below.

	30% Insecticide	50% Insecticide	42% Insecticide
Liters of Solution	■	■	■
Liters of Insecticide	■	■	■

b. Write a system of equations that describes the situation. Solve the system.

Standards Mastery

Cumulative Practice

Some questions ask you to find the solution to a system of linear equations. Read the question at the right. Then follow the tips to answer the sample question.

A system of linear equations is shown below.

$$10x + \frac{3}{2}y = 10$$
$$-\frac{5}{2}y + 10x = -30$$

Which ordered pair is the solution of the system?

(A) $(10, -60)$ (B) $(10, -\frac{1}{2})$ (C) $(-\frac{1}{2}, 10)$ (D) $(-32, 10)$

Tip 1
Look at the form in which the equations are written to determine which method to use in solving the system.

Tip 2
Test the choices by substituting for x and y in the equations. The solution will make each equation true.

Think It Through

Since the coefficient of x in both equations is 10, subtract the equations to eliminate x. Then $4y = 40$ and $y = 10$. When you substitute 10 for y in either equation, x is $-\frac{1}{2}$. The answer is C.

Vocabulary Review

As you solve problems, you must understand the meanings of mathematical terms. Match each term with its mathematical meaning.

A. consecutive integers
B. y-intercept
C. system of linear equations
D. linear inequality

I. describes a region of the coordinate plane that has a boundary line
II. a point where a graph crosses the y-axis
III. two or more linear equations
IV. integers that differ by 1

Read each question. Then write the letter of the correct answer on your paper.

1. Which equation describes a line with a slope of 2 that passes through point P on the graph? **(Lesson 5-4)**

(A) $y = 2x - \frac{1}{2}$
(B) $y = 2x + \frac{1}{2}$
(C) $y = 2x + 1$
(D) $y = 2x + 4$

2. Which equation describes a line with a slope of 12 and y-intercept of 4? **(Lesson 5-2)**

(A) $y = 12x + 4$ (B) $y = 12(x + 4)$ (C) $y = 4x + 12$ (D) $y = x + 3$

3. Which linear function includes the points $(2, -6)$ and $(-3, 4)$? **(Lesson 5-4)**

(A) $y = \frac{1}{2}x - 7$ (B) $y = 2x - 10$ (C) $y = -\frac{1}{2}x - 5$ (D) $y = -2x - 2$

4. Which step below can be justified by the Associative Property of Addition? **(Lesson 2-2)**

Step 1: $\frac{1}{2}(3 - x) + 10x = -9$
Step 2: $(3 - x) + 20x = -18$
Step 3: $3 + (-x + 20x) = -18$
Step 4: $3 + 19x = -18$
Step 5: $19x = -21$
Step 6: $x = -\frac{21}{19}$

(A) Step 2 (B) Step 3 (C) Step 4 (D) Step 5

5. Carroll took three fourths of a number, multiplied by 2, subtracted 7, and then added the original number. The result was 13. What was the original number? **(Lesson 2-5)**

(A) -16 (B) 8 (C) 9 (D) 50

6. Greg's school paid \$1012.50 for 135 T-shirts. How much would it cost the school to purchase 235 T-shirts? **(Lesson 2-4)**

Ⓐ \$750.00 Ⓒ \$2025.00

Ⓑ \$1762.50 Ⓓ \$2775.00

7. Rhonda has 25 coins in her pocket. All of the coins are either dimes or nickels. If Rhonda has a total of \$2.30, which system can be used to find the number of dimes d and the number of nickels n she has? **(Lesson 6-4)**

Ⓐ $d + n = 2.30$, $5d + 10n = 25$

Ⓒ $d + n = 25$, $0.1d + 0.05n = 2.30$

Ⓑ $d + n = 25$, $0.05d + 0.1n = 2.30$

Ⓓ $d + n = 2.30$, $0.05d + 0.1n = 25$

8. Which system of equations can be used to find the number of toppings t Sam needs to order for the cost of a large pizza c to be the same at either restaurant in the ad below? **(Lesson 6-4)**

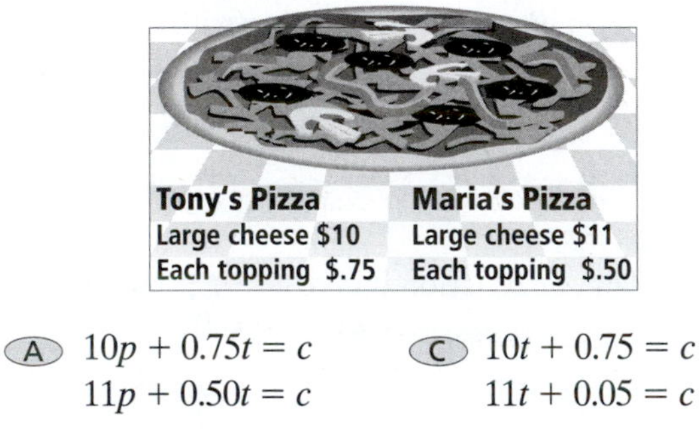

Ⓐ $10p + 0.75t = c$, $11p + 0.50t = c$

Ⓒ $10t + 0.75 = c$, $11t + 0.05 = c$

Ⓑ $10 + 0.75t = c$, $11 + 0.50t = c$

Ⓓ $10t + 11p = c$, $0.75t + 0.50p = c$

9. A group of students is going on a field trip. If the students take 3 vans and 1 car, they can transport 22 people. If they take 2 vans and 4 cars, they can transport 28 people. Which system of equations can be used to find c, the number of people that can fit in each car, and v, the number of people that can fit in each van? **(Lesson 6-4)**

Ⓐ $3v = 22$, $2v + 4c = 28$

Ⓒ $3v + 2c = 22$, $v + 4c = 28$

Ⓑ $3v + c = 22$, $2v + 4c = 28$

Ⓓ $v + 4c = 22$, $3v + 2c = 28$

10. Kris buys 1 pound of a mix of walnuts and dried fruit for \$4.04. Walnuts are \$4.80 per pound and dried fruit is \$2.90 per pound. How much dried fruit was in the mixture? **(Lesson 2-6)**

Ⓐ 0.4 lb Ⓑ 0.5 lb Ⓒ 0.6 lb Ⓓ 0.7 lb

11. Which graph represents the solution to this system of inequalities? **(Lesson 6-6)**

$x \geq -3y + 3$

$4x + 3y \leq -6$

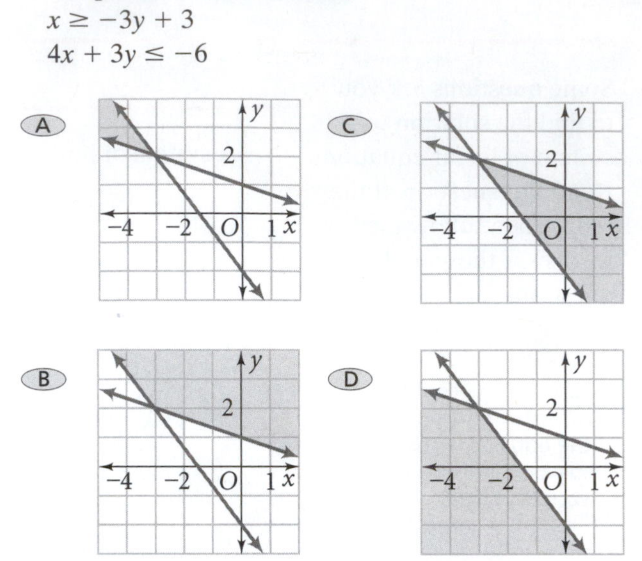

12. If a, b, and c are three consecutive positive integers, which of the following is true? **(Lesson 2-5)**

I. $a + c < 2b$ **III.** $a + c > 2b$

II. $a + b < c$ **IV.** $b + c > a$

Ⓐ I only Ⓒ IV only

Ⓑ I and II Ⓓ III and IV

13. Rob and Kenji are running a half-marathon (about 13.1 miles). Groups of runners start at different times. Rob starts first and runs at a pace of 4 miles per half hour. Kenji starts 3 minutes later and runs at a pace of 4.3 miles per half hour. After how many minutes will Kenji catch up to Rob? **(Lesson 2-5)**

Ⓐ 40 Ⓑ 43 Ⓒ 60 Ⓓ 63

14. A school band sells fruit to raise money. One student collected \$226.74 for 6 boxes of grapefruit and 5 boxes of oranges. Another student collected \$254.52 for 4 boxes of grapefruit and 9 boxes of oranges. How much do one box of grapefruit and one box of oranges cost together? **(Lesson 6-4)**

Ⓐ \$40.83 Ⓒ \$38.77

Ⓑ \$41.25 Ⓓ \$43.76

15. Which point can be used as a counterexample to the following statement? **(Lesson 5-2)**

If $x > 7$, then the point is on the line $4x + y = 81$.

Ⓐ (1, 77) Ⓒ (8, 49)

Ⓑ (9, 46) Ⓓ (10, 41)

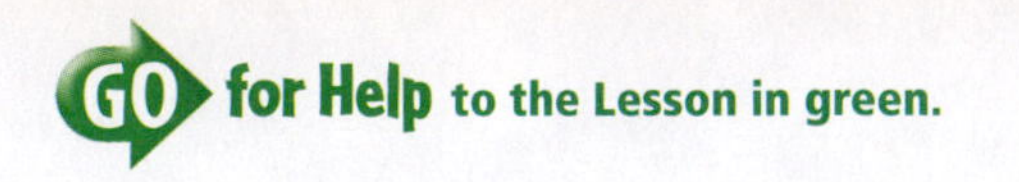

Standards Mastery

16. Which of the following points are solutions of the equation $4x + 5y = 30$? **(Lesson 5-2)**

I. $(5, 2)$ **II.** $(-5, 10)$ **III.** $(4, 7)$

Ⓐ II and III
Ⓑ I and III
Ⓒ I and II
Ⓓ III only

17. Eva is thinking of three consecutive integers. The sum of the first plus twice the second plus one half of the third is 52. What is the middle number? **(Lesson 2-5)**

Ⓐ 13
Ⓑ 14
Ⓒ 15
Ⓓ 16

18. A chemist makes 100 L of a 76%-acid solution using a 52%-acid solution and an 82%-acid solution. How many liters of 52%-acid solution does the chemist use? **(Lesson 2-6)**

Ⓐ 80 L
Ⓑ 50 L
Ⓒ 40 L
Ⓓ 20 L

19. Which ordered pair is the solution of the system $7y - 4x = 29$ and $x = y - 5$? **(Lesson 6-2)**

Ⓐ $(3, 8)$
Ⓑ $(-2, 3)$
Ⓒ $(11, 16)$
Ⓓ $(-2, -7)$

20. On a map, the town in which a museum is located is 3.45 inches away from your town. The map's scale is 0.5 inch : 10 miles. About how many miles away is the museum? **(Lesson 2-4)**

Ⓐ 2 mi
Ⓑ 35 mi
Ⓒ 69 mi
Ⓓ 350 mi

21. Which relation is a function? **(Lesson 4-2)**

Ⓐ $\{(-1, 2\frac{1}{3}), (0, 3), (1, 3\frac{1}{3}), (2, 3\frac{2}{3})\}$
Ⓑ $\{(-2, 4), (-1, 5), (-2, 6), (0, 2)\}$
Ⓒ $\{(5, -1), (5, 0), (5, 1), (5, 2)\}$
Ⓓ $\{(3, 2), (-1, 4), (2, 1), (3, 1)\}$

22. Which ordered pair could you add to the set below and have the relation still be a function?
$\{(2, 12), (7, 8), (-3, -1), (5, 8)\}$ **(Lesson 4-2)**

Ⓐ $(2, -3)$
Ⓑ $(7, 0)$
Ⓒ $(4, -1)$
Ⓓ $(-3, 1)$

23. To solve this system of equations by using substitution, what substitution would you perform? **(Lesson 6-2)**

$4x + y = 9$
$x - 9y = 22$

Ⓐ $9 + 4x$ for y
Ⓑ $22 - 9y$ for x
Ⓒ $9 - 4x$ for y
Ⓓ $22 - x$ for y

24. Which point can be used as a counterexample to the following statement? **(Lesson 6-6)**

If $x < 1$, then the point is a solution of the system of inequalities $-x + 2y > 5$ and $x + y \leq 4$.

Ⓐ $(-3, 4)$
Ⓑ $(-2, 1)$
Ⓒ $(-1, 2.5)$
Ⓓ $(0, 3)$

25. The sum of three consecutive even integers is 84. What is the smallest integer? **(Lesson 2-5)**

Ⓐ 12 Ⓑ 24 Ⓒ 26 Ⓓ 30

Standards Reference Guide

California Content Standard	Item Number(s)
Alg1 5.0	5, 6, 17, 20, 25
Alg1 7.0	1–3, 16
Alg1 9.0	7–9, 11, 14, 19, 23
Alg1 15.0	10, 13, 18
Alg1 16.0	21, 22
Alg1 24.3	15
Alg1 25.1	4, 24
Alg1 25.3	12

For additional review and practice, see the *California Standards Review and Practice Workbook* or go online to use the

Visit: PHSchool.com, **Web Code:** baq-9045

Exponents

What You've Learned

California Content Standards

1.0 Identify and use the arithmetic properties of subsets of integers and rational, irrational, and real numbers for the four basic arithmetic operations.

2.0 Understand and use such operations as taking the opposite and finding the reciprocal.

4.0 Simplify expressions before solving linear equations and inequalities in one variable.

Check Your Readiness

GO for Help to the Lesson in green.

Converting Fractions to Decimals (Skills Handbook page 599)

Write as a decimal.

1. $\frac{7}{10}$ **2.** $6\frac{2}{5}$ **3.** $\frac{8}{1000}$ **4.** $\frac{7}{2}$ **5.** $\frac{3}{11}$

Using the Order of Operations (Lesson 1-2)

Simplify each expression.

6. $(9 \div 3 + 4)^2$ **7.** $5 + (0.3)^3$ **8.** $3 - (1.5)^2$ **9.** $64 \div 2^4$

Evaluating Expressions (Lessons 1-4 to 1-6)

Evaluate each expression for $a = -2$ and $b = 5$.

10. $(ab)^2$ **11.** $(a - b)^2$ **12.** $a^3 + b^2$ **13.** $b - (3a)^2$

Simplifying Algebraic Expressions (Lesson 1-7)

Simplify each expression.

14. $3(3b + 4)$ **15.** $\frac{1}{2}\left(1 - \frac{3}{8}h\right)$ **16.** $3x^2 + 12x^2$ **17.** $rst - t^2 - 11rst$

Identifying Properties (Lesson 1-8)

Name the property that each equation illustrates.

18. $5^2 \cdot 1 = 5^2$ **19.** $3^4 \cdot \frac{1}{3^4} = 1$ **20.** $2^6(8 - 1) = 2^6(8) - 2^6(1)$

Evaluating a Function Rule (Lesson 4-3)

Find the range of each function with domain {−2, 0, 3.5}.

21. $f(x) = -2x^2$ **22.** $g(x) = 10 - x^3$ **23.** $y = 5x - 1$

▲ Dust particles are usually less than 2×10^{-6} meter in size and can travel thousands of kilometers on strong winds.

What You'll Learn Next

California Content Standards

2.0 Understand and use the rules of exponents.

10.0 Multiply and divide monomials. Solve multi-step problems, including word problems, by using these techniques.

New Vocabulary

English and Spanish Audio Online

- **scientific notation** (p. 334)

7-1 Zero and Negative Exponents

California Content Standards

2.0 Understand and use the rules of exponents. ***Develop***

What You'll Learn

- To simplify expressions with zero and negative exponents
- To evaluate exponential expressions

. . . And Why

To find the size of a population, as in Example 4

Check Skills You'll Need

GO for Help Lessons 1-2 and 1-6

Simplify each expression.

1. 2^3 **2.** $\frac{1}{4^2}$ **3.** $4^2 \div 2^2$

4. $(-3)^3$ **5.** -3^3 **6.** $6^2 \div 12$

Evaluate each expression for $a = 2$, $b = -1$, and $c = 0.5$.

7. $\frac{a}{2a}$ **8.** $\frac{bc}{c}$ **9.** $\frac{ab}{bc}$

Zero and Negative Exponents

CA Standards Investigation Exponents

1. a. Copy the table below. Replace each blank with the value of the power in simplest form.

2^x	5^x	10^x
$2^4 = \blacksquare$	$5^4 = \blacksquare$	$10^4 = \blacksquare$
$2^3 = \blacksquare$	$5^3 = \blacksquare$	$10^3 = \blacksquare$
$2^2 = \blacksquare$	$5^2 = \blacksquare$	$10^2 = \blacksquare$

b. Look at the values that you used to replace the blanks. What pattern do you see as you go down each column?

2. Copy the table below. Use the pattern you described in Question 1 to complete the table.

2^x	5^x	10^x
$2^1 = \blacksquare$	$5^1 = \blacksquare$	$10^1 = \blacksquare$
$2^0 = \blacksquare$	$5^0 = \blacksquare$	$10^0 = \blacksquare$
$2^{-1} = \blacksquare$	$5^{-1} = \blacksquare$	$10^{-1} = \blacksquare$
$2^{-2} = \blacksquare$	$5^{-2} = \blacksquare$	$10^{-2} = \blacksquare$

3. Critical Thinking What pattern do you notice in the row with 0 as an exponent?

4. Copy and complete each expression.

a. $2^{-1} = \frac{1}{2^{\blacksquare}}$ **b.** $2^{-2} = \frac{1}{2^{\blacksquare}}$ **c.** $2^{-3} = \frac{1}{2^{\blacksquare}}$

Consider 3^3, 3^2, and 3^1. Decreasing the exponent by one is the same as dividing by 3. Continuing the pattern, 3^0 equals 1 and 3^{-1} equals $\frac{1}{3}$.

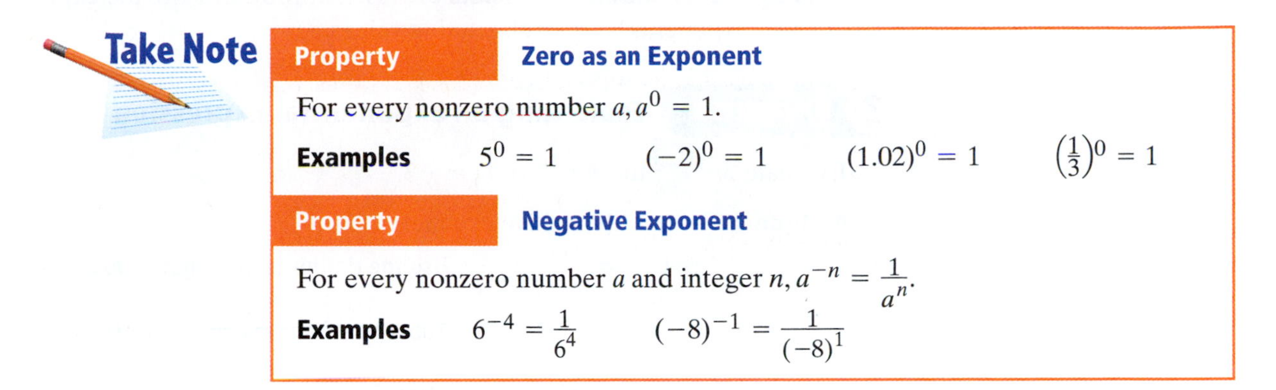

Take Note

Property **Zero as an Exponent**

For every nonzero number a, $a^0 = 1$.

Examples $5^0 = 1$ $\quad (-2)^0 = 1$ $\quad (1.02)^0 = 1$ $\quad \left(\frac{1}{3}\right)^0 = 1$

Property **Negative Exponent**

For every nonzero number a and integer n, $a^{-n} = \frac{1}{a^n}$.

Examples $6^{-4} = \frac{1}{6^4}$ $\quad (-8)^{-1} = \frac{1}{(-8)^1}$

Why can't you use 0 as a base? By the first property, $3^0 = 1$, $2^0 = 1$, and $1^0 = 1$, which implies $0^0 = 1$. However, the pattern $0^3 = 0$, $0^2 = 0$, and $0^1 = 0$ implies $0^0 = 0$. Since both 1 and 0 cannot be the answer, 0^0 is undefined. In the second property, using 0 as a base results in division by zero, which you know is undefined.

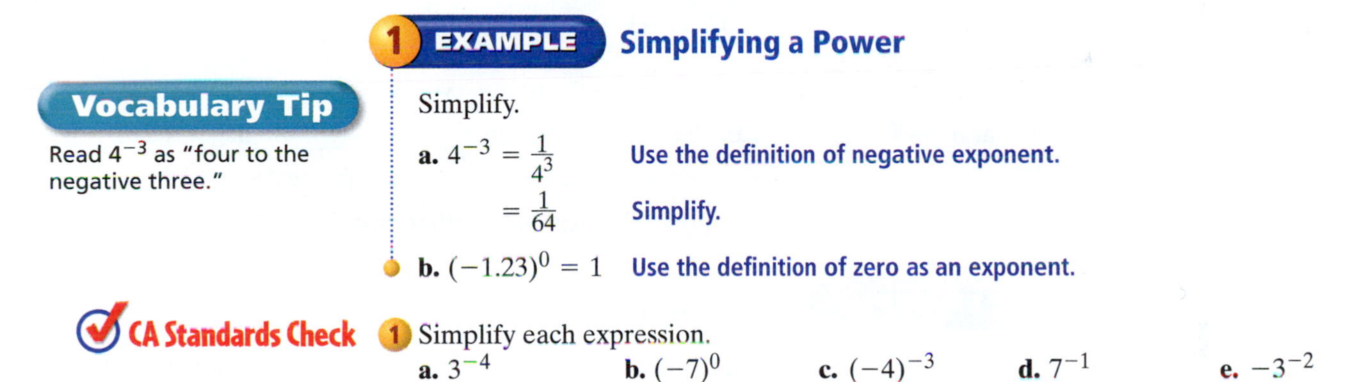

1 EXAMPLE Simplifying a Power

Vocabulary Tip

Read 4^{-3} as "four to the negative three."

Simplify.

a. $4^{-3} = \frac{1}{4^3}$ Use the definition of negative exponent.

$= \frac{1}{64}$ Simplify.

b. $(-1.23)^0 = 1$ Use the definition of zero as an exponent.

CA Standards Check

1 Simplify each expression.

a. 3^{-4} **b.** $(-7)^0$ **c.** $(-4)^{-3}$ **d.** 7^{-1} **e.** -3^{-2}

An algebraic expression is in simplest form when it is written with only positive exponents. If the expression is a fraction in simplest form, the only common factor of the numerator and denominator is 1.

2 EXAMPLE Simplifying an Exponential Expression

Simplify each expression.

a. $4yx^{-3} = 4y\left(\frac{1}{x^3}\right)$ Use the definition of negative exponent.

$= \frac{4y}{x^3}$ Simplify.

b. $\frac{1}{w^{-4}} = 1 \div w^{-4}$ Rewrite using a division symbol.

$= 1 \div \frac{1}{w^4}$ Use the definition of negative exponent.

$= 1 \cdot w^4$ Multiply by the reciprocal of $\frac{1}{w^4}$, which is w^4.

$= w^4$ Identity Property of Multiplication

CA Standards Check

2 Simplify each expression.

a. $11m^{-5}$ **b.** $7s^{-4}t^2$ **c.** $\frac{2}{a^{-3}}$ **d.** $\frac{n^{-5}}{v^2}$

Evaluating Exponential Expressions

When you evaluate an exponential expression, you can write the expression with positive exponents before substituting values.

3 EXAMPLE Evaluating an Exponential Expression

Evaluate $3m^2t^{-2}$ for $m = 2$ and $t = -3$.

Method 1 Write with positive exponents first.

$3m^2t^{-2} = \frac{3m^2}{t^2}$ **Use the definition of negative exponent.**

$= \frac{3(2)^2}{(-3)^2}$ **Substitute 2 for m and -3 for t.**

$= \frac{12}{9} = 1\frac{1}{3}$ **Simplify.**

Method 2 Substitute first.

$3m^2t^{-2} = 3(2)^2(-3)^{-2}$ **Substitute 2 for m and -3 for t.**

$= \frac{3(2)^2}{(-3)^2}$ **Use the definition of negative exponent.**

$= \frac{12}{9} = 1\frac{1}{3}$ **Simplify.**

CA Standards Check 3 Evaluate each expression for $n = -2$ and $w = 5$.

a. $n^{-3}w^0$ **b.** $\frac{n^{-1}}{w^2}$ **c.** $\frac{w^0}{n^4}$ **d.** $\frac{1}{nw^{-2}}$

You can also evaluate exponential expressions that model real-world situations.

4 EXAMPLE Application

During the months of June and July, green peach aphids in a field of potato plants can double in population every three days.

A biologist is studying green peach aphids, like the one shown at the left. In the lab, the population doubles every week. The expression $1000 \cdot 2^w$ models an initial population of 1000 insects after w weeks of growth.

a. Evaluate the expression for $w = 0$. Then describe what the value of the expression represents in the situation.

$1000 \cdot 2^w = 1000 \cdot 2^0$ **Substitute 0 for w.**

$= 1000 \cdot 1$ **Simplify.**

$= 1000$

The value of the expression represents the initial population of insects. This makes sense because when $w = 0$, no time has passed.

b. Evaluate the expression for $w = -3$. Then describe what the value of the expression represents in the situation.

$1000 \cdot 2^w = 1000 \cdot 2^{-3}$ **Substitute -3 for w.**

$= 1000 \cdot \frac{1}{8}$ **Simplify.**

$= 125$

There were 125 aphids 3 weeks before the present population of 1000 insects.

CA Standards Check 4 A sample of bacteria triples each month. The expression $5400 \cdot 3^m$ models a population of 5400 bacteria after m months of growth. Evaluate the expression for $m = -2$ and $m = 0$. Describe what each value of the expression represents.

EXERCISES
Standards Practice

For more exercises, see *Extra Skills and Word Problem Practice.*

Alg1 2.0

A Practice by Example

Example 1 (page 329)

GO for Help

Simplify each expression.

1. $-(2.57)^0$
2. 4^{-2}
3. $(-5)^{-2}$
4. -5^{-2}
5. $(-4)^{-2}$
6. -3^{-4}
7. 2^{-6}
8. -12^{-1}
9. $\frac{1}{2^0}$
10. 78^{-1}
11. $(-4)^{-3}$
12. -4^{-3}

Example 2 (page 329)

Copy and complete each equation.

13. $4n^{\blacksquare} = \frac{4}{n^2}$
14. $\frac{x^{\blacksquare}}{2y^{\blacksquare}} = \frac{1}{2x^{-3}y^4}$
15. $\frac{a^{\blacksquare}}{3b^{\blacksquare}} = \frac{b^3}{3}$
16. $3xy^{\blacksquare} = \frac{3x}{y^5}$

Simplify each expression.

17. $3ab^0$
18. $5x^{-4}$
19. $\frac{1}{x^{-7}}$
20. $\frac{1}{c^{-1}}$
21. $\frac{5^{-2}}{p}$
22. $a^{-4}c^0$
23. $\frac{3x^{-2}}{y}$
24. $\frac{7ab^{-2}}{3w}$
25. $x^{-5}y^{-7}$
26. $x^{-5}y^7$
27. $\frac{8}{2c^{-3}}$
28. $\frac{7s}{5t^{-3}}$
29. $\frac{6a^{-1}c^{-3}}{d^0}$
30. $2^{-3}x^2z^{-7}$
31. $9^0y^7t^{-11}$
32. $\frac{7s^0t^{-5}}{2^{-1}m^2}$

Example 3 (page 330)

Evaluate each expression for $r = -3$ and $s = 5$.

33. s^{-2}
34. r^{-2}
35. $-r^{-2}$
36. s^0
37. $3s^{-2}$
38. $(2s)^{-2}$
39. $r^{-4}s^2$
40. $\frac{1}{r^{-4}s^2}$
41. s^2r^{-3}
42. r^0s^{-2}
43. $5r^3s^{-1}$
44. $2^{-4}r^3s^{-2}$

Example 4 (page 330)

45. Suppose your allowance doubles every week. This week you receive \$2.56. How much will your allowance be three weeks from now? How much was your allowance three weeks ago?

B Apply Your Skills

Mental Math **Is the value of each expression *positive* or *negative*?**

46. -2^2
47. $(-2)^2$
48. 2^{-2}
49. $(-2)^3$
50. $(-2)^{-3}$

Write each number as a power of 10 using negative exponents.

51. $\frac{1}{10}$
52. $\frac{1}{100}$
53. $\frac{1}{1000}$
54. $\frac{1}{10{,}000}$
55. $\frac{1}{100{,}000}$

Write each expression as a decimal.

56. 10^{-3}
57. 10^{-6}
58. $7 \cdot 10^{-1}$
59. $3 \cdot 10^{-2}$
60. $5 \cdot 10^{-4}$

61. a. Complete the pattern using powers of 5.
   $\frac{1}{5^2} = \blacksquare$ $\quad \frac{1}{5^1} = \blacksquare$ $\quad \frac{1}{5^0} = \blacksquare$ $\quad \frac{1}{5^{-1}} = \blacksquare$ $\quad \frac{1}{5^{-2}} = \blacksquare$
   b. Write $\frac{1}{5^{-4}}$ using a positive exponent.
   c. Rewrite $\frac{1}{a^{-n}}$ so that the power of a is in the numerator.

62. Which expression is equivalent to $\frac{3x^{-2}y^3}{9x^3y^{-5}}$?
   (A) $\frac{3x^{-5}}{y^8}$ (B) $\frac{xy^2}{3}$ (C) $3xy^2$ (D) $\frac{y^8}{3x^5}$

Visit: PHSchool.com
Web Code: bae-0701

Simplify each expression.

63. $45 \cdot (0.5)^0$ **64.** $54 \cdot 3^{-2}$ **65.** $\frac{5^{-2}}{10^{-3}}$ **66.** $\frac{4^{-1}}{9^0}$ **67.** $\frac{(-3)^{-4}}{-3}$

Evaluate each expression for $a = 3, b = 2$, and $c = -4$.

68. c^b **69.** $a^{-b}b$ **70.** b^{-a} **71.** b^c **72.** $c^{-a}b^{ab}$

73. Copy and complete the table below.

a	4	■	■	$\frac{7}{8}$	■
a^{-1}	■	3	$\frac{1}{6}$	■	0.5

74. a. Critical Thinking Simplify $a^n \cdot a^{-n}$.
b. What is the mathematical relationship of a^n and a^{-n}? Justify your answer.

75. Which expressions equal $\frac{1}{4}$?
A. 4^{-1} **B.** 2^{-2} **C.** -4^1 **D.** $\frac{1}{2^2}$ **E.** 1^4 **F.** -2^{-2}

76. Choose a fraction to use as a value for the variable a. Find the values of a^{-1}, a^2, and a^{-2}.

77. Critical Thinking Are $3x^{-2}$ and $3x^2$ reciprocals? Explain.

78. Writing Explain why the value of -3^0 is negative but the value of $(-3)^0$ is positive.

Error Analysis **Two students simplified the expressions as shown below. Find the error in each of their work and simplify each expression.**

79. **80.**

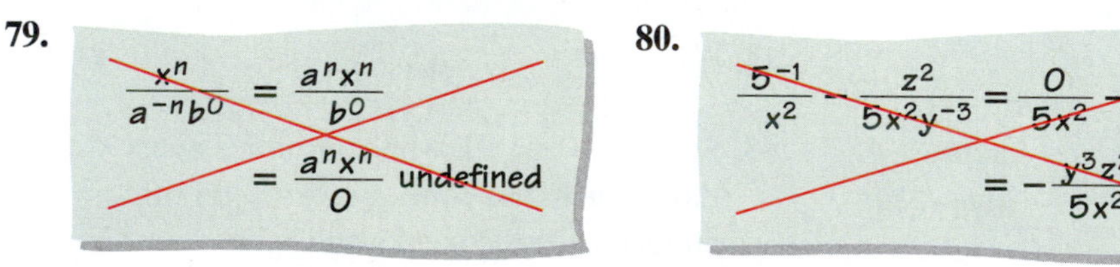

81. Suppose you are the only person in your class who knows a certain story. After a minute you tell a classmate. Every minute after that, every student who knows the story tells another student (sometimes the person being told already will have heard it). In a class of 30 students, the expression $\frac{30}{1 + 29 \cdot 2^{-t}}$ predicts the approximate number of people who will have heard the story after t minutes. About how many students will have heard your story after 2 min? After 5 min? After 10 min?

Simplify each expression.

82. $2^3(5^0 - 6m^2)$ **83.** $(-5)^2 - (0.5)^{-2}$ **84.** $\frac{6}{m^2} + \frac{5m^{-2}}{3^{-3}}$

85. $(0.8)^{-3} + 19^0 - 2^{-6}$ **86.** $\frac{2r^{-5}y^5}{n^2} \div \frac{y^5}{2n}$ **87.** $2^{-1} - \frac{1}{3^{-2}} + 5\left(\frac{1}{2^2}\right)$

88. For what values of n is $n^{-3} = \left(\frac{1}{n}\right)^5$?

89. Simplify the expression $\frac{3^{-2}q^2}{p^0q^2}$.

Multiple Choice Practice

For California Standards Tutorials, visit PHSchool.com. Web Code: baq-9045

Alg1 2.0

90. Elisa is plotting points on the graph of $f(x) = \frac{1}{2x^{-3}}$. What is the value of $f(x)$ when $x = 2$?

(A) $\frac{1}{16}$ (B) $\frac{1}{4}$ (C) 4 (D) 16

Alg1 24.0

91. Charlie made a stack of cans that is 4 cans high, as shown at the right. If Eli makes a similar stack that is 6 cans high, how many cans will be in Eli's stack?

(A) 36
(B) 61
(C) 91
(D) 729

Alg1 6.0

92. Which graph represents the line $y = x$?

(A) (B) (C) (D)

Alg1 24.3

93. What value for x can you use to show that $x^{-2} \leq x^2$ is NOT always true?

(A) -2 (B) $-\frac{1}{2}$ (C) 1 (D) 2

Alg1 8.0

94. Which equation represents a line that is perpendicular to the line $y = x$ and has a y-intercept of 3?

(A) $y = x - 3$ (B) $y = x + 3$ (C) $y = -x - 3$ (D) $y = -x + 3$

Mixed Review

Lesson 6-6

Solve each system by graphing.

95. $y > 3x + 4$, $y \leq -3x + 1$

96. $y \leq -2x + 1$, $y < 2x - 1$

97. $y \geq 0.5x$, $y \leq x + 2$

98. $y < -3x$, $y \leq x - 6$

99. $y - 1 > x$, $-2 < x$

100. $\frac{2}{3}y + \frac{8}{3} \geq x$, $y < -\frac{2}{3}x - 4$

GO for Help

Lesson 5-5

Write an equation for the line that passes through the given point and is parallel to the given line.

101. $y = 5x + 1; (0, 0)$

102. $y = 3x - 2; (0, 1)$

103. $y = -2x + 5; (4, 0)$

104. $y = 0.4x + 5; (2, -3)$

Lesson 5-2

Write an equation of the line with the given slope and y-intercept.

105. $m = -1, b = 4$

106. $m = 5, b = -2$

107. $m = \frac{2}{5}, b = -3$

108. $m = -\frac{3}{11}, b = -17$

109. $m = \frac{5}{9}, b = \frac{1}{3}$

110. $m = 1.25, b = -3.79$

7-2 Scientific Notation

California Content Standards

2.0 Understand and use the rules of exponents. ***Develop***

What You'll Learn

- To write numbers in scientific and standard notation
- To use scientific notation

. . . And Why

To order planets based on their masses, as in Example 4

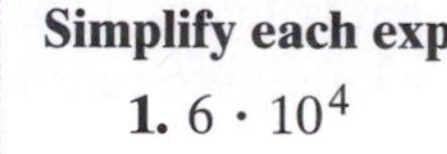

Check Skills You'll Need

GO for Help Lesson 7-1

Simplify each expression.

1. $6 \cdot 10^4$ **2.** $7 \cdot 10^{-2}$ **3.** $8.2 \cdot 10^5$

4. $3 \cdot 10^{-3}$ **5.** $3.4 \cdot 10^1$ **6.** $5.24 \cdot 10^2$

7. Simplify $3 \times 10^2 + 6 \times 10^1 + 7 \times 10^0 + 8 \times 10^{-1}$.

New Vocabulary • scientific notation

Writing Numbers in Scientific and Standard Notation

The planet Jupiter has an average radius of 69,111 km. What is Jupiter's volume?

Since Jupiter is a sphere, to answer this question you use the formula for the volume of a sphere.

$V = \frac{4}{3}\pi r^3$

$= \frac{4}{3}\pi(69{,}111)^3$ **Substitute 69,111 for *r*.**

$\approx 1{,}382{,}706{,}933{,}000{,}000$ **Simplify.**

The number 1,382,706,933,000,000 is written in standard notation. In scientific notation, you write the number as $1.382706933 \times 10^{15}$. Scientific notation is a shorthand way to write very large or very small numbers.

Take Note

Definition **Scientific Notation**

A number in **scientific notation** is written as the product of two factors in the form $a \times 10^n$, where n is an integer and $1 \le a < 10$.

Examples 3.4×10^6 5.43×10^{13} 2.1×10^{-10}

1 EXAMPLE Recognizing Scientific Notation

Is each number written in scientific notation? If not, explain.

a. 56.29×10^{12} No; 56.29 is greater than 10.

b. 0.84×10^{-3} No; 0.84 is less than 1.

c. 6.11×10^5 yes

CA Standards Check **1** Is each number written in scientific notation? If not, explain.

a. 3.42×10^{-7} **b.** 52×10^4 **c.** 0.04×10^{-5}

In scientific notation, you use positive exponents to write a number greater than 1. You use negative exponents to write a number between 0 and 1.

2 EXAMPLE Writing a Number in Scientific Notation

Write each number in scientific notation.

a. 56,900,000

56,900,000. $= 5.69 \times 10^7$ Move the decimal point 7 places to the left and use 7 as an exponent. Drop the zeros after the 9.

b. 0.00985

$0.00985 = 9.85 \times 10^{-3}$ Move the decimal point 3 places to the right and use −3 as an exponent. Drop the zeros before the 9.

CA Standards Check 2 Write each number in scientific notation.

a. 267,000 **b.** 46,205,000 **c.** 0.0000325 **d.** 0.000000009

e. Critical Thinking You express 1 billion as 10^9. Explain why you express 436 billion as 4.36×10^{11} in scientific notation.

3 EXAMPLE Writing a Number in Standard Notation

Write each number in standard notation.

a. temperature at the sun's core: 1.55×10^6 kelvins

$1.55 \times 10^6 = 1\ 550000.$ A positive exponent indicates a number greater than 10. Move the decimal point 6 places to the right.

$= 1,550,000$

b. lowest temperature recorded in a lab: 2×10^{-11} kelvin

$2 \times 10^{-11} = 0.00000000002$ A negative exponent indicates a number between 0 and 1. Move the decimal point 11 places to the left.

$= 0.00000000002$

CA Standards Check 3 Write each number in standard notation.

a. 3.2×10^{12} **b.** 5.07×10^4 **c.** 5.6×10^{-4} **d.** 8.3×10^{-2}

Using Scientific Notation

Masses of Planets (kilograms)

You can compare and order numbers in scientific notation. First compare the powers of 10, and then compare the decimals.

4 EXAMPLE Application

List the planets in order from least to greatest mass.

Order the powers of 10. Arrange the decimals with the same power of 10 in order.

8.7×10^{25}	1.0×10^{26}	5.7×10^{26}	3.7×10^{27}
Uranus	Neptune	Saturn	Jupiter

From least to greatest mass, the order is Uranus, Neptune, Saturn, and Jupiter.

CA Standards Check 4 The following masses of parts of an atom are measured in grams. Order the parts of an atom from least to greatest mass.

neutron: 1.6749×10^{-24}, electron: 9.1096×10^{-28}, proton: 1.6726×10^{-24}

You can write numbers like 815×10^5 and 0.078×10^{-2} in scientific notation.

$815 \times 10^5 = 81{,}500{,}000 = 8.15 \times 10^7$ $\quad$ $0.078 \times 10^{-2} = 0.00078 = 7.8 \times 10^{-4}$

The examples above show this pattern: When you move a decimal n places left, the exponent of 10 increases by n; when you move a decimal point n places right, the exponent of 10 decreases by n.

5 EXAMPLE Using Scientific Notation to Order Numbers

Order 0.052×10^7, 5.12×10^5, 53.2×10, and 534 from least to greatest.

Problem Solving Tip

Remember that 53.2×10 is 53.2×10^1.

Write each number in scientific notation.

0.052×10^7	5.12×10^5	53.2×10	534
↓	↓	↓	↓
5.2×10^5	5.12×10^5	5.32×10^2	5.34×10^2

Order the powers of 10. Arrange the decimals with the same power of 10 in order.

$5.32 \times 10^2 \quad 5.34 \times 10^2 \quad 5.12 \times 10^5 \quad 5.2 \times 10^5$

Write the original numbers in order.

$53.2 \times 10 \quad 534 \quad 5.12 \times 10^5 \quad 0.052 \times 10^7$

CA Standards Check 5 Order 60.2×10^{-5}, 63×10^4, 0.067×10^3, and 61×10^{-2} from least to greatest.

You can multiply a number that is in scientific notation by another number. If the product is less than one or greater than 10, rewrite the product in scientific notation.

6 EXAMPLE Multiplying a Number in Scientific Notation

Simplify. Write each answer using scientific notation.

a. $7(4 \times 10^5) = (7 \cdot 4) \times 10^5$ — Use the Associative Property of Multiplication.

$= 28 \times 10^5$ — Simplify inside the parentheses.

$= 2.8 \times 10^6$ — Write the product in scientific notation.

b. $0.5(1.2 \times 10^{-3}) = (0.5 \cdot 1.2) \times 10^{-3}$ — Use the Associative Property of Multiplication.

$= 0.6 \times 10^{-3}$ — Simplify inside the parentheses.

$= 6 \times 10^{-4}$ — Write the product in scientific notation.

CA Standards Check 6 Simplify. Write each answer using scientific notation.

a. $2.5(6 \times 10^3)$ $\qquad$ **b.** $0.4(2 \times 10^{-9})$

EXERCISES

Standards Practice

For more exercises, see *Extra Skills and Word Problem Practice.*

Alg1 2.0

A Practice by Example

GO for Help Example 1 (page 334)

Is each number written in scientific notation? If not, explain.

1. 55×10^4 $\qquad$ **2.** 3.2×10^5 $\qquad$ **3.** 0.9×10^{-2}

4. 7.3×10^{-5} $\qquad$ **5.** 1.12×10^1 $\qquad$ **6.** 46×10^7

Example 2 (page 335)

Write each number in scientific notation.

7. 9,040,000,000 **8.** 0.02 **9.** 9.3 million **10.** 21,700

11. 0.00325 **12.** 8,003,000 **13.** 0.00092 **14.** 0.0156

Example 3 (page 335)

Write each number in standard notation.

15. 5×10^2 **16.** 5×10^{-2} **17.** 2.04×10^3 **18.** 7.2×10^5

19. 8.97×10^{-1} **20.** 1.3×10^0 **21.** 2.74×10^{-5} **22.** 4.8×10^{-3}

Examples 4, 5 (pages 335, 336)

Order the numbers in each list from least to greatest.

23. $10^5, 10^{-3}, 10^0, 10^{-1}, 10^1$

24. $9 \times 10^{-7}, 8 \times 10^{-8}, 7 \times 10^{-6}, 6 \times 10^{-10}$

25. $50.1 \times 10^{-3}, 4.8 \times 10^{-1}, 0.52 \times 10^{-3}, 56 \times 10^{-2}$

26. $0.53 \times 10^7, 5300 \times 10^{-1}, 5.3 \times 10^5, 530 \times 10^8$

27. Measuring instruments may have different degrees of precision. Instrument A is precise to 10^{-2} cm, Instrument B is precise to 5×10^{-2} cm, and Instrument C is precise to 8×10^{-3} cm. Order the instruments from most precise (least possible error) to least precise (greatest possible error).

Example 6 (page 336)

Simplify. Write each answer using scientific notation.

28. $8(7 \times 10^{-3})$ **29.** $8(3 \times 10^{14})$ **30.** $0.2(3 \times 10^2)$

31. $6(5.3 \times 10^{-4})$ **32.** $0.3(8.2 \times 10^{-3})$ **33.** $0.5(6.8 \times 10^5)$

B Apply Your Skills

Elephant calves weigh from 1.0×10^2 to 1.45×10^2 kilograms.

For Exercises 34–39, find the missing value.

Selected Masses (kilograms)

		Standard Notation	Scientific Notation
34.	Elephant	■	5.4×10^3
35.	Adult human	70	■
36.	Dog	10	■
37.	Golf ball	0.046	■
38.	Paper clip	■	5×10^{-4}
39.	Oxygen atom	0.00000000000000000000000003	■

40. **Critical Thinking** Is the number 10^5 in scientific notation? Explain.

41. **Writing** Explain how to write 48 million and 48 millionths in scientific notation.

42. In 2010, the population in the United States will be about 3.09×10^8. Spending for health care will be about $8754 per person. About how much will the United States spend on health care in 2010? Use scientific notation.

43. A computer can perform 4.66×10^8 instructions per second. How many instructions is that per minute? Per hour? Use scientific notation.

44. The national debt at the beginning of 2005 was about $7,600,000,000,000. Write this number in scientific notation.

Visit: PHSchool.com
Web Code: bae-0702

45. The world population in 2025 may reach 7.84×10^9 persons. This is about 3 times the world population in 1950. What was the world population in 1950?

46. Use a calculator to find the volume of each planet with the given radius.
  a. Mercury: 2439 km b. Earth: 6378 km c. Saturn: 60,268 km

47. Write $\frac{1}{300}$ using scientific notation.

Multiple Choice Practice

For California Standards Tutorials, visit PHSchool.com. Web Code: baq-9045

Alg1 2.0

48. Florence Griffith-Joyner set the world record for the women's 100-meter sprint in 1988. Which expression equals her winning time of 1.748×10^{-1} minutes?
  A 0.1748 B 17.48 C 1748×10^{-3} D 1748×10^{3}

Alg1 6.0

49. What is the equation of the line with an x-intercept of 3 and a y-intercept of 2?
  A $2y = 3x$ B $3y = 2x$ C $3x + 2y = 6$ D $2x + 3y = 6$

Alg1 5.0

50. Abby will receive 1 free football ticket for every 30 tickets she sells for a raffle. How many raffle tickets must she sell to get 5 free football tickets?
  A 6 B 35 C 150 D 305

Mixed Review

GO for Help

Lesson 7-1

Simplify each expression.

51. $4(1.8)^0$ 52. $12 \cdot 2^{-2}$ 53. $6 \cdot 3^{-2}$ 54. $\frac{4^3}{7^2}$ 55. $\frac{3^{-2}}{9^0}$

Lesson 6-5

Graph each linear inequality.

56. $y < -\frac{1}{4}x + 2$ 57. $y \geq \frac{2}{3}x$ 58. $y < 3x - 4$

Lesson 3-5

Solve each compound inequality.

59. $5 \leq 2a < 13$ 60. $-7 \leq b + 8 \leq 23$ 61. $-16 < 4m - 2 < -3$

62. $y + 5 < -1$ or $3y + 1 > -2$ 63. $\frac{1}{2}(p - 2) < \frac{5}{2}$ or $3p \leq -9$

Checkpoint Quiz 1

Lessons 7-1 through 7-2

Simplify each expression.

1. $5^{-1}(3^{-2})$ 2. $r^{-5}s^{-4}$ 3. $2x^5 3y^{-12}$ 4. $\frac{mn^{-4}}{p^0 q^{-2}}$

5. $a^2 b^0 c^{-3}$ 6. $(3^2)(4m^2)$ 7. $\frac{2t^0}{3s^{-2}}$ 8. $5^{-3} 15n^6$

9. A certain bacteria population doubles in size every day. Suppose a sample starts with 500 bacteria. The expression $500 \cdot 2^x$ models the number of bacteria in the sample after x days. Evaluate the expression for $x = 0, 2, 5$.

10. Saturn is about 1,433,500,000 km from the sun. Mars is located about 22.79×10^7 km from the sun. Which planet is farther from the sun?

7-3 Multiplication Properties of Exponents

California Content Standards

2.0 Understand and use the rules of exponents. ***Develop***

10.0 Multiply monomials. Solve multi-step problems, including word problems, by using this technique. ***Develop***

What You'll Learn

- To multiply powers
- To work with scientific notation

. . . And Why

To find the number of red blood cells in the human body, as in Example 5

Check Skills You'll Need

GO for Help Lesson 1-6

Rewrite each expression using exponents.

1. $t \cdot t \cdot t \cdot t \cdot t \cdot t \cdot t$

2. $(6 - m)(6 - m)(6 - m)$

3. $(r + 5)(r + 5)(r + 5)(r + 5)(r + 5)$

4. $5 \cdot 5 \cdot 5 \cdot s \cdot s \cdot s$

Simplify.

5. -5^4

6. $(-5)^4$

7. $(-5)^0$

8. $(-5)^{-4}$

Multiplying Powers

CA Standards Investigation: Exponents With the Same Base and Multiplication

1. Copy and complete the table.

2. What is true for $2^2 \cdot 2^2$ and $2^3 \cdot 2^1$?

3. **Patterns** What relationship do you see between the sum of the exponents of 2 in the first column and the exponent of 2 in the third column?

Factors	Product Using Repeated Factors	Power of 2
$2^1 \cdot 2^1$	$2 \cdot 2$	2^2
$2^2 \cdot 2^2$	■	■
$2^3 \cdot 2^1$	■	■
$2^4 \cdot 2^2$	■	■
$2^3 \cdot 2^3$	■	■

You can write the product of powers with the same base, like $2^4 \cdot 2^2$, using one exponent.

$$2^4 \cdot 2^2 = (2 \cdot 2 \cdot 2 \cdot 2) \cdot (2 \cdot 2) = 2^6$$

Notice that the sum of the exponents of the expression $2^4 \cdot 2^2$ equals the exponent of 2^6.

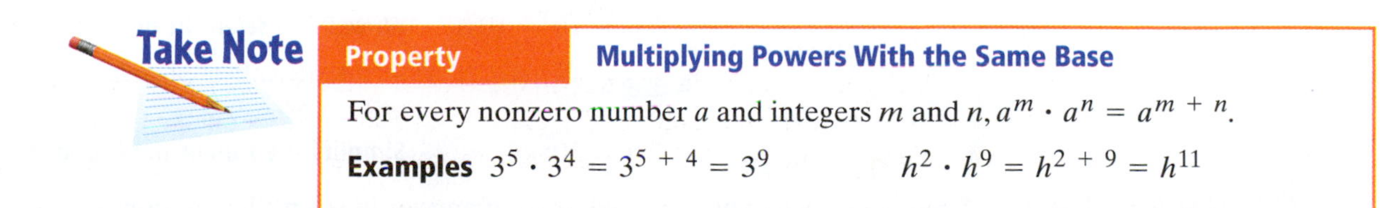

Take Note

Property | **Multiplying Powers With the Same Base**

For every nonzero number a and integers m and n, $a^m \cdot a^n = a^{m+n}$.

Examples $3^5 \cdot 3^4 = 3^{5+4} = 3^9$ $\qquad h^2 \cdot h^9 = h^{2+9} = h^{11}$

1 EXAMPLE Multiplying Powers

Rewrite each expression using each base only once.

a. $11^4 \cdot 11^3 = 11^{4+3}$ — Add exponents of powers with the same base.

$= 11^7$ — Simplify the sum of the exponents.

b. $5^{-2} \cdot 5^2 = 5^{-2+2}$ — Add exponents of powers with the same base.

$= 5^0$ — Simplify the sum of the exponents.

$= 1$ — Use the definition of zero as an exponent.

CA Standards Check **1** Rewrite each expression using each base only once.

a. $5^3 \cdot 5^6$ **b.** $2^4 \cdot 2^{-3}$ **c.** $7^{-3} \cdot 7^2 \cdot 7^6$

When variable factors have more than one base, be careful to combine only those powers with the same base.

2 EXAMPLE Multiplying Powers in an Algebraic Expression

Simplify each expression.

a. $2n^5 \cdot 3n^{-2} = (2 \cdot 3)(n^5 \cdot n^{-2})$ — Commutative Property of Multiplication

$= 6(n^{5+(-2)})$ — Add exponents of powers with the same base.

$= 6n^3$ — Simplify.

b. $5x \cdot 2y^4 \cdot 3x^8 = (5 \cdot 2 \cdot 3)(x \cdot x^8)(y^4)$ — Commutative and Associative Properties of Multiplication

$= 30(x^1 \cdot x^8)(y^4)$ — Multiply the coefficients. Write x as x^1.

$= 30(x^{1+8})(y^4)$ — Add exponents of powers with the same base.

$= 30x^9y^4$ — Simplify.

Problem Solving Tip

Remember that $x = x^1$.

CA Standards Check **2** Simplify each expression.

a. $n^2 \cdot n^3 \cdot 7n$ **b.** $2y^3 \cdot 7x^2 \cdot 2y^4$ **c.** $m^2 \cdot n^{-2} \cdot 7m$

Working With Scientific Notation

You can use the property for multiplying powers with the same base to write numbers and to multiply numbers in scientific notation.

3 EXAMPLE Multiplying Numbers in Scientific Notation

Simplify $(7 \times 10^2)(4 \times 10^5)$. Write the answer in scientific notation.

$(7 \times 10^2)(4 \times 10^5) = (7 \cdot 4)(10^2 \cdot 10^5)$ — Commutative and Associative Properties of Multiplication

$= 28 \times 10^7$ — Simplify.

$= 2.8 \times 10^1 \cdot 10^7$ — Write 28 in scientific notation.

$= 2.8 \times 10^{1+7}$ — Add exponents of powers with the same base.

$= 2.8 \times 10^8$ — Simplify the sum of the exponents.

CA Standards Check **3** Simplify each expression. Write each answer in scientific notation.

a. $(2.5 \times 10^8)(6 \times 10^3)$ **b.** $(1.5 \times 10^{-2})(3 \times 10^4)$ **c.** $(9 \times 10^{-6})(7 \times 10^{-9})$

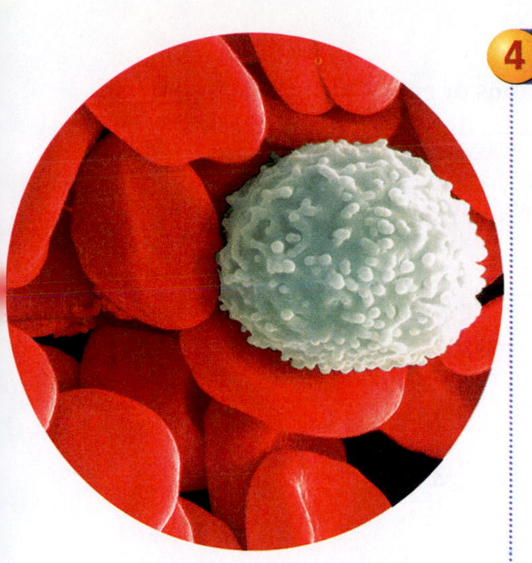

The blood cells shown in the photo above are magnified 5×10^3 times their actual size.

4 EXAMPLE Application

A human body contains about 3.2×10^4 μL (microliters) of blood for each pound of body weight. Each microliter of blood contains about 5×10^6 red blood cells. Find the approximate number of red blood cells in the body of a 125-lb person.

$$\text{red blood cells} = \text{pounds} \cdot \frac{\text{microliters}}{\text{pound}} \cdot \frac{\text{cells}}{\text{microliter}}$$ **Use dimensional analysis.**

$$= 125 \text{ lb} \cdot (3.2 \times 10^4)\frac{\mu L}{\text{lb}} \cdot (5 \times 10^6)\frac{\text{cells}}{\mu L}$$ **Substitute.**

$$= (125 \cdot 3.2 \cdot 5) \times (10^4 \cdot 10^6)$$ **Commutative and Associative Properties of Multiplication**

$$= (2000) \times (10^{4+6})$$ **Simplify.**

$$= 2000 \times 10^{10}$$ **Add exponents.**

$$= 2 \times 10^3 \cdot 10^{10}$$ **Write 2000 in scientific notation.**

$$= 2 \times 10^{13}$$ **Add the exponents.**

There are about 2×10^{13} red blood cells in a 125-lb person.

CA Standards Check 4 About how many red blood cells are in the body of a 160-lb soccer player?

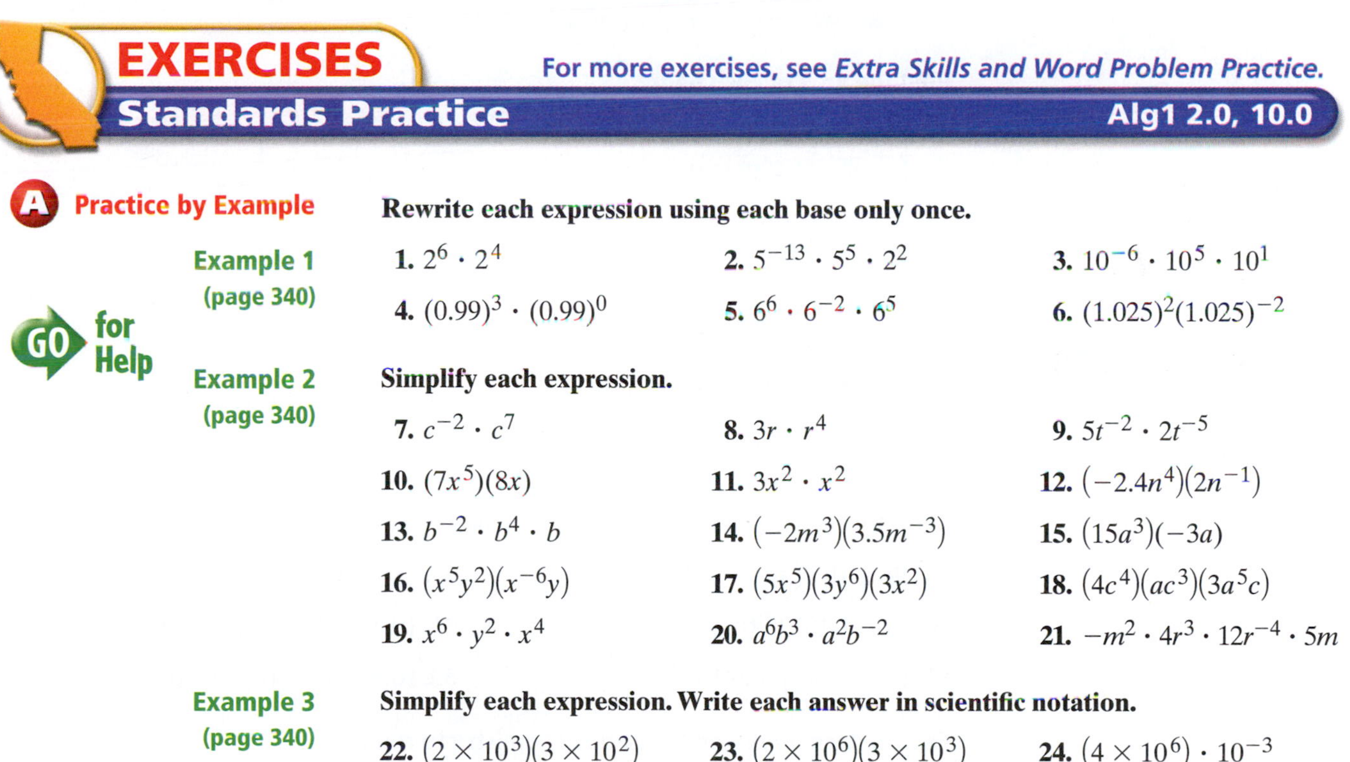

EXERCISES

Standards Practice

For more exercises, see *Extra Skills and Word Problem Practice.*

Alg1 2.0, 10.0

A Practice by Example

GO for Help

Example 1 (page 340)

Rewrite each expression using each base only once.

1. $2^6 \cdot 2^4$
2. $5^{-13} \cdot 5^5 \cdot 2^2$
3. $10^{-6} \cdot 10^5 \cdot 10^1$
4. $(0.99)^3 \cdot (0.99)^0$
5. $6^6 \cdot 6^{-2} \cdot 6^5$
6. $(1.025)^2(1.025)^{-2}$

Example 2 (page 340)

Simplify each expression.

7. $c^{-2} \cdot c^7$
8. $3r \cdot r^4$
9. $5t^{-2} \cdot 2t^{-5}$
10. $(7x^5)(8x)$
11. $3x^2 \cdot x^2$
12. $(-2.4n^4)(2n^{-1})$
13. $b^{-2} \cdot b^4 \cdot b$
14. $(-2m^3)(3.5m^{-3})$
15. $(15a^3)(-3a)$
16. $(x^5y^2)(x^{-6}y)$
17. $(5x^5)(3y^6)(3x^2)$
18. $(4c^4)(ac^3)(3a^5c)$
19. $x^6 \cdot y^2 \cdot x^4$
20. $a^6b^3 \cdot a^2b^{-2}$
21. $-m^2 \cdot 4r^3 \cdot 12r^{-4} \cdot 5m$

Example 3 (page 340)

Simplify each expression. Write each answer in scientific notation.

22. $(2 \times 10^3)(3 \times 10^2)$
23. $(2 \times 10^6)(3 \times 10^3)$
24. $(4 \times 10^6) \cdot 10^{-3}$
25. $(1 \times 10^3)(3.4 \times 10^{-8})$
26. $(8 \times 10^{-5})(7 \times 10^{-3})$
27. $(5 \times 10^7)(3 \times 10^{14})$

Example 4 (page 341)

Write each answer in scientific notation.

28. The distance light travels in one year is about 5.88×10^{12} miles. This distance is a light-year. The closest star to Earth (other than the sun) is Alpha Centauri, which is 4.35 light-years from Earth. About how many miles from Earth is Alpha Centauri?

Write each answer in scientific notation.

29. Earth's crust contains about 120 trillion metric tons of gold. One metric ton of gold is worth about \$9 million. What is the value of the gold in Earth's crust?

30. Light travels through space at a constant speed of about 3×10^5 km/s. Sunlight reflecting from the moon takes about 1.28×10^0 s to reach Earth. Find the distance from the moon to Earth.

B Apply Your Skills

Complete each equation.

31. $5^2 \cdot 5^{\blacksquare} = 5^{11}$ **32.** $5^7 \cdot 5^{\blacksquare} = 5^3$ **33.** $2^{\blacksquare} \cdot 2^4 = 2^1$

34. $c^{-5} \cdot c^{\blacksquare} = c^6$ **35.** $m^{\blacksquare} \cdot m^{-4} = m^{-9}$ **36.** $a \cdot a \cdot a^3 = a^{\blacksquare}$

37. $a^{\blacksquare} \cdot a^4 = 1$ **38.** $a^{12} \cdot a^{\blacksquare} = a^{12}$ **39.** $x^3y^{\blacksquare} \cdot x^{\blacksquare} = y^2$

Error Analysis **Correct each error.**

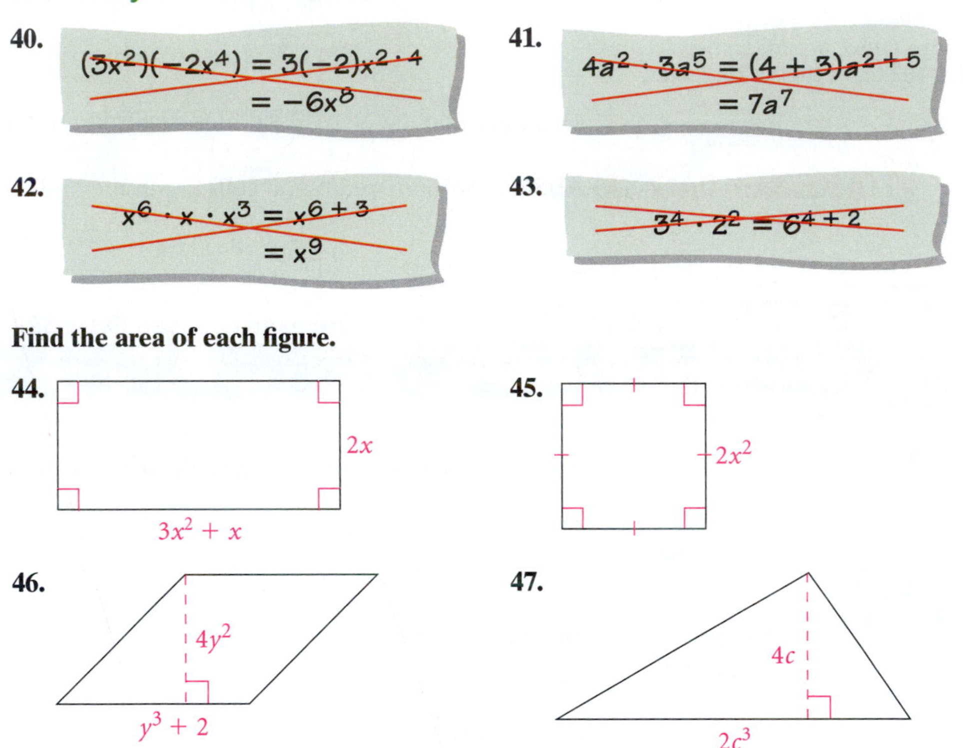

Visit: PHSchool.com
Web Code: bae-0703

Simplify each expression. Write each answer in scientific notation.

48. $(9 \times 10^7)(3 \times 10^{-16})$ **49.** $(8 \times 10^{-3})(0.1 \times 10^9)$

50. $(0.7 \times 10^{-12})(0.3 \times 10^8)$ **51.** $(0.4 \times 10^0)(3 \times 10^{-4})$

52. $(0.2 \times 10^5)(4 \times 10^{-12})$ **53.** $(0.5 \times 10^{13})(0.3 \times 10^{-4})$

54. The term *mole* can be used in chemistry to refer to 6.02×10^{23} atoms of a substance. The mass of a single hydrogen atom is approximately 1.67×10^{-24} gram. What is the mass of 1 mole of hydrogen atoms?

55. a. Write y^8 as a product of two powers with the same base in four different ways. Use only positive exponents.

b. Write y^8 as a product of two powers with the same base in four different ways using negative or zero exponents in each.

c. **Reasoning** How many ways are there to write y^8 as the product of two powers? Explain your reasoning.

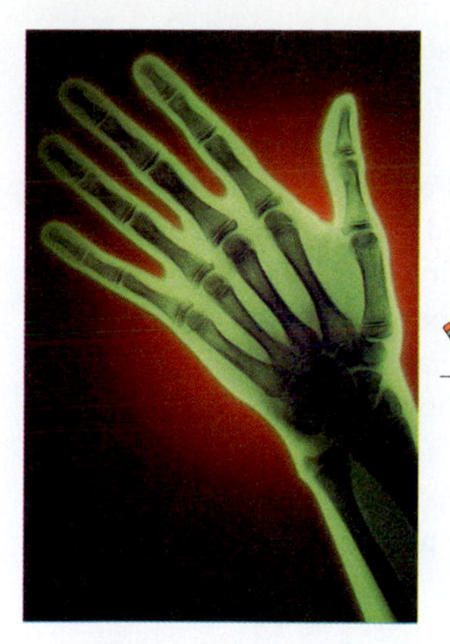

Light used to "see" an object cannot have a wavelength that is larger than the object. Only gamma rays are smaller than X-rays. They have lengths that are as small as 10^{-15} meter.

56. Medical X-rays, with a wavelength of about 10^{-10} meter, can penetrate your skin.
   a. Ultraviolet rays, which cause sunburn by penetrating only the top layers of skin, have a wavelength about 1000 times the wavelength of an X-ray. Find the wavelength of ultraviolet rays.
   b. Critical Thinking The wavelengths of visible light are between 4×10^{-7} meter and 7.5×10^{-7} meter. Are these wavelengths longer or shorter than those of ultraviolet rays? Explain.

57. Writing Explain why $x^3 \cdot y^5$ cannot be written with fewer bases.

58. A CD-ROM stores about 650 megabytes (6.5×10^8 bytes) of information along a spiral track. Each byte uses about 9 micrometers (9×10^{-6} m) of space along the track. Find the length of the track.

Simplify each expression. Write each answer in scientific notation.

59. $(6.12 \times 10^5)(12.5 \times 10^8)$ **60.** $(1.9 \times 10^{-3})(2.04 \times 10^{11})$

61. $(9.55 \times 10^7)(7.3 \times 10^{-15})$ **62.** $(6.9 \times 10^{-9})(2.5 \times 10^{-4})$

63. There are about 3.35×10^{25} molecules in a liter of water. Clear Lake, in California, has about 1.4×10^{12} liters of water. About how many molecules of water are in Clear Lake?

64. About 8.4×10^{11} drops of water flow over Niagara Falls each minute. Each drop of water contains about 1.7×10^{21} molecules of water. About how many molecules of water flow over the falls each minute?

Simplify each expression.

65. $\frac{1}{x^2 \cdot x^{-5}}$ **66.** $\frac{1}{a^3 \cdot a^{-2}}$ **67.** $\frac{5}{c \cdot c^{-4}}$

68. $2a^2(3a + 5)$ **69.** $8m^3(m^2 + 7)$ **70.** $-4x^3(2x^2 - 9x)$

Simplify.

71. $3^x \cdot 3^{2-x} \cdot 3^2$ **72.** $2^n \cdot 2^{n+2} \cdot 2$ **73.** $3^x \cdot 2^y \cdot 3^2 \cdot 2^x$

74. $(a + b)^2(a + b)^{-3}$ **75.** $(t + 3)^7(t + 3)^{-5}$ **76.** $5^{x+1} \cdot 5^{1-x}$

77. a. Find the volume of a rectangular prism with length 1.3×10^{-3} km, width 1.5×10^{-3} km, and height 9.4×10^{-4} km. Write your answer in scientific notation.
   b. What is the volume of the prism in cubic meters?

78. A protozoan is 1.1×10^{-4} meter long. A diagram of a protozoan in a science book is 7.7 centimeters long. The diagram is how many times greater than the protozoan in length?

Multiple Choice Practice

For California Standards Tutorials, visit PHSchool.com. Web Code: baq-9045

Alg1 2.0

79. Which expression is equivalent to $2(3a^2b)(a^{-2}b)$?

(A) $5b^2$ (B) $6b^2$ (C) $6ab^2$ (D) $6a^{-4}b$

Alg1 17.0

80. Which value is NOT in the range of the function $f(x) = x^2 - 1$?

(A) -2 (B) -1 (C) 0 (D) 1

GO Online Lesson Quiz Visit: PHSchool.com, Web Code: baa-0703

Alg1 5.0

81. Which problem is best represented by the number sentence $5x + 3(x + 2) = 26$?

Ⓐ Mia spent \$5 on a pizza and \$3 on 2 drinks. How much did she spend in all?

Ⓑ Devin spent 5 hours studying for a math test and 2 more hours studying for 3 other tests. How many tests did he study for in 26 hours?

Ⓒ Angela bought 5 notebooks and 3 binders for \$26. If a binder costs \$2 more than a notebook, how much does a notebook cost?

Ⓓ Steve's class has 2 more boys than girls. There are 26 students in the class. If 5 girls and 3 boys play a sport, how many girls do NOT play a sport?

Alg1 17.0

82. Which graph below has a range that includes only negative real numbers?

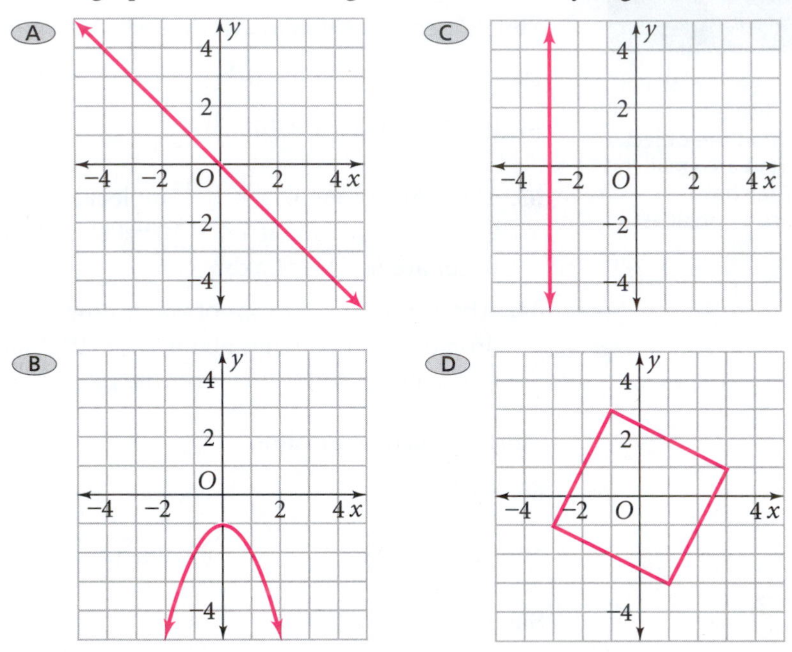

Mixed Review

GO for Help

Lesson 7-2

Write each number in scientific notation.

83. 1,280,000 **84.** 0.0035 **85.** 0.00009 **86.** 6.2 million

Write each number in standard form.

87. 8.76×10^{8} **88.** 1.052×10^{-3} **89.** 9.1×10^{11} **90.** 2.9×10^{-4}

Lesson 6-6

Solve each system by graphing.

91. $y < 3x + 2$
$2x + y \geq 4$

92. $y < x + 6$
$x - 3y \leq 6$

93. $y > x + 4$
$x + 2y \leq 6$

Lesson 4-7

Find the third, seventh, and tenth terms of each sequence.

94. $A(n) = 10 + (n - 1)(4)$

95. $A(n) = -5 + (n - 1)(2)$

96. $A(n) = 12 + (n - 1)(-4)$

97. $A(n) = 1.2 + (n - 1)(-4)$

98. $A(n) = 8 + (n - 1)(3)$

99. $A(n) = 8 + (n - 1)(-3)$

More Multiplication Properties of Exponents

California Content Standards

2.0 Understand and use the rules of exponents. ***Develop***

10.0 Multiply monomials. Solve multi-step problems, including word problems, by using this technique. ***Develop***

What You'll Learn

- To raise a power to a power
- To raise a product to a power

. . . And Why

To find the resting energy of an object, as in Example 5

Check Skills You'll Need

GO for Help Lesson 7-3

Rewrite each expression using each base only once.

1. $3^2 \cdot 3^2 \cdot 3^2$
2. $2^3 \cdot 2^3 \cdot 2^3 \cdot 2^3$
3. $5^7 \cdot 5^7 \cdot 5^7 \cdot 5^7$
4. $7 \cdot 7 \cdot 7$

Simplify.

5. $x^3 \cdot x^3$
6. $a^2 \cdot a^2 \cdot a^2$
7. $y^{-2} \cdot y^{-2} \cdot y^{-2}$
8. $n^{-3} \cdot n^{-3}$

Raising a Power to a Power

CA Standards Investigation Powers of Powers

Online active math

For: Exponent Activity
Use: Interactive Textbook, 7-4

You can use what you learned in the previous lesson to find a shortcut for simplifying expressions with powers. Copy and complete each statement.

1. $(3^6)^2 = 3^6 \cdot 3^6 = 3^{\blacksquare + \blacksquare} = 3^{6 \cdot \blacksquare} = 3^{\blacksquare}$
2. $(5^4)^3 = 5^4 \cdot 5^4 \cdot 5^4 = 5^{\blacksquare + \blacksquare + \blacksquare} = 5^{4 \cdot \blacksquare} = 5^{\blacksquare}$
3. $(2^7)^4 = 2^7 \cdot 2^7 \cdot 2^7 \cdot 2^7 = 2^{\blacksquare + \blacksquare + \blacksquare + \blacksquare} = 2^{7 \cdot \blacksquare} = 2^{\blacksquare}$
4. $(a^3)^2 = a^3 \cdot a^3 = a^{\blacksquare + \blacksquare} = a^{3 \cdot \blacksquare} = a^{\blacksquare}$
5. $(g^4)^3 = g^4 \cdot g^4 \cdot g^4 = g^{\blacksquare + \blacksquare + \blacksquare} = g^{4 \cdot \blacksquare} = g^{\blacksquare}$
6. $(c^3)^4 = c^3 \cdot c^3 \cdot c^3 \cdot c^3 = c^{\blacksquare + \blacksquare + \blacksquare + \blacksquare} = c^{3 \cdot \blacksquare} = c^{\blacksquare}$
7. a. **Make a Conjecture** What pattern do you see in your answers to Questions 1–6?
   b. Use your pattern to simplify $(8^6)^3$.

Raising a power to a power is the same as raising the base to the product of the exponents.

Property **Raising a Power to a Power**

For every nonzero number a and integers m and n, $(a^m)^n = a^{mn}$.

Examples $(5^4)^2 = 5^{4 \cdot 2} = 5^8$ $(x^2)^5 = x^{2 \cdot 5} = x^{10}$

1 EXAMPLE Simplifying a Power Raised to a Power

Simplify $(x^3)^6$.

$(x^3)^6 = x^{3 \cdot 6}$ Multiply exponents when raising a power to a power.

$= x^{18}$ Simplify.

CA Standards Check 1 Simplify $(a^4)^7$ and $(a^{-4})^7$.

Be sure to use the order of operations. Simplify expressions in parentheses first.

GO Online

Video Tutor Help
Visit: PHSchool.com
Web Code: bae-0775

2 EXAMPLE Simplifying an Expression With Powers

Simplify $c^5(c^3)^{-2}$.

$c^5(c^3)^{-2} = c^5 \cdot c^{3 \cdot (-2)}$ Multiply exponents in $(c^3)^{-2}$.

$= c^5 \cdot c^{-6}$ Simplify.

$= c^{5 + (-6)}$ Add exponents when multiplying powers with the same base.

$= c^{-1}$ Simplify.

$= \frac{1}{c}$ Write using only positive exponents.

CA Standards Check 2 Simplify each expression. **a.** $t^2(t^7)^{-2}$ **b.** $(a^4)^2 \cdot (a^2)^5$

Raising a Product to a Power

You can use repeated multiplication to simplify expressions like $(5y)^3$.

$$(5y)^3 = 5y \cdot 5y \cdot 5y$$
$$= 5 \cdot 5 \cdot 5 \cdot y \cdot y \cdot y$$
$$= 5^3y^3$$
$$= 125y^3$$

Notice that $(5y)^3 = 5^3y^3$. This illustrates another property of exponents.

Take Note

Property	Raising a Product to a Power

For every nonzero number a and b and integer n, $(ab)^n = a^nb^n$.

Example $(3x)^4 = 3^4x^4 = 81x^4$

3 EXAMPLE Simplifying a Product Raised to a Power

Problem Solving Tip

When raising a product to a power, make sure each factor of the product is raised to the power.

Simplify $(2x^4)^2$.

$(2x^4)^2 = 2^2(x^4)^2$ Raise each factor to the 2nd power.

$= 2^2x^8$ Multiply exponents of a power raised to a power.

$= 4x^8$ Simplify.

The correct answer is D.

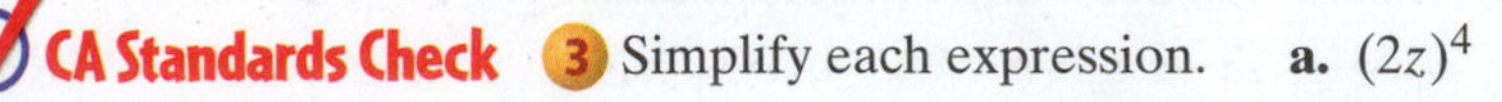

CA Standards Check 3 Simplify each expression. **a.** $(2z)^4$ **b.** $(4g^5)^{-2}$

Some expressions have more than one power raised to a power.

4 EXAMPLE Simplifying a Product Raised to a Power

Simplify $(x^{-2})^2(3xy^2)^4$.

$(x^{-2})^2(3xy^2)^4 = (x^{-2})^2 \cdot 3^4x^4(y^2)^4$ — Raise the three factors to the 4th power.

$= x^{-4} \cdot 3^4x^4y^8$ — Multiply the exponents of a power raised to a power.

$= 3^4 \cdot x^{-4} \cdot x^4 \cdot y^8$ — Use the Commutative Property of Multiplication.

$= 3^4x^0y^8$ — Add exponents of powers with the same base.

$= 81y^8$ — Simplify.

CA Standards Check 4 Simplify each expression.

a. $(c^2)^3(3c^5)^4$ **b.** $(2a^3)^5(3ab^2)^3$ **c.** $(6mn)^3(5m^{-3})^2$

Albert Einstein is famous for discovering that the amount of energy in an object, measured in joules, is equal to its mass in kg multiplied by $(3 \times 10^8 \text{ m/s})^2$.

You can use the property of raising a product to a power to solve problems involving scientific notation. For an expression like $(3 \times 10^8)^2$, raise both 3 and 10^8 to the second power.

5 EXAMPLE Application

All objects, even resting ones, contain energy. A raisin has a mass of 10^{-3} kg. The expression $10^{-3} \cdot (3 \times 10^8)^2$ describes the amount of resting energy, in joules, the raisin contains. Simplify the expression.

$10^{-3} \cdot (3 \times 10^8)^2 = 10^{-3} \cdot 3^2 \cdot (10^8)^2$ — Raise each factor within parentheses to the second power.

$= 10^{-3} \cdot 3^2 \cdot 10^{16}$ — Simplify $(10^8)^2$.

$= 3^2 \cdot 10^{-3} \cdot 10^{16}$ — Use the Commutative Property of Multiplication.

$= 3^2 \cdot 10^{-3+16}$ — Add exponents of powers with the same base.

$= 9 \times 10^{13}$ — Simplify. Write in scientific notation.

CA Standards Check 5 **a.** The mass of a feather is 10^{-5} kg. Simplify the expression $(10^{-5})(3 \times 10^8)^2$ to find the amount of resting energy in joules the feather contains.

b. The mass of a drop of water is 2.5×10^{-2} kg. Simplify the expression $(2.5 \times 10^{-2})(3 \times 10^8)^2$ to find the amount of resting energy in joules the drop of water contains.

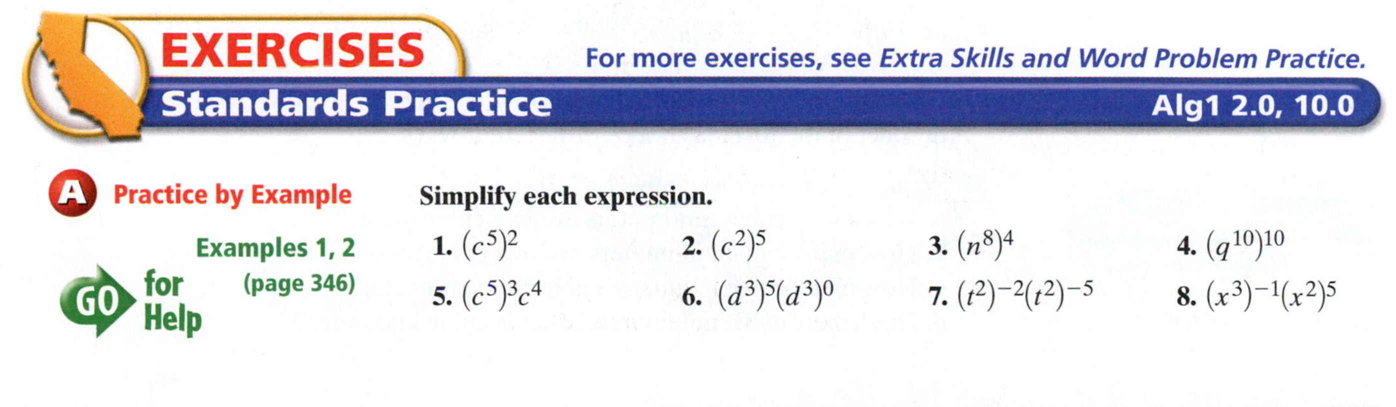

EXERCISES

For more exercises, see *Extra Skills and Word Problem Practice.*

Standards Practice — Alg1 2.0, 10.0

A Practice by Example

Examples 1, 2 (page 346) GO for Help

Simplify each expression.

1. $(c^5)^2$ **2.** $(c^2)^5$ **3.** $(n^8)^4$ **4.** $(q^{10})^{10}$

5. $(c^5)^3c^4$ **6.** $(d^3)^5(d^3)^0$ **7.** $(t^2)^{-2}(t^2)^{-5}$ **8.** $(x^3)^{-1}(x^2)^5$

Example 3 (page 346)

Simplify each expression.

9. $(5y)^4$
10. $(4m)^5$
11. $(7a)^2$
12. $(12g^4)^{-1}$
13. $(6y^2)^2$
14. $(3n^6)^4$
15. $(2y^4)^{-3}$
16. $(2p^6)^0$

Example 4 (page 347)

17. $(x^2)^5(x^3)^2$
18. $(2xy)^3x^2$
19. $(mg^4)^{-1}(mg^4)$
20. $(c^{-2})^3c^{-12}$
21. $(3b^{-2})^2(a^2b^4)^3$
22. $(2a^2c^4)^{-5}(c^{-1}a^7)^6$

Example 5 (page 347)

Simplify. Write each answer in scientific notation.

23. $(4 \times 10^5)^2$
24. $(3 \times 10^5)^2$
25. $(2 \times 10^{-10})^3$
26. $(2 \times 10^{-3})^3$
27. $(7 \times 10^4)^2$
28. $(6 \times 10^{12})^2$
29. $(4 \times 10^8)^{-2}$
30. $(3.5 \times 10^{-4})^3$

31. The length of one side of a cube is 9.5×10^{-4} m. What is the volume of the cube?

B Apply Your Skills

Complete each equation.

32. $(x^2)^{\blacksquare} = x^6$
33. $(m^{\blacksquare})^3 = m^{-12}$
34. $(b^2)^{\blacksquare} = b^8$
35. $(y^{-4})^{\blacksquare} = y^{12}$
36. $(n^9)^{\blacksquare} = 1$
37. $7(c^1)^{\blacksquare} = 7c^8$
38. $(5x^{\blacksquare})^2 = 25x^{-4}$
39. $(3x^3y^{\blacksquare})^3 = 27x^9$
40. $(m^2n^3)^{\blacksquare} = \frac{1}{m^6n^9}$

41. **Error Analysis** One student simplified $x^5 + x^5$ to x^{10}. A second student simplified $x^5 + x^5$ to $2x^5$. Which student is correct? Explain.

Simplify each expression.

42. $(4.1)^5 \cdot (4.1)^{-5}$
43. $3^2(3x)^3$
44. $(b^5)^3b^2$
45. $(-5x)^2 + 5x^2$
46. $(2x^{-3})^2 \cdot (0.2x)^2$
47. $(-2a^2b)^3(ab)^3$
48. $(3^7)^2 \cdot (3^{-4})^3$
49. $(10^3)^4(4.3 \times 10^{-8})$
50. $(4xy^2)^4(-y)^{-3}$

51. a. Write an expression for the surface area of each cube.
    b. How many times greater than the surface area of the small cube is the surface area of the large cube?
    c. Write an expression for the volume of each cube.
    d. How many times greater than the volume of the small cube is the volume of the large cube?

2x

4x

Write each expression with only one exponent. Use parentheses.

52. $m^4 \cdot n^4$
53. $(a^5)(b^5)(a^0)$
54. $49x^2y^2z^2$
55. $\frac{12x^2}{3y^2}$

56. Choose a value of n for the expression a^n. Express the power you wrote as a product of the form $(a^c)^d$ in four different ways.

57. Write each answer as a power of 10.
    a. How many cubic centimeters are in a cubic meter?
    b. How many cubic millimeters are in a cubic meter?
    c. How many cubic meters are in a cubic kilometer?
    d. How many cubic millimeters are in a cubic kilometer?

Homework Video Tutor

Visit: PHSchool.com
Web Code: bae-0704

58. Write each answer as a power of 2.

a. Computer capacity is often measured in bits and bytes. A bit is the smallest unit, a 1 or 0 in the computer's memory. A byte is 2^3 bits. A megabyte (MB) is 2^{20} bytes. How many bits are in a megabyte?

b. A gigabyte (GB) is 2^{10} megabytes. How many bytes are there in a gigabyte? How many bits are there in a gigabyte?

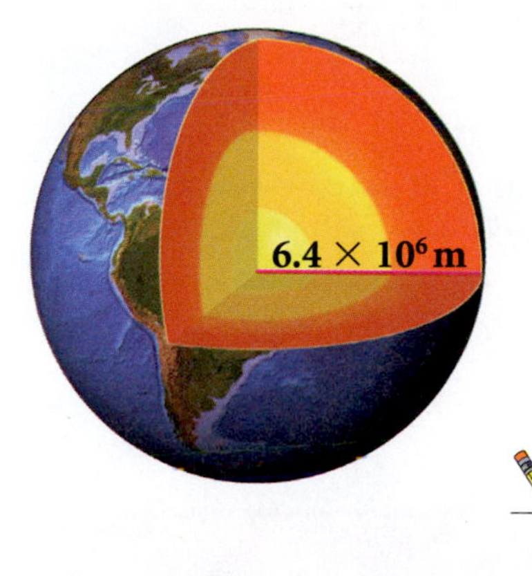

59. a. Earth has a radius of about 6.4×10^6 m. Approximate the surface area of Earth using the formula for the surface area of a sphere, $S = 4\pi r^2$.

b. Earth's surface is about 70% water, almost all of it in oceans. About how many square meters of Earth's surface are covered with water?

c. The oceans have an average depth of 3795 m. Estimate the volume of water on Earth.

60. Which expression or expressions do *not* equal 64?

A. $2^5 \cdot 2$ **B.** 2^6 **C.** $2^2 \cdot 2^3$ **D.** $(2^3)^2$ **E.** $(2^2)(2^2)^2$

61. **Writing** Explain how you know when to add the exponents of powers and when to multiply the exponents.

Challenge

Solve each equation.

Sample

$25^3 = 5^x$

$(5^2)^3 = 5^x$ Write 25 as a power of 5.

$5^6 = 5^x$ Simplify $(5^2)^3$.

$6 = x$ Since the bases are the same, the exponents are equal.

62. $5^6 = 25^x$

63. $8^2 = 2^x$

64. $3^x = 27^4$

65. $4^x = 2^6$

66. $3^{2x} = 9^4$

67. $2^x = \frac{1}{32}$

68. **Critical Thinking** Simplify $(x^3)^4$ and x^{3^4}. Are the expressions equivalent?

Multiple Choice Practice

For California Standards Tutorials, visit PHSchool.com. Web Code: baq-9045

Alg1 2.0

69. Which expression is equivalent to $(x^3y)^3$?

(A) x^3y^3 (B) x^6y^3 (C) x^6y^4 (D) x^9y^3

Alg1 2.0

70. Evaluate $3a^2$ for $a = 5.1 \times 10^{-5}$.

(A) 1.53×10^{-10}

(B) 1.53×10^{-9}

(C) 7.803×10^{-10}

(D) 7.803×10^{-9}

Alg1 18.0

71. Which relation is NOT a function?

(A) $\{(2, -1), (3, -1), (5, -1), (9, -1)\}$

(B) $\{(1, 2), (3, 4), (1, 4), (3, 5)\}$

(C) $\{(3, 4), \left(\frac{1}{2}, -3\right), (-2, 4), (-5, 7)\}$

(D) $\{(0, 0), (-1, -1), (-2, -3), (1, 4)\}$

Alg1 17.0

72. Which solution set describes the range of the function $y = -3x + 1$ for the domain $\{1.5, 1.75, 2, 2.25\}$?

(A) $\{5.5, 6.25, 7, 7.75\}$

(B) $\{-3.5, -4.25, -5, -5.75\}$

(C) $\{-7.5, -8.25, -9, -9.75\}$

(D) $\{7.5, 8.25, 9, 9.75\}$

73. Which graph represents the function rule $f(x) = 3x + \frac{1}{2}$?

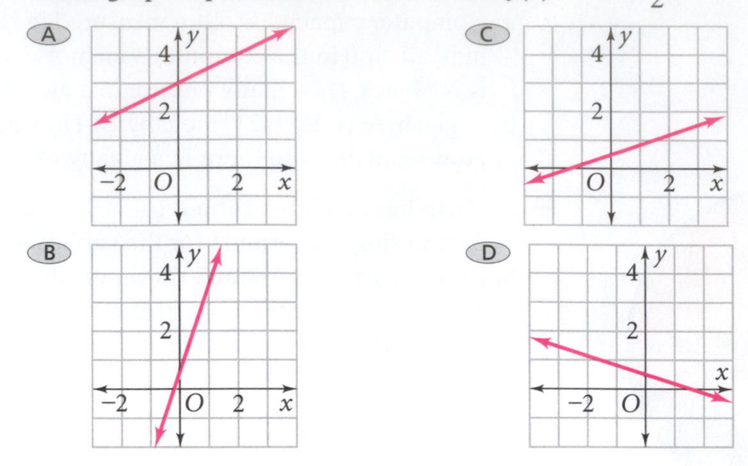

Mixed Review

GO for Help

Lesson 7-3 **Simplify each expression.**

74. $bc^{-6} \cdot b$ **75.** $(a^2b^3)(a^6)$ **76.** $9m^3(6m^2n^4)$ **77.** $2t(-2t^4)$

Lesson 6-2 **Solve each system using substitution.**

78. $y = 3x + 5$, $y = -4x + 12$

79. $y = 0.5x - 1$, $y = 0.2x + 0.4$

80. $y = 5x - 9$, $y = 3x + 5$

81. $y = x + 4$, $y = -5$

Lesson 5-1 **Find the slope of the line that passes through each pair of points.**

82. $(0, 3), (4, 0)$ **83.** $(2, -5), (3, 1)$ **84.** $(-3, 6), (1, 0)$ **85.** $(0, 0), (11, -9)$

Find the slope of each line.

86.

87.

Checkpoint Quiz 2 — Lessons 7-3 through 7-4

1. $m^{-3}n^0m^1$ **2.** $5c^2 \cdot 7c^{-2}$ **3.** $a^3b \cdot a^{-6}b^{-2}$ **4.** $-3r^2 \cdot 2^{-6} \cdot r^{-7}$

5. $(p^4)^2(p^0)^9$ **6.** $(a^{-3})^{-2}$ **7.** $(2^5)^{-1}(3b)^3$ **8.** $(c^2d^{-2})^3$

9. In 2000, about 1.4×10^4 ships passed through the Panama Canal. About 5.2×10^7 gallons of water flow out of the canal with each ship. About how many gallons of water flowed out of the canal with the ships in 2000? Write your answer in scientific notation.

10. The moon has a radius of about 1.7×10^6 km.

a. Approximate the surface area of the moon using the formula $S = 4\pi r^2$.

b. Approximate the volume of the moon using the formula $V = \frac{4}{3}\pi r^3$.

Division Properties of Exponents

California Content Standards

2.0 Understand and use the rules of exponents. ***Develop***

10.0 Divide monomials. Solve multi-step problems, including word problems, by using this technique. ***Develop***

What You'll Learn

- To divide powers with the same base
- To raise a quotient to a power

. . . And Why

To find the amount of paper recycled per person in the United States, as in Example 2

Check Skills You'll Need

GO for Help Skills Handbook page 598

Write each fraction in simplest form.

1. $\frac{5}{20}$	**2.** $\frac{125}{25}$	**3.** $\frac{60}{100}$	**4.** $\frac{124}{4}$
5. $\frac{6}{15}$	**6.** $\frac{8}{30}$	**7.** $\frac{10}{35}$	**8.** $\frac{18}{63}$
9. $\frac{5xy}{15x}$	**10.** $\frac{6y^2}{3x}$	**11.** $\frac{3ac}{12a}$	**12.** $\frac{24m}{6mn^2}$

Dividing Powers With the Same Base

You can use repeated multiplication to simplify fractions. Expand the numerator and the denominator using repeated multiplication. Then cancel like terms.

$$\frac{5^6}{5^2} = \frac{\cancel{5} \cdot \cancel{5} \cdot 5 \cdot 5 \cdot 5 \cdot 5}{\cancel{5} \cdot \cancel{5}} = 5^4$$

Take Note

Property | **Dividing Powers With the Same Base**

For every nonzero number a and integers m and n, $\frac{a^m}{a^n} = a^{m-n}$.

Example $\frac{3^7}{3^3} = 3^{7-3} = 3^4$

Since division by zero is undefined, assume that no base is equal to zero.

1 EXAMPLE Simplifying an Algebraic Expression

Simplify each expression.

a. $\frac{a^6}{a^{14}} = a^{6-14}$ Subtract exponents when dividing powers with the same base.

$= a^{-8}$ Simplify the exponents.

$= \frac{1}{a^8}$ Rewrite using positive exponents.

b. $\frac{c^{-1}d^3}{c^5d^{-4}} = c^{-1-5}d^{3-(-4)}$ Subtract exponents when dividing powers with the same base.

$= c^{-6}d^7$ Simplify.

$= \frac{d^7}{c^6}$ Rewrite using positive exponents.

GO Online

Video Tutor Help
Visit: PHSchool.com
Web Code: bae-0775

CA Standards Check **1** Simplify each expression.

a. $\frac{b^4}{b^9}$ **b.** $\frac{z^{10}}{z^5}$ **c.** $\frac{a^2b}{a^4b^3}$ **d.** $\frac{m^{-1}n^2}{m^3n}$ **e.** $\frac{x^2y^{-1}z^4}{xy^4z^{-3}}$

When you divide numbers that are in scientific notation, you can use the property of dividing powers with the same base. In real-world situations, decide whether to write the result in standard or scientific notation.

California generates nearly 1.4×10^7 tons of postconsumer paper annually.

2 EXAMPLE Application

In 2000, the total amount of paper and paperboard recycled in the United States was 37 million tons. The population of the United States in 2000 was 281.4 million. On average, how much paper and paperboard did each person recycle?

$\frac{\text{37 million tons}}{\text{281.4 million people}} = \frac{3.7 \times 10^7 \text{ tons}}{2.814 \times 10^8 \text{ people}}$ Write in scientific notation.

$= \frac{3.7}{2.814} \times 10^{7-8}$ Subtract exponents when dividing powers with the same base.

$= \frac{3.7}{2.814} \times 10^{-1}$ Simplify the exponent.

$\approx 1.3 \times 10^{-1}$ Divide. Round to the nearest tenth.

$= 0.13$ Write in standard notation.

There was about 0.13 ton of paper and paperboard recycled per person in 2000.

CA Standards Check **2** Find each quotient. Write each answer in scientific notation.

a. $\frac{2 \times 10^3}{8 \times 10^8}$ **b.** $\frac{7.5 \times 10^{12}}{2.5 \times 10^{-4}}$ **c.** $\frac{4.2 \times 10^5}{12.6 \times 10^2}$

d. In 2000 the total amount of glass recycled in the United States was 2.7 million tons. The population of the United States in 2000 was 281.4 million people. On average, about how many tons of glass were recycled per person?

Raising a Quotient to a Power

You can use repeated multiplication to simplify the expression $\left(\frac{x}{y}\right)^3$.

$$\left(\frac{x}{y}\right)^3 = \frac{x}{y} \cdot \frac{x}{y} \cdot \frac{x}{y} = \frac{x \cdot x \cdot x}{y \cdot y \cdot y} = \frac{x^3}{y^3}$$

This illustrates another property of exponents.

Take Note

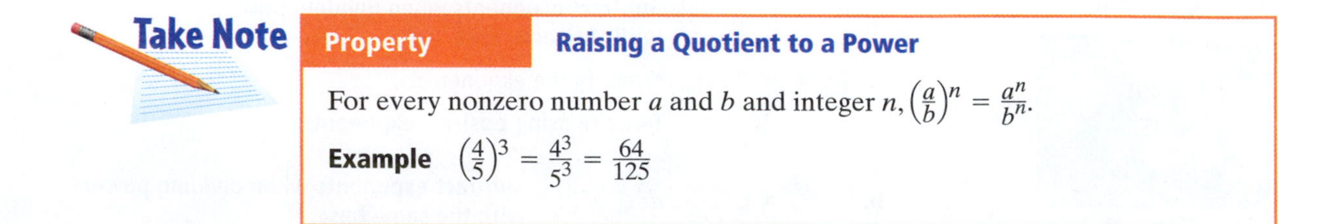

Property **Raising a Quotient to a Power**

For every nonzero number a and b and integer n, $\left(\frac{a}{b}\right)^n = \frac{a^n}{b^n}$.

Example $\left(\frac{4}{5}\right)^3 = \frac{4^3}{5^3} = \frac{64}{125}$

3 EXAMPLE Raising a Quotient to a Power

Quick Review

Check your answer when simplifying by substituting a value for the variable.
For $x = 2$,
$\left(\frac{4}{2^2}\right)^3 = \left(\frac{4}{4}\right)^3 = 1^3 = 1$
$\frac{64}{2^6} = \frac{64}{64} = 1$

Which expression is equivalent to $\left(\frac{4}{x^2}\right)^3$?

(A) $\frac{12}{x^5}$ (B) $\frac{12}{x^6}$ (C) $\frac{64}{x^5}$ (D) $\frac{64}{x^6}$

$\left(\frac{4}{x^2}\right)^3 = \frac{4^3}{(x^2)^3}$ **Raise the numerator and the denominator to the third power.**

$= \frac{4^3}{x^6}$ **Multiply the exponents in the denominator.**

$= \frac{64}{x^6}$ **Simplify.**

The correct answer is D.

CA Standards Check 3 Simplify each expression. **a.** $\left(\frac{3}{x^2}\right)^2$ **b.** $\left(\frac{x}{y^2}\right)^3$

You can use what you know about exponents to rewrite an expression in the form $\left(\frac{a}{b}\right)^{-n}$ using positive exponents.

$\left(\frac{a}{b}\right)^{-n} = \frac{1}{\left(\frac{a}{b}\right)^n}$ Use the definition of negative exponent.

$= \frac{1}{\frac{a^n}{b^n}}$ Raise the quotient to a power.

$= \frac{1}{\frac{a^n}{b^n}} \cdot \frac{b^n}{b^n}$ Use the Identity Property of Multiplication to multiply by $\frac{b^n}{b^n}$.

$= \frac{b^n}{a^n}$ Simplify.

$= \left(\frac{b}{a}\right)^n$ Write the quotient using one exponent.

So, $\left(\frac{a}{b}\right)^{-n} = \left(\frac{b}{a}\right)^n$.

4 EXAMPLE Simplifying an Exponential Expression

Simplify each expression.

a. $\left(\frac{3}{5}\right)^{-2} = \left(\frac{5}{3}\right)^2$ **Rewrite using the reciprocal of $\frac{3}{5}$.**

$= \frac{5^2}{3^2}$ **Raise the numerator and denominator to the second power.**

$= \frac{25}{9}$ or $2\frac{7}{9}$ **Simplify.**

b. $\left(-\frac{2x}{y}\right)^{-4} = \left(-\frac{y}{2x}\right)^4$ **Rewrite using the reciprocal of $-\frac{2x}{y}$.**

$= \left(\frac{-y}{2x}\right)^4$ **Write the fraction with a negative numerator.**

$= \frac{(-y)^4}{(2x)^4}$ **Raise the numerator and denominator to the fourth power.**

$= \frac{y^4}{16x^4}$ **Simplify.**

CA Standards Check 4 Simplify each expression.
a. $\left(\frac{3}{4}\right)^{-3}$ **b.** $\left(\frac{-1}{2}\right)^{-5}$ **c.** $\left(\frac{2r}{s}\right)^{-1}$ **d.** $\left(\frac{7a}{m}\right)^{-2}$

EXERCISES

For more exercises, see *Extra Skills and Word Problem Practice.*

Standards Practice

Alg1 2.0, 10.0, 25.0

A Practice by Example

Example 1 (page 351)

Copy and complete each equation.

1. $\frac{5^9}{5^2} = 5^{■}$
2. $\frac{2^4}{2^3} = 2^{■}$
3. $\frac{3^2}{3^5} = 3^{■}$
4. $\frac{5^2 5^3}{5^3 5^2} = 5^{■}$

Simplify each expression.

5. $\frac{2^5}{2^7}$
6. $\frac{2^7}{2^5}$
7. $\frac{c^{12}}{c^{15}}$
8. $\frac{m^{-2}}{m^{-5}}$
9. $\frac{3s^{-9}}{6s^{-11}}$
10. $\frac{x^{13}y^2}{x^{13}y}$
11. $\frac{c^2d^{-3}}{c^3d^{-1}}$
12. $\frac{3^2m^3t^6}{3^5m^7t^{-5}}$

Example 2 (page 352)

Simplify each quotient. Write each answer in scientific notation.

13. $\frac{6.5 \times 10^{15}}{1.3 \times 10^8}$
14. $\frac{2.7 \times 10^{-8}}{9 \times 10^{-4}}$
15. $\frac{4.2 \times 10^8}{7 \times 10^5}$
16. $\frac{8.4 \times 10^{-5}}{2 \times 10^{-8}}$
17. $\frac{4.65 \times 10^{-4}}{3.1 \times 10^2}$
18. $\frac{3.5 \times 10^6}{5 \times 10^8}$

19. In 2000, people in the United States over age 2 watched television a total of 386 billion hours. The population of the United States over age 2 was about 265 million people.
    a. Write each number in scientific notation.
    b. Find the average number of hours of TV viewing per person older than age 2 for 2000.
    c. On average, how many hours per day did each person older than age 2 watch television in 2000?

20. The speed of computers is measured in number of calculations per picosecond. There are 3.6×10^{15} picoseconds per hour. What fraction of a second is a picosecond?

Example 3 (page 353)

Simplify each expression.

21. $\left(\frac{3}{5}\right)^2$
22. $\left(\frac{1}{x}\right)^3$
23. $\left(\frac{2x}{y}\right)^5$
24. $\left(\frac{3a}{2b}\right)^4$
25. $\left(\frac{2^2}{5}\right)^3$
26. $\left(\frac{3^3}{3^4}\right)^2$
27. $\left(\frac{6}{n^6}\right)^2$
28. $\left(\frac{2p}{5}\right)^3$

Example 4 (page 353)

29. $\left(\frac{2}{3}\right)^{-1}$
30. $\left(\frac{2}{3}\right)^{-2}$
31. $\left(-\frac{2}{3}\right)^{-2}$
32. $\left(-\frac{2}{3}\right)^{-3}$
33. $\left(\frac{3x^4}{15}\right)^2$
34. $\left(\frac{4n}{2n^2}\right)^3$
35. $\left(\frac{c^5}{c^9}\right)^3$
36. $\left(\frac{3b^2}{5}\right)^0$

B Apply Your Skills

Explain why each expression is *not* in simplest form.

37. 5^3m^3
38. x^5y^{-2}
39. $(2c)^4$
40. x^0y
41. $\frac{d^7}{d}$

Simplify each expression.

42. $\frac{3^2 \cdot 5^0}{2^3}$
43. $\left(\frac{2m^5}{m^2}\right)^{-4}$
44. $\frac{5x^3}{(5x)^3}$
45. $\frac{(2a^7)(3a^2)}{6a^3}$
46. $\left(\frac{7t^3}{21t}\right)^3$
47. $\left(\frac{n^4n}{n^{-2}}\right)^{-4}$
48. $\left(\frac{2k^3}{3k^{-2}}\right)^{-2}$
49. $\frac{7^9 \cdot (10)^2}{7^7}$

In 2003, about 2.0×10^7 people in California had cell phones.

50. At the end of 2003, there were about 158.7 million wireless telephone subscribers in the United States. These subscribers made about 23.7 billion calls and used about 80.5 billion minutes per month.

a. Write each number in scientific notation.

b. What was the average number of minutes used by each subscriber per month? Round to the nearest whole number.

c. What was the average length of a phone call? Round to the nearest tenth.

51. a. Writing While simplifying the expression $\frac{c^4}{c^6}$, Kneale said, "I've found a property of exponents that's not in my algebra book!" Write an explanation of why Kneale's method works.

b. Apply Kneale's method to an example you create.

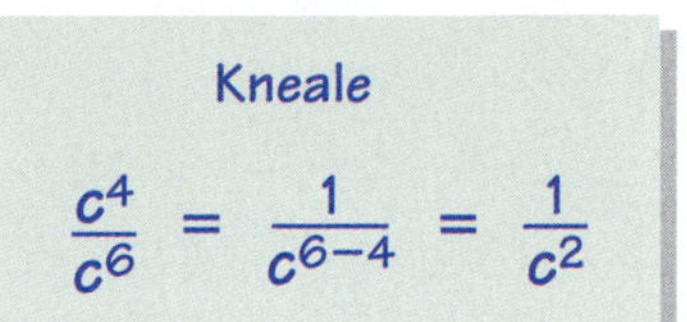

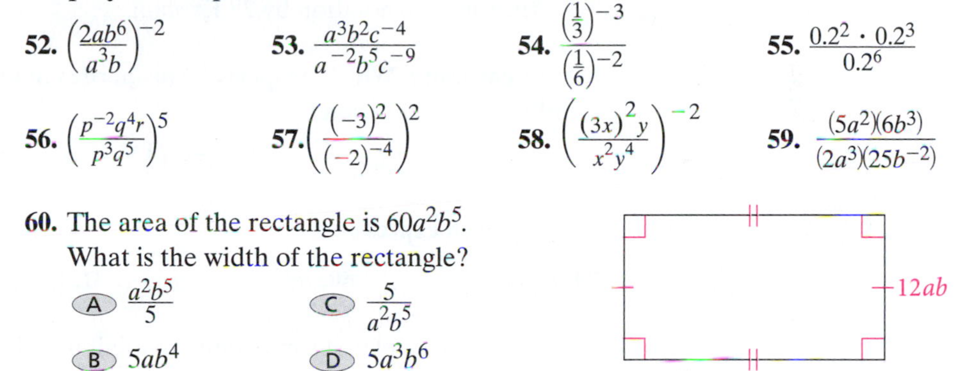

Simplify each expression.

52. $\left(\frac{2ab^6}{a^3b}\right)^{-2}$ **53.** $\frac{a^3b^2c^{-4}}{a^{-2}b^5c^{-9}}$ **54.** $\frac{\left(\frac{1}{3}\right)^{-3}}{\left(\frac{1}{6}\right)^{-2}}$ **55.** $\frac{0.2^2 \cdot 0.2^3}{0.2^6}$

56. $\left(\frac{p^{-2}q^4r}{p^3q^5}\right)^5$ **57.** $\left(\frac{(-3)^2}{(-2)^{-4}}\right)^2$ **58.** $\left(\frac{(3x)^2y}{x^2y^4}\right)^{-2}$ **59.** $\frac{(5a^2)(6b^3)}{(2a^3)(25b^{-2})}$

60. The area of the rectangle is $60a^2b^5$. What is the width of the rectangle?

Ⓐ $\frac{a^2b^5}{5}$ Ⓒ $\frac{5}{a^2b^5}$

Ⓑ $5ab^4$ Ⓓ $5a^3b^6$

$12ab$

61. Critical Thinking Lena and Jared used different methods to simplify $\left(\frac{b^7}{b^3}\right)^2$. Why are both methods correct?

62. a. In 2000, the United States government owed \$5.67 trillion to its creditors. The population of the United States was 282.2 million people. How much did the government owe per person in 2000? Round to the nearest dollar.

b. In 2005 the debt had grown to \$7.93 trillion, with a population of 296.4 million. How much did the government owe per person? Round to the nearest dollar.

c. What was the percent of increase in the average amount owed per person from 2000 to 2005?

Visit: PHSchool.com
Web Code: bae-0705

63. a. Error Analysis What error did the student make in simplifying the expression at the right?

b. What is the correct answer?

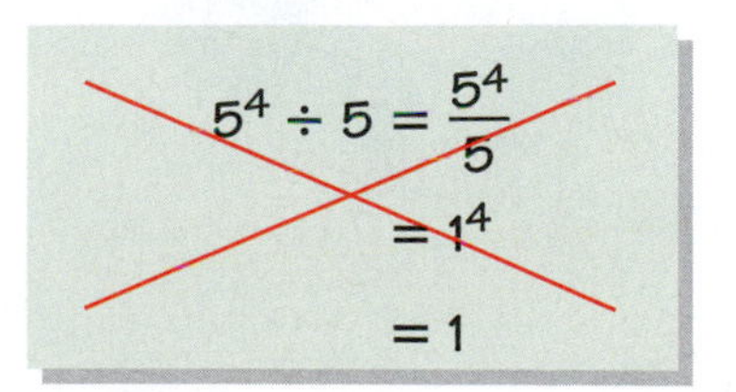

Write each expression with only one exponent. You may need to use parentheses.

64. $\frac{3^5}{5^5}$ **65.** $\frac{m^7}{n^7}$ **66.** $\frac{d^8}{d^5}$ **67.** $\frac{10^7 \cdot 10^0}{10^{-3}}$

68. $\frac{27x^3}{8y^3}$ **69.** $\frac{4m^2}{169m^4}$ **70.** $\frac{49m^2}{25n^2}$ **71.** $\frac{125c^7}{216c^4}$

72. If you donate blood regularly, the American Red Cross recommends a 56-day waiting period between donations. One pint of blood contains about 2.4×10^{12} red blood cells. Your body normally produces about 2×10^6 red blood cells per second.

a. At its normal rate, in how many seconds will your body replace the red blood cells lost by giving one pint of blood?

b. Convert your answer from part (a) to days.

73. a. Write three numbers in scientific notation.

b. Divide each number by 2.

c. Critical Thinking Is the power of 10 divided by 2 when you divide a number in scientific notation by 2? Explain.

Math Reasoning Which property or properties of exponents would you use to simplify each expression?

74. 2^{-3} **75.** $\frac{2^2}{2^5}$ **76.** $\left(\frac{1}{2}\right)^3$ **77.** $\frac{1}{2^{-4}2^7}$ **78.** $\frac{(2^4)^3}{2^{15}}$

C Challenge

Simplify each expression.

79. $n^{x+2} \div n^x$ **80.** $n^{5x} \div n^x$ **81.** $\left(\frac{x^m}{x^{m-2}}\right)^2$ **82.** $\frac{\left(\frac{n^5}{n^4}\right)}{n^3}$

83. The ratio of a planet's maximum to minimum distance from the sun is related to how circular its orbit is.

a. Copy and complete the table below. Round decimals to the nearest hundredth.

b. Reasoning How can you use the ratio maximum : minimum to determine whether a planet's orbit is close to circular?

c. Which planet has the least circular orbit? The most circular orbit?

Distance From the Sun (kilometers)

Planet	Maximum	Minimum	Maximum : Minimum
Mercury	6.97×10^7	4.59×10^7	■ : ■ = $\frac{6.97 \times 10^7}{4.59 \times 10^7} = \frac{6.97}{4.59} \approx 1.52$
Venus	1.089×10^8	1.075×10^8	1.089×10^8 : ■ ≈ ■
Earth	1.521×10^8	1.471×10^8	■ : 1.471×10^8 ≈ ■
Mars	2.491×10^8	2.067×10^8	■ : ■ ≈ ■
Jupiter	8.157×10^8	7.409×10^8	■ : ■ ≈ ■
Saturn	1.507×10^9	1.347×10^9	■ : ■ ≈ ■
Uranus	3.004×10^9	2.735×10^9	■ : ■ ≈ ■
Neptune	4.537×10^9	4.457×10^9	■ : ■ ≈ ■

Maximum
Minimum

Multiple Choice Practice

For California Standards Tutorials, visit PHSchool.com. Web Code: baq-9045

Alg1 2.0

84. Which expression is equivalent to $\left(\frac{3^2 s^{-3}}{3s^2}\right)^{-2}$?

Ⓐ -5 Ⓑ $\frac{1}{s^5}$ Ⓒ $\frac{1}{3s^3}$ Ⓓ $\frac{s^{10}}{9}$

Alg1 7.0

85. Look at the line shown on the graph. What is the equation of the line with half the slope and the same y-intercept?

Ⓐ $y = -\frac{2}{3}x + 2$ Ⓒ $y = -\frac{1}{3}x + 2$

Ⓑ $y = -\frac{3}{2}x + 3$ Ⓓ $y = -\frac{3}{4}x + 3$

Alg1 2.0

86. Which expression is NOT equivalent to $\left(\frac{4n}{3m^5}\right)^{-2}$?

Ⓐ $\left(\frac{3m^5}{4n}\right)^2$ Ⓑ $\frac{4n^{-2}}{3m^3}$ Ⓒ $\frac{9m^{10}}{16n^2}$ Ⓓ $\left(\frac{16n^2}{9m^{10}}\right)^{-1}$

Alg1 5.0

87. A radio station is organizing a fundraiser to build a new public library. The radio station will donate \$.50 for every dollar donated by the listeners. If the listeners donated \$530 on the first day of the fundraiser, how much did the radio station donate on the first day?

Ⓐ \$106 Ⓑ \$265 Ⓒ \$1060 Ⓓ \$2650

Mixed Review

GO for Help

Lesson 7-4 **Simplify each expression.**

88. $(3y^2)^3$ **89.** $(2m^{-7})^3$ **90.** $(r^2t^{-5})^{-4}$

91. $2(3s^{-2})^{-3}$ **92.** $(2^3c^2)^{-1}$ **93.** $(-3)^2(-r^3)^2$

94. $(7^0n^{-3})^2(n^5)^2$ **95.** $(7^2y^{12})^0$ **96.** $(5x^3)^2$

Lesson 6-1 **Solve each system by graphing.**

97. $y = 3x$, $y = -2x$ **98.** $y = 2x + 1$, $y = x - 3$ **99.** $y = 5$, $x = 3$ **100.** $y = 7$, $y = 8$

Lesson 4-5 **Write an equation of the direct variation that includes the given point.**

101. (3, 8) **102.** (−5, 2) **103.** (6, −7)

104. (−3, −5) **105.** (4, 7) **106.** (−16, 4)

107. (9, 5) **108.** (4, −2) **109.** (7, 1)

GPS Guided Problem Solving

For Use With Page 356, Exercise 72

2.0 Understand and use the rules of exponents. ***Develop***

Understanding Word Problems **Read the exercise below and then follow along with what Casey thinks and writes. Check your understanding with the exercise at the bottom of the page.**

If you donate blood regularly, the American Red Cross recommends a 56-day waiting period between donations. One pint of blood contains about 2.4×10^{12} red blood cells (RBCs). Your body normally produces about 2×10^6 red blood cells per second.

a. At its normal rate, in how many seconds will your body replace the red blood cells lost by giving one pint of blood?

b. Convert your answer from part (a) to days.

What Casey Thinks	What Casey Writes
First, I'll read the problem and write down the important information.	1 pint of blood contains 2.4×10^{12} RBCs. Body produces 2×10^6 RBCs per second.
To answer part (a), I'll write an equation relating the information in the problem.	Number of RBCs produced = rate body produces RBCs × time
Since I need to find out how many seconds it will take to replace the RBCs, I'll solve this equation for time by dividing each side of the equation by the rate.	$\text{Time} = \frac{\text{number of RBCs produced}}{\text{rate body produces RBCs}}$
Now I'll substitute the information from the problem into my equation and simplify.	$\text{Time} = \frac{2.4 \times 10^{12}}{2 \times 10^6} = \frac{2.4}{2} \times 10^{12-6}$ $= 1.2 \times 10^6$ seconds
To answer part (b), I need to find out how many days there are in 1.2×10^6 seconds. First, I will find out how many seconds there are in one day.	$60 \frac{\text{seconds}}{\text{minute}} \times 60 \frac{\text{minutes}}{\text{hour}} \times 24 \frac{\text{hour}}{\text{day}} =$ $86{,}400 \frac{\text{seconds}}{\text{day}} = 8.64 \times 10^4$
Now I will divide my answer to part (a) by the number of seconds in a day. I'll write my answer in a sentence.	$\frac{1.2 \times 10^6}{8.64 \times 10^4} = \frac{1.2}{8.64} \times 10^{6-4} =$ $0.139 \times 10^2 = 13.9$ days. It will take about 1.2×10^6 seconds, or 13.9 days, to replace the red blood cells lost in 1 pint of blood.

EXERCISE

Hair growth rates differ for every person. Suppose your hair grows at a rate of 3.2×10^{-4} m per day. About how many days will it take for your hair to grow 3.5×10^{-1} m? About how many years is this?

Remembering Properties

There are many rules of exponents in this chapter. To remember these rules, it may help you to make a flash card.

EXAMPLE

Follow the steps below to make a card for the rule Zero as an Exponent.

1. Write the name of the rule.
2. Describe the rule in words.
3. Give an arithmetic example of the rule.
4. Give an algebraic example of the rule.

Zero as an Exponent

Word description: Any number other than zero raised to the zero exponent equals 1.

Arithmetic	Algebra
$5^0 = 1$	For every nonzero number a, $a^0 = 1$.

EXERCISES

Follow the steps above to make a card for each rule of exponents.

1. Negative Exponent
2. Multiplying Powers With the Same Base
3. Raising a Power to a Power
4. Dividing Powers With the Same Base
5. Raising a Quotient to a Power
6. **Error Analysis** A student made a card for the rule Raising a Product to a Power. Which parts are incorrect? Explain.

Raising a Product to a Power

Word description: A product raised to a power equals the product of each factor raised to that power.

Arithmetic	Algebra
$(2x)^6 = 2x^6$	For every number a, b, and n, $(ab)^n = a^n b^n$.

Test-Taking Strategies

Testing Multiple Choices

One advantage of multiple-choice tests is that the correct answer is always among the choices. A strategy is to work backward by taking answers and testing them in the original problem.

EXAMPLE

Which is always a correct conclusion about the quantities in the function $y = 2x - 1$?

Ⓐ The variable y is always 1 less than x.

Ⓑ As the value of x increases, the value of y decreases.

Ⓒ The variable y is always greater than x.

Ⓓ When the value of x is negative, the value of y is also negative.

When testing statements, testing a single value or case is often not enough.

In this case, making a table of values for the function $y = 2x - 1$ will make it easier to test all the statements.

x	$2x-1$	y
-2	$2(-2)-1$	-5
-1	$2(-1)-1$	-3
0	$2(0)-1$	-1
1	$2(1)-1$	1
2	$2(2)-1$	3

Choice A: When $x = 0$, y is 1 less than x. However, this is not true for any other number in the table, so A is not correct.

Choice B: The table shows that as the x-values increase from -2 to 2, the y-values increase from -5 to 3. So B is not correct.

Choice C: When $x = 2$, y is greater than x. For all the other values in the table, y is less than or equal to x. So C is not correct.

Choice D: For every negative x-value in the table, y is negative. Since 2 times a negative number is always negative, and a negative number minus 1 is always negative, D is always true.

Multiple Choice Practice

1. Marie recorded the number of pages she read in her history book and the amount of time it took in the table at the right. Which equation best represents the relationship between the number of pages p and the amount of time t?

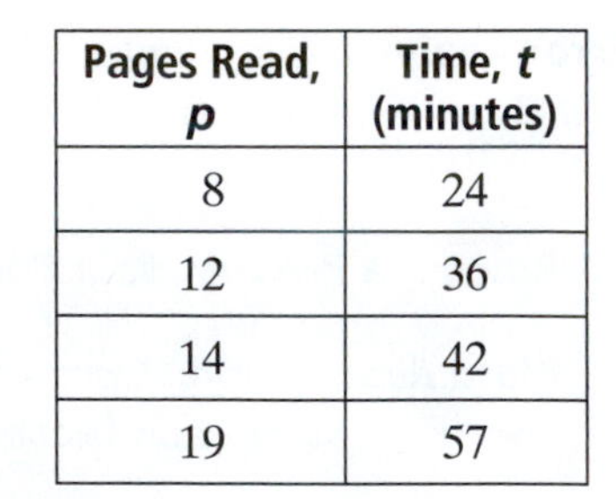

Pages Read, p	Time, t (minutes)
8	24
12	36
14	42
19	57

Ⓐ $t = p + 16$

Ⓑ $t = 3p$

Ⓒ $t = \frac{p}{3}$

Ⓓ $t = p^2 - 40$

2. Which statement is always a correct conclusion about the quantities in the function $y = 2x$?

Ⓐ The value of y is always twice the value of x.

Ⓑ When the value of x is negative, the value of y is negative.

Ⓒ When the value of x is a positive integer, y is an odd number.

Ⓓ As the value of x increases, the value of y decreases.

Chapter 7 Review

Vocabulary Review

🔊 English and Spanish Audio Online

scientific notation (p. 334)

For: Vocabulary quiz
Web Code: baj-0751

Choose the correct term to complete each sentence.

1. (*Scientific notation, Standard notation*) is a shorthand way to write very large and very small numbers.

2. In the expression 8^4, the (*power, exponent*) 4 shows that 8 is used as a factor four times.

Skills and Concepts

Lesson 7-1

- To simplify expressions with zero and negative exponents (p. 328)
- To evaluate exponential expressions (p. 330)

Alg1 2.0

You can use zero and negative integers as exponents. For every nonzero number a, $a^0 = 1$. For every nonzero number a and any integer n, $a^{-n} = \frac{1}{a^n}$. You cannot use 0 as a base. Both 0^0 and 0^{-n} are undefined.

Copy and complete each equation.

3. $\frac{1}{3a^{■}} = \frac{a^2}{3}$ **4.** $\frac{4m^{■}}{n^{■}} = 4n^5$ **5.** $\frac{x^{■}}{9y^{■}} = \frac{1}{9x^6y^4}$

Simplify each expression.

6. $b^{-4}c^0d^6$ **7.** $\frac{x^{-2}}{y^{-8}}$ **8.** $7k^{-8}h^3$

9. $\frac{1}{p^2q^{-4}r^0}$ **10.** $\left(\frac{2}{5}\right)^{-4}$ **11.** $(-2)^{-3}$

12. -2^{-3} **13.** $7^{-2}y^{-4}$ **14.** $\frac{9w^{-4}}{x^{-2}y^7}$

15. $\frac{5^{-2}m^0}{m^{-6}n^{11}}$ **16.** $8g^{-3}h^0k^6$ **17.** $\frac{z^{-1}}{4^{-2}x^3y^{-5}}$

Evaluate each expression for $p = 2$, $q = -3$, and $r = 0$.

18. p^2q^2 **19.** $(-p)^2q^{-2}$ **20.** p^qq^p **21.** p^rq^r **22.** $-p^2q^3$

23. Copy and complete the table below.

2^a	4	■	8	$\frac{1}{4}$	■
2^{-a}	■	2	■	■	$\frac{1}{2}$

24. Which expression has the greatest value for $a = 4$, $b = -3$, and $c = 0$?

A. a^b **B.** b^c **C.** $\frac{1}{b^{-a}}$ **D.** $\frac{a^c}{b^c}$ **E.** $\frac{c}{a^{-b}}$

25. Critical Thinking Is $(-3b)^4 = -12b^4$? Explain why or why not.

Lesson 7-2

- To write numbers in scientific and standard notation (p. 334)
- To use scientific notation (p. 335)

Alg1 2.0

You can use **scientific notation** to express very large or very small numbers. A number is in scientific notation if it is in the form $a \times 10^n$, where $1 \leq a < 10$, and n is an integer.

Is each number written in scientific notation? If not, explain.

26. 950×10^5 **27.** 72.35×10^8 **28.** 1.6×10^{-6} **29.** 0.84×10^{-5}

30. 0.12×10^2 **31.** 5.471×10^{-1} **32.** 10×10^{13} **33.** 0.71×10^{-6}

34. The space probe Voyager 2 traveled 2,793,000 miles. Write the number of miles in scientific notation.

35. There are 189 million passenger cars and trucks in use in the United States. Write the number of passenger cars and trucks using scientific notation.

Order the numbers in each list from least to greatest.

36. $7^{-2}, 7^{12}, 7^0, 7^{-4}, 7^6, 7^1$

37. $3.1 \times 10^2, 30 \times 10^{-1}, 0.3 \times 10^4, 300 \times 10^{-4}$

38. $6.73 \times 10^2, 0.6 \times 10^3, 60.8 \times 10^1, 5.6 \times 10^3$

39. $100 \times 10^{-4}, 5 \times 10^{-3}, 50 \times 10^{-2}, 150 \times 10^{-3}$

Simplify. Write each answer using scientific notation.

40. $11(3 \times 10^{12})$ **41.** $0.2(7.5 \times 10^{-2})$ **42.** $1.4(1.4 \times 10^{-3})$

Lesson 7-3

- To multiply powers (p. 339)
- To work with scientific notation (p. 340)

Alg1 2.0, 10.0

To multiply powers with the same base, add the exponents.

$$a^m \cdot a^n = a^{m+n}$$

Simplify each expression.

43. a^2a^{-4} **44.** t^3st^7 **45.** $4x^6 \cdot x^{-1}$

46. $n^1 \cdot n^5 \cdot n^{-3}$ **47.** $4p \cdot p^8$ **48.** $(a^4b)(2b^5)$

49. $(rs^2)(r^8s^4)$ **50.** $11x(4xy^{-3})(y^7)$ **51.** $w^4 \cdot q \cdot w^{10}$

52. $(4v^2)(5z^9)(12v^{-3})$ **53.** $-2a^2 \cdot (-5n)^{-2} \cdot 13a^6$ **54.** $(-2c^{10})(bc^9)(b^5c^{-18})$

Simplify each expression. Write each answer in scientific notation.

55. $(2 \times 10^1)(6 \times 10^4)$ **56.** $(7 \times 10^{-7})(3 \times 10^6)$

57. $(11 \times 10^3)(2 \times 10^5)$ **58.** $(0.5 \times 10^4)(4 \times 10^{-2})$

59. $(1.2 \times 10^{-3})(0.6 \times 10^{-2})$ **60.** $(5 \times 10^5)(2.7 \times 10^{-6})$

Complete each equation.

61. $4^2 \cdot 4^{\blacksquare} = 4^{11}$ **62.** $12^{-1} \cdot 12^{\blacksquare} = 12^3$ **63.** $3^{\blacksquare} \cdot 3^5 = 3^2$

64. $a^{-5} \cdot a^{\blacksquare} = a^{-7}$ **65.** $v^2 \cdot v^2 \cdot v^{\blacksquare} = v^7$ **66.** $rs^{\blacksquare} \cdot r^{\blacksquare} = r^4s^{-3}$

67. Each square inch of your body has about 6.5×10^2 pores. Suppose the back of your hand has an area of about 0.12×10^2 in.^{2}. About how many pores are on the back of your hand?

Lesson 7-4

- To raise a power to a power (p. 345)
- To raise a product to a power (p. 346)

Alg1 2.0, 10.0

To raise a power to a power, multiply the exponents.

$$(a^m)^n = a^{mn}$$

To raise a product to a power, raise each factor in the product to the power.

$$(ab)^n = a^n b^n$$

Simplify each expression.

68. $(m^2)^6$ **69.** $(b^7)^{-4}$ **70.** $(h^{-1})^3$

71. $(6y^3)^4$ **72.** $(10h^7)^{-1}$ **73.** $(5x^0)^2$

74. $(2d^2)^3$ **75.** $(q^3r)^4$ **76.** $(5c^{-4})(-4m^8)^2$

77. $(1.34^2)^5(1.34)^{-8}$ **78.** $(12x^2y^{-2})^5(4xy^{-3})^{-8}$ **79.** $(-2r^{-4})^2(-3r^2z^8)^{-1}$

Simplify each expression. Write each answer in scientific notation.

80. $(3 \times 10^4)^2$ **81.** $(4 \times 10^{-5})^2$ **82.** $(2 \times 10^7)^3$

83. $(10^3)^2(2 \times 10^{-4})$ **84.** $(1.5^{-2})^2\,(1.5 \times 10^1)^2$ **85.** $(0.6 \times 10^{-1})^3$

86. Rewrite the expression $27x^3y^3$ with only one exponent.

87. Write and solve a problem that involves multiplying exponents.

Lesson 7-5

- To divide powers with the same base (p. 351)
- To raise a quotient to a power (p. 352)

Alg1 2.0, 10.0

To divide powers with the same base, subtract the exponents.

$$\frac{a^m}{a^n} = a^{m-n}$$

To raise a quotient to a power, raise the dividend and the divisor to the power.

$$\left(\frac{a}{b}\right)^n = \frac{a^n}{b^n}$$

Copy and complete each equation.

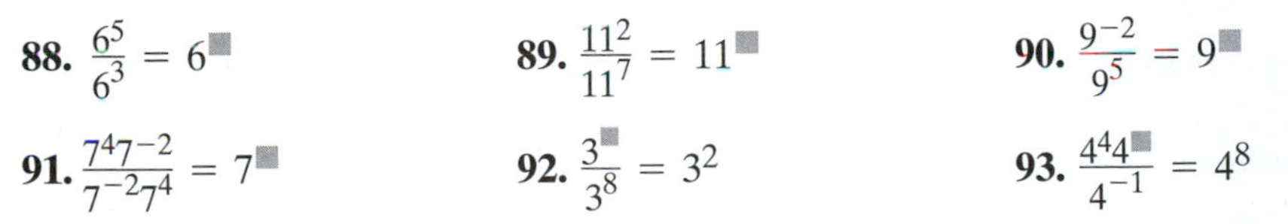

88. $\frac{6^5}{6^3} = 6^{■}$ **89.** $\frac{11^2}{11^7} = 11^{■}$ **90.** $\frac{9^{-2}}{9^5} = 9^{■}$

91. $\frac{7^4 7^{-2}}{7^{-2} 7^4} = 7^{■}$ **92.** $\frac{3^{■}}{3^8} = 3^2$ **93.** $\frac{4^4 4^{■}}{4^{-1}} = 4^8$

Simplify each expression.

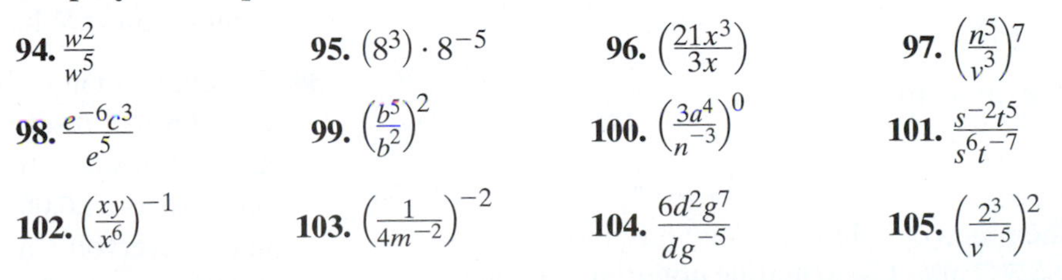

94. $\frac{w^2}{w^5}$ **95.** $(8^3) \cdot 8^{-5}$ **96.** $\left(\frac{21x^3}{3x}\right)$ **97.** $\left(\frac{n^5}{v^3}\right)^7$

98. $\frac{e^{-6}c^3}{e^5}$ **99.** $\left(\frac{b^5}{b^2}\right)^2$ **100.** $\left(\frac{3a^4}{n^{-3}}\right)^0$ **101.** $\frac{s^{-2}t^5}{s^6t^{-7}}$

102. $\left(\frac{xy}{x^6}\right)^{-1}$ **103.** $\left(\frac{1}{4m^{-2}}\right)^{-2}$ **104.** $\frac{6d^2g^7}{dg^{-5}}$ **105.** $\left(\frac{2^3}{v^{-5}}\right)^2$

Simplify each quotient. Give your answer in scientific notation.

106. $\frac{4.2 \times 10^8}{2.1 \times 10^{11}}$ **107.** $\frac{3.1 \times 10^4}{12.4 \times 10^2}$ **108.** $\frac{4.5 \times 10^3}{9 \times 10^7}$ **109.** $\frac{5.1 \times 10^5}{1.7 \times 10^2}$

110. Writing List the steps that you would use to simplify $\left(\frac{5a^8}{10a^6}\right)^{-3}$.

Chapter 7 Test

Go Online PHSchool.com For: Chapter Test Web Code: baa-0752

Simplify each expression.

1. $\frac{r^3t^{-7}}{t^5}$
2. $\left(\frac{a^3}{m}\right)^{-4}$
3. $\frac{t^{-8}m^2}{m^{-3}}$
4. $c^3v^9c^{-1}c^0$
5. $h^2k^{-5}d^3k^2$
6. $9y^4j^2y^{-9}$
7. $(w^2k^0p^{-5})^{-7}$
8. $2y^{-9}h^2(2y^0h^{-4})^{-6}$
9. $(1.2)^5(1.2)^{-2}$
10. $(-3q^{-1})^3\,q^2$

Evaluate each expression for $a = 5, b = -3$, and $c = 2$.

11. $c^2 \cdot 5^b$
12. $\frac{a^3}{b^2}$
13. $\left(\frac{1}{bc}\right)^{-3}$
14. $a^2(-5)^{-1}c^4$
15. $2^c \cdot ab \cdot 7^c$
16. $(4c^3)^2(c^b)$
17. $\left(\frac{ac}{2bc}\right)^c$
18. $\frac{2b^5}{b^4c^3}$
19. $(a^{-1}5bc)^{-2}$
20. $(0.6)^a(0.6)^b$

21. If $n = -3$, which expression has the least value?

    A. n^2n^0 **C.** n^n
    B. n^8n^{-5} **D.** $-n^nn^{-4}$

Write each number in scientific notation.

22. There were about 62,041,000 votes cast for George Bush in the 2004 presidential election.
23. More than 450,000 households in the United States have reptiles as pets.

Is each number written in scientific notation? If not, explain.

24. 76×10^{-9}
25. 7.3×10^5
26. $4.05 \times 10 \times 10^{-8}$
27. 32.5×10^{13}

28. **a.** The speed of light in a vacuum is about 186,300 mi/s. Use scientific notation to express how far light travels in one hour.
    b. At its farthest, Saturn is about 1.03×10^9 mi from Earth. About how many hours does it take for light to travel from Earth to Saturn?

29. Which answer has the numbers listed from least to greatest?
    A. $50 \times 10^{-2}, 15 \times 10^{-1}, 105 \times 10^{-2}$
    B. $71 \times 10^2, 6.5 \times 10^1, 0.08 \times 10^2$
    C. $12 \times 10^2, 210 \times 10^{-1}, 0.0012 \times 10^{-3}$
    D. $3.6 \times 10^0, 0.603 \times 10^1, 6030 \times 10^{-1}$

30. The length of a rectangle measures $7d^2$ cm and the width measures 3^2d^5 cm. What is the area of the rectangle?

31. The mass of Mercury is about 3.3×10^{23} kg. A student made a model of Mercury that weighs 60 g. Mercury is about how many times larger than the model?

    A. 5.5×10^{24} **C.** 1.8×10^{-27}
    B. 5.5×10^{18} **D.** 1.8×10^{19}

32. Write and solve a problem that involves raising a power to a power.

33. Which expression does NOT equal 32?

    A. $2 \cdot 2^4$ **B.** $2\left(\frac{1}{4^2}\right)^{-1}$ **C.** $2^3 \cdot 2^2$ **D.** $(2^1)^4$

34. The human body contains about 5×10^6 red blood cells per microliter of blood, and 3.2×10^4 μL (microliters) of blood for each pound of body weight. How much does a person with 2.24×10^{13} red blood cells weigh?

Write each expression using only one exponent.

35. $x^2(y^3)^2 \cdot 64z^6 \cdot x^4$
36. $\frac{a^3}{125b^3}$

37. Lola is putting up a fence around her rectangular garden that has an area of $35p^3q^5$ ft^2. The garden's length is $5p^2q$. What is the garden's width?

38. Folsom Dam in California holds 1 million acre-feet of water in a reservoir. An acre-foot of water is the amount of water that covers an acre to the depth of one foot, or 326,000 gallons. How many gallons are in the reservoir? Write your answer in scientific notation.

39. Which expression equals $d^{-3}e^9f^{-1} \cdot 14d^3$?

    A. 0 **B.** $\frac{14e^9}{d^9f}$ **C.** $\frac{e^9}{14f}$ **D.** $\frac{14e^9}{f}$

Cumulative Practice

Some questions ask you to solve a problem using exponents. Read the question at the right. Then follow the tips to answer the sample question.

If the side length of a square can be represented by the expression $4x^2y^6$, which expression could represent the area of the square?

Ⓐ $2xy^3$

Ⓑ $8x^4y^{12}$

Ⓒ $16x^4y^{12}$

Ⓓ $16x^4y^{36}$

Tip 1
Think about how the information given in the problem can be used to answer the question.

Tip 2
Look for answer choices that make sense in the context of the problem.

Think It Through

The side length of the square is $4x^2y^6$, so the area is $4x^2y^6 \times 4x^2y^6$. The answer must contain $4 \times 4 = 16$. Remember, add the exponents when multiplying with like bases. So, $x^2y^6 \times x^2y^6 = x^{2+2}y^{6+6} = x^4y^{12}$. The correct answer is C.

Vocabulary Review

As you solve problems, you must understand the meanings of mathematical terms. Choose the correct term to complete each sentense.

A. If a line passes through the point $(a, 0)$, then $(a, 0)$ is called the (*x-intercept*, *y-intercept*).

B. A system of linear equations has (*infinitely many solutions*, *no solution*) when the graphs of the equations are parallel.

C. Lines in the same plane that never intersect are (*parallel*, *perpendicular*) lines.

D. A (*linear inequality*, *solution of an inequality*) describes a region of the coordinate plane that has a boundary line.

E. The product of two numbers is -1 if one number is the (*multiplicative inverse*, *negative reciprocal*) of the other.

Read each question. Then write the letter of the correct answer on your paper.

1. What is the y-intercept of the function shown on the graph at the right? **(Lesson 5-2)**

Ⓐ $(-2, 0)$

Ⓑ $(0, -3)$

Ⓒ $\left(-\frac{2}{3}, 0\right)$

Ⓓ $\left(0, \frac{2}{3}\right)$

2. Where is the x-intercept of the line represented by the equation $8x - 3y = 24$? **(Lesson 5-3)**

Ⓐ $x = -8$ Ⓑ $x = -3$ Ⓒ $x = 3$ Ⓓ $x = 8$

3. The data shown in the table at the right represent points on a line. What is the x-intercept of the line? **(Lesson 5-3)**

x	y
0	−4
1	4
2	12
3	20

Ⓐ $\left(\frac{1}{2}, 0\right)$

Ⓑ $(0, -4)$

Ⓒ $(2, 0)$

Ⓓ $\left(0, \frac{1}{4}\right)$

4. If a is positive and b is negative, which of the following is negative? **(Lesson 3-6)**

Ⓐ $a + |b|$

Ⓑ $|a|b$

Ⓒ $a|b|$

Ⓓ $|a| - b$

5. What is the solution of the following system of equations? **(Lesson 6-2)**

$\frac{1}{3}x - y = 4$

$x + 3y = 0$

Ⓐ $(9, -1)$

Ⓑ $(6, -2)$

Ⓒ $(-6, 2)$

Ⓓ $(-9, 1)$

6. Which number has the least value? **(Lesson 7-2)**

Ⓐ 2.8×10^{-5}

Ⓑ 8.3×10^{-7}

Ⓒ 5.3×10^{-4}

Ⓓ 1.6×10^{-8}

7. Which expression is equivalent to $(j^2k^3)(jk^2)$? **(Lesson 7-3)**

Ⓐ j^2k^2 Ⓑ j^3k^5 Ⓒ j^2k^6 Ⓓ j^3k^6

Cumulative Practice (continued)

8. The dimensions of a rectangular prism are shown in the diagram at the right. Which expression represents the volume of the rectangular prism? **(Lesson 7-3)**

a^2b ab^3 ab^2

Ⓐ a^2b^5 Ⓒ a^4b^5

Ⓑ a^2b^6 Ⓓ a^4b^6

9. Which expression is equivalent to $\frac{3x^3y}{(3y)^{-2}}$? **(Lesson 7-5)**

Ⓐ $9x^3y^3$ Ⓒ $\frac{x^3}{y}$

Ⓑ $27x^3y^3$ Ⓓ $\frac{x^3y^3}{3}$

10. Which system of equations is shown in the graph at the right? **(Lesson 6-1)**

Ⓐ $3x + 2y = 6$
$y = \frac{1}{4}x + 2$

Ⓒ $2x + 3y = 12$
$y = -\frac{1}{4}x + 2$

Ⓑ $3x + 3y = 9$
$y = \frac{1}{4}x + 2$

Ⓓ $3x - 2y = 12$
$y = 4x + 2$

11. Which statement is true for every solution of the following system? **(Lesson 6-6)**

$y > x + 4$

$y + x > 4$

Ⓐ $x \leq -3$ Ⓑ $x > 4$ Ⓒ $y < 5$ Ⓓ $y > 4$

12. Simplify $-3a^8 \cdot cb^{-3} \cdot b^{12} \cdot 9c^5$. **(Lesson 7-3)**

Ⓐ $6a^9b^5c^6$ Ⓒ $-27a^8b^9c^6$

Ⓑ $-27a^8b^{15}c^6$ Ⓓ $-3abc$

13. All of the students in Haley's class received between 36 and 48 points on the last quiz. Each question was worth 2 points, and there was no partial credit. How many questions could Haley have answered correctly? **(Lesson 3-5)**

Ⓐ 12 Ⓑ 21 Ⓒ 44 Ⓓ 72

14. Mr. Kent sells calculators for \$35 each. If an order is placed from a business account, there is a \$50 shipping fee, and no fewer than 100 calculators can be purchased. Which is a reasonable amount of money that a business would spend when ordering calculators? **(Lesson 3-5)**

Ⓐ \$750 Ⓑ \$1070 Ⓒ \$2990 Ⓓ \$3585

15. Alejandro bought 6 notebooks and 2 binders for \$23.52. Cassie bought 3 notebooks and 4 binders for \$25.53. Which system of equations can be used to find the cost of a notebook n and a binder b? **(Lesson 6-4)**

Ⓐ $6n + 2b = 23.52$
$3n + 4b = 25.53$

Ⓒ $6n + 3n = 23.52$
$2b + 4b = 25.53$

Ⓑ $6n + 4b = 23.52$
$3n + 2b = 25.53$

Ⓓ $9n + 6b = 49.05$
$n + b = 49.05$

16. Megan's company pays \$20,000 per year plus a 5% sales commission. Laurie's company pays \$32,000 per year plus a 1% sales commission. Which system of equations can be used to determine the amount Megan and Laurie must sell s to receive the same pay p? **(Lesson 6-4)**

Ⓐ $p = 5s + 20{,}000$
$p = s + 32{,}000$

Ⓒ $p + 0.5s = 20{,}000$
$p + 0.1s = 32{,}000$

Ⓑ $p + 5s = 20{,}000$
$p + s = 32{,}000$

Ⓓ $p = 0.05s + 20{,}000$
$p = 0.01s + 32{,}000$

17. A library is packing its books to move to a new building. If 4 large and 2 small boxes are used, 124 books can be packed. If 3 large and 5 small boxes are used, 135 books can be packed. Which system of equations can be used to find the number of books s that can be packed in a small box and the number ℓ in a large box? **(Lesson 6-4)**

Ⓐ $\ell + s = 14$
$7\ell + 7s = 259$

Ⓒ $3\ell + 4\ell = 124$
$2s + 5s = 135$

Ⓑ $4\ell + 2s = 124$
$3\ell + 5s = 135$

Ⓓ $4\ell + 5s = 124$
$3\ell + 2s = 135$

18. What is the solution set of the inequality $3|2x - 1| > 15$? **(Lesson 3-6)**

Ⓐ $x < -2$ or $x > 3$ Ⓒ $-2 < x < 3$

Ⓑ $x > -2$ Ⓓ $-3 < x < 2$

19. Which equation represents a line that is parallel to $y = -\frac{1}{4}x + 2$? **(Lesson 5-5)**

Ⓐ $-y = 4x$ Ⓒ $y = 4x - 12$

Ⓑ $4y + x = 5$ Ⓓ $-\frac{1}{4}x - y = -3$

20. Which equation represents a line that is perpendicular to $3y = x$ and passes through the point $(0, -6)$? **(Lesson 5-5)**

Ⓐ $y = -3(x + 6)$ Ⓒ $y = 3(x + 6)$

Ⓑ $y = -3x - 6$ Ⓓ $y = 3x - 6$

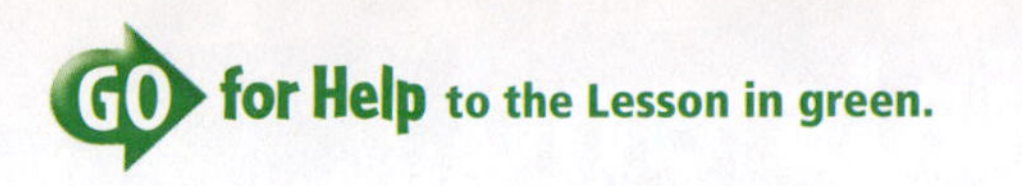

Standards Mastery

21. Which value below is NOT a solution to the inequality $|6x + 1| \geq 11$? **(Lesson 3-6)**

Ⓐ -3 Ⓑ -1 Ⓒ 2 Ⓓ 3

22. Which equation represents a line that is perpendicular to the line shown and passes through the point shown? **(Lesson 5-5)**

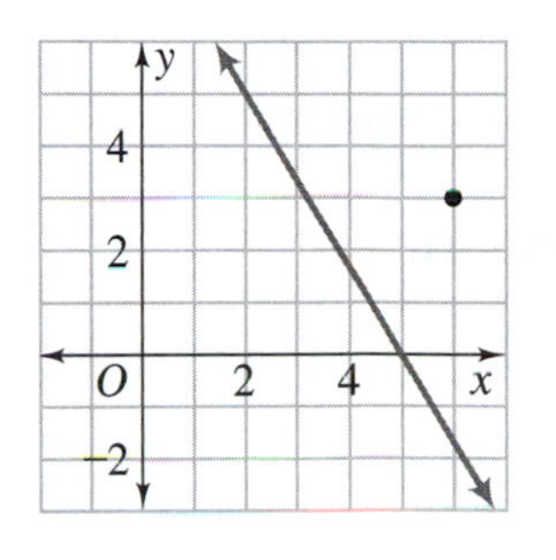

Ⓐ $y = -\frac{5}{3}(x - 6)$

Ⓑ $y = -\frac{5}{3}(x - 6) + 3$

Ⓒ $y = \frac{3}{5}(x - 6) + 3$

Ⓓ $y = \frac{3}{5}(x - 6)$

23. Which statement is true about the lines shown in the graph? **(Lesson 5-5)**

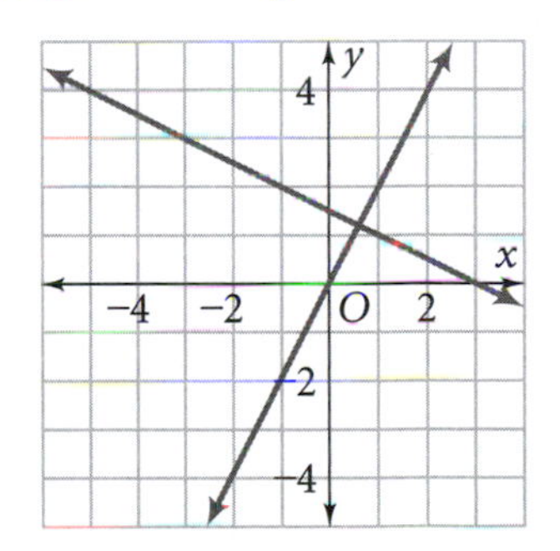

Ⓐ The slopes of the lines are the same.

Ⓑ The slopes of the lines are negative reciprocals.

Ⓒ The lines have the same y-intercept.

Ⓓ The lines have the same x-intercept.

24. Simplify $(4m + 7v^2 - v) - (11v - 12m)$. **(Lesson 1-7)**

Ⓐ $-8m + 7v^2 + 10v$

Ⓑ $16m^2 + 7v^2 + 10v$

Ⓒ $16m + 7v^2 - 12v$

Ⓓ $-8m + 7v^2 - 12v$

25. Simplify $-3x^4 \cdot 2y^2 \cdot 4x^{-6}$. **(Lesson 7-3)**

Ⓐ $3x^{-2}y^2$

Ⓑ $3x^{-24}y^2$

Ⓒ $-24x^{-2}y^2$

Ⓓ $-24x^{-24}y^2$

26. The diameter of Earth is about 1.28×10^4 km. About what is Earth's radius? **(Lesson 7-3)**

Ⓐ 2.56×10^8 km

Ⓑ 6.4×10^3 km

Ⓒ 6.4×10^4 km

Ⓓ 2.56×10^6 km

27. Which inequality is shown on the graph below? **(Lesson 6-5)**

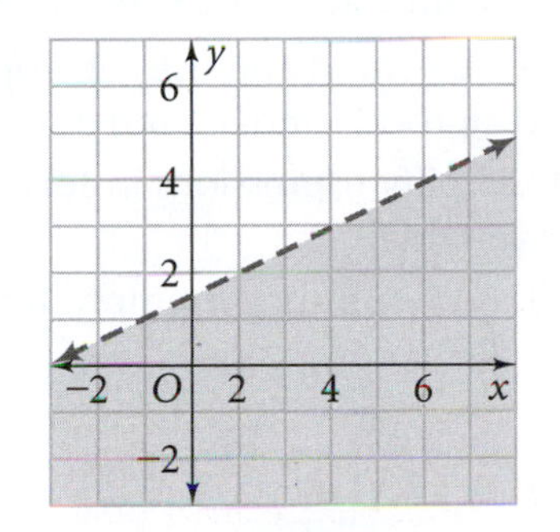

Ⓐ $y - 1 > \frac{2}{5}(x + 1)$

Ⓑ $y + 1 > \frac{2}{5}(x - 1)$

Ⓒ $y - 1 < \frac{2}{5}(x + 1)$

Ⓓ $y + 1 < \frac{2}{5}(x - 1)$

Standards Reference Guide

California Content Standard	Item Number(s)
Alg1 2.0	6–9, 12, 26
Alg1 3.0	4, 18, 21
Alg1 5.0	13, 14
Alg1 6.0	1–3, 27
Alg1 8.0	19, 20, 22, 23
Alg1 9.0	5, 10, 11, 15–17
Alg1 10.0	24, 25

For additional review and practice, see the *California Standards Review and Practice Workbook* or go online to use

Visit: PHSchool.com, **Web Code:** baq-9045

CALIFORNIA CHECK SYSTEM

CHAPTER 8

Polynomials and Factoring

What You've Learned

California Content Standards

2.0 Understand and use such operations as taking the opposite and finding the reciprocal. Understand and use the rules of exponents.

4.0 Simplify expressions before solving linear equations and inequalities in one variable.

10.0 Add, subtract, multiply, and divide monomials.

Check Your Readiness

GO for Help to the Lesson in green.

Finding Factors of Composite Numbers (Skills Handbook page 595)

List all the factors of each number.

1. 12 **2.** 56 **3.** 31 **4.** 27

5. 110 **6.** 65 **7.** 50 **8.** 200

9. 11 **10.** 42 **11.** 66 **12.** 73

Simplifying Expressions (Lesson 1-7)

Simplify each expression.

13. $2x^2 - x + x^2 - 3x$

14. $-b + 2 + 3b + 4$

15. $-5y - y^2 + 4y^2 - 6y$

16. $(3w - 2w^2 + 4w - 2w^2)\frac{1}{6}$

17. $-8(z + 2) + 5(3z - 10)$

18. $2(x + 4x^2 - 2x - 2x^2)$

19. $12t - 5t^2 - 2t - t^2$

20. $p - 3 - (p^2 - 3) - 3p$

Multiplying Expressions With Exponents (Lessons 7-3 and 7-4)

Simplify each expression.

21. $(7w)^2$ **22.** $(-5n^2)(-5n)$ **23.** $(3z^2)^2$ **24.** $(2t^3)(5t^4)$

25. $(4y^3)^2$ **26.** $(-9ab)^2$ **27.** $4(x^2)^2$ **28.** $(-6p^4)^2$

Dividing Expressions With Exponents (Lesson 7-5)

Simplify each expression.

29. $\frac{x^5y^8}{x^3y^4}$ **30.** $\frac{(3c)^2}{(3c)}$ **31.** $\frac{-5t}{(10t^3)(2t)}$ **32.** $\frac{(3a)(4a^3)}{6a^2}$

▲ These Labrador retrievers have the same parents. In Lesson 8-4, you will multiply polynomials to determine the chances that a puppy will have dark fur or yellow fur.

What You'll Learn Next

California Content Standards

10.0 Add, subtract, multiply, and divide monomials and polynomials. Solve multi-step problems, including word problems, by using these techniques.

11.0 Apply basic factoring techniques to second- and simple third-degree polynomials. These techniques include finding a common factor for all terms in a polynomial, recognizing the difference of two squares, and recognizing perfect squares of binomials.

New Vocabulary

English and Spanish Audio Online

- **binomial** (p. 371)
- **degree of a monomial** (p. 371)
- **degree of a polynomial** (p. 371)
- **difference of squares** (p. 390)
- **factor by grouping** (p. 410)
- **monomial** (p. 370)
- **perfect-square trinomial** (p. 404)
- **polynomial** (p. 371)
- **standard form of a polynomial** (p. 371)
- **trinomial** (p. 371)

8-1 Adding and Subtracting Polynomials

California Content Standards

10.0 Add and subtract polynomials. Solve multi-step problems, including word problems, by using these techniques. ***Develop***

What You'll Learn

- To describe polynomials
- To add and subtract polynomials

. . . And Why

To combine and simplify polynomials, as in Example 4

Check Skills You'll Need

GO for Help Lesson 1-7

Simplify each expression.

1. $6t + 13t$ **2.** $5g + 34g$ **3.** $7k - 15k$

4. $2b - 6 + 9b$ **5.** $4n^2 - 7n^2$ **6.** $8x^2 - x^2$

New Vocabulary

- monomial
- degree of a monomial
- polynomial
- standard form of a polynomial
- degree of a polynomial
- binomial
- trinomial

Describing Polynomials

CA Standards Investigation Using Polynomials

Suppose you work at a pet store. The table below shows the details of several customers' orders.

	A	B	C	D	E	F
1	Customer	Seed	Cuttlebone	Millet	G. Paper	Perches
2	Davis			✔		
3	Brooks	✔	✔			
4	Casic	✔		✔		
5	Martino	✔			✔	✔

The following variables represent the number of each item ordered.

s = bags of birdseed m = bags of millet
c = packages of cuttlebone g = packages of gravel paper
p = packages of perches

1. Which expression represents the cost of Casic's order?

   A. $27.99(s + m)$ **B.** $3.99s + 24m$ **C.** $27.99sm$

2. Write expressions to represent each of the other customers' orders.

3. Martino buys 10 bags of birdseed, 4 packages of gravel paper, and 2 packages of perches. What is the total cost of his order?

A **monomial** is an expression that is a number, a variable, or a product of a number and one or more variables. Each of the following is a monomial.

$$12 \qquad y \qquad -5x^2y \qquad \frac{c}{3}$$

EXERCISES
Standards Practice

For more exercises, see *Extra Skills and Word Problem Practice.*

Alg1 10.0

A Practice by Example

Example 1 (page 371)

GO for Help

Find the degree of each monomial.

1. $4x$
2. $7c^3$
3. -16
4. $6y^2w^8$
5. $8ab^3$
6. 6
7. $-9x^4$
8. 11

Example 2 (page 371)

Name each expression based on its degree and number of terms.

9. $5x^2 - 2x + 3$
10. $\frac{3}{4}z + 5$
11. $7a^3 + 4a - 12$
12. $\frac{3}{x} + 5$
13. -15
14. $w^2 + 2$

Write each polynomial in standard form. Then name each polynomial based on its degree and number of terms.

15. $4x - 3x^2$
16. $4x + 9$
17. $c^2 - 2 + 4c$
18. $9z^2 - 11z^2 + 5z - 5$
19. $y - 7y^3 + 15y^8$
20. $-10 + 4q^4 - 8q + 3q^2$

Example 3 (page 372)

Simplify each sum.

21. $\begin{array}{r} 5m^2 + 9 \\ +\ 3m^2 + 6 \\ \hline \end{array}$
22. $\begin{array}{r} 3k - 8 \\ +\ 7k + 12 \\ \hline \end{array}$
23. $\begin{array}{r} w^2 + w - 4 \\ +\ 7w^2 - 4w + 8 \\ \hline \end{array}$
24. $(8x^2 + 1) + (12x^2 + 6)$
25. $(g^4 + 4g) + (9g^4 + 7g)$
26. $(a^2 + a + 1) + (5a^2 - 8a + 20)$
27. $(7y^3 - 3y^2 + 4y) + (8y^4 + 3y^2)$

Example 4 (page 372)

Simplify each difference.

28. $\begin{array}{r} 6c - 5 \\ -\ (4c + 9) \\ \hline \end{array}$
29. $\begin{array}{r} 2b + 6 \\ -(b + 5) \\ \hline \end{array}$
30. $\begin{array}{r} 7h^2 + 4h - 8 \\ -\ (3h^2 - 2h + 10) \\ \hline \end{array}$
31. $(17n^4 + 2n^3) - (10n^4 + n^3)$
32. $(24x^5 + 12x) - (9x^5 + 11x)$
33. $(6w^2 - 3w + 1) - (w^2 + w - 9)$
34. $(-5x^4 + x^2) - (x^3 + 8x^2 - x)$

B Apply Your Skills

Simplify. Write each answer in standard form.

35. $(7y^2 - 3y + 4y) + (8y^2 + 3y^2 + 4y)$
36. $(2x^3 - 5x^2 - 1) - (8x^3 + 3 - 8x^2)$
37. $(-7z^3 + 3z - 1) - (-6z^2 + z + 4)$
38. $(7a^3 - a + 3a^2) + (8a^2 - 3a - 4)$

Find an expression for the perimeter of each figure.

39.

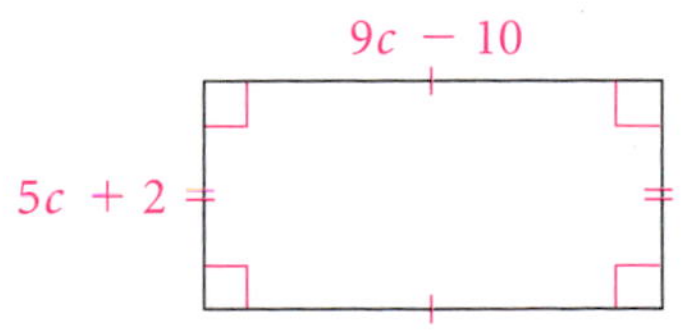

40.

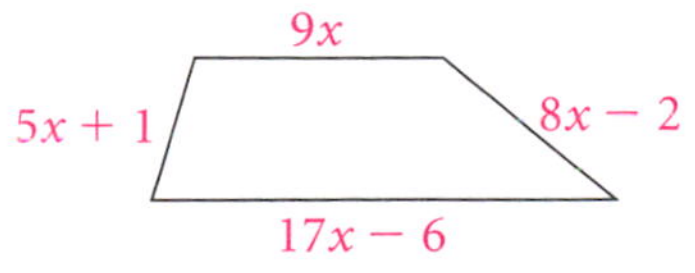

Vocabulary Tip

The prefix mono means "one."

The fraction $\frac{c}{3}$ is a monomial, but the expression $\frac{c}{x}$, or cx^{-1}, is *not* a monomial because the exponent of the variable is negative.

The **degree of a monomial** is the sum of the exponents of its variables. For a nonzero constant, the degree is 0. Zero has no degree.

1 EXAMPLE Degree of a Monomial

Find the degree of each monomial.

a. $\frac{2}{3}x$ Degree: 1 $\frac{2}{3}x = \frac{2}{3}x^1$. The exponent is 1.

b. $7x^2y^3$ Degree: 5 The exponents are 2 and 3. Their sum is 5.

c. -4 Degree: 0 The degree of a nonzero constant is 0.

CA Standards Check 1 Find the degree of $-5xy^2$.

A **polynomial** is a sum of one or more monomials.

$$\begin{array}{lcccc} & 3x^4 & +\ 5x^2 & -\ 7x & +\ 1 \\ & \uparrow & \uparrow & \uparrow & \uparrow \\ \text{degree} \rightarrow & 4 & 2 & 1 & 0 \end{array}$$

The polynomial shown above is in standard form. **Standard form of a polynomial** means that the degrees of its monomial terms decrease from left to right. The **degree of a polynomial** in one variable is the same as the degree of the monomial with the greatest exponent. The degree of $3x^4 + 5x^2 - 7x + 1$ is 4.

After you simplify a polynomial by combining like terms, you can name the polynomial based on its degree or the number of monomial terms it contains.

Polynomial	Degree	Name Using Degree	Number of Terms	Name Using Number of Terms
$7x + 4$	1	linear	2	**binomial**
$3x^2 + 2x + 1$	2	quadratic	3	**trinomial**
$4x^3$	3	cubic	1	monomial
$9x^4 + 11x$	4	fourth degree	2	binomial
5	0	constant	1	monomial

2 EXAMPLE Classifying Polynomials

Write each polynomial in standard form. Then name each polynomial based on its degree and the number of its terms.

a. $5 - 2x$

$-2x + 5$ Place terms in order.

linear binomial

b. $3x^4 - 4 + 2x^2 + 5x^4$

$3x^4 + 5x^4 + 2x^2 - 4$ Place terms in order.

$8x^4 + 2x^2 - 4$ Combine like terms.

fourth degree trinomial

CA Standards Check 2 Write each polynomial in standard form. Then name each polynomial based on its degree and the number of its terms.

a. $6x^2 + 7 - 9x^4$ b. $3y - 4 - y^3$ c. $8 + 7v - 11v$

Adding and Subtracting Polynomials

You can add polynomials by adding like terms.

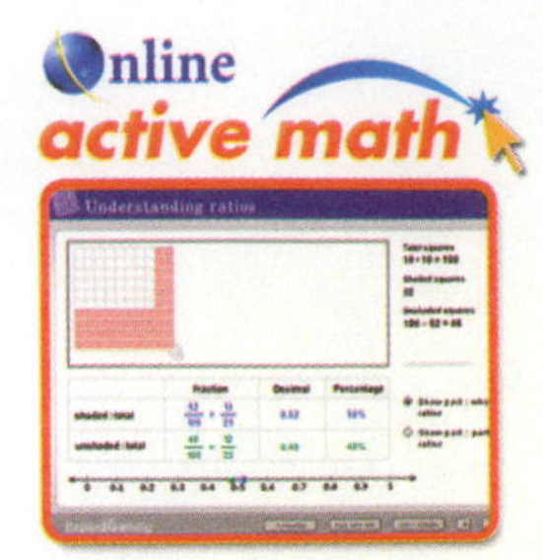

For: Polynomial Addition Activity
Use: Interactive Textbook, 8-1

3 EXAMPLE Adding Polynomials

Simplify $(4x^2 + 6x + 7) + (2x^2 - 9x + 1)$.

Method 1 Add vertically.

Line up like terms. Then add the coefficients.

$$\begin{array}{r} 4x^2 + 6x + 7 \\ + \; 2x^2 - 9x + 1 \\ \hline 6x^2 - 3x + 8 \end{array}$$

Method 2 Add horizontally.

Group like terms. Then add the coefficients.

$$\begin{aligned}(4x^2 + 6x + 7) + (2x^2 - 9x + 1) &= (4x^2 + 2x^2) + (6x - 9x) + (7 + 1) \\ &= 6x^2 - 3x + 8\end{aligned}$$

CA Standards Check 3 Simplify each sum.

a. $(12m^2 + 4) + (8m^2 + 5)$
b. $(t^2 - 6) + (3t^2 + 11)$
c. $(9w^3 + 8w^2) + (7w^3 + 4)$
d. $(2p^3 + 6p^2 + 10p) + (9p^3 + 11p^2 + 3p)$

In Chapter 1, you learned that subtraction means to add the opposite. So when you subtract a polynomial, change each of the terms to its opposite. Then add the coefficients.

4 EXAMPLE Subtracting Polynomials

Simplify $(2x^3 + 5x^2 - 3x) - (x^3 - 8x^2 + 11)$.

Method 1 Subtract vertically.

$$\begin{array}{r} 2x^3 + 5x^2 - 3x \qquad \\ - \; (x^3 - 8x^2 \qquad + 11) \\ \hline \end{array}$$ Line up like terms.

$$\begin{array}{r} 2x^3 + 5x^2 - 3x \qquad \\ -x^3 + 8x^2 \qquad - 11 \\ \hline x^3 + 13x^2 - 3x - 11 \end{array}$$ Then add the opposite of each term in the polynomial being subtracted.

Method 2 Subtract horizontally.

$(2x^3 + 5x^2 - 3x) - (x^3 - 8x^2 + 11)$

$= 2x^3 + 5x^2 - 3x - x^3 + 8x^2 - 11$ Write the opposite of each term in the polynomial being subtracted.

$= (2x^3 - x^3) + (5x^2 + 8x^2) - 3x - 11$ Group like terms.

$= x^3 + 13x^2 - 3x - 11$ Simplify.

CA Standards Check 4 Simplify each difference.

a. $(v^3 + 6v^2 - v) - (9v^3 - 7v^2 + 3v)$
b. $(30d^3 - 29d^2 - 3d) - (2d^3 + d^2)$

8-2 Multiplying and Factoring

California Content Standards

10.0 Multiply monomials and polynomials. Solve multi-step problems, including word problems, by using these techniques. *Develop*

11.0 Apply basic factoring techniques to second-degree polynomials. These techniques include finding a common factor for all terms in a polynomial. *Introduce*

What You'll Learn

- To multiply a polynomial by a monomial
- To factor a monomial from a polynomial

. . . And Why

To factor a monomial out of a polynomial, as in Example 3

Check Skills You'll Need

GO for Help Lesson 1-7

Multiply.

1. $3(302)$
2. $41(7)$
3. $9(504)$

Simplify each expression.

4. $4(6 + 5x)$
5. $-8(2y + 1)$
6. $(5v - 1)5$
7. $7(p - 2)$
8. $(6 - x)9$
9. $-2(4x - 1)$

Distributing a Monomial

In Chapter 1, you used the Distributive Property to multiply a number by a sum or difference.

$5(a + 3) = 5a + 15 \quad (x - 2)(3) = 3x - 6 \quad -2(2y + 7) = -4y - 14$

You can also use the Distributive Property or an area model to multiply polynomials. Consider the product $2x(3x + 1)$.

$$\begin{aligned}2x(3x + 1) &= 2x(3x) + 2x(1) \\ &= 6x^2 + 2x\end{aligned}$$

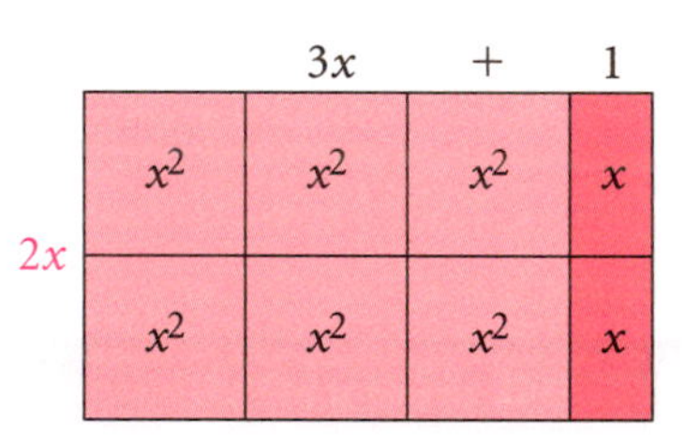

You can use the Distributive Property for multiplying powers with the same base when multiplying by a monomial.

1 EXAMPLE Multiplying a Monomial and a Trinomial

Problem Solving Tip

When you distribute a negative expression such as $-4y^2$, be sure to apply the negative sign to each term within the parentheses.

Simplify $-4y^2(5y^4 - 3y^2 + 2)$.

$-4y^2(5y^4 - 3y^2 + 2)$

$= -4y^2(5y^4) - 4y^2(-3y^2) - 4y^2(2)$ Use the Distributive Property.

$= -20y^{2+4} + 12y^{2+2} - 8y^2$ Multiply the coefficients and add the exponents of powers with the same base.

$= -20y^6 + 12y^4 - 8y^2$ Simplify.

CA Standards Check 1 Simplify each product.

a. $4b(5b^2 + b + 6)$
b. $-7h(3h^2 - 8h - 1)$
c. $2x(x^2 - 6x + 5)$

Factoring a Monomial From a Polynomial

Vocabulary Tip

The greatest common factor is the greatest factor that divides evenly into each term of an expression.

Factoring a polynomial reverses the multiplication process. To factor a monomial from a polynomial, first find the common factor of its terms.

2 EXAMPLE Finding the Common Factor

Find the common factor of the terms of $4x^3 + 12x^2 - 8x$.

$4x^3 = 2 \cdot 2 \cdot x \cdot x \cdot x$

$12x^2 = 2 \cdot 2 \cdot 3 \cdot x \cdot x$

$8x = 2 \cdot 2 \cdot 2 \cdot x$

List the prime factors of each term. Identify the factors common to all terms.

The common factor is $2 \cdot 2 \cdot x$ or $4x$.

CA Standards Check 2 Find the common factor of the terms of each polynomial.

a. $5v^5 + 10v^3$ **b.** $3t^2 - 18$ **c.** $4b^3 - 2b^2 - 6b$

To factor a polynomial completely, you must factor until there are no common factors other than 1.

3 EXAMPLE Factoring Out a Monomial

Factor $3x^3 - 12x^2 + 15x$.

Step 1 Find the common factor.

$3x^3 = 3 \cdot x \cdot x \cdot x$

$12x^2 = 2 \cdot 2 \cdot 3 \cdot x \cdot x$

$15x = 3 \cdot 5 \cdot x$

The common factor is $3 \cdot x$ or $3x$.

Step 2 Factor out the common factor.

$3x^3 - 12x^2 + 15x$

$= 3x(x^2) + 3x(-4x) + 3x(5)$

$= 3x(x^2 - 4x + 5)$

CA Standards Check 3 Use the common factor to factor each polynomial.

a. $8x^2 - 12x$ **b.** $5d^3 + 10d$ **c.** $6m^3 - 12m^2 - 24m$

EXERCISES Standards Practice

For more exercises, see *Extra Skills and Word Problem Practice.*

Alg1 10.0, 11.0

A Practice by Example

GO for Help Example 1 (page 376)

Simplify each product.

1. $8m(m + 6)$ **2.** $(x + 10)3x$ **3.** $9k(7k + 4)$

4. $-5a(a - 1)$ **5.** $2x^2(9 + x)$ **6.** $-p^2(p - 11)$

7. $2x(6x^3 - x^2 + 5x)$ **8.** $4y^2(9y^3 + 8y^2 - 11)$ **9.** $-5c^3(9c^2 - 8c - 5)$

10. $-7q^2(6q^5 - 2q - 7)$ **11.** $-3g^7(g^4 - 6g^2 + 5)$ **12.** $-4x^6(10x^3 + 3x^2 - 7)$

Example 2 (page 377)

Find the common factor of the terms of each polynomial.

13. $15w + 21$ **14.** $6a^2 - 8a$ **15.** $36v + 24$

16. $x^3 + 7x^2 - 5x$ **17.** $5b^3 + 15b - 30$ **18.** $9x^3 - 6x^2 + 12x$

Example 3 (page 377)

Factor each polynomial.

19. $6x - 4$ **20.** $v^2 + 4v$ **21.** $10x^3 - 25x^2 + 20$

22. $2t^2 - 10t^4$ **23.** $15n^3 - 3n^2 + 12n$ **24.** $6p^6 + 24p^5 + 18p^3$

B Apply Your Skills

25. Error Analysis Kevin said that $-2x(4x - 3) = -8x^2 - 6x$. Karla said that $-2x(4x - 3) = -8x^2 + 6x$. Who is correct? Explain.

26. Write and factor a polynomial that has a common factor in each term.

Simplify. Write in standard form.

27. $-3a(4a^2 - 5a + 9)$ **28.** $-7p^2(-2p^3 + 5p)$ **29.** $12c(-5c^2 + 3c - 4)$

30. $y(y + 3) - 5y(y - 2)$ **31.** $x^2(x + 1) - x(x^2 - 1)$ **32.** $4t(3t^2 - 4t) - t(7t)$

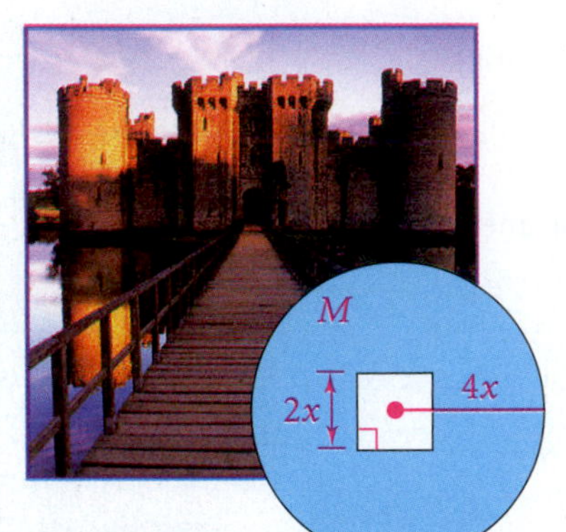

33. Suppose you are building a model of the square castle shown at the left. The moat of the model castle is made of blue paper.

a. Find the area of the moat using the diagram with the photo.

b. Write your answer in factored form.

Factor each polynomial.

34. $9m^{12} - 36m^7 + 81m^5$ **35.** $24x^3 - 96x^2 + 48x$ **36.** $16n^3 + 48n^2 - 80n$

37. $5x^4 + 4x^3 + 3x^2$ **38.** $13ab^3 + 39a^2b^4$ **39.** $7g^2k^3 - 35g^5k^2$

40. The common factor of two numbers p and q is 5. What is the common factor of p^2 and q^2? Explain your answer.

41. a. Factor $n^2 - n$.

b. Math Reasoning Suppose n is an integer. Is $n^2 - n$ *always, sometimes,* or *never* even? Justify your answer.

42. A triangular number is a number you can represent with a triangular arrangement of objects. A triangular number can also be written as a product of two factors, as in the table.

a. Find the values of a, b, c, and d, and then write an expression in factored form for the nth triangular number.

	1	2	3	4
Triangular Number	1	3	6	10
Factored Form	$\frac{a}{2}(a + 1)$	$\frac{b}{2}(b + 1)$	$\frac{c}{2}(c + 1)$	$\frac{d}{2}(d + 1)$

b. Use the expression you wrote to find the 100th triangular number.

Homework Video Tutor

Visit: PHSchool.com
Web Code: bae-0802

C Challenge

43. a. How many sides does the polygon have? How many of its diagonals come from one vertex?

b. Suppose a polygon has n sides. How many diagonals will it have from one vertex?

c. The number of diagonals from all the vertices is $\frac{n}{2}(n - 3)$. Multiply the two factors.

d. For a polygon with 8 sides, what is the total number of diagonals that can be drawn from the vertices?

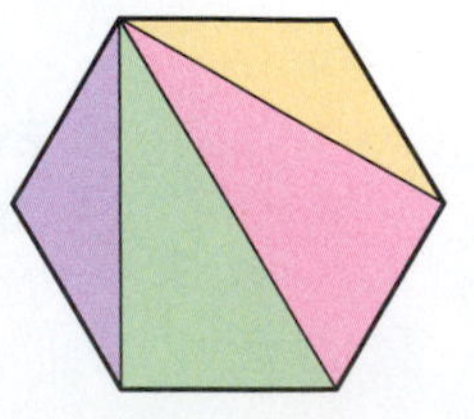

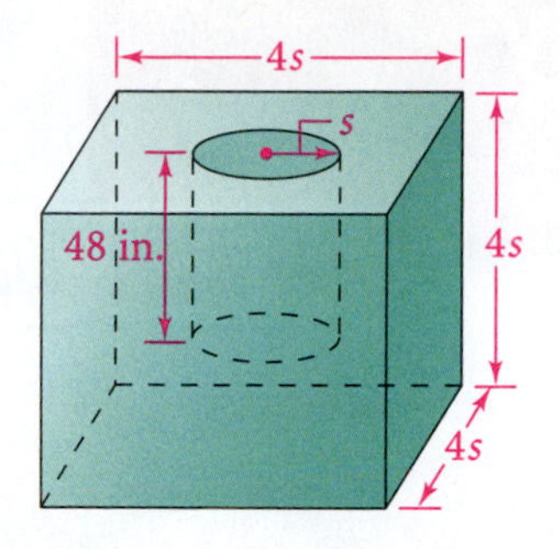

44. The diagram shows a cube with a cylinder cut out of it. The formula for the volume of a cylinder is $V = \pi r^2 h$, where r is the radius and h is the height.

a. Write a formula for the volume of the cube in terms of s.

b. Write a formula for the volume of the cylinder in terms of s.

c. Write a formula in terms of s for the volume V that is left after the cylinder has been removed from the cube.

d. Factor your formula from part (c).

e. Find V in cubic inches for $s = 15$ in.

Multiple Choice Practice

For California Standards Tutorials, visit PHSchool.com. Web Code: baq-9045

Alg1 10.0

45. Simplify the algebraic expression $x(6x^2 - 4x - 2)$.

(A) $6x^3 - 4x - 2$
(B) $6x^3 - 4x^2 - 2x$
(C) $6x^3 - 4x^2 - 2$
(D) $7x^3 - 5x^2 - 3x$

Alg1 17.0

46. What is the greatest value in the range of $y = x^2 - 7$ given the domain $\{-2, 0, 1\}$?

(A) -7
(B) -3
(C) -2
(D) 1

Alg1 10.0

47. Which sum is equivalent to $11k^2 + 3k + 1$?

(A) $(4k^2 + k - 5) + (7k^2 + 2k + 6)$
(B) $(k^2 - 2) + (11k^2 + 3k + 3)$
(C) $(8k^2 + k) + (3k + 1)$
(D) $(5k + 1) + (6k - 3)$

Alg1 8.0

48. Which equation represents a line that is perpendicular to the line shown in the graph and passes through the point (1, –2)?

(A) $y = -\frac{1}{3}x + \frac{5}{3}$
(B) $y = -\frac{1}{3}x - \frac{5}{3}$
(C) $y = \frac{1}{3}x + \frac{7}{3}$
(D) $y = \frac{1}{3}x - \frac{7}{3}$

Mixed Review

GO for Help

Lesson 8-1

Simplify. Write each answer in standard form.

49. $(x^2 + 3) - (4x^2 - 7)$

50. $(m^3 + 8m + 6) + (-5m^2 + 4m)$

51. $(g^2 + 6g - 2) + (4g^2 - 7g + 2)$

52. $(3r^2 - 8r + 7) - (2r^2 + 8r - 9)$

53. $(t^4 - t^3 + 1) + (t^3 + 5t^2 - 10)$

54. $(3b^3 - b^2) - (5b^2 + 12)$

Lesson 7-1

Simplify each expression.

55. 5^{-1}

56. 5^{-2}

57. $(-2)^{-3}$

58. 8^0

59. $n^{-3}m^2$

60. v^3w^{-5}

61. $\frac{4}{c^{-3}}$

62. $\frac{ab^{-8}}{c^5}$

Lesson 6-3

Solve by elimination.

63. $7x + 6y = 33$
$2x - 6y = -6$

64. $8x + 4y = 28$
$3x - 2y = 21$

65. $4x + 2y = 16$
$11x - 3y = -7$

GO Online Lesson Quiz Visit: PHSchool.com, Web Code: baa-0802

Activity Lab: Using Models to Multiply

FOR USE WITH LESSON 8-3

10.0 Multiply polynomials. ***Develop***

You can use models to multiply two binomials.

1 EXAMPLE Multiplying Binomials

Find the product $(2x + 1)(x + 5)$.

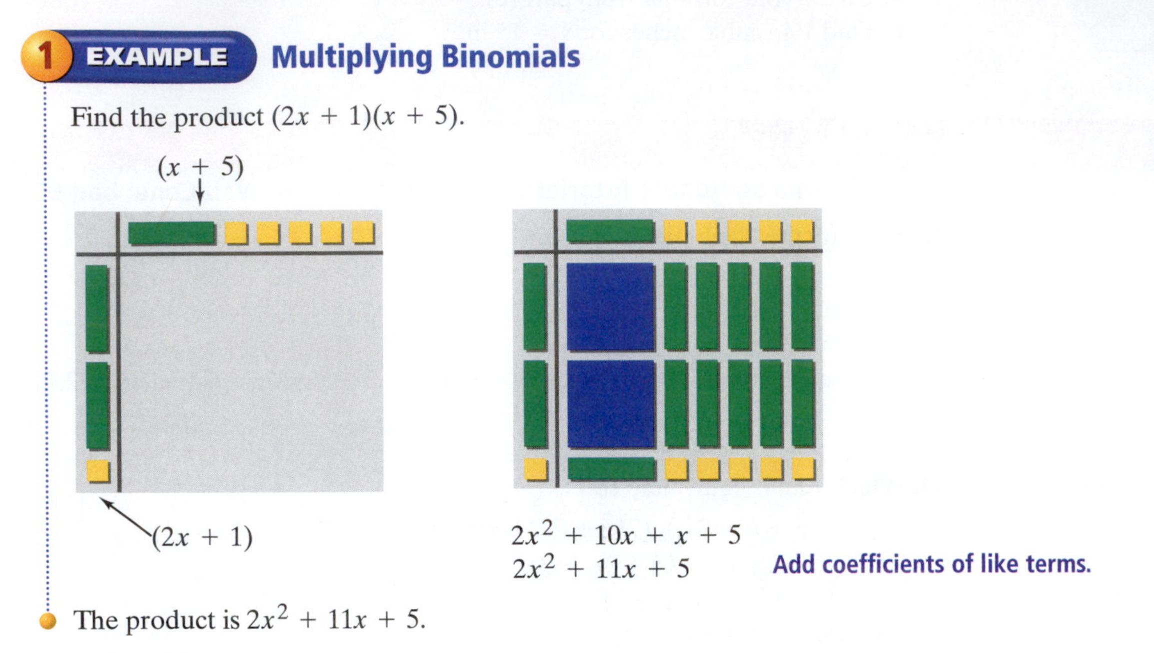

$2x^2 + 10x + x + 5$

$2x^2 + 11x + 5$ **Add coefficients of like terms.**

The product is $2x^2 + 11x + 5$.

You can also model products that involve subtraction. Negative variables and negative numbers are represented in red.

2 EXAMPLE Multiplying Binomials Involving Subtraction

Find the product $(x - 2)(3x + 1)$.

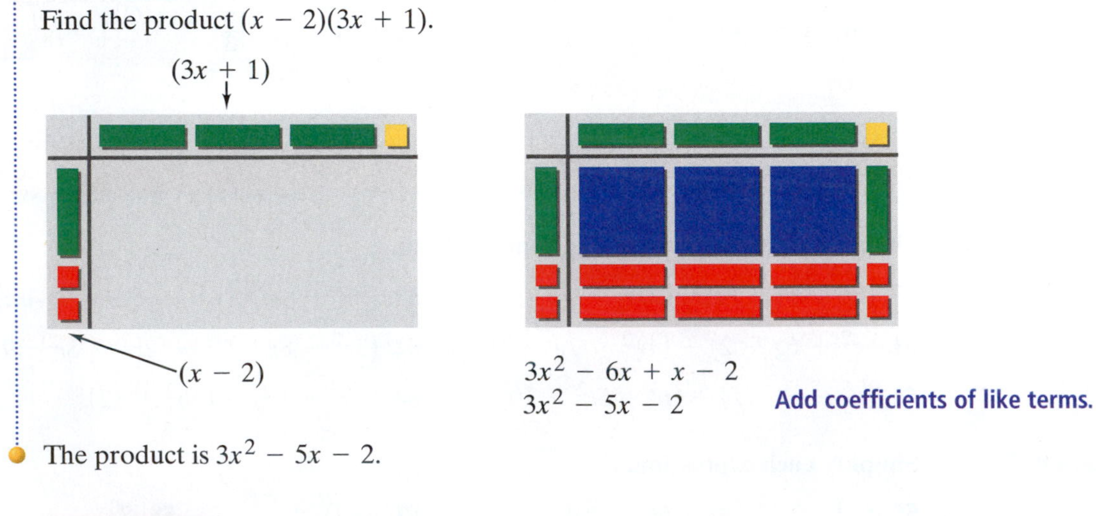

$3x^2 - 6x + x - 2$

$3x^2 - 5x - 2$ **Add coefficients of like terms.**

The product is $3x^2 - 5x - 2$.

EXERCISES

Use models to find each product.

1. $(x + 1)(x + 6)$

2. $(x + 1)(x - 2)$

3. $(x + 1)(4x - 1)$

4. $(x + 4)(2x + 1)$

5. $(x - 3)(3x + 5)$

6. $(2x + 3)(3x + 5)$

8-3 Multiplying Binomials

California Content Standards

10.0 Add, subtract, and multiply monomials and polynomials. Solve multi-step problems, including word problems, by using these techniques. ***Develop***

What You'll Learn

- To multiply binomials using FOIL
- To multiply trinomials by binomials

. . . And Why

To find the area of a geometric figure, as in Example 3

Check Skills You'll Need

GO for Help Lessons 8-1 and 8-2

Find each product.

1. $4r(r - 1)$ **2.** $6h(h^2 + 8h - 3)$ **3.** $y^2(2y^3 - 7)$

Simplify. Write each answer in standard form.

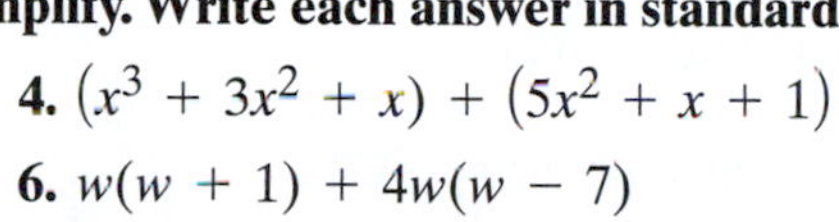

4. $(x^3 + 3x^2 + x) + (5x^2 + x + 1)$ **5.** $(3t^3 - 6t + 8) + (5t^3 + 7t - 2)$

6. $w(w + 1) + 4w(w - 7)$ **7.** $6b(b - 2) - b(8b + 3)$

8. $m(4m^2 - 6) + 3m^2(m + 9)$ **9.** $3d^2(d^3 - 6) - d^3(2d^2 + 4)$

Multiplying Two Binomials

You can use an area model to multiply two binomials. The diagram below shows $(2x + 3)(x + 4)$.

$2x(x + 4)$ → $2x^2 + 8x$

$3(x + 4)$ → $3x + 12$

$2x^2 + 11x + 12$

You can also use the Distributive Property to find the product of two binomials.

1 EXAMPLE Using the Distributive Property

Simplify $(2x + 3)(x + 4)$.

$(2x + 3)(x + 4) = 2x(x + 4) + 3(x + 4)$ **Distribute $x + 4$.**

$= 2x^2 + 8x + 3x + 12$ **Now distribute $2x$ and 3.**

$= 2x^2 + 11x + 12$ **Simplify.**

CA Standards Check 1 Simplify each product.

a. $(6h - 7)(2h + 3)$ **b.** $(5m + 2)(8m - 1)$ **c.** $(9a - 8)(7a + 4)$

One way to organize multiplying two binomials is to use FOIL, which stands for "First, Outer, Inner, Last." The term FOIL is a memory device for applying the Distributive Property to the product of two binomials.

Video Tutor Help
Visit: PHSchool.com
Web Code: bae-0775

2 EXAMPLE Multiplying Using FOIL

Simplify $(3x - 5)(2x + 7)$.

		First		Outer		Inner		Last
	$=$	$(3x)(2x)$	$+$	$(3x)(7)$	$-$	$(5)(2x)$	$-$	$(5)(7)$
$(3x - 5)(2x + 7)$	$=$	$6x^2$	$+$	$21x$	$-$	$10x$	$-$	35
	$=$	$6x^2$	$+$		$11x$		$-$	35

The product is $6x^2 + 11x - 35$.

CA Standards Check

2 Simplify each product using FOIL.

a. $(3x + 4)(2x + 5)$ **b.** $(3x - 4)(2x + 5)$
c. $(3x + 4)(2x - 5)$ **d.** $(3x - 4)(2x - 5)$

3 EXAMPLE Applying Multiplication of Polynomials

Study Tip

When you use the FOIL method to multiply binomials, draw arrows to keep the products organized.

Which expression best describes the area of the shaded region?

Ⓐ $x^2 + 2x$ Ⓒ $5x^2 + 15x + 5$
Ⓑ $6x^2 + 17x + 5$ Ⓓ $7x^2 + 9x + 5$

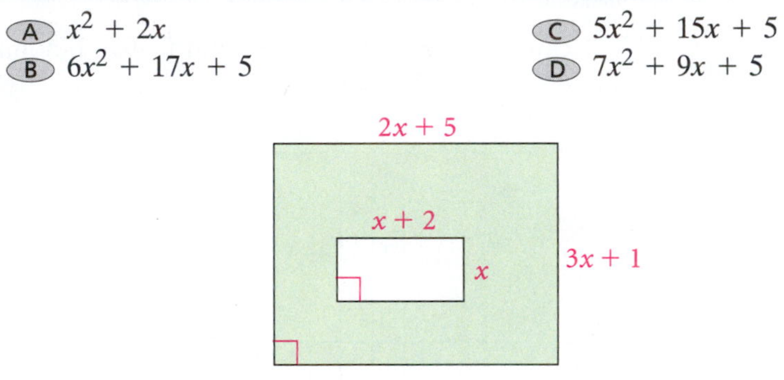

area of outer rectangle $= (3x + 1)(2x + 5)$ area of hole $= x(x + 2)$

area of shaded region

$= $ area of outer rectangle $-$ area of hole

$= (3x + 1)(2x + 5) - x(x + 2)$ **Substitute.**

$= 6x^2 + 15x + 2x + 5 - x^2 - 2x$ **Use FOIL to simplify $(3x + 1)(2x + 5)$ and the Distributive Property to simplify $-x(x + 2)$.**

$= 6x^2 - x^2 + 15x + 2x - 2x + 5$ **Group like terms.**

$= 5x^2 + 15x + 5$ **Simplify.**

So C is the correct answer.

CA Standards Check

3 Find an expression for the area of each shaded region. Simplify.

a.

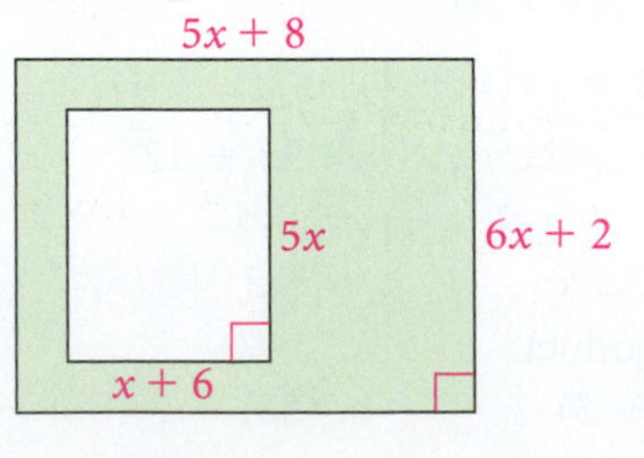

b.

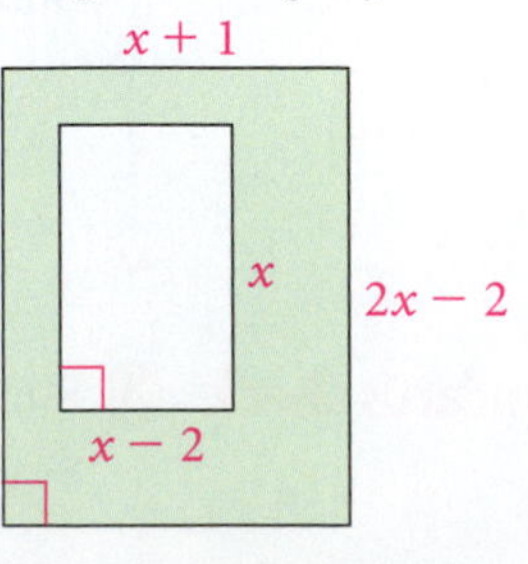

Multiplying a Trinomial and a Binomial

When you multiply polynomials with more than two terms, you can use the vertical method or the horizontal method to distribute each term in such factors.

4 EXAMPLE Multiplying a Trinomial and a Binomial

Simplify the product $(4x^2 + x - 6)(2x - 3)$.

Method 1 Multiply using the vertical method.

$$\begin{array}{rrrrl} & 4x^2 & + x & - 6 & \\ & & 2x & - 3 & \\ \hline & -12x^2 & - 3x & + 18 & \text{Multiply by } -3. \\ 8x^3 & + 2x^2 & - 12x & & \text{Multiply by } 2x. \\ \hline 8x^3 & - 10x^2 & - 15x & + 18 & \text{Add like terms.} \end{array}$$

Method 2 Multiply using the horizontal method.

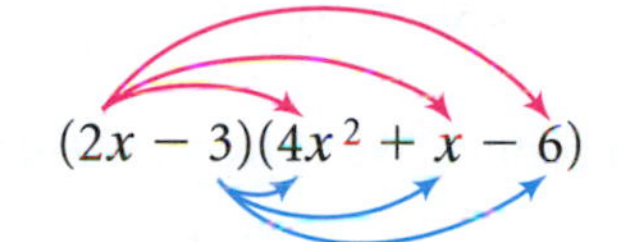

$= 2x(4x^2) + 2x(x) + 2x(-6) - 3(4x^2) - 3(x) - 3(-6)$

$= 8x^3 + 2x^2 - 12x - 12x^2 - 3x + 18$

$= 8x^3 - 10x^2 - 15x + 18$ Add like terms.

The product is $8x^3 - 10x^2 - 15x + 18$.

CA Standards Check 4 Simplify $(6n - 8)(2n^2 + n + 7)$ using both methods shown in Example 4.

EXERCISES

For more exercises, see *Extra Skills and Word Problem Practice*.

Standards Practice Alg1 10.0

A Practice by Example

Example 1 (page 381)

GO for Help

Copy and fill in each blank.

1. $(5a + 2)(6a - 1) = \blacksquare a^2 + 7a - 2$
2. $(3c - 7)(2c - 5) = 6c^2 - 29c + \blacksquare$
3. $(z - 4)(2z + 1) = 2z^2 - \blacksquare z - 4$
4. $(2x + 9)(x + 2) = 2x^2 + \blacksquare x + 18$

Simplify each product using the Distributive Property.

5. $(x + 2)(x + 5)$
6. $(h + 3)(h + 4)$
7. $(k + 7)(k - 6)$
8. $(a - 8)(a - 9)$
9. $(2x - 1)(x + 2)$
10. $(2y + 5)(y - 3)$

Example 2 (page 382)

Simplify each product using FOIL.

11. $(r + 6)(r - 4)$
12. $(y + 4)(5y - 8)$
13. $(x + 6)(x - 7)$
14. $(m - 6)(m - 9)$
15. $(4b - 2)(b + 3)$
16. $(8w + 2)(w + 5)$
17. $(x - 7)(x + 9)$
18. $(a + 11)(a + 5)$
19. $(p - 1)(p + 10)$

Example 3 (page 382)

Find an expression for the area of each shaded region. Simplify.

20.

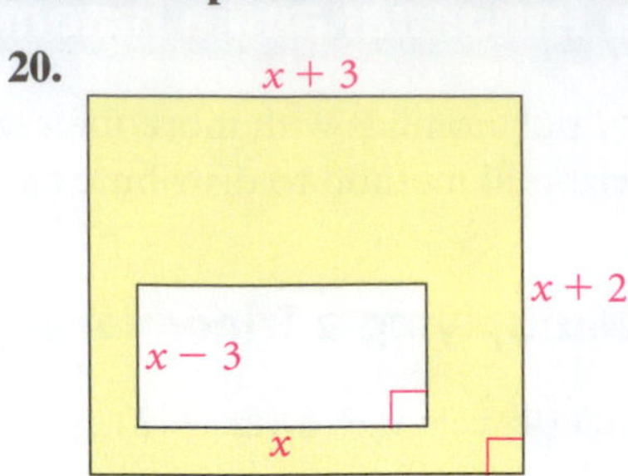

21.

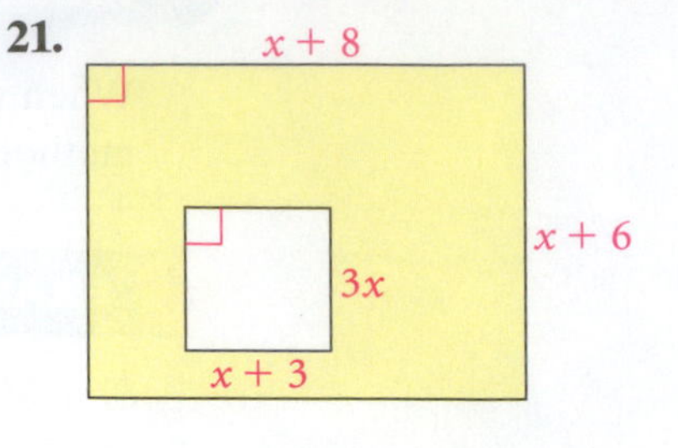

Example 4 (page 383)

Simplify. Use the vertical method.

22. $(x + 9)(x^2 - 4x + 1)$

23. $(a - 4)(a^2 - 2a + 1)$

24. $(g - 3)(2g^2 + 3g + 3)$

25. $(k + 8)(3k^2 - 5k + 7)$

Simplify. Use the horizontal method.

26. $(x^2 + 2x + 1)(9x - 3)$

27. $(t^2 - 6t + 3)(2t - 5)$

28. $(7p^2 + 5p - 1)(8p + 9)$

29. $(12w^2 - w - 1)(4w - 2)$

Apply Your Skills

Simplify each product. Write in standard form.

30. $(p - 7)(p + 8)$

31. $(-7 + p)(8 + p)$

32. $(p^2 - 7)(p + 8)$

33. $(5c - 9)(5c + 1)$

34. $(n^2 + 3)(n + 11)$

35. $(3k^2 + 2)(k + 5k^2)$

36. $(6h - 1)(4h^2 + h + 3)$

37. $(9y^2 + 2)(y^2 - y - 1)$

38. $(8q - 4)(6q^2 + q + 1)$

Homework Video Tutor

Visit: PHSchool.com
Web Code: bae-0803

39. You are planning a rectangular garden. Its length is twice its width x. You want a walkway 2 ft wide around the garden.

a. Write an expression for the area of the garden and walk.

b. Write an expression for the area of the walk only.

c. You have enough gravel to cover 76 ft^2 and want to use it all on the walk. How big should you make the garden?

40. Write a binomial and a trinomial. Find their product.

41. Writing Which method do you prefer for multiplying a binomial and a trinomial? Explain.

Write and simplify an expression for the area of each shaded region.

For a guide to solving Exercise 42, see p. 387.

42. **43.**

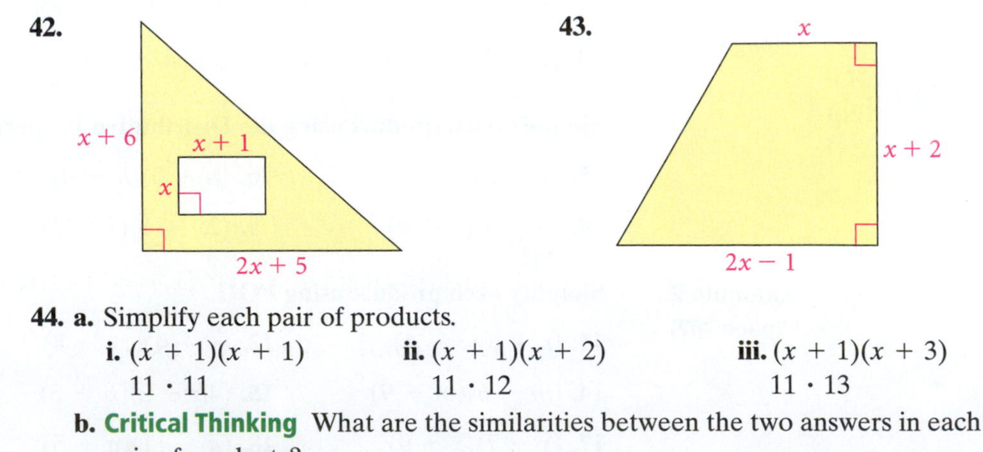

44. a. Simplify each pair of products.

i. $(x + 1)(x + 1)$
$11 \cdot 11$

ii. $(x + 1)(x + 2)$
$11 \cdot 12$

iii. $(x + 1)(x + 3)$
$11 \cdot 13$

b. Critical Thinking What are the similarities between the two answers in each pair of products?

45. Use the formula $V = \ell wh$ to write a polynomial in standard form for the volume of the box.

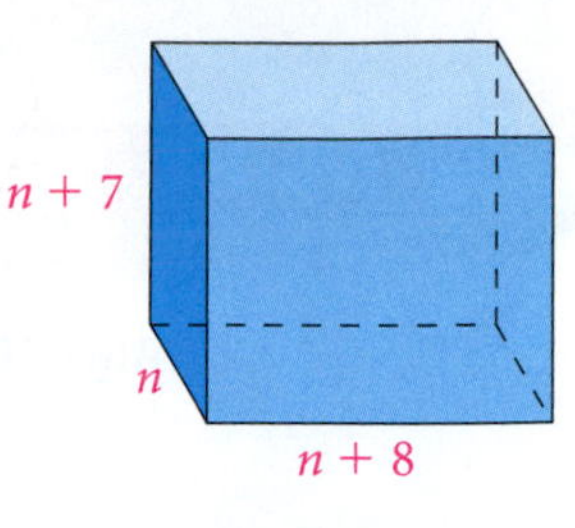

46. If n represents an even number, which expression represents the product of the next two even numbers?

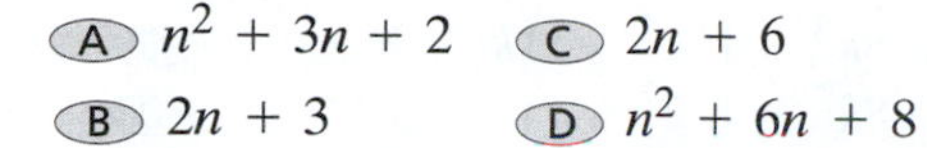

(A) $n^2 + 3n + 2$ (C) $2n + 6$
(B) $2n + 3$ (D) $n^2 + 6n + 8$

Math Reasoning **Determine whether each statement is *sometimes*, *always*, or *never* true. Explain.**

47. The expression $x^2 - 8x + 16$ is negative.

48. If $x^2 - 2xy + y^2 = 0$, then $x = y$.

49. The degree of the product of a binomial and a trinomial is 3.

50. The sum of the degrees of the terms in two binomials is equal to the sum of the degrees of the terms in their product.

Error Analysis **Explain the error in the work. Find the correct product.**

51. 52.

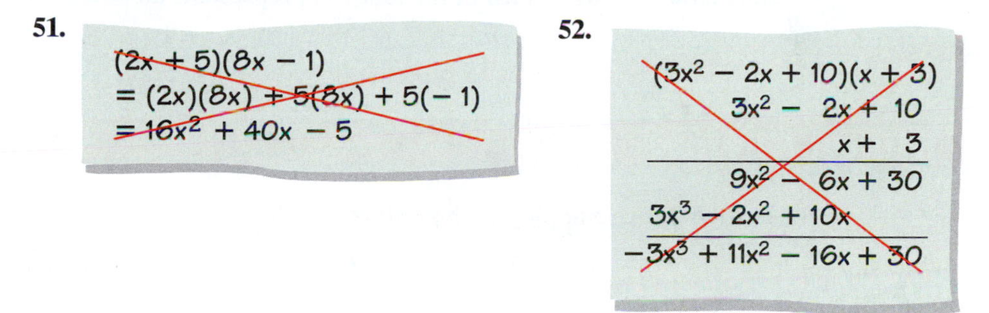

Challenge **For Exercises 53–55, each expression represents the side length of a cube. Write an expression in standard form for the surface area of each cube.**

53. $x + 3$ 54. $4t + 1$ 55. $2w^2 + 7$

In 2004, the U.S. consumption of fresh tomatoes was 19.3 lb per person.

56. a. Multiply the expressions on the right side of each equation to create a model for the total number of pounds of fresh vegetables $V(t)$ consumed in a year in the United States.

$C(t) = 2.2t + 183$ the U.S. annual per capita consumption of fresh vegetables, in pounds, from 1995 to 2004

$P(t) = 2.8t + 282$ the U.S. population, in millions, from 1995 to 2004

b. Evaluate the equation you found in part (a) with $t = 9$ to find the total vegetable consumption for 2004. ($t = 0$ corresponds to the year 1995.)

57. Suppose you deposit \$2000 for college in a savings account that has an annual interest rate r. At the end of three years, the value of your account will be $2000(1 + r)^3$ dollars.

a. Rewrite the expression $2000(1 + r)^3$ by finding the product $2000(1 + r)(1 + r)(1 + r)$. Write your answer in standard form.

b. Find the amount of money in the account if the interest rate is 3%.

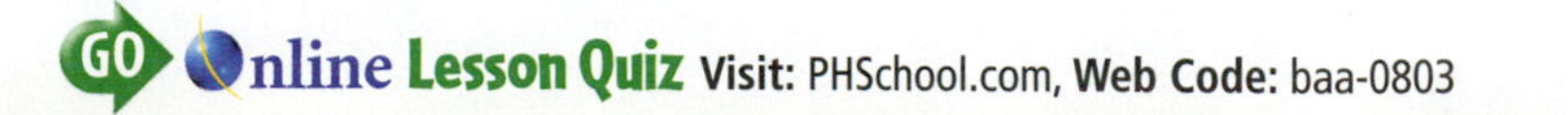

Multiple Choice Practice

For California Standards Tutorials, visit PHSchool.com. Web Code: baq-9045

Alg1 10.0

58. Which expression is equivalent to $(8k - 3)(k^2 - k + 1)$?

A $8k^3 + 11k^2 - 11k - 3$
C $9k^3 - 8k^2 + 8k - 2$
B $8k^3 - 11k^2 + 11k - 3$
D $9k^3 - 3k^2 + 3k - 3$

Alg1 5.0

59. Nigel brought a \$50 bill to the grocery store to buy coffee. The coffee costs \$2.25 per pound. Which equation best represents the change c Nigel will receive when he buys x pounds of coffee?

A $c = 50 - x$
C $50 = c - 2.25x$
B $c = 50 - 2.25x$
D $50 = c - 2.25 - x$

Alg1 10.0

60. How many terms does the following sum have when it is written in standard form? $(4x^9 - 3x^2 + 10x - 4) + (4x^9 + x^3 + 2x)$

A 7 B 5 C 3 D 1

Alg1 25.0

61. Which of the following represents an odd number for any integer n?

A $n + 1$ B $2n + 1$ C $3n$ D $3n + 1$

Mixed Review

GO for Help

Lesson 8-2

Simplify each product.

62. $4v(5v - 7)$ **63.** $(c - 9)3c$ **64.** $8t^2(t + 6)$ **65.** $y(3y - 10)$

66. $5x^2(11 - x)$ **67.** $-t^3(6t - 1)$ **68.** $4r(3 - r^5)$ **69.** $9b^2(b^3 + 2b)$

Factor.

70. $5w + 45$ **71.** $3x^2 - 11x$ **72.** $4a^2 + 12a$ **73.** $9n^2 - n^3$

74. $34t - 51$ **75.** $63v^2 + 45v$ **76.** $25m - 60m^3$ **77.** $11k + 77k^6$

Lesson 7-5

Simplify each expression.

78. $\frac{3^5}{3^2}$ **79.** $\frac{3^2}{3^5}$ **80.** $\frac{y^{12}}{y^8}$ **81.** $\frac{2w^{-3}}{6w^2}$ **82.** $\frac{x^{-8}}{2x^3}$

83. $\left(\frac{5}{3}\right)^{-1}$ **84.** $\left(\frac{5}{3}\right)^{-2}$ **85.** $\left(\frac{5}{3}\right)^{0}$ **86.** $\left(\frac{4x}{7}\right)^{-2}$ **87.** $\left(\frac{y^{-2}}{8}\right)^{-2}$

Checkpoint Quiz 1

Lessons 8-1 through 8-3

Simplify each expression.

1. $(4x^2 + x + 3) + (5x^2 + 9x - 2)$

2. $(7b^2 - 5b + 3) - (b^2 + 8b - 6)$

3. $3w(12w - 1) - 8w$

4. $6k(4k + k^2) + 9k(2k - 6k^2)$

5. $(x + 3)(x - 5)$

6. $(2n^3 - 5)(6n^2 + n)$

Factor each polynomial.

7. $12y^2 - 10$

8. $5t^6 + 25t^3 - 10t$

9. $18v^4 + 27v^3 + 36v^2$

10. $36m^4 + 12m^2 + 6m^8$

GPS Guided Problem Solving

For Use With Page 384, Exercise 42

> **10.0** Add, subtract, and multiply monomials and polynomials. Solve multi-step problems by using these techniques. *Develop*

Understanding Math Problems **Read the exercise below and then follow along with what Terry thinks and writes. Check your understanding with the exercise at the bottom of the page.**

Write an expression for the area of the shaded region. Write your answer in simplest form.

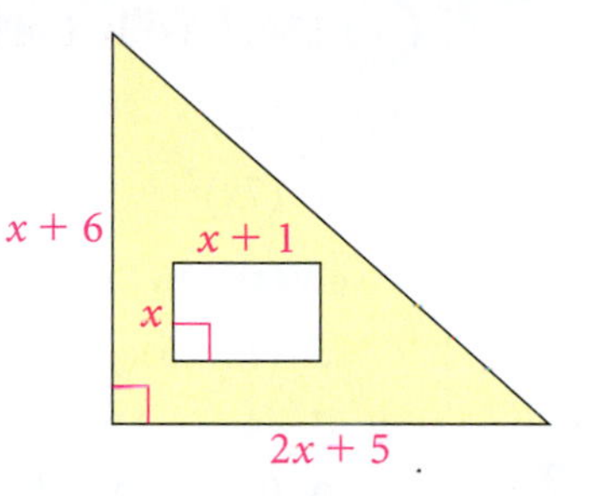

What Terry Thinks	What Terry Writes
There are two figures—a right triangle and a rectangle inside it. I'll write down the dimensions of each shape.	Triangle: base $= 2x + 5$, height $= x + 6$ Rectangle: length $= x$, width $= x + 1$
The area of the shaded region is the difference between the area of the triangle and the area of the rectangle.	Area of shaded region = Area of triangle − Area of rectangle
I can rewrite my equation using the area formulas for each shape.	$= \frac{1}{2}$(base)(height) − (length)(width)
Next, I'll substitute the expressions for the dimensions of the triangle and rectangle into the formula.	$= \frac{1}{2}(2x + 5)(x + 6) - x(x + 1)$
I can use FOIL and the Distributive Property to simplify the expressions. Lastly, I combine like terms and write my answer in simplest form.	$= \frac{1}{2}(2x^2 + 12x + 5x + 30) - (x^2 + x)$ $= x^2 + \frac{17}{2}x + 15 - x^2 - x$ $= 7.5x + 15$

EXERCISE

Write an expression for the area of the colored region. Write your answer in simplest form.

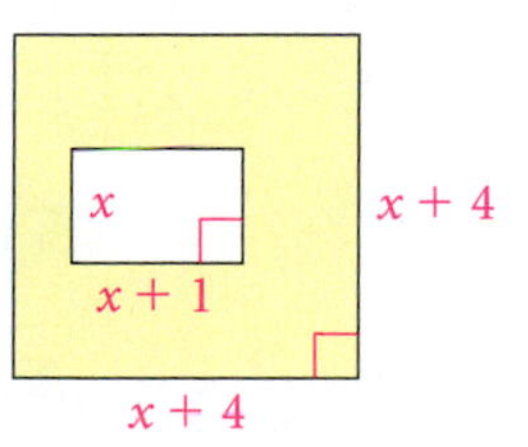

8-4 Multiplying Special Cases

California Content Standards

10.0 Add, subtract, and multiply monomials and polynomials. Solve multi-step problems, including word problems, by using these techniques. *Develop*

What You'll Learn

- To find the square of a binomial
- To find the difference of squares

. . . And Why

To find the probability of a Labrador retriever inheriting dark fur, as in Example 2

Check Skills You'll Need

GO for Help Lessons 7-4 and 8-3

Simplify.

1. $(7x)^2$
2. $(3v)^2$
3. $(-4c)^2$
4. $(5g^3)^2$

Use FOIL to find each product.

5. $(j + 5)(j + 7)$
6. $(2b - 6)(3b - 8)$
7. $(4y + 1)(5y - 2)$
8. $(x + 3)(x - 4)$
9. $(8c^2 + 2)(c^2 - 10)$
10. $(6y^2 - 3)(9y^2 + 1)$

New Vocabulary • difference of squares

Finding the Square of a Binomial

CA Standards Investigation Exploring Special Products

1. Find each product.

   Row 1: $(x + 8)(x + 8)$ $(y + 5)(y + 5)$ $(2p + 3)(2p + 3)$

   Row 2: $(d - 3)(d - 3)$ $(t - 1)(t - 1)$ $(9r - 2)(9r - 2)$

   Row 3: $(x + 4)(x - 4)$ $(k + 9)(k - 9)$ $(3c + 7)(3c - 7)$

2. Describe the pattern or patterns you found in each row.
3. Based on the patterns you found, predict each product.

   $(p + 6)(p + 6)$ $(v - 5)(v - 5)$ $(x + 8)(x - 8)$

4. Use FOIL to find each product in Question 2. Were your predictions correct?

You can write the expression $(a + b)^2$ as $(a + b)(a + b)$. You can find $(a + b)^2$ using the methods you learned in Lesson 8-3.

Area Model

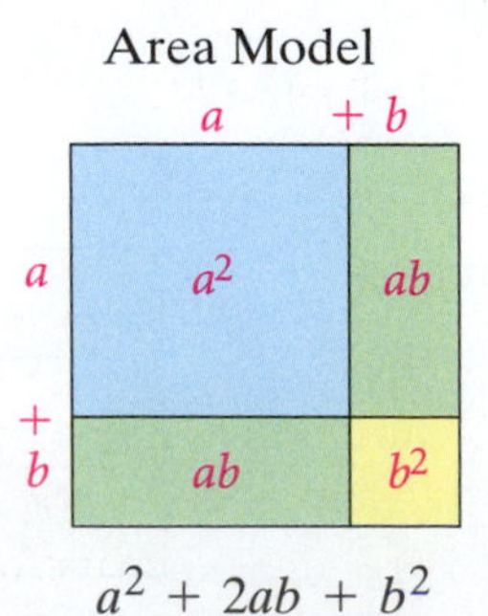

$a^2 + 2ab + b^2$

FOIL

$(a + b)(a + b)$

$= a^2 + ab + ba + b^2$ **Use FOIL.**

$= a^2 + 2ab + b^2$ **Simplify.**

The expressions $(a - b)^2$ and $(a + b)^2$ are squares of binomials. To square a binomial, you can use FOIL or the following rule.

Take Note

Rule **The Square of a Binomial**

$(a + b)^2 = a^2 + 2ab + b^2$

$(a - b)^2 = a^2 - 2ab + b^2$

The square of a binomial is the square of the first term plus twice the product of the two terms plus the square of the last term.

1 EXAMPLE Squaring a Binomial

a. Find $(x + 7)^2$.

$(x + 7)^2 = x^2 + 2x(7) + 7^2$ **Square the binomial.**

$= x^2 + 14x + 49$ **Simplify.**

b. Find $(4k - 3)^2$.

$(4k - 3)^2 = (4k)^2 - 2(4k)(3) + 3^2$ **Square the binomial.**

$= 16k^2 - 24k + 9$ **Simplify.**

CA Standards Check **1** Find each square.

a. $(t + 6)^2$ **b.** $(5y + 1)^2$ **c.** $(7m - 2p)^2$ **d.** $(9c - 8)^2$

You can square binomials to find probabilities that apply to real-world situations.

2 EXAMPLE Application

Among Labrador retrievers, the dark-fur gene D is dominant, and the yellow-fur gene Y is recessive. This means that a dog with at least one dominant gene (DD or DY) will have dark fur. A dog with two recessive genes (YY) will have yellow fur.

The color of a Labrador retriever is determined by a pair of genes. The offspring inherits a single gene at random from each of its parents.

The Punnett square at the right models the possible combinations of color genes that parents who carry both genes can pass on to their offspring. Since YY is $\frac{1}{4}$ of the outcomes, the probability that a puppy has yellow fur is $\frac{1}{4}$.

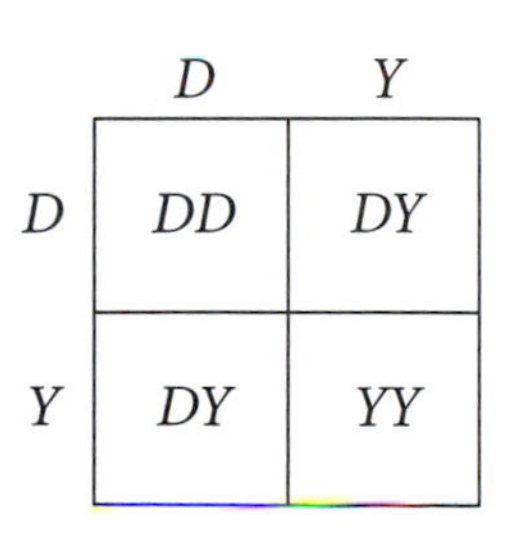

	D	Y
D	DD	DY
Y	DY	YY

You can model the probabilities found in the Punnett square with the expression $(\frac{1}{2}D + \frac{1}{2}Y)^2$. Show that this product gives the same result as the Punnett square.

$(\frac{1}{2}D + \frac{1}{2}Y)^2 = \left(\frac{1}{2}D\right)^2 + 2\left(\frac{1}{2}D\right)\left(\frac{1}{2}Y\right) + \left(\frac{1}{2}Y\right)^2$ **Square the binomial.**

$= \frac{1}{4}D^2 + \frac{1}{2}DY + \frac{1}{4}Y^2$ **Simplify.**

The expressions $\frac{1}{4}D^2$ and $\frac{1}{4}Y^2$ indicate that the probability offspring will have either two dominant genes or two recessive genes is $\frac{1}{4}$. The expression $\frac{1}{2}DY$ indicates that there is $\frac{1}{2}$ chance that the offspring will inherit both genes. These are the same probabilities shown in the Punnett square.

2 When you play a game with two number cubes, you can find probabilities by squaring a binomial. Let A represent rolling 1 or 2 and B represent rolling 3, 4, 5, or 6. The probability of A is $\frac{1}{3}$, and the probability of B is $\frac{2}{3}$.

a. Find $\left(\frac{1}{3}A + \frac{2}{3}B\right)^2$.

b. What is the probability that both number cubes you roll show 1 or 2?

c. What is the probability that one number cube shows a 1 or 2 and the other shows 3, 4, 5, or 6?

d. What is the probability that both number cubes show 3, 4, 5, or 6?

Using mental math, you can square a binomial to find the square of a number.

3 EXAMPLE Mental Math

a. Find 51^2 using mental math.

$51^2 = (50 + 1)^2$

$= 50^2 + 2(50 \cdot 1) + 1^2$ ← Square the binomial.

$= 2500 + 100 + 1 = 2601$ ← Simplify.

b. Find 49^2 using mental math.

$49^2 = (50 - 1)^2$

Square the binomial. → $= 50^2 - 2(50 \cdot 1) + 1^2$

Simplify. → $= 2500 - 100 + 1 = 2401$

CA Standards Check

3 Find each square using mental math.

a. 31^2 **b.** 29^2 **c.** 98^2 **d.** 203^2

Difference of Squares

The product of the sum and difference of the same two terms also produces a pattern.

$$(a + b)(a - b) = a^2 - ab + ba - b^2$$
$$= a^2 - b^2$$

Notice that the sum of $-ab$ and ba is 0, leaving $a^2 - b^2$. This product is called the **difference of squares.**

Rule **The Difference of Squares**

$(a + b)(a - b) = a^2 - b^2$

The product of the sum and difference of the same two terms is the difference of their squares.

4 EXAMPLE Finding the Difference of Squares

Find $(t^3 - 6)(t^3 + 6)$.

$(t^3 - 6)(t^3 + 6) = (t^3)^2 - (6)^2$ Find the difference of squares.

$= t^6 - 36$ Simplify.

CA Standards Check

4 Find each product.

a. $(d + 11)(d - 11)$ **b.** $(c^2 + 8)(c^2 - 8)$ **c.** $(9v^3 + w^4)(9v^3 - w^4)$

You can use the difference of squares to calculate products using mental math.

5 EXAMPLE Mental Math

Find $82 \cdot 78$.

$82 \cdot 78 = (80 + 2)(80 - 2)$ Express each factor using 80 and 2.

$= 80^2 - 2^2$ Find the difference of squares.

$= 6400 - 4 = 6396$ Simplify.

CA Standards Check 5 Find each product.

a. $18 \cdot 22$ **b.** $19 \cdot 21$ **c.** $59 \cdot 61$ **d.** $87 \cdot 93$

EXERCISES

Standards Practice

For more exercises, see *Extra Skills and Word Problem Practice.*

Alg1 10.0

A Practice by Example

Examples 1, 2 (page 389)

GO for Help

Find each square.

1. $(c + 1)^2$ **2.** $(x + 4)^2$ **3.** $(2v + 11)^2$ **4.** $(3m + 7)^2$

5. $(w - 12)^2$ **6.** $(b - 5)^2$ **7.** $(6x - 8)^2$ **8.** $(9j - 2)^2$

9. Suppose you play a game with two spinners like the one shown at the right. Let C represent spinning an even number. Let D represent spinning an odd number. The probability of C is $\frac{1}{4}$. The probability of D is $\frac{3}{4}$.

1 4 9 5

a. Simplify $(\frac{1}{4}C + \frac{3}{4}D)^2$.

b. Find $P(C \text{ and } C)$.

c. How does the answer in part (b) relate to the polynomial in part (a)?

Example 3 (page 390)

Mental Math Find each square.

10. 61^2 **11.** 99^2 **12.** 48^2 **13.** 302^2 **14.** 499^2

Example 4 (page 390)

Find each product.

15. $(x + 4)(x - 4)$ **16.** $(a + 8)(a - 8)$ **17.** $(d + 7)(d - 7)$

18. $(h + 15)(h - 15)$ **19.** $(y + 12)(y - 12)$ **20.** $(k + 5)(k - 5)$

Example 5 (page 391)

Mental Math Find each product.

21. $31 \cdot 29$ **22.** $89 \cdot 91$ **23.** $52 \cdot 48$ **24.** $197 \cdot 203$ **25.** $299 \cdot 301$

B Apply Your Skills

Find an expression for the area of each shaded region. Write your answers in standard form.

26.

$x + 3$

x

x

$x + 3$

27.

$x - 1$

$x - 1$

$x + 4$

$x + 4$

Find each square.

28. $(x + 3y)^2$
29. $(5p - q)^2$
30. $(6m + n)^2$
31. $(x - 7y)^2$
32. $(4k + 7j)^2$
33. $(2y - 9x)^2$
34. $(3w + 10t)^2$
35. $(6a + 11b)^2$
36. $(5p - 6q)^2$
37. $(6h - 8p)^2$
38. $(y^5 - 9x^4)^2$
39. $(8k + 4h)^2$

The cow in the photo shows a typical roan coat. This cow has the genes *RW*.

40. The coat color of shorthorn cattle is determined by two genes, Red R and White W. RR produces red, WW produces white, and RW produces a third type of coat color called roan.
    a. Model the Punnett square with the square of a binomial.
    b. If both parents have RW, what is the probability the offspring will also be RW?
    c. Write an expression to model a situation where one parent is RW while the other is RR.
    d. What is the probability that the offspring of the parents in part (c) will have a white coat?

	R	*W*
R	*RR*	*RW*
W	*RW*	*WW*

41. a. Copy and complete the table.
    b. Describe any patterns you see.
    c. **Writing** How does the difference of squares account for the pattern in the table?

$4^2 = 16$	$3 \cdot 5 = 15$
$5^2 = ■$	$4 \cdot 6 = 24$
$6^2 = ■$	$5 \cdot 7 = ■$
$7^2 = ■$	$6 \cdot 8 = ■$

42. **Math Reasoning** Give a counterexample to show that $(x + y)^2 = x^2 + y^2$ is false.

43. **Critical Thinking** Does $\left(3\frac{1}{2}\right)^2 = 9\frac{1}{4}$? Explain.

Visit: PHSchool.com
Web Code: bae-0804

Find each product.

44. $(3y + 5w)(3y - 5w)$
45. $(p + 9q)(p - 9q)$
46. $(2d + 7g)(2d - 7g)$
47. $(7b - 8c)(7b + 8c)$
48. $(g + 7h)(g - 7h)$
49. $(g^3 + 7h^2)(g^3 - 7h^2)$
50. $(2a^2 + b)(2a^2 - b)$
51. $(11x - y^3)(11x + y^3)$
52. $(4k - 3h^2)(4k + 3h^2)$

53. Write the expression $(a + b + c)^2$ in standard form.

54. Suppose you play a game by tossing 3 coins. You can find the probabilities by simplifying $\left(\frac{1}{2}H + \frac{1}{2}T\right)^3$.
    a. Simplify the expression.
    b. Use part (a) to find the probability of getting a head and two tails $\left(HT^2\right)$.

55. You can use factoring to show that the sum of two multiples of 3 is also a multiple of 3.

    If m and n are integers, then $3n$ and $3m$ are multiples of three.
    $3m + 3n = 3(m + n)$
    Since $(m + n)$ is an integer, $3(m + n)$ is a multiple of three.

    a. Show that if a number is one more than a multiple of 3, then its square is also one more than a multiple of 3.
    b. **Reasoning** If a number is two more than a multiple of 3, is its square also two more than a multiple of 3? Explain.

56. The formula $V = \frac{4}{3}\pi r^3$ gives the volume of a sphere. Find the formula for the volume of a sphere that has a radius 3 more than r. Write your answer in standard form.

57. The area of the shaded region in the diagram is $9^2 - 2^2$.

a. Copy the figure. Make a single cut across the shaded region and reassemble it to show that $9^2 - 2^2 = (9 - 2)(9 + 2)$.

b. Draw your reassembled figure. Include its dimensions.

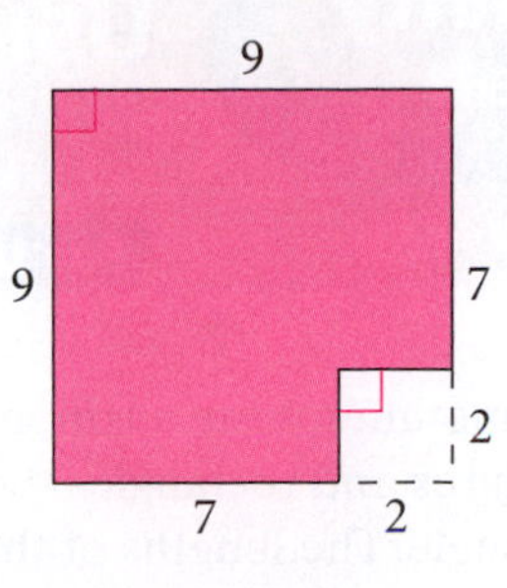

Multiple Choice Practice

For California Standards Tutorials, visit PHSchool.com. Web Code: baq-9045

Alg1 10.0

58. Which expression is equivalent to $(3x - 4y)^2$?

Ⓐ $6x^2 - 12xy - 8y^2$

Ⓑ $9x^2 - 14xy + 16y^2$

Ⓒ $9x^2 - 24xy + 16y^2$

Ⓓ $9x^2 - 24xy - 16y^2$

Alg1 7.0

59. The table at the right shows Sonia's total earnings after working at her job for a given number of weeks. What is the slope of the line that can be used to model this data?

Ⓐ 71

Ⓑ 87

Ⓒ 100

Ⓓ 261

Week	Earnings
2	$174
5	$435
7	$609
11	$957

Alg1 5.0

60. Jeff's car holds 16 gallons of gasoline. One gallon allows him to travel an average of 32 miles. Last week, Jeff filled his car with gasoline and drove 84 miles. He then drove to his uncle's house without stopping for gasoline. Which inequality represents the number of miles m Jeff drove to his uncle's house?

Ⓐ $84 + m < 16$

Ⓑ $84 + m > 32$

Ⓒ $84 + m < 16(32)$

Ⓓ $84 + m > 16(32)$

Alg1 6.0

61. Which point is NOT a solution to the inequality shown at the right?

Ⓐ $(0, -2)$

Ⓑ $(2, 0)$

Ⓒ $(2, -1)$

Ⓓ $(4, 0)$

Mixed Review

Lesson 8-3 GO for Help

Find each product.

62. $(k + 7)(k - 9)$ **63.** $(2x - 11)(x - 6)$ **64.** $(5p + 4)(3p - 1)$

65. $(3y + 1)(y + 1)$ **66.** $(4h - 2)(6h + 1)$ **67.** $(9b + 7)(8b + 2)$

68. $(2w^2 + 5)(w + 8)$ **69.** $(r - 7)(r^2 + 3r - 9)$ **70.** $(5m^2 - 2)(6m^3 + 4m)$

Lesson 7-2

Write each number in scientific notation.

71. 8713 **72.** 0.031 **73.** 68,952 **74.** 1.2 million

75. 11 **76.** 523 **77.** 6 billion **78.** 0.72

Activity Lab: Using Models to Factor

FOR USE WITH LESSON 8-5

11.0 Apply basic factoring techniques to second-degree polynomials. ***Develop***

You can sometimes write a trinomial as the product of two binomial factors. You can use squares and rectangles to find the factors by arranging the shapes to form a larger rectangle. The lengths of the sides of the rectangle are the factors of the trinomial.

EXAMPLE

Write $2x^2 + 7x + 6$ as the product of two binomial factors.

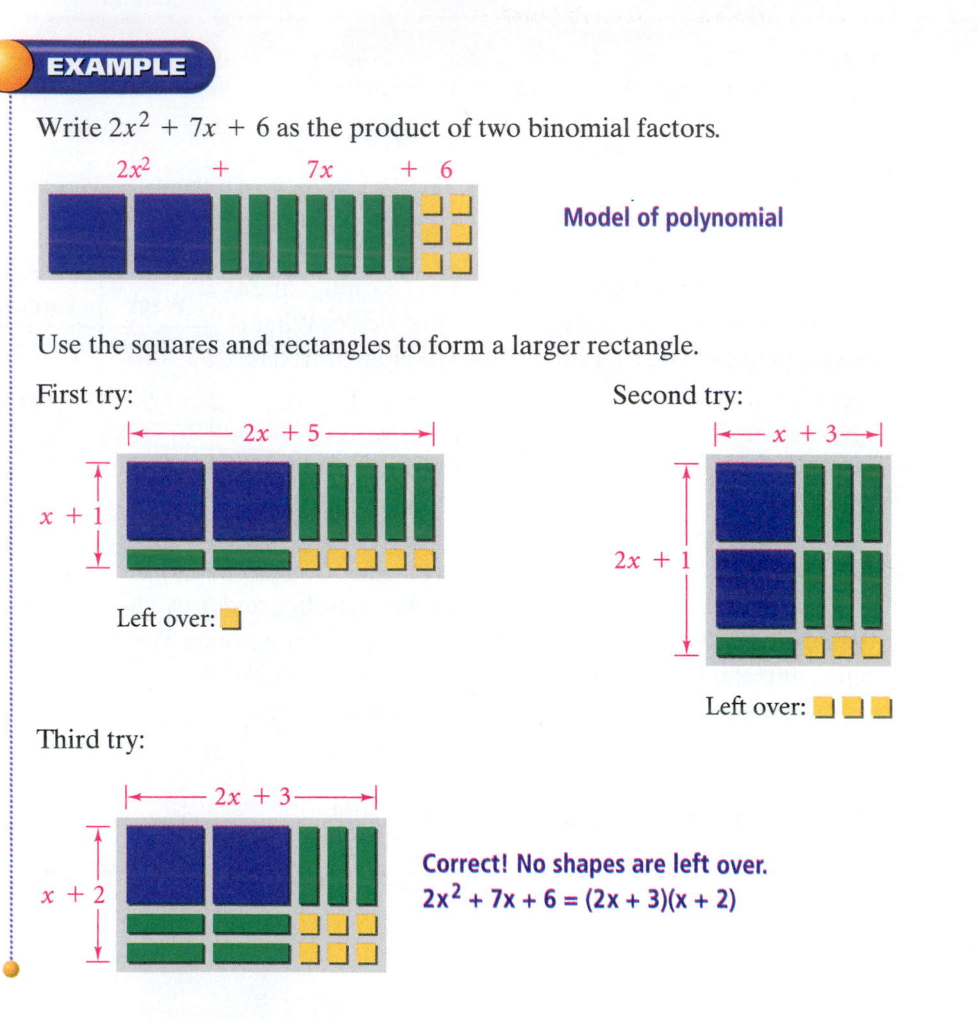

EXERCISES

Use a model to find binomial factors of each trinomial.

1. $x^2 + 8x + 15$
2. $x^2 + 4x + 4$
3. $x^2 + 8x + 7$
4. $2x^2 + 7x + 3$
5. $4x^2 + 12x + 5$
6. $6x^2 + 7x + 2$
7. **Critical Thinking** Explain why the trinomial $x^2 + 3x + 5$ cannot be represented as a rectangle.
8. **Critical Thinking** Complete $2x^2 + \blacksquare x + 6$ with three different integers so that each trinomial has two binomial factors. Write each trinomial as the product of binomial factors.

8-5 Factoring Trinomials of the Type $x^2 + bx + c$

California Content Standards

11.0 Apply basic factoring techniques to second-degree polynomials. ***Develop***

What You'll Learn

- To factor trinomials

. . . And Why

To factor trinomials like $h^2 - 4hk - 77k^2$, as in Example 4

Check Skills You'll Need

GO for Help Skills Handbook p. 595

List all of the factors of each number.

1. 24 **2.** 12 **3.** 54 **4.** 15

5. 36 **6.** 56 **7.** 64 **8.** 96

Factoring Trinomials

In earlier courses, you learned how to find the factors of whole numbers like 15. Since $3 \times 5 = 15$, 3 and 5 are factors of 15. You can also find the factors of some trinomials. Consider the product below.

$$(x + 3)(x + 5) = x^2 + 5x + 3x + 3 \cdot 5$$
$$= x^2 + (5 + 3)x + 15$$
$$= x^2 + 8x + 15$$

Notice that the coefficient of the middle term $8x$ is the sum of 3 and 5. Also the constant term 15 is the product of 3 and 5. To factor a trinomial of the form $x^2 + bx + c$, you must find two numbers that have a sum of b and a product of c.

The next example shows how to use a table to list the factors of the constant term c and how to add the factors until the sum is the middle term b.

1 EXAMPLE Factoring $x^2 + bx + c$

Factor $x^2 + 7x + 12$.

Find the factors of 12. Identify the pair that has a sum of 7.

Factors of 12	Sum of Factors
1 and 12	13
2 and 6	8
3 and 4	7 ✓

$x^2 + 7x + 12 = (x + 3)(x + 4)$

Check $x^2 + 7x + 12 \stackrel{?}{=} (x + 3)(x + 4)$

$= x^2 + 4x + 3x + 12$

$= x^2 + 7x + 12$ ✓

Online active math

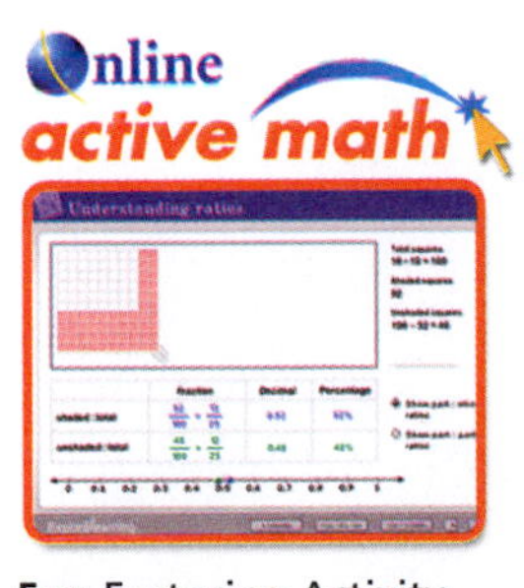

For: Factoring Activity
Use: Interactive Textbook, 8-5

CA Standards Check

1 Factor each expression. Check your answer.

a. $g^2 + 7g + 10$ **b.** $v^2 + 21v + 20$ **c.** $a^2 + 13a + 30$

Some factorable trinomials have a negative middle term and a positive constant term. If the middle term is negative, you need to inspect the negative factors of c to find the factors of the trinomial.

2 EXAMPLE Factoring $x^2 - bx + c$

Factor $d^2 - 17d + 42$.

Since the middle term is negative, find the negative factors of 42 until you find the pair that has a sum of -17.

Factors of 42	Sum of Factors
-1 and -42	-43
-2 and -21	-23
-3 and -14	-17 ✓

$d^2 - 17d + 42 = (d - 3)(d - 14)$

CA Standards Check 2 Factor each expression.

a. $k^2 - 10k + 25$ **b.** $x^2 - 11x + 18$ **c.** $q^2 - 15q + 36$

When you factor trinomials with a negative constant, you will need to inspect pairs of positive and negative factors of c.

3 EXAMPLE Factoring Trinomials With a Negative c

a. Factor $m^2 + 6m - 27$.

Identify the pair of factors of -27 that has a sum of 6.

Factors of -27	Sum of Factors
1 and -27	-26
27 and -1	26
3 and -9	-6
9 and -3	6 ✓

$m^2 + 6m - 27 = (m - 3)(m + 9)$

b. Factor $p^2 - 3p - 18$.

Identify the pair of factors of -18 that has a sum of -3.

Factors of -18	Sum of Factors
1 and -18	-17
18 and -1	17
-6 and 3	-3 ✓

$p^2 - 3p - 18 = (p + 3)(p - 6)$

CA Standards Check 3 Factor each expression.

a. $m^2 + 8m - 20$ **b.** $p^2 - 3p - 40$ **c.** $y^2 - y - 56$

You can also factor some trinomials that have more than one variable. Consider the product $(p + 10q)(p + 3q)$.

$$(p + 10q)(p + 3q) = p^2 + 3pq + 10pq + 10q \cdot 3q$$
$$(3 + 10)pq$$
$$= p^2 + 13pq + 30q^2$$

The first term is the square of the first variable, the middle term includes both variables, and the last term includes the square of the second variable.

4 EXAMPLE Factoring Trinomials With Two Variables

Factor $h^2 - 4hk - 77k^2$.

Find the factors of -77. Identify the pair that has a sum of -4.

Factors of -77	Sum of Factors
1 and -77	-76
77 and -1	76
7 and -11	-4 ✓

$h^2 - 4hk - 77k^2 = (h + 7k)(h - 11k)$

CA Standards Check 4 Factor each expression.

a. $x^2 + 11xy + 24y^2$ **b.** $v^2 + 2vw - 48w^2$ **c.** $m^2 - 17mn - 60n^2$

EXERCISES

Standards Practice

For more exercises, see *Extra Skills and Word Problem Practice*.

Alg1 11.0

A Practice by Example

Examples 1, 2 (pages 395, 396)

Complete.

1. $t^2 + 7t + 10 = (t + 2)(t + \blacksquare)$

2. $y^2 - 13y + 36 = (y - 4)(y - \blacksquare)$

3. $x^2 - 8x + 7 = (x - 1)(x - \blacksquare)$

4. $x^2 + 9x + 18 = (x + 3)(x + \blacksquare)$

Factor each expression. Check your answer.

5. $r^2 + 4r + 3$ **6.** $n^2 - 3n + 2$ **7.** $k^2 + 5k + 6$

8. $y^2 + 6y + 8$ **9.** $x^2 - 2x + 1$ **10.** $p^2 + 19p + 18$

11. $k^2 - 16k + 28$ **12.** $w^2 + 6w + 5$ **13.** $m^2 - 9m + 8$

14. $d^2 + 21d + 38$ **15.** $t^2 - 13t + 42$ **16.** $q^2 - 18q + 45$

Example 3 (page 396)

Complete.

17. $m^2 + 3m - 10 = (m - 2)(m + \blacksquare)$

18. $v^2 - 2v - 24 = (v + 4)(v - \blacksquare)$

19. $k^2 - 8k - 9 = (k + 1)(k - \blacksquare)$

20. $q^2 + 3q - 18 = (q - 3)(q + \blacksquare)$

Factor each expression.

21. $x^2 + 3x - 4$ **22.** $q^2 - 2q - 8$ **23.** $y^2 + y - 20$

24. $h^2 + 16h - 17$ **25.** $x^2 - 14x - 32$ **26.** $d^2 + 6d - 40$

27. $m^2 - 13m - 30$ **28.** $p^2 + 3p - 54$ **29.** $p^2 - 15p - 54$

Example 4 (page 397)

Choose the correct factoring for each expression.

30. $p^2 + 10pq + 9q^2$ **A.** $(p + 9q)(p + q)$ **B.** $(p + 9)(p + q^2)$

31. $m^2 + 4mn + 3n^2$ **A.** $(m + n)(3m + n)$ **B.** $(m + 3n)(m + n)$

32. $x^2 + 8xy + 15y^2$ **A.** $(x + 15y^2)(x + 1)$ **B.** $(x + 5y)(x + 3y)$

Factor each expression.

33. $t^2 + 7tv - 18v^2$ **34.** $x^2 + 12xy + 35y^2$ **35.** $p^2 - 10pq + 16q^2$

36. $m^2 - 3mn - 54n^2$ **37.** $h^2 + 18hj + 17j^2$ **38.** $x^2 - 10xy - 39y^2$

B Apply Your Skills

Find three different values to complete each expression so that it can be factored into the product of two binomials. Show each factorization.

39. $x^2 - 3x - ■$ **40.** $x^2 + x - ■$ **41.** $x^2 + ■x + 12$

42. Writing Suppose you can factor $x^2 + bx + c$ into the product of two binomials.
a. Explain what you know about the factors if $c > 0$.
b. Explain what you know about the factors if $c < 0$.

Factor each expression.

43. $k^2 + 10k + 16$ **44.** $m^2 + 10m - 24$ **45.** $n^2 + 10n - 56$

46. $g^2 + 20g + 96$ **47.** $x^2 + 8x - 65$ **48.** $t^2 + 28t + 75$

49. $x^2 - 11x - 42$ **50.** $k^2 + 23k + 42$ **51.** $m^2 + 14m - 51$

52. $x^2 + 29xy + 100y^2$ **53.** $t^2 - 10t - 75$ **54.** $d^2 - 19de + 48e^2$

Write the standard form for each polynomial modeled below. Then factor.

55. **56.**

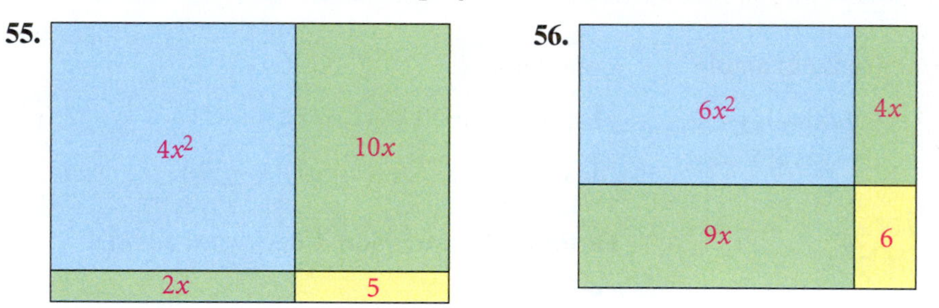

Visit: PHSchool.com
Web Code: bae-0805

57. Critical Thinking Let $x^2 - 12x - 28 = (x + a)(x + b)$.
a. What do you know about the signs of a and b?
b. Suppose $|a| > |b|$. Which number, a or b, is a negative integer? Explain.

58. Critical Thinking Let $x^2 + 12x - 28 = (x + a)(x + b)$.
a. What do you know about the signs of a and b?
b. Suppose $|a| > |b|$. Which number, a or b, is a negative integer? Explain.

C Challenge

Factor each trinomial.

Sample $n^6 + n^3 - 56 = n^{3+3} + n^3 - 56$
$= (n^3 + 8)(n^3 - 7)$

59. $x^{12} + 12x^6 + 35$ **60.** $t^8 + 5t^4 - 24$ **61.** $r^6 - 21r^3 + 80$

62. $m^{10} + 18m^5 + 17$ **63.** $x^{12} - 19x^6 - 120$ **64.** $p^6 + 14p^3 - 72$

Multiple Choice Practice

For California Standards Tutorials, visit PHSchool.com. Web Code: baq-9045

Alg1 10.0

65. The rectangle at the right is labeled with the area of each region. Which product represents the total area?

x^2	$9x$
$2x$	18

A $(x + 1)(x + 18)$
B $(x + 3)(x + 6)$
C $(x - 1)(x - 18)$
D $(x + 2)(x + 9)$

Alg1 16.0

66. Which situation can be represented by a linear function?

A The area of a square as the side length increases
B The distance a car travels, moving at a steady rate
C The value of a stock fund that is fluctuating
D The number of cells in a petri dish if the number of cells doubles every hour

Alg1 2.0

67. Which of the following lists is ordered from least to greatest?

A $3 \times 10^2, 2.9 \times 10^3, 30 \times 10^{-1}$
B $7.2 \times 10^1, 0.72 \times 10^3, 7.22 \times 10^2$
C $1.34 \times 10^5, 1.4 \times 10^5, 34 \times 10^3$
D $2 \times 10^8, 4 \times 10^6, 6 \times 10^4$

Alg1 15.0

68. Kimberly installed a swimming pool that is 18 feet long, 9 feet wide, and has an average depth of 8 feet. She can fill the pool with water at a rate of 280 cubic inches per minute. About how long will it take to fill her pool?

A 1 hour B 5 hours C 2 days D 6 days

Mixed Review

Lesson 8-4

GO for Help

Simplify each product.

69. $(x + 4)(x + 4)$ **70.** $(w - 6)(w - 6)$ **71.** $(r - 5)(r + 5)$

72. $(2q + 7)(2q + 7)$ **73.** $(8v - 2)(8v + 2)$ **74.** $(3a - 9)(3a - 9)$

75. $(3a - 5)(3a + 5)$ **76.** $(6t + 9)(6t + 9)$ **77.** $(2x + 8y)(2x - 8y)$

Lesson 6-4

78. You start with \$40 in your bank account and deposit \$18 each week. At the same time, your friend starts with \$220 but withdraws \$12 each week. When will your accounts have the same balance?

79. The sum of the two numbers is 42. The smaller number is 63 less than twice the larger number. Find both numbers.

80. A department store sells two types of DVD players. Total sales of players for the year were \$16,918.71. The total number of players sold was 129. The basic model costs \$119.99. The deluxe model costs \$149.99.
a. Find the number sold of each type of player.
b. What were the sales for the basic player?

Lesson 6-1

Solve each system by graphing.

81. $y = -2x - 1$
$y = 2x + 3$

82. $y = x + 4$
$y = 0.5x + 5$

83. $2x + 4y = 12$
$x - y = 3$

8-6 Factoring Trinomials of the Type $ax^2 + bx + c$

California Content Standards

11.0 Apply basic factoring techniques to second-degree polynomials. These techniques include finding a common factor for all terms in a polynomial. ***Develop***

What You'll Learn

- To factor trinomials of the type $ax^2 + bx + c$

. . . And Why

To factor trinomials in order to solve equations in Chapter 9

Check Skills You'll Need

GO for Help Lessons 8-2 and 8-5

Find the common factor of the terms of each polynomial.

1. $12x^2 + 6x$ **2.** $28m^2 - 35m + 14$ **3.** $4v^3 + 36v^2 + 10$

Factor each expression.

4. $x^2 + 5x + 4$ **5.** $y^2 - 3y - 28$ **6.** $t^2 - 11t + 30$

Factoring $ax^2 + bx + c$

To understand how to factor $ax^2 + bx + c$, where a is a positive integer greater than 1, consider the following product simplified using FOIL.

$$(2x + 3)(5x + 4) = \underset{F}{10x^2} + \underset{O}{8x} + \underset{I}{15x} + \underset{L}{12} = 10x^2 + 23x + 12$$

To factor $ax^2 + bx + c$, look for binomials that have the following characteristics:

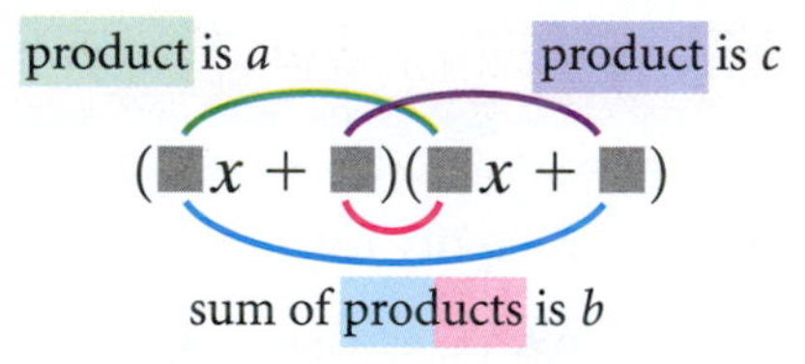

If c is positive and b is positive, the two factors of c are positive. If c is positive and b is negative, the two factors of c are negative.

1 EXAMPLE c Is Positive

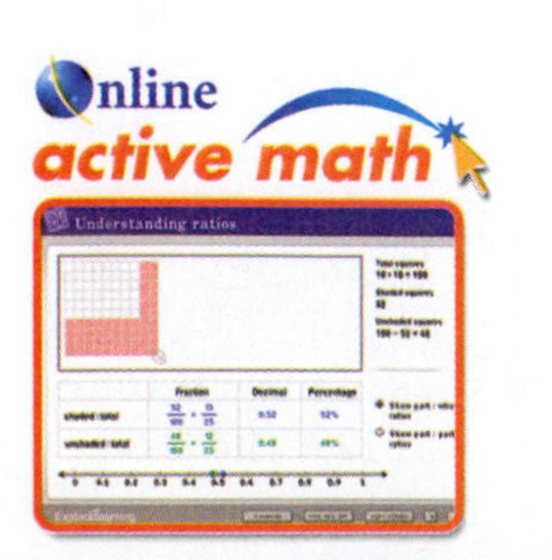

For: Factoring Activity
Use: Interactive Textbook, 8-6

Factor $6n^2 + 23n + 7$.

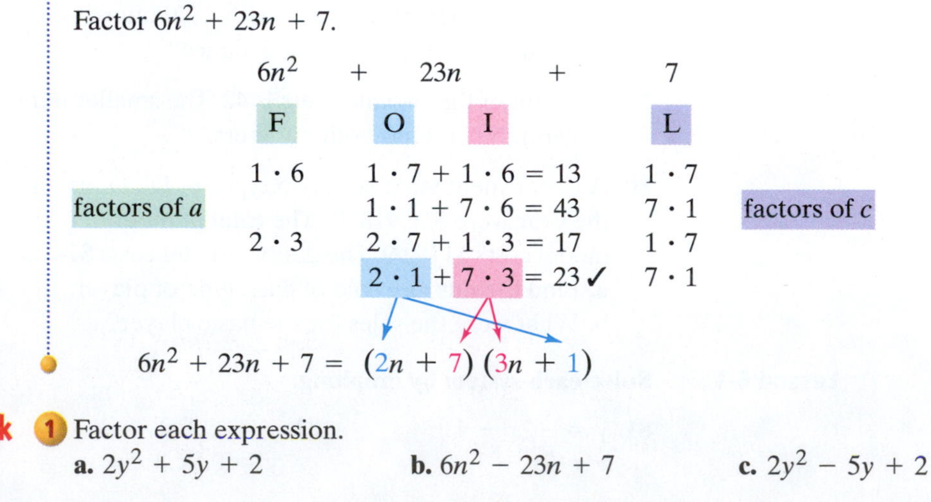

$$6n^2 + 23n + 7 = (2n + 7)(3n + 1)$$

CA Standards Check 1 Factor each expression.

a. $2y^2 + 5y + 2$ **b.** $6n^2 - 23n + 7$ **c.** $2y^2 - 5y + 2$

In the next example, c is negative. In this case, you need to consider combinations that equal -8, like $(-8)(1)$. You must also consider $(-1)(8)$.

2 EXAMPLE c Is Negative

Factor $7x^2 - 26x - 8$.

$7x^2$	$-26x$	-8
$1 \cdot 7$	$(1)(-8) + (1)(7) = -1$	$(1)(-8)$
	$(1)(1) + (-8)(7) = -55$	$(-8)(1)$
	$(1)(-4) + (2)(7) = 10$	$(2)(-4)$
	$(1)(2) + (-4)(7) = -26$ ✓	$(-4)(2)$

$$7x^2 - 26x - 8 = (1x + -4)(7x + 2)$$

CA Standards Check 2 Factor each expression.

a. $5d^2 - 14d - 3$ **b.** $2n^2 + n - 3$ **c.** $20p^2 - 31p - 9$

Some polynomials can be factored repeatedly. Continue the process of factoring until there are no common factors other than 1. If a trinomial has a common monomial factor, factor it out before trying to find binomial factors.

3 EXAMPLE Factoring Out a Monomial First

Factor $20x^2 + 80x + 35$ completely.

$20x^2 + 80x + 35 = 5(4x^2 + 16x + 7)$ Factor out the common factor.

$4x^2$	$16x$	7	Factor $4x^2 + 16x + 7$.
$1 \cdot 4$	$1 \cdot 7 + 1 \cdot 4 = 11$	$1 \cdot 7$	
	$1 \cdot 1 + 7 \cdot 4 = 29$	$7 \cdot 1$	
$2 \cdot 2$	$2 \cdot 7 + 1 \cdot 2 = 16$ ✓	$1 \cdot 7$	

$$4x^2 + 16x + 7 = (2x + 1)(2x + 7)$$

$20x^2 + 80x + 35 = 5(2x + 1)(2x + 7)$ Include the common factor in your final answer.

CA Standards Check 3 Factor each expression.

a. $2v^2 - 12v + 10$ **b.** $4y^2 + 14y + 6$ **c.** $18k^2 - 12k - 6$

EXERCISES

Standards Practice

For more exercises, see *Extra Skills and Word Problem Practice.*

Alg1 11.0

A Practice by Example

Example 1 (page 400)

GO for Help

Factor each expression.

1. $2n^2 + 15n + 7$ **2.** $7d^2 + 50d + 7$ **3.** $11w^2 - 14w + 3$

4. $3x^2 - 17x + 10$ **5.** $6t^2 + 25t + 11$ **6.** $3d^2 - 17d + 20$

7. $16m^2 + 26m + 9$ **8.** $15p^2 - 26p + 11$ **9.** $8y^2 + 30y + 13$

10. $2y^2 + 35y + 17$ **11.** $7x^2 - 30x + 27$ **12.** $8x^2 + 18x + 9$

Example 2 (page 401)

Factor each expression.

13. $2t^2 - t - 3$ **14.** $8y^2 - 10y - 3$ **15.** $2q^2 - 11q - 21$

16. $7x^2 - 20x - 3$ **17.** $13p^2 + 8p - 5$ **18.** $5k^2 - 2k - 7$

19. $10w^2 + 11w - 8$ **20.** $12d^2 - d - 20$ **21.** $14n^2 + 23n - 15$

Example 3 (page 401)

22. $24m^2 - 32m + 8$ **23.** $21v^2 - 70v + 49$ **24.** $6t^2 + 26t + 24$

25. $25x^2 - 10x - 15$ **26.** $11p^2 + 77p + 66$ **27.** $24v^2 + 10v - 6$

B Apply Your Skills

Find three different values that complete each expression so that the trinomial can be factored into the product of two binomials. Factor your trinomials.

28. $4g^2 + ■g + 10$ **29.** $15m^2 + ■m - 24$ **30.** $35g^2 + ■g - 16$

31. a. Write each area as a product of two binomials.

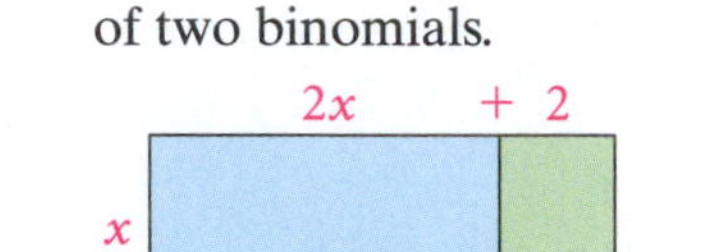

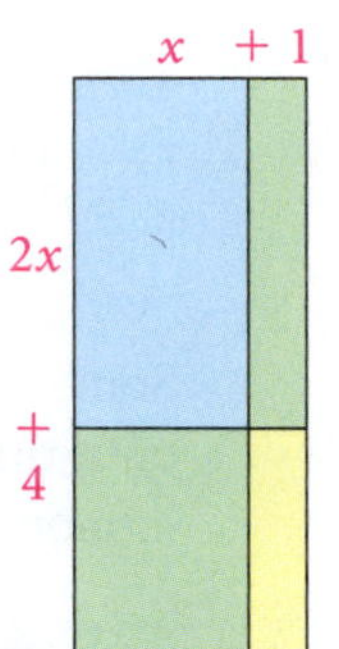

b. Are the products equal?

c. Critical Thinking Explain how the two products you found in part (a) can equal the same trinomial.

32. Writing Explain how you would factor the expression $50x^2 - 90x + 16$.

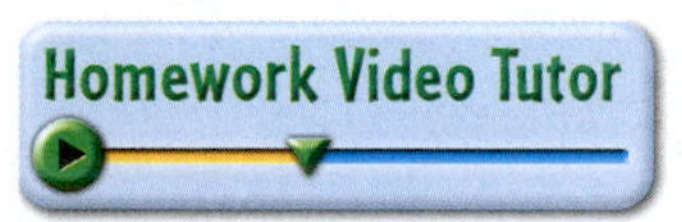

Visit: PHSchool.com
Web Code: bae-0806

Factor each expression.

33. $54p^2 + 87p + 28$ **34.** $66r^2 + 57r + 12$ **35.** $14x^2 - 53x + 14$

36. $28m^2 + 28m - 56$ **37.** $21h^2 + 72h - 48$ **38.** $55n^2 - 52n + 12$

39. $36y^2 + 114y - 20$ **40.** $63w^2 - 89w + 30$ **41.** $99q^2 - 92q + 9$

42. Critical Thinking If a and c in $ax^2 + bx + c$ are prime numbers, and the trinomial is factorable, how many positive values are possible for b?

43. Write three different factorable trinomials that are of the form $■x^2 - 12x + ■$. Factor your trinomials.

C Challenge

Factor each expression.

44. $56x^3 + 43x^2 + 5x$ **45.** $49p^2 + 63pq - 36q^2$ **46.** $108g^2h - 162gh + 54h$

47. The graph of the function $y = x^2 + 5x + 6$ is shown at the right.

a. What are the x-intercepts?

b. Factor $x^2 + 5x + 6$.

c. Critical Thinking Describe the relationship between the binomial factors you found in part (b) and the x-intercepts.

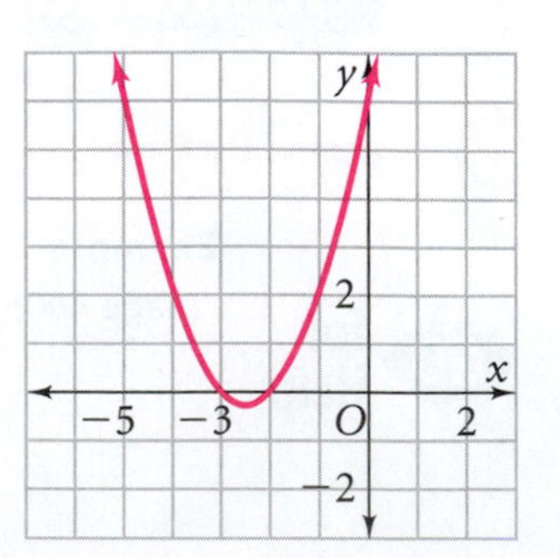

Multiple Choice Practice

For California Standards Tutorials, visit PHSchool.com. Web Code: baq-9045

Alg1 10.0

48. The area of a rectangle can be represented by the expression $3x^2 + 22x + 24$. If the factors of $3x^2 + 22x + 24$ represent the length and width, which expression represents the perimeter?

(A) $4x + 10$ (B) $4x + 25$ (C) $8x + 20$ (D) $8x + 50$

Alg1 6.0

49. Rafael recorded the average temperature outside his home during the first 10 weeks of spring. He modeled his data with the graph shown at the right. Which equation best represents his data?

(A) $y = \frac{1}{5}x + 55$ (C) $y = \frac{5}{2}x + 55$

(B) $y = \frac{2}{5}x + 55$ (D) $y = 5x + 55$

Alg1 2.0

50. Find the quotient $\frac{1.8 \times 10^{-4}}{3.6 \times 10^{3}}$.

(A) 5×10^{-8} (B) 5×10^{-6} (C) 5×10^{-2} (D) 5×10^{-1}

Alg1 9.0

51. Which is NOT a solution of the following system of equations?

$y - 2x < -5$

$2y + 3x < 5$

(A) $(4, -4)$ (B) $(5, 5)$ (C) $(6, 0)$ (D) $(7, -3)$

Mixed Review

GO for Help

Lesson 8-5

Factor each expression.

52. $y^2 + 8y + 7$
53. $t^2 - 7t + 12$
54. $p^2 - p - 20$
55. $m^2 - 15m + 36$
56. $k^2 + 16k - 36$
57. $g^2 + 17g + 72$
58. $h^2 - 13h - 48$
59. $x^2 - 13x - 30$
60. $d^2 - 18d + 56$

Lesson 8-4

Mental Math Find each square.

61. 89^2
62. 401^2
63. 903^2
64. 197^2

Mental Math Find each product.

65. $39 \cdot 41$
66. $38 \cdot 42$
67. $198 \cdot 202$
68. $73 \cdot 67$

Lesson 3-3

Solve each inequality.

69. $3g \leq 21$
70. $15 \leq \frac{5}{3}t$
71. $-16 < -4m$
72. $-\frac{1}{6}x < 5$
73. $4.9 \leq 7b$
74. $\frac{k}{7} < -24$

Write three solutions to each inequality.

75. $3a < 14$
76. $-7 \leq \frac{2c}{3}$
77. $16 < -5s$

GO Online Lesson Quiz Visit: PHSchool.com, Web Code: baa-0806

8-7 Factoring Special Cases

California Content Standards

11.0 Apply basic factoring techniques to second-degree polynomials. These techniques include finding a common factor for all terms in a polynomial, recognizing the difference of two squares, and recognizing perfect squares of binomials. ***Develop***

What You'll Learn

- To factor perfect-square trinomials
- To factor the difference of squares

. . . And Why

To find the length of a side of a square, as in Example 2

Check Skills You'll Need

GO for Help Lessons 7-4 and 8-4

Simplify each expression.

1. $(3x)^2$ **2.** $(5y)^2$ **3.** $(15h^2)^2$ **4.** $(2ab^2)^2$

Simplify each product.

5. $(c - 6)(c + 6)$ **6.** $(p - 11)(p - 11)$ **7.** $(4d + 7)(4d + 7)$

New Vocabulary

- perfect-square trinomial

Factoring Perfect-Square Trinomials

CA Standards Investigation Perfect-Square Trinomials

1. Factor each trinomial.

$x^2 + 6x + 9$ $x^2 + 10x + 9$ $m^2 + 15m + 36$

$m^2 + 12m + 36$ $k^2 + 26k + 25$ $k^2 + 10k + 25$

2. a. Which trinomials have pairs of binomial factors that are identical?

b. Describe the relationship between the middle and last terms of the trinomials that have identical pairs of factors.

In Lesson 8-4 you found the square of a binomial.

$$(a + b)^2 = (a + b)(a + b) = a^2 + 2ab + b^2 \text{ and}$$
$$(a - b)^2 = (a - b)(a - b) = a^2 - 2ab + b^2$$

Any trinomial of the form $a^2 + 2ab + b^2$ or $a^2 - 2ab + b^2$ is a **perfect-square trinomial.** You can factor a perfect-square trinomial into identical binomial factors.

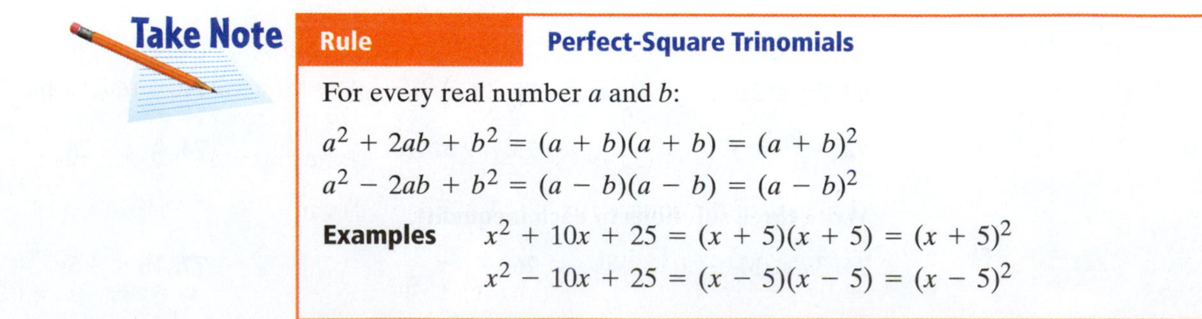

Take Note

Rule **Perfect-Square Trinomials**

For every real number a and b:

$a^2 + 2ab + b^2 = (a + b)(a + b) = (a + b)^2$

$a^2 - 2ab + b^2 = (a - b)(a - b) = (a - b)^2$

Examples $x^2 + 10x + 25 = (x + 5)(x + 5) = (x + 5)^2$

$x^2 - 10x + 25 = (x - 5)(x - 5) = (x - 5)^2$

You can factor a perfect-square trinomial using the method shown in the previous lesson. Or you can recognize a perfect-square trinomial and then factor it quickly. Here is how to recognize a perfect-square trinomial.

- The first and the last terms can both be written as the product of two identical factors.
- The middle term is twice the product of one factor from the first term and one factor from the last term.

Consider the following trinomials.

$4x^2 \quad + \quad 12x \quad + \quad 9$

$2x \cdot 2x \qquad\qquad 3 \cdot 3$

$2(2x \cdot 3) = 12x$

This is a perfect-square trinomial. In factored form the trinomial is $(2x + 3)(2x + 3)$, or $(2x + 3)^2$.

$4x^2 \quad + \quad 20x \quad + \quad 9$

$2x \cdot 2x \qquad\qquad 3 \cdot 3$

$2(2x \cdot 3) \neq 20x$

This is not a perfect-square trinomial. Factor by listing factors, as shown in Lesson 8-6.

When you factor a perfect-square trinomial, it may help to write the first and last terms as the products of identical factors.

1 EXAMPLE Factoring a Perfect-Square Trinomial With $a = 1$

Factor $x^2 - 8x + 16$.

$x^2 - 8x + 16 = x \cdot x - 8x + 4 \cdot 4$ — **Rewrite first and last terms.**

$= x \cdot x - 2(x \cdot 4) + 4 \cdot 4$ — **Does the middle term equal $2ab$? $8x = 2(x \cdot 4)$**

$= (x - 4)^2$ — **Write the factors as the square of a binomial.**

CA Standards Check

1 Factor each expression.

a. $x^2 + 8x + 16$ **b.** $n^2 + 16n + 64$ **c.** $n^2 - 16n + 64$

Problem Solving Tip

For $a \neq 0$, $b \neq 0$, and all integers n, $a^nb^n = (ab)^n$.

$9g^2 = 3^2g^2 = (3g)^2$

When you write the identical factors of the first and last terms, you can write them as square terms. Notice in Example 2, $9g^2$ is written as $(3g)^2$ and 4 is written as 2^2.

2 EXAMPLE Factoring a Perfect-Square Trinomial With $a \neq 1$

The area of the square shown at the right is $(9g^2 + 12g + 4)$ cm^2. Find an expression for the length of a side.

$9g^2 + 12g + 4 = (3g)^2 + 12g + 2^2$ — **Rewrite $9g^2$ as $(3g)^2$ and 4 as 2^2.**

$= (3g)^2 + 2(3g)(2) + 2^2$ — **Does the middle term equal $2ab$? $12g = 2(3g)(2)$ ✓**

$= (3g + 2)^2$ — **Write the factors as the square of a binomial.**

The side of the square has length of $(3g + 2)$ cm.

CA Standards Check

2 Factor each expression.

a. $9g^2 - 12g + 4$ **b.** $4t^2 + 36t + 81$ **c.** $4t^2 - 36t + 81$

Factoring the Difference of Squares

Recall from Lesson 8-4 that $(a + b)(a - b) = a^2 - b^2$. So you can factor a difference of two squares as $(a + b)(a - b)$.

Take Note

Rule **Difference of Two Squares**

For every real number a and b:

$a^2 - b^2 = (a + b)(a - b)$

Examples $x^2 - 81 = (x + 9)(x - 9)$

$16x^2 - 49 = (4x + 7)(4x - 7)$

3 EXAMPLE The Difference of Two Squares for $a = 1$

Factor $x^2 - 64$.

$x^2 - 64 = x^2 - 8^2$ Rewrite 64 as 8^2.

$= (x + 8)(x - 8)$ Factor.

Check Use FOIL to multiply.

$(x + 8)(x - 8)$

$x^2 - 8x + 8x - 64$

$x^2 - 64$ ✓

CA Standards Check 3 Factor each expression. Check your answer.

a. $x^2 - 36$ **b.** $m^2 - 100$ **c.** $p^2 - 49$

4 EXAMPLE The Difference of Two Squares for $a \neq 1$

Factor $4x^2 - 121$.

$4x^2 - 121 = (2x)^2 - (11)^2$ Rewrite $4x^2$ as $(2x)^2$ and 121 as 11^2.

$= (2x + 11)(2x - 11)$ Factor.

CA Standards Check 4 Factor each expression.

a. $9v^2 - 4$ **b.** $25x^2 - 64$ **c.** $4w^2 - 49$

Online active math

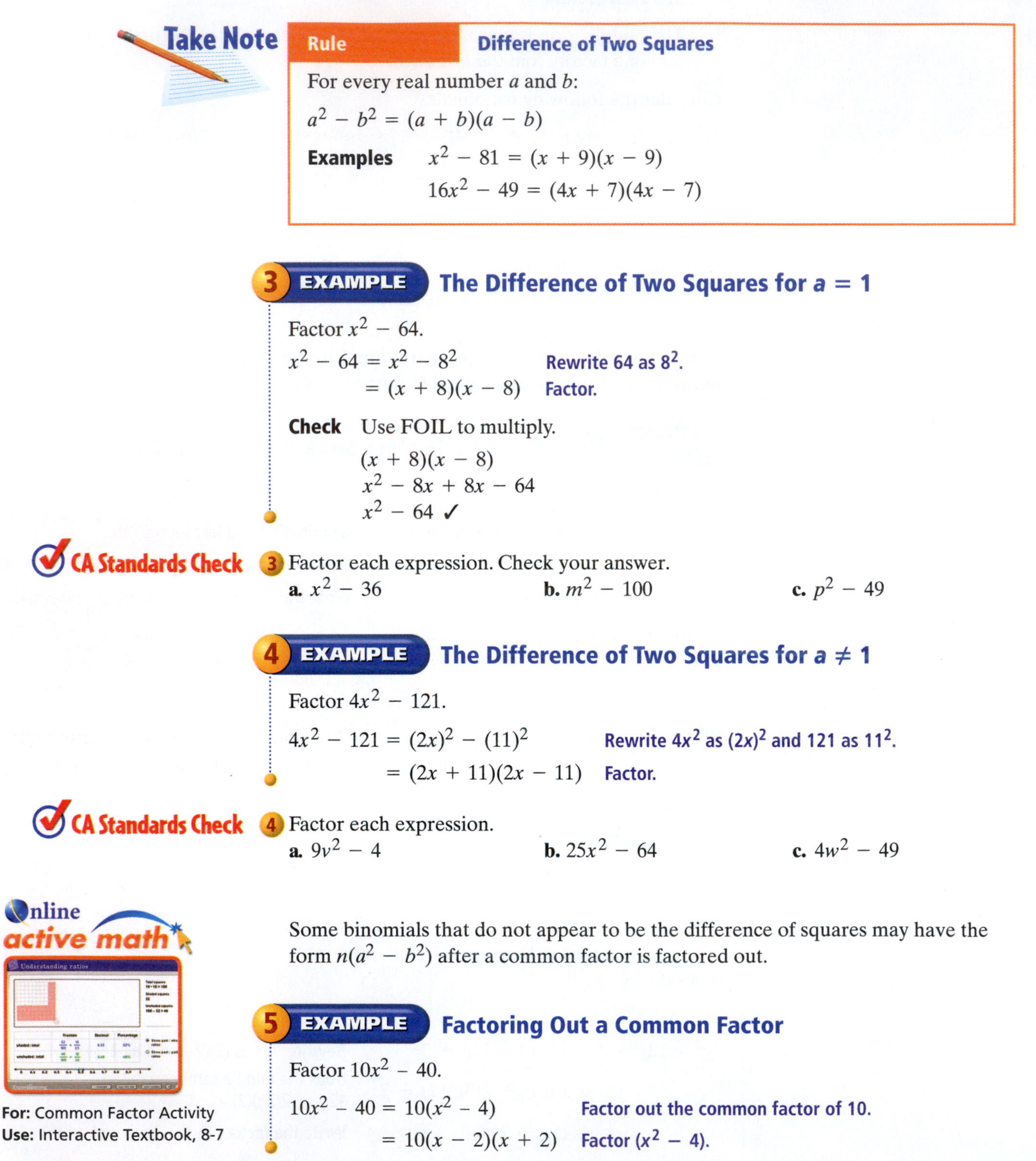

For: Common Factor Activity
Use: Interactive Textbook, 8-7

Some binomials that do not appear to be the difference of squares may have the form $n(a^2 - b^2)$ after a common factor is factored out.

5 EXAMPLE Factoring Out a Common Factor

Factor $10x^2 - 40$.

$10x^2 - 40 = 10(x^2 - 4)$ Factor out the common factor of 10.

$= 10(x - 2)(x + 2)$ Factor $(x^2 - 4)$.

CA Standards Check 5 Factor each expression.

a. $8y^2 - 50$ **b.** $3c^2 - 75$ **c.** $28k^2 - 7$

EXERCISES

For more exercises, see *Extra Skills and Word Problem Practice.*

Standards Practice

Alg1 11.0

A Practice by Example

Example 1 (page 405)

Factor each expression.

1. $c^2 + 10c + 25$ **2.** $x^2 - 2x + 1$ **3.** $h^2 + 12h + 36$

4. $m^2 - 24m + 144$ **5.** $k^2 - 16k + 64$ **6.** $t^2 - 14t + 49$

Example 2 (page 405)

The given expression represents the area. Find the side length of each square.

7.

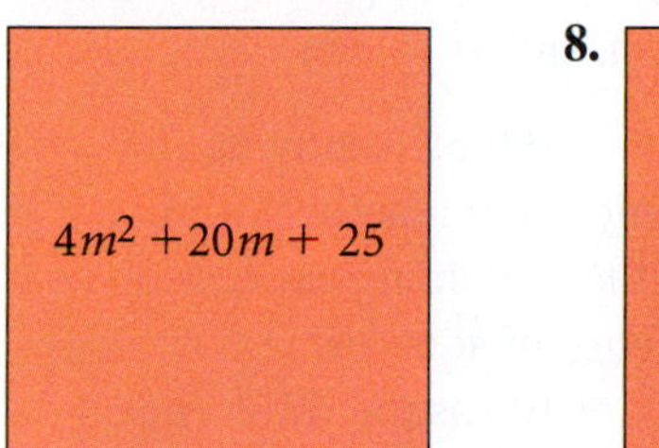

8.

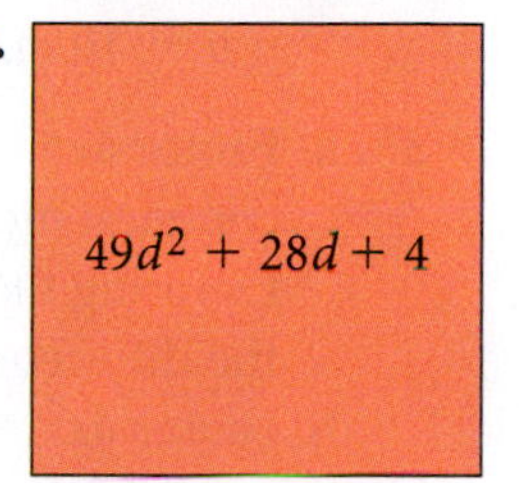

9.

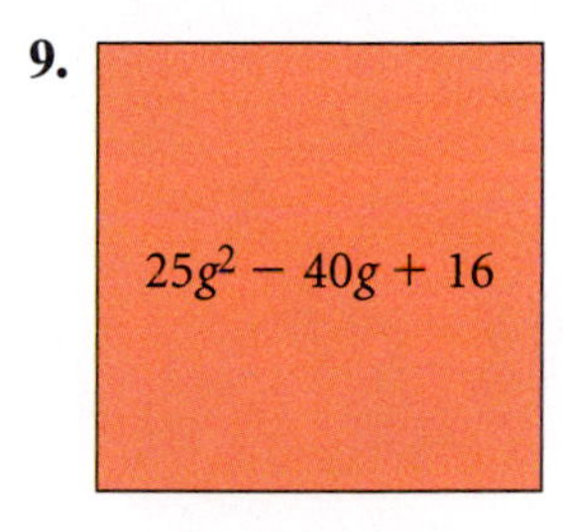

Factor each expression. Check your answer.

10. $25g^2 - 30g + 9$ **11.** $64r^2 - 144r + 81$ **12.** $100v^2 - 220v + 121$

Example 3 (page 406)

13. $x^2 - 4$ **14.** $y^2 - 81$ **15.** $k^2 - 196$

16. $r^2 - 144$ **17.** $h^2 - 100$ **18.** $m^2 - 225$

19. $w^2 - 256$ **20.** $x^2 - 400$ **21.** $y^2 - 900$

Example 4 (page 406)

22. $25q^2 - 9$ **23.** $49y^2 - 4$ **24.** $9c^2 - 64$

25. $4m^2 - 81$ **26.** $16k^2 - 49$ **27.** $144p^2 - 1$

28. $81v^2 - 100$ **29.** $400n^2 - 121$ **30.** $25w^2 - 196$

Example 5 (page 406)

31. $3m^2 - 12$ **32.** $5k^2 - 245$ **33.** $3x^2 + 48x + 192$

34. $2t^2 - 36t + 162$ **35.** $6r^3 - 150r$ **36.** $7h^2 - 56h + 112$

B Apply Your Skills

37. Writing Summarize the procedure for factoring a perfect-square trinomial. Give at least two examples.

38. Error Analysis Suppose a classmate factored the binomial at the right. What error did your classmate make?

~~$4x^2 - 121 = (4x - 11)(4x - 11)$~~
~~$= (4x - 11)^2$~~

Find a pair of factors for each number by using the difference of two squares.

Sample $143 = 144 - 1$ Write 143 as the difference of two squares.

$= 12^2 - 1^2$ Rewrite 144 as 12^2 and 1 as 1^2.

$= (12 - 1)(12 + 1)$ Factor.

$= (11)(13)$ Simplify.

39. 99 **40.** 91 **41.** 75 **42.** 117 **43.** 224

44. a. Write an expression that is a perfect-square trinomial.

b. Explain how you know your trinomial is a perfect-square trinomial.

Visit: PHSchool.com
Web Code: bae-0807

Factor each expression.

45. $100v^2 - 25w^2$
46. $16p^2 - 48pq + 36q^2$
47. $28c^2 + 140cd + 175d^2$
48. $\frac{1}{4}m^2 - \frac{1}{9}$
49. $x^2 + x + \frac{1}{4}$
50. $64g^2 - 192gh + 144h^2$
51. $\frac{1}{4}p^2 - 2p + 4$
52. $\frac{1}{9}n^2 - \frac{1}{25}$
53. $\frac{1}{25}k^2 + \frac{6}{5}k + 9$

54. a. Write an expression in terms of n and m for the area of the top of the block that was drilled at the right. Use 3.14 for π. Factor your expression.
b. Find the area of the top of the block if $n = 10$ in. and $m = 3$ in.

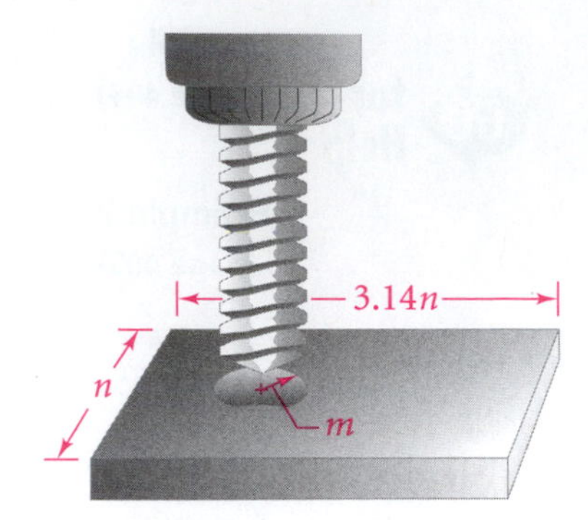

55. a. Factor $4x^2 - 100$ by removing the common monomial factor and then factoring the remaining expression as the difference of squares.
b. Factor $4x^2 - 100$ as the difference of squares, and then remove the common monomial factors.
c. **Critical Thinking** Why can $4x^2 - 100$ be factored in two different ways?
d. Can you factor $3x^2 - 75$ in the two ways you factored $4x^2 - 100$ in parts (a) and (b)? Explain your answer.

Factor each expression.

56. $64r^6 - 144r^3 + 81$
57. $p^6 + 40p^3q + 400q^2$
58. $36m^4 + 84m^2 + 49$
59. $81p^{10} + 198p^5 + 121$
60. $108m^6 - 147$
61. $x^{20} - 4x^{10}y^5 + 4y^{10}$
62. $256g^4 - 100h^6$
63. $45x^4 - 60x^2y + 20y^2$
64. $37g^8 - 37h^8$

65. a. The expression $(t - 3)^2 - 16$ is a difference of two squares. Identify a and b.
b. Factor $(t - 3)^2 - 16$ and simplify.

66. The binomial $16 - 81n^4$ can be factored twice as the difference of squares.
a. Factor $16 - 81n^4$ completely.
b. **Critical Thinking** What characteristics do 16 and $81n^4$ share that make this possible?
c. Write a binomial that can be factored twice as the difference of squares.

Multiple Choice Practice

For California Standards Tutorials, visit PHSchool.com. Web Code: baq-9045

Alg1 10.0

67. The area of the square at the right can be represented by the expression $4x^2 + 28x + 49$. What is the value of $a + b$?

Ⓐ 2
Ⓑ 4
Ⓒ 7
Ⓓ 9

$ax + b$

$ax + b$

Alg1 6.0

68. At what x-value does the graph of $y = 8x - 4$ cross the x-axis?

Ⓐ -4
Ⓑ $-\frac{1}{2}$
Ⓒ $\frac{1}{2}$
Ⓓ 4

Alg1 5.0

69. Autumn is decorating cookies with chocolate chip happy faces. If Autumn used 168 chocolate chips to decorate 24 cookies, how many chocolate chips will she need to decorate 140 cookies?

(A) 20 (B) 164 (C) 308 (D) 980

Alg1 2.0

70. Which of the following statements is true?

(A) Any number raised to the zero power equals zero.

(B) Any number raised to a negative power equals a negative number.

(C) A number $a \times 10^n$ is written in scientific notation when n is an integer and $1 \leq a \leq 10$.

(D) The product of two powers with the same base equals the base raised to the sum of the exponents.

Mixed Review

GO for Help

Lesson 8-6 **Factor each expression.**

71. $2d^2 + 11d + 5$ **72.** $2x^2 - 11x + 12$ **73.** $4t^2 + 16t + 7$

74. $5w^2 - 44w - 9$ **75.** $6t^2 + 19t + 8$ **76.** $21m^2 - 20m - 9$

77. $14x^2 - 11x - 9$ **78.** $4y^2 + 32y + 55$ **79.** $12k^2 - 5k - 2$

Lesson 4-4 **Write a function rule for each table.**

80.

x	f(x)
−1	−7
0	0
1	7
2	14

81.

x	f(x)
0	−5
1	−4
2	−3
3	−2

82.

x	f(x)
−2	1
−1	2
0	3
1	4

Lesson 4-1 **Write the coordinates of a point that satisfies each condition.**

83. The point is located in Quadrant II.

84. The point is located on the y-axis.

85. The x-value is greater than the y-value.

Checkpoint Quiz 2 — Lessons 8-4 through 8-7

Simplify each expression.

1. $(k - 7)^2$ **2.** $(5t + 9)^2$

3. $(h - 11)(h - 11)$ **4.** $(x^3 - 2y)(5x^2 + y^2)$

Factor each expression.

5. $v^2 + 20v + 100$ **6.** $k^2 - 17k + 60$ **7.** $2x^2 + 13x + 11$

8. $10m^2 + 19m + 7$ **9.** $3w^2 - 6w - 24$ **10.** $9t^2 - 25$

8-8

Factoring by Grouping

California Content Standards

11.0 Apply basic factoring techniques to second- and simple third-degree polynomials. These techniques include finding a common factor for all terms in a polynomial. ***Master***

What You'll Learn

- To factor polynomials with four terms
- To factor trinomials by grouping

. . . And Why

To find expressions for the dimensions of a packaging box, as in Example 4

Check Skills You'll Need

GO for Help Lessons 8-2 and 8-3

Find the common factor of the terms of each polynomial.

1. $6y^2 + 12y - 4$
2. $9r^3 + 15r^2 + 21r$
3. $30h^3 - 25h^2 - 40h$
4. $16m^3 - 12m^2 - 36m$

Find each product.

5. $(v + 3)(v^2 + 5)$
6. $(2q^2 - 4)(q - 5)$
7. $(2t - 5)(3t + 4)$
8. $(4x - 1)(x^2 + 2x + 3)$

New Vocabulary • factor by grouping

Factoring Polynomials With Four Terms

You can use the Distributive Property to **factor by grouping** if two groups of terms have the same factor.

$$y^3 + 3y^2 + 4y + 12$$
$$y^2(y + 3) + 4(y + 3)$$
$$(y^2 + 4)(y + 3)$$

These factors are the same, so factor again.

To factor by grouping, look for a common binomial factor of two pairs of terms.

1 EXAMPLE Factoring a Four-Term Polynomial

Factor $4n^3 + 8n^2 - 5n - 10$.

$4n^3 + 8n^2 - 5n - 10 = 4n^2(n + 2) - 5(n + 2)$ Factor out the common factor from each group of two terms.

$= (4n^2 - 5)(n + 2)$ Factor out $(n + 2)$.

Check $4n^3 + 8n^2 - 5n - 10 \stackrel{?}{=} (4n^2 - 5)(n + 2)$

$= 4n^3 + 8n^2 - 5n - 10$ ✓ Use FOIL.

CA Standards Check 1 Factor each expression. Check your answer.

a. $5t^4 + 20t^3 + 6t + 24$

b. $2w^3 + w^2 - 14w - 7$

Before you factor by grouping, you may need to factor out the common factor of all the terms of a polynomial. Remember, a polynomial is not completely factored until there are no common factors other than 1.

2 EXAMPLE Factoring Completely

Factor $12p^4 + 10p^3 - 36p^2 - 30p$.

$$12p^4 + 10p^3 - 36p^2 - 30p = 2p(6p^3 + 5p^2 - 18p - 15)$$ **Factor out $2p$.**

$$= 2p[(p^2(6p + 5) - 3(6p + 5)]$$ **Factor by grouping.**

$$= 2p(p^2 - 3)(6p + 5)$$ **Factor again.**

CA Standards Check 2 Factor $45m^4 - 9m^3 + 30m^2 - 6m$.

Factoring Trinomials by Grouping

You can also factor by grouping to find the factors of a trinomial of the form $ax^2 + bx + c$. You may want to use this method when you cannot quickly factor a trinomial using the method you learned in Lesson 8-6.

You can use these steps to factor a trinomial such as $48x^2 + 46x + 5$.

Video Tutor Help
Visit: PHSchool.com
Web Code: bae-0775

Step 1 Find the product ac.

$48 \cdot 5 = 240$

Step 2 Find the two factors of ac that have sum b.

Factors	→	Sum	Factors	→	Sum
$1 \cdot 240$	→	$1 + 240 = 241$	$4 \cdot 60$	→	$4 + 60 = 64$
$2 \cdot 120$	→	$2 + 120 = 122$	$5 \cdot 48$	→	$5 + 48 = 53$
$3 \cdot 80$	→	$3 + 80 = 83$	$6 \cdot 40$	→	$6 + 40 = 46$ ✓

Step 3 Rewrite the trinomial using the sum.

$$48x^2 + 46x + 5 = 48x^2 + (6 + 40)x + 5$$
$$= 48x^2 + 6x + 40x + 5$$

Step 4 Factor by grouping.

$$48x^2 + 6x + 40x + 5$$
$$6x(8x + 1) + 5(8x + 1)$$
$$(6x + 5)(8x + 1)$$

3 EXAMPLE Factoring a Trinomial by Grouping

Factor $24q^2 + 25q - 25$.

Step 1 $24(-25) = -600$ — **Find the product ac.**

Step 2 Factors → Sum — **Find two factors of ac that have sum b.**

$(-12)(50) \rightarrow -12 + 50 = 38$

$(-15)(40) \rightarrow -15 + 40 = 25$ ✓

Step 3 $24q^2 - 15q + 40q - 25$ — **Rewrite the trinomial.**

Step 4 $3q(8q - 5) + 5(8q - 5)$ — **Factor by grouping.**

$(3q + 5)(8q - 5)$ — **Factor again.**

Problem Solving Tip

As you look for factors of ac, use mental math to eliminate those factors that give sums too great or too small to be reasonable choices.

CA Standards Check 3 Factor each trinomial by grouping.

a. $63d^2 + 44d + 5$ **b.** $11k^2 + 49k + 20$ **c.** $4y^2 + 33y - 70$

Given a polynomial expression for the volume of a rectangular prism, you can sometimes factor to find possible expressions for the length, width, and height.

4 EXAMPLE Application

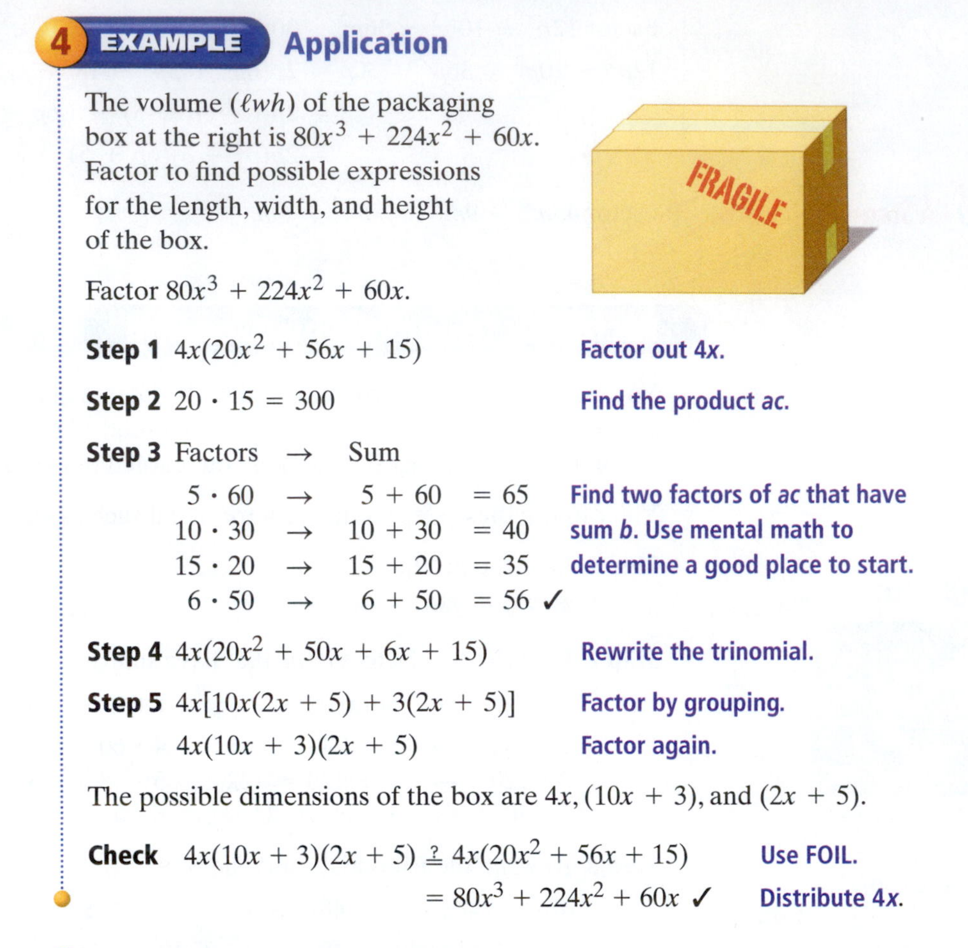

The volume (ℓwh) of the packaging box at the right is $80x^3 + 224x^2 + 60x$. Factor to find possible expressions for the length, width, and height of the box.

Factor $80x^3 + 224x^2 + 60x$.

Step 1 $4x(20x^2 + 56x + 15)$ — **Factor out $4x$.**

Step 2 $20 \cdot 15 = 300$ — **Find the product ac.**

Step 3 Factors $\rightarrow$ Sum

Factors		Sum	
$5 \cdot 60$	$\rightarrow$	$5 + 60$	$= 65$
$10 \cdot 30$	$\rightarrow$	$10 + 30$	$= 40$
$15 \cdot 20$	$\rightarrow$	$15 + 20$	$= 35$
$6 \cdot 50$	$\rightarrow$	$6 + 50$	$= 56$ ✓

Find two factors of ac that have sum b. Use mental math to determine a good place to start.

Step 4 $4x(20x^2 + 50x + 6x + 15)$ — **Rewrite the trinomial.**

Step 5 $4x[10x(2x + 5) + 3(2x + 5)]$ — **Factor by grouping.**

$4x(10x + 3)(2x + 5)$ — **Factor again.**

The possible dimensions of the box are $4x$, $(10x + 3)$, and $(2x + 5)$.

Check $4x(10x + 3)(2x + 5) \stackrel{?}{=} 4x(20x^2 + 56x + 15)$ — **Use FOIL.**

$= 80x^3 + 224x^2 + 60x$ ✓ — **Distribute $4x$.**

CA Standards Check **4** Find expressions for the possible dimensions of each rectangular prism.

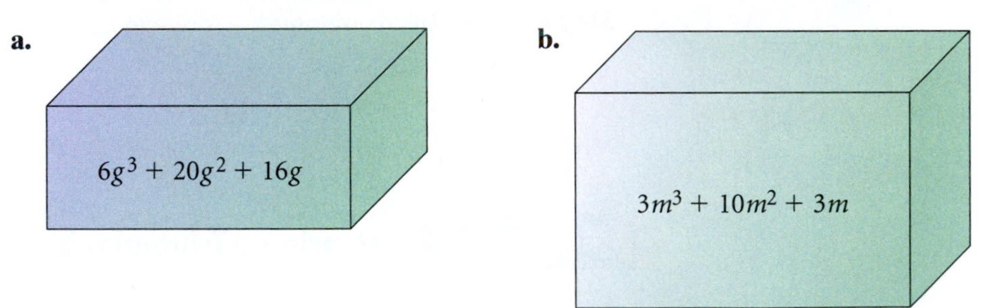

Here is a summary of what to remember as you factor polynomials.

Take Note

Summary **Factoring Polynomials**

1. Factor out the common factor.
2. If the polynomial has two terms or three terms, look for a difference of two squares, a product of two squares, or a pair of binomial factors.
3. If there are four or more terms, group terms and factor to find common binomial factors.
4. As a final check, make sure there are no common factors other than 1.

EXERCISES

For more exercises, see *Extra Skills and Word Problem Practice.*

Standards Practice Alg1 11.0

A Practice by Example

Example 1 (page 410)

GO for Help

Find the common factor of the first two terms and of the last two terms.

1. $2m^3 + 6m^2 + 3m + 9$

2. $10p^3 - 25p^2 + 4p - 10$

3. $2z^3 + 12z^2 - 5z - 30$

4. $6n^3 + 3n^2 + 2n + 1$

Factor each expression.

5. $6n^3 + 8n^2 + 3n + 4$

6. $14t^3 + 21t^2 + 16t + 24$

7. $27t^3 + 45t^2 - 3t - 5$

8. $13y^3 - 8y^2 + 13y - 8$

9. $45x^3 + 20x^2 + 9x + 4$

10. $10w^3 + 16w^2 - 15w - 24$

Example 2 (page 411)

Factor completely.

11. $12v^3 - 32v^2 + 6v - 16$

12. $7q^4 - 4q^3 + 28q^2 - 16q$

13. $20m^3 - 18m^2 + 40m - 36$

14. $6x^4 + 4x^3 - 6x^2 - 4x$

15. $12y^3 - 20y^2 + 30y - 50$

16. $9c^3 - 12c^2 + 18c - 24$

Example 3 (page 411)

Factor by grouping.

17. $12p^2 + 16p + 5$

18. $16t^2 + 24t + 9$

19. $18n^2 + 57n - 10$

20. $9w^2 - 27w + 20$

21. $24m^2 + 8m - 2$

22. $36v^2 - 9v - 7$

23. $6x^2 + 11x - 10$

24. $20v^2 - 41v + 9$

25. $63q^2 - 52q - 20$

Example 4 (page 412)

Find expressions for the possible dimensions of each rectangular prism.

26. $3m^3 + 7m^2 + 2m$

27. $5k^3 + 30k^2 + 40k$

B Apply Your Skills

Factor completely.

28. $7h^3 - 35h^2 - 42h$

29. $60t^3 - 200t^2 - 66t + 220$

30. $8d^3 + 16d^2 + 24d + 48$

31. $12x^2 - 4xy - 56y^2$

32. $54r^3 - 45r^2 + 9r$

33. $150k^3 + 350k^2 + 180k + 420$

34. a. Factor $(28x^3 - 7x^2) + (36x - 9)$.

b. Factor $(28x^3 + 36x) + (-7x^2 - 9)$.

c. Why can you factor the same polynomial using different pairs of terms?

Write each expression in standard form and factor.

35. $-8w + 49w^2 + 14w^3 - 28$

36. $2m^3 + 16 - m - 32m^2$

37. $-6 + 44t^3 - 4t^2 + 66t$

38. $2 - 50x - x^2 + 25x^3$

GO Online Lesson Quiz Visit: PHSchool.com, Web Code: baa-0808

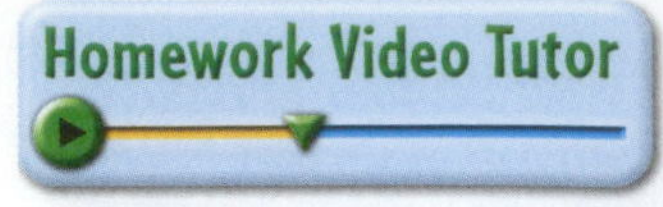

Visit: PHSchool.com
Web Code: bae-0808

39. The polynomial shown at the right represents the volume of the rectangular prism. Factor the polynomial to find possible expressions for the length, width, and height of the prism.

$84w^3 + 82w^2 + 10w$

40. Write a four-term polynomial that can be factored by grouping. Factor your polynomial.

41. Writing Describe how to factor the expression $10x^3 - 15x^2 + 2x - 3$ by grouping.

42. Error Analysis Find the error in the student's work. Factor the expression correctly.

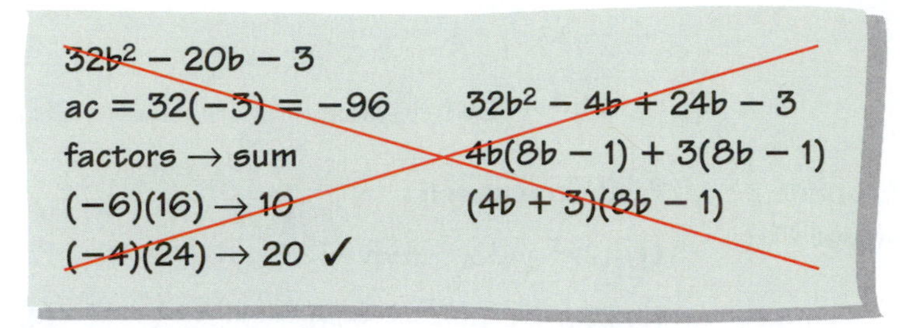

C Challenge

Factor by grouping.

43. $30m^5 + 24m^3n - 35m^2n^2 - 28n^3$

44. $x^2p + x^2q^5 + yp + yq^5$

45. $h^3 + 11h^2 - 4h - 44$

46. $w^6 - w^4 - 9w^2 + 9$

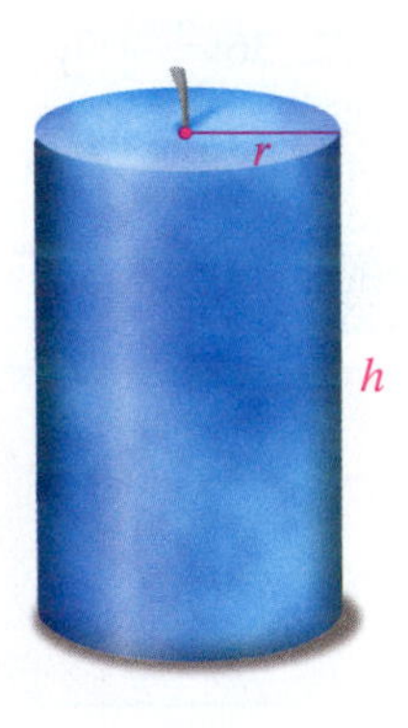

47. The polynomial $2\pi x^3 + 12\pi x^2 + 18\pi x$ represents the volume of a cylindrical candle. The formula for the volume of a cylinder is $V = \pi r^2 h$.

a. Factor $2\pi x^3 + 12\pi x^2 + 18\pi x$.

b. Based on your answer to part (a), write an expression for a possible radius of the candle.

The number 63 can be written as $2^5 + 2^4 + 2^3 + 2^2 + 2^1 + 2^0$. For Exercises 48 and 49, factor each expression by grouping. Then simplify the powers of 2 to write 63 as the product of two numbers.

48. $(2^5 + 2^4 + 2^3) + (2^2 + 2^1 + 2^0)$

49. $(2^5 + 2^4) + (2^3 + 2^2) + (2^1 + 2^0)$

50. a. For the rectangular prism below, let $x = 3$. Write linear expressions for the length, width, and height of the prism.

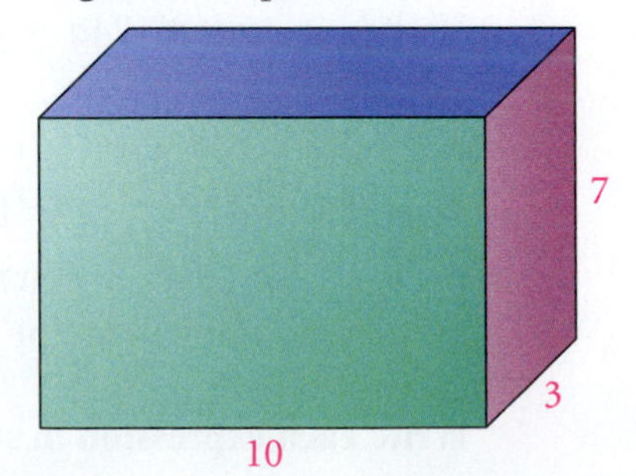

b. Using your answers from part (a), write a polynomial that represents the volume of the prism.

Multiple Choice Practice

For California Standards Tutorials, visit PHSchool.com. Web Code: baq-9045

Alg1 11.0

51. The volume of the square prism is $96x^3 + 48x^2 + 6x$. Which expression could describe the perimeter of one of the prism's square faces?

(A) $4x + 1$ (B) $24x$ (C) $6x$ (D) $16x + 4$

Alg1 10.0

52. Simplify the expression $(5c^3 + 2c^2 + 3c - 12) - (2c^2 + 10c + 7)$.

(A) $5c^3 + 13c + 5$ (B) $5c^3 - 7c - 19$ (C) $5c^3 - 4c^2 - 7c - 19$ (D) $5c^3 - 7c - 5$

Alg1 2.0

53. Evaluate $\frac{-5x^3y^5}{15x^{-7}y^5z^{-2}}$ for $x = -1$, $y = 5$, and $z = 3$.

(A) -9 (B) -3 (C) -1 (D) 0

Alg1 6.0

54. Which of the following graphs represents a direct variation?

(A) (B) (C) (D)

Mixed Review

Lesson 8-7

Factor each expression.

55. $k^2 + 14k + 49$ **56.** $r^2 + 6r + 9$ **57.** $y^2 - 16y + 64$

58. $2t^2 + 12t + 18$ **59.** $m^2 - 64$ **60.** $4g^2 + 40g + 100$

61. $4d^2 - 25$ **62.** $5n^2 - 45$ **63.** $25q^2 + 40q + 16$

GO for Help

Lesson 7-4

Simplify each expression.

64. $(b^2)^2$ **65.** $x^4 \cdot x^{-2}$ **66.** $(t^3)^5$ **67.** $(c^5d)^7$

68. $(2y)^3$ **69.** $(9m)^0$ **70.** $(x^3)(x^7)^{-2}$ **71.** $(3w^2v^3)^4$

Simplify. Write each answer in scientific notation.

72. $(2 \times 10^5)^4$ **73.** $(3 \times 10^6)^2$ **74.** $(7 \times 10^{-6})^2$ **75.** $(2 \times 10^7)^5$

76. $(5.3 \times 10^2)^2$ **77.** $(8.1 \times 10^{-3})^2$ **78.** $(1.9 \times 10^8)^3$ **79.** $(4 \times 10^{-3})^{-2}$

Lesson 6-2

Solve each system using substitution.

80. $y = -7x + 12$, $y = 3x + 2$

81. $y = -3x + 4$, $y = -5x + 12$

82. $10x + 2y = 15$, $y = -4x + 7$

83. $x + y = -28$, $y = -2x - 26$

84. $8x + 2y = 50$, $y = -4x + 25$

85. $y = x - 5$, $11x - 6y = 65$

Test-Taking Strategies

Eliminating Answers

Before you do all the work involved in solving a multiple-choice problem, you usually can eliminate some answer choices. This can save you time in arriving at the answer to the problem, or in making an "educated" guess if you do not actually know how to find the answer.

1 EXAMPLE

One factor of $x^3 + x^2 + x - 3$ is $x - 1$. Which of the following is also a factor?

(A) $x^2 + 2x - 3$ (B) $x^2 + 2x + 3$ (C) $x^3 + 2x + 3$ (D) $x^2 - 2x + 3$

Look at the degrees of the polynomials. The original polynomial has degree 3 and the given factor has degree 1. The answer must have degree less than or equal to $3 - 1 = 2$. Choice C has degree 3, so you can eliminate it.

Look at the constant terms of the polynomials. The constant term of the original polynomial is -3. Since the constant term of the factor is -1, the other constant term must be 3 for the product of the two factors to be -3. The constant term of answer choice A is -3, so you can eliminate choice A.

The correct answer is either B or D.

2 EXAMPLE

$(3x + 5)(x - 2) = ■$

(A) $3x^2 - 2x - 10$ (B) $3x^2 - 5x - 2$ (C) $3x^2 + 2x - 10$ (D) $3x^2 - x - 10$

Substitute a number. The original polynomial has $x - 2$ as a factor. If x equals 2, then the polynomial equals 0. The correct answer will equal 0 when x is 2.

Choice A: $3(2)^2 - 2(2) - 10 = 3(4) - 4 - 10 = 12 - 4 - 10 = -2$. You can eliminate A.

Choice B: $3(2)^2 - 5(2) - 2 = 3(4) - 10 - 2 = 12 - 10 - 2 = 0$. B is a possible answer.

Choice C: $3(2)^2 + 2(2) - 10 = 3(4) + 4 - 10 = 12 + 4 - 10 = 6$. You can eliminate C.

Choice D: $3(2)^2 - 2 - 10 = 3(4) - 2 - 10 = 12 - 2 - 10 = 0$. D is a possible answer.

The correct answer is either B or D.

Multiple Choice Practice

1. One factor of $3x^3 + 2x^2 + x - 6$ is $x - 1$. What is the other factor?

   (A) $3x^2 - 5x - 6$ (B) $3x^2 + 5x + 6$ (C) $3x^3 + x^2 - 3$ (D) $3x^2 - 5x + 6$

2. Simplify the product $(2m - 1)(m + 5)$.

   (A) $2m^2 + 11m + 5$ (B) $2m^2 - 11m + 5$ (C) $2m^2 + 9m - 5$ (D) $2m^2 - 9m - 5$

3. If the expression $10x^2 + 17x + 3$ represents the area of a rectangle and $2x + 3$ represents its length, which expression best describes the width of the rectangle?

   (A) $5x + 3$ (B) $5x + 1$ (C) $4x + 1$ (D) $5x^2 + 1$

Chapter 8 Review

Vocabulary Review

English and Spanish Audio Online

binomial (p. 371)
degree of a monomial (p. 371)
degree of a polynomial (p. 371)
difference of squares (p. 390)
factor by grouping (p. 410)
monomial (p. 370)
perfect-square trinomial (p. 404)
polynomial (p. 371)
standard form of a polynomial (p. 371)
trinomial (p. 371)

Go Online PHSchool.com
For: Vocabulary quiz
Web Code: baj-0851

Match the vocabulary term in the column on the left with the most accurate description in the column on the right.

1. binomial
2. degree of a monomial
3. monomial
4. perfect-square trinomial
5. standard form of a polynomial

A. a polynomial with two terms
B. a polynomial in which the terms decrease in degree from left to right and there are no like terms
C. a polynomial with two identical binomial factors
D. the sum of the exponents of the variables
E. an expression that is a number, a variable, or a product of a number and one or more variables

Skills and Concepts

Lesson 8-1

- To describe polynomials (p. 370)
- To add and subtract polynomials (p. 372)

Alg1 10.0

The degree of a term with one variable is the exponent of the variable. A **polynomial** is a sum of one or more monomials. The **degree of a polynomial** is the same as the degree of the term with the highest degree. A polynomial can be named by its degree or by the number of its terms. You can simplify polynomials by adding the coefficients of like terms.

Write each polynomial in standard form. Then name each polynomial based on its degree and number of terms.

6. $5y + 2 - 6y^2 + 3y$
7. $1 + 9h^2$
8. $k^3 + 3k^5 + k - k^3$
9. $6t^3 + 9 + 8t + 7t^2 - 6t^3$
10. x^2y^2
11. $5 + x^2 + x^3$

Simplify. Write each answer in standard form.

12. $(-4b^5 + 3b^3 - b + 10) + (3b^5 - b^3 + b - 4)$
13. $(3g^4 + 5g^2 + 5) + (5g^4 - 10g^2 + 11g)$
14. $(3x^3 + 8x^2 + 2x + 9) - (-4x^3 + 5x - 3)$
15. $(2t^3 - 4t^2 + 9t - 7) - (t^3 + t^2 - 3t + 1)$
16. $(7w^5 - 7w^3 + 3w) - (5w^4 - w^2 + 3)$

Lesson 8-2

- To multiply a polynomial by a monomial (p. 376)
- To factor a monomial from a polynomial (p. 377)

Alg1 10.0, 11.0

You can multiply a monomial and a polynomial using the Distributive Property. You can factor a polynomial by finding the common factor of its terms.

Simplify each product. Write in standard form.

17. $8x(2 - 5x)$
18. $5g(3g + 7g^2 - 9)$
19. $8t^2(3t - 4 - 5t^2)$
20. $5m(3m + m^2)$
21. $-2w^2(4w - 10 + 3w^2)$
22. $b(10 + 5b - 3b^2)$

Find the common factor of the terms of each polynomial. Then factor.

23. $9x^4 + 12x^3 + 6x$
24. $4t^5 - 12t^3 + 8t^2$
25. $40n^5 + 70n^4 - 30n^3$
26. $3d^2 - 6d$
27. $2k^4 + 4k^3 - 6k - 8$
28. $10m^4 - 12m^3 + 4m^2$
29. $10v - 5$
30. $12w^3 + 8w^2 + 20w$
31. $18d^5 + 6d^4 + 9d^3$

32. Critical Thinking The common factor of two numbers x and y is 3. Can you predict the common factor of $4x$ and $4y$? Explain your answer.

Lessons 8-3 and 8-4

- To multiply binomials using FOIL (p. 381)
- To multiply trinomials by binomials (p. 383)
- To find the square of a binomial (p. 388)
- To find the difference of squares (p. 390)

Alg1 10.0

You can use tiles or the Distributive Property to multiply polynomials. You can use the FOIL method (First, Outer, Inner, Last) to multiply two binomials.

Simplify each product. Write in standard form.

33. $(x + 3)(x + 5)$
34. $(5v + 2)(3v - 7)$
35. $(2b + 5)(3b - 2)$
36. $(k - 1)(-k + 4)$
37. $(p + 2)(p^2 + p + 1)$
38. $(4a - 1)(a - 5)$
39. $(3x + 4)(x + 2)$
40. $(y - 4)(y^2 - 5y - 2)$
41. $(-2h^2 + h - 1)(h - 5)$
42. $(q - 4)(q - 4)$
43. $(2k^3 + 5)^2$
44. $(8 - 3t^2)(8 + 3t^2)$
45. $(w - 4)(w + 4)$
46. $(2m^2 + 5)(2m^2 - 5)$
47. $(4g^2 - 5h^4)(4g^2 + 5h^4)$

48. A rectangle has dimensions $2x + 1$ and $x + 4$. Write an expression for the area of the rectangle as a product and as a polynomial in standard form.

49. Error Analysis Suppose a classmate claims that the difference between $(x^2 - y^2)$ and $(x - y)^2$ must be 0. Is your classmate correct? Explain your answer.

Lessons 8-5 and 8-6

- To factor trinomials (p. 395)
- To factor trinomials of the type $ax^2 + bx + c$ (p. 400)

Alg1 11.0

Some quadratic trinomials are the product of two binomial factors. You can factor trinomials using tiles or by using FOIL. Factor any common monomial factors first.

Factor each expression.

50. $x^2 + 3x + 2$
51. $y^2 - 9y + 14$
52. $x^2 - 2x - 15$
53. $2w^2 - w - 3$
54. $b^2 - 7b + 12$
55. $2t^2 + 3t - 2$
56. $x^2 + 5x - 6$
57. $6x^2 + 10x + 4$
58. $21x^2 - 22x - 8$
59. $3x^2 + x - 2$
60. $15y^2 + 16y + 1$
61. $15y^2 - 16y + 1$

Lesson 8-7

- To factor perfect-square trinomials (p. 404)
- To factor the difference of squares (p. 406)

When you factor a **perfect-square trinomial,** the two binomial factors are the same.

$$a^2 + 2ab + b^2 = (a + b)(a + b) = (a + b)^2 \text{ and}$$
$$a^2 - 2ab + b^2 = (a - b)(a - b) = (a - b)^2$$

When you factor the difference of squares of two terms, the two binomial factors are the sum and the difference of the two terms.

$$a^2 - b^2 = (a + b)(a - b)$$

Factor each expression.

62. $q^2 + 2q + 1$

63. $b^2 - 16$

64. $x^2 - 4x + 4$

65. $4t^2 - 121$

66. $4d^2 - 20d + 25$

67. $9c^2 + 6c + 1$

68. $9k^2 - 25$

69. $x^2 + 6x + 9$

70. $24y^2 - 6$

71. Find an expression for the length of a side of the square with an area of $\frac{1}{4}d^2 + d + 1$.

72. The area of a rectangle is $25u^2 + 65u + 36$. If the dimensions of the rectangle are factors of $25u^2 + 65u + 36$, could the rectangle be a square? Explain.

Lesson 8-8

- To factor polynomials with four terms (p. 410)
- To factor trinomials by grouping (p. 411)

Alg1 11.0

To factor a polynomial, first see if you can factor out the common factor. If the polynomial has four or more terms, you can group the terms and look for a common binomial factor. Then you can use the Distributive Property to factor the polynomial. If you do not quickly recognize the binomial factors of a polynomial of the form $ax^2 + bx + c$, try grouping the terms.

Find the common factor of the first two terms and of the last two terms for each polynomial.

73. $16x^3 + 12x^2 - 8x - 6$

74. $9k^3 + 15k^2 - 6k - 10$

75. $72y^3 + 24y^2 - 12y - 4$

76. $20n^4 - 10n^3 + 14n - 7$

Factor completely.

77. $6x^3 + 3x^2 + 8x + 4$

78. $20y^4 - 45y^2$

79. $9g^2 + 15g - 6$

80. $6c^2 - 5cd + d^2$

81. $15p^2 + 14p + 3$

82. $3u^2 - 21u + 18$

83. $15h^3 + 11h^2 - 45h - 33$

84. $30x^3 + 42x^2 - 5x - 7$

85. $12s^4t + 20s^3t - 8s^2t$

86. $2x^3 + 7x^2 + 4x + 14$

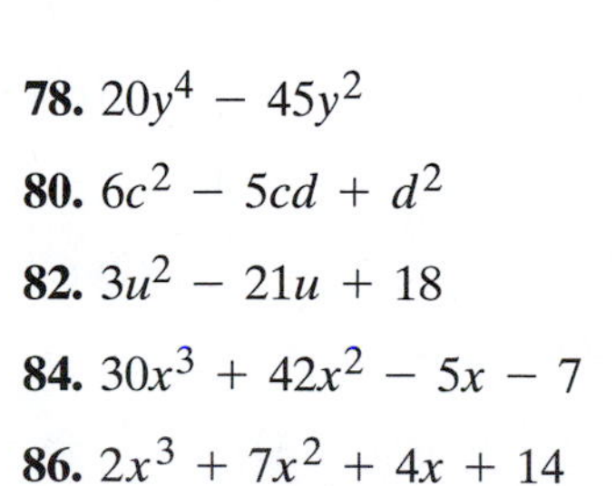

87. The volume of the rectangular prism is $6p^3 + 38p^2 + 40p$. Find expressions for the possible dimensions of the prism.

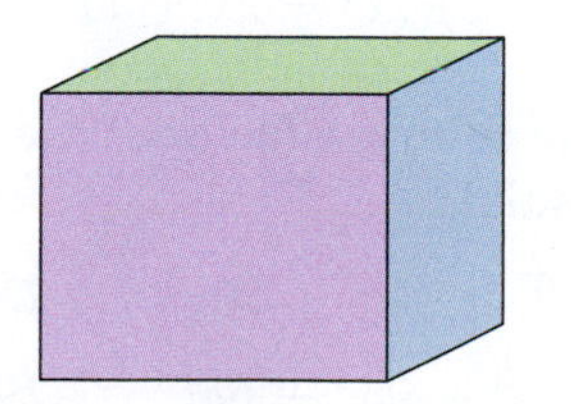

Chapter 8 Test

Go Online PHSchool.com For: Chapter Test Web Code: baa-0852

Write each polynomial in standard form. Then name each polynomial based on its degree and number of terms.

1. $y^2 + 2y + 5 - 3y^2 - 5y$
2. $4 - 5v - 12v - 6v^2 - 4 - 2v^3$
3. $-4x^4 + x^2 - 10 + 12x^4 - 7x^2$
4. $3k^5 + 4k^2 - 6k^5 - 5k^2$

Simplify. Write each answer in standard form.

5. $(4x^2 + 2x + 5) + (7x^2 - 5x + 2)$
6. $(9a^2 - 4 - 5a) - (12a - 6a^2 + 3)$
7. $(-4m^2 + m - 10) + (3m + 12 - 7m^2)$
8. $(3c - 4c^2 + c^3) - (5c^2 + 8c^3 - 6c)$
9. Write the standard form for the polynomial modeled below. Then factor the expression.

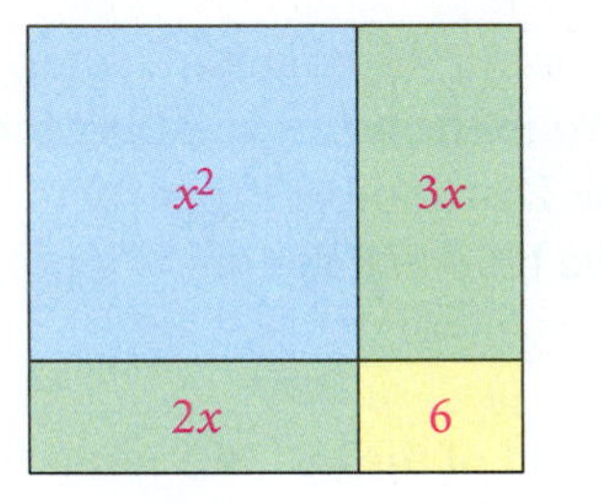

10. Write a trinomial with a degree of 6.

Simplify each product. Write in standard form.

11. $8b(3b + 7 - b^2)$
12. $-t(5t^2 + t)$
13. $3q(4 - q + 3q^3)$
14. $2c(c^5 + 4c^3)$
15. $(x + 6)(x + 1)$
16. $(d + 4)(d - 3)$
17. $(2h - 1)(h - 4)$
18. $(2m + 5)(3m - 7)$
19. $(p + 2)(2p^2 - 5p + 4)$
20. $(a - 4)(6a^2 + 10a - 3)$
21. $(3x + 5)(7x^2 - 2x + 1)$

Find the common factor of the terms of each polynomial.

22. $21x^4 + 18x^2 + 36x^3$
23. $3t^2 - 5t - 2t^4$
24. $-3a^{10} + 9a^5 + 6a^{15}$
25. $9m^3 - 7m^4 + 8m^2$
26. **Writing** Explain how to use the Distributive Property to multiply polynomials. Include an example.

Write an expression for each situation as a product. Then write each expression in standard form.

27. A plot of land has width x meters. The length of the plot of land is 5 meters more than 3 times its width. What is the area of the land?
28. The height of a box is 2 in. less than its width w. The length of the box is 3 in. more than 4 times its width. What is the volume of the box in terms of w?

Write an expression for the area of each shaded region. Write your answer in simplest form.

29. 30.

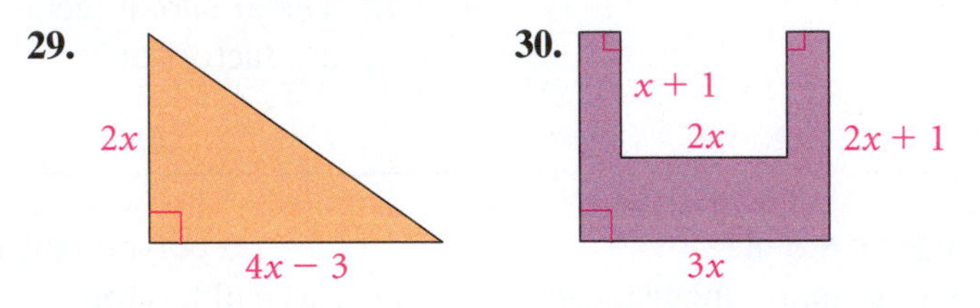

Factor each expression.

31. $w^2 - 5w - 14$
32. $g^2 + 10g + 25$
33. $9k^2 + 24k + 16$
34. $n^2 - 100$
35. $y^2 - 4y + 4$
36. $4x^2 - 49$
37. $4p^2 + 164p + 81$
38. $13c^2 - 52$

Find the missing value in each perfect-square trinomial.

39. $x^2 + \blacksquare x + 49$
40. $\blacksquare t^2 + 12t + 9$
41. $9x^2 - 30x + \blacksquare$
42. $4w^2 - \blacksquare w + 81$

Factor completely.

43. $12n^3 + 15n^2 + 4n + 5$
44. $4x^2 - 10x + 6$
45. $x^3 - 5x^2 + 5x - 25$
46. $6r^3 - 9r^2 - 4r + 6$
47. $12y^3 + 28y^2 - 3y - 7$
48. $3n^3 - 4n^2 - 6n + 8$
49. Find the common factor for the first two terms and the common factor for the last two terms of $6x^4 + 9x^3 - 8x + 12$.
50. Find three different values to complete $x^2 + \blacksquare x + 30$ so that it can be factored into the product of two binomials. Show each factorization.

Standards Mastery

Cumulative Practice

Some questions ask you to use polynomials to represent perimeter, area, and volume. Read the question at the right. Then follow the tips to answer the sample question.

A rectangular prism is shown below.

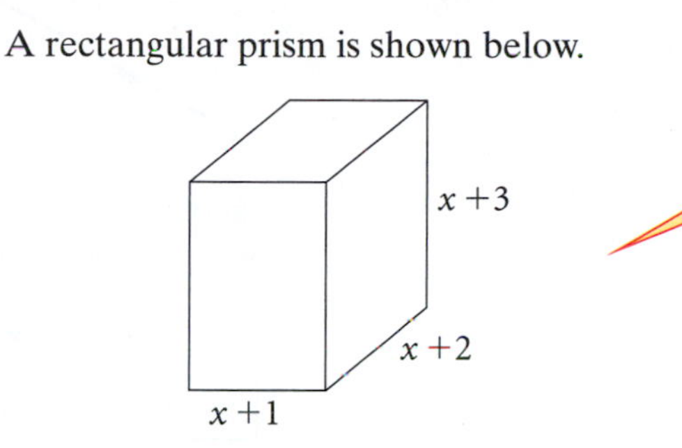

Which expression best represents the volume of the prism?

(A) $x^3 + 6$
(B) $x^2 + 2x + 2$
(C) $x^3 + x^2 + 10x + 6$
(D) $x^3 + 6x^2 + 11x + 6$

Tip 1
Make sure you look at the picture and understand what it means. This is a rectangular prism, and the lengths of the sides are represented by the expressions $x + 1$, $x + 2$, and $x + 3$.

Tip 2
Look for what the question is asking. You need to find the volume of a rectangular prism.

Think It Through

The formula for the volume of a prism is $V = \ell wh$. It can be represented by the expression $(x + 1)(x + 2)(x + 3)$. First, find the product $(x + 1)(x + 2)$, then multiply the result by $(x + 3)$.
$(x + 1)(x + 2) = x^2 + 3x + 2$.
$(x^2 + 3x + 2)(x + 3) =$
$x^3 + 6x^2 + 11x + 6$.
The correct answer is D.

Vocabulary Review

As you solve problems, you must understand the meanings of mathematical terms. Match each term with its mathematical meaning.

A. term
B. function
C. like terms
D. coefficient
E. constant

I. a numerical factor of a term
II. a term that has no variable
III. terms with the same variable factors
IV. a relation where each domain value has exactly one range value
V. a number, a variable, or the product of a number and one or more variables

Read each question. Then write the letter of the correct answer on your paper.

1. If $b = 2a - 16$ and $b = a + 2$, then what is the value of a? **(Lesson 6-1)**

(A) 5 (B) 6 (C) 18 (D) 20

2. Which is NOT a solution of the inequalities $y < 3$ and $y \geq 2x - 2$? **(Lesson 6-1)**

(A) (0, 0) (B) (2, 0) (C) (2, 1) (D) (3, 0)

3. The graphs of $y = -7x + 12$ and $y = -\frac{2}{3}x - \frac{2}{3}$ are shown below.

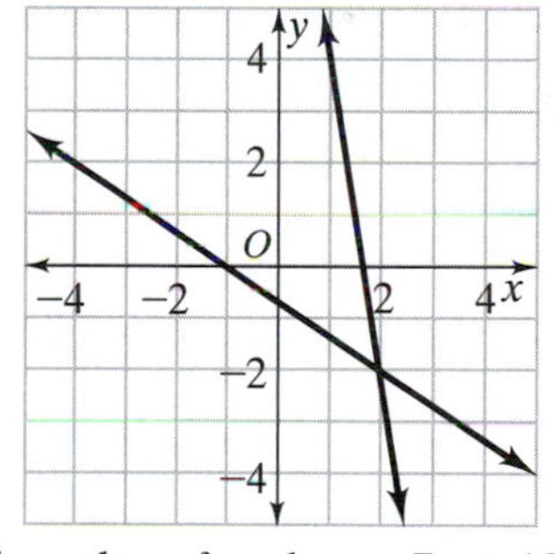

What is the value of y when $-7x + 12 = -\frac{2}{3}x - \frac{2}{3}$? **(Lesson 6-1)**

(A) −2 (B) 2 (C) $11\frac{1}{3}$ (D) $12\frac{2}{3}$

4. Corin bought candlesticks for \$11.78 and candles for \$.62 each. If she spent a total of \$18.60, how many candles did she buy? **(Lesson 2-5)**

(A) 11 (B) 19 (C) 25 (D) 30

5. Which statement is true about factoring $x^2 + 5x + 6$? **(Lesson 8-5)**

(A) In factored form, each x term has a coefficient of 1.
(B) It is a "difference of squares" problem.
(C) It is a "trinomial square" problem.
(D) $x^2 + 5x + 6$ cannot be factored.

Cumulative Practice (continued)

6. Factor $24x^2 + 82x + 70$. **(Lesson 8-6)**

(A) $2(2x + 5)(6x + 7)$

(B) $3(8x^2 + 27x + 23)$

(C) $2(3x + 5)(4x + 7)$

(D) It cannot be factored using only rational numbers.

7. The width of a rectangle can be represented by the expression $x + 2$. If the length of the rectangle is twice the width, what is the area of the rectangle? **(Lesson 8-3)**

(A) $2x + 4$

(B) $2x^2 + 6x + 4$

(C) $2x^2 + 8x + 8$

(D) $4x^2 + 16x + 16$

8. The area of a rectangle can be represented by $3n^2 + 10n + 3$. If the expression $n + 3$ represents the width, which expression represents the length? **(Lesson 8-6)**

(A) $3n + 1$

(B) $3n + 10$

(C) $3n^2 + 10$

(D) $3n^2 + 9$

9. The lengths of the sides of a rectangle can be represented by the factors of $6n^2 + n - 2$. Which expression could represent the perimeter of the rectangle? **(Lesson 8-6)**

(A) $2n - 1$ (B) $3n + 2$ (C) $5n + 1$ (D) $10n + 2$

10. Simplify $(5x^3y^4z)^3$. **(Lesson 7-4)**

(A) $15x^9y^4z$

(B) $15x^9y^4z^3$

(C) $125x^6y^7z^4$

(D) $125x^9y^{12}z^3$

11. Simplify $\left(\frac{-10m^3n}{2rt^2}\right)^2$. **(Lesson 7-5)**

(A) $\frac{25m^6n^2}{r^2t^4}$

(B) $\frac{-50m^5n}{r^2t^4}$

(C) $\frac{-5m^5n^3}{r^3t^4}$

(D) $\frac{-8m^5n^3}{r^3t^4}$

12. Simplify $(p^2 - 3) - (5 - p + 2p^2) - (4p + 5 - 2p^2)$. What is the coefficient of p^2? **(Lesson 8-1)**

(A) 7 (B) 5 (C) 3 (D) 1

13. Which expression equals $\left(\frac{m^{-2}2^2n}{n^8p^{-9}}\right)^{-3}$? **(Lesson 7-5)**

(A) $\frac{m^6n^{21}}{729p^{27}}$

(B) $\frac{64p^{27}}{m^6n^{21}}$

(C) $\frac{-12p^{-27}}{m^{-6}n^{-21}}$

(D) $\frac{m^6n^{21}}{64p^{27}}$

14. Look at the graph shown below.

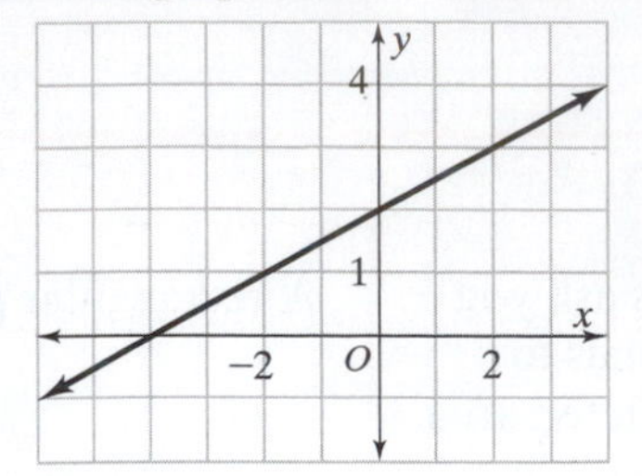

Which table models the linear function shown on the graph? **(Lesson 4-3)**

(A)

x	y
−2	1
0	2
1	3
4	4

(B)

x	y
−6	−1
−3	$\frac{1}{2}$
0	2
6	5

(C)

x	y
−1	−6
0	−4
3	2
4	4

(D)

x	y
0	−4
$\frac{1}{2}$	−3
1	−2
2	0

15. Ed is drawing the graph of a function. Each time the x-value increases by 3, the y-value decreases by 4. If the function includes the point (1, 3), which could be Ed's graph? **(Lesson 4-3)**

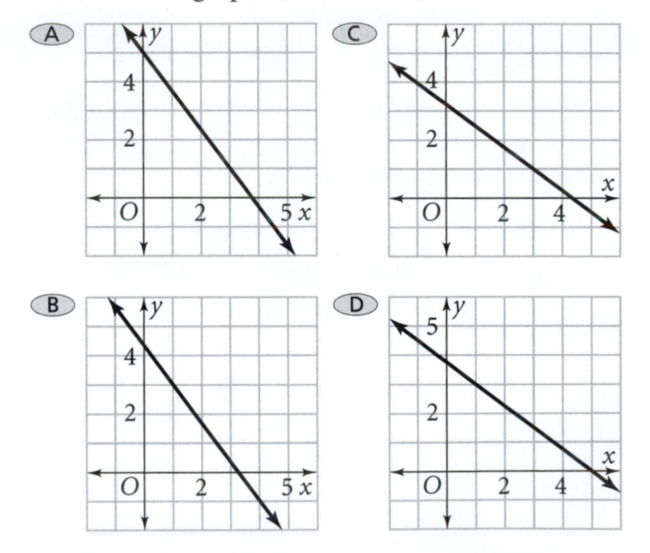

16. Which linear function never intersects the x-axis? **(Lesson 4-3)**

(A) $y = x$

(B) $y = -1$

(C) $y = x + 1$

(D) $y = -x - 1$

17. Simplify. Arrange the terms of your answer in descending order. **(Lesson 8-1)**

$(-2m + 7m^3 - 6) + (9m^2 - 7 + 4m)$

(A) $-13 + 2m + 9m^2 - 7m^3$

(B) $-13 + 2m + 15m^3$

(C) $7m^3 + 9m^2 + 2m - 13$

(D) $-7 - 5m + 16m^2 + 4m^3$

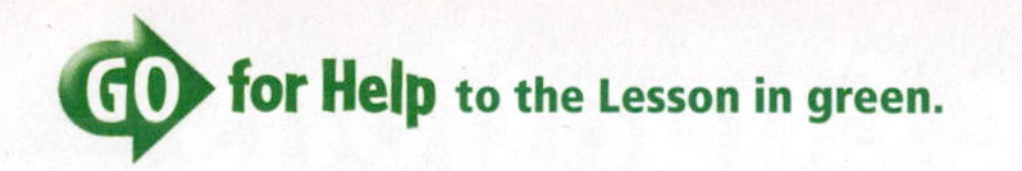

Standards Mastery

18. Which statement about $4x^2 - 5x + 3$ is true? **(Lesson 8-1)**

Ⓐ This trinomial has numerical coefficients 4, −5, and 3.

Ⓑ This binomial has numerical coefficients 4, −5, and 3.

Ⓒ This polynomial is written in ascending order.

Ⓓ The degree of this polynomial is 0.

19. Maria and Molly went apple picking and used the apples to bake 3 apple pies. They had enough apples left over for $1\frac{1}{2}$ pies. If they picked 27 apples, how many apples did they need for one pie? **(Lesson 2-1)**

Ⓐ 2 Ⓑ 3 Ⓒ 6 Ⓓ 9

20. Which of the following graphs represents a line perpendicular to the line $y = -x$? **(Lesson 5-5)**

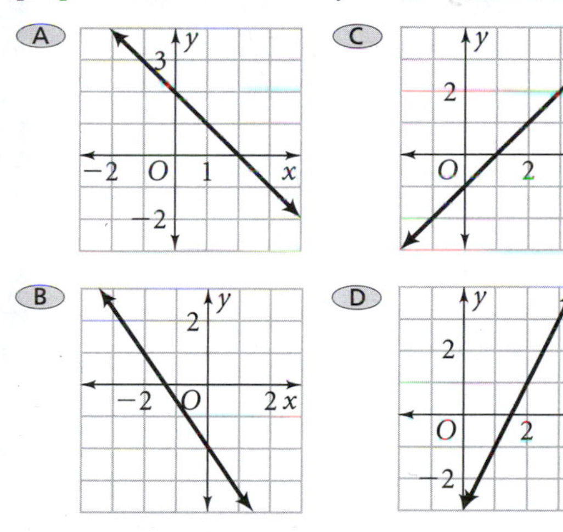

21. A school is putting up a wall to divide a large rectangular room into two equal-sized classrooms. The length of the wall is the same as the width of the room. The perimeter of the original room is 88 ft, and the length of the wall is 16 ft. What is the length of each of the classrooms? **(Lesson 2-2)**

Ⓐ 14 ft Ⓒ 18 ft

Ⓑ 16 ft Ⓓ 28 ft

22. Which equation represents a line with a y-intercept of 4? **(Lesson 5-2)**

Ⓐ $y = 4x - 4$ Ⓒ $y = -4x + \frac{1}{4}$

Ⓑ $y = \frac{1}{4}x - 4$ Ⓓ $y = -\frac{1}{4}x + 4$

23. Which equation represents a line perpendicular to the line $3x = 2y$ and passes through the point $(-3, -1)$? **(Lesson 5-4)**

Ⓐ $y = \frac{3}{2}x - 1$ Ⓒ $y = -\frac{3}{2}x + 3$

Ⓑ $y = \frac{2}{3}x - 1$ Ⓓ $y = -\frac{2}{3}x - 3$

24. Which inequality represents the graph shown below? **(Lesson 6-5)**

Ⓐ $y > 3x$

Ⓑ $y > 3x + 8$

Ⓒ $y < 3x$

Ⓓ $y < 3x + 8$

25. Find the x-intercept of the graph of $3x - 2y = 14$. **(Lesson 5-4)**

Ⓐ $\frac{3}{14}$ Ⓑ $\frac{2}{7}$ Ⓒ $\frac{14}{3}$ Ⓓ 7

Standards Reference Guide

California Content Standard	Item Number(s)
Alg1 2.0	10–13
Alg1 5.0	4, 19, 21
Alg1 6.0	22, 24, 25
Alg1 8.0	20, 23
Alg1 9.0	1–3
Alg1 10.0	7, 17, 18
Alg1 11.0	5, 6, 8, 9
Alg1 16.0	14–16

For additional review and practice, see the *California Standards Review and Practice Workbook* or go online to use the

Visit: PHSchool.com, **Web Code:** baq-9045

CALIFORNIA CHECK SYSTEM

CHAPTER 9

Quadratic Equations and Functions

What You've Learned

California Content Standards

2.0 Understand and use such operations as taking a root.

6.0 Graph a linear equation and compute the x- and y-intercepts. Sketch the region defined by linear inequalities.

11.0 Apply basic factoring techniques to second-degree polynomials. These techniques include finding a common factor for all terms in a polynomial, recognizing the difference of two squares, and recognizing perfect squares of binomials.

Check Your Readiness

GO for Help to the Lesson in green.

Evaluating Expressions (Lesson 1-6)

Evaluate each expression for $a = -1$, $b = 3$, and $c = -2$.

1. $2a - b^2 + c$ **2.** $\frac{c^2 - ab}{2a}$ **3.** $bc - 3a^2$

4. $\frac{b^2 - 4ac}{2a}$ **5.** $5a + 2b(c - 1)$ **6.** $c^2 + 2ab - 1$

Evaluating Function Rules (Lesson 4-3)

Evaluate each function rule for $x = -6$.

7. $f(x) = -3x^2$ **8.** $y = x^2 - 10$ **9.** $h(x) = x^2 + 6x$ **10.** $y = (x - 1)^2$

11. $y = 5 - 2x^2$ **12.** $y = (1 + x)^2$ **13.** $g(x) = \frac{2}{3}x^2$ **14.** $y = (2x)^2$

Graphing Functions (Lesson 4-3)

Graph each function.

15. $y = x$ **16.** $y = -x^2$ **17.** $y = |x|$

Multiplying Binomials (Lesson 8-3)

Simplify each product using FOIL.

18. $(x + 2)(x - 3)$ **19.** $(2y + 1)(2y + 3)$ **20.** $(3x - 7)(x + 4)$

Factoring (Lessons 8-5 and 8-6)

Factor each expression.

21. $4x^2 + 4x + 1$ **22.** $5x^2 + 32x - 21$ **23.** $8x^2 - 10x + 3$

24. $m^2 - 7m - 18$ **25.** $12y^2 + 8y - 15$ **26.** $x^2 - 18x + 81$

▲ The San Diego-Coronado Bridge is in the shape of a curve. In this chapter, you will study the graphs of quadratic functions called parabolas, which are U-shaped curves.

What You'll Learn Next

California Content Standards

14.0 Solve a quadratic equation by factoring or completing the square.

19.0 Know the quadratic formula and be familiar with its proof.

20.0 Use the quadratic formula to find the roots of a second-degree polynomial and to solve quadratic equations.

21.0 Graph quadratic functions and know that their roots are the x-intercepts.

22.0 Determine whether the graph of a quadratic function will intersect the x-axis in zero, one, or two points.

23.0 Apply quadratic equations to physical problems.

New Vocabulary

English and Spanish Audio Online

- **axis of symmetry** (p. 427)
- **completing the square** (p. 457)
- **discriminant** (p. 470)
- **maximum** (p. 427)
- **minimum** (p. 427)
- **parabola** (p. 426)
- **quadratic equation** (p. 446)
- **quadratic formula** (p. 463)
- **quadratic function** (p. 426)
- **radicand** (p. 440)
- **roots of the equation** (p. 446)
- **square root** (p. 440)
- **vertex** (p. 427)
- **Zero-Product Property** (p. 452)
- **zeros of the function** (p. 446)

9-1 Exploring Quadratic Graphs

California Content Standards

21.0 Graph quadratic functions. ***Introduce***

23.0 Apply quadratic equations to physical problems. ***Introduce***

What You'll Learn

- To graph quadratic functions of the form $y = ax^2$
- To graph quadratic functions of the form $y = ax^2 + c$

. . . And Why

To model a problem involving gravity, as in Example 5

Check Skills You'll Need

GO for Help Lessons 1-2 and 4-3

Evaluate each expression for $h = 3, k = 2,$ and $j = -4$.

1. hkj **2.** kh^2 **3.** hk^2 **4.** $kj^2 + h$

Graph each equation.

5. $y = 2x - 1$ **6.** $y = |x| + 1$ **7.** $y = x^2 + 2$

New Vocabulary • quadratic function • standard form of a quadratic function • quadratic parent function • parabola • axis of symmetry • vertex • minimum • maximum

Graphing $y = ax^2$

CA Standards Investigation — Plotting Quadratic Curves

1. Graph the equations $y = x^2$ and $y = 3x^2$ on the same coordinate plane.

2. a. Describe how the graphs are alike.

b. Describe how the graphs are different.

3. Predict how the graph of $y = \frac{1}{3}x^2$ will be similar to and different from the graph of $y = x^2$.

4. Graph $y = \frac{1}{3}x^2$. Were your predictions correct? Explain.

The functions shown above are quadratic functions.

Take Note

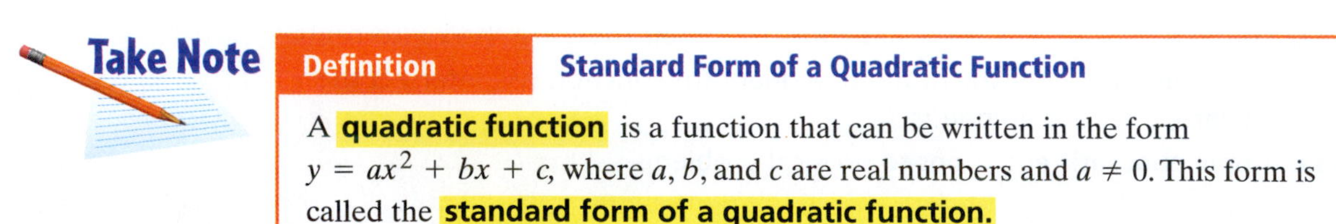

Definition — Standard Form of a Quadratic Function

A **quadratic function** is a function that can be written in the form $y = ax^2 + bx + c$, where a, b, and c are real numbers and $a \neq 0$. This form is called the **standard form of a quadratic function.**

Examples $y = 5x^2$ $y = x^2 + 7$ $y = x^2 - x - 3$

The simplest quadratic function, $f(x) = x^2$, or $y = x^2$, is the **quadratic parent function.**

The graph of a quadratic function is a U-shaped curve called a **parabola.** The graph of $y = x^2$, shown at the right, is a parabola.

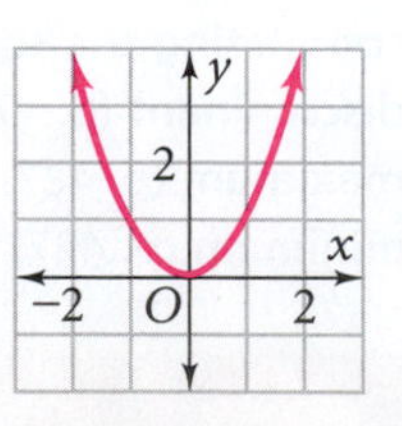

This bouncing ball follows a parabolic path.

You can fold a parabola so that the two sides match exactly. This property is called *symmetry*. The fold or line that divides the parabola into two matching halves is called the **axis of symmetry.**

The highest or lowest point of a parabola is its **vertex,** which is on the axis of symmetry.

If $a > 0$ in $y = ax^2 + bx + c$,
↓
the parabola opens upward.
↓
The vertex is the **minimum** point or lowest point of the parabola.

If $a < 0$ in $y = ax^2 + bx + c$,
↓
the parabola opens downward.
↓
The vertex is the **maximum** point or highest point of the parabola.

1 EXAMPLE Identifying a Vertex

Identify the vertex of each graph. Tell whether it is a minimum or maximum.

a.

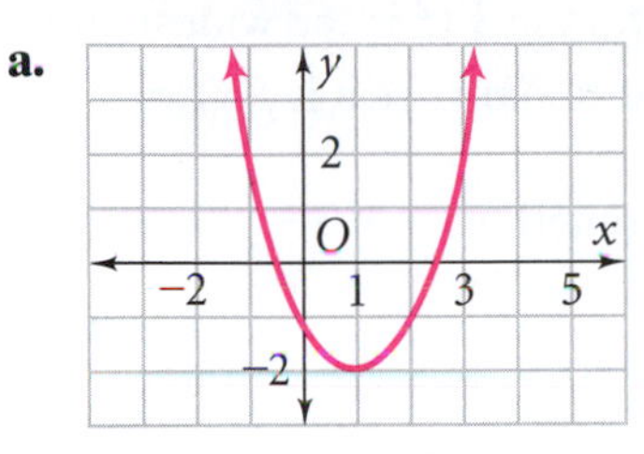

b.

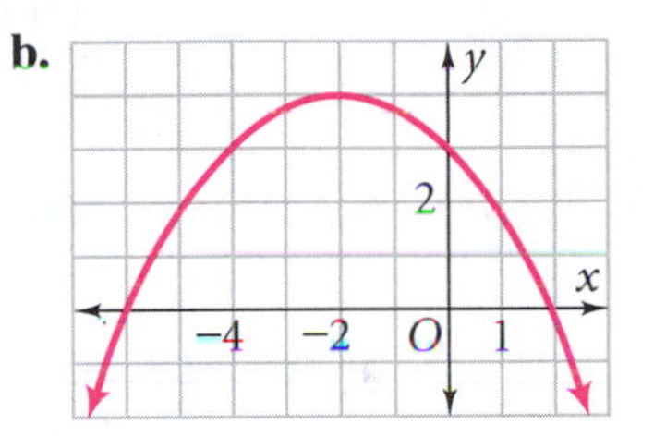

The vertex is $(1, -2)$. It is a minimum. The vertex is $(-2, 4)$. It is a maximum.

CA Standards Check 1 Identify the vertex of each graph. Tell whether it is a minimum or maximum.

a.

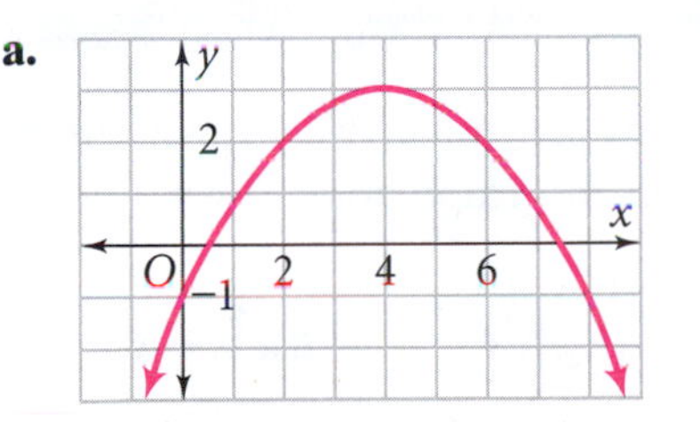

b.

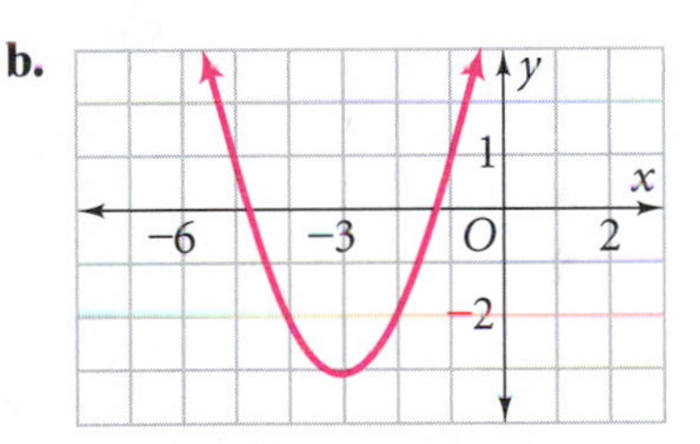

You can use the fact that a parabola is symmetric to graph it quickly. First find the coordinates of the vertex and several points on either side of the vertex. Then reflect the points across the axis of symmetry. For functions of the form $y = ax^2$, the vertex is at the origin.

2 EXAMPLE Graphing $y = ax^2$

Make a table of values and graph the quadratic function $y = \frac{1}{2}x^2$.

x	$y = \frac{1}{2}x^2$	(x, y)
0	$\frac{1}{2}(0)^2 = 0$	(0, 0)
2	$\frac{1}{2}(2)^2 = 2$	(2, 2)
4	$\frac{1}{2}(4)^2 = 8$	(4, 8)

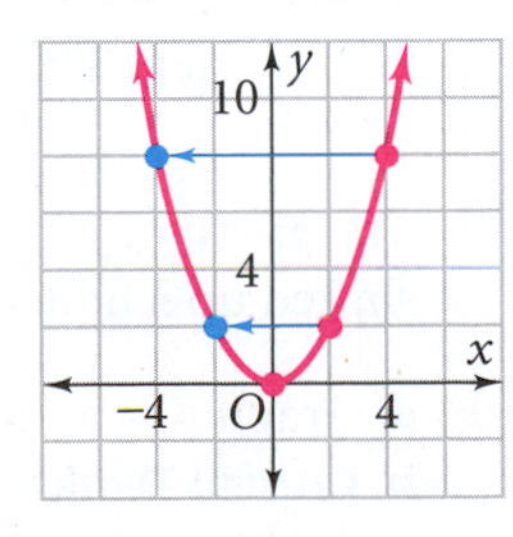

Find the corresponding points on the other side of the axis of symmetry.

CA Standards Check 2 Make a table of values and graph the quadratic function $f(x) = -2x^2$.

The value of a, the coefficient of the x^2 term in a quadratic function, affects the width of a parabola as well as the direction in which it opens.

3 EXAMPLE Comparing Widths of Parabolas

Use the graphs below. Order the quadratic functions $f(x) = -4x^2, f(x) = \frac{1}{4}x^2$, and $f(x) = x^2$ from widest to narrowest graph.

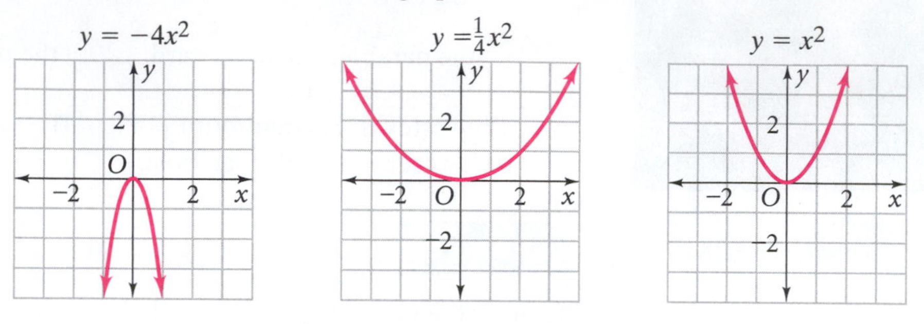

Of the three graphs, $f(x) = \frac{1}{4}x^2$ is the widest and $f(x) = -4x^2$ is the narrowest. So, the order from widest to narrowest is $f(x) = \frac{1}{4}x^2, f(x) = x^2$, and $f(x) = -4x^2$.

CA Standards Check 3 Order the quadratic functions $y = x^2, y = \frac{1}{2}x^2$, and $y = -2x^2$ from widest to narrowest graph.

When $|m| < |n|$, the graph of $y = mx^2$ is wider than the graph of $y = nx^2$.

Graphing $y = ax^2 + c$

The y-axis is the axis of symmetry for functions in the form $y = ax^2 + c$. The value of c translates the graph up or down.

4 EXAMPLE Graphing $y = ax^2 + c$

Problem Solving Tip

You can use symmetry of the parabola to check calculated (x, y) coordinates or points on the graph.

How is the graph of $y = 2x^2 + 3$ different from the graph of $y = 2x^2$?

Ⓐ It is shifted 3 units up.

Ⓑ It is shifted 3 units to the right.

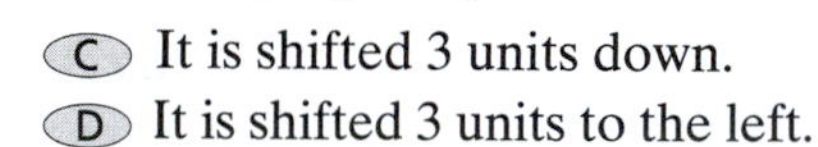

Ⓒ It is shifted 3 units down.

Ⓓ It is shifted 3 units to the left.

x	$y = 2x^2$	$y = 2x^2 + 3$
−2	8	11
−1	2	5
0	0	3
−1	2	5
−2	8	11

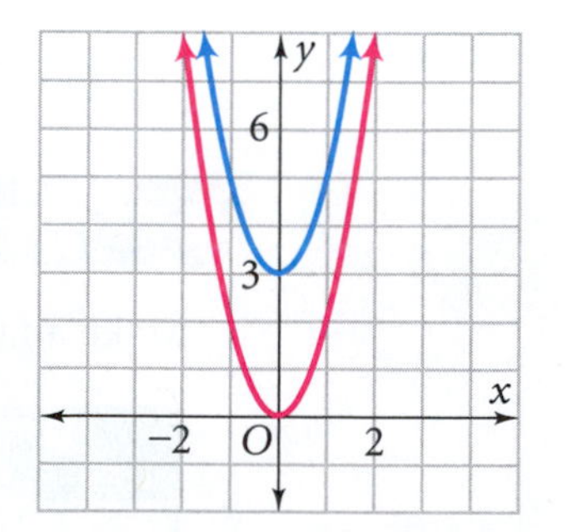

The graph of $y = 2x^2 + 3$ has the same shape as the graph of $y = 2x^2$, but it is shifted up 3 units. So A is the correct answer.

CA Standards Check 4 **a.** Graph $y = x^2$ and $y = x^2 - 4$. Compare the graphs.

b. Critical Thinking Describe what positive and negative values of c do to the position of the vertex.

You can model the height of an object moving under the influence of gravity by using a quadratic function. As an object falls, its speed continues to increase. Ignoring air resistance, you can find the approximate height of a falling object using the function $h = -16t^2 + c$. The height h is in feet, the time t is in seconds, and the initial height of the object c is in feet.

5 EXAMPLE Application

Suppose you see an eagle flying over a canyon. The eagle is 30 ft above the level of the canyon's edge when it drops a stick from its claws. The force of gravity causes the stick to fall toward Earth. The function $h = -16t^2 + 30$ gives the height of the stick h in feet after t seconds. Graph this quadratic function.

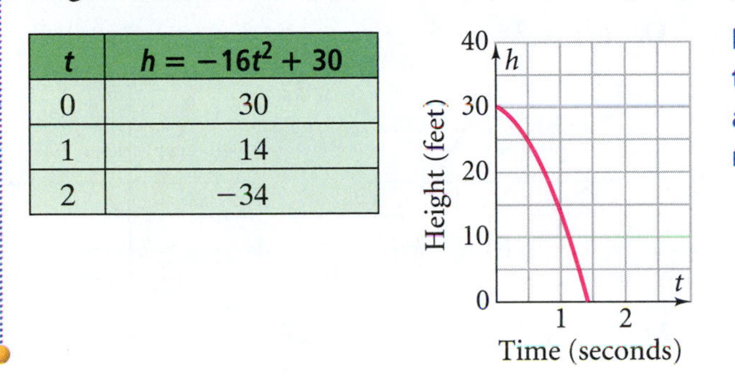

t	$h = -16t^2 + 30$
0	30
1	14
2	−34

Height h is dependent on time t. Graph t on the x-axis and h on the y-axis. Use nonnegative values for t.

CA Standards Check 5 **a.** Suppose a squirrel is in a tree 24 ft above the ground. She drops an acorn. The function $h = -16t^2 + 24$ gives the height of the acorn in feet after t seconds. Graph this function.

b. Critical Thinking Describe a reasonable domain and range for the function in Example 5.

EXERCISES

Standards Practice

For more exercises, see *Extra Skills and Word Problem Practice.*

Alg1 21.0, 23.0

A Practice by Example

GO for Help

Example 1 (page 427)

Identify the vertex of each graph. Tell whether it is a minimum or maximum.

1.

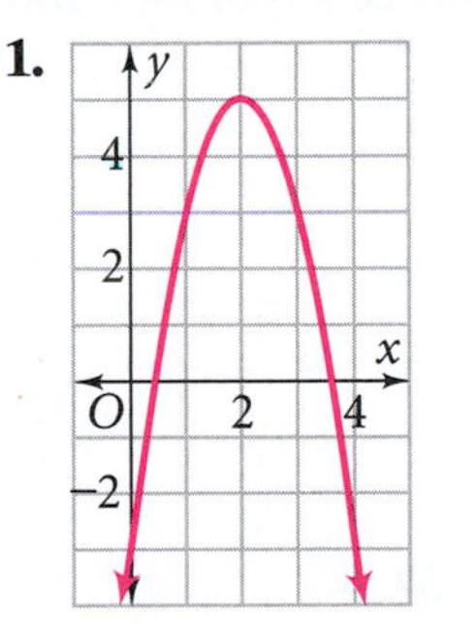

2.

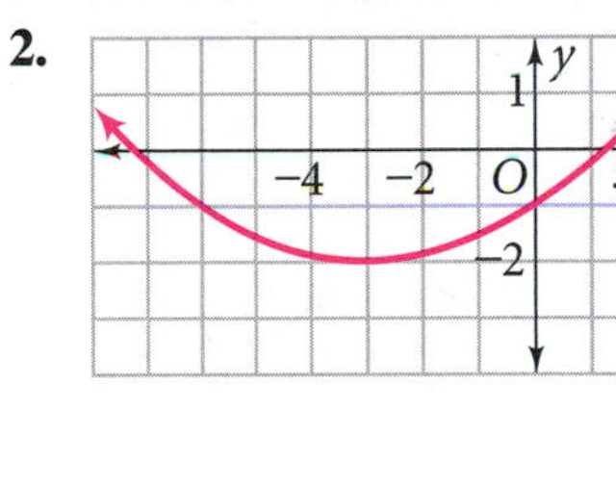

3.

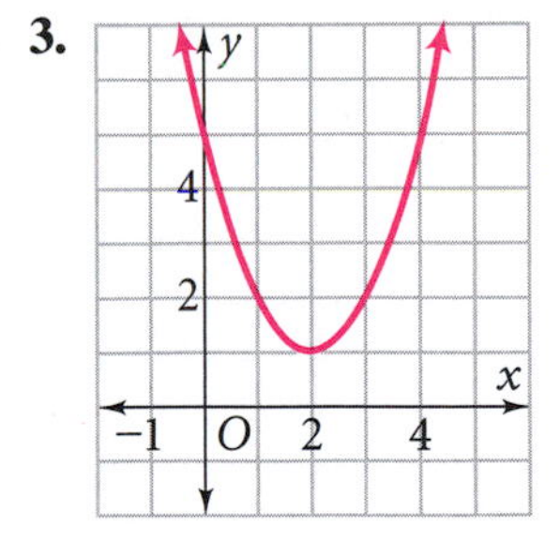

Example 2 (page 427)

Graph each function.

4. $y = -4x^2$
5. $f(x) = 1.5x^2$
6. $y = \frac{2}{3}x^2$
7. $f(x) = -\frac{1}{2}x^2$
8. $y = -\frac{1}{3}x^2$
9. $f(x) = 3x^2$

Example 3 (page 428)

Order each group of quadratic functions from widest to narrowest graph.

10. $y = 3x^2, y = \frac{1}{2}x^2, y = 4x^2$
11. $f(x) = 5x^2, f(x) = \frac{1}{3}x^2, f(x) = x^2$
12. $y = -\frac{1}{2}x^2, y = 5x^2, y = -\frac{1}{4}x^2$
13. $f(x) = -2x^2, f(x) = -\frac{2}{3}x^2, f(x) = -4x^2$

Example 4 (page 428)

Graph each function.

14. $f(x) = x^2 + 2$ **15.** $y = x^2 - 3$ **16.** $y = \frac{1}{2}x^2 + 4$

17. $f(x) = -x^2 - 1$ **18.** $y = -2x^2 + 2$ **19.** $f(x) = 4x^2 - 7$

Example 5 (page 429)

20. A gull drops a clam shell onto some rocks from a height of 50 ft. The function $h = -16t^2 + 50$ gives the shell's approximate height h in feet after t seconds. Graph the function.

B Apply Your Skills

Match each graph with its function.

A. $f(x) = x^2 - 1$ **B.** $f(x) = x^2 + 4$ **C.** $f(x) = -x^2 + 2$

D. $f(x) = 3x^2 - 5$ **E.** $f(x) = -3x^2 + 8$ **F.** $f(x) = -0.2x^2 + 5$

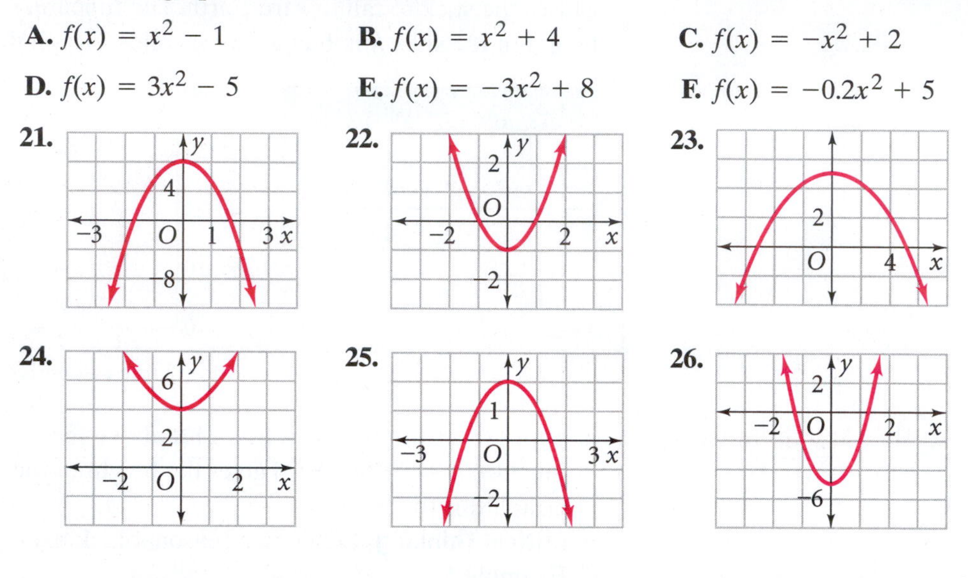

Writing **Without graphing, describe how each graph differs from the graph of $y = x^2$.**

27. $y = 2x^2$ **28.** $y = -x^2$ **29.** $y = 1.5x^2$ **30.** $y = \frac{1}{2}x^2$

Graph each function.

31. $y = -\frac{1}{4}x^2 + 3$ **32.** $f(x) = -1.5x^2 + 5$ **33.** $y = 3x^2 - 6$

Trace each parabola on a sheet of paper and draw its axis of symmetry.

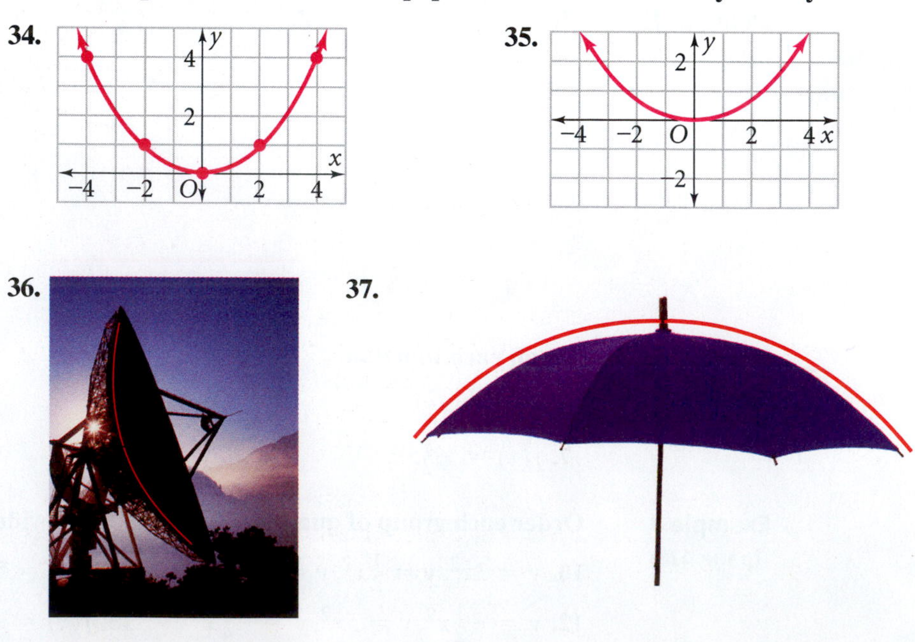

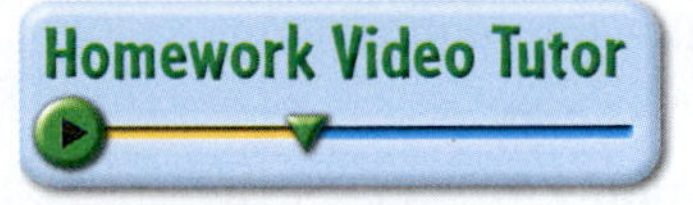

Visit: PHSchool.com
Web Code: bae-0901

38. A bungee jumper dives from a platform. The function $h = -16t^2 + 200$ gives her approximate height h in feet after t seconds.
a. Graph the function. Graph t on the x-axis and h on the y-axis.
b. What will the jumper's height be after 1 second?
c. What will the jumper's height be after 3 seconds?

39. Suppose that a pizza must fit into a box with a base that is 12 in. long and 12 in. wide. You can use the quadratic function $A = \pi r^2$ to find the area of a pizza in terms of its radius.

a. What values of r make sense for the function?
b. What values of A make sense for the function?
c. Graph the function. Round values of A to the nearest tenth.

Three graphs are shown below. For Exercises 40–43, identify the graph(s) that fit each description.

40. $a > 0$

41. $a < 0$

42. $|a|$ has the greatest value.

43. $|a|$ has the least value.

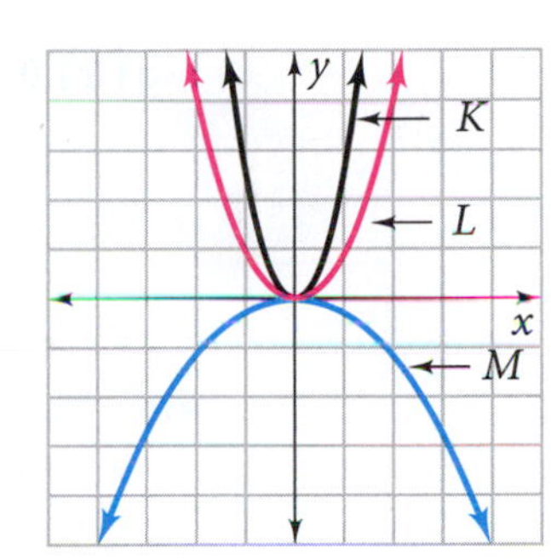

44. Suppose a person is riding in a hot-air balloon 144 feet above the ground. He drops an apple. The height of the apple above the ground is given by the formula $h = -16t^2 + 144$, where h is height in feet and t is time in seconds.
a. Graph the function.
b. How far has the apple fallen from time $t = 0$ to $t = 1$?
c. **Critical Thinking** Does the apple fall as far from time $t = 1$ to $t = 2$ as it does from time $t = 0$ to $t = 1$? Explain.

45. Which function has a graph that is the same as the graph of $f(x) = x^2 + 1$ shifted 4 units down?

(A) $f(x) = x^2 + 5$
(B) $f(x) = x^2 - 3$
(C) $f(x) = x^2 - 4$
(D) $f(x) = x^2 + 4$

C Challenge

46. **Critical Thinking** Complete each statement. Assume $a \neq 0$.
a. The graph of $y = ax^2 + c$ intersects the x-axis in two places when __?__.
b. The graph of $y = ax^2 + c$ does not intersect the x-axis when __?__.

47. The plan for a 20 ft-by-12 ft patio has a square garden in the middle of it. If each side of the garden is x ft, the function $y = 240 - x^2$ gives the area of the patio without the garden in square feet.
a. Graph the function.
b. What values make sense for the domain? Explain.
c. What is the range of the function? Explain.
d. Use the graph to estimate the side length of the garden if the area of the patio is 200 ft^2.

48. Consider the graphs of $y = ax^2$ and $y = (ax)^2$. Assume $a \neq 0$.
a. For what values of a will both graphs lie in the same quadrants?
b. For what values of a will the graph of $y = ax^2$ be wider than the graph of $y = (ax)^2$?

49. An architect wants to design an archway with the following requirements.

- The archway is 6 ft wide and has vertical sides 7 ft high.
- The top of the archway is modeled by the function $y = -\frac{1}{3}x^2 + 10$.

a. Sketch the archway by drawing vertical lines 7 units high at $x = -3$ and $x = 3$ and graphing the portion of the quadratic function that lies between $x = -3$ and $x = 3$.

b. The plan for the archway is then changed so that the top is modeled by the function $y = -0.5x^2 + 11.5$. Make a revised sketch of the archway.

Multiple Choice Practice

For California Standards Tutorials, visit PHSchool.com. Web Code: baq-9045

Alg1 21.0

50. If the graph of $y = x^2$ is shifted 2 units down, what will be the equation of the new graph?

(A) $y = x^2 + 2$ (B) $y = x^2 - 2$ (C) $y = (x + 2)^2$ (D) $y = (x - 2)^2$

Alg1 21.0

51. Which equation does the graph at the right represent?

(A) $0.5x^2 + 3$
(B) $0.5x^2 - 3$
(C) $-0.5x^2 + 3$
(D) $-0.5x^2 - 3$

Alg1 10.0

52. Simplify $(-3x^2 - 5x + 6) - (4x^2 + 2x - 5)$.

(A) $-7x^2 - 7x + 1$
(B) $-7x^2 - 7x + 11$
(C) $-7x^2 - 3x + 1$
(D) $-7x^2 - 3x + 11$

Alg1 11.0

53. Which is a factor of $x^2 + 5x - 24$?

(A) $x + 2$ (B) $x - 3$ (C) $x - 8$ (D) $x - 4$

Alg1 2.0

54. Which expression is equivalent to $4x^{-4} \cdot 6x^6$?

(A) $3x^{-5} \cdot 8x^3$ (B) $2x^4 \cdot 12x^{-6}$ (C) $6x^2 \cdot 4x$ (D) $24x \cdot x$

Mixed Review

GO for Help

Lesson 8-8

Factor each expression.

55. $x^3 - 4x^2 + 2x - 8$
56. $15a^3 - 18a^2 - 10a + 12$
57. $7b^3 + 14b^2 + b + 2$
58. $y^3 + 3y^2 - 4y - 12$

Lesson 8-2

Simplify each expression.

59. $5x(3x - 4)$
60. $(n - 7)9n$
61. $-2t^2(6t - 11)$
62. $4m^2(3m^4 - m^3 + 5)$
63. $-5y(3y^5 + 2y^3 - 4)$
64. $3c^3(-4c^2 + 7c - 8)$

Lesson 6-4

65. The City Council invites your art club to sell helium balloons during a citywide celebration. The rental of the helium tank is $27.00 for the day. Each balloon costs $.20. If the balloons sell for $2.00 each, how many will your art club have to sell to break even?

9-2 Quadratic Functions

California Content Standards

17.0 Determine domain and range. ***Develop***
21.0 Graph quadratic functions. ***Develop***
23.0 Apply quadratic equations to physical problems. ***Develop***

What You'll Learn

- To graph quadratic functions of the form $y = ax^2 + bx + c$
- To graph quadratic inequalities

. . . And Why

To model height of fireworks, as in Example 2

GO for Help Lessons 1-6 and 9-1

Evaluate the expression $\frac{-b}{2a}$ for the following values of a and b.

1. $a = -6, b = 4$ **2.** $a = 15, b = 20$

3. $a = -8, b = -56$ **4.** $a = -9, b = 108$

Graph each function.

5. $y = x^2$ **6.** $y = -x^2 + 2$ **7.** $y = \frac{1}{2}x^2 - 1$

Graphing $y = ax^2 + bx + c$

In Lesson 9-1, you investigated the graphs of $y = ax^2$ and $y = ax^2 + c$. In the quadratic function $y = ax^2 + bx + c$, the value of b affects the position of the axis of symmetry.

Consider the graphs of the following functions.

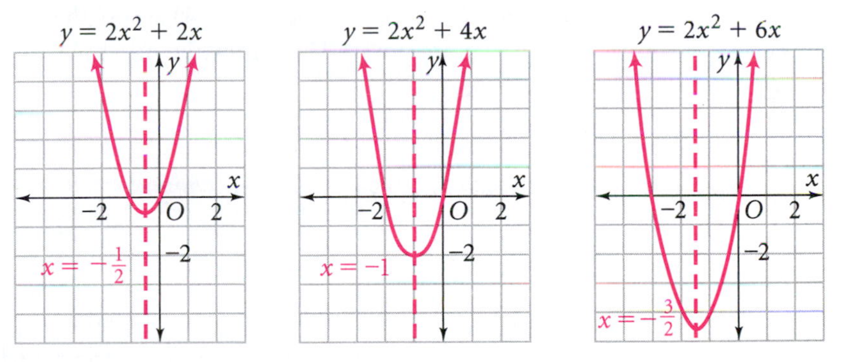

Notice that all three graphs have the same y-intercept. This is because in all three equations $c = 0$. The axis of symmetry changes with each change in the b value. The equation of the axis of symmetry is related to the ratio $\frac{b}{a}$.

equation:	$y = 2x^2 + 2x$	$y = 2x^2 + 4x$	$y = 2x^2 + 6x$
$\frac{b}{a}$:	$\frac{2}{2} = 1$	$\frac{4}{2} = 2$	$\frac{6}{2} = 3$
axis of symmetry:	$x = -\frac{1}{2}$	$x = -1$, or $-\frac{2}{2}$	$x = -\frac{3}{2}$

The equation of the axis of symmetry is $x = -\frac{1}{2}\left(\frac{b}{a}\right)$, or $\frac{-b}{2a}$.

Property **Graph of a Quadratic Function**

The graph of $y = ax^2 + bx + c$, where a, b, and c are real numbers and $a \neq 0$, has the line $x = \frac{-b}{2a}$ as its axis of symmetry. The x-coordinate of the vertex is $\frac{-b}{2a}$.

When you substitute $x = 0$ into the equation $y = ax^2 + bx + c$, $y = c$. So the y-intercept of a quadratic function is the value of c. You can use the axis of symmetry and the y-intercept to help you graph a quadratic function.

1 EXAMPLE Graphing $y = ax^2 + bx + c$

Online active math

For: Quadratic Function Activity
Use: Interactive Textbook, 9-2

Graph the function $y = -3x^2 + 6x + 5$. Find the domain and range.

Step 1 Find the axis of symmetry and the vertex.

$x = \frac{-b}{2a} = \frac{-6}{2(-3)} = 1$ **Find the equation of the axis of symmetry.**

The axis of symmetry is $x = 1$.

$y = -3x^2 + 6x + 5$

$y = -3(1)^2 + 6(1) + 5$ **To find the y-coordinate of the vertex, substitute 1 for x.**

$= 8$

The vertex is $(1, 8)$.

Step 2 Find two other points on the graph.

Use the y-intercept. For $x = 0, y = 5$, so one point is $(0, 5)$.

Choose a value for x on the same side of the vertex as the y-intercept. Let $x = -1$.

$y = -3(-1)^2 + 6(-1) + 5$ **Find the y-coordinate for $x = -1$.**

$= -4$

For $x = -1, y = -4$, so another point is $(-1, -4)$.

Step 3 Reflect $(0, 5)$ and $(-1, -4)$ across the axis of symmetry to get two more points. Then draw the parabola.

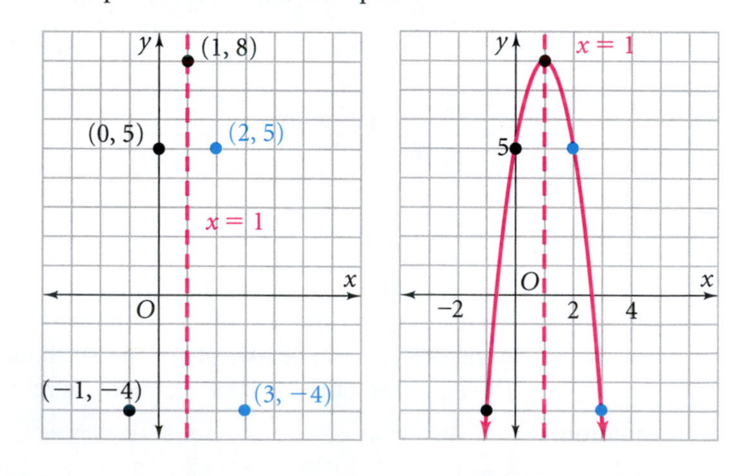

The domain is the set of all real numbers. The range is $\{y: y \leq 8\}$.

CA Standards Check 1 Graph $f(x) = x^2 - 6x + 9$. Label the axis of symmetry and the vertex.

The formula $h = -16t^2 + c$ describes the height above the ground at time t of an object falling from an initial height c. If an object is given an initial upward velocity v and continues with no force acting on it but gravity, the formula $h = -16t^2 + vt + c$ describes its approximate height above the ground.

Aerial fireworks like those shown above follow a parabolic path.

2 EXAMPLE Application

In professional fireworks displays, aerial fireworks carry "stars" upward, ignite them, and project them into the air.

Suppose a particular star is projected from an aerial firework at a starting height of 520 ft with an initial upward velocity of 72 ft/s. How long will it take for the star to reach its maximum height? How far above the ground will it be?

The equation $h = -16t^2 + 72t + 520$ gives the star's height h in feet at time t in seconds. Since the coefficient of t^2 is negative, the curve opens downward, and the vertex is the maximum point.

Step 1 Find the t-coordinate of the vertex.

$$\frac{-b}{2a} = \frac{-(72)}{2(-16)} = 2.25$$

After 2.25 seconds, the star will be at its greatest height.

Step 2 Find the h-coordinate of the vertex.

$h = -16(2.25)^2 + 72(2.25) + 520$ **Substitute 2.25 for t.**

$h = 601$ **Simplify.**

The maximum height of the star will be 601 ft.

CA Standards Check 2 A ball is thrown into the air with an initial upward velocity of 48 ft/s. Its height h in feet after t seconds is given by the function $h = -16t^2 + 48t + 4$.

a. In how many seconds will the ball reach its maximum height?

b. What is the ball's maximum height?

Graphing Quadratic Inequalities

Graphing a quadratic inequality is similar to graphing a linear inequality. The curve is dashed if the inequality involves $<$ or $>$. The curve is solid if the inequality involves $\leq$ or $\geq$.

3 EXAMPLE Graphing Quadratic Inequalities

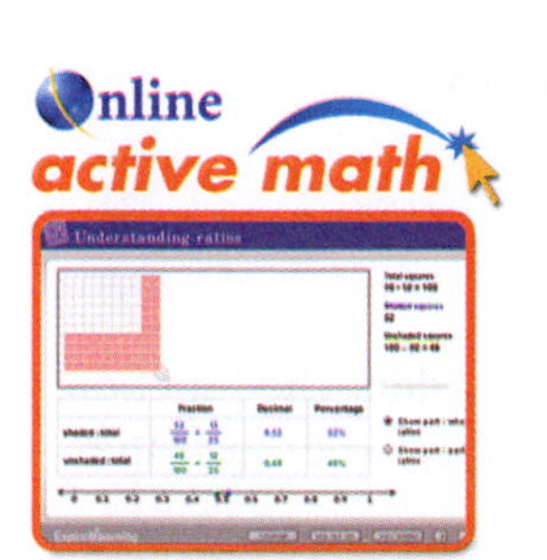

Online active math

For: Quadratic Inequality Activity
Use: Interactive Textbook, 9-2

Graph the quadratic inequality $y \leq x^2 - 3x - 4$.

Graph the boundary curve, $y = x^2 - 3x - 4$. Use a solid line because the solution of the inequality $y \leq x^2 - 3x - 4$ includes the boundary. Shade below the curve.

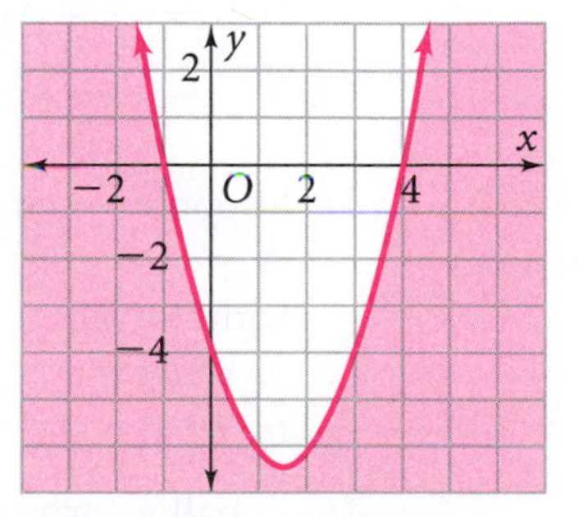

CA Standards Check 3 Graph each quadratic inequality.

a. $y \leq x^2 + 2x - 5$

b. $y > x^2 + x + 1$

EXERCISES
Standards Practice

For more exercises, see *Extra Skills and Word Problem Practice.*

Alg1 17.0, 21.0, 23.0, 25.3

A Practice by Example

Example 1 (page 434)

GO for Help

Find the equation of the axis of symmetry and the coordinates of the vertex of the graph of each function. Find the domain and range.

1. $y = 2x^2 + 4$

2. $f(x) = 2x^2 + 4x - 5$

3. $y = x^2 - 8x - 9$

4. $y = 3x^2 - 9x + 5$

Match each graph with its function.

A. $y = x^2 - 2x$ **B.** $y = x^2 + 2x$ **C.** $y = -x^2 - 2x$

D. $y = -x^2 + 2x$ **E.** $y = -x^2 + 2$ **F.** $y = x^2 - 2$

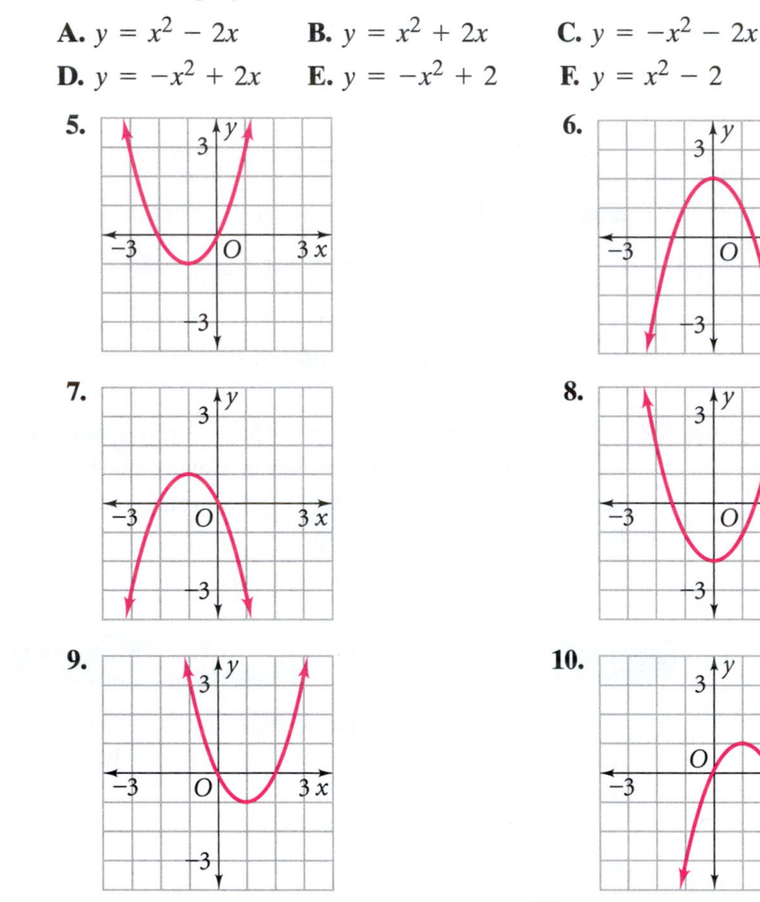

Graph each function. Label the axis of symmetry and the vertex.

11. $f(x) = x^2 + 4x + 3$

12. $y = 2x^2 - 6x$

13. $y = -x^2 + 4x - 4$

14. $y = 2x^2 + 3x + 1$

Example 2 (page 435)

15. Suppose you have 80 ft of fence to enclose a rectangular garden. The function $A = 40x - x^2$ gives you the area of the garden in square feet, where x is the width in feet.

a. What width gives you the maximum gardening area?

b. What is the maximum area?

16. A ball is thrown into the air with an upward velocity of 40 ft/s. Its height h in feet after t seconds is given by the function $h = -16t^2 + 40t + 6$.

a. In how many seconds does the ball reach its maximum height?

b. What is the ball's maximum height?

Example 3 (page 435)

Graph each quadratic inequality.

17. $y > x^2$ **18.** $f(x) < -x^2$ **19.** $y \leq x^2 + 3$

20. $y < -x^2 + 4$ **21.** $y \geq -2x^2 + 6$ **22.** $f(x) > -x^2 + 4x - 4$

B Apply Your Skills

Graph each function. Label the axis of symmetry and the vertex. Find the domain and range.

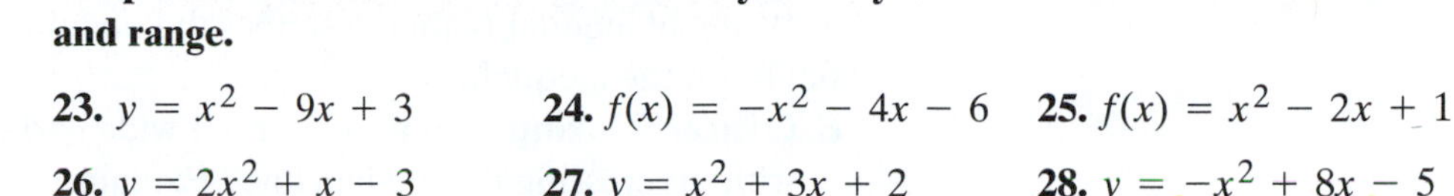

23. $y = x^2 - 9x + 3$ **24.** $f(x) = -x^2 - 4x - 6$ **25.** $f(x) = x^2 - 2x + 1$

26. $y = 2x^2 + x - 3$ **27.** $y = x^2 + 3x + 2$ **28.** $y = -x^2 + 8x - 5$

29. $y = \frac{1}{2}x^2 + 2x + 1$ **30.** $y = \frac{1}{4}x^2 + 2x + 1$ **31.** $y = -\frac{1}{4}x^2 + 2x - 3$

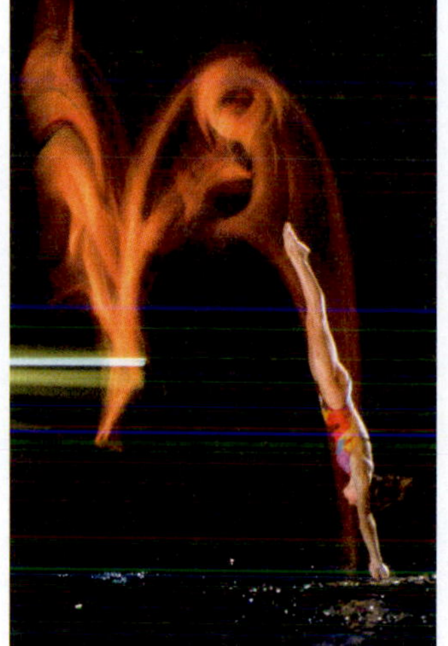

After turning a somersault, the diver followed a parabolic path.

Critical Thinking For Exercises 32–34, give an example of a quadratic function for each description.

32. Its axis of symmetry is to the right of the y-axis.

33. Its graph opens downward and has its vertex at (0, 0).

34. Its graph lies entirely above the x-axis.

35. An athlete dives from the 3-meter springboard. Her height y, at horizontal distance x, can be approximated by the function $y = -1.2x^2 + 3.12x + 3$. Both the height and distance are in meters.

a. How far has she traveled horizontally when she reaches her maximum height? Round to the nearest tenth of a meter.

b. What is her maximum height? Round to the nearest tenth of a meter.

36. Math Reasoning Suppose you graph a quadratic function $y = ax^2 + bx + c$, where $a < 0$ and $b > 0$. Would the axis of symmetry *sometimes, always,* or *never* be located to the right of the y-axis? Explain.

37. A small company markets a new toy. The function $S = -64p^2 + 1600p$ predicts the total sales S in dollars as a function of the price p of the toy. What price will produce the highest total sales?

Ⓐ \$64.00 Ⓑ \$25.00 Ⓒ \$12.50 Ⓓ \$8.00

For each of the graphs below, estimate the area enclosed by the parabola, the x-axis, and the vertical lines $x = 1$ and $x = 7$. Follow the instructions below.

- Count the number of whole grid squares in the region.
- If half a square or more is included in the region, count it as one.
- If less than half a square is included in the region, do *not* count it.
- Add the counted squares to estimate the area.

38.

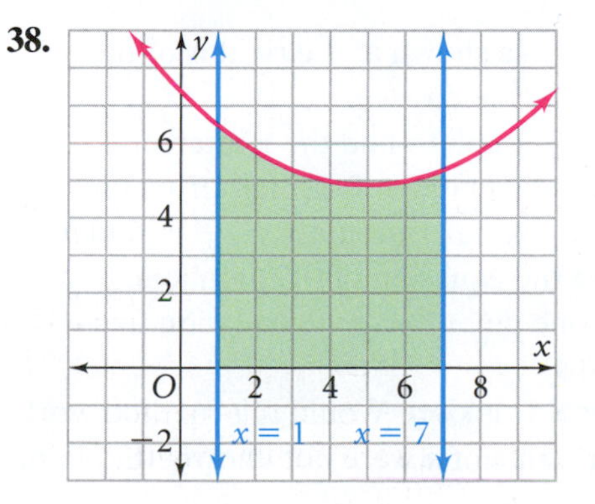

39.

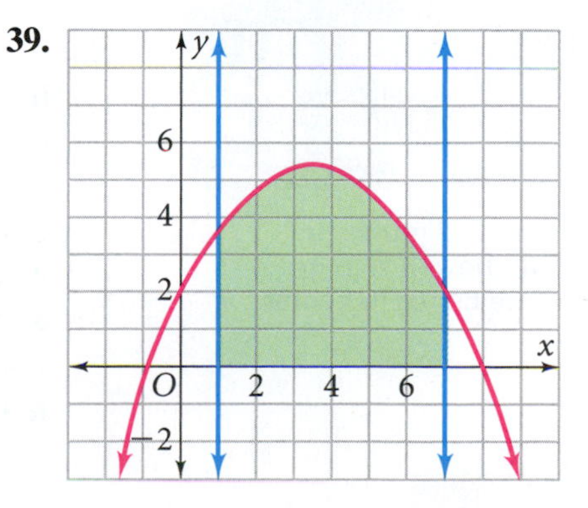

Visit: PHSchool.com
Web Code: bae-0902

40. **Writing** Explain how changing the values of a, b, and c in a quadratic function affects the graph of the function.

41. An archway over a road is cut out of rock. Its shape is modeled by the quadratic function $y = -0.1x^2 + 12$ for $y \geq 0$.
   a. Write an inequality that describes the opening of the archway.
   b. Graph the inequality.
   c. **Critical Thinking** Can a camper 6 ft wide and 7 ft high fit under the arch without crossing the median line? Explain.

42. Suppose a volleyball player serves from 1 m behind the back line. If no other player touches the ball, it will land in bounds. The equation $h = -4.9t^2 + 3.82t + 1.7$ gives the ball's height h in meters in terms of time t in seconds.

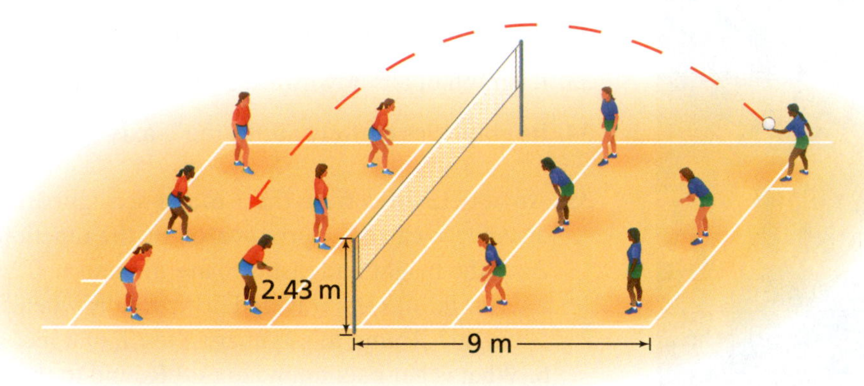

   a. When will the ball be at its highest point? Round to the nearest tenth of a second.
   b. The ball will reach the net at $t = 0.6$ s. Will it clear the net? Explain.

Challenge

43. An architect designs a monument for a new park. The solution of the following system of inequalities describes the shape of the monument. Make a graph of the monument.

$$y \geq -x^2 + 6 \qquad y \leq -\tfrac{1}{2}x^2 + 8 \qquad y \geq 0$$

A tennis ball must reach a height above 3 ft in order to clear the net at its center.

44. Suppose a tennis player hits a ball over the net. The ball leaves his racket 0.5 m above the ground. The equation $h = -4.9t^2 + 3.8t + 0.5$ gives the ball's height h in meters at time t in seconds.
   a. When will the ball be at the highest point in its path? Round to the nearest tenth of a second.
   b. **Critical Thinking** If you double the answer from part (a), will you find the amount of time the ball is in the air before it hits the court? Explain.

45. The parabola shown at the right is of the form $y = x^2 + bx + c$.
   a. Use the graph to find the y-intercept.
   b. Find the equation of the axis of symmetry.
   c. Use the vertex formula $x = \frac{-b}{2a}$ to find b.
   d. Write the equation of the parabola.
   e. Test one point using the equation from part (d).
   f. **Critical Thinking** Would this method work if the value of a were not known? Explain.

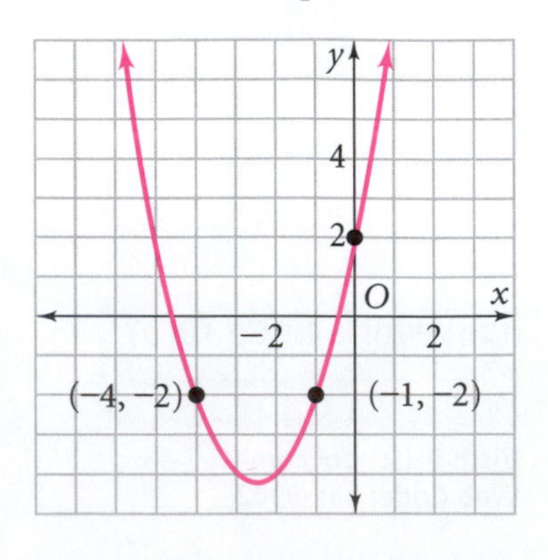

Multiple Choice Practice

For California Standards Tutorials, visit PHSchool.com. Web Code: baq-9045

Alg1 21.0

46. How would the graph of the function $y = x^2 - 3$ be affected if the function were changed to $y = x^2 + 1$?

- (A) The graph would shift 2 units up.
- (B) The graph would shift 2 units down.
- (C) The graph would shift 4 units up.
- (D) The graph would shift 4 units down.

Alg1 7.0

47. Which equation best represents the line shown on the graph?

- (A) $y = \frac{3}{4}x - \frac{5}{4}$
- (B) $y = \frac{3}{4}x - 3$
- (C) $y = \frac{4}{3}x - \frac{5}{4}$
- (D) $y = \frac{4}{3}x - 3$

Alg1 16.0

48. Which situation can be represented by a linear function?

- (A) The volume of a cube given its side length
- (B) The amount of taxes paid given a person's age
- (C) The life expectancy of a person given his or her occupation
- (D) The distance a car travels given a constant speed

Alg1 23.0

49. An arrow is shot into the air. It follows a path given by the equation $y = -0.009x^2 + 0.3x + 4.5$, where x and y are in feet. What is the arrow's maximum height to the nearest foot?

- (A) 5 ft
- (B) 6 ft
- (C) 7 ft
- (D) 8 ft

Mixed Review

GO for Help

Lesson 9-1

Match each graph with its function.

A. $y = \frac{1}{8}x^2 + 2$ **B.** $y = \frac{1}{2}x^2 + 2$ **C.** $y = -x^2 - 2$

D. $y = x^2 + 2$ **E.** $y = -x^2 + 2$ **F.** $y = -\frac{1}{2}x^2 - 2$

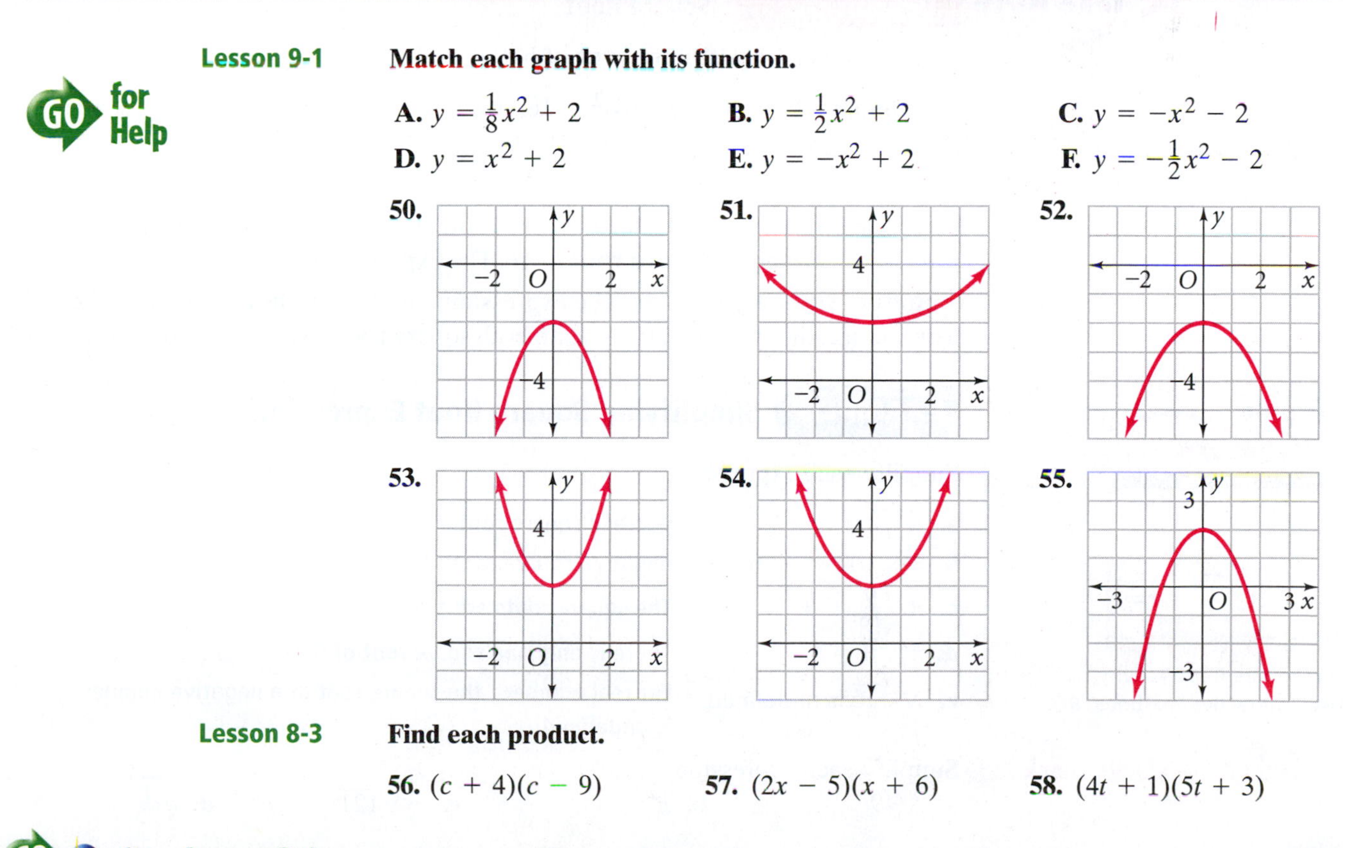

Lesson 8-3

Find each product.

56. $(c + 4)(c - 9)$ **57.** $(2x - 5)(x + 6)$ **58.** $(4t + 1)(5t + 3)$

9-3 Finding and Estimating Square Roots

California Content Standards

2.0 Understand and use such operations as taking a root. ***Develop***

23.0 Apply quadratic equations to physical problems. ***Develop***

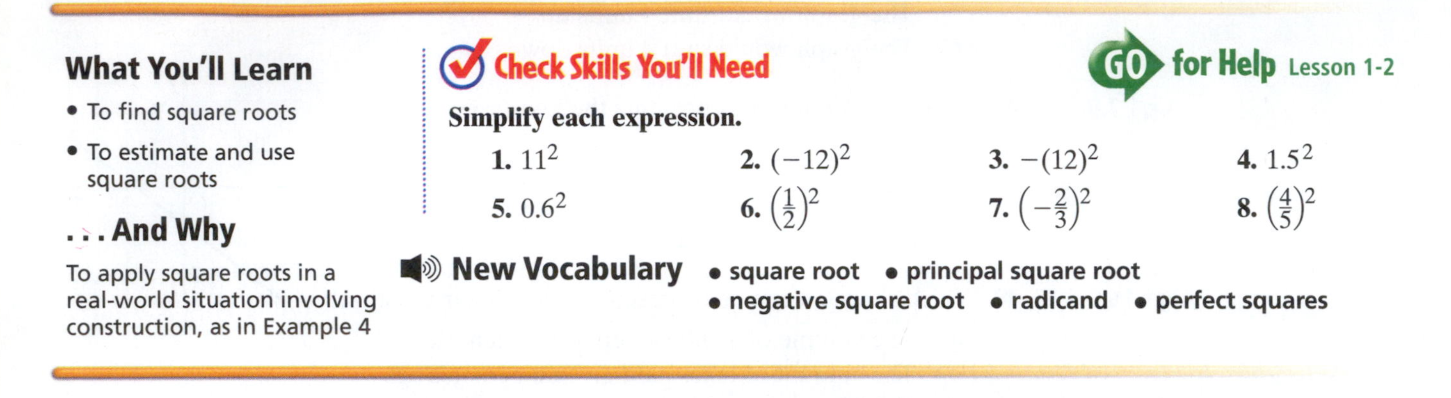

What You'll Learn

- To find square roots
- To estimate and use square roots

. . . And Why

To apply square roots in a real-world situation involving construction, as in Example 4

Check Skills You'll Need

GO for Help Lesson 1-2

Simplify each expression.

1. 11^2 **2.** $(-12)^2$ **3.** $-(12)^2$ **4.** 1.5^2

5. 0.6^2 **6.** $\left(\frac{1}{2}\right)^2$ **7.** $\left(-\frac{2}{3}\right)^2$ **8.** $\left(\frac{4}{5}\right)^2$

New Vocabulary

- square root
- principal square root
- negative square root
- radicand
- perfect squares

Finding Square Roots

The diagram at the right shows the relationship between squares and square roots. Every positive number has *two* square roots.

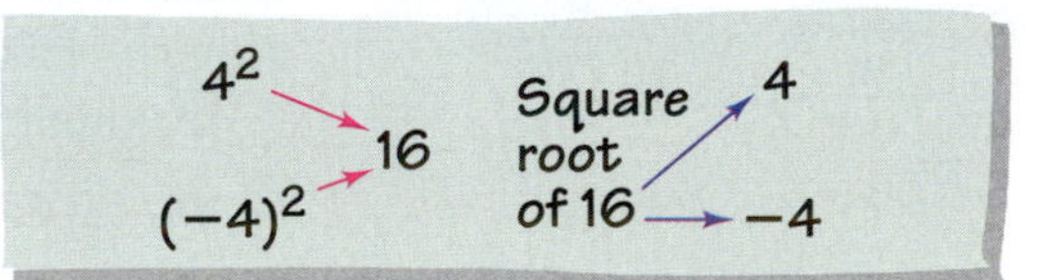

Take Note

Definition **Square Root**

The number a is a **square root** of b if $a^2 = b$.

Example $4^2 = 16$ and $(-4)^2 = 16$, so 4 and -4 are square roots of 16.

A radical symbol $\sqrt{}$ indicates a square root. The expression $\sqrt{16}$ means the positive, or **principal square root** of 16. The expression $-\sqrt{16}$ means the **negative square root** of 16. The expression under the radical sign is a **radicand.** You can use the symbol $\pm$ to indicate both square roots. Read $\pm$ as "plus or minus."

1 EXAMPLE Simplifying Square Root Expressions

Simplify each expression.

a. $\sqrt{64} = 8$ positive square root

b. $-\sqrt{100} = -10$ negative square root

c. $\pm\sqrt{\frac{9}{16}} = \pm\frac{3}{4}$ The square roots are $\frac{3}{4}$ and $-\frac{3}{4}$.

d. $\pm\sqrt{0} = 0$ There is only one square root of 0.

e. $\sqrt{-16}$ is undefined. For real numbers, the square root of a negative number is undefined.

Online active math

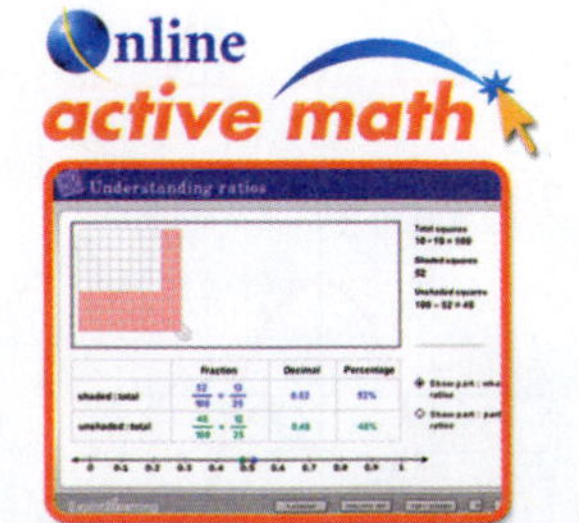

For: Square Root Activity
Use: Interactive Textbook, 9-3

CA Standards Check 1 Simplify each expression.

a. $\sqrt{49}$ **b.** $\pm\sqrt{36}$ **c.** $-\sqrt{121}$ **d.** $\sqrt{\frac{1}{25}}$

Vocabulary Tip

In decimal form, a rational number terminates or repeats. In decimal form, an irrational number continues without repeating.

Some square roots are rational numbers and some are irrational numbers.

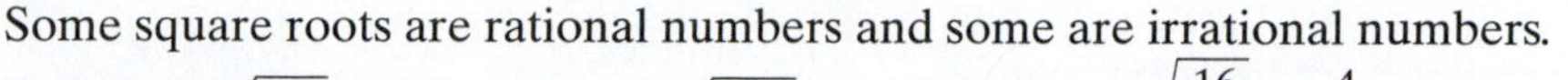

Rational: $\sqrt{100} = 10$ $\qquad \pm\sqrt{0.36} = \pm 0.6$ $\qquad \sqrt{\frac{16}{121}} = \frac{4}{11}$

Irrational: $\sqrt{10} \approx 3.16227766$ $\qquad \sqrt{\frac{1}{7}} \approx 0.377964473$

2 EXAMPLE Rational and Irrational Square Roots

Tell whether each expression is *rational* or *irrational*.

a. $\pm\sqrt{81} = \pm 9$ rational

b. $-\sqrt{5} \approx -2.23606798$ irrational

c. $-\sqrt{1.44} = -1.2$ rational

d. $\sqrt{\frac{4}{9}} = \frac{2}{3}$ rational

CA Standards Check 2 Tell whether each expression is *rational* or *irrational*.

a. $\sqrt{8}$ **b.** $\pm\sqrt{225}$ **c.** $-\sqrt{75}$ **d.** $\sqrt{\frac{1}{4}}$

Estimating and Using Square Roots

The squares of integers are called **perfect squares.**

consecutive integers:	1	2	3	4	5	6
	↓	↓	↓	↓	↓	↓
consecutive perfect squares:	1	4	9	16	25	36

You can estimate square roots by using perfect squares.

3 EXAMPLE Estimating Square Roots

Estimation Between what two consecutive integers is $\sqrt{14.52}$?

$\sqrt{9} < \sqrt{14.52} < \sqrt{16}$ **14.52 is between the two consecutive perfect squares 9 and 16.**

↓ ↓ ↓

$3 < \sqrt{14.52} < 4$ **The square roots of 9 and 16 are 3 and 4, respectively.**

$\sqrt{14.52}$ is between 3 and 4.

CA Standards Check 3 Between what two consecutive integers is $-\sqrt{105}$?

Many real-world formulas involve square roots.

4 EXAMPLE Application

The formula $d = \sqrt{x^2 + (2x)^2}$ gives the length d of each wire for the tower at the left. Find the length of the wire if $x = 12$ ft.

$d = \sqrt{x^2 + (2x)^2}$

$d = \sqrt{12^2 + (2 \cdot 12)^2}$ **Substitute 12 for *x*.**

$d = \sqrt{144 + 576}$ **Simplify.**

$d = \sqrt{720}$

$d \approx 26.8$ **Use a calculator. Round to the nearest tenth.**

The wire is about 26.8 ft long.

CA Standards Check 4 Suppose the tower is 140 ft tall. How long is the supporting wire? Round to the nearest tenth of a foot.

EXERCISES

For more exercises, see *Extra Skills and Word Problem Practice*.

Standards Practice

Alg1 2.0, 23.0, 24.3

A Practice by Example

Example 1 (page 440)

Simplify each expression.

1. $\sqrt{169}$
2. $\sqrt{400}$
3. $\sqrt{\frac{1}{9}}$
4. $\sqrt{900}$
5. $\sqrt{0.25}$
6. $\sqrt{\frac{36}{49}}$
7. $-\sqrt{1.21}$
8. $\sqrt{1.96}$
9. $\sqrt{0.36}$
10. $-\sqrt{144}$
11. $\sqrt{\frac{25}{16}}$
12. $\pm\sqrt{0.01}$

GO for Help

Example 2 (page 441)

Tell whether each expression is *rational* or *irrational*.

13. $\sqrt{37}$
14. $-\sqrt{0.04}$
15. $\pm\sqrt{\frac{1}{5}}$
16. $-\sqrt{\frac{16}{121}}$

Example 3 (page 441)

Between what two consecutive integers is each square root?

17. $\sqrt{35}$
18. $\sqrt{27}$
19. $-\sqrt{130}$
20. $\sqrt{170}$

Example 4 (page 441)

21. The elasticity coefficient e of a ball relates the height r of its rebound to the height h from which it is dropped. You can use the function $e = \sqrt{\frac{r}{h}}$ to find the elasticity coefficient. What is the elasticity coefficient of a tennis ball that rebounds 3 ft after it is dropped from a height of 3.5 ft? Round to the nearest hundredth.

B Apply Your Skills

Find the square root(s) of each number.

22. 400
23. 0
24. 625
25. $\frac{9}{49}$
26. 1.69
27. $\frac{1}{81}$
28. 729
29. 2.25
30. 256
31. 0.01
32. $\frac{64}{121}$
33. 40,804

34. **Critical Thinking** What number other than 0 is its own square root?

35. The formula $d = \sqrt{12{,}800h + h^2}$ gives the distance d in kilometers to the horizon from a satellite h kilometers above Earth. Find the distance to the horizon from a satellite 4200 km above Earth. Round to the nearest kilometer.

Find the value of each expression. If necessary, round to the nearest hundredth.

36. $\sqrt{441}$
37. $-\sqrt{\frac{4}{25}}$
38. $\sqrt{2}$
39. $\sqrt{1.6}$
40. $-\sqrt{30}$
41. $-\sqrt{1089}$
42. $-\sqrt{0.64}$
43. $\sqrt{41}$
44. $\sqrt{75}$

45. **Writing** Explain the difference between $-\sqrt{1}$ and $\sqrt{1}$.

Visit: PHSchool.com
Web Code: bae-0903

46. **Critical Thinking** Find two integers a and b between 1 and 20 such that $a^2 + b^2$ is a perfect square.

47. In the cartoon, to what number is the golfer referring?

48. If you drop an object, the time t in seconds that it takes to fall d feet is given by the formula $t = \sqrt{\frac{d}{16}}$.
   a. Find the time it takes an object to fall 400 ft.
   b. Find the time it takes an object to fall 1600 ft.
   c. **Critical Thinking** In part (b), the object falls four times as far as in part (a). Does it take four times as long to fall? Explain.

C Challenge

Math Reasoning For Exercises 49–52, tell whether each statement is *true* or *false*. If the statement is false, give a counterexample.

49. Every nonnegative number has two square roots.

50. The square root of a positive number is always less than the number.

51. The square root of an even perfect square is always an even number.

52. $\sqrt{p} + \sqrt{q} = \sqrt{p + q}$

53. a. What is the total area of the large square shown at the right?
   b. What is the area of each shaded triangle?
   c. What is the area of the shaded square?
   d. What is the length of the diagonal of each 1×1 square?

Multiple Choice Practice

For California Standards Tutorials, visit PHSchool.com. Web Code: baq-9045

Alg1 2.0

54. Simplify $\sqrt{4^2 + 3^2 + 11}$.
   (A) 4 (B) 5 (C) 6 (D) 7

Alg1 21.0

55. Which of the following equations has a graph that is narrower than the graph of $y = 2x^2 + 3$?
   (A) $y = 2x^2 - 3$
   (B) $y = 0.5x^2 + 3$
   (C) $y = -3x^2 + 2$
   (D) $y = -0.5x^2 - 2$

Alg1 8.0

56. A line perpendicular to $y = 3x - 2$ passes through the point $(0, 6)$. Which other point lies on the line?
   (A) $(9, 3)$ (B) $(-9, 3)$ (C) $(-9, -3)$ (D) $(9, -3)$

Alg1 5.0

57. Jack's age is 3 less than twice Dean's age, and Jack is 5 years older than Dean. How old is Dean?
   (A) 5 years (B) 8 years (C) 10 years (D) 13 years

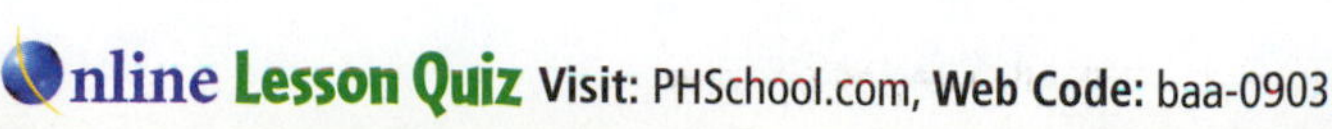

Alg1 9.0

58. Mandy has \$2.40 in coins, all in dimes and nickels. The total number of coins is 30. If she has d dimes and n nickels, which system models the situation?

Ⓐ $d + n = 30$
$10d + 5n = 240$

Ⓑ $d + n = 30$
$10d + 5n = 2.40$

Ⓒ $d + n = 240$
$10d + 5n = 30$

Ⓓ $d + n = 2.40$
$10d + 5n = 30$

Mixed Review

Lesson 8-5

Factor each expression.

59. $x^2 + 5x - 24$ **60.** $h^2 - 3h - 10$ **61.** $m^2 - 11m + 18$

Lesson 2-5

62. Marcus and Beth leave college traveling in opposite directions on a straight road. Beth drives 13 mi/h faster than Marcus. After 4 hours, they are 452 miles apart. Find their rates.

Lesson 1-8

Simplify each expression. Justify each step.

63. $8 \cdot 7 \cdot 5$ **64.** $14 + 23 + 56$ **65.** $16\left(\frac{1}{16}\right) + 5$

66. $(6^8 - 6^9)(11 - 11)$ **67.** $-7(3w)$ **68.** $8m + 145 + 4m$

Mathematical Reasoning

24.0 Use and know simple aspects of a logical argument. ***Develop***

The Square Root of 5 Is Irrational

You can show that $\sqrt{5}$ is irrational by using a *proof by contradiction.* This involves assuming that $\sqrt{5}$ is rational and then showing that the assumption leads to a contradiction. The proof also uses the fact that if a prime number p is a factor of a^2, then p is a factor of a.

Assume that $\sqrt{5}$ is rational. So $\sqrt{5}$ can be written as a ratio of two integers. Let a and b be two integers where $b \neq 0$ and the greatest common factor of a and b is 1.

$\sqrt{5} = \frac{a}{b}$ Assumption

$5 = \frac{a^2}{b^2}$ Square each side.

$5b^2 = a^2$ Multiply each side by b^2.

The equation $5b^2 = a^2$ implies that 5 is a factor of a^2. Since 5 is a prime number, 5 is also a factor of a. So $a = 5k$ for some integer k.

$5b^2 = (5k)^2$ Substitute $5k$ for a.

$5b^2 = 25k^2$ Raise each factor to the 2nd power.

$b^2 = 5k^2$ Divide each side by 5.

The equation $b^2 = 5k^2$ implies that 5 is a factor of b^2, and therefore a factor of b. So 5 is factor of both a and b. But the greatest common factor of a and b is 1. This contradiction shows that our assumption is false. So $\sqrt{5}$ is irrational.

EXERCISE

Show that $\sqrt{3}$ is irrational.

9-4 Solving Quadratic Equations

California Content Standards

21.0 Graph quadratic functions and know that their roots are the x-intercepts. ***Master***
23.0 Apply quadratic equations to physical problems. ***Develop***

What You'll Learn

- To solve quadratic equations by graphing
- To solve quadratic equations using square roots

. . . And Why

To use square roots in a real-world situation involving city planning, as in Example 3

Check Skills You'll Need

GO for Help Lesson 9-3

Simplify each expression.

1. $\sqrt{36}$
2. $-\sqrt{81}$
3. $\pm\sqrt{121}$
4. $\sqrt{1.44}$
5. $\sqrt{0.25}$
6. $\pm\sqrt{1.21}$
7. $\sqrt{\frac{1}{4}}$
8. $\pm\sqrt{\frac{1}{9}}$
9. $\sqrt{\frac{49}{100}}$

New Vocabulary • quadratic equation • standard form of a quadratic equation • roots of the equation • zeros of the function

Solving Quadratic Equations by Graphing

CA Standards Investigation Finding x-intercepts

1. Find the x-intercepts of each graph.
   a. $y = 2x - 3$
   b. $y = x^2 + 3x - 4$

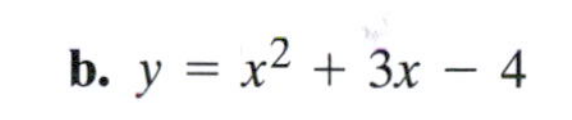

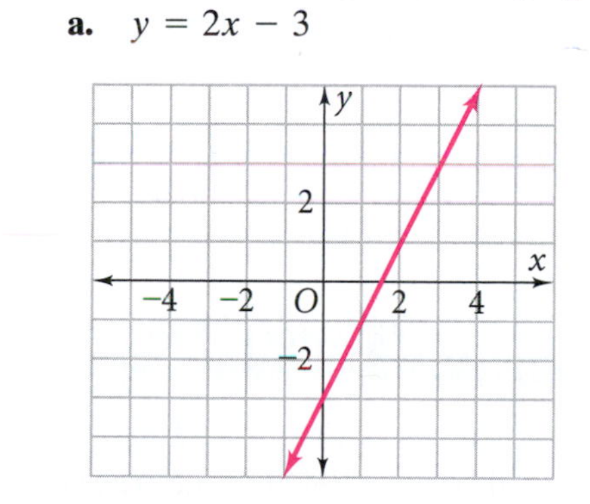

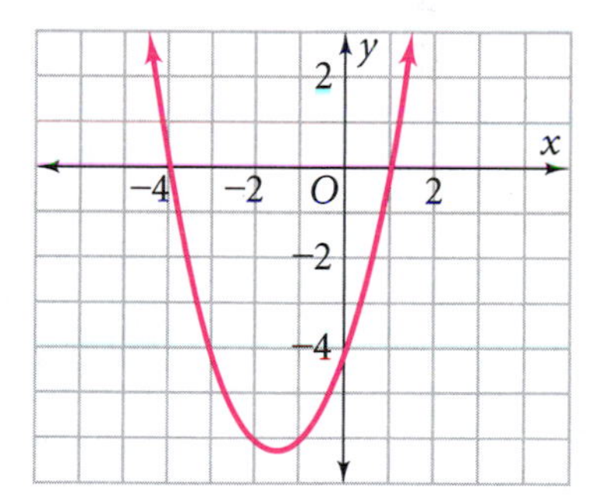

2. Solve $2x - 3 = 0$. Is the solution of $2x - 3 = 0$ the same as the x-intercept of $y = 2x - 3$?
3. Do the x-intercepts that you found in Question 1b satisfy the equation $x^2 + 3x - 4 = 0$?
4. a. Graph $y = x^2 + x - 6$.
   b. Find the x-intercepts of the graph of $y = x^2 + x - 6$.
   c. Do the values you found in part (b) satisfy the equation $x^2 + x - 6 = 0$?

The equation $x^2 + 3x - 4 = 0$ is called a quadratic equation, and its related quadratic function is $y = x^2 + 3x - 4$. The solutions of a quadratic equation and the x-intercepts of its related quadratic function are the same.

Take Note

Definition — **Standard Form of a Quadratic Equation**

A **quadratic equation** is an equation that can be written in the form $ax^2 + bx + c = 0$, where a, b, and c are real numbers and $a \neq 0$. This form is called the **standard form of a quadratic equation.**

A quadratic equation can have two, one, or no real-number solutions. In a future course you will learn about solutions of quadratic equations that are not real numbers. In this course *solutions* refers to real-number solutions.

The solutions of a quadratic equation and the related x-intercepts are often called **roots of the equation** or **zeros of the function.**

1 EXAMPLE Solving by Graphing

Solve each equation by graphing the related function.

a. $x^2 - 4 = 0$
Graph $y = x^2 - 4$.

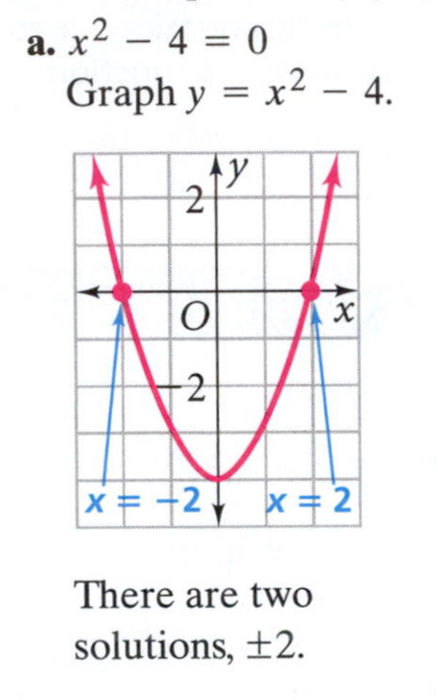

There are two solutions, ± 2.

b. $x^2 = 0$
Graph $y = x^2$.

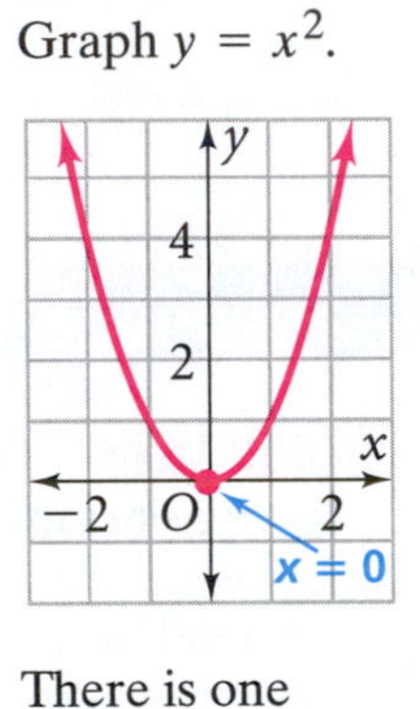

There is one solution, 0.

c. $x^2 + 4 = 0$
Graph $y = x^2 + 4$.

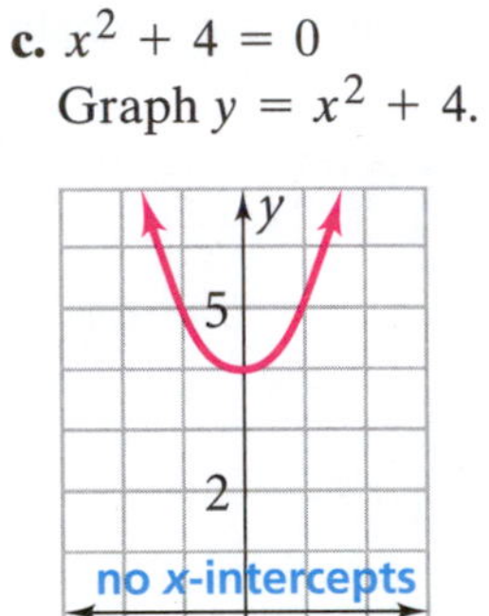

There is no solution.

CA Standards Check 1 Solve each equation by graphing the related function.

a. $x^2 - 1 = 0$ **b.** $2x^2 + 4 = 0$ **c.** $x^2 - 16 = -16$

Solving Quadratic Equations Using Square Roots

You can solve equations of the form $x^2 = a$ by finding the square roots of each side. Since $6^2 = 36$ and $(-6)^2 = 36$ are both true statements, 6 and -6 are both solutions to the equation $x^2 = 36$. We write the solution to $x^2 = 36$ as $\pm\sqrt{36}$, or ± 6.

2 EXAMPLE Using Square Roots

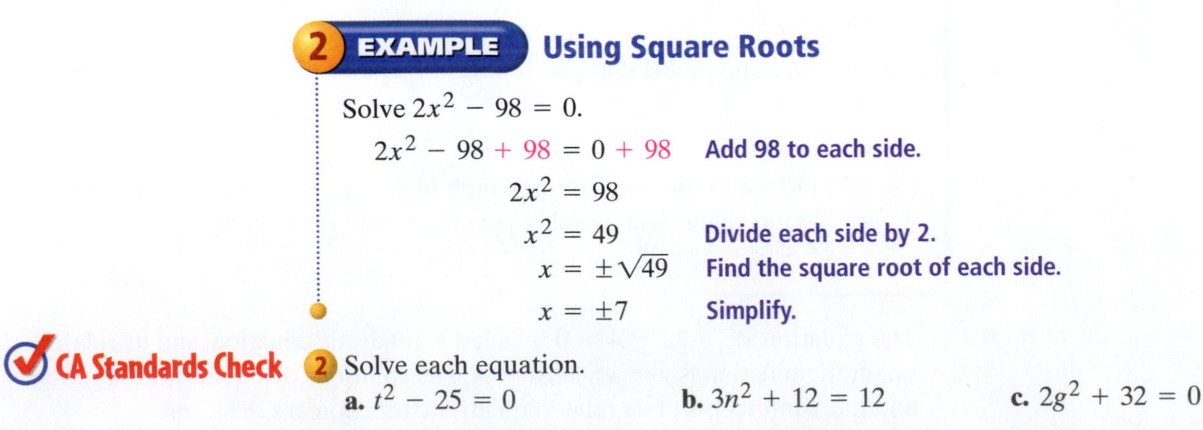

Solve $2x^2 - 98 = 0$.

$2x^2 - 98 + 98 = 0 + 98$ — Add 98 to each side.

$2x^2 = 98$

$x^2 = 49$ — Divide each side by 2.

$x = \pm\sqrt{49}$ — Find the square root of each side.

$x = \pm 7$ — Simplify.

CA Standards Check 2 Solve each equation.

a. $t^2 - 25 = 0$ **b.** $3n^2 + 12 = 12$ **c.** $2g^2 + 32 = 0$

You can solve real-world problems by finding square roots. In many cases, the negative solution of a quadratic equation will not be a reasonable solution to the original problem.

Problem Solving Tip

You can check answers such as 39.9 by rounding to 40 and substituting it into the original formula. If you get a value close to the one given in the problem, your answer is probably correct.

3 EXAMPLE Application

A city is planning a circular duck pond for a new park. The depth of the pond will be 4 ft and the volume will be 20,000 ft^3. Find the radius of the pond to the nearest tenth of a foot. Use the equation $V = \pi r^2 h$, where V is the volume, r is the radius, and h is the depth.

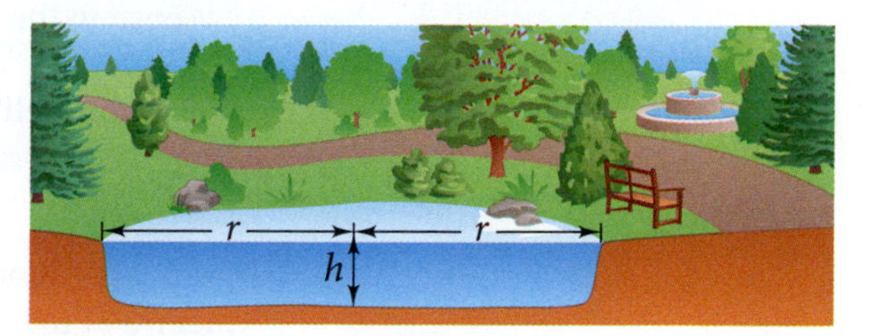

$$V = \pi r^2 h$$

$$20{,}000 = \pi r^2(4)$$ Substitute 20,000 for V and 4 for h.

$$\frac{20{,}000}{(\pi \cdot 4)} = r^2$$ Divide each side by $\pi \cdot 4$.

$$\sqrt{\frac{20{,}000}{(\pi \cdot 4)}} = r$$ Find the principal square root.

$$39.89422804 \approx r$$ Simplify using a calculator.

The pond will have a radius of 39.9 ft.

CA Standards Check 3 A city is planning a circular fountain. The depth of the fountain will be 3 ft and the volume will be 1800 ft^3. Find the radius of the fountain.

EXERCISES

Standards Practice

For more exercises, see *Extra Skills and Word Problem Practice*.

Alg1 21.0, 23.0

A Practice by Example

Solve each equation by graphing the related function. If the equation has no solution, write *no solution*.

Example 1 (page 446)

GO for Help

1. $x^2 - 9 = 0$ **2.** $x^2 + 5 = 0$ **3.** $4x^2 = 0$

4. $2x^2 - 8 = 0$ **5.** $x^2 + 16 = 0$ **6.** $\frac{1}{3}x^2 - 3 = 0$

7. $\frac{1}{2}x^2 + 1 = 0$ **8.** $x^2 + 7 = 7$ **9.** $\frac{1}{4}x^2 - 1 = 0$

Example 2 (page 446)

Solve each equation by finding square roots. If the equation has no solution, write *no solution*.

10. $k^2 = 49$ **11.** $b^2 = 441$ **12.** $m^2 - 225 = 0$

13. $c^2 + 25 = 25$ **14.** $x^2 - 9 = -16$ **15.** $4r^2 = 25$

16. $64p^2 = 4$ **17.** $6w^2 - 24 = 0$ **18.** $27 - y^2 = 0$

Example 3 (page 447)

Model each problem with a quadratic equation. Then solve. If necessary, round to the nearest tenth.

19. Find the side of a square with an area of 256 m^2.

20. Find the side of a square with an area of 90 ft^2.

21. Find the radius of a circle with an area of 80 cm^2.

B **Apply Your Skills**

22. Suppose a map company wants to produce a globe with a surface area of 450 in.^{2}. Use the formula $A = 4\pi r^2$, where A is the surface area and r is the radius of the sphere.

a. What should the radius be? Round to the nearest tenth of an inch.

b. **Critical Thinking** Why is the principal square root the only root that makes sense in this situation?

Mental Math **Tell the number of solutions each equation has.**

23. $y^2 = -36$ **24.** $a^2 - 12 = 6$ **25.** $n^2 - 15 = -15$

26. Find dimensions for the square picture at the right that would make the area of the picture equal to 75% of the total area enclosed by the square frame. Round to the nearest tenth of an inch.

27. Suppose you have a can of paint that will cover 400 ft^2.

a. Find the radius of the largest circle you can paint. Round to the nearest tenth of a foot. (*Hint:* Use the formula $A = \pi r^2$.)

b. Suppose you have two cans of paint, which will cover a total of 800 ft^2. Find the radius of the largest circle you can paint. Round to the nearest tenth of a foot.

Solve each equation by finding square roots. If the equation has no solution, write *no solution*. If the value is irrational, round to the nearest tenth.

28. $1.2q^2 - 7 = -34$ **29.** $49t^2 - 16 = -7$ **30.** $3d^2 - \frac{1}{12} = 0$

31. $\frac{1}{2}x^2 - 4 = 0$ **32.** $7h^2 + 0.12 = 1.24$ **33.** $-\frac{1}{4}x^2 + 3 = 0$

34. The equation $d = \frac{1}{2}at^2$ gives the distance d an object starting at rest travels given acceleration a and time t. Suppose a ball rolls down the ramp shown at the right with acceleration $a = 2$ ft/s^2. Find the time it will take to roll from the top of the ramp to the bottom. Round to the nearest tenth of a second.

12 ft

35. Find a value for c such that the equation $x^2 - c = 0$ has 11 and -11 as solutions.

36. **a.** **Critical Thinking** For what values of n will $x^2 = n$ have two solutions?

b. For what value of n will $x^2 = n$ have exactly one solution?

c. For what values of n will $x^2 = n$ have no solution?

37. **Error Analysis** Michael's work is shown at the right. Explain the error that he made.

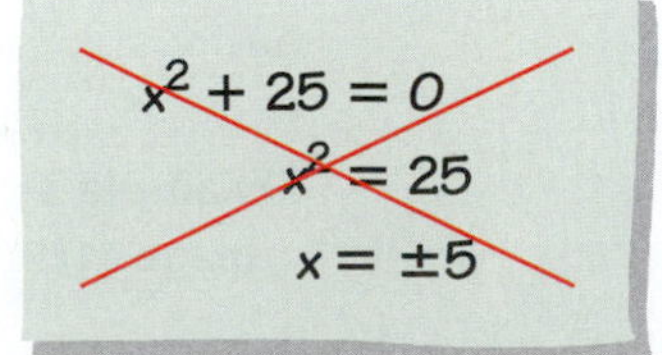

38. **a.** Solve $x^2 - 4 = 0$ and $2x^2 - 8 = 0$ by graphing their related functions.

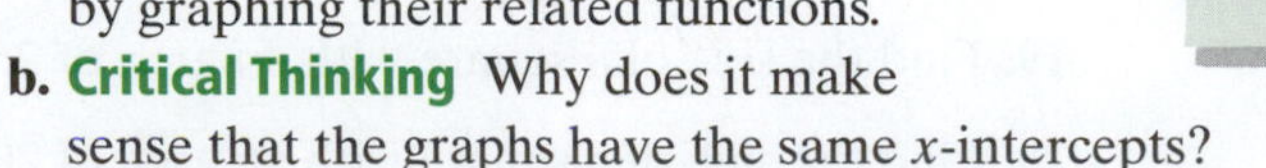

b. **Critical Thinking** Why does it make sense that the graphs have the same x-intercepts?

Homework Video Tutor

Visit: PHSchool.com
Web Code: bae-0904

39. Suppose your class wants to design a T-shirt logo similar to the one shown at the left. You want the orange region to have an area of 80 in.^{2}.

a. Write expressions for the area of the square and of the circle.

b. Write an equation for the area of the orange region.

c. Solve the equation to find the radius of the circle and the side of the square. Round to the nearest tenth of an inch.

40. Write and solve equations in the form $ax^2 + c = 0$ for each of the following.

a. The equation has no solutions.

b. The equation has one solution.

c. The equation has two solutions.

Find the value of *h* for each triangle. If necessary, round to the nearest tenth.

41. **42.**

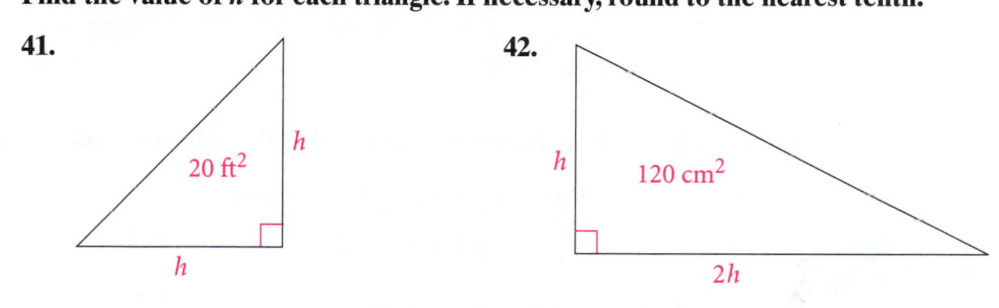

C Challenge

43. The time t a pendulum takes to make a complete swing back and forth depends on the length of the pendulum. The formula $\ell = \frac{2.45t^2}{\pi^2}$ relates the length of a pendulum ℓ in meters to the time t in seconds.

a. Find the length of the pendulum if $t = 1$ s. Round to the nearest tenth.

b. Find t if $\ell = 1.6$ m. Round to the nearest tenth.

c. Find t if $\ell = 2.2$ m. Round to the nearest tenth.

d. **Writing** You can adjust a clock that has a pendulum by making the pendulum longer or shorter. If a clock is running slowly, would you lengthen or shorten the pendulum to make the clock run faster? Explain.

44. **a.** Solve the equation $(x + 7)^2 = 0$.

b. Find the vertex of the related function $y = (x + 7)^2$.

c. Choose a value for h and repeat parts (a) and (b) using $(x + h)^2 = 0$ and $y = (x + h)^2$.

d. Where would you expect to find the vertex of $y = (x - 4)^2$? Explain.

45. The trapezoid has an area of 1960 cm^2. Use the formula $A = \frac{1}{2}h(b_1 + b_2)$ to find the value of y.

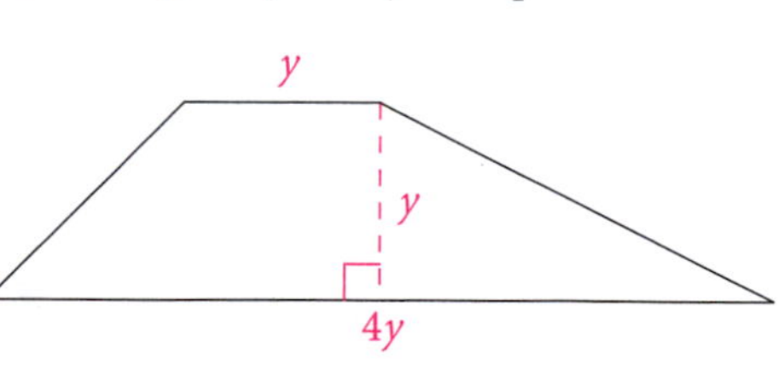

Multiple Choice Practice

For California Standards Tutorials, visit PHSchool.com. Web Code: baq-9045

Alg1 21.0

46. Which graph could represent the function $y = x^2 - 1$?

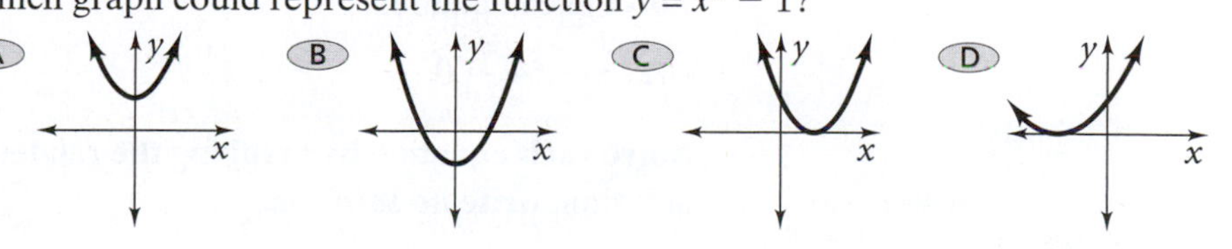

Alg1 6.0

47. What will happen to the graph of $y = 3x - 2$ if the y-intercept is changed to 1?

- (A) The graph will shift 1 unit up.
- (B) The graph will shift 1 unit down.
- (C) The graph will shift 3 units up.
- (D) The graph will shift 3 units down.

Alg1 2.0

48. Between which two consecutive integers is $\sqrt{52}$?

(A) 5 and 6 (B) 6 and 7 (C) 7 and 8 (D) 8 and 9

Alg1 9.0

49. How many solutions are there for the equations $y = x - 3$ and $6y - x = 24$?

(A) 0 (B) 1 (C) 2 (D) 3

Mixed Review

GO for Help

Lesson 9-2

Graph each function. Label the axis of symmetry and the vertex.

50. $y = x^2 + 4x + 3$ **51.** $y = x^2 + 2$ **52.** $y = 2x^2 - 8x - 5$

53. $y = -x^2 + 6x - 1$ **54.** $y = 6x^2 - 12x + 1$ **55.** $y = -3x^2 + 18x$

Lesson 8-5

Factor each expression.

56. $x^2 + 5x + 4$ **57.** $y^2 - 15y + 26$ **58.** $a^2 + 3a - 10$

59. $z^2 - 6z - 72$ **60.** $c^2 - 14cd + 24d^2$ **61.** $t^2 + tu - 2u^2$

Lesson 7-2

Write each number in scientific notation.

62. 3,613,500 **63.** 0.0000348 **64.** 8.12

Write each number in standard notation.

65. 3.1×10^4 **66.** 7.01×10^5 **67.** 6.2×10^{-4}

Checkpoint Quiz 1

Lessons 9-1 through 9-4

Graph each function. Label the axis of symmetry and the vertex.

1. $y = x^2 - 4$ **2.** $y = 8x^2 - 2x$ **3.** $f(x) = x^2 + 5x - 6$

4. Suppose you throw a ball up in the air. Its height h in feet after t seconds is given by the function $h = -16t^2 + 24t + 6$.

a. When does the ball reach its maximum height?

b. What is the ball's maximum height?

Simplify each expression.

5. $\pm\sqrt{0.36}$ **6.** $-\sqrt{4}$

Solve each equation.

7. $t^2 - 64 = 0$ **8.** $6m^2 - 150 = 0$

Solve each equation by graphing the related function. If the equation has no solution, write *no solution*.

9. $3x^2 - 27 = 0$ **10.** $x^2 + 25 = 0$

Mathematical Reasoning

Using Logical Reasoning

FOR USE WITH LESSON 9-4

24.0 Use and know simple aspects of a logical argument. ***Master***
25.3 Given a specific algebraic statement, determine whether the statement is true sometimes, always, or never. ***Master***

When you determine whether or not a statement is true or make a conclusion, it is important to justify your answer with a logical argument. Knowing how to reason logically will help you in later math courses when you learn formal proofs.

1 EXAMPLE

Is the equation $(p + q)^2 = 2pq$ true *sometimes*, *always*, or *never*? Explain your reasoning.

$(p + q)^2 = 2pq$

$p^2 + 2pq + q^2 = 2pq$ **Use FOIL.**

$p^2 + q^2 = 0$ **Subtract $2pq$ from each side.**

$p^2 = -q^2$ **Subtract q^2 from each side.**

The square of a nonzero number is always positive, so p^2 and q^2 are positive and p^2 does not equal $-q^2$ for all nonzero numbers. The equation $p^2 = -q^2$ is true, however, when $p = 0$ and $q = 0$. So the equation $(p + q)^2 = 2pq$ is sometimes true.

2 EXAMPLE

Identify the step below in which an error occurs. Explain your answer.

Step 1: Let $a = 1$ and $b = 1$.
Step 2: $b^2 = ab$
Step 3: $2b^2 = 2ab$
Step 4: $b^2 + b^2 = 2ab$
Step 5: $-2ab + b^2 = -b^2$
Step 6: $a^2 - 2ab + b^2 = a^2 - b^2$
Step 7: $(a - b)(a - b) = (a + b)(a - b)$
Step 8: $a - b = a + b$
Step 9: $-b = b$

Since $a = 1$ and $b = 1$, $a - b = 0$. The error occurs in Step 8, since the equation results from dividing by $a - b$, or zero, which is undefined.

EXERCISES

1. Is the equation $(x + y)^2 = x^2 + y^2$ true *sometimes*, *always*, or *never*? Explain your reasoning.

2. Identify the step below in which an error occurs. Explain your answer.

Step 1: Let $a = 1$ and $b = 2$.
Step 2: $(a - b)^2 > 0$
Step 3: $a^2 - 2ab + b^2 > 0$
Step 4: $a^2 - ab + b^2 - ab > 0$
Step 5: $a^2 - ab > ab - b^2$
Step 6: $a(a - b) > b(a - b)$
Step 7: $a > b$

9-5

Factoring to Solve Quadratic Equations

California Content Standards

14.0 Solve a quadratic equation by factoring. ***Introduce, Develop***
23.0 Apply quadratic equations to physical problems. ***Develop***
25.1 Use properties of numbers to construct valid arguments for claimed assertions. ***Master***

What You'll Learn

- To solve quadratic equations by factoring

. . . And Why

To find the dimensions of a box, as in Example 4

Check Skills You'll Need

GO for Help Lessons 2-1 and 8-6

Solve and check each equation.

1. $6 + 4n = 2$ **2.** $\frac{a}{8} - 9 = 4$ **3.** $7q + 16 = -3$

Factor each expression.

4. $2c^2 + 29c + 14$ **5.** $3p^2 + 32p + 20$ **6.** $4x^2 - 21x - 18$

New Vocabulary • Zero-Product Property

Solving Quadratic Equations

In the previous lesson, you solved quadratic equations by finding square roots. This method works if $b = 0$. You can solve some quadratic equations when $b \neq 0$ by using the Zero-Product Property.

Take Note

Property **Zero-Product Property**

For every real number a and b, if $ab = 0$, then $a = 0$ or $b = 0$.

Example If $(x + 3)(x + 2) = 0$, then $x + 3 = 0$ or $x + 2 = 0$.

1 EXAMPLE Using the Zero-Product Property

Solve $(x + 5)(2x - 6) = 0$.

$(x + 5)(2x - 6) = 0$

$x + 5 = 0$ or $2x - 6 = 0$ Use the Zero-Product Property.

$2x = 6$ Solve for x.

$x = -5$ or $x = 3$

Check Substitute -5 for x.

$(x + 5)(2x - 6) = 0$

$(-5 + 5)[2(-5) - 6] \stackrel{?}{=} 0$

$(0)(-16) = 0$ ✓

Substitute 3 for x.

$(x + 5)(2x - 6) = 0$

$(3 + 5)[2(3) - 6] \stackrel{?}{=} 0$

$(8)(0) = 0$ ✓

CA Standards Check 1 Solve each equation.

a. $(x + 7)(x - 4) = 0$ **b.** $(3y - 5)(y - 2) = 0$

c. $(6k + 9)(4k - 11) = 0$ **d.** $(5h + 1)(h + 6) = 0$

You can also use the Zero-Product Property to solve equations of the form $ax^2 + bx + c = 0$ if the quadratic expression $ax^2 + bx + c$ can be factored.

Problem Solving Tip

Recall that you can use models to factor polynomials.

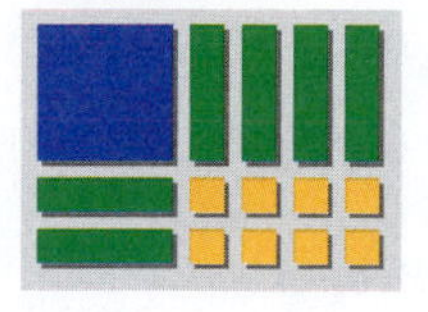

2 EXAMPLE Solving by Factoring

Solve $x^2 + 6x + 8 = 0$.

$x^2 + 6x + 8 = 0$			
$(x + 2)(x + 4) = 0$			Factor $x^2 + 6x + 8$.
$x + 2 = 0$	or	$x + 4 = 0$	Use the Zero-Product Property.
$x = -2$	or	$x = -4$	Solve for x.

CA Standards Check 2 Solve $x^2 - 8x - 48 = 0$ by factoring.

Before solving a quadratic equation, you may need to add or subtract terms in order to write the equation in standard form. Then factor the quadratic expression.

3 EXAMPLE Solving by Factoring

Solve $2x^2 - 5x = 88$.

$2x^2 - 5x - 88 = 0$			Subtract 88 from each side.
$(2x + 11)(x - 8) = 0$			Factor $2x^2 - 5x - 88$.
$2x + 11 = 0$	or	$x - 8 = 0$	Use the Zero-Product Property.
$2x = -11$	or	$x = 8$	Solve for x.
$x = -5.5$			

CA Standards Check 3 Solve $x^2 - 12x = -36$.

4 EXAMPLE Application

The diagram shows a pattern for an open-top box. The total area of the sheet of material used to make the box is 288 in.^{2}. The height of the box is 3 in. Therefore, 3-in. × 3-in. squares are cut from each corner. Find the dimensions of the box.

waste material

3

3

$x + 2$

x

Define Let x = width of a side of the box.
Then the width of the material $= x + 3 + 3 = x + 6$.
The length of the material $= x + 2 + 3 + 3 = x + 8$.

Relate length × width = area of the sheet

Write $(x + 8)(x + 6) = 288$

$x^2 + 14x + 48 = 288$			Find the product $(x + 8)(x + 6)$.
$x^2 + 14x - 240 = 0$			Subtract 288 from each side.
$(x + 24)(x - 10) = 0$			Factor $x^2 + 14x - 240$.
$x + 24 = 0$	or	$x - 10 = 0$	Use the Zero-Product Property.
$x = -24$	or	$x = 10$	Solve for x.

The only reasonable solution is 10. So the dimensions of the box are 10 in. × 12 in. × 3 in.

CA Standards Check 4 Suppose that a box has a base with a width of x, a length of $x + 1$, and a height of 2 in. It is cut from a rectangular sheet of material with an area of 182 in.^{2}. Find the dimensions of the box.

EXERCISES

For more exercises, see *Extra Skills and Word Problem Practice.*

Standards Practice

Alg1 14.0, 23.0, 25.1

A Practice by Example

Example 1 (page 452)

GO for Help

Use the Zero-Product Property to solve each equation.

1. $(x - 3)(x - 7) = 0$ **2.** $(x + 4)(2x - 9) = 0$ **3.** $t(t + 1) = 0$

4. $-3n(2n - 5) = 0$ **5.** $(7x + 2)(5x + 4) = 0$ **6.** $(4a - 7)(3a + 8) = 0$

Factor each polynomial. Then solve using the Zero-Product Property.

7. $x^2 + 7x + 10 = 0$ **8.** $k^2 + 7k + 12 = 0$

Example 2 (page 453)

Solve by factoring.

9. $b^2 + 3b - 4 = 0$ **10.** $m^2 - 5m - 14 = 0$ **11.** $w^2 - 8w = 0$

12. $x^2 - 16x + 55 = 0$ **13.** $k^2 - 3k - 10 = 0$ **14.** $n^2 + n - 12 = 0$

Example 3 (page 453)

15. $x^2 + 8x = -15$ **16.** $t^2 - 3t = 28$ **17.** $n^2 = 6n$

18. $2c^2 - 7c = -5$ **19.** $3q^2 + 16q = -5$ **20.** $4y^2 = 25$

Example 4 (page 453)

21. The sides of a square are all increased by 3 cm. The area of the new square is 64 cm^2. Find the length of a side of the original square.

22. A rectangular box has volume 280 $in.^3$. Its dimensions are 4 in. $\times$ $(n + 2)$ in. $\times$ $(n + 5)$ in. Find n. Use the formula $V = \ell wh$.

23. You are building a rectangular wading pool. You want the area of the bottom to be 90 ft^2. You want the length of the pool to be 3 ft longer than twice its width. What will the dimensions of the pool be?

$2x + 2$

x

24. Suppose the area of the sail shown in the photo at the left is 110 ft^2. Find the dimensions of the sail.

25. The product of two consecutive numbers is 14 less than 10 times the smaller number. Find each number.

B Apply Your Skills

Write each equation in standard form. Then solve.

26. $2q^2 + 22q = -60$ **27.** $4 = -5n + 6n^2$

28. $6y^2 + 12y + 13 = 2y^2 + 4$ **29.** $3a^2 + 4a = 2a^2 - 2a - 9$

30. $3t^2 + 8t = t^2 - 3t - 12$ **31.** $4x^2 + 20 = 10x + 3x^2 - 4$

32. The length of an open box is 2 in. greater than its width. The box was made from an 80-$in.^2$ rectangular sheet of material. The height of the box is 1 in. Therefore 1-in. $\times$ 1-in. squares are cut from each corner. What were the dimensions of the original sheet of material? (*Hint:* Draw a diagram.)

33. Suppose you throw a baseball into the air with an initial upward velocity of 29 ft/s and an initial height of 6 ft. The formula $h = -16t^2 + 29t + 6$ gives the ball's height h in feet at time t in seconds.

a. The ball's height h is 0 when it is on the ground. Find the number of seconds that pass before the ball lands by solving $0 = -16t^2 + 29t + 6$.

b. Graph the related function for the equation in part (a). Use your graph to estimate the maximum height of the ball.

Homework Video Tutor

Visit: PHSchool.com
Web Code: bae-0905

34. **Writing** Summarize the procedure for solving a quadratic equation by factoring. Include an example.

35. In the diagram below, a, b, and x represent positive integers. List several possible values for x, a, and b such that the large rectangle has an area of 56 square units.

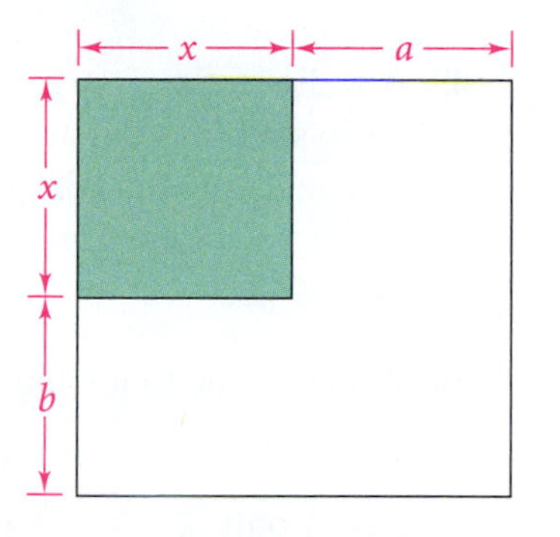

36. Write and solve a quadratic equation using the Zero-Product Property.

37. **a.** Solve $x^2 = x$ and $x^2 = -x$ by factoring.
    b. What number is a solution to both equations?

Solve each cubic equation.

Sample $x^3 + 7x^2 + 12x = 0$

$x(x^2 + 7x + 12) = 0$	Factor out the GCF.
$x(x + 3)(x + 4) = 0$	Factor the quadratic trinomial.
$x = 0$ or $x + 3 = 0$ or $x + 4 = 0$	Use the Zero-Product Property.
$x = 0$ or $x = -3$ or $x = -4$	Solve for x.

38. $x^3 - 10x^2 + 24x = 0$

39. $x^3 - 5x^2 + 4x = 0$

40. $3x^3 - 9x^2 = 0$

41. $x^3 + 3x^2 - 70x = 0$

42. $3x^3 - 30x^2 + 27x = 0$

43. $2x^3 = -2x^2 + 40x$

Challenge

44. You are building a rectangular patio with two rectangular openings for gardens. You have 124 one-foot-square paving stones. Using the diagram below, what value of x would allow you to use all of the stones?

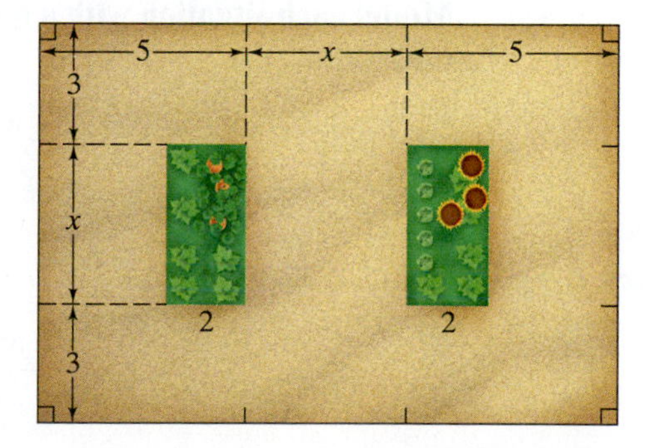

45. Find an equation that has the given numbers as solutions. For example, 4 and -3 are solutions to $x^2 - x - 12 = 0$.
    a. $-5, 8$ **b.** $3, -2$ **c.** $\frac{1}{2}, -10$ **d.** $\frac{2}{3}, -\frac{5}{7}$

Factor the expression on the left side of each equation by grouping. Then solve.

46. $x^3 + 5x^2 - x - 5 = 0$

47. $x^3 + x^2 - 4x - 4 = 0$

Multiple Choice Practice

For California Standards Tutorials, visit PHSchool.com. Web Code: baq-9045

GO for Help

Alg1 21.0

48. The graph of $y = x^2 - 2$ is shifted 5 units up. How many times will the shifted graph intersect the x-axis?

(A) 0 (B) 1 (C) 2 (D) 3

Alg1 5.0

49. A radio station is organizing a fundraiser to build a new public library. The radio station is donating $.50 for every dollar donated by the listeners. If the listeners donated $532 on the first day of the fundraiser, how many dollars did the radio station donate on the first day?

(A) $26.60 (B) $266 (C) $1064 (D) $10,640

Alg1 14.0

50. Which of the following solve(s) $x^2 + 4x + 4 = 49$?

I. 5 **II.** -9 **III.** $\sqrt{47}$ **IV.** $-\sqrt{47}$

(A) I only (B) III and IV (C) III only (D) I and II

Alg1 23.0

51. The length of a rectangle is 6 m less than twice its width. The area of the rectangle is 140 m^2. What is the length of the shorter side of the rectangle?

(A) 8 m (B) 10 m (C) 12 m (D) 13 m

Alg1 16.0

52. Which function is modeled by the table at the right?

(A) $f(x) = x - 2$
(B) $f(x) = 2x + 1$
(C) $f(x) = -x - 2$
(D) $f(x) = 2x - 1$

x	$f(x)$
-3	-5
0	1
2	5
3	7

Alg1 5.0

53. Solve $-5n + 16 \leq -7n$.

(A) $n \leq -8$
(B) $n \geq -8$
(C) $n \leq 8$
(D) $n \geq 8$

Alg1 10.0

54. Simplify $9a + 3b - 3 - 4a + 7 - 8b$.

(A) $12ab - 12ab + 4$
(B) $5b - 5a - 4$
(C) $5a - 5b + 4$
(D) $5ab + 4$

Mixed Review

Lesson 9-4

Model each situation with a quadratic equation. Then solve. Round answers to the nearest tenth.

55. Find the side of a square with an area of 320 ft^2.

56. Find the radius of a circle with an area of 38 ft^2.

Lesson 9-1

Graph each function.

57. $y = -2x^2$ **58.** $f(x) = \frac{1}{4}x^2$ **59.** $f(x) = x^2 + 4$

60. $y = -x^2 - 2$ **61.** $y = 3x^2 + 1$ **62.** $y = -\frac{1}{2}x^2 + 1$

Lesson 8-6

Factor each expression.

63. $2x^2 + 13x + 15$ **64.** $3y^2 - 10y + 3$

65. $4t^2 + 5t - 6$ **66.** $6n^2 + 7n - 3$

67. $15a^3 - 50a^2 - 40a$ **68.** $-18b^3 + 42b^2 - 20b$

9-6 Completing the Square

California Content Standards

14.0 Solve a quadratic equation by completing the square. ***Master***
23.0 Apply quadratic equations to physical problems. ***Develop***

What You'll Learn

- To solve quadratic equations by completing the square

. . . And Why

To solve real-world problems involving carpentry, as in Example 4

GO for Help Lessons 8-4 and 8-7

Find each square.

1. $(d - 4)^2$ **2.** $(x + 11)^2$ **3.** $(k - 8)^2$

Factor.

4. $b^2 + 10b + 25$ **5.** $t^2 + 14t + 49$ **6.** $n^2 - 18n + 81$

New Vocabulary • completing the square

Solving by Completing the Square

In previous lessons, you solved quadratic equations by finding square roots and by factoring. These methods work in some cases. A third method, completing the square, works with every quadratic equation. Completing the square turns every quadratic equation into the form $m^2 = n$. You can model completing the square of a quadratic expression using squares and rectangles.

The model at the right represents the expression $x^2 + 8x$.

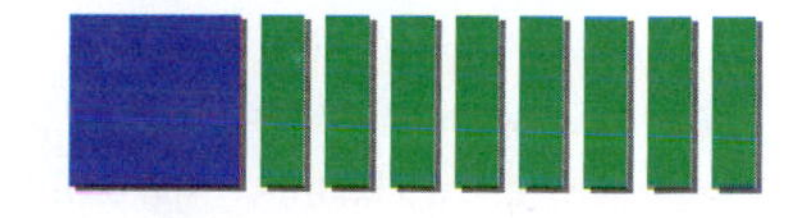

Here is the same expression rearranged to form part of a square. Notice that the x-rectangles have been split evenly into two groups of four.

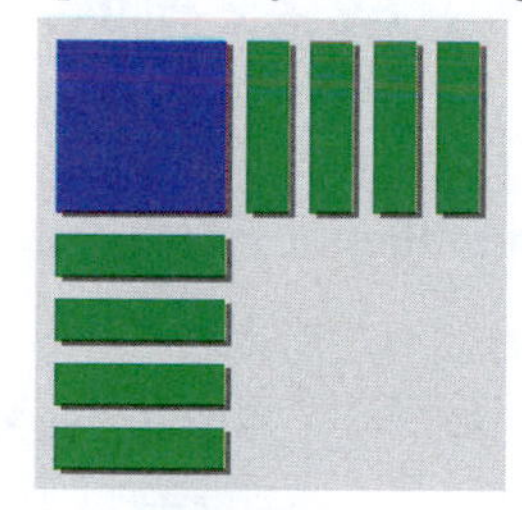

You can complete the square by adding 4^2, or 16, single squares. The completed square is $x^2 + 8x + 16$ or $(x + 4)^2$.

To explore this method algebraically, consider the equation below. In a perfect square trinomial, with $a = 1$, c must be the square of half of b.

$$\begin{aligned}(x + 4)^2 &= x^2 + 2(4)x + 4^2 \\ &= x^2 + 8x + 16\end{aligned}$$

$$8x \downarrow \quad \frac{8}{2} = 4 \rightarrow 4^2 \uparrow 16$$

You can change an expression like $x^2 + bx$ into a perfect square trinomial by adding $\left(\frac{b}{2}\right)^2$ to $x^2 + bx$. This process is called **completing the square.** The process is the same whether b is positive or negative.

1 EXAMPLE Finding n to Complete the Square

Find the value of n such that $x^2 - 12x + n$ is a perfect square trinomial.

The value of b is -12. The term to add to $x^2 - 12x$ is $\left(-\frac{12}{2}\right)^2$, or 36. So $n = 36$.

CA Standards Check 1 Find the value of n such that $x^2 + 22x + n$ is a perfect square trinomial.

The simplest equations in which to complete the square have the form $x^2 + bx = c$.

2 EXAMPLE Solving $x^2 + bx = c$

Solve the equation $x^2 + 9x = 136$.

Step 1 Write the left side of $x^2 + 9x = 136$ as a perfect square.

$$x^2 + 9x = 136$$

$$x^2 + 9x + \left(\frac{9}{2}\right)^2 = 136 + \left(\frac{9}{2}\right)^2$$ Add $\left(\frac{9}{2}\right)^2$, or $\frac{81}{4}$, to each side of the equation.

$$\left(x + \frac{9}{2}\right)^2 = \frac{544}{4} + \frac{81}{4}$$ Write $x^2 + 9x + \left(\frac{9}{2}\right)^2$ as a square. Rewrite 136 as a fraction with denominator 4.

$$\left(x + \frac{9}{2}\right)^2 = \frac{625}{4}$$ Simplify the right side of the equation.

Step 2 Solve the equation.

$$\left(x + \frac{9}{2}\right) = \pm\sqrt{\frac{625}{4}}$$ Find the square root of each side.

$$x + \frac{9}{2} = \pm\frac{25}{2}$$ Simplify.

$$x + \frac{9}{2} = \frac{25}{2} \quad \text{or} \quad x + \frac{9}{2} = -\frac{25}{2}$$ Write as two equations.

$$x = 8 \quad \text{or} \quad x = -17$$ Solve for x by subtracting $\frac{9}{2}$ from each side of the equations and simplifying.

CA Standards Check 2 Solve the equation $m^2 - 6m = 247$.

To solve an equation in the form $x^2 + bx + c = 0$, first subtract the constant term c from each side of the equation.

3 EXAMPLE Solving $x^2 + bx + c = 0$

Solve $x^2 - 20x + 32 = 0$.

Step 1 Rewrite the equation in the form $x^2 + bx = c$ and complete the square.

$$x^2 - 20x + 32 = 0$$

$$x^2 - 20x = -32$$ Subtract 32 from each side.

$$x^2 - 20x + 100 = -32 + 100$$ Add $\left(-\frac{20}{2}\right)^2$, or 100, to each side of the equation.

$$(x - 10)^2 = 68$$ Write $x^2 - 20x + 100$ as a square.

Step 2 Solve the equation.

$$(x - 10) = \pm\sqrt{68}$$ Find the square root of each side.

$$x - 10 \approx \pm 8.25$$ Approximate $\sqrt{68}$.

$$x - 10 \approx 8.25 \quad \text{or} \quad x - 10 \approx -8.25$$ Write as two equations.

$$x \approx 8.25 + 10 \quad \text{or} \quad x \approx -8.25 + 10$$ Add 10 to each side.

$$x \approx 18.25 \quad \text{or} \quad x \approx 1.75$$ Simplify.

CA Standards Check **3** Solve each equation. Round to the nearest hundredth.

a. $x^2 + 5x + 3 = 0$ **b.** $x^2 - 14x + 16 = 0$

The method of completing the square works when $a = 1$. To solve an equation like $3x^2 + 6x - 9 = 0$, you need to divide each side by 3 before completing the square.

$$3x^2 + 6x - 9 = 0 \rightarrow \frac{3x^2 + 6x - 9}{3} = \frac{0}{3} \rightarrow x^2 + 2x - 3 = 0$$

Video Tutor Help
Visit: PHSchool.com
Web Code: bae-0775

4 EXAMPLE Application

Suppose a woodworker wants to build a tabletop like the one shown at the right. If the surface area is 26 ft^2, what is the value of x?

x
1
1 x x x 1

Define width $= x + 1$

length $= x + x + x + 1 + 1 = 3x + 2$

Relate length × width = area

Write $(3x + 2)(x + 1) = 26$

$3x^2 + 5x + 2 = 26$

Step 1 Rewrite the equation in the form $x^2 + bx = c$.

$3x^2 + 5x + 2 = 26$

$3x^2 + 5x = 24$ **Subtract 2 from each side.**

$x^2 + \frac{5}{3}x = 8$ **Divide each side by 3.**

Step 2 Complete the square.

$x^2 + \frac{5}{3}x + \frac{25}{36} = 8 + \frac{25}{36}$ **Add $\left(\frac{5}{6}\right)^2$, or $\frac{25}{36}$, to each side.**

$\left(x + \frac{5}{6}\right)^2 = \frac{288}{36} + \frac{25}{36}$ **Write $x^2 + \frac{5}{3}x + \frac{25}{36}$ as a square. Rewrite 8 as a fraction with denominator 36.**

$\left(x + \frac{5}{6}\right)^2 = \frac{313}{36}$ **Simplify.**

Step 3 Solve the equation.

$\left(x + \frac{5}{6}\right) = \pm\sqrt{\frac{313}{36}}$ **Take the square root of each side.**

$x + \frac{5}{6} \approx \pm 2.95$ **Approximate. $\sqrt{\frac{313}{36}} \approx 2.95$**

$x + \frac{5}{6} \approx 2.95$ or $x + \frac{5}{6} \approx -2.95$ **Write as two equations.**

$x \approx 2.95 - \frac{5}{6}$ or $x \approx -2.95 - \frac{5}{6}$ **Subtract $\frac{5}{6}$ from each side.**

$x \approx 2.95 - 0.83$ or $x \approx -2.95 - 0.83$ **$\frac{5}{6} \approx 0.83$, so substitute 0.83 for $\frac{5}{6}$.**

$x \approx 2.12$ or $x \approx -3.78$ **Use the positive answer for this problem.**

The value of x is about 2.12 ft.

CA Standards Check **4** Solve each equation. Round to the nearest hundredth.

a. $4a^2 - 8a = 24$ **b.** $5n^2 - 3n - 15 = 10$

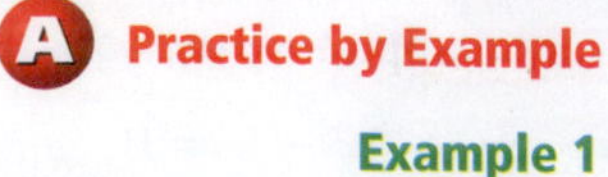

EXERCISES

For more exercises, see *Extra Skills and Word Problem Practice.*

Standards Practice

Alg1 14.0, 23.0

A Practice by Example

GO for Help

Example 1 (page 458)

Find the value of n such that each expression is a perfect square trinomial.

1. $k^2 + 14k + n$ **2.** $m^2 - 8m + n$ **3.** $y^2 - 40y + n$

4. $p^2 - 6p + n$ **5.** $v^2 + 24v + n$ **6.** $w^2 - 36w + n$

Example 2 (page 458)

Solve each equation by completing the square. If necessary, round to the nearest hundredth.

7. $r^2 + 8r = 48$ **8.** $x^2 - 10x = 40$ **9.** $q^2 + 22q = -85$

10. $m^2 + 6m = 9$ **11.** $r^2 + 20r = 261$ **12.** $g^2 - 2g = 323$

Example 3 (page 458)

13. $r^2 - 2r - 35 = 0$ **14.** $x^2 + 10x + 17 = 0$ **15.** $p^2 - 12p + 11 = 0$

16. $w^2 + 3w - 5 = 0$ **17.** $m^2 + m - 28 = 0$ **18.** $a^2 + 9a - 682 = 0$

Example 4 (page 459)

What term do you need to add to each side to complete the square?

19. $2k^2 + 4k = 10$ **20.** $3x^2 + 12x = 24$ **21.** $5t^2 + 9t = 15$

Solve each equation by completing the square. If necessary, round to the nearest hundredth.

22. $4y^2 + 8y - 36 = 0$ **23.** $3q^2 - 12q = 15$ **24.** $2x^2 - 10x - 20 = 8$

25. a. Write an expression for the total area of the model below.

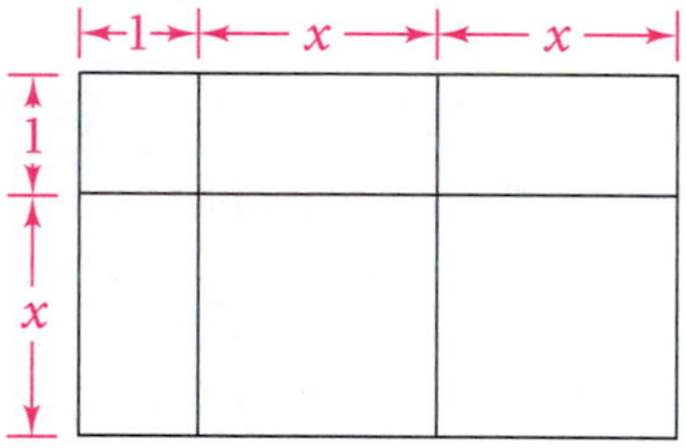

b. The total area is 28 square units. Write an equation to find x.

c. Solve by completing the square.

B Apply Your Skills

Solve each equation. If necessary, round to the nearest hundredth. If there is no solution, write *no solution*.

26. $b^2 + 4b + 1 = 0$ **27.** $c^2 + 7c = -12$ **28.** $h^2 + 6h - 40 = 0$

29. $y^2 - 8y = -12$ **30.** $4m^2 - 40m + 56 = 0$ **31.** $k^2 + 4k + 11 = -10$

32. $2x^2 - 15x + 6 = 41$ **33.** $3d^2 - 24d = 3$ **34.** $x^2 + 9x + 20 = 0$

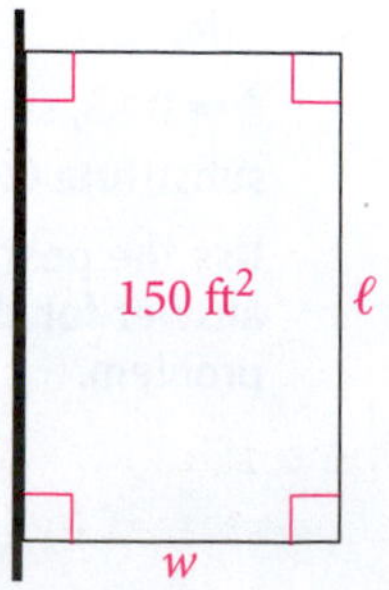

35. Suppose you want to enclose a rectangular garden plot against a house using fencing on three sides, as shown at the left. Assume you have 50 ft of fencing material and want to create a garden with an area of 150 ft^2.

a. Let w = the width. Write an expression for the length of the plot.

b. Write and solve an equation for the area of the plot. Round to the nearest tenth of a foot.

c. What dimensions should the garden have?

Visit: PHSchool.com
Web Code: bae-0906

36. Error Analysis A classmate was completing the square to solve $4x^2 + 10x = 0$. For her first step she wrote $4x^2 + 10x + 25 = 25$. What was her error?

37. Writing Explain to a classmate how to solve $x^2 + 30x - 1 = 0$ by completing the square.

38. Write a quadratic equation and solve it by completing the square. Show your work.

Use each graph to estimate the values of x for which $f(x) = 5$. Write and solve an equation to find the values of x such that $f(x) = 5$. Round to the nearest hundredth.

39. $f(x) = x^2 - 4x - 1$

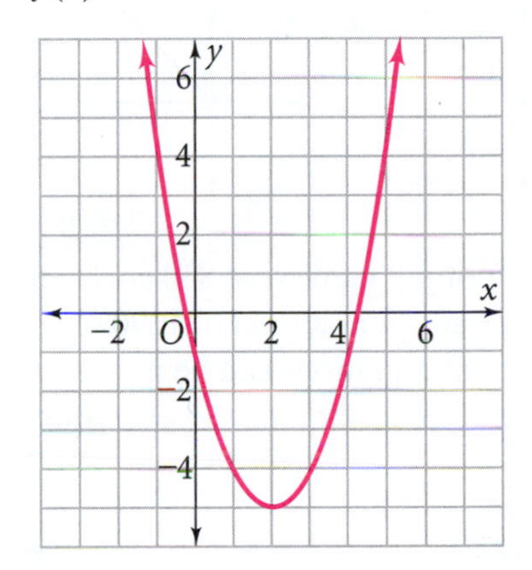

40. $f(x) = -\frac{1}{2}x^2 + 4x + 1$

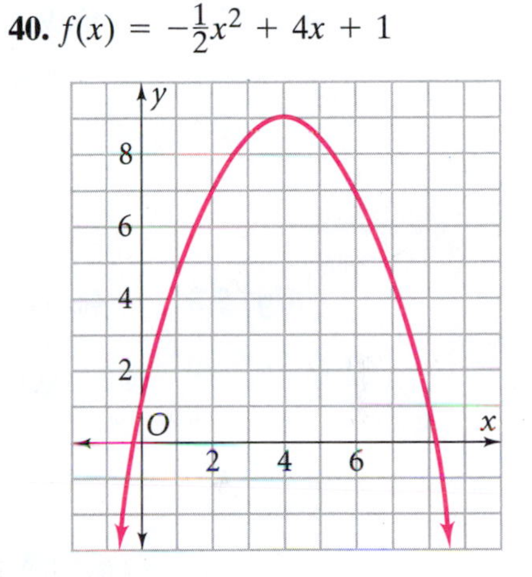

41. A rectangle has a length of x. Its width is 3 feet longer than twice the length. Find the dimensions if its area is 80 ft^2. Round to the nearest tenth of a foot.

Challenge

42. Suppose the prism shown at the right has the same surface area as an 8-in. cube.

a. Write an expression for the surface area of the prism shown at the right.

b. Write an equation that relates the surface area of the prism to the surface area of the 8-in. cube.

c. Solve the equation you wrote in part (b) to find the dimensions of the prism.

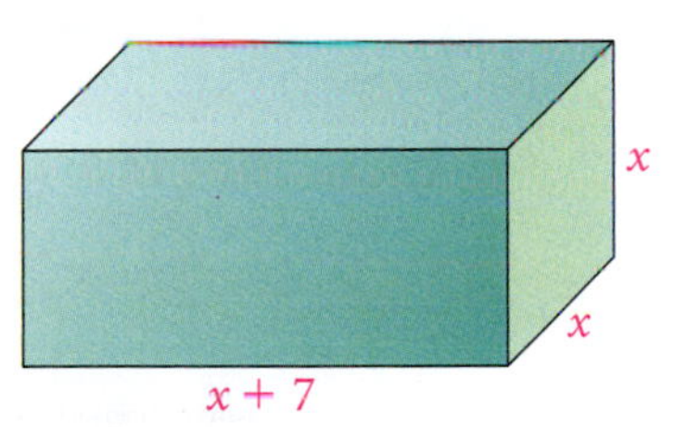

43. Suppose you want to design a patio like the one shown below.

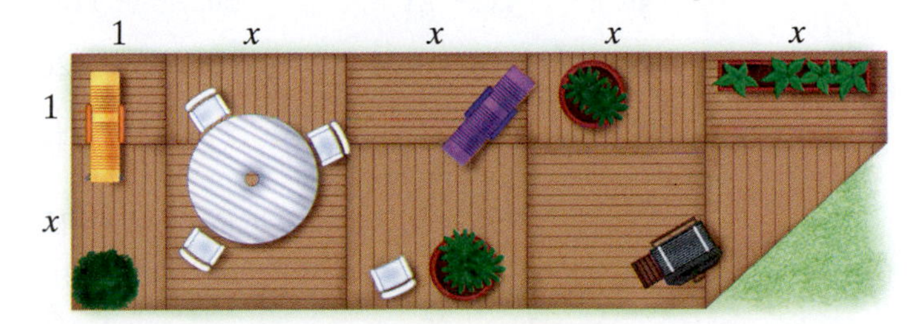

a. Write an expression for the total area.

b. If you want the total area to be 200 ft^2, what is the value of x?

c. If you rounded the value of x to the nearest integer, what would the total area be?

44. a. Solve the equation $x^2 - 6x + 4 = 0$, but leave your answers in the form $p \pm \sqrt{q}$.

b. Use the vertex formula $x = \frac{-b}{2a}$ to find the coordinates of the vertex of $y = x^2 - 6x + 4$.

c. Critical Thinking Explain the relationship between your answers in part (a) and part (b).

Multiple Choice Practice

For California Standards Tutorials, visit PHSchool.com. Web Code: baq-9045

Alg1 21.0

45. Which is the best representation of the function $y = x^2$?

(A) (B) (C) (D)

Alg1 9.0

46. Tickets to a football game cost \$40 each, and tickets to a basketball game cost \$25 each. Nathan spent a total of \$390 on 11 football and basketball tickets. Which system of equations can be used to find the number of football tickets f and the number of basketball tickets b that Nathan bought?

(A) $f + b = 11$
$40f + 25b = 390$

(B) $f + b = 11$
$65(f + b) = 390$

(C) $f - b = 11$
$40f + 25b = 390$

(D) $f - b = 11$
$65(f + b) = 390$

Alg1 14.0

47. Which values of b will make the expression $x^2 + bx + 100$ a perfect square trinomial?

(A) $-10, 10$

(B) $-20, 20$

(C) $-25, 25$

(D) $-50, 50$

Alg1 14.0

48. Which of the following is the sum of the solutions of $4x^2 - 35x - 9 = 0$?

(A) -8 (B) 8 (C) 8.75 (D) 9.25

Mixed Review

GO for Help

Lesson 9-5

Solve each equation.

49. $x^2 - 4x - 21 = 0$ **50.** $n^2 + 11n + 30 = 0$ **51.** $t^2 - 5t = 0$

52. $9v^2 - 64 = 0$ **53.** $4c^2 + 12c = -9$ **54.** $12w^2 = 28w + 5$

Lesson 8-7

Factor each expression.

55. $x^2 + 4x + 4$ **56.** $t^2 - 22t + 121$ **57.** $b^2 - 25$

58. $16c^2 + 24c + 9$ **59.** $49s^2 - 169$ **60.** $8m^3 - 18m$

61. $25m^2 + 120m + 144$ **62.** $400k^2 - 9$ **63.** $256g^2 - 121$

Lesson 7-4

Simplify.

64. $(r^3)^4$ **65.** $p(p^2)^6$ **66.** $-y^3(y^{-1})^2$

67. $(m^5)^{-8}$ **68.** $-w^7(w^8)^{-1}$ **69.** $t^8(t^{-7})^{-3}$

9-7 Using the Quadratic Formula

California Content Standards

19.0 Know the quadratic formula and are familiar with its proof by completing the square. ***Introduce, Develop, Master***

20.0 Use the quadratic formula to find the roots of a second-degree polynomial and to solve quadratic equations. ***Introduce, Develop***

23.0 Apply quadratic equations to physical problems. ***Develop***

What You'll Learn

- To use the quadratic formula to solve quadratic equations
- To choose an appropriate method for solving a quadratic equation

. . . And Why

To solve sports problems, as in Example 3

Check Skills You'll Need

GO for Help Lesson 9-6

Find the value of c to complete the square for each expression.

1. $x^2 + 6x + c$ **2.** $x^2 + 7x + c$ **3.** $x^2 - 9x + c$

Solve each equation by completing the square.

4. $x^2 - 10x + 24 = 0$ **5.** $x^2 + 16x - 36 = 0$

6. $3x^2 + 12x - 15 = 0$ **7.** $2x^2 - 2x - 112 = 0$

New Vocabulary • quadratic formula

Using the Quadratic Formula

The path of a golf ball can be modeled with a quadratic function.

In Lesson 9-6, you solved quadratic equations by completing the square. If you complete the square of the general equation $ax^2 + bx + c = 0$, you can derive the **quadratic formula,** which will solve any quadratic equation.

Step 1 Write $ax^2 + bx + c = 0$ so the coefficient of x^2 is 1.

$$ax^2 + bx + c = 0$$

$$x^2 + \frac{b}{a}x + \frac{c}{a} = 0 \quad \text{Divide each side by } a.$$

Step 2 Complete the square.

$$x^2 + \frac{b}{a}x = -\frac{c}{a} \quad \text{Subtract } \tfrac{c}{a} \text{ from each side.}$$

$$x^2 + \frac{b}{a}x + \left(\frac{b}{2a}\right)^2 = -\frac{c}{a} + \left(\frac{b}{2a}\right)^2 \quad \text{Add } \left(\tfrac{b}{2a}\right)^2 \text{ to each side.}$$

$$\left(x + \frac{b}{2a}\right)^2 = -\frac{c}{a} + \left(\frac{b}{2a}\right)^2 \quad \text{Write the trinomial as a perfect square.}$$

$$= -\frac{4ac}{4a^2} + \frac{b^2}{4a^2} \quad \text{Multiply } -\tfrac{c}{a} \text{ by } \tfrac{4a}{4a} \text{ to get like denominators, and simplify } \left(\tfrac{b}{2a}\right)^2.$$

$$= \frac{b^2 - 4ac}{4a^2} \quad \text{Simplify the right side.}$$

Step 3 Solve the equation.

$$\sqrt{\left(x + \frac{b}{2a}\right)^2} = \sqrt{\frac{b^2 - 4ac}{4a^2}} \quad \text{Take the square root of each side.}$$

$$x + \frac{b}{2a} = \pm\frac{\sqrt{b^2 - 4ac}}{2a} \quad \text{Simplify the right side. } \tfrac{1}{\sqrt{4a^2}} = \pm\tfrac{1}{2a}$$

$$x = -\frac{b}{2a} \pm \frac{\sqrt{b^2 - 4ac}}{2a} \quad \text{Subtract } \tfrac{b}{2a} \text{ from each side.}$$

$$x = \frac{-b \pm \sqrt{b^2 - 4ac}}{2a} \quad \text{Simplify.}$$

Take Note

Rule — **Quadratic Formula**

If $ax^2 + bx + c = 0$, a, b, and c are real numbers, and $a \neq 0$, then

$$x = \frac{-b \pm \sqrt{b^2 - 4ac}}{2a}$$

Be sure to write a quadratic equation in standard form before using the quadratic formula.

1 EXAMPLE Using the Quadratic Formula

GO Online

Video Tutor Help
Visit: PHSchool.com
Web Code: bae-0775

Solve $x^2 + 6 = 5x$.

$x^2 - 5x + 6 = 0$ — Subtract $5x$ from each side and write in standard form.

$x = \frac{-b \pm \sqrt{b^2 - 4ac}}{2a}$ — Use the quadratic formula.

$x = \frac{-(-5) \pm \sqrt{(-5)^2 - (4)(1)(6)}}{2(1)}$ — The coefficient of x^2 is 1. Substitute 1 for a, -5 for b, and 6 for c.

$x = \frac{5 \pm \sqrt{1}}{2}$ — Simplify $-(-5)$ and the radicand.

$x = \frac{5 + 1}{2}$ or $x = \frac{5 - 1}{2}$ — Write as two equations.

$x = 3$ or $x = 2$ — Simplify.

Check Substitute 3 for x.

$(3)^2 + 6 \overset{?}{=} 5(3)$

$9 + 6 \overset{?}{=} 15$

$15 = 15$ ✓

Substitute 2 for x.

$(2)^2 + 6 \overset{?}{=} 5(2)$

$4 + 6 \overset{?}{=} 10$

$10 = 10$ ✓

CA Standards Check 1 Use the quadratic formula to solve each equation.

a. $x^2 - 2x - 8 = 0$ **b.** $x^2 - 4x = 117$

Vocabulary Tip

The radicand is the quantity inside the radical symbol. The radicand of $\sqrt{b^2 - 4ac}$ is $b^2 - 4ac$.

When the radicand in the quadratic formula is not a perfect square, you can use a calculator to approximate the solutions of an equation.

2 EXAMPLE Finding Approximate Solutions

Solve $2x^2 + 4x - 7 = 0$. Round the solutions to the nearest hundredth.

$x = \frac{-b \pm \sqrt{b^2 - 4ac}}{2a}$ — Use the quadratic formula.

$x = \frac{-4 \pm \sqrt{4^2 - (4)(2)(-7)}}{2(2)}$ — Substitute 2 for a, 4 for b, and -7 for c.

$x = \frac{-4 \pm \sqrt{72}}{4}$

$x = \frac{-4 + \sqrt{72}}{4}$ or $x = \frac{-4 - \sqrt{72}}{4}$ — Write as two equations.

$x \approx \frac{-4 + 8.49}{4}$ or $x \approx \frac{-4 - 8.49}{4}$ — Approximate. $\sqrt{72} \approx 8.49$

$x \approx 1.12$ or $x \approx -3.12$ — Simplify. Round to the nearest hundredth.

CA Standards Check 2 Solve each equation. Round to the nearest hundredth.

a. $-3x^2 + 5x - 2 = 0$ **b.** $7x^2 - 2x - 8 = 0$

You can use the quadratic formula to solve real-world problems. You must decide whether a solution makes sense in the real-world situation. For example, a negative value for time would not be a reasonable solution in most situations.

3 EXAMPLE Application

Suppose a football player kicks a ball and gives it an initial upward velocity of 47 ft/s. The starting height of the football is 3 ft. If no one catches the football, how long will it be in the air?

Step 1 Use the vertical motion formula.

$h = -16t^2 + vt + c$ — The initial upward velocity is v, and the starting height is c.

$0 = -16t^2 + 47t + 3$ — Substitute 0 for h, 47 for v, and 3 for c.

Step 2 Use the quadratic formula.

$$x = \frac{-b \pm \sqrt{b^2 - 4ac}}{2a}$$

$$t = \frac{-47 \pm \sqrt{(47)^2 - (4)(-16)(3)}}{2(-16)}$$ Substitute −16 for a, 47 for b, 3 for c, and t for x.

$$t = \frac{-47 \pm \sqrt{2209 + 192}}{-32}$$ Simplify.

$$t = \frac{-47 \pm \sqrt{2401}}{-32}$$

$$t = \frac{-47 + 49}{-32} \quad \text{or} \quad t = \frac{-47 - 49}{-32}$$ Write as two equations.

$$t \approx -0.06 \quad \text{or} \quad t = 3$$ Simplify. Use the positive answer because it is the only reasonable answer in this situation.

The football will be in the air for 3 seconds.

CA Standards Check 3 A football player kicks a ball with an initial upward velocity of 38.4 ft/s from a starting height of 3.5 ft.

a. Substitute the values into the vertical motion formula. Let $h = 0$.

b. Solve. If no one catches the ball, how long will it be in the air? Round to the nearest tenth of a second.

Choosing an Appropriate Method

There are many methods for solving a quadratic equation. You can always use the quadratic formula, but sometimes another method may be easier.

Method	When to Use
Graphing	Use if the equation has the form $y = ax^2$ or $y = ax^2 + c$.
Square Roots	Use if the equation has no x term.
Factoring	Use if you can factor the equation easily.
Completing the Square	Use if the coefficient of the x^2 term is 1, but you cannot factor the equation easily.
Quadratic Formula	Use if the equation cannot be factored easily or at all.

4 EXAMPLE Choosing an Appropriate Method

Which method(s) would you choose to solve each equation? Justify your reasoning.

a. $2x^2 - 6 = 0$ — Square roots; there is no x term.

b. $6x^2 + 13x - 17 = 0$ — Quadratic formula; the equation cannot be factored easily.

c. $x^2 + 2x - 15 = 0$ — Factoring; the equation is easily factorable.

d. $16x^2 - 96x + 45 = 0$ — Quadratic formula; the equation cannot be factored easily, and the numbers are large.

e. $x^2 - 7x + 4 = 0$ — Quadratic formula, completing the square, or graphing; the coefficient of the x^2 term is 1, but the equation is not factorable.

CA Standards Check 4 Which method(s) would you choose to solve each equation? Justify your reasoning.

a. $13x^2 - 5x + 21 = 0$ **b.** $x^2 - x - 30 = 0$ **c.** $144x^2 = 25$

EXERCISES Standards Practice

For more exercises, see *Extra Skills and Word Problem Practice*.

Alg1 19.0, 20.0, 23.0

A Practice by Example

Example 1 (page 464)

GO for Help

Use the quadratic formula to solve each equation. If necessary, round answers to the nearest hundredth.

1. $2x^2 + 5x + 3 = 0$ **2.** $5x^2 + 16x - 84 = 0$ **3.** $4x^2 - 12x + 9 = 0$

4. $3x^2 + 47x = -30$ **5.** $12x^2 - 77x - 20 = 0$ **6.** $3x^2 + 39x + 108 = 0$

7. $3x^2 + 40x - 128 = 0$ **8.** $2x^2 - 9x - 221 = 0$ **9.** $5x^2 - 68x = 192$

Example 2 (page 464)

10. $5x^2 + 13x - 1 = 0$ **11.** $2x^2 - 24x + 33 = 0$ **12.** $7x^2 + 100x - 4 = 0$

13. $8x^2 - 3x - 7 = 0$ **14.** $6x^2 + 5x - 40 = 0$ **15.** $3x^2 - 11x - 2 = 0$

Example 3 (page 465)

For Exercises 16 and 17, use the vertical motion formula $h = -16t^2 + vt + c$.

16. A ball is tossed upward with a starting velocity of 10 ft/s from a height of 3 ft.
a. Substitute the values into the vertical motion formula. Let $h = 0$.
b. Solve. If it is not caught, how long will the ball be in the air? Round to the nearest tenth of a second.

17. A soccer ball is kicked with a starting upward velocity of 50 ft/s from a starting height of 3.5 ft.
a. Substitute the values into the vertical motion formula. Let $h = 0$.
b. Solve. If no one touches the ball, how long will the ball be in the air? Round to the nearest tenth of a second.

Example 4 (page 466)

Which method(s) would you choose to solve each equation? Justify your reasoning.

18. $x^2 + 2x - 13 = 0$ **19.** $4x^2 - 81 = 0$ **20.** $9x^2 - 31x = 51$

21. $3x^2 - 5x + 9 = 0$ **22.** $x^2 + 4x - 60 = 0$ **23.** $-4x^2 + 3x + 2 = 0$

B Apply Your Skills

Use any method you choose to solve each equation. If necessary, round to the nearest hundredth.

24. $2t^2 = 72$ **25.** $3x^2 + 2x - 4 = 0$ **26.** $5b^2 - 10 = 0$

27. $3x^2 + 4x = 10$ **28.** $m^2 - 4m = -4$ **29.** $13n^2 - 117 = 0$

30. $3s^2 - 4s = 2$ **31.** $5b^2 - 2b - 7 = 0$ **32.** $15x^2 - 12x - 48 = 0$

For a guide to solving Exercise 33, see p. 469.

33. Suppose you throw a ball upward with a starting velocity of 30 ft/s. The ball is 6 ft high when it leaves your hand. After how many seconds will it hit the ground? Use the vertical motion formula $h = -16t^2 + vt + c$.

34. Suppose a rectangle has an area of 60 ft^2 and dimensions x and $(x + 1)$.

a. Estimate each dimension of the rectangle to the nearest integer.

b. Write a quadratic equation and use the quadratic formula to find each dimension to the nearest hundredth.

35. Writing Compare the way you solve the linear equation $mx + b = 0$ with the way you solve the quadratic equation $ax^2 + bx + c = 0$.

Find the base and height of each triangle below. If necessary, round to the nearest hundredth.

36. **37.**

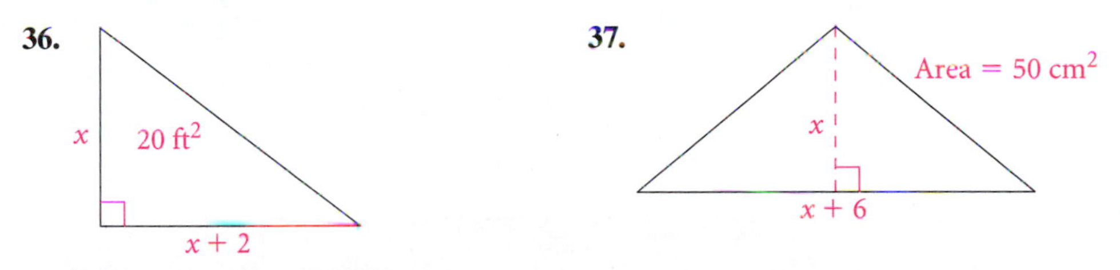

Visit: PHSchool.com
Web Code: bae-0907

38. Write a problem that you can solve using a quadratic equation in which you find the area of a rectangle. Draw a diagram and solve.

39. Critical Thinking How you can tell from the quadratic formula that a quadratic equation has one solution? Explain.

40. Refer to the cartoon. Suppose the man's starting upward velocity v is 5 ft/s. Use $0 = -16t^2 + vt + c$, where c is the starting height. Find the number of seconds t before he hits the water.

Ⓐ about 1.6 s
Ⓑ about 1.9 s
Ⓒ about 3.0 s
Ⓓ about 3.2 s

CLOSE TO HOME by John McPherson

THERE ARE TIMES WHEN BEING A WHIZ AT PHYSICS CAN BE A DEFINITE DRAWBACK.

C Challenge

41. The function below models the United States population P in millions since 1900, where t is the number of years after 1900.

$P = 0.0089t^2 + 1.1149t + 78.4491$

a. Use the function to estimate the United States population the year you graduate from high school.

b. Estimate the United States population in 2025.

42. **Critical Thinking** The two solutions of any quadratic equation are $\frac{-b + \sqrt{b^2 - 4ac}}{2a}$ and $\frac{-b - \sqrt{b^2 - 4ac}}{2a}$.

a. Find a formula for the sum of the solutions.

b. One solution of $2x^2 + 3x - 104 = 0$ is -8. Use the formula you found in part (a) to find the second solution.

Multiple Choice Practice

For California Standards Tutorials, visit PHSchool.com. Web Code: baq-9045

Alg1 17.0

43. Which of the following is NOT in the range of $y = x^2 - 6$?

(A) -8 (B) -6 (C) -2 (D) 0

Alg1 7.0

44. The graph of the line shown at the right contains the points $(-4, 1)$ and $(2, -2)$. If the slope of this line were doubled while the y-intercept remained fixed, which point would lie on the new line?

(A) $(4, -4)$
(B) $(-2, 0)$
(C) $(-3, 2)$
(D) $(1, -1.5)$

Alg1 20.0

45. Which equation does $\frac{9 \pm \sqrt{(-9)^2 - 4(5)(-7)}}{2(5)}$ give the solutions to?

(A) $-9x + 5x = -7$
(B) $5x^2 - 9x = -7$
(C) $5x^2 + 7x = 9$
(D) $5x^2 - 9x = 7$

Mixed Review

GO for Help

Lesson 9-6

Solve each equation by completing the square. If necessary, round to the nearest hundredth.

46. $d^2 - 10d + 13 = 0$
47. $z^2 + 3z = -2$
48. $3x^2 + 18x - 1 = 0$

Lesson 8-8

Factor by grouping.

49. $2c^2 + 11c + 15$
50. $3z^2 + 10z - 8$
51. $5n^2 - 33n - 14$
52. $12v^2 + 32v - 35$
53. $6x^2 - 13x + 5$
54. $15t^2 + 19t + 6$

Checkpoint Quiz 2

Lessons 9-5 through 9-7

Solve each equation. If necessary, round to the nearest tenth. If there is no solution, write *no solution*.

1. $(x + 3)(x - 7) = 0$
2. $x^2 + 12x + 27 = 0$
3. $x^2 - 5x = 50$
4. $x^2 + 2x - 1 = 0$
5. $x^2 - 5x - 4 = 0$
6. $x^2 - 8x - 33 = 0$
7. $4x^2 - x - 3 = 0$
8. $4x^2 - x + 3 = 0$
9. $2x^2 - 3x + 1 = 0$

10. Kevin's office cubicle measures 8 ft by 12 ft.

a. Write an equation to find the amount x that should be added to the current length and width to double the area.

b. Solve the equation. What will the new dimensions be?

GPS Guided Problem Solving

FOR USE WITH PAGE 467, EXERCISE 33

20.0 Use the quadratic formula to solve quadratic equations. ***Master***
23.0 Apply quadratic equations to physical problems. ***Develop***

Understanding Word Problems **Read the exercise below and then follow along with what Hannah thinks and writes. Check your understanding with the exercise at the bottom of the page.**

Suppose you throw a ball in the air with a starting upward velocity of 30 ft/s. The ball is 6 ft high when it leaves your hand. After how many seconds will it hit the ground? Use the vertical motion formula $h = -16t^2 + vt + c$.

What Hannah Thinks	What Hannah Writes
First, I'll write the values from the word problem and the vertical motion formula.	starting upward velocity = 30 ft/s starting height = 6 ft $h = -16t^2 + vt + c$
Next, I will substitute the starting upward velocity and the initial height into the formula.	$h = -16t^2 + 30t + 6$
When the ball hits the ground, the height will be zero. So h is zero.	$0 = -16t^2 + 30t + 6$
I can use the quadratic formula to solve the equation. I'll write the quadratic formula and the values of a, b, and c.	$x = \frac{-b \pm \sqrt{b^2 - 4ac}}{2a}$ $a = -16 \quad b = 30 \quad c = 6$
I'll substitute t for x and substitute the values of a, b, and c into the quadratic formula. Then I simplify to find t when h equals zero.	$t = \frac{-30 \pm \sqrt{30^2 - (4(-16)(6))}}{2(-16)}$ $= \frac{-30 \pm \sqrt{900 - (-384)}}{-32}$ $t = \frac{-30 \pm \sqrt{1284}}{-32}$ $t \approx 2.1$ or $t \approx -0.2$
Only the positive answer makes sense because I solved for time. So I'll write the positive answer with the units.	about 2.1 seconds

EXERCISE

Find the base and height of the triangle. If necessary, round to the nearest hundredth.

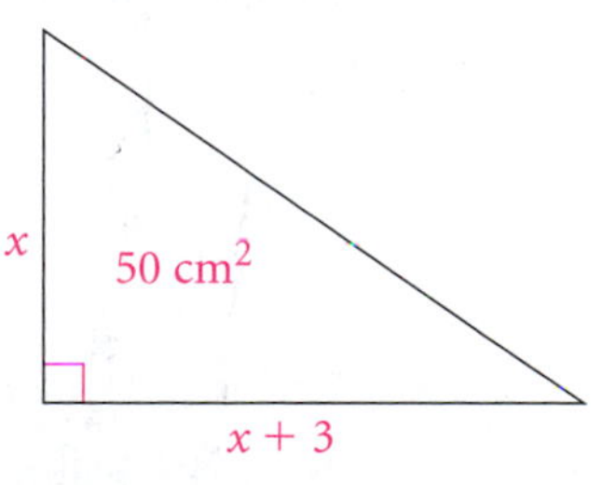

9-8 Using the Discriminant

CALIFORNIA CHECK SYSTEM

California Content Standards

22.0 Determine whether the graph of a quadratic function will intersect the x-axis in zero, one, or two points. ***Introduce, Develop, Master***

23.0 Apply quadratic equations to physical problems. ***Master***

What You'll Learn

- To find the number of times the graph of a quadratic function will intersect the x-axis and the number of solutions of a quadratic equation

. . . And Why

To solve physics problems, as in Example 2

Check Skills You'll Need

Evaluate $b^2 - 4ac$ for the given values of a, b, and c.

1. $a = 3, b = 4, c = 8$ **2.** $a = -2, b = 0, c = 9$ **3.** $a = 11, b = -5, c = 7$

Solve using the quadratic formula. If necessary, round to the nearest hundredth.

4. $3x^2 - 7x + 1 = 0$ **5.** $4x^2 + x - 1 = 0$ **6.** $x^2 - 12x + 35 = 0$

New Vocabulary • discriminant

Number of Real Solutions and x-intercepts

Quadratic equations can have two, one, or no solutions. You can determine how many solutions a quadratic equation has, before you solve it, by using the discriminant. The **discriminant** is the expression under the radical in the quadratic formula.

$$x = \frac{-b \pm \sqrt{b^2 - 4ac}}{2a} \quad \leftarrow \text{the discriminant}$$

Consider the graphs and discriminants of the functions below.

	$y = x^2 - 6x + 3$	$y = x^2 - 6x + 9$	$y = x^2 - 6x + 12$
	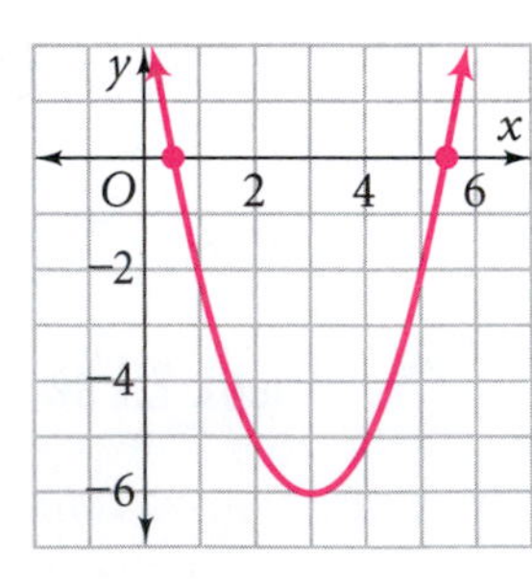	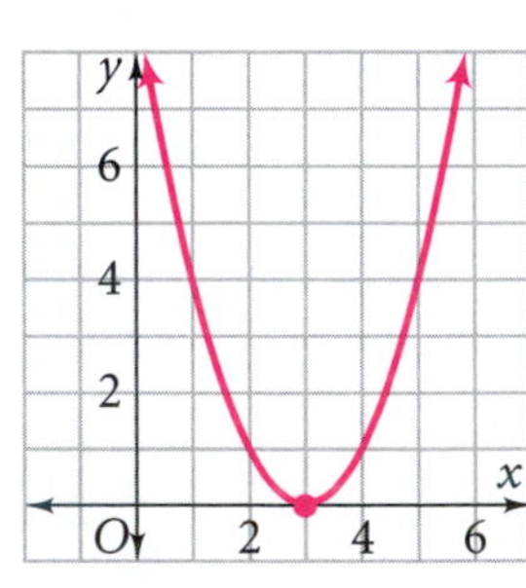	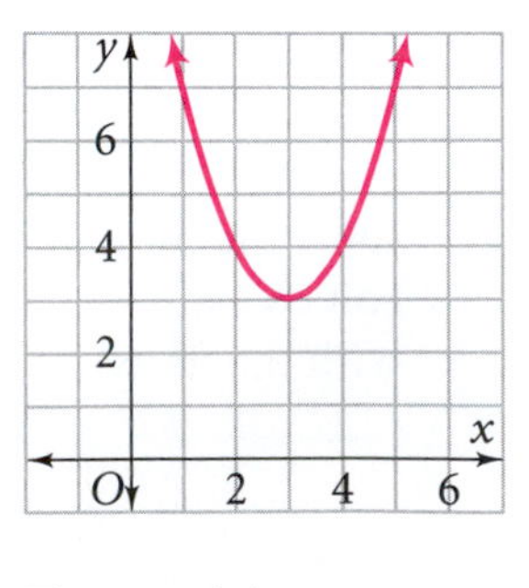
	The graph has two x-intercepts.	The graph has one x-intercept.	The graph has no x-intercepts.
	$x^2 - 6x + 3 = 0$	$x^2 - 6x + 9 = 0$	$x^2 - 6x + 12 = 0$
$b^2 - 4ac$:	$(-6)^2 - 4(1)(3)$	$(-6)^2 - 4(1)(9)$	$(-6)^2 - 4(1)(12)$
	$= 36 - 12$	$= 36 - 36$	$= 36 - 48$
	$= 24$	$= 0$	$= -12$

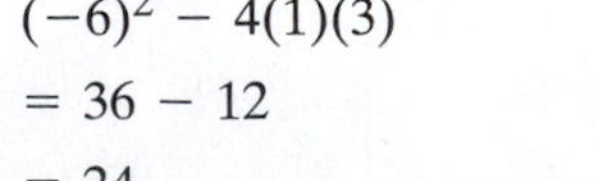

The relationship you see between the graphs and discriminants above is true for all cases. If the discriminant is positive, there are two solutions. If the discriminant is zero, there is one solution. If the discriminant is negative, there are no solutions.

Take Note

Property **Property of the Discriminant**

For real numbers a, b, and c, where $a \neq 0$, the quadratic function is $y = ax^2 + bx + c$, and its related quadratic equation is $ax^2 + bx + c = 0$.

If $b^2 - 4ac > 0$, then

- the graph of the quadratic function intersects the x-axis in two points
- the related quadratic equation has two solutions

If $b^2 - 4ac = 0$, then

- the graph of the quadratic function intersects the x-axis in one point
- the related quadratic equation has one solution

If $b^2 - 4ac < 0$, then

- the graph of the quadratic function intersects the x-axis in zero points
- the related quadratic equation has no solutions

1 EXAMPLE Finding the Number of x-intercepts

Determine whether the graph of $y = 4x^2 - 12x + 9$ intersects the x-axis in zero, one, or two points.

Method 1 Use the discriminant.

$b^2 - 4ac = (-12)^2 - (4)(4)(9)$ **Evaluate the discriminant. Substitute for *a*, *b*, and *c*.**

$= 144 - 144$ **Use the order of operations.**

$= 0$ **Simplify.**

Since the discriminant is 0, the graph intersects the x-axis in one point.

Method 2 Factor.

$4x^2 - 12x + 9 = 0$ **Set the expression equal to zero.**

$(2x - 3)^2 = 0$ **Factor.**

$2x - 3 = 0$ **Use the Zero-Product Property.**

$x = \frac{3}{2}$ **Solve for *x*.**

The function has one zero, so the graph intersects the x-axis in one point.

CA Standards Check 1 Determine whether the graph of $y = 3x^2 + 6x - 7$ intersects the x-axis in zero, one, or two points.

2 EXAMPLE Finding the Number of Solutions

Find the number of solutions of $3x^2 - 5x = 1$.

$3x^2 - 5x - 1 = 0$ **Write in standard form.**

$b^2 - 4ac = (-5)^2 - (4)(3)(-1)$ **Evaluate the discriminant. Substitute for *a*, *b*, and *c*.**

$= 25 - (-12)$ **Use the order of operations.**

$= 37$ **Simplify.**

Since $37 > 0$, the equation has two solutions.

CA Standards Check 2 Find the number of solutions of $3x^2 - 4x = 7$.

You can use the discriminant to solve real-world problems.

3 EXAMPLE Application

A construction worker on the ground tosses an apple to a fellow worker who is 20 ft above the ground. The starting height of the apple is 5 ft. Its initial upward velocity is 30 ft/s. Will the apple reach the second worker?

$h = -16t^2 + vt + c$	Use the vertical motion formula.
$20 = -16t^2 + 30t + 5$	Substitute 20 for *h*, 30 for *v*, and 5 for *c*.
$0 = -16t^2 + 30t - 15$	Write in standard form.
$b^2 - 4ac = (30)^2 - 4(-16)(-15)$	Evaluate the discriminant.
$= 900 - 960$	Use the order of operations.
$= -60$	Simplify.

The discriminant is negative. The apple will not reach the second worker.

CA Standards Check 3 Suppose the same construction worker tosses an apple with an initial upward velocity of 32 ft/s. Will the apple reach the second worker?

EXERCISES

For more exercises, see *Extra Skills and Word Problem Practice.*

Standards Practice

Alg1 22.0, 23.0, 25.3

A Practice by Example

Example 1 (page 471)

GO for Help

For which discriminant is each graph possible?

1.

2.

3.

A. $b^2 - 4ac = 4$ **B.** $b^2 - 4ac = 0$ **C.** $b^2 - 4ac = -4$

Use the discriminant or factoring techniques to determine whether the graph of each quadratic function intersects the *x*-axis in zero, one, or two points.

4. $y = x^2 - 6x + 5$ **5.** $y = x^2 + 3x + 5$ **6.** $y = x^2 + 4x + 4$

7. $y = x^2 - 2x - 3$ **8.** $y = 6x^2 + x - 2$ **9.** $y = 4x^2 + 7x - 15$

10. $y = 2x^2 + 4x$ **11.** $y = 3x^2 - 2x + 8$ **12.** $y = 9x^2 - 6x + 1$

Example 2 (page 471)

Find the number of solutions of each equation.

13. $x^2 - 3x + 4 = 0$ **14.** $x^2 - 6x + 9 = 0$ **15.** $x^2 + 4x - 2 = 0$

16. $x^2 - 1 = 0$ **17.** $x^2 + x = 0$ **18.** $2x^2 - 3x + 4 = 0$

19. $x^2 - 7x + 6 = 0$ **20.** $x^2 + 2x + 1 = 0$ **21.** $0 = x^2 + 2x + 9$

Example 3 (page 472)

22. The Reeves family's garden is 18 ft long and 15 ft wide. They want to decrease the length by *x* feet and increase the width by the same amount. The equation $A = (18 - x)(15 + x)$ models the new area of the garden. What value of *x*, if any, will give a new area of 280 ft^2?

Visit: PHSchool.com
Web Code: bae-0908

23. An apartment rental agency uses the formula $I = 5400 + 300n - 50n^2$ to find its monthly income I based on renting n apartments. Will the agency's monthly income ever reach \$7000? Explain.

24. Suppose the equation $h = -16t^2 + 35t$ models the altitude a football will reach t seconds after it is kicked. Is the given altitude possible?
a. $h = 16$ ft **b.** $h = 20$ ft **c.** $h = 30$ ft **d.** $h = 35$ ft

B Apply Your Skills

Find the number of x-intercepts of the related function of each equation.

25. $2x^2 + 4x = -15$ **26.** $4x^2 + 5x = -2$ **27.** $x^2 - 8x = -12$

28. $\frac{1}{2}x^2 + 4x = 7$ **29.** $0.25x^2 - 1.2x + 3.2 = 0$ **30.** $5x^2 = 3.5 + 4.7x$

31. A software company is producing a new computer application. The equation $S = p(54 - 0.75p)$ relates price p in dollars to total sales S in thousands of dollars.
a. Write the equation in standard form.
b. Use the discriminant to determine if it is possible for the company to earn \$1,000,000 in sales.
c. According to the model, what price would generate the greatest sales?

32. Math Reasoning For the equation $x^2 + 4x + k = 0$, find all values of k such that the equation has the given number of solutions.
a. none **b.** one **c.** two

33. The function $P = 3i^2 - 2i + 450$ models the power P in an electric circuit with a current i. Can the power in this circuit ever be zero? If so, what is the value of i?

34. Error Analysis Kenji claimed that the discriminant of $2x^2 + 5x - 1 = 0$ was 17. What error did he make?

35. Find the value of the discriminant and the solutions of each equation. If necessary, round to the nearest hundredth.
a. $x^2 - 6x + 5 = 0$ **b.** $x^2 + x - 20 = 0$ **c.** $2x^2 - 7x - 3 = 0$
d. Reasoning When the discriminant is a perfect square, are the solutions rational or irrational? Explain.

Does the graph of each function cross the x-axis? If so, find the x-intercepts.

36. $y = x^2 - 2x + 5$ **37.** $y = 2x^2 - 4x + 3$ **38.** $y = 4x^2 + x - 5$

39. $y = -3x^2 - x + 2$ **40.** $y = x^2 - 5x + 7$ **41.** $y = 2x^2 - 3x - 5$

42. Writing How can you use the discriminant to write an equation that has two solutions?

C Challenge

Math Reasoning For each condition given, tell whether $ax^2 + bx + c = 0$ will have two solutions *sometimes*, *always*, or *never*.

43. $b^2 < 4ac$ **44.** $b^2 = 0$ **45.** $ac < 0$

46. Critical Thinking The graph of a quadratic equation includes the points $(2, -1)$ and $(3, 2)$. How many solutions does the related equation have? Explain.

47. Critical Thinking The discriminant of $0 = 2x^2 + 6x + 7$ is -20. The discriminant of $0 = 2x^2 + 8x + 10$ is -16. Without graphing, determine which related function has a vertex closer to the x-axis. Explain.

Multiple Choice Practice

For California Standards Tutorials, visit PHSchool.com. Web Code: baq-9045

Alg1 21.0

48. If the graph of $y = x^2 + 16$ were shifted down 2 units, which equation could represent the shifted graph?

Ⓐ $y = x^2 + 2$ Ⓑ $y = x^2 + 4$ Ⓒ $y = x^2 + 8$ Ⓓ $y = x^2 + 14$

Alg1 6.0

49. Where does the graph of $4x - 2y = 3$ intersect the x-axis?

Ⓐ $x = -\frac{3}{2}$ Ⓑ $x = -\frac{3}{4}$ Ⓒ $x = \frac{3}{4}$ Ⓓ $x = \frac{3}{2}$

Alg1 6.0

50. Which graph represents the equation $x - 2y = 4$?

Ⓐ Ⓑ Ⓒ Ⓓ

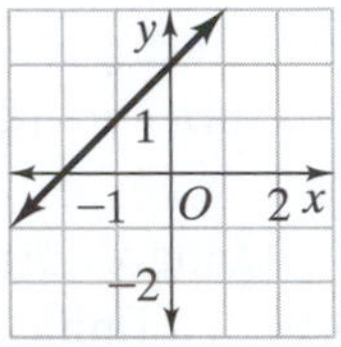

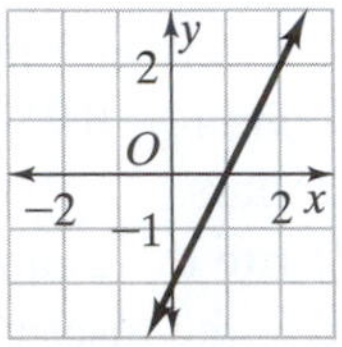

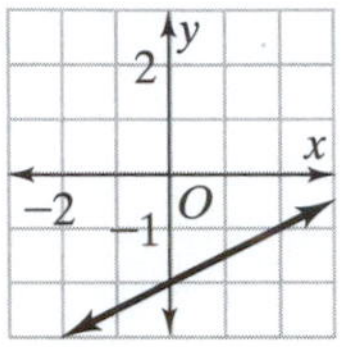

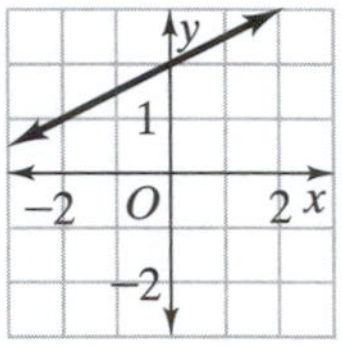

Alg1 22.0

51. Which of the following equations has NO real-number solutions?

Ⓐ $3x^2 - 5x + 1 = 0$
Ⓑ $-3x^2 - 11x + 4 = 0$
Ⓒ $3x^2 - 5x + 4 = 0$
Ⓓ $-2x^2 - 3x + 1 = 0$

Alg1 21.0

52. The table at the right shows x- and y-values for a given quadratic function. Based on the table, which of the following statements is NOT true?

Ⓐ The related equation has a solution between 0 and 1.
Ⓑ The parabola opens upward.
Ⓒ The related equation has more than one solution.
Ⓓ The maximum y-value of the function is 1.

x	y
−1	−7
0	−1
1	1
2	−1
3	−7

Alg1 14.0

53. Which of the following is a solution of $(2n - 5)(10n + 3) = 0$?

Ⓐ −3 Ⓑ 0.3 Ⓒ 0 Ⓓ 2.5

Mixed Review

GO for Help

Lesson 9-7

Use the quadratic formula to solve each equation. If necessary, round to the nearest hundredth.

54. $4x^2 + 4x - 3 = 0$ **55.** $x^2 + 2x - 7 = 0$ **56.** $6x^2 - 2x - 1 = 0$

57. $x^2 + x = 5$ **58.** $3x^2 - 8x + 1 = 0$ **59.** $2x^2 - 7x = -6$

Lesson 9-6

Solve by completing the square. If there is no solution, write *no solution.*

60. $x^2 + 12x + 1 = 0$ **61.** $x^2 + 6x + 20 = 0$

62. $x^2 + 8x = 11$ **63.** $x^2 + 7x + 1 = 13$

64. $2x^2 + 8x + 7 = 9$ **65.** $x^2 - 18x + 65 = 0$

Lesson 8-7

Factor each expression.

66. $n^2 - 400$ **67.** $x^2 - 30x + 225$

68. $100p^2 - 49$ **69.** $\frac{1}{2}d^2 - \frac{9}{4}$

Vocabulary Builder

Connecting Ideas With Concept Maps

You can show connections among ideas by making a diagram called a concept map. The lines in a concept map connect related ideas.

EXAMPLE

Make a concept map using terms from Chapter 9 for *quadratic relationships.*

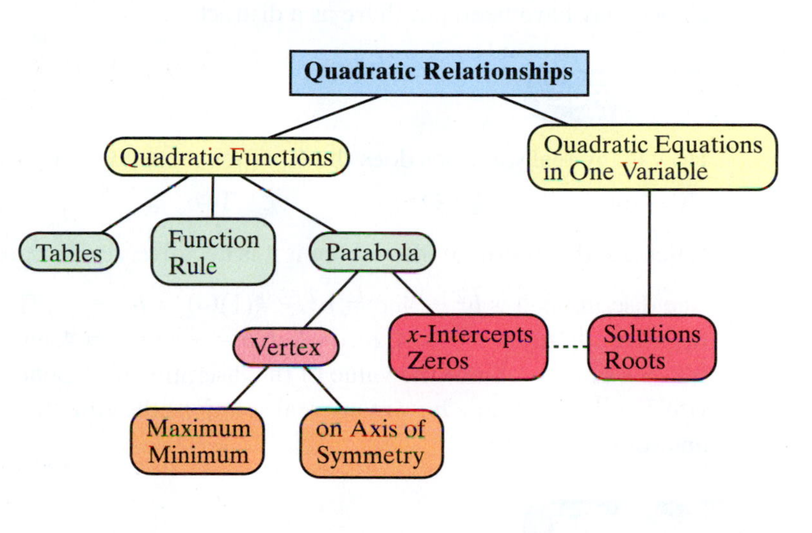

EXERCISES

1. Copy and complete the concept map for *polynomial.* Fill in the ovals using the appropriate terms listed below.

binomial
constant
linear
monomial
trinomial
cubic
fourth power
quadratic

Polynomial
Named by Degree
Named by Number of Terms
? ? ? ? ?
? ? ?

2. Copy and complete the concept map for *power.* Give an example of each term in the outer ovals.

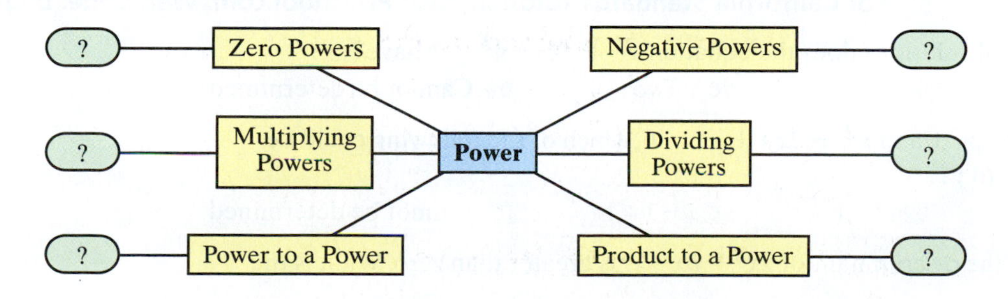

Test-Taking Strategies

Choosing "Cannot Be Determined"

Some multiple-choice questions do not contain enough information. One of the answer choices will then be "Cannot be determined." In such cases, you will not be able to find a specific answer. However, just because the answer choice "Cannot be determined" appears, do not assume that you cannot answer the question; the choice may have been put there as a distraction.

1 EXAMPLE

How many real solutions does the equation $x^2 + bx + 4 = 0$ have if $b > 0$?

(A) None (B) One (C) Two (D) Cannot be determined

Calculate the discriminant and see if it is negative, zero, or positive when $b > 0$.

The discriminant is $b^2 - 4ac = b^2 - 4(1)(4) = b^2 - 16$. This expression is negative when $-4 < b < 4$, zero when $b = -4$ or $b = 4$, and positive when $b < -4$ or $b > 4$. Since the value of the discriminant depends on the value of b, you cannot determine how many real solutions the equation has. The correct answer is D.

2 EXAMPLE

A parabola passes through the points (2, 8), (6, 2), and (8, 8). What is the x-coordinate of its vertex?

(A) 4 (B) 5 (C) 7 (D) Cannot be determined

The x-coordinate of the vertex of $y = ax^2 + bx + c$ is $-\frac{b}{2a}$. However, you don't have an equation for the parabola, so you can't use the formula. You might think that the answer is D.

Graph the points and you will notice that (2, 8) and (8, 8) have the same y value, so they are symmetrically placed about the axis of symmetry. The axis of symmetry will be $x = \frac{2 + 8}{2} = 5$. Since the x-coordinate of the vertex is on the axis of symmetry, the correct answer is B. Choice D is a distraction; it was put there in case you thought that the problem could not be done.

Multiple Choice Practice

For California Standards Tutorials, visit PHSchool.com. Web Code: baq-9045

1. How many real solutions does the equation $x^2 + 4x - n^2 = 0$ have?

   (A) None (B) One (C) Two (D) Cannot be determined

2. If $x \neq 0$ and $y \neq 0$, and $x^2 + 2xy + y^2 = 0$, which of the following could be the ratio of x to y?

   (A) 1 : 1 (B) 2 : 1 (C) −1 : 1 (D) Cannot be determined

3. The value of the discriminant of $2x^2 + bx + 3$ is greater than zero. What is the value of b?

   (A) 4 (B) 5 (C) 6 (D) Cannot be determined

Chapter 9 Review

Vocabulary Review

English and Spanish Audio Online

axis of symmetry (p. 427)
completing the square (p. 457)
discriminant (p. 470)
maximum (p. 427)
minimum (p. 427)
negative square root (p. 440)
parabola (p. 426)
perfect squares (p. 441)
principal square root (p. 440)
quadratic equation (p. 446)
quadratic formula (p. 463)
quadratic function (p. 426)
quadratic parent function (p. 426)
radicand (p. 440)
roots of the equation (p. 446)
square root (p. 440)
standard form of a quadratic equation (p. 446)
standard form of a quadratic function (p. 426)
vertex (p. 427)
Zero-Product Property (p. 452)
zeros of the function (p. 446)

Choose the term that correctly completes each sentence.

1. The U-shaped graph of a quadratic function is a *(parabola, perfect square).*

2. If $ax^2 + bx + c$ *cannot* be factored, one good way to solve the equation $ax^2 + bx + c = 0$ is to use (*completing the square, the Zero-Product Property*).

3. If $a^2 = b$ and $a > 0$, then a is the (*negative , principal*) square root of b.

4. The (*radicand, vertex*) of a parabola is the point at which the parabola intersects the axis of symmetry.

5. The (*discriminant, axis of symmetry*) can be used to determine the number of solutions of a quadratic equation.

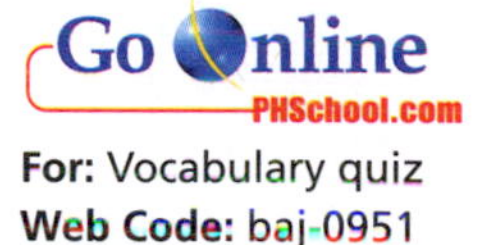

For: Vocabulary quiz
Web Code: baj-0951

Skills and Concepts

Lessons 9-1 and 9-2

- To graph quadratic functions of the form $y = ax^2$ (p. 426)
- To graph quadratic functions of the form $y = ax^2 + c$ (p. 428)
- To graph quadratic functions of the form $y = ax^2 + bx + c$ (p. 433)
- To graph quadratic inequalities (p. 435)

Alg1 17.0, 21.0, 23.0

A function of the form $y = ax^2 + bx + c$, where $a \neq 0$, is a **quadratic function.** The shape of its graph is a **parabola.** The **axis of symmetry** of a parabola divides it into two congruent halves. The **vertex** of a parabola is the point at which the parabola intersects the axis of symmetry. The axis of symmetry is the line with the equation $x = \frac{-b}{2a}$. The x-coordinate of the vertex of the parabola is $\frac{-b}{2a}$.

The value of a in a quadratic function $y = ax^2 + bx + c$ determines the width of the parabola and whether it opens upward or downward. The value of c is the y-intercept of the graph. Changing the value of c shifts the parabola up or down.

When the parabola opens downward, the y-coordinate of the vertex is a **maximum** point of the function. When the parabola opens upward, the y-coordinate of the vertex is a **minimum** point of the function.

Give an example of a quadratic function for each description.

6. Its graph opens downward.

7. Its vertex is at the origin.

8. Its graph opens upward.

9. Its graph is wider than $y = x^2$.

Graph each function.

10. $y = \frac{2}{3}x^2$

11. $y = -x^2 + 1$

12. $y = x^2 - 4$

13. $y = 5x^2 + 8$

State whether each function has a *maximum* or *minimum* point.

14. $y = 4x^2 + 1$ **15.** $y = -3x^2 - 7$ **16.** $y = \frac{1}{2}x^2 + 9$ **17.** $y = -x^2 + 6$

Graph each function. Label the axis of symmetry and the vertex. Find the domain and range.

18. $y = -\frac{1}{2}x^2 + 4x + 1$ **19.** $y = -2x^2 - 3x + 10$

20. $y = x^2 + 6x - 2$ **21.** $y = \frac{1}{2}x^2 + 2x - 3$

Graph each quadratic inequality.

22. $y \leq 3x^2 + x - 5$ **23.** $y > 3x^2 + x - 5$

24. $y \geq -x^2 - x - 8$ **25.** $y < x^2 - 4x$

Lesson 9-3

- To find square roots (p. 440)
- To estimate and use square roots (p. 441)

Alg1 2.0, 23.0

If $a^2 = b$, then a is a **square root** of b. The positive or **principal square root** of b is indicated by $\sqrt{b}$. The **negative square root** is indicated by $-\sqrt{b}$. The squares of integers are called **perfect squares.**

Tell whether each expression is *rational* or *irrational*. Then find the value of each expression. If necessary, round to the nearest hundredth.

26. $\sqrt{86}$ **27.** $-\sqrt{121}$ **28.** $\pm\sqrt{\frac{1}{2}}$ **29.** $\sqrt{2.55}$ **30.** $-\sqrt{\frac{4}{25}}$

Between which two consecutive integers is each square root?

31. $\sqrt{95}$ **32.** $\sqrt{48}$ **33.** $-\sqrt{127}$ **34.** $-\sqrt{23}$

Lessons 9-4 and 9-5

- To solve quadratic equations by graphing (p. 445)
- To solve quadratic equations using square roots (p. 446)
- To solve quadratic equations by factoring (p. 452)

The **standard form of a quadratic equation** is $ax^2 + bx + c = 0$, where a, b, and c are real numbers and $a \neq 0$. Quadratic equations can have two, one, or no solutions. You can solve some quadratic equations by graphing the related function and finding the x-intercepts. If the quadratic expression $ax^2 + bx + c$ can be factored, you can use the **Zero-Product Property** to find the solutions of the equation $ax^2 + bx + c = 0$. This property states that for all real numbers a and b, if $ab = 0$, then $a = 0$ or $b = 0$.

Solve each equation. If the equation has no solution, write *no solution.*

35. $6(x^2 - 2) = 12$ **36.** $-5m^2 = -125$ **37.** $9(w^2 + 1) = 9$

38. $3r^2 + 27 = 0$ **39.** $4 = 9k^2$ **40.** $4n^2 = 64$

Write each equation in standard form. Then solve by factoring.

41. $x^2 + 7x + 12 = 0$ **42.** $5x^2 - 10x = 0$

43. $2x^2 - 9x = x^2 - 20$ **44.** $2x^2 + 5x = 3$

45. $3x^2 - 5x = -3x^2 + 6$ **46.** $x^2 - 5x + 4 = 0$

47. The area of a circle is given by the formula $A = \pi r^2$. Find the radius of a circle with area 16 in.^{2}. Round to the nearest tenth of an inch.

Lesson 9-6

- To solve quadratic equations by completing the square (p. 457)

Alg1 14.0, 23.0

You can solve any quadratic equation by writing it in the form $x^2 + bx = c$, **completing the square,** and finding the square roots of each side of the equation.

Find the value of n such that each expression is a perfect square trinomial.

48. $a^2 - 10a + n$ **49.** $r^2 + 4r + n$ **50.** $g^2 - 30g + n$

51. $p^2 + 18p + n$ **52.** $w^2 + 26w + n$ **53.** $c^2 - 42c + n$

What term do you need to add to each side to complete the square?

54. $3x^2 + 24x = 48$ **55.** $2s^2 - 32s = 56$ **56.** $4m^2 + 7m = 25$

Solve each equation by completing the square. If necessary, round to the nearest hundredth.

57. $x^2 + 6x - 5 = 0$ **58.** $x^2 = 3x - 1$ **59.** $2x^2 + 7x = -6$

60. Alice is planning a rectangular garden. Its length is 3 ft less than twice its width. Its area is 170 ft^2. Find the dimensions of the garden.

Lessons 9-7 and 9-8

- To use the quadratic formula to solve quadratic equations (p. 463)
- To choose an appropriate method for solving a quadratic equation (p. 465)
- To find the number of times the graph of a quadratic function will intersect the x-axis and the number of solutions of a quadratic equation (p. 470)

Alg1 19.0, 20.0, 22.0, 23.0

You can solve $ax^2 + bx + c = 0$ when $a \neq 0$ by using the **quadratic formula** $x = \frac{-b \pm \sqrt{b^2 - 4ac}}{2a}$. The **discriminant** is $b^2 - 4ac$. You can use the discriminant to find the number of solutions of an equation $ax^2 + bx + c = 0$ $(a \neq 0)$ and the number of x-intercepts in the graph of a function $y = ax^2 + bx + c$ $(a \neq 0)$.

If $b^2 - 4ac > 0$, the equation has two solutions, and the graph has two x-intercepts.
If $b^2 - 4ac = 0$, the equation has one solution, and the graph has one x-intercept.
If $b^2 - 4ac < 0$, the equation has no solution, and the graph has no x-intercepts.

Find the number of solutions of each equation.

61. $x^2 - 10 = 3$ **62.** $3x^2 = 27$

63. $x^2 + 3 = 2x$ **64.** $x^2 + 10x = -25$

Solve each equation using the quadratic formula. Round to the nearest hundredth.

65. $4x^2 + 3x - 8 = 0$ **66.** $2x^2 - 7x = -3$

67. $-x^2 + 8x + 4 = 5$ **68.** $9x^2 - 270 = 0$

Writing Solve each equation. Explain why you chose the method you used.

69. $5x^2 - 10 = x^2 + 90$ **70.** $9x^2 + 30x - 29 = 0$

71. $2x^2 - 9x = x^2 - 20$ **72.** $x^2 - 6x + 9 = 0$

73. $x^2 + 3x - 225 = 3x$ **74.** $x^2 + 8x = 4$

75. A square pool has side length p. The border of the pool is 1 ft wide. The area of the border and the pool is 400 ft^2. Find the length and the area of the pool.

76. Suppose you throw a ball in the air. The ball is 6 ft high when it leaves your hand. Use the equation $0 = -16t^2 + 20t + 6$ to find the number of seconds t that the ball is in the air.

Chapter 9 Test

Go Online PHSchool.com For: Chapter Test Web Code: baa-0952

Match each graph with its function.

A. $y = 3x^2$ **B.** $y = -3x^2 + 1$

C. $y = -2x^2$ **D.** $y = x^2 - 3$

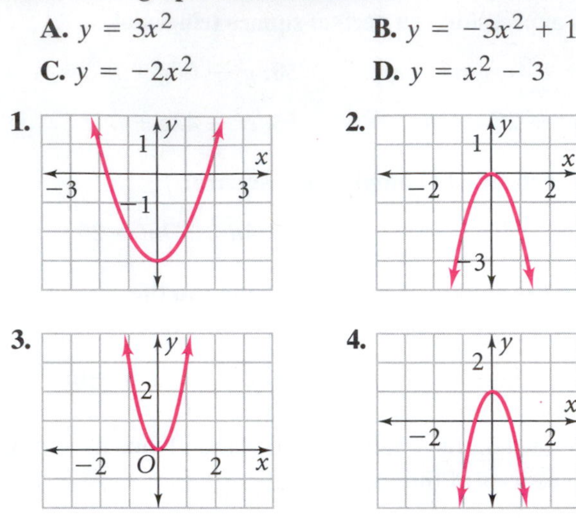

Find the equation of the axis of symmetry and the coordinates of the vertex of the graph of each function. Is the vertex a maximum or a minimum?

5. $y = 3x^2 - 7$

6. $y = x^2 - 3x + 2$

7. $y = -2x^2 + 10x - 1$

8. $y = \frac{1}{2}x^2 + 6x$

Graph each function.

9. $y = x^2 - 4$

10. $y = -x^2 + 1$

11. $y = 5x^2$

12. $y = \frac{1}{2}x^2 + 3x$

13. $y = x^2 - 3x + 5$

14. $y = 2x^2 - 5$

15. Writing Explain what you can determine about the shape of a parabola from its equation alone.

Find the number of x-intercepts of each function.

16. $y = 5x^2$

17. $y = 3x^2 + 10$

18. $y = -2x^2 + x + 7$

19. $y = x^2 - 4x$

Graph each inequality.

20. $y \leq 2x^2 - 1$

21. $y > \frac{1}{2}x^2$

Solve each equation.

22. $x^2 + 11x - 26 = 0$

23. $x^2 - 2x = 35$

24. $x^2 - 19x + 80 = -8$

25. $x^2 - 5x = -4x$

26. $2x^2 = 7 + 13x$

27. $5x^2 - 8x = 8 - 5x$

Find the number of solutions of each equation.

28. $x^2 + 4x = -4$

29. $x^2 + 8 = 0$

30. $2x^2 + x = 0$

31. $3x^2 - 9x = -5$

32. Find a nonzero value of k such that $kx^2 - 10x + 25 = 0$ has one solution.

Solve each equation. If necessary, round to the nearest hundredth.

33. $2x^2 = 50$

34. $-3x^2 + 7x = -10$

35. $x^2 + 6x + 9 = 25$

36. $-x^2 - x + 2 = 0$

37. $x^2 + 4x = 1$

38. $12x^2 + 16x - 28 = 0$

39. Write an equation of a parabola that has two x-intercepts and a maximum value. Include a graph of your parabola.

Model each problem with a quadratic equation. Then solve.

40. The volume V of a cylinder is given by the formula $V = \pi r^2 h$, where r is the radius of the cylinder, and h is the height. A cylinder with height 10 ft has volume 140 ft^3. To the nearest tenth of a foot, what is the radius of the cylinder?

41. The area of a rectangular patio is 800 ft^2. The patio's length is twice its width. Find the dimensions of the patio.

Between which two consecutive integers is each square root?

42. $\sqrt{28}$

43. $\sqrt{136}$

44. $\sqrt{332}$

45. $-\sqrt{8.99}$

Tell whether each number is *rational* or *irrational*.

46. $\sqrt{\frac{8}{5}}$

47. $\sqrt{\frac{121}{100}}$

48. $\sqrt{11}$

49. $-\sqrt{0.81}$

Use the quadratic formula to solve each equation. If necessary, round to the nearest hundredth.

50. $4x^2 + 4x - 3 = 0$

51. $x^2 + 2x - 7 = 0$

52. $6x^2 - 2x - 1 = 0$

53. $x^2 + x = 5$

Standards Mastery

Cumulative Practice

Some questions ask you to describe a change in an equation based on a change in the graph that the equation represents. Read the question at the right. Then follow the tips to answer the sample question.

The graph of $y = x^2 - 1$ is shown below.

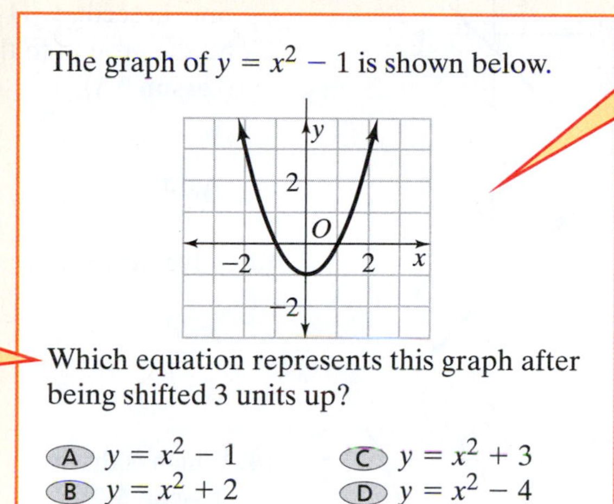

Which equation represents this graph after being shifted 3 units up?

(A) $y = x^2 - 1$ (C) $y = x^2 + 3$
(B) $y = x^2 + 2$ (D) $y = x^2 - 4$

Tip 1
Think about how the equation relates to the graph.

Tip 2
Read the question carefully. The correct answer describes the graph after a shift.

Think It Through

The question asks you to find the equation of the graph after a shift. The original graph has a minimum at $y = -1$. If you shift the graph up 3 units, the minimum will be at $y = -1 + 3 = 2$. So, the equation of the shifted graph is $y = x^2 + 2$. The correct answer is B.

Vocabulary Review

As you solve problems, you must understand the meanings of mathematical terms. Choose the correct term to complete each sentence.

A. The (*quotient, difference*) is the result of subtraction.

B. The (*roots, zeros*) of a quadratic function are the x-intercepts of the graph of the function.

C. The (*slope, x-intercept*) of a line defines a rate of change.

D. (*Completing the square, Factoring*) turns every quadratic equation into the form $x^2 = c$.

E. A (*linear, quadratic*) function has exactly 1 minimum or exactly 1 maximum.

Read each question. Then write the letter of the correct answer on your paper.

1. What is the solution set of the quadratic equation $x^2 + 2x - 15 = 0$? **(Lesson 9-5)**

(A) $\{3, 5\}$ (C) $\{-3, 5\}$
(B) $\{3, -5\}$ (D) $\{-3, -5\}$

2. Which term should be added to both sides of the equation $x^2 + \frac{8}{7}x + 2 = 0$ to complete the square? **(Lesson 9-6)**

(A) 225 (B) $\frac{64}{49}$ (C) $\frac{8}{7}$ (D) $\frac{16}{49}$

3. The sum of $2x^2$ and $-6x$ is 56. Which of the following could be the value of x? **(Lesson 9-5)**

(A) -8 (B) 4 (C) 7 (D) 8

4. The difference between Ann and Jay's height is half of Jay's height. Which equation represents the relationship between Jay's height j and Ann's height a? **(Lesson 2-3)**

(A) $\frac{1}{2}j = a - j$ (C) $a = \frac{1}{2}j - j$
(B) $\frac{1}{2}j = a + j$ (D) $j = \frac{1}{2}(a - j)$

5. Kevin ran 2 more than $\frac{3}{4}$ the number of miles that Cierra ran. Which equation represents the relationship between the number of miles Kevin ran k and the number of miles Cierra ran c? **(Lesson 2-3)**

(A) $c = \frac{3}{4}k + 2$ (C) $c = \frac{3}{4}k - 2$
(B) $k = \frac{3}{4}c + 2$ (D) $k = \frac{3}{4}c - 2$

6. Laura rented a car that cost \$20 for the day plus \$.12 for each mile driven. She returned the car later that day. Laura gave the salesperson \$50 and received change. Which inequality represents the number of miles m that she could have driven? **(Lesson 3-4)**

(A) $50 > 0.12m + 20$ (C) $50 > 0.12m - 20$
(B) $50 < 0.12m + 20$ (D) $50 < 0.12m - 20$

Cumulative Practice (continued)

7. Which graph shows a line with a positive slope and a positive x-intercept? **(Lesson 5-2)**

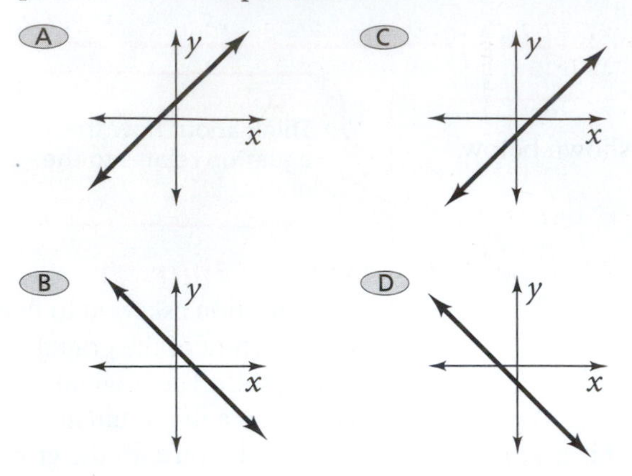

8. What is the equation of the line shown on the coordinate grid at the right? **(Lesson 5-3)**

y
−2 O 2 4 x
−2
−4

Ⓐ $2x - 6 = y$

Ⓑ $x - 2y = 12$

Ⓒ $2x + y = 3$

Ⓓ $x + 2y = 6$

9. The table shows the number of volunteers needed v based on the number of children c who will go on a field trip. Which equation best represents the relationship between the number of volunteers and the number of children? **(Lesson 4-4)**

c	v
20	6
25	7
30	8

Ⓐ $v = \frac{1}{4}c + 10$

Ⓑ $v = 5c - 10$

Ⓒ $v = 4c + 2$

Ⓓ $v = \frac{1}{5}c + 2$

10. The equation $h = -16t^2 + vt + c$ describes the height h of an object at time t seconds when it is projected upward with initial velocity v feet per second from a height c feet off the ground. Suppose Sofia is standing on a bridge 15 feet above a river. She throws a rock straight up with an initial velocity of 8 feet per second. In how many seconds will the rock hit the water? **(Lesson 9-5)**

Ⓐ 0.75 s Ⓑ 1.25 s Ⓒ 1.75 s Ⓓ 2.25 s

11. If a ball is thrown upward into the air from ground level with an initial velocity of 48 feet per second, in how many seconds will the ball hit the ground? (*Hint*: $h = -16t^2 + vt + c$) **(Lesson 9-2)**

Ⓐ 3 s

Ⓑ 10 s

Ⓒ 16 s

Ⓓ 48 s

12. A construction worker drops a tool from the top of a building that is 200 ft high. The height of the tool above the ground can be modeled by $h = -16t^2 + 200$, where h is height in feet and t is time in seconds. How long will it take for the tool to hit the ground to the nearest tenth of a second? **(Lesson 9-1)**

Ⓐ 5.6 s

Ⓑ 4.2 s

Ⓒ 3.5 s

Ⓓ 0.08 s

13. Solve $2x^2 + 7x + 9 = 0$. **(Lesson 9-7)**

Ⓐ $x = \frac{-7 \pm \sqrt{23}}{4}$

Ⓑ $\left\{-1, \frac{9}{2}\right\}$

Ⓒ $\left\{-\frac{9}{2}, 1\right\}$

Ⓓ no real solutions

14. Which is the best representation of $y = x$? **(Lesson 5-2)**

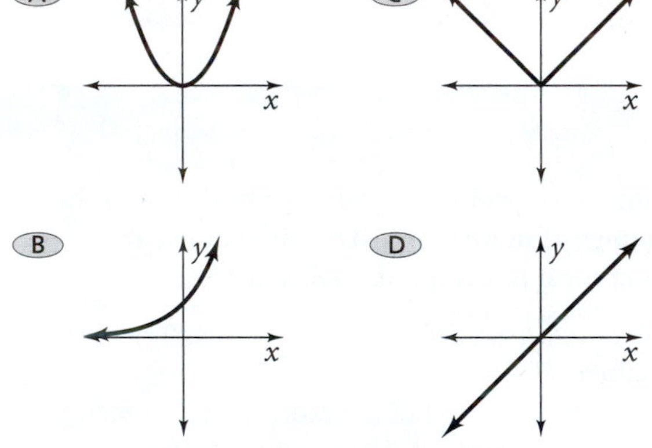

15. Which is the best representation of a quadratic function? **(Lesson 9-1)**

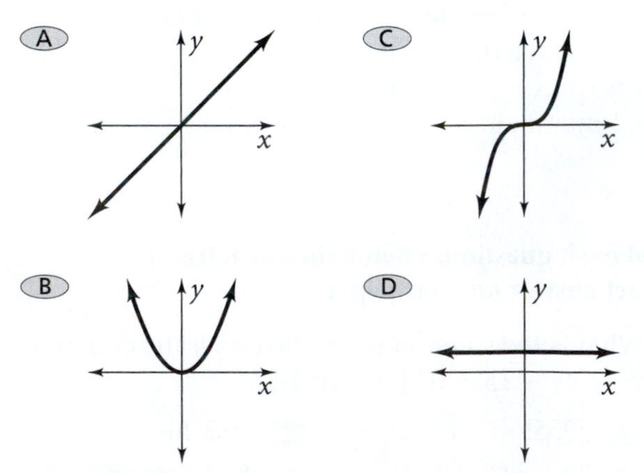

16. If the graph of the function $y = x^2 - 6$ were shifted 3 units down, which equation could represent the shifted graph? **(Lesson 9-1)**

Ⓐ $y = x^2 - 2$

Ⓑ $y = x^2 - 3$

Ⓒ $y = x^2 - 9$

Ⓓ $y = x^2 - 18$

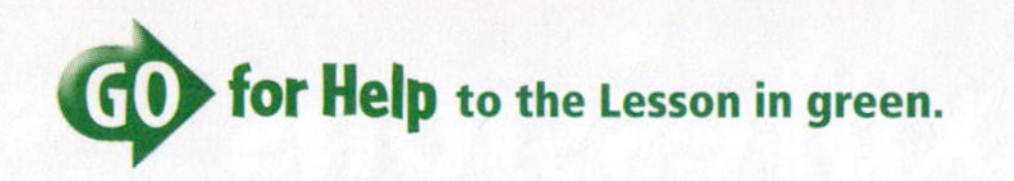

Standards Mastery

17. How would the graph of the function $y = x^2 - 5$ be affected if the function were changed to $y = x^2 + 2$? **(Lesson 9-1)**

A The graph would shift 2 units down.
B The graph would shift 3 units up.
C The graph would shift 7 units up.
D The graph would shift 10 units down.

18. Which equation best represents the graph of the function shown at the right? **(Lesson 9-1)**

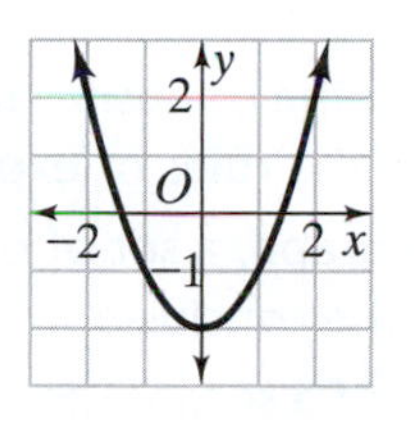

A $y = x^2$ C $y = x^2 - 2$
B $y = -x^2$ D $y = x^2 + 2$

19. Chi's solution to the equation $x^2 + 3x - 10 = 0$ is shown below.

Step 1: $(x - 2)(x + 5)$
Step 2: $x - 2 = 0$ or $x + 5 = 0$
Step 3: $x = 2$ or $x = -5$

Which property of real numbers justifies Step 2? **(Lesson 9-5)**

A Multiplication Property of Equality
B Zero-Product Property
C Distributive Property
D Commutative Property of Multiplication

20. A student mistakenly claimed that the graph of a linear equation with positive slope never enters the fourth quadrant. Which equation is a counterexample to this statement? **(Lesson 5-2)**

A $y = 2x - 3$ C $y = 2$
B $y = 2x + 3$ D $y = x + 1$

21. Which is one of the solutions to the equation $3x^2 + x - 5 = 0$? **(Lesson 9-7)**

A $\frac{1}{6} - \sqrt{61}$ C $\frac{1 - \sqrt{61}}{6}$
B $-\frac{1}{6} + \sqrt{61}$ D $\frac{-1 + \sqrt{61}}{6}$

22. What is the solution set of the quadratic equation $5x^2 - 2x - 1 = 0$? **(Lesson 9-7)**

A $\left\{\frac{-1+2\sqrt{6}}{5}, \frac{-1-2\sqrt{6}}{5}\right\}$ C $\left\{-\frac{1}{5}, \frac{3}{5}\right\}$
B $\left\{\frac{2+\sqrt{22}}{10}, \frac{2-\sqrt{22}}{10}\right\}$ D $\left\{\frac{1+\sqrt{6}}{5}, \frac{1-\sqrt{6}}{5}\right\}$

23. Suppose a, b, and c are distinct real numbers. Which relation is NOT a function? **(Lesson 4-2)**

A $\{(a, b), (b, c), (c, a)\}$
B $\{(a, a), (b, b), (c, c)\}$
C $\{(a, a), (a, b), (a, c)\}$
D $\{(a, a), (b, a), (c, a)\}$

24. Which ordered pair should be removed to make the relation below a function? **(Lesson 4-2)**

$\{(0, 0), (1, 2), (2, -2), (-2, 1), (-1, -2), (2, -1)\}$

A $(0, 0)$ C $(-1, -2)$
B $(2, -1)$ D $(-2, 1)$

25. For which equation should $12\frac{1}{4}$ be added to each side in order to complete the square? **(Lesson 9-6)**

A $x^2 + x = 24$ C $x^2 + 2x + 9 = 0$
B $x^2 + \frac{7}{2}x = -5$ D $x^2 + 7x - 16 = 0$

Standards Reference Guide

California Content Standard	Item Number(s)
Alg1 5.0	4–6
Alg1 6.0	7, 8, 14
Alg1 14.0	1–3, 25
Alg1 16.0	9, 23, 24
Alg1 20.0	13, 21, 22
Alg1 21.0	15–18
Alg1 23.0	10–12
Alg1 25.1	19, 20

For additional review and practice, see the *California Standards Review and Practice Workbook* or go online to use the

Visit: PHSchool.com, **Web Code:** baq-9045

CALIFORNIA CHECK SYSTEM

CHAPTER 10 Radical Expressions and Equations

What You've Learned

California Content Standards

2.0 Understand and use such operations as taking the opposite, finding the reciprocal, and taking a root. Understand and use the rules of exponents.

18.0 Determine whether a relation defined by a graph, a set of ordered pairs, or a symbolic expression is a function and justify the conclusion.

20.0 Use the quadratic formula to find the roots of a second-degree polynomial and to solve quadratic equations.

Check Your Readiness

GO for Help to the Lesson in green.

Solving Proportions (Lesson 2-4)

Solve each proportion.

1. $\frac{8}{x} = \frac{24}{9}$ **2.** $\frac{k-4}{27} = \frac{1}{3}$ **3.** $\frac{5}{6} = \frac{25}{c}$

4. $\frac{42}{x+8} = \frac{7}{2}$ **5.** $\frac{9}{13} = \frac{y}{65}$ **6.** $\frac{6}{x-5} = \frac{1}{2}$

7. $\frac{3n-1}{14} = \frac{4}{7}$ **8.** $\frac{4}{33} = \frac{8}{w}$ **9.** $\frac{y-1}{5} = \frac{y+3}{7}$

Properties of Exponents (Lesson 7-5)

Simplify each expression.

10. $\left(\frac{3}{4}\right)^{-2}$ **11.** $\left(\frac{1}{y^2}\right)^3$ **12.** $\frac{6m^3}{(6m)^2}$ **13.** $\frac{(9a)(2a^5)}{18a^3}$

Finding Square Roots (Lesson 9-3)

Simplify each expression.

14. $\sqrt{4}$ **15.** $\sqrt{225}$ **16.** $\sqrt{\frac{9}{25}}$ **17.** $-\sqrt{0.0036}$

Simplify each expression. Round to the nearest hundredth.

18. $\sqrt{40}$ **19.** $\sqrt{84}$ **20.** $\sqrt{104}$ **21.** $\sqrt{3.2}$

Using the Discriminant (Lesson 9-8)

Find the number of real solutions of each equation.

22. $x^2 + 6x + 1 = 0$ **23.** $x^2 - 5x - 6 = 0$ **24.** $x^2 - 2x + 9 = 0$

25. $4x^2 - 4x = -1$ **26.** $6x^2 + 5x - 2 = -3$ **27.** $(2x - 5)^2 = 121$

▲ Smoke jumpers parachute to remote areas to fight wildfire. In this chapter, you will work with radical equations such as the formula for the time it takes an object to fall a given distance.

What You'll Learn Next

California Content Standards

2.0 Understand and use such operations as taking the opposite, finding the reciprocal, taking a root, and raising to a fractional power. Understand and use the rules of exponents.

17.0 Determine the domain of independent variables and the range of dependent variables defined by a graph.

24.2 Identify the hypothesis and conclusion in logical deduction.

New Vocabulary

English and Spanish Audio Online

- **conjugates** (p. 501)
- **extraneous solution** (p. 509)
- **hypotenuse** (p. 493)
- **leg** (p. 493)
- **like radicals** (p. 500)
- **Pythagorean Theorem** (p. 493)
- **radical equation** (p. 507)
- **radical expression** (p. 486)
- **rationalize** (p. 489)
- **square root function** (p. 514)
- **unlike radicals** (p. 500)

10-1 Simplifying Radicals

California Content Standards

2.0 Understand and use such operations as taking a root. ***Develop***

What You'll Learn

- To simplify radicals involving products
- To simplify radicals involving quotients

. . . And Why

To find the distance to the horizon, as in Example 4

Check Skills You'll Need

GO for Help Lessons 8-3 and 9-3

Complete each equation.

1. $a^3 = a^2 \cdot a^{■}$ **2.** $b^7 = b^6 \cdot b^{■}$ **3.** $c^6 = c^3 \cdot c^{■}$ **4.** $d^8 = d^4 \cdot d^{■}$

Find the value of each expression.

5. $\sqrt{4}$ **6.** $\sqrt{169}$ **7.** $\sqrt{25}$ **8.** $\sqrt{49}$

New Vocabulary • radical expression • rationalize

Simplifying Radical Expressions Involving Products

Radical expressions like $2\sqrt{3}$ and $\sqrt{x + 3}$ contain a radical. You read $\sqrt{x + 3}$ as "the square root of the quantity x plus three." You can simplify a radical expression by removing perfect-square factors from the radicand.

Take Note

Property **Multiplication Property of Square Roots**

For every number $a \geq 0$ and $b \geq 0$, $\sqrt{ab} = \sqrt{a} \cdot \sqrt{b}$.

Example $\sqrt{54} = \sqrt{9} \cdot \sqrt{6} = 3 \cdot \sqrt{6} = 3\sqrt{6}$

You can simplify radical expressions by rewriting the radicand as a product of the perfect-square factors times the remaining factors.

1 EXAMPLE Removing Perfect-Square Factors

Simplify $\sqrt{192}$.

$\sqrt{192} = \sqrt{64 \cdot 3}$ 64 is a perfect square and a factor of 192.

$= \sqrt{64} \cdot \sqrt{3}$ Use the Multiplication Property of Square Roots.

$= 8\sqrt{3}$ Simplify $\sqrt{64}$.

CA Standards Check **1** Simplify each radical expression.

a. $\sqrt{50}$ **b.** $-5\sqrt{300}$ **c.** $\sqrt{18}$

You can simplify radical expressions that contain variables. A variable with a nonzero, even exponent is a perfect square. Variables with odd exponents (other than 1 and -1) are the product of a perfect square and the variable. For example, $n^3 = n^2 \cdot n$, so $\sqrt{n^3} = \sqrt{n^2 \cdot n}$. Assume that all variables of all radicands represent nonnegative numbers.

2 EXAMPLE Removing Variable Factors

Simplify $\sqrt{45a^5}$.

(A) $a^2\sqrt{45}$ (B) $3a^2\sqrt{5a}$ (C) $5\sqrt{3a^5}$ (D) $9a^4\sqrt{5a}$

$\sqrt{45a^5} = \sqrt{9a^4 \cdot 5a}$ $9a^4$ is a perfect square and a factor of $45a^5$.

$= \sqrt{9a^4} \cdot \sqrt{5a}$ Use the Multiplication Property of Square Roots.

$= 3a^2\sqrt{5a}$ Simplify $\sqrt{9a^4}$.

So B is the correct answer.

CA Standards Check 2 Simplify each radical expression.

a. $\sqrt{27n^2}$ b. $-a\sqrt{60a^7}$ c. $\sqrt{x^2y^5}$

You can use the Multiplication Property of Square Roots to write $\sqrt{a} \cdot \sqrt{b} = \sqrt{ab}$. Sometimes the product of two radical expressions has a perfect-square factor.

3 EXAMPLE Multiplying Two Radicals

Problem Solving Tip

Another method of simplifying is using prime factors.

$\sqrt{8} \cdot \sqrt{12}$
$= \sqrt{2 \cdot 2 \cdot 2 \cdot 2 \cdot 2 \cdot 3}$
$= \sqrt{2^2 \cdot 2^2 \cdot 2 \cdot 3}$
$= 2 \cdot 2\sqrt{6}$
$= 4\sqrt{6}$

Simplify each radical expression.

a. $\sqrt{8} \cdot \sqrt{12} = \sqrt{8 \cdot 12}$ Use the Multiplication Property of Square Roots.

$= \sqrt{96}$ Simplify under the radical.

$= \sqrt{16 \cdot 6}$ 16 is a perfect square and a factor of 96.

$= \sqrt{16} \cdot \sqrt{6}$ Use the Multiplication Property of Square Roots.

$= 4\sqrt{6}$ Simplify $\sqrt{16}$.

b. $3\sqrt{2b} \cdot 4\sqrt{10b} = 12\sqrt{20b^2}$ Multiply the whole numbers and use the Multiplication Property of Square Roots.

$= 12\sqrt{4b^2 \cdot 5}$ $4b^2$ is a perfect square and a factor of $20b^2$.

$= 12\sqrt{4b^2} \cdot \sqrt{5}$ Use the Multiplication Property of Square Roots.

$= 12 \cdot 2b\sqrt{5}$ Simplify $\sqrt{4b^2}$.

$= 24b\sqrt{5}$ Simplify.

CA Standards Check 3 Simplify each radical expression.

a. $\sqrt{13} \cdot \sqrt{52}$ b. $5\sqrt{3c} \cdot \sqrt{6c}$ c. $2\sqrt{5a^2} \cdot 6\sqrt{10a^3}$

4 EXAMPLE Application

You can use the formula $d = \sqrt{1.5h}$ to estimate the distance d in miles to a horizon when h is the height of the viewer's eyes above the ground in feet. Estimate the distance a visitor at the Washington Monument can see to the horizon from the observation windows. Round your answer to the nearest mile.

$d = \sqrt{1.5h}$

$= \sqrt{1.5 \cdot 500}$ Substitute 500 for h.

$= \sqrt{750}$ Multiply.

≈ 27 Use a calculator.

The distance a visitor can see is about 27 miles.

CA Standards Check 4 Suppose you are looking out a second floor window 25 ft above the ground. Find the distance you can see to the horizon. Round your answer to the nearest mile.

Simplifying Radical Expressions Involving Quotients

You can use the Division Property of Square Roots to simplify expressions.

Take Note

Property **Division Property of Square Roots**

For every number $a \geq 0$ and $b > 0$, $\sqrt{\frac{a}{b}} = \frac{\sqrt{a}}{\sqrt{b}}$.

Example $\sqrt{\frac{16}{25}} = \frac{\sqrt{16}}{\sqrt{25}} = \frac{4}{5}$

When the denominator of the radicand is a perfect square, it is easier to simplify the numerator and denominator separately.

5 EXAMPLE Simplifying Fractions Within Radicals

Vocabulary Tip

Read $\frac{\sqrt{2}}{3}$ as "the square root of 2 over 3," and $\sqrt{\frac{2}{3}}$ as "the square root of two thirds."

Simplify each radical expression.

a. $\sqrt{\frac{11}{49}} = \frac{\sqrt{11}}{\sqrt{49}}$ Use the Division Property of Square Roots.

$= \frac{\sqrt{11}}{7}$ Simplify $\sqrt{49}$.

b. $\sqrt{\frac{25}{b^4}} = \frac{\sqrt{25}}{\sqrt{b^4}}$ Use the Division Property of Square Roots.

$= \frac{5}{b^2}$ Simplify $\sqrt{25}$ and $\sqrt{b^4}$.

CA Standards Check 5 Simplify each radical expression.

a. $\sqrt{\frac{144}{9}}$ **b.** $\sqrt{\frac{25p^3}{q^2}}$ **c.** $\sqrt{\frac{75}{16t^2}}$

When the denominator of the radicand is not a perfect square, it may be easier to divide first and then simplify the radical expression.

6 EXAMPLE Simplifying Radicals by Dividing

Online active math

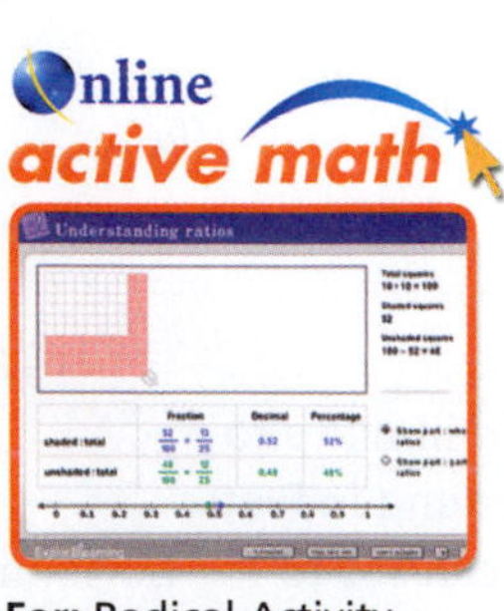

For: Radical Activity
Use: Interactive Textbook, 10-1

Simplify each radical expression.

a. $\sqrt{\frac{88}{11}} = \sqrt{8}$ Divide.

$= \sqrt{4 \cdot 2}$ 4 is a perfect square and a factor of 8.

$= \sqrt{4} \cdot \sqrt{2}$ Use the Multiplication Property of Square Roots.

$= 2\sqrt{2}$ Simplify $\sqrt{4}$.

b. $\sqrt{\frac{12a^3}{27a}} = \sqrt{\frac{4a^2}{9}}$ Divide the numerator and denominator by $3a$.

$= \frac{\sqrt{4a^2}}{\sqrt{9}}$ Use the Division Property of Square Roots.

$= \frac{\sqrt{4} \cdot \sqrt{a^2}}{\sqrt{9}}$ Use the Multiplication Property of Square Roots.

$= \frac{2a}{3}$ Simplify $\sqrt{4}$, $\sqrt{a^2}$ and $\sqrt{9}$.

CA Standards Check 6 Simplify each radical expression.

a. $\sqrt{\frac{90}{5}}$ **b.** $\sqrt{\frac{48}{75}}$ **c.** $\sqrt{\frac{27x^3}{3x}}$

A radicand in the denominator of a radical expression may not be a perfect square. To simplify, you may need to **rationalize** the denominator. To do this, you multiply the numerator and the denominator by the same radical expression. You choose a radical expression that will make the denominator a perfect square.

7 EXAMPLE Rationalizing a Denominator

Simplify by rationalizing the denominator.

a. $\frac{2}{\sqrt{5}} = \frac{2}{\sqrt{5}} \cdot \frac{\sqrt{5}}{\sqrt{5}}$ Multiply by $\frac{\sqrt{5}}{\sqrt{5}}$ to make the denominator a perfect square.

$= \frac{2\sqrt{5}}{\sqrt{25}}$ Use the Multiplication Property of Square Roots.

$= \frac{2\sqrt{5}}{5}$ Simplify $\sqrt{25}$.

b. $\frac{\sqrt{7}}{\sqrt{8n}} = \frac{\sqrt{7}}{\sqrt{8n}} \cdot \frac{\sqrt{2n}}{\sqrt{2n}}$ Multiply by $\frac{\sqrt{2n}}{\sqrt{2n}}$ to make the denominator a perfect square.

$= \frac{\sqrt{14n}}{\sqrt{16n^2}}$ Use the Multiplication Property of Square Roots.

$= \frac{\sqrt{14n}}{4n}$ Simplify $\sqrt{16n^2}$.

CA Standards Check 7 Simplify by rationalizing the denominator.

a. $\frac{3}{\sqrt{3}}$ **b.** $\frac{\sqrt{5}}{\sqrt{18t}}$ **c.** $\sqrt{\frac{7m}{10}}$

The summary below can help you determine whether a radical expression is in simplest radical form.

Take Note

Summary Simplest Radical Form

A radical expression is in simplest radical form when all three statements are true.

- The radicand has no perfect-square factors other than 1.
- The radicand has no fractions.
- The denominator of a fraction has no radical.

EXERCISES Standards Practice

For more exercises, see *Extra Skills and Word Problem Practice*.

Alg1 2.0

A Practice by Example

Simplify each radical expression.

Examples 1, 2

GO for Help (pages 486, 487)

1. $\sqrt{200}$ **2.** $\sqrt{98}$ **3.** $\sqrt{75}$ **4.** $-\sqrt{80}$

5. $-3\sqrt{120}$ **6.** $5\sqrt{320}$ **7.** $\sqrt{28n^2}$ **8.** $\sqrt{108b^4}$

9. $3\sqrt{12x^2}$ **10.** $\sqrt{4n^3}$ **11.** $\sqrt{20a^5}$ **12.** $-\sqrt{48b^4}$

Example 3

(page 487)

13. $\sqrt{10} \cdot \sqrt{40}$ **14.** $3\sqrt{6} \cdot \sqrt{6}$ **15.** $\sqrt{22} \cdot \sqrt{11}$ **16.** $2\sqrt{18} \cdot 7\sqrt{6}$

17. $\sqrt{7} \cdot \sqrt{21}$ **18.** $-3\sqrt{20} \cdot \sqrt{15}$ **19.** $\sqrt{3n} \cdot \sqrt{24n}$ **20.** $2\sqrt{7t} \cdot \sqrt{14t}$

21. $\sqrt{3x} \cdot \sqrt{51x^3}$ **22.** $5\sqrt{8t} \cdot \sqrt{32t^5}$ **23.** $\sqrt{2a^2} \cdot \sqrt{9a^4}$ **24.** $-2\sqrt{6a^3} \cdot \sqrt{3a}$

Example 4 (page 487)

For Exercises 25–27, use the formula $d = \sqrt{1.5h}$ to approximate distance d in miles to a horizon when h is the height in feet of the viewer's eyes above the ground. Round your answer to the nearest mile.

25. Find the distance you can see to the horizon from a height of 6 feet.

26. Find the distance you can see to the horizon from a height of 100 feet.

27. Find the distance you can see to the horizon from a height of 200 feet.

Example 5 (page 488)

Simplify each radical expression.

28. $\sqrt{\frac{21}{49}}$ **29.** $3\sqrt{\frac{3}{4}}$ **30.** $\sqrt{\frac{625}{100}}$ **31.** $\sqrt{\frac{120}{121}}$

32. $\sqrt{\frac{5}{9a^2}}$ **33.** $\sqrt{\frac{7}{16c^2}}$ **34.** $\sqrt{\frac{75a}{49}}$ **35.** $\sqrt{\frac{8n^3}{81}}$

Example 6 (page 488)

36. $\sqrt{\frac{15}{5}}$ **37.** $\sqrt{\frac{54}{24}}$ **38.** $\sqrt{\frac{60}{5}}$ **39.** $-\sqrt{\frac{160}{8}}$

40. $\sqrt{\frac{140x^3}{5x}}$ **41.** $\sqrt{\frac{3s^3}{27s}}$ **42.** $\sqrt{\frac{30a^5}{40a}}$ **43.** $\sqrt{\frac{63y}{7y^3}}$

Example 7 (page 489)

Simplify each radical expression by rationalizing the denominator.

44. $\frac{3}{\sqrt{2}}$ **45.** $\frac{5}{\sqrt{5}}$ **46.** $\frac{\sqrt{3}}{\sqrt{7x}}$ **47.** $\frac{2\sqrt{2}}{\sqrt{5n}}$

48. $\frac{9}{\sqrt{8}}$ **49.** $\frac{12}{\sqrt{12}}$ **50.** $\frac{3\sqrt{2}}{\sqrt{9b}}$ **51.** $\frac{5\sqrt{11}}{\sqrt{20y}}$

B Apply Your Skills

Writing **Explain why each radical expression is or is not in simplest radical form.**

52. $\frac{13}{\sqrt{4}}$ **53.** $\frac{3}{\sqrt{3}}$ **54.** $4\sqrt{3}$ **55.** $5\sqrt{30}$

56. Suppose a and b are positive integers.
  a. Verify that if $a = 18$ and $b = 10$, then $\sqrt{a} \cdot \sqrt{b} = 6\sqrt{5}$.
  b. Find two other pairs of positive integers a and b such that $\sqrt{a} \cdot \sqrt{b} = 6\sqrt{5}$.

Simplify each radical expression.

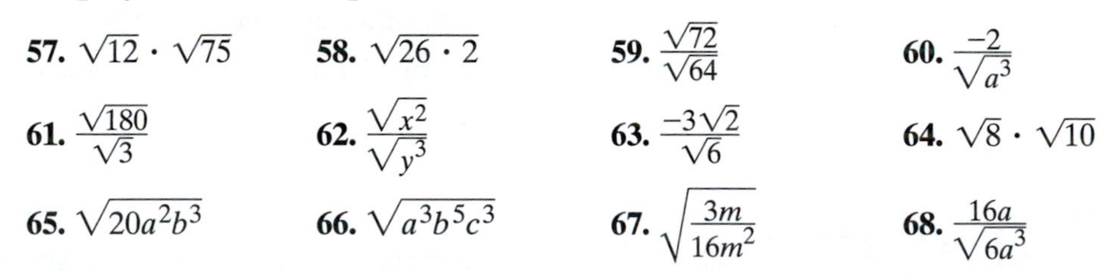

57. $\sqrt{12} \cdot \sqrt{75}$ **58.** $\sqrt{26 \cdot 2}$ **59.** $\frac{\sqrt{72}}{\sqrt{64}}$ **60.** $\frac{-2}{\sqrt{a^3}}$

61. $\frac{\sqrt{180}}{\sqrt{3}}$ **62.** $\frac{\sqrt{x^2}}{\sqrt{y^3}}$ **63.** $\frac{-3\sqrt{2}}{\sqrt{6}}$ **64.** $\sqrt{8} \cdot \sqrt{10}$

65. $\sqrt{20a^2b^3}$ **66.** $\sqrt{a^3b^5c^3}$ **67.** $\sqrt{\frac{3m}{16m^2}}$ **68.** $\frac{16a}{\sqrt{6a^3}}$

Solve each equation. Leave your answer in simplest radical form.

69. $x^2 + 6x - 9 = 0$ **70.** $n^2 - 2n + 1 = 5$ **71.** $3y^2 - 4y - 2 = 0$

72. a. Show work to verify that $\sqrt{50}$ equals $5\sqrt{2}$.
  b. Writing Explain why $5\sqrt{2}$ is in simplest radical form.

73. What are three numbers whose square roots can be written in the form $a\sqrt{3}$ for some integer value of a?

Visit: PHSchool.com
Web Code: bae-1001

74. A square picture on the front page of a newspaper occupies an area of 24 in.^{2}.
  a. Find the length of each side in simplest radical form.
  b. Calculate the length of each side to the nearest hundredth of an inch.

C Challenge

Simplify each radical expression.

75. $\sqrt{24} \cdot \sqrt{2x} \cdot \sqrt{3x}$

76. $2b(\sqrt{5b})^2$

77. $\sqrt{45a^7} \cdot \sqrt{20a}$

78. The time that a pendulum of a grandfather clock takes to swing back and forth one cycle is the period of the pendulum. The formula for finding the period T in seconds is $T = 2\pi\sqrt{\frac{L}{32}}$, where L is the length of the pendulum in feet. Find the period of a pendulum that is 8 feet long. Write your answer in terms of π.

Multiple Choice Practice

For California Standards Tutorials, visit PHSchool.com. Web Code: baq-9045

Alg1 16.0

79. Which equation best represents the function shown on the graph?

Ⓐ $y = x$
Ⓑ $y = -x$
Ⓒ $y = x^2$
Ⓓ $y = -x^2$

y
x

Alg1 2.0

80. Simplify $\sqrt{\frac{36x^{16}}{4900}}$.

Ⓐ $-\frac{3x^4}{35}$
Ⓑ $\frac{3x^4}{35}$
Ⓒ $\frac{6}{7}x^4$
Ⓓ $\frac{3x^8}{35}$

Alg1 14.0

81. Which of the following is a solution to the equation $x^2 + 6x = 20$?

Ⓐ $-3 - \sqrt{29}$
Ⓑ $3 + \sqrt{29}$
Ⓒ $3 - \sqrt{38}$
Ⓓ $3 + \sqrt{38}$

Alg1 17.0

82. What is the range of the function shown at the right?

Ⓐ $\{y: y \geq -1\}$
Ⓑ $\{y: y = 1\}$
Ⓒ $\{y: y \geq 1\}$
Ⓓ $\{y: y \geq 2\}$

y
2
O
2
4 x

Mixed Review

GO for Help

Lesson 9-8

Find the number of solutions of each equation.

83. $2x^2 - x - 4 = 0$

84. $7x^2 + x + 20 = 0$

85. $9x^2 + 6x + 1 = 0$

86. $2x^2 - 6x + 2 = 0$

87. $x^2 + 3x + 5 = 0$

88. $-2x^2 + 8x - 8 = 0$

Lesson 9-2

Graph each function. Label the axis of symmetry and the vertex.

89. $f(x) = x^2 + 8x - 4$

90. $y = x^2 - 10x + 7$

91. $y = 3x^2 + 12x - 5$

Lesson 8-1

Simplify. Write each answer in standard form.

92. $(n^2 + 5n - 1) + (2n^2 + 6)$

93. $(4v^2 + 8v - 2) - (v^2 + 9v + 7)$

94. $(5t^3 - 14t) + (8t^2 - 11)$

95. $(2b^2 - 12b - 8) - (5b^2 + 11b + 13)$

96. $(5p^2 - p + 21) - (p^3 + 6p^2 - p - 1)$

97. $(7y^3 + 5y^2 - y) + (y^3 + y^2 - 5y)$

GO Online Lesson Quiz Visit: PHSchool.com, Web Code: baa-1001

Activity Lab Rational Exponents

FOR USE WITH LESSON 10-1

2.0 Understand and use such operations as taking a root and raising to a fractional power. Understand and use the rules of exponents. ***Develop***

You can have roots other than square roots. The third root of a number x is written as $\sqrt[3]{x}$. For example, $\sqrt[3]{8} = 2$ because $2^3 = 8$. You can also express roots using exponents. The expression $a^{\frac{1}{n}}$ is defined as $\sqrt[n]{a}$. An example is $9^{\frac{1}{2}} = \sqrt[2]{9} = 3$.

Rational exponents follow the same rules as integer exponents, so $9^{\frac{1}{2}} \cdot 9^{\frac{1}{2}} = 9^{\left(\frac{1}{2} + \frac{1}{2}\right)} = 9^1 = 9$, just as $\sqrt{9} \cdot \sqrt{9} = 9$.

1 EXAMPLE

Simplify $16^{\frac{1}{4}}$.

$16^{\frac{1}{4}} = 2$ **$16 = 2 \cdot 2 \cdot 2 \cdot 2$, so $\sqrt[4]{16} = 2$**

An exponent can be any rational number. You can simplify rational exponents using the property of raising a power to a power, $a^{mn} = (a^m)^n$.

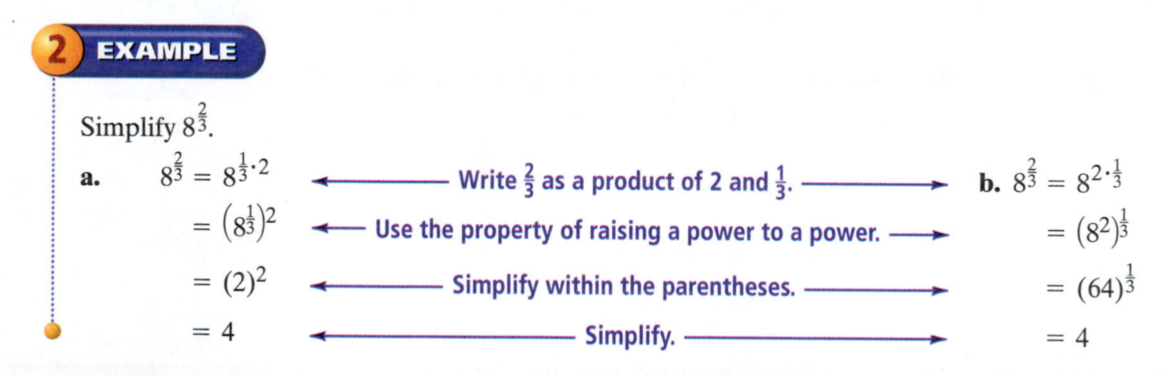

2 EXAMPLE

Simplify $8^{\frac{2}{3}}$.

a. $8^{\frac{2}{3}} = 8^{\frac{1}{3} \cdot 2}$ ← **Write $\frac{2}{3}$ as a product of 2 and $\frac{1}{3}$.** → **b.** $8^{\frac{2}{3}} = 8^{2 \cdot \frac{1}{3}}$

$= \left(8^{\frac{1}{3}}\right)^2$ ← **Use the property of raising a power to a power.** → $= (8^2)^{\frac{1}{3}}$

$= (2)^2$ ← **Simplify within the parentheses.** → $= (64)^{\frac{1}{3}}$

$= 4$ ← **Simplify.** → $= 4$

3 EXAMPLE

Simplify $\left(x^{\frac{3}{4}}\right)^5\left(y^{\frac{1}{2}}\right)y^{\frac{2}{5}}$.

$\left(x^{\frac{3}{4}}\right)^5\left(y^{\frac{1}{2}}\right)y^{\frac{2}{5}} = \left(x^{\frac{15}{4}}\right)\left(y^{\frac{1}{2}} \cdot y^{\frac{2}{5}}\right)$ **Multiply exponents in $\left(x^{\frac{3}{4}}\right)^5$.**

$= x^{\frac{15}{4}}\left(y^{\frac{1}{2} + \frac{2}{5}}\right)$ **Add exponents of powers with the same base.**

$= x^{\frac{15}{4}}y^{\frac{9}{10}}$ **Simplify fractions. $\frac{1}{2} + \frac{2}{5} = \frac{9}{10}$. Leave $\frac{15}{4}$ as an improper fraction.**

EXERCISES

Simplify each expression.

1. $100^{\frac{1}{2}}$ **2.** $25^{\frac{1}{2}}$ **3.** $8^{\frac{1}{3}}$ **4.** $\left(49^{\frac{1}{2}}\right)^3$

5. $\left(8^{\frac{1}{3}}\right)^2$ **6.** $8^{\frac{4}{3}}$ **7.** $25^{\frac{3}{2}}$ **8.** $64^{\frac{4}{3}}$

9. $\left(x^{\frac{1}{3}}\right)^6$ **10.** $\left(b^{\frac{1}{4}}\right)^4$ **11.** $\left(m^{\frac{2}{5}}\right)^{\frac{5}{3}}$ **12.** $\left(m^{\frac{2}{5}}\right)\left(m^{\frac{3}{5}}\right)$

10-2 The Pythagorean Theorem

California Content Standards

2.0 Understand and use such operations as taking a root. Understand and use the rules of exponents. ***Develop***

24.2 Identify the hypothesis and conclusion in logical deduction. ***Master***

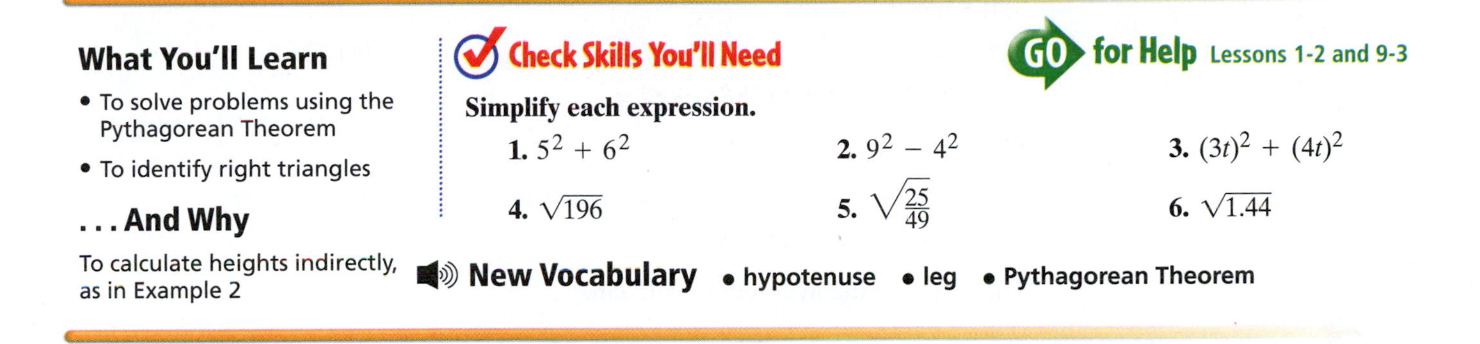

What You'll Learn

- To solve problems using the Pythagorean Theorem
- To identify right triangles

. . . And Why

To calculate heights indirectly, as in Example 2

Check Skills You'll Need

GO for Help Lessons 1-2 and 9-3

Simplify each expression.

1. $5^2 + 6^2$ **2.** $9^2 - 4^2$ **3.** $(3t)^2 + (4t)^2$

4. $\sqrt{196}$ **5.** $\sqrt{\frac{25}{49}}$ **6.** $\sqrt{1.44}$

New Vocabulary • hypotenuse • leg • Pythagorean Theorem

Solving Problems Using the Pythagorean Theorem

CA Standards Investigation The Pythagorean Theorem

1. Copy and complete the table.

a	b	c	a^2	b^2	$a^2 + b^2$	c^2
3	4	5	■	■	■	■
5	12	13	■	■	■	■
$\frac{3}{5}$	$\frac{4}{5}$	1	■	■	■	■
0.9	1.2	1.5	■	■	■	■

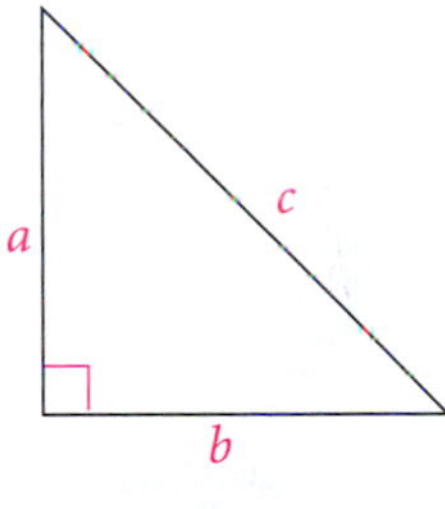

2. Compare the values of $a^2 + b^2$ for each row to the values of c^2.

3. Complete the following statement: For a right triangle, the square of the longest side __?__ the sum of the squares of the other two sides.

Vocabulary Tip

The Pythagorean Theorem is named after Pythagoras, a Greek philosopher and mathematician who taught about 530 B.C.

In a right triangle, the side opposite the right angle is the **hypotenuse.** It is the longest side. Each of the sides forming the right angle is a **leg.**

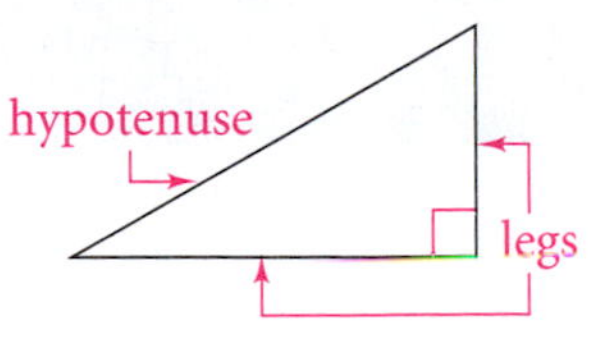

The **Pythagorean Theorem** describes the relationship of the lengths of the sides of a right triangle.

Take Note

Theorem **The Pythagorean Theorem**

In any right triangle, the sum of the squares of the lengths of the legs is equal to the square of the length of the hypotenuse.

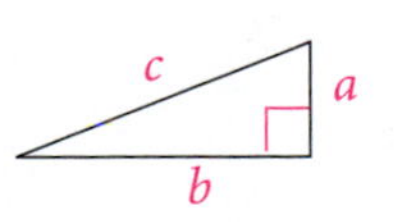

$$a^2 + b^2 = c^2$$

Sometimes you will need to find square roots to determine the length of a side or of a hypotenuse of a triangle. In real-world situations, $x^2 = a^2$, you find the principal square root of each side. So $\sqrt{x^2} = \sqrt{a^2}$, and $x = a$.

1 EXAMPLE Using the Pythagorean Theorem

What is the length of the hypotenuse of the triangle at the right?

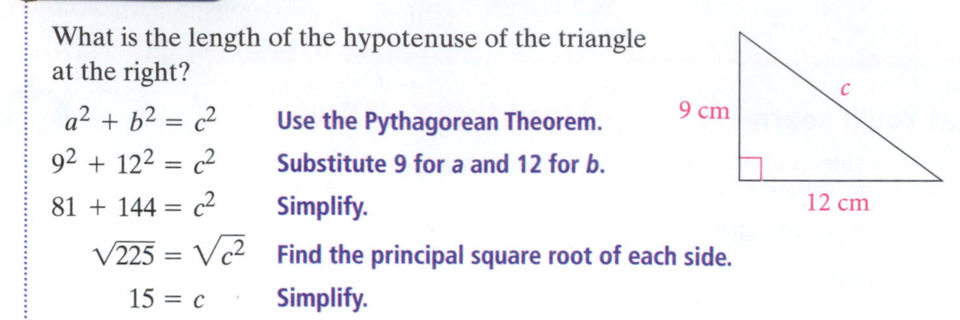

$a^2 + b^2 = c^2$ **Use the Pythagorean Theorem.**

$9^2 + 12^2 = c^2$ **Substitute 9 for *a* and 12 for *b*.**

$81 + 144 = c^2$ **Simplify.**

$\sqrt{225} = \sqrt{c^2}$ **Find the principal square root of each side.**

$15 = c$ **Simplify.**

The length of the hypotenuse is 15 cm.

CA Standards Check 1 What is the length of the hypotenuse of a right triangle with legs of lengths 7 cm and 24 cm?

You can also use the Pythagorean Theorem to find the length of a leg of a right triangle when you know the lengths of the hypotenuse and the other leg.

2 EXAMPLE Application

A fire truck parks beside a building such that the base of the ladder is 16 ft from the building. The fire truck extends its ladder 30 ft as shown at the left. How high is the top of the ladder above the ground?

Define Let b = height (in feet) of the ladder from a point 10 ft above the ground.

Relate The triangle formed is a right triangle. Use the Pythagorean Theorem.

Write $a^2 + b^2 = c^2$

$16^2 + b^2 = 30^2$ **Substitute.**

$256 + b^2 = 900$ **Simplify.**

$b^2 = 644$ **Subtract 256 from each side.**

$\sqrt{b^2} = \sqrt{644}$ **Find the principal square root of each side.**

$b \approx 25.4$ **Use a calculator and round to the nearest tenth.**

The height to the top of the ladder is 10 feet higher than 25.4 ft, so it is about 35.4 ft from the ground.

CA Standards Check 2 Use the figure at the right. About how many miles is it from downtown to the harbor? Round to the nearest tenth of a mile.

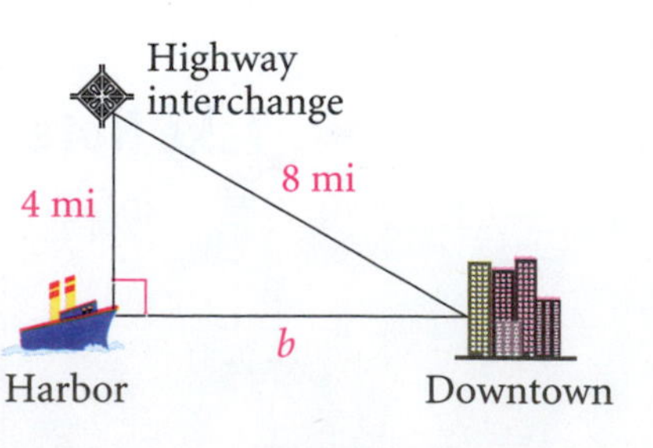

Identifying Right Triangles

Recall that an *if-then* statement is called a conditional and has two parts. The part following *if* is the hypothesis, and the part following *then* is the conclusion. The converse of a conditional switches the hypothesis and the conclusion. Sometimes the converse of a conditional is not true.

You can rewrite the Pythagorean Theorem as an *if-then* statement, "If a triangle is a right triangle with legs of lengths a and b and hypotenuse of length c, then $a^2 + b^2 = c^2$." The Pythagorean Theorem has a converse that is always true.

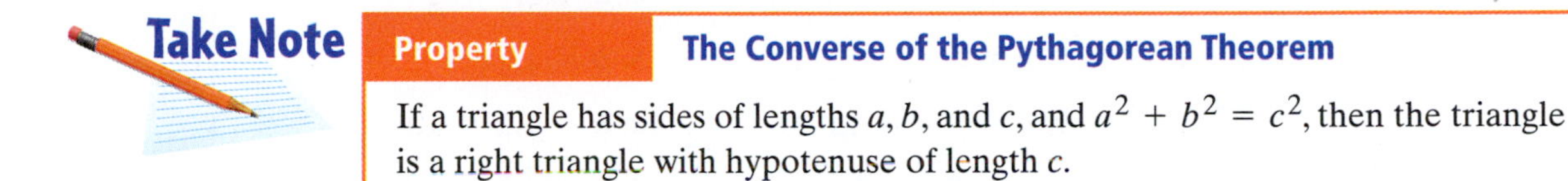

Take Note

Property **The Converse of the Pythagorean Theorem**

If a triangle has sides of lengths a, b, and c, and $a^2 + b^2 = c^2$, then the triangle is a right triangle with hypotenuse of length c.

You can use the converse of the Pythagorean Theorem to determine whether a triangle is a right triangle. Since the Pythagorean Theorem and its converse are always true, you can also determine whether a triangle is *not* a right triangle.

3 EXAMPLE Using the Converse of the Pythagorean Theorem

Determine whether the given lengths can be sides of a right triangle.

a. 5 in., 12 in., and 13 in.

$5^2 + 12^2 \stackrel{?}{=} 13^2$

$25 + 144 \stackrel{?}{=} 169$

$169 = 169$ ✓

The triangle is a right triangle.

Determine whether $a^2 + b^2 = c^2$, where c is the longest side.

b. 7 m, 9 m, and 12 m

$7^2 + 9^2 \stackrel{?}{=} 12^2$

$49 + 81 \stackrel{?}{=} 144$

$130 \neq 144$

The triangle is not a right triangle.

CA Standards Check 3 A triangle has sides of lengths 10 m, 24 m, and 26 m. Is the triangle a right triangle?

You can use the converse of the Pythagorean Theorem to solve a physics problem involving force.

4 EXAMPLE Application

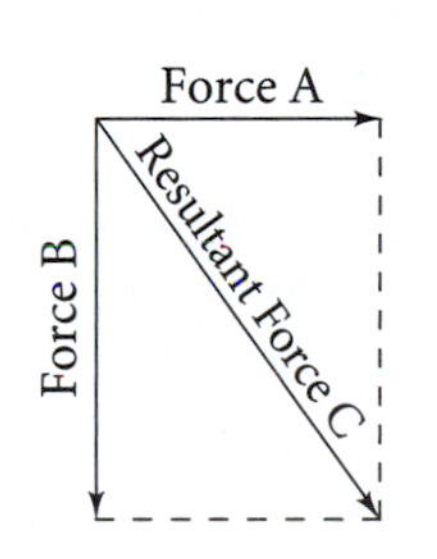

If two forces pull at right angles to each other, the resultant force is represented as the diagonal of a rectangle, as shown at the left. The diagonal forms a right triangle with two of the perpendicular sides of the rectangle. For a 30-lb force and a 40-lb force, the resultant force is 50 lb. Are the forces pulling at right angles to each other?

$30^2 + 40^2 \stackrel{?}{=} 50^2$ Determine whether $a^2 + b^2 = c^2$, where c is the greatest force.

$900 + 1600 \stackrel{?}{=} 2500$

$2500 = 2500$ ✓

Yes, the 30-lb and 40-lb forces are pulling at right angles to each other.

CA Standards Check 4 For a 70-lb force and a 60-lb force, the resultant force is 100 lb. Are the forces pulling at right angles to each other?

EXERCISES
Standards Practice

For more exercises, see *Extra Skills and Word Problem Practice.*

Alg1 2.0, 24.2

A Practice by Example

Example 1 (page 494)

GO for Help

Use the triangle at the right. Find the length of the missing side. If necessary, round to the nearest tenth.

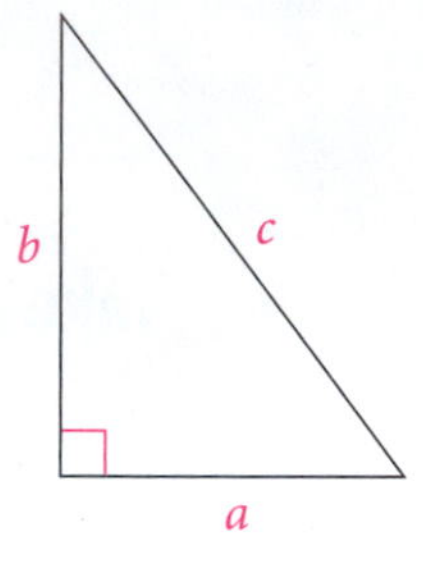

1. $a = 6, b = 8$　　**2.** $a = 15, b = 20$

3. $a = 8, b = 15$　　**4.** $a = 10, b = 24$

5. $a = 1.5, b = 2$　　**6.** $a = \frac{3}{5}, b = \frac{4}{5}$

Example 2 (page 494)

7. $a = 3, c = 5$　　**8.** $b = 12, c = 13$

9. $a = 9, c = 15$　　**10.** $b = 7, c = 10$

11. $a = 5, c = 9$　　**12.** $a = 0.8, c = 1$

13. Use the diagram at the right. Find the width w that the box needs to be for the fishing rod to fit flat inside of it.

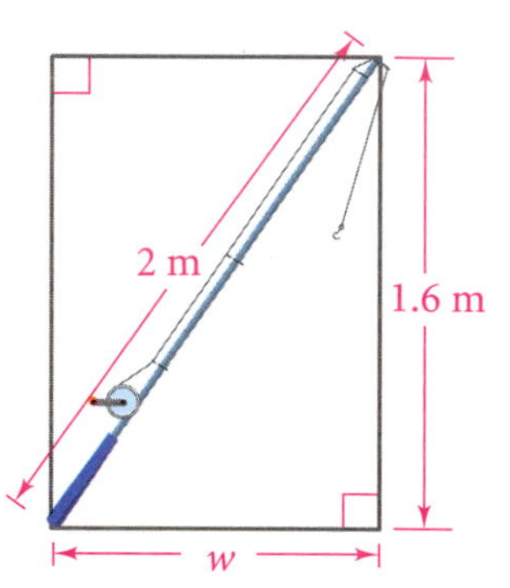

14. A 16-ft ladder is placed 4 ft from the base of a building. How high on the building will the ladder reach?

15. A pigeon leaves its nest in New York City and flies 5 km due east. The pigeon then flies 3 km due north. How far is the pigeon from its nest?

Example 3 (page 495)

Determine whether the given lengths can be sides of a right triangle.

16. 9 ft, 12 ft, 15 ft　　**17.** 1 in., 2 in., 3 in.　　**18.** 2 m, 4 m, 5 m

19. 16 cm, 30 cm, 34 cm　　**20.** 4 m, 4 m, 8 m　　**21.** 10 in., 24 in., 26 in.

Example 4 (page 495)

Determine whether the forces in each pair are pulling at right angles to each other.

22. 45 lb, 24 lb, resultant force 51 lb　　**23.** 3.5 lb, 6.2 lb, resultant force 9.1 lb

24. 20 lb, 10 lb, resultant force 30 lb　　**25.** 1.25 lb, 3 lb, resultant force 3.25 lb

B Apply Your Skills

For the values given, a and b are legs of a right triangle, and c is the hypotenuse. Find the length of the missing side. If necessary, round to the nearest tenth.

26. $a = 1.2, b = 0.9$　　**27.** $a = \frac{1}{5}, c = \frac{1}{3}$　　**28.** $a = 1, c = 2$

29. $a = \frac{3}{4}, b = 1$　　**30.** $a = 2.4, b = 1.0$　　**31.** $a = 2\frac{1}{2}, b = 6\frac{1}{2}$

32. Error Analysis The length of the hypotenuse of a right triangle is 7.5 cm, and the length of a leg is 4.5 cm. Sylvie solved the equation $(7.5)^2 + (4.5)^2 = c^2$ and found the length of the missing leg to be 8.75 cm. Explain her mistake and find the correct answer.

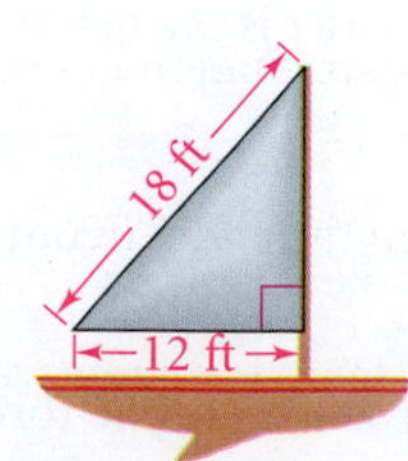

33. The diagram at the left shows a sailboat.

a. Use the Pythagorean Theorem to find the height of the sail. Round to the nearest tenth.

b. Use the result of part (a) and the formula for the area of a triangle to find the area of the sail. Round to the nearest tenth.

34. What is the diameter of the smallest circular opening through which the rectangular rod shown at the right will fit? Round to the nearest tenth.

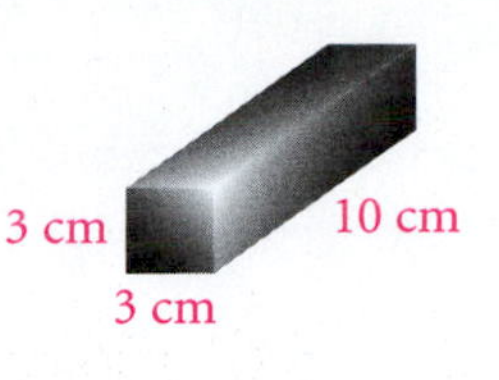

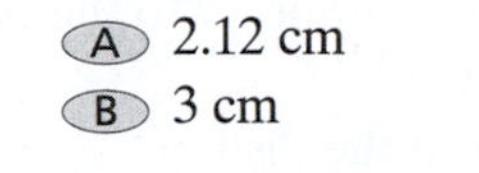

Ⓐ 2.12 cm　　Ⓒ 4.3 cm

Ⓑ 3 cm　　Ⓓ 9 cm

35. Two utility vehicles at a 90° angle to each other try to pull a third vehicle out of the snow. If one utility vehicle exerts a force of 600 lb, and the other exerts a force of 800 lb, what is the resulting force on the vehicle stuck in the snow?

Find the missing length to the nearest tenth.

36. **37.** **38.**

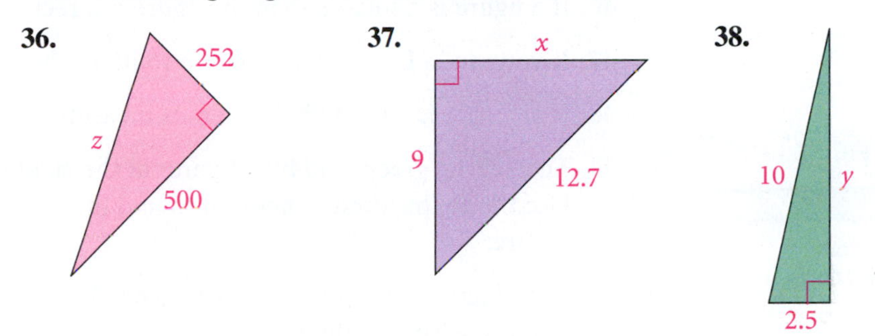

39. You know that two sides of a right triangle measure 10 in. and 8 in.

a. **Writing** Explain why this is not enough information to be sure of finding the length of the third side.

b. Give two possible values for the length of the third side.

40. Any set of three positive integers that satisfies the relationship $a^2 + b^2 = c^2$ is called a *Pythagorean triple.*

a. Verify that the numbers 6, 8, and 10 form a Pythagorean triple.

b. Copy the table at the right. Complete the table so that the values in each row form a Pythagorean triple.

c. Find a Pythagorean triple that does not appear in the table.

a	b	c
3	4	■
5	■	13
■	24	25
9	40	■

41. Solar cars use panels built out of photovoltaic cells, which convert sunlight into electricity. Consider a car like the one shown. Not counting the driver's "bubble," the panels form a rectangle.

a. The length of the rectangle is 13 ft and the diagonal is 14.7 ft. Find the width. Round to the nearest tenth of a foot.

b. Find the area of the rectangle.

c. The panels produce a maximum power of about 11 watts/ft^2. Find the maximum power produced by the panels on the car. Round to the nearest watt.

This solar-powered car weighs only 110 lb. It can reach a top speed of 80 mi/h.

42. A carpenter braces an 8-ft × 10-ft wall by nailing a board diagonally across the wall. How long is the bracing board?

43. **a.** Find a right triangle that has legs with irrational lengths and a hypotenuse with a rational length.

b. Use a calculator to find the area of your triangle. Round to the nearest tenth.

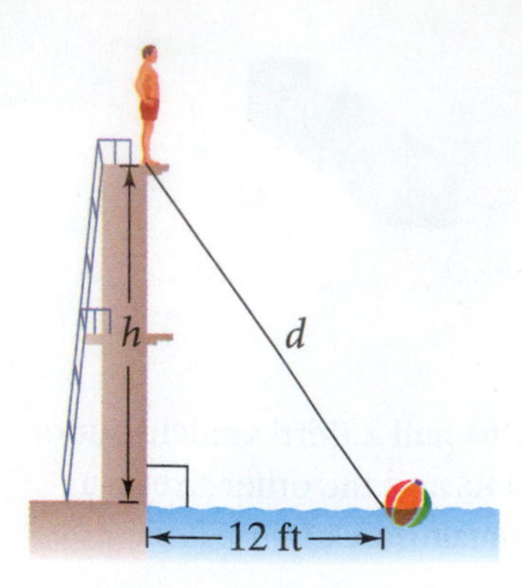

44. Suppose you are standing at the top of a diving platform h feet tall. Looking down, you see a ball on the water 12 feet from the bottom of the diving platform, as in the diagram at the left.
   a. Find the distance d to the ball if $h = 6$ feet; if $h = 12$ feet.
   b. Suppose you know the distance d to the ball is 16 feet. About how tall is the diving platform?
   c. **Critical Thinking** Could the distance d to the ball be 7 feet? Explain.

Math Reasoning State the hypothesis and the conclusion of each conditional. Then write the converse. Tell whether the converse is true or false.

45. If an integer has 2 as a factor, then the integer is even.

46. If a figure is a square, then the figure is a rectangle.

47. If you are in Brazil, then you are south of the equator.

48. If an angle is a right angle, then its measure is 90°.

Visit: PHSchool.com
Web Code: bae-1002

49. The yellow, green, and blue figures at the right are squares. Use the Pythagorean Theorem to find the area of the blue square.

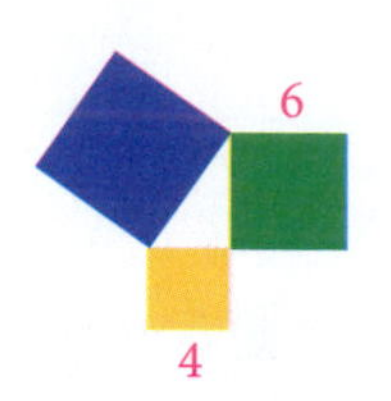

50. The diagonal of a square measures $6\sqrt{2}$ in. Find the length of the side of the square.

For any two points $P(x_1, y_1)$ and $Q(x_2, y_2)$ not on the same horizontal or vertical line, you can graph the points and form a right triangle as shown at the right. You can then use the Pythagorean Theorem to find the distance between the points. The result is called the Distance Formula.

$$PQ = \sqrt{(x_2 - x_1)^2 + (y_2 - y_1)^2}$$

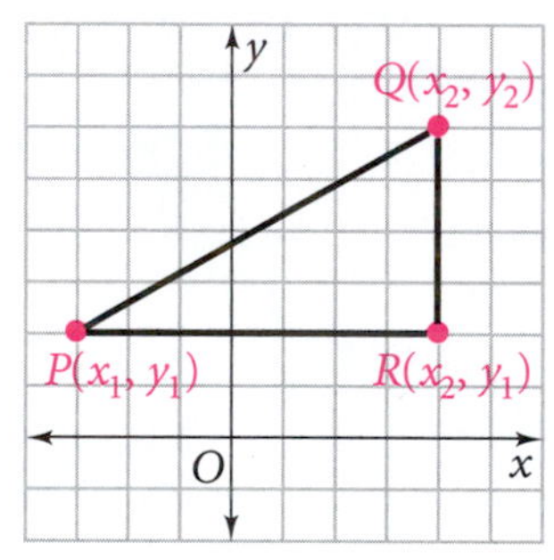

Use the Distance Formula to find the distance between each pair of points. Where necessary, round to the nearest tenth.

51. (7, −3), (−8, −3)
52. (−2, 7), (−3, −7)
53. (0, 0), (6, −8)
54. (−4, −4), (4, 4)
55. (9, 10), (11, 12)
56. (3, −2), (−1, 5)

Use the Pythagorean Theorem to find s.

57. 58. 59.

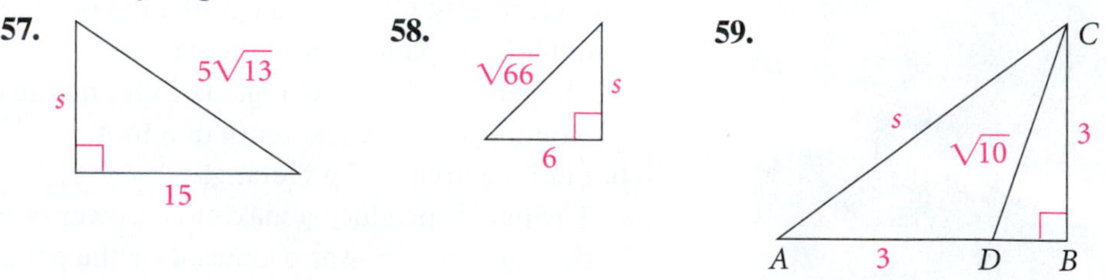

60. The lengths of the sides of a right triangle are three consecutive integers. Write and solve an equation to find the three integers.

61. a. **Critical Thinking** The vertex of the right angle of a right triangle is at the origin of coordinate axes. The length of the horizontal side is 5 units. The length of the vertical side is 7 units. The triangle is located in Quadrant II. Sketch the graph.
   b. Find the length of the hypotenuse. Round to the nearest tenth.

62. On graph paper, draw a right triangle like the one at the right. Then draw the square by drawing four right triangles as shown.

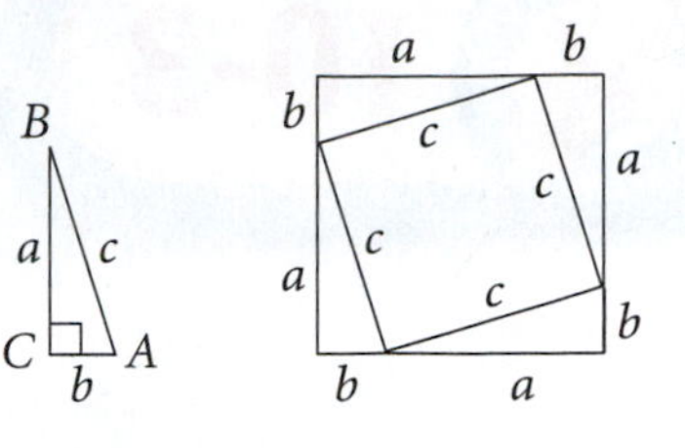

a. Find the area of the larger square. Write your answer as a trinomial.

b. Find the area for the smaller square. Write your answer as a monomial.

c. Find the area of each triangle in terms of a and b.

d. The area of the larger square equals the sum of the area of the smaller square and the areas of the four triangles. Write this equation and simplify.

e. What do you notice about the equation you wrote for part (d)?

Multiple Choice Practice

For California Standards Tutorials, visit PHSchool.com. Web Code: baq-9045

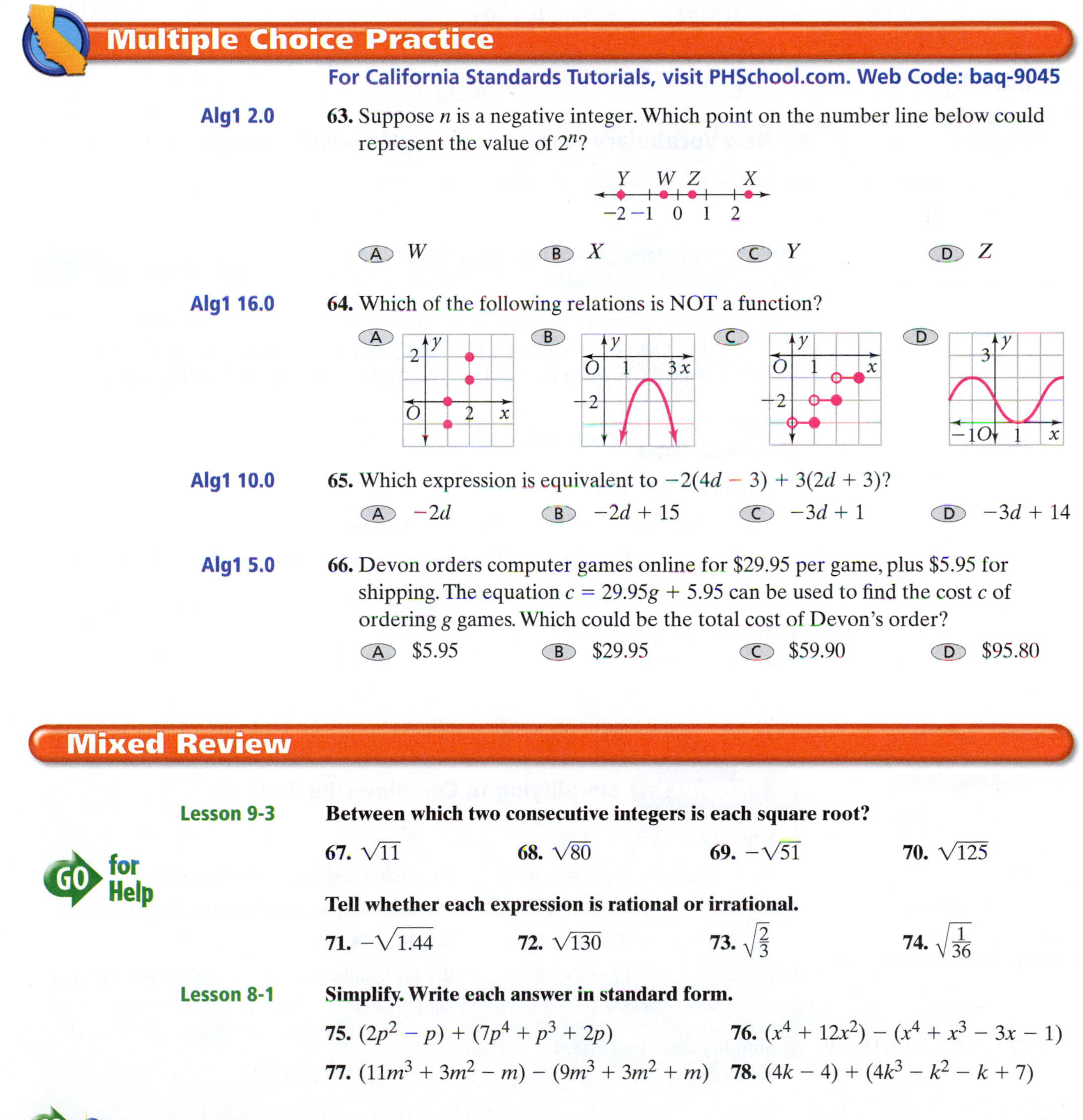

Alg1 2.0

63. Suppose n is a negative integer. Which point on the number line below could represent the value of 2^n?

Ⓐ W Ⓑ X Ⓒ Y Ⓓ Z

Alg1 16.0

64. Which of the following relations is NOT a function?

Ⓐ Ⓑ Ⓒ Ⓓ

Alg1 10.0

65. Which expression is equivalent to $-2(4d - 3) + 3(2d + 3)$?

Ⓐ $-2d$ Ⓑ $-2d + 15$ Ⓒ $-3d + 1$ Ⓓ $-3d + 14$

Alg1 5.0

66. Devon orders computer games online for \$29.95 per game, plus \$5.95 for shipping. The equation $c = 29.95g + 5.95$ can be used to find the cost c of ordering g games. Which could be the total cost of Devon's order?

Ⓐ \$5.95 Ⓑ \$29.95 Ⓒ \$59.90 Ⓓ \$95.80

Mixed Review

GO for Help

Lesson 9-3

Between which two consecutive integers is each square root?

67. $\sqrt{11}$ **68.** $\sqrt{80}$ **69.** $-\sqrt{51}$ **70.** $\sqrt{125}$

Tell whether each expression is rational or irrational.

71. $-\sqrt{1.44}$ **72.** $\sqrt{130}$ **73.** $\sqrt{\frac{2}{3}}$ **74.** $\sqrt{\frac{1}{36}}$

Lesson 8-1

Simplify. Write each answer in standard form.

75. $(2p^2 - p) + (7p^4 + p^3 + 2p)$

76. $(x^4 + 12x^2) - (x^4 + x^3 - 3x - 1)$

77. $(11m^3 + 3m^2 - m) - (9m^3 + 3m^2 + m)$

78. $(4k - 4) + (4k^3 - k^2 - k + 7)$

GO Online Lesson Quiz Visit: PHSchool.com, Web Code: baa-1002

Operations With Radical Expressions

California Content Standards

2.0 Understand and use such operations as taking a root. ***Develop***

25.0 Use properties of the number system to judge the validity of results and to prove or disprove statements. ***Master***

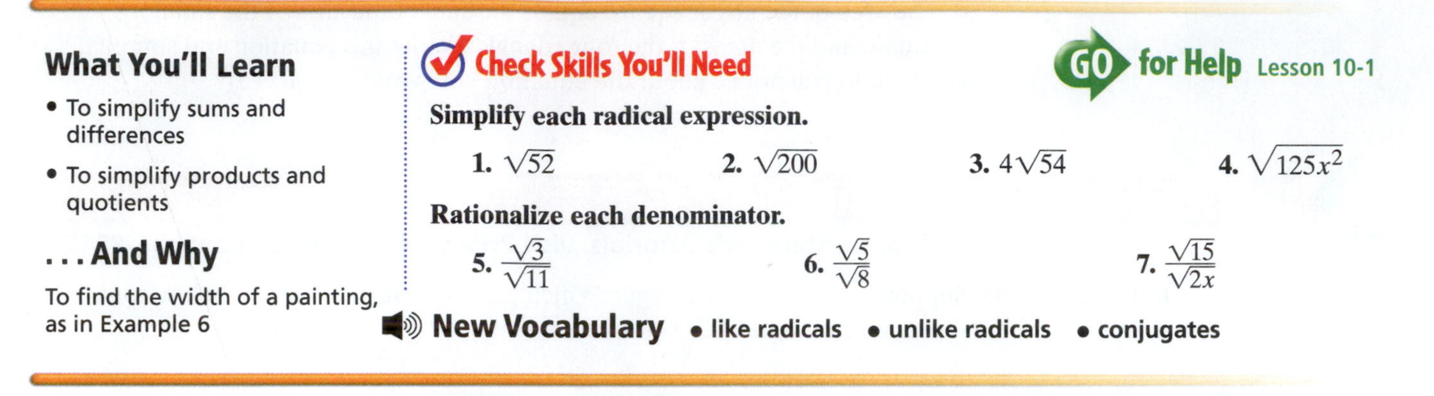

What You'll Learn

- To simplify sums and differences
- To simplify products and quotients

. . . And Why

To find the width of a painting, as in Example 6

Check Skills You'll Need — GO for Help Lesson 10-1

Simplify each radical expression.

1. $\sqrt{52}$ **2.** $\sqrt{200}$ **3.** $4\sqrt{54}$ **4.** $\sqrt{125x^2}$

Rationalize each denominator.

5. $\frac{\sqrt{3}}{\sqrt{11}}$ **6.** $\frac{\sqrt{5}}{\sqrt{8}}$ **7.** $\frac{\sqrt{15}}{\sqrt{2x}}$

New Vocabulary • like radicals • unlike radicals • conjugates

Simplifying Sums and Differences

For radical expressions, **like radicals** have the same radicand and **unlike radicals** do not. For example, $4\sqrt{7}$ and $-12\sqrt{7}$ are like radicals, but $3\sqrt{11}$ and $2\sqrt{5}$ are unlike radicals. You can use the Distributive Property to combine like radicals.

1 EXAMPLE Combining Like Radicals

Simplify $\sqrt{2} + 3\sqrt{2}$.

$\sqrt{2} + 3\sqrt{2} = 1\sqrt{2} + 3\sqrt{2}$ Both terms contain $\sqrt{2}$.

$= (1 + 3)\sqrt{2}$ Use the Distributive Property to combine like radicals.

$= 4\sqrt{2}$ Simplify.

CA Standards Check 1 Simplify each expression.

a. $-3\sqrt{5} - 4\sqrt{5}$ **b.** $\sqrt{10} - 5\sqrt{10}$

Online active math

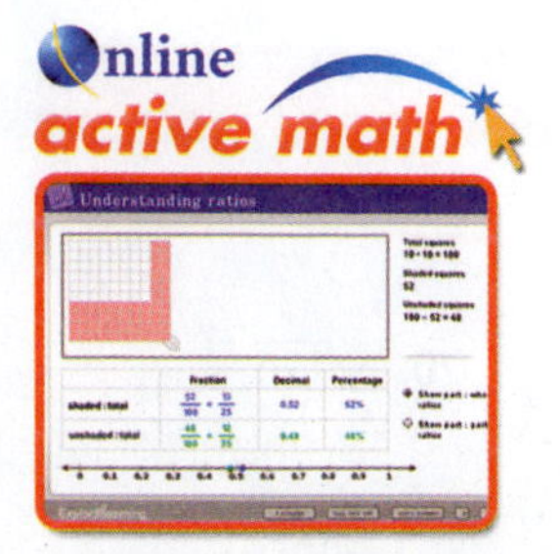

For: Radical Activity
Use: Interactive Textbook, 10-3

You may need to simplify a radical expression to determine if you have like radicals.

2 EXAMPLE Simplifying to Combine Like Radicals

Simplify $7\sqrt{3} - \sqrt{12}$.

$7\sqrt{3} - \sqrt{12} = 7\sqrt{3} - \sqrt{4 \cdot 3}$ 4 is a perfect square and a factor of 12.

$= 7\sqrt{3} - \sqrt{4} \cdot \sqrt{3}$ Use the Multiplication Property of Square Roots.

$= 7\sqrt{3} - 2\sqrt{3}$ Simplify $\sqrt{4}$.

$= (7 - 2)\sqrt{3}$ Use the Distributive Property to combine like radicals.

$= 5\sqrt{3}$ Simplify.

CA Standards Check 2 Simplify each expression.

a. $3\sqrt{20} + 2\sqrt{5}$ **b.** $3\sqrt{3} - 2\sqrt{27}$

Simplifying Products and Quotients

When simplifying a radical expression like $\sqrt{3}(\sqrt{6}+7)$, use the Distributive Property to multiply $\sqrt{3}$ times $(\sqrt{6}+7)$.

3 EXAMPLE Using the Distributive Property

Simplify $\sqrt{3}(\sqrt{6}+7)$.

$\sqrt{3}(\sqrt{6}+7) = \sqrt{18} + 7\sqrt{3}$ — Use the Distributive Property.

$= \sqrt{9}\cdot\sqrt{2} + 7\sqrt{3}$ — Use the Multiplication Property of Square Roots.

$= 3\sqrt{2} + 7\sqrt{3}$ — Simplify.

CA Standards Check 3 Simplify each radical expression.

a. $\sqrt{5}(2+\sqrt{10})$ **b.** $\sqrt{2x}(\sqrt{6x}-11)$ **c.** $\sqrt{5a}(\sqrt{5a}+3)$

If both radical expressions have two terms, you can multiply the same way you find the product of two binomials, by using FOIL.

4 EXAMPLE Simplifying Using FOIL

Simplify $(\sqrt{5}-2\sqrt{15})(\sqrt{5}+\sqrt{15})$.

$(\sqrt{5}-2\sqrt{15})(\sqrt{5}+\sqrt{15})$

$= \sqrt{25} + \sqrt{75} - 2\sqrt{75} - 2\sqrt{225}$ — Use FOIL.

$= 5 - \sqrt{75} - 2(15)$ — Combine like radicals and simplify $\sqrt{25}$ and $\sqrt{225}$.

$= 5 - \sqrt{25\cdot 3} - 30$ — 25 is a perfect square factor of 75.

$= 5 - \sqrt{25}\cdot\sqrt{3} - 30$ — Use the Multiplication Property of Square Roots.

$= 5 - 5\sqrt{3} - 30$ — Simplify $\sqrt{25}$.

$= -25 - 5\sqrt{3}$ — Simplify.

CA Standards Check 4 Simplify each radical expression.

a. $(2\sqrt{6}+3\sqrt{3})(\sqrt{6}-5\sqrt{3})$ **b.** $(\sqrt{7}+4)^2$

Go Online

Video Tutor Help

Visit: PHSchool.com

Web Code: bae-0775

Conjugates are the sum and the difference of the same two terms. The radical expressions $\sqrt{5}+\sqrt{2}$ and $\sqrt{5}-\sqrt{2}$ are conjugates. The product of two conjugates results in a difference of two squares.

$$(\sqrt{5}+\sqrt{2})(\sqrt{5}-\sqrt{2}) = (\sqrt{5})^2 - (\sqrt{2})^2$$
$$= 5 - 2$$
$$= 3$$

Notice that the product of these conjugates has no radical.

You recall that a simplified radical expression has no radical in the denominator. When a denominator contains a sum or a difference including radical expressions, you can rationalize the denominator by multiplying the numerator and the denominator by the conjugate of the denominator. For example, to simplify a radical expression like $\frac{6}{\sqrt{5}-\sqrt{2}}$, you multiply by $\frac{\sqrt{5}+\sqrt{2}}{\sqrt{5}+\sqrt{2}}$.

5 EXAMPLE Rationalizing a Denominator Using Conjugates

Simplify $\frac{6}{\sqrt{5} - \sqrt{2}}$.

$\frac{6}{\sqrt{5} - \sqrt{2}} = \frac{6}{\sqrt{5} - \sqrt{2}} \cdot \frac{\sqrt{5} + \sqrt{2}}{\sqrt{5} + \sqrt{2}}$ **Multiply the numerator and the denominator by the conjugate of the denominator.**

$= \frac{6(\sqrt{5} + \sqrt{2})}{5 - 2}$ **Multiply in the denominator.**

$= \frac{6(\sqrt{5} + \sqrt{2})}{3}$ **Simplify the denominator.**

$= 2(\sqrt{5} + \sqrt{2})$ **Divide 6 and 3 by the common factor 3.**

$= 2\sqrt{5} + 2\sqrt{2}$ **Simplify the expression.**

CA Standards Check 5 Simplify each expression.

a. $\frac{4}{\sqrt{7} + \sqrt{5}}$ b. $\frac{-4}{\sqrt{10} + \sqrt{8}}$ c. $\frac{-5}{\sqrt{11} - \sqrt{3}}$

You can solve a ratio involving radical expressions.

6 EXAMPLE Application

The ratio length : width of this painting by Mondrian is approximately equal to the *golden ratio* $(1 + \sqrt{5}) : 2$. The length of the painting is 81 inches. Find the width of the painting in simplest radical form. Then find the approximate width to the nearest inch.

Define 81 = length of painting
x = width of painting

Relate $(1 + \sqrt{5}) : 2$ = length : width

Write $\frac{1 + \sqrt{5}}{2} = \frac{81}{x}$

$x(1 + \sqrt{5}) = 162$ **Cross multiply.**

$\frac{x(1 + \sqrt{5})}{(1 + \sqrt{5})} = \frac{162}{(1 + \sqrt{5})}$ **Divide both sides by $(1 + \sqrt{5})$.**

$x = \frac{162}{(1 + \sqrt{5})} \cdot \frac{(1 - \sqrt{5})}{(1 - \sqrt{5})}$ **Multiply the numerator and the denominator by the conjugate of the denominator.**

$x = \frac{162(1 - \sqrt{5})}{1 - 5}$ **Multiply in the denominator.**

$x = \frac{162(1 - \sqrt{5})}{-4}$ **Simplify the denominator.**

$x = \frac{-81(1 - \sqrt{5})}{2}$ **Divide 162 and −4 by the common factor −2.**

$x = 50.06075309$ **Use a calculator.**

$x \approx 50$

The exact width of the painting is $\frac{-81(1 - \sqrt{5})}{2}$ in. The approximate width is 50 in.

CA Standards Check 6 Another painting has a length : width ratio approximately equal to the golden ratio $(1 + \sqrt{5}) : 2$. Find the length of the painting if the width is 34 inches.

EXERCISES

For more exercises, see *Extra Skills and Word Problem Practice.*

Standards Practice

Alg1 2.0, 25.0

A Practice by Example

Example 1 (page 500)

GO for Help

Simplify each expression.

1. $-3\sqrt{6} + 8\sqrt{6}$
2. $16\sqrt{10} + 2\sqrt{10}$
3. $\sqrt{5} - 3\sqrt{5}$
4. $6\sqrt{7} - 4\sqrt{7}$
5. $15\sqrt{2} - \sqrt{2}$
6. $-5\sqrt{3} - 3\sqrt{3}$

Example 2 (page 500)

Tell whether each pair of expressions can be simplified to like radicals.

7. $\sqrt{2}, \sqrt{32}$
8. $\sqrt{3}, \sqrt{75}$
9. $\sqrt{5}, \sqrt{50}$

Simplify each expression.

10. $\sqrt{18} + \sqrt{2}$
11. $2\sqrt{12} - 7\sqrt{3}$
12. $\sqrt{8} + 2\sqrt{2}$
13. $4\sqrt{5} - 2\sqrt{45}$
14. $3\sqrt{7} - \sqrt{28}$
15. $-4\sqrt{10} + 6\sqrt{40}$

Example 3 (page 501)

16. $\sqrt{2}(\sqrt{8} - 4)$
17. $\sqrt{3}(\sqrt{27} + 1)$
18. $2\sqrt{3}(\sqrt{3} - 1)$
19. $\sqrt{3}(\sqrt{15} + 2)$
20. $\sqrt{2}(3 + 3\sqrt{2})$
21. $\sqrt{6}(\sqrt{6} - 5)$

Example 4 (page 501)

22. $(3\sqrt{2} + \sqrt{3})(\sqrt{2} - 5\sqrt{3})$
23. $(2\sqrt{5} - \sqrt{6})(4\sqrt{5} - 3\sqrt{6})$
24. $(\sqrt{7} - 2)^2$
25. $(2\sqrt{10} + \sqrt{3})^2$
26. $(2\sqrt{11} + 5)(\sqrt{11} + 2)$
27. $(4 - \sqrt{13})(9 + \sqrt{13})$

Example 5 (page 502)

28. $\dfrac{8}{\sqrt{7} - \sqrt{3}}$
29. $\dfrac{-12}{\sqrt{8} - \sqrt{2}}$
30. $\dfrac{48}{\sqrt{6} - \sqrt{18}}$
31. $\dfrac{3}{\sqrt{10} - \sqrt{5}}$
32. $\dfrac{-40}{\sqrt{11} - \sqrt{3}}$
33. $\dfrac{9}{\sqrt{12} - \sqrt{11}}$

Example 6 (page 502)

Find an exact solution for each equation. Find the approximate solution to the nearest tenth.

34. $\dfrac{5\sqrt{2}}{\sqrt{2} - 1} = \dfrac{x}{\sqrt{2}}$
35. $\dfrac{3}{1 + \sqrt{5}} = \dfrac{1 - \sqrt{5}}{x}$
36. $\dfrac{\sqrt{2} - 1}{\sqrt{2} + 1} = \dfrac{x}{2}$

37. The ratio of the length to the width of a painting is $(1 + \sqrt{5}) : 2$. The length is 12 ft. What is the width?

B Apply Your Skills

Simplify each expression.

38. $\sqrt{40} + \sqrt{90}$
39. $3\sqrt{2}(2 + \sqrt{6})$
40. $\sqrt{12} + 4\sqrt{75} - \sqrt{36}$
41. $(\sqrt{3} + \sqrt{5})^2$
42. $\dfrac{\sqrt{13} + \sqrt{10}}{\sqrt{13} - \sqrt{5}}$
43. $(\sqrt{7} + \sqrt{8})(\sqrt{7} + \sqrt{8})$
44. $2\sqrt{2}(-2\sqrt{32} + \sqrt{8})$
45. $4\sqrt{50} - 7\sqrt{18}$
46. $\dfrac{2\sqrt{12} + 3\sqrt{6}}{\sqrt{9} - \sqrt{6}}$

47. The ratio of the rates of diffusion of two gases is given by the formula $\frac{r_1}{r_2} = \frac{\sqrt{m_2}}{\sqrt{m_1}}$, where m_1 and m_2 are the masses of the molecules of the gases. Find $\frac{r_1}{r_2}$ if $m_1 = 12$ units and $m_2 = 30$ units.

Geometry **Find the exact perimeter of each figure below.**

48. **49.**

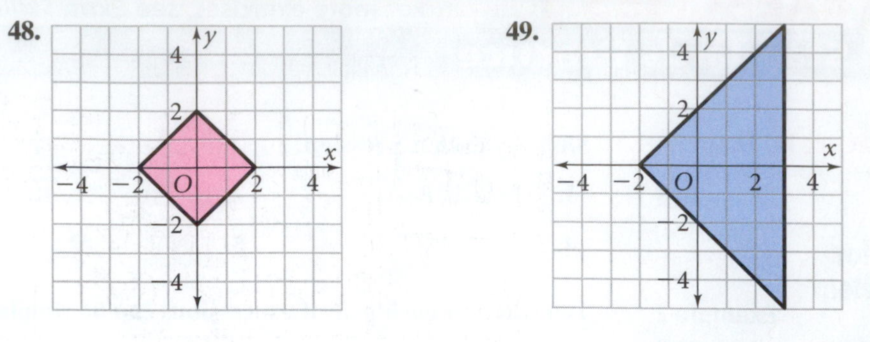

Error Analysis **Find the error in each student's work. Then simplify correctly.**

50.

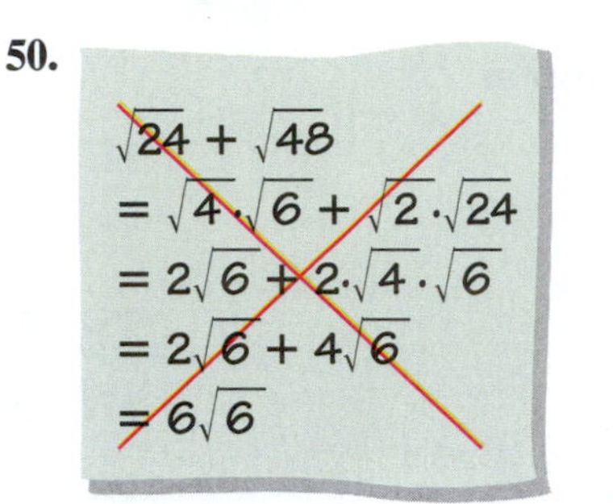

51.

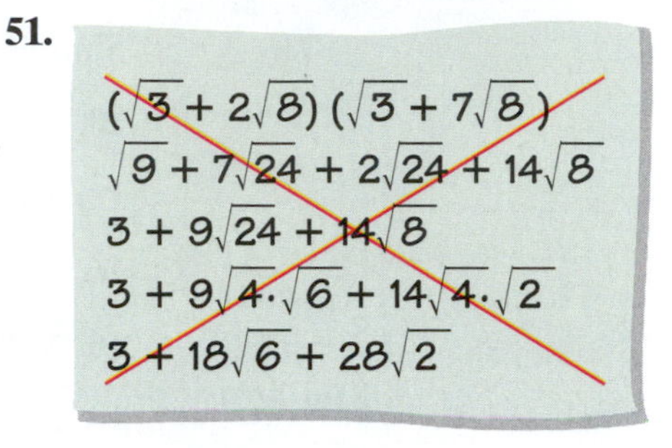

52. Write three sums that are less than or equal to 50. Use the square roots of 2, 3, 5, or 7, and the whole numbers less than 10.
For example, $8\sqrt{5} + 9\sqrt{7} \leq 50$.

53. You can make a box kite like the one at the right in the shape of a rectangular solid. The opening at each end of the kite is a square.

a. Suppose the sides of the square are 2 ft long. How long are the diagonal struts used for bracing?

b. Suppose each side of the square has length s. Find the length of the diagonal struts in terms of s. Write your answer in simplest form.

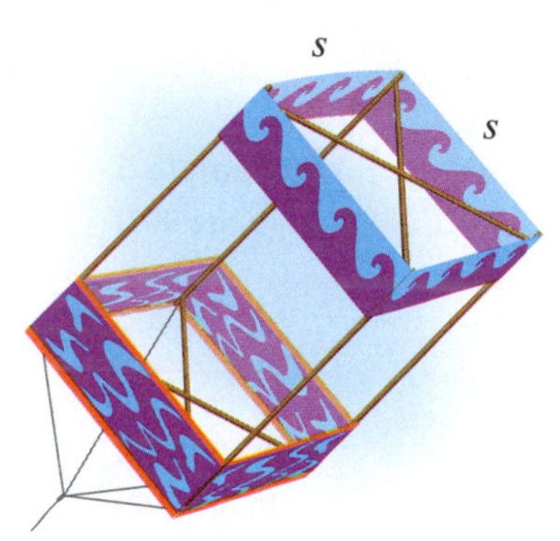

For Exercises 54–56, the formula $r = \sqrt{\frac{A}{P}} - 1$ gives the interest rate r that will allow principal P to grow into amount A in two years, if the interest is compounded annually. Use the formula to find the interest rate you would need to meet each goal.

54. Suppose you have \$500 to deposit into an account. Your goal is to have \$595 in that account at the end of the second year.

55. Suppose you have \$550 to deposit into an account. Your goal is to have \$700 in that account at the end of two years.

56. Suppose you have \$600 to deposit into an account. Your goal is to have \$800 in that account at the end of two years.

Visit: PHSchool.com
Web Code: bae-1003

57. a. Suppose n is an even number. Simplify $\sqrt{x^n}$.

b. Suppose n is an odd number greater than 1. Simplify $\sqrt{x^n}$.

58. **Critical Thinking** Simplify $\frac{a\sqrt{b}}{b\sqrt{a}}$.

59. Find the value of the numerical expression for Professor Hinkle's age in the cartoon.

60. Writing Explain why $\sqrt{3} + \sqrt{6}$ cannot be simplified.

61. a. Copy and complete the table.

a	b	$\sqrt{a}$	$\sqrt{b}$	$\sqrt{a}+\sqrt{b}$	$\sqrt{a+b}$
1	0	■	■	■	■
16	1	■	■	■	■
25	9	■	■	■	■
64	36	■	■	■	■
100	81	■	■	■	■

b. Does $\sqrt{a} + \sqrt{b}$ always equal $\sqrt{a + b}$? Explain.

62. Error Analysis Explain the error in the work below.

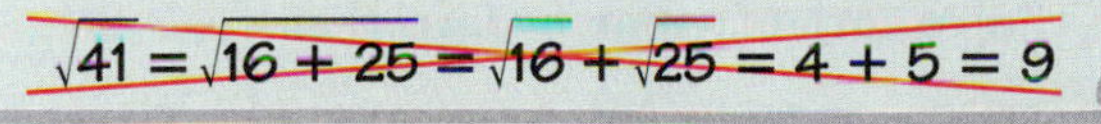

$\sqrt{41} = \sqrt{16 + 25} = \sqrt{16} + \sqrt{25} = 4 + 5 = 9$

63. Simplify $4\sqrt{75} + \sqrt{27}$.

Ⓐ $12\sqrt{3}$ Ⓑ $23\sqrt{3}$ Ⓒ $4\sqrt{102}$ Ⓓ $5\sqrt{102}$

Challenge

Simplify each expression.

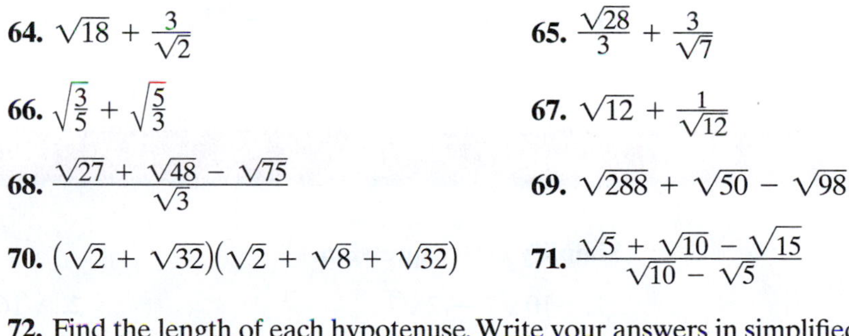

64. $\sqrt{18} + \frac{3}{\sqrt{2}}$

65. $\frac{\sqrt{28}}{3} + \frac{3}{\sqrt{7}}$

66. $\sqrt{\frac{3}{5}} + \sqrt{\frac{5}{3}}$

67. $\sqrt{12} + \frac{1}{\sqrt{12}}$

68. $\frac{\sqrt{27} + \sqrt{48} - \sqrt{75}}{\sqrt{3}}$

69. $\sqrt{288} + \sqrt{50} - \sqrt{98}$

70. $(\sqrt{2} + \sqrt{32})(\sqrt{2} + \sqrt{8} + \sqrt{32})$

71. $\frac{\sqrt{5} + \sqrt{10} - \sqrt{15}}{\sqrt{10} - \sqrt{5}}$

72. Find the length of each hypotenuse. Write your answers in simplified radical form.

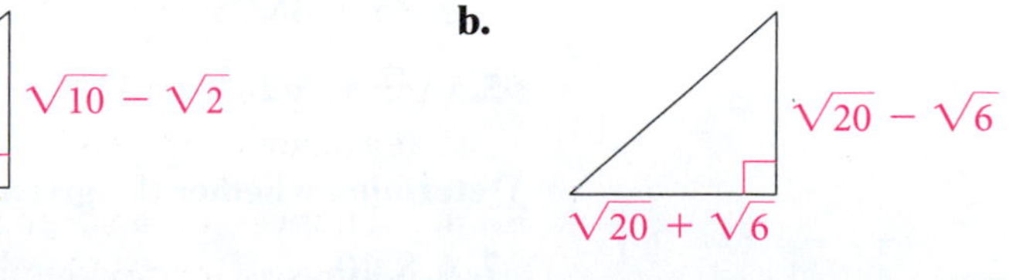

c. If the length of the legs of a right triangle are $\sqrt{p} + \sqrt{q}$ and $\sqrt{p} - \sqrt{q}$, write an expression for the length of the hypotenuse.

Multiple Choice Practice

For California Standards Tutorials, visit PHSchool.com. Web Code: baq-9045

Alg1 2.0

73. Which radical expression is NOT equal to $5\sqrt{2}$?

A $\sqrt{8} + \sqrt{18}$
C $\sqrt{98} - \sqrt{8}$
B $-\sqrt{32} + \sqrt{162}$
D $\sqrt{48} + \sqrt{2}$

Alg1 2.0

74. Which expression is equivalent to $(3x^{-2}y)^4(x^2y)$?

A $12x^4y^5$
B $81x^{10}y^5$
C $12x^{-6}y^5$
D $81x^{-6}y^5$

Alg1 5.0

75. Which problem can be solved using the equation $2x + (2x + 2) + (2x + 4) = 156$?

A The sum of 3 consecutive integers and 6 is 156. What is the first integer?
B The sum of 3 consecutive integers is 156. What is the first integer?
C The sum of 3 consecutive odd integers is 156. What is the first integer?
D The sum of 3 consecutive even integers is 156. What is the first integer?

Mixed Review

GO for Help

Lesson 10-1

Simplify each radical expression.

76. $\sqrt{8} \cdot \sqrt{6}$
77. $\frac{\sqrt{12}}{\sqrt{18}}$
78. $\sqrt{5 \cdot 10}$
79. $\sqrt{40b^5}$
80. $\frac{\sqrt{2x^2}}{\sqrt{4x^6}}$
81. $\sqrt{\frac{24v}{v^8}}$

Lesson 9-5

Solve each equation by factoring.

82. $5t^2 - 35t = 0$
83. $p^2 - 7p - 18 = 0$
84. $k^2 + 12k + 27 = 0$
85. $y^2 - 2y = 24$
86. $m^2 + 30 = -17m$
87. $2a^2 = -7a - 3$

Lesson 8-4

Find each product.

88. $(b + 11)(b + 11)$
89. $(2p + 7)(2p + 7)$
90. $(5g - 7)(5g + 7)$
91. $(3x + 1)(3x - 1)$
92. $\left(\frac{1}{3}k - 9\right)\left(\frac{1}{3}k + 9\right)$
93. $(d - 1.1)(d - 1.1)$

Checkpoint Quiz 1

Lessons 10-1 through 10-3

Simplify each expression.

1. $-10\sqrt{7} + 2\sqrt{7}$
2. $\sqrt{16} - 5\sqrt{2}$
3. $2\sqrt{5} + 3\sqrt{25}$
4. $\sqrt{6}(\sqrt{12} - \sqrt{3})$
5. $(\sqrt{3} + \sqrt{2})^2$
6. $\frac{\sqrt{8} - \sqrt{27}}{\sqrt{6} - \sqrt{5}}$

Determine whether the given lengths can be sides of a right triangle.

7. 6, 8, 10
8. 4, 8, 11
9. 12, 13, 15

10. A house is 12 miles east of a school. Another house is 9 miles north of the school. How far apart are the houses?

10-4 Solving Radical Equations

California Content Standards

2.0 Understand and use such operations as taking a root. ***Develop***

25.2 Judge the validity of an argument according to whether the properties of the real number system and the order of operations have been applied correctly at each step. ***Master***

What You'll Learn

- To solve equations containing radicals
- To identify extraneous solutions

. . . And Why

To design an amusement park ride, as in Example 2

Check Skills You'll Need

GO for Help Lesson 9-3

Evaluate each expression for the given value.

1. $\sqrt{x} - 3$ for $x = 16$ **2.** $\sqrt{x + 7}$ for $x = 9$ **3.** $2\sqrt{x + 3}$ for $x = 1$

Simplify each expression.

4. $(\sqrt{3})^2$ **5.** $(\sqrt{x + 1})^2$ **6.** $(\sqrt{2x - 5})^2$

New Vocabulary

- radical equation
- extraneous solution

Video Tutor Help

Visit: PHSchool.com
Web Code: bae-0775

Solving Radical Equations

A **radical equation** is an equation that has a variable in a radicand. You can often solve a radical equation by getting the radical by itself on one side of the equation. Then you square both sides. Remember that the expression under a radical must be nonnegative. When $x \geq 0, (\sqrt{x})^2 = x$.

1 EXAMPLE Solving by Isolating the Radical

Solve each equation. Check your solution.

a. $\sqrt{x} - 3 = 4$

$\sqrt{x} = 7$ Get the radical on the left side of the equation.

$(\sqrt{x})^2 = 7^2$ Square both sides.

$x = 49$

Check $\sqrt{x} - 3 = 4$

$\sqrt{49} - 3 \stackrel{?}{=} 4$ Substitute 49 for *x*.

$7 - 3 = 4$ ✓

b. $\sqrt{x - 3} = 4$

$(\sqrt{x - 3})^2 = 4^2$ Square both sides.

$x - 3 = 16$ Solve for *x*.

$x = 19$

Check $\sqrt{x - 3} = 4$

$\sqrt{19 - 3} \stackrel{?}{=} 4$ Substitute 19 for *x*.

$\sqrt{16} = 4$ ✓

CA Standards Check

1 Solve each equation. Check your solution.

a. $\sqrt{x} + 7 = 12$ **b.** $\sqrt{a} - 4 = 5$ **c.** $\sqrt{c - 2} = 6$

For an equation like $2\sqrt{x} = 8$, you could square both sides first, or you could divide by 2 to get $\sqrt{x}$ alone on one side of the equation.

When the roller coaster cars are upside down, the riders and the cars fall at the same rate and stay together.

2 EXAMPLE Application

On a roller coaster ride, your speed in a loop depends on the height of the hill you have just come down and the radius of the loop in feet. The equation $v = 8\sqrt{h - 2r}$ gives the velocity v in feet per second of a car at the top of the loop.

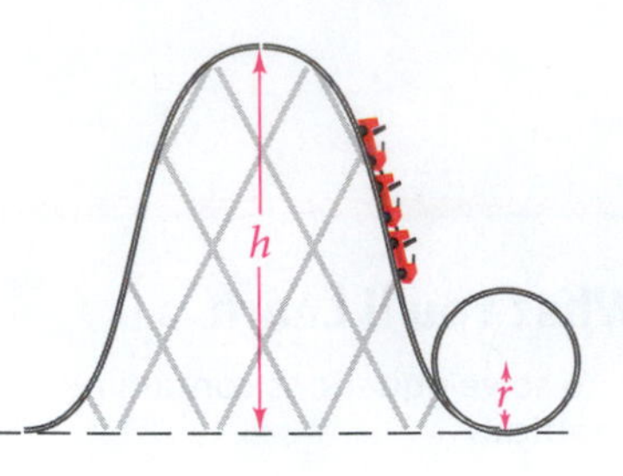

Suppose the loop has a radius of 18 ft. You want the car to have a velocity of 30 ft/s at the top of the loop. How high should the hill be?

Solve $v = 8\sqrt{h - 2r}$ for h when $v = 30$ and $r = 18$.

$30 = 8\sqrt{h - 2(18)}$ **Substitute 30 for *v* and 18 for *r*.**

$\frac{30}{8} = \frac{8\sqrt{h - 2(18)}}{8}$ **Divide each side by 8 to isolate the radical.**

$3.75 = \sqrt{h - 36}$ **Simplify.**

$(3.75)^2 = (\sqrt{h - 36})^2$ **Square both sides.**

$14.0625 = h - 36$

$50.0625 = h$

The hill should be about 50 ft high.

CA Standards Check 2 **a.** Find the height of the hill when the velocity at the top of the loop is 35 ft/s and the radius of the loop is 24 ft.

b. Critical Thinking Would you expect the velocity of the car to increase as the radius of the loop increases? Explain.

You can square both sides of an equation to solve an equation involving radical expressions.

3 EXAMPLE Solving With Radical Expressions on Both Sides

Solve $\sqrt{3n - 2} = \sqrt{n + 6}$.

$(\sqrt{3n - 2})^2 = (\sqrt{n + 6})^2$ **Square both sides.**

$3n - 2 = n + 6$ **Simplify.**

$3n = n + 8$ **Add 2 to each side.**

$2n = 8$ **Subtract *n* from each side.**

$n = 4$ **Divide each side by 2.**

Check $\sqrt{3n - 2} = \sqrt{n + 6}$

$\sqrt{3(4) - 2} \stackrel{?}{=} \sqrt{4 + 6}$ **Substitute 4 for *n*.**

$\sqrt{10} = \sqrt{10}$ ✓

The solution is 4.

CA Standards Check 3 Solve $\sqrt{3t + 4} = \sqrt{5t - 6}$. Check your answer.

Solving Equations With Extraneous Solutions

When you solve an equation by squaring each side, you create a new equation. This new equation may have solutions that do not solve the original equation.

Original equation		Square of each side		New equation		Solutions of new equation
$x = 2$	$\longrightarrow$	$(x)^2 = (2)^2$	$\longrightarrow$	$x^2 = 4$	$\longrightarrow$	$2, -2$

In the example above, -2 is an extraneous solution. An **extraneous solution** is a solution that does not satisfy the original equation. Be sure to check all solutions in the original equation to determine whether a solution is extraneous.

4 EXAMPLE Identifying Extraneous Solutions

Solve $x = \sqrt{x + 6}$.

$$(x)^2 = (\sqrt{x + 6})^2 \quad \text{Square both sides.}$$
$$x^2 = x + 6 \quad \text{Simplify.}$$
$$x^2 - x - 6 = 0 \quad \text{Subtract } x \text{ and 6 from both sides.}$$
$$(x - 3)(x + 2) = 0 \quad \text{Solve the quadratic equation by factoring.}$$
$$(x - 3) = 0 \text{ or } (x + 2) = 0 \quad \text{Use the Zero-Product Property.}$$
$$x = 3 \text{ or } x = -2 \quad \text{Solve for } x.$$

Check $x = \sqrt{x + 6}$

$$3 \stackrel{?}{=} \sqrt{3 + 6} \qquad -2 \stackrel{?}{=} \sqrt{-2 + 6} \quad \text{Substitute 3 and 2 for } x.$$
$$3 = 3 \checkmark \qquad -2 \neq 2$$

The solution to the original equation is 3. The value -2 is an extraneous solution.

Problem Solving Tip

For CA Standards Check 4b, you can use any method to solve a quadratic equation: graphing, factoring, or the quadratic formula.

CA Standards Check 4

a. Critical Thinking How could you determine that -2 was not a solution of $x = \sqrt{x + 6}$ without going through all the steps of the check?

b. Solve $y = \sqrt{y + 2}$. Check your solutions.

It is possible that the only solution you get after squaring both sides of an equation is extraneous. In that case, the original equation has no solution.

5 EXAMPLE No Solution

Solve $\sqrt{2x} + 6 = 4$.

$$\sqrt{2x} = -2$$
$$(\sqrt{2x})^2 = (-2)^2 \quad \text{Square both sides.}$$
$$2x = 4$$
$$x = 2$$

Check $\sqrt{2x} + 6 = 4$

$$\sqrt{2(2)} + 6 \stackrel{?}{=} 4 \quad \text{Substitute 2 for } x.$$
$$\sqrt{4} + 6 \stackrel{?}{=} 4$$
$$2 + 6 \neq 4 \quad x = 2 \text{ does not solve the original equation.}$$

$\sqrt{2x} + 6 = 4$ has no solution.

CA Standards Check 5 Solve $8 - \sqrt{2n} = 20$. Check your solution.

EXERCISES

For more exercises, see *Extra Skills and Word Problem Practice.*

Standards Practice

Alg1 2.0, 25.2

A Practice by Example

GO for Help

Example 1 (page 507)

Solve each radical equation. Check your solution.

1. $\sqrt{x} + 3 = 5$
2. $\sqrt{t} + 2 = 9$
3. $\sqrt{s} - 1 = 5$
4. $\sqrt{n + 7} = 12$
5. $\sqrt{a - 6} = 3$
6. $\sqrt{z} - 7 = -3$

Example 2 (page 508)

7. The time t in seconds it takes an object to fall d feet is given by $t = \sqrt{\frac{d}{16}}$. Find the distance an object falls after 6 seconds.

8. The current of an electrical circuit I in amps is related to the power P in watts and the resistance R in ohms by the formula $I = \sqrt{\frac{P}{R}}$. Find the power (to the nearest watt) when the current is 8 amps and the resistance is 9.4 ohms.

Example 3 (page 508)

Solve each radical equation. Check your solution.

9. $\sqrt{3x + 1} = \sqrt{5x - 8}$
10. $\sqrt{2y} = \sqrt{9 - y}$
11. $\sqrt{7v - 4} = \sqrt{5v + 10}$
12. $\sqrt{s + 10} = \sqrt{6 - s}$
13. $\sqrt{n + 5} = \sqrt{5n - 11}$
14. $\sqrt{3m + 1} = \sqrt{7m - 9}$

Examples 4, 5 (page 509)

Tell which solutions, if any, are extraneous for each equation.

15. $-z = \sqrt{-z + 6}; z = -3, z = 2$
16. $\sqrt{12 - n} = n; n = -4, n = 3$
17. $y = \sqrt{2y}; y = 0, y = 2$
18. $2a = \sqrt{4a + 3}; a = \frac{3}{2}, a = -\frac{1}{2}$
19. $x = \sqrt{28 - 3x}; x = 4, x = -7$
20. $-t = \sqrt{-6t - 5}; t = -5, t = -1$

Solve each radical equation. Check your solution. If there is no solution, write *no solution.*

21. $x = \sqrt{2x + 3}$
22. $n = \sqrt{4n + 5}$
23. $\sqrt{3b} = -3$
24. $2y = \sqrt{5y + 6}$
25. $-2\sqrt{2r + 5} = 6$
26. $\sqrt{d + 12} = d$
27. $\sqrt{z + 5} = 2z$
28. $2t = \sqrt{5t - 1}$

B Apply Your Skills

Determine whether each statement is true or false. Rewrite each false statement using $<$, $=$, or $>$ to make the statement true.

29. $\sqrt{16a^2b^3} = 4ab\sqrt{b}$
30. $2m^2\sqrt{144} > 24m^2$
31. $3\sqrt{24} < \sqrt{150}$
32. $3 + 4\sqrt{2} = -2\sqrt{8} + \sqrt{9}$

33. The volume V in cubic units for a cylindrical can is given by the formula $V = \pi r^2 h$, where r is the radius of the can and h is the height. The volume of the can is 98 in.^{3}, and the height of the can is 5 in. Find the radius of the can.

34. **Writing** Explain what is meant by an extraneous solution.

35. Write two radical equations that have 3 for a solution.

36. The formula $t = \sqrt{\frac{n}{16}}$ gives the time t in seconds for an object that is initially at rest to fall n feet. Find the distance an object falls in the first 10 seconds.

Homework Video Tutor

Visit: PHSchool.com
Web Code: bae-1004

Solve each radical equation. Check your solution. If there is no solution, write *no solution.*

37. $\sqrt{5x + 10} = 5$

38. $-6 - \sqrt{3y} = -3$

39. $\sqrt{7p + 5} = \sqrt{p - 3}$

40. $a = \sqrt{7a - 6}$

41. $\sqrt{y + 12} = 3\sqrt{y}$

42. $\sqrt{x - 10} = 1$

43. $\frac{x}{2} = \sqrt{3x}$

44. $\frac{c}{3} = \sqrt{c - 2}$

45. $7 = \sqrt{x + 5}$

46. $3 - \sqrt{4a + 1} = 12$

47. a. The equation $v = 8\sqrt{h - 2r}$ gives the velocity v in feet per second of a car at the top of the loop of a roller coaster. Find the radius of the loop when the hill is 150 ft high and the velocity of the car is 30 ft/s.

b. Find the approximate speed in mi/h for 30 ft/s. (*Hint:* 1 mi = 5280 ft)

c. Critical Thinking Would you expect the velocity of the car to increase or decrease as the radius of the loop increases? As the height of the hill decreases?

d. Explain your reasoning in your answer for part (c).

48. Math Reasoning Is the equation $\sqrt{x^2 + y^2} = \sqrt{x^2} + \sqrt{y^2}$ *sometimes*, *always*, or *never* true? Give examples to support your answer.

For a guide to solving Exercise 49, see p. 513.

49. The diagram at the right shows a piece of cardboard that makes a box when sections of it are folded and taped. The ends of the box are x inches by x inches and the body of the box is 10 inches long.

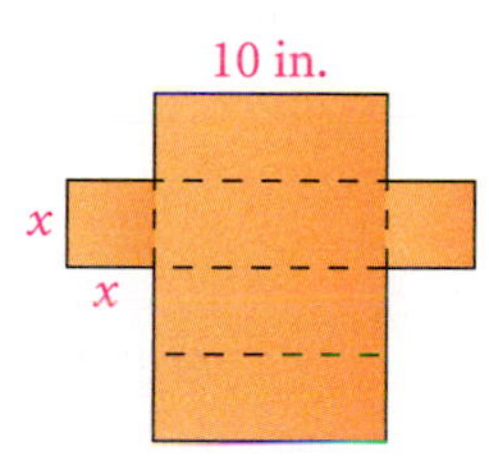

a. Write an equation for the volume V of the box.

b. Solve the equation in part (a) for x.

c. Find the integer values of x that would give the box a volume between 40 in.^{3} and 490 in.^{3}, inclusive.

50. a. Solve $x^2 - 3 = 4$.

b. Solve $\sqrt{x} - 3 = 4$.

c. How are solving part (a) and solving part (b) alike? How are they different?

C Challenge

Solve each radical equation. Check your solution. If there is no solution, write *no solution.*

51. $\sqrt{x^2 - 6x} = 4$

52. $\sqrt{2x^2 + 8x} = x$

53. $\sqrt{x^2 + 4x + 5} = x$

54. $x + 3 = \sqrt{x^2 - 4x - 1}$

55. Writing Explain how you would solve the equation $\sqrt{2x} + \sqrt{x + 2} = 0$.

56. Critical Thinking Explain the difference between squaring $\sqrt{x - 1}$ and squaring $\sqrt{x} - 1$.

In the yo-yo trick called "Around the World," the yo-yo is a satellite circling a person's hand. The person's hand is the center of the orbit.

57. The equation $T = \sqrt{\frac{2\pi^2 r}{F}}$ gives the time T in seconds it takes a satellite with mass 0.5 kilograms to complete one orbit of radius r meters. The force F in newtons pulls the body toward the center of the orbit.

a. It takes 2 seconds for an object to make one revolution with a force of 10 newtons. Find the radius of the orbit.

b. Find the radius of the orbit if the force is 160 newtons and $T = 2$.

Multiple Choice Practice

For California Standards Tutorials, visit PHSchool.com. Web Code: baq-9045

Alg1 9.0

58. Tina has \$350 in her savings account and Cliff has \$175 in his savings account. Each month, Tina adds \$25 to her account and Cliff adds \$35 to his account. Which system of equations can be used to find how many months m it will take for Tina and Cliff to have the same account balance b?

A $b = 25m + 175$, $b = 35m + 350$

B $m = 25b + 350$, $m = 35b + 175$

C $b = 25m + 350$, $b = 35m + 175$

D $m = 25b + 175$, $m = 35b + 350$

Alg1 2.0

59. Which radical equation has no solution?

A $-\sqrt{x} = -25x$

B $-3\sqrt{3x} = -5$

C $\sqrt{3x + 1} = -10$

D $\frac{x}{2} = \sqrt{x - 1}$

Alg1 21.0

60. Which graph represents a quadratic equation with 2 as a solution?

A B C D

Alg1 14.0

61. Which of the following is a solution to the equation $x^2 - 3x - 28 = 0$?

A -1 B -2 C -3 D -4

Mixed Review

Lesson 10-3

GO for Help

Simplify each expression.

62. $\sqrt{20} + \sqrt{45}$

63. $\sqrt{3}(\sqrt{6} + 4)$

64. $\sqrt{72} - \sqrt{50}$

65. $\sqrt{2}(2\sqrt{8} + 4\sqrt{18})$

66. $\frac{8}{\sqrt{5} + \sqrt{3}}$

67. $\sqrt{12}(7\sqrt{6} + \sqrt{24})$

Lesson 9-6

Solve by completing the square. If necessary, round to the nearest tenth.

68. $w^2 + 2w - 11 = 0$

69. $k^2 - 8k = 3$

70. $d^2 + 5d + 1 = 0$

71. $2a^2 + 20a = 16$

72. $\frac{1}{5}x^2 + 2x = 4$

73. $6g^2 - 9g - 30 = 0$

Lessons 8-5, 8-6

Factor each expression.

74. $x^2 + 10x - 24$

75. $m^2 - 14m + 13$

76. $b^2 + 16b - 36$

77. $2p^2 + 15p + 7$

78. $3d^2 + 12d - 15$

79. $4v^2 - 25v + 25$

80. $2y^2 + 21y - 11$

81. $3k^2 + 10k + 7$

GPS Guided Problem Solving

FOR USE WITH PAGE 511, EXERCISE 49

2.0 Understand and use such operations as taking a root. ***Develop***

Understanding Word Problems **Read the problem below and then follow along with what Lily thinks as she solves the problem. Check your understanding by solving the exercise at the bottom of the page.**

The diagram at the right shows a piece of cardboard that makes a box when sections of it are folded and taped. The ends of the box are x inches by x inches and the box is 10 inches long.

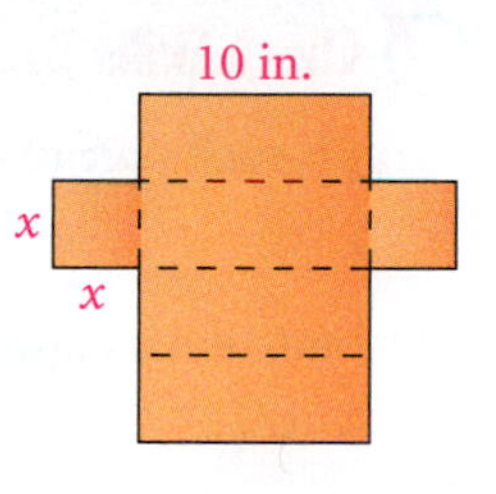

a. Write an equation for the volume V of the box.

b. Solve the equation in part (a) for x.

c. Find the integer values of x that give the box a volume between 40 in.^{3} and 490 in.^{3}, inclusive.

What Lily Thinks

What will this box look like? I'll draw a sketch.

Okay, I can see now that the box has length 10 in., width x in., and height x in. I can substitute these into the formula for the volume of a rectangular prism.

Part (b) asks me to solve the equation for x. Since x is a dimension of the box, it can't be negative. So the solution is the positive square root only.

Part (c) asks me to write a sentence showing that the volume is between 40 in.^{3} and 490 in.^{3}. Oh, I can write an inequality! Then I can solve for x.

Wait! The problem asks for *integer values* only.

What Lily Writes

a. $V = lwh$

$V = 10 \cdot x \cdot x$

$V = 10x^2$

b. $V = 10x^2$

$\frac{V}{10} = x^2$

$\pm\sqrt{\frac{V}{10}} = x$

$x = \sqrt{\frac{V}{10}} = \frac{\sqrt{10V}}{10}$

c. $40 \le \text{Volume} \le 490$

$40 \le 10x^2 \le 490$

$4 \le x^2 \le 49$

$2 \le x \le 7$

The possible integer values of x are 2, 3, 4, 5, 6, and 7.

EXERCISE

Each edge of a cube has length e.

a. Write an equation for the surface area of the cube S in terms of e.

b. Find the integer values of e that will give the cube a surface area between 726 cm^2 and 1176 cm^2, inclusive.

Graphing Square Root Functions

California Content Standards

17.0 Determine the domain of independent variables and the range of dependent variables defined by a graph or a symbolic expression. ***Master***

What You'll Learn

- To graph square root functions

. . . And Why

To solve problems involving police work, as in Example 3

Check Skills You'll Need

GO for Help Lessons 9-1 and 9-3

Graph each pair of quadratic functions on the same graph.

1. $y = x^2, y = x^2 + 3$ **2.** $y = x^2, y = x^2 - 4$

Evaluate each expression for the given value of *x*.

3. $\sqrt{x}$ for $x = 4$ **4.** $\sqrt{x + 7} - 3$ for $x = 2$ **5.** $3\sqrt{x} + 2$ for $x = 9$

New Vocabulary • square root function

Graphing Square Root Functions

Vocabulary Tip

The square root function is the simplest example of a radical function.

A **square root function** is a function that contains the independent variable in the radicand. The function $y = \sqrt{x}$ is the simplest square root function. For *x*-values that are not perfect squares, you can approximate the *y*-values to the nearest tenth.

For real numbers, the value of the radicand cannot be negative. So the domain is limited to those values of *x* that make the radicand greater than or equal to 0. Use the least value in the domain and several other values to find the range.

1 EXAMPLE Finding Domain and Range

Find the domain and range of each function.

a. $y = \sqrt{x + 3}$

$x + 3 \geq 0$ ← Make the radicand ≥ 0. →

$x \geq -3$

The domain is $\{x: x \geq -3\}$.

x	$y = \sqrt{x + 3}$
−3	0
−2	1
−1	1.4
0	1.7

The range is $\{y: y \geq 0\}$.

b. $y = \sqrt{2x - 8} - 3$

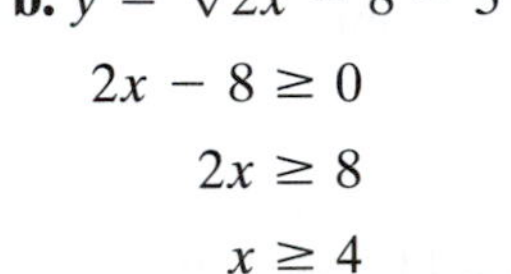

$2x - 8 \geq 0$

$2x \geq 8$

$x \geq 4$

The domain is $\{x: x \geq 4\}$.

x	$y = \sqrt{2x - 8} - 3$
4	−3
5	−1.6
6	−1
7	−0.6

The range is $\{y: y \geq -3\}$.

CA Standards Check **1** Find the domain and range of each function.

a. $y = \sqrt{x - 7}$ **b.** $y = \sqrt{3x - 1}$

You can graph a square root function by plotting points. Plot the least value in the domain and several other points. Then join the points using a curve.

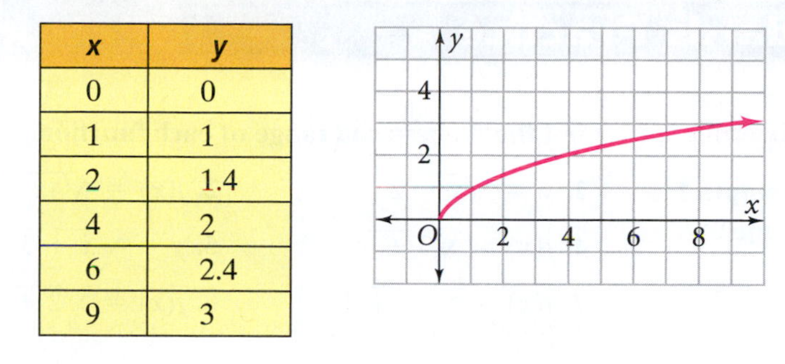

x	y
0	0
1	1
2	1.4
4	2
6	2.4
9	3

Online active math

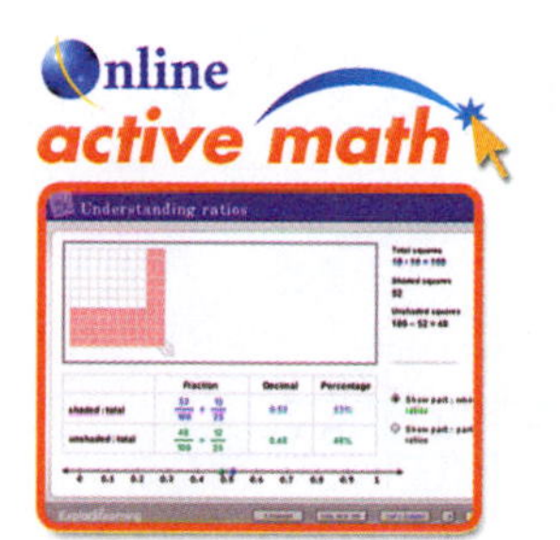

For: Square Root Function Activity
Use: Interactive Textbook, 10-5

2 EXAMPLE Graphing a Square Root Function

Graph $f(x) = \sqrt{x + 4}$.

$x + 4 \geq 0$ — Make the radicand ≥ 0.

$x \geq -4$

Step 1 Make a table of values.

x	$y = \sqrt{x + 4}$
−4	0
−3	1
−2	1.4
−1	1.7

Step 2 Plot the points.

Step 3 Joint the points to form a curve.

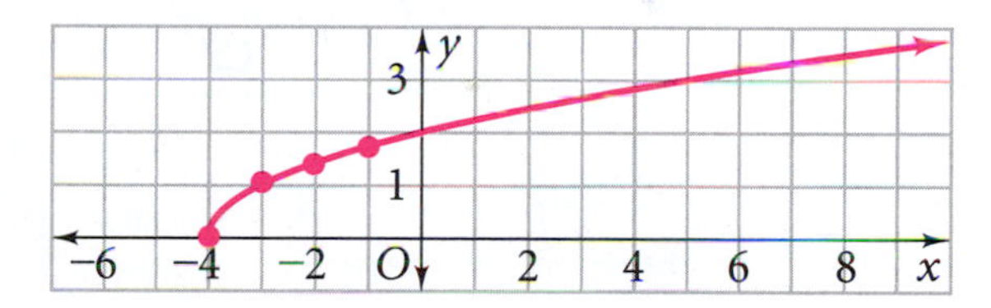

CA Standards Check 2 Graph each function.

a. $f(x) = \sqrt{x - 3}$

b. $f(x) = \sqrt{x} + 1$

You can represent real-world applications with square root functions.

Police officers use mathematics and logical reasoning to analyze accidents.

3 EXAMPLE Application

In good weather conditions, police can use the formula $r = 2\sqrt{5L}$ to find the approximate speed r of a car that leaves a skid mark of length L in feet. Graph the function.

Length of Skid Mark (ft)	Speed (mi/h)
0	0
10	14.1
20	20
30	24.5
40	28.3

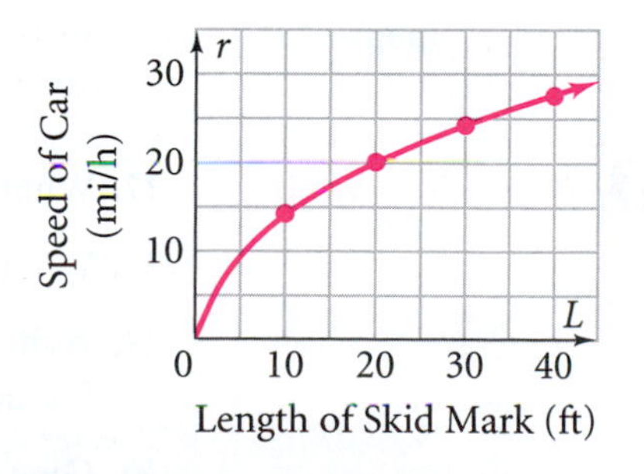

CA Standards Check 3 **a.** Copy and extend the graph in Example 3 for skid mark lengths from 60 ft to 100 ft.

b. Critical Thinking How long is the skid mark when a car's speed before putting on the brakes is 85 mi/h?

EXERCISES
For more exercises, see *Extra Skills and Word Problem Practice.*

Standards Practice
Alg1 17.0, 25.3

A Practice by Example

Example 1 (page 514)

GO for Help

Find the domain and range of each function.

1. $y = \sqrt{x - 2}$
2. $f(x) = \sqrt{4x - 3}$
3. $y = \sqrt{1.5x}$
4. $f(x) = \sqrt{7 + x}$
5. $y = \sqrt{x + 3} - 1$
6. $f(x) = \sqrt{x - 5} + 1$
7. $f(x) = \sqrt{3x + 5}$
8. $f(x) = \sqrt{2 + x}$
9. $f(x) = \sqrt{6x - 8} + 1$

Example 2 (page 515)

Match each graph with its function.

10. $y = \sqrt{x + 4}$
11. $y = \sqrt{x - 2}$
12. $y = \sqrt{x} + 4$
13. $y = \sqrt{x} - 2$

A.

B.

C.

D.

Make a table of values and graph each function.

14. $y = \sqrt{2x}$
15. $f(x) = 2\sqrt{x}$
16. $y = \sqrt{4x - 8}$
17. $y = \sqrt{3x}$
18. $f(x) = 3\sqrt{x}$
19. $y = -3\sqrt{x}$
20. $y = \sqrt{x} + 5$
21. $y = \sqrt{x} - 3$
22. $f(x) = \sqrt{x - 2}$
23. $f(x) = 2\sqrt{x - 4}$
24. $y = \sqrt{x + 1}$
25. $y = \sqrt{x - 1} + 3$

Example 3 (page 515)

26. You can use the function $v = \sqrt{64h}$ to find the velocity v of an object, ignoring air resistance, after it has fallen h feet. Make a table of values and graph the function.

B Apply Your Skills

27. What are the domain and the range of the function $y = \sqrt{2x - 8}$?
28. What are the domain and the range of the function $y = \sqrt{8 - 2x}$?
29. **Writing** Explain how to find the domain of a square root function. Include an example.
30. Give an example of a square root function in each form. Choose $n \neq 0$.
    a. $y = \sqrt{x} + n$ **b.** $y = \sqrt{x + n}$ **c.** $y = n\sqrt{x}$
    d. Graph each function in parts (a)–(c).

Visit: PHSchool.com
Web Code: bae-1005

Math Reasoning **Describe how the graph of each function relates to the graph of $y = \sqrt{x}$.**

31. $y = \sqrt{x + 8}$

32. $f(x) = \sqrt{x} - 10$

33. $f(x) = \sqrt{x} + 12$

34. $y = \sqrt{x - 9}$

Make a table of values and graph each function.

35. $y = \sqrt{x - 2.5}$

36. $f(x) = 4\sqrt{x}$

37. $y = \sqrt{x + 6}$

38. $y = \sqrt{0.5x}$

39. $y = \sqrt{x - 2} + 3$

40. $f(x) = \sqrt{x + 2} - 4$

41. Which graph best models the function $y = \sqrt{x - 1} + 3$?

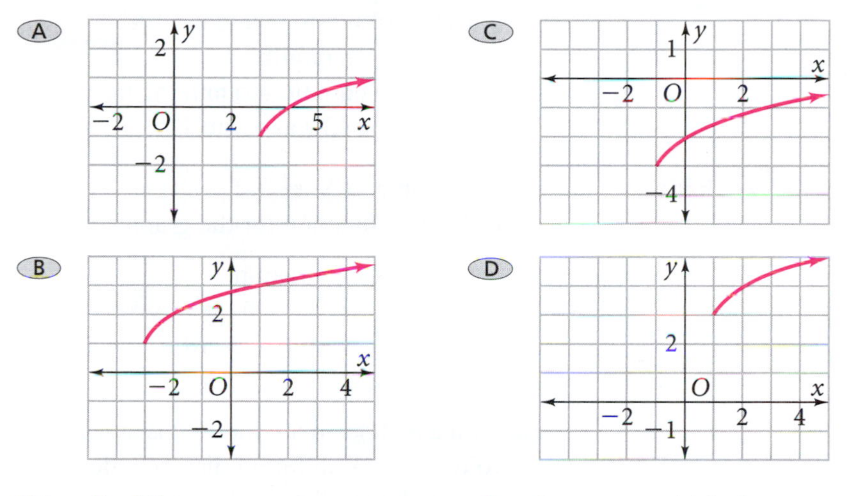

To fight a fire on the ground, a fire hose needs about 150 pounds per square inch of water pressure.

42. When firefighters are trying to put out a fire, the rate at which they can spray water on the fire depends on the nozzle pressure. You can find the flow rate f in gallons per minute (gal/min) using the function $f = 120\sqrt{p}$, where p is the nozzle pressure in pounds per square inch (lb/in.^{2}).

a. What is the domain of the function?

b. Graph the function.

c. Use the graph to estimate the pressure when the flow rate is 800 gal/min.

43. The graph of $x = y^2$ is shown at the right.

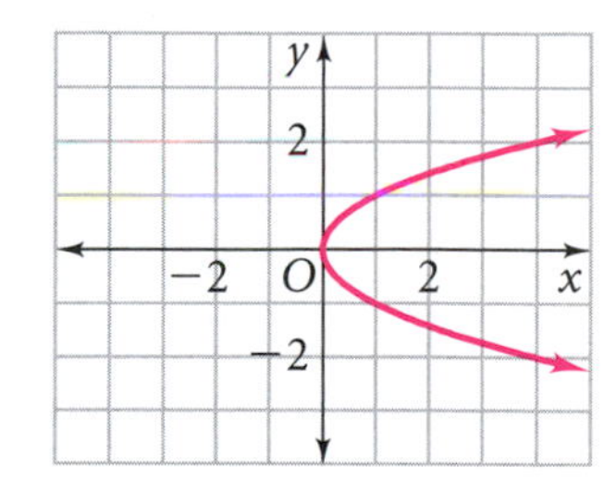

a. Is this the graph of a function?

b. How does $x = y^2$ relate to the square root function $y = \sqrt{x}$?

c. **Critical Thinking** What is a function for the part of the graph that is shown in Quadrant IV?

44. Without graphing, determine which graph rises more steeply, $y = \sqrt{3x}$ or $y = 3\sqrt{x}$. Explain your answer.

Math Reasoning **Determine whether each statement is *sometimes*, *always*, or *never* true. If it is not always true, explain why.**

45. If $\sqrt{x} = 9$, then $x = 3$.

46. The expression $3 + 4\sqrt{x}$ is equivalent to $7\sqrt{x}$.

47. For $\sqrt{x + 5} = 12$, $x = 139$.

48. $\sqrt{x + 5} = 2$ has no solution.

Since the year 2000, the number of rolls of film sold in the United States has decreased each year. The number of single-use cameras has increased.

49. Last year a store had an advertising campaign. The graph shows the sales for single-use cameras. The function $n = 27\sqrt{5t} + 53$ models the sales volume n for the cameras as a function of time t, the number of months after the start of the advertising campaign.

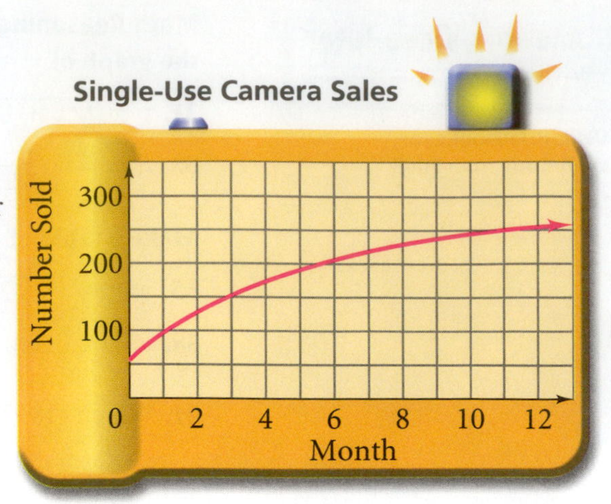

a. Evaluate the function to find how many disposable cameras the store sold in the seventh month.

b. Solve an equation to find the month in which the number of single-use cameras sold was about 175.

C Challenge

50. a. Graph $y = \sqrt{x^2} + 5$.

b. Write a function for the graph you drew that does not require a radical.

51. a. Graph each function.

i. $y = \sqrt{4x}$ **ii.** $y = \sqrt{5x}$ **iii.** $y = \sqrt{6x}$ **iv.** $y = \sqrt{-6x}$

b. Critical Thinking Describe how the graph of $y = \sqrt{nx}$ changes as the value of n varies.

52. Roll a ball down a ramp that is at least 6 ft long. Record the time the ball takes to roll several different distances down the ramp, up to its full length.

a. Graph your data with time as a function of distance (d, t).

b. Describe your graph. Explain why it is *not* linear.

Multiple Choice Practice

For California Standards Tutorials, visit PHSchool.com. Web Code: baq-9045

Alg1 16.0

53. Which is the best representation of a linear function?

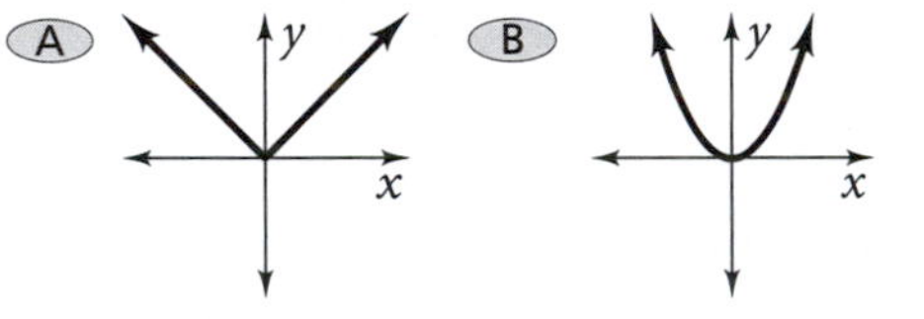

Ⓐ Ⓑ Ⓒ Ⓓ

Alg1 16.0

54. Which table of values is generated by the function $y = 6x - 3$?

Ⓐ

x	y
1	6
2	12
3	18
4	24
5	30

Ⓑ

x	y
−1	−6
0	−3
1	0
2	3
3	6

Ⓒ

x	y
−2	−15
0	−3
2	9
4	21
6	33

Ⓓ

x	y
−3	0
3	1
9	2
15	3
21	4

Alg1 2.0

55. Which of the following is the solution of the equation $\sqrt{2x + 1} = \sqrt{3x - 5}$?

Ⓐ −1 Ⓑ 0 Ⓒ 4 Ⓓ 6

Alg1 17.0

56. Which of the following graphs has a range $\{y: y \leq 1\}$?

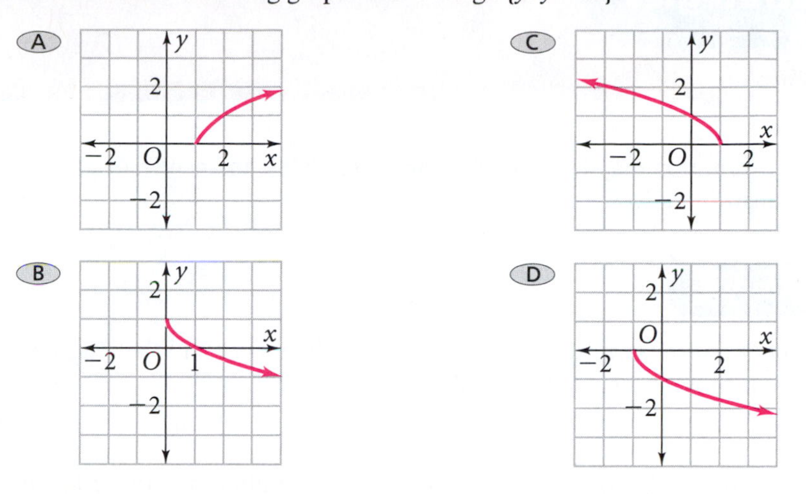

Mixed Review

GO for Help

Lesson 10-4

Solve each equation. Check your solutions.

57. $\sqrt{x} + 7 = 11$

58. $\sqrt{c + 1} = \sqrt{2c - 6}$

59. $\sqrt{x} - 4 = 9$

60. $13 = 5\sqrt{m - 8}$

61. $\sqrt{k + 3} + 12 = 6$

62. $\sqrt{5h - 2} = \sqrt{2h}$

Lesson 9-7

Use the quadratic formula to solve each equation.

63. $2x^2 + 4x - 7 = 0$

64. $x^2 - 8x - 23 = 0$

65. $5x^2 - x + 11 = 0$

66. $9x^2 + 6x - 10 = 0$

67. $1.2x^2 + x + 6 = 0$

68. $9x^2 + 13x - 7 = 0$

Lesson 8-6

Factor completely.

69. $2x^2 - 7x - 4$

70. $3x^2 + x - 10$

71. $4x^2 + 20x + 9$

72. $2x^2 - 10x - 48$

73. $4x^2 - 4x - 60$

74. $x^3 - 12x^2 - 13x$

Checkpoint Quiz 2

Lessons 10-4 through 10-5

Solve each radical equation.

1. $4 - \sqrt{m} = -12$

2. $\sqrt{t + 5} = \sqrt{2t - 3}$

3. $r = \sqrt{4r + 5}$

4. If $a = \sqrt{24}$ and $\frac{a}{\sqrt{b}} = \sqrt{\frac{6}{c}}$, what is the value of $\frac{c}{b}$?

Find the domain and range of each function.

5. $y = 2\sqrt{x} + 3$

6. $y = \sqrt{2x + 6}$

7. $y = \sqrt{3x - 3} - 2$

Graph each equation.

8. $y = \sqrt{x} - 5$

9. $y = \sqrt{x + 2}$

10. $y = 3\sqrt{x} - 4$

Test-Taking Strategies

Using Estimation

Using estimation may help you find answers, check an answer, or eliminate one or more answer choices.

EXAMPLE

The length of the hypotenuse of a right triangle is 9 cm and the length of one leg is 4 cm. Which is closest to the length of the other leg?

(A) 7.7 cm (B) 7.8 cm (C) 8.1 cm (D) 9 cm

First, use the Pythagorean Theorem to find the length of the other leg in radical form. Then use estimation to see which answer choice is closest to it.

$a^2 + b^2 = c^2$ **Use the Pythagorean Theorem.**

$4^2 + b^2 = 9^2$ **Substitute 4 for *a* and 9 for *c*.**

$16 + b^2 = 81$ **Simplify.**

$b^2 = 65$ **Subtract 16 from each side.**

$b = \sqrt{65}$ **Take the square root of each side.**

A good estimate for $\sqrt{65}$ is 8, since $\sqrt{65}$ is close to $\sqrt{64}$. You can now eliminate answer choices A, B, and D, which are not as close to 8 as C. C is the correct answer.

Multiple Choice Practice

For California Standards Tutorials, visit PHSchool.com. Web Code: baq-9045

1. Tim's family is building a ramp like the one shown below. They plan on installing railings on both sides of the ramp.

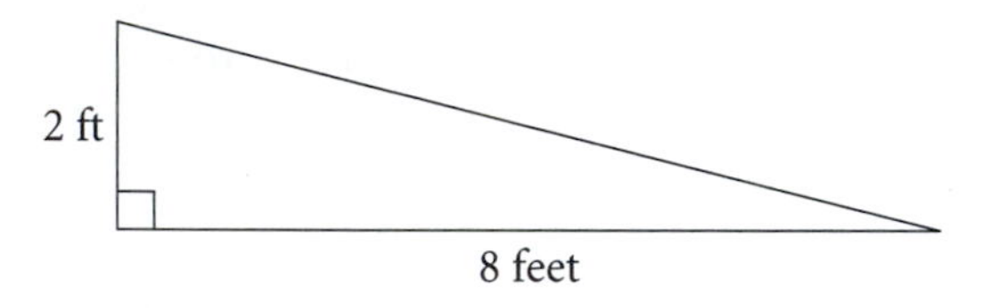

Which of the following is the best estimate for the length of railing they need?

(A) 15 feet (B) 17 feet (C) 19 feet (D) 21 feet

2. Isabel traveled by car to visit relatives in the next state. For each hour of her trip, she recorded how many miles she had traveled from home. Her data are shown below.

Time (hours)	1	2	3	4
Distance from home (miles)	53	108	172	225

If Isabel modeled her data with a linear function and graph, which of the following would be the best estimate for the slope of the line?

(A) 45 mph (B) 55 mph (C) 65 mph (D) 75 mph

Chapter 10 Review

Vocabulary Review

English and Spanish Audio Online

conjugates (p. 501)	**like radicals** (p. 500)	**rationalize** (p. 489)
extraneous solution (p. 509)	**Pythagorean Theorem** (p. 493)	**square root function** (p. 514)
hypotenuse (p. 493)	**radical equation** (p. 507)	**unlike radicals** (p. 500)
leg (p. 493)	**radical expression** (p. 486)	

Choose the vocabulary term that correctly completes each sentence.

1. Two radical expressions that are the sum and the difference of the same two terms are _?_.

2. One method of simplifying a radical expression is to _?_ the denominator.

3. A(n) _?_ is a value that satisfies the new equation but not the original equation.

4. Radicals with the same radicand are _?_.

5. In a right triangle, the _?_ is the side opposite the right angle and is the longest side.

6. A(n) _?_ is a function that contains the independent variable in the radicand.

7. The _?_ states that in any right triangle, the sum of the squares of the lengths of the legs is equal to the square of the length of the hypotenuse.

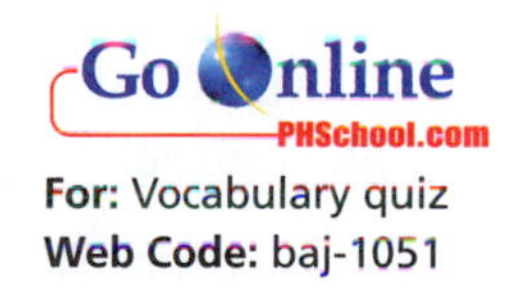

For: Vocabulary quiz
Web Code: baj-1051

8. The expressions $4\sqrt{5}$ and $3\sqrt{15}$ are examples of _?_.

9. You can simplify a(n) _?_ such as $\sqrt{x-6}$ by removing perfect square factors from the radicand.

Skills and Concepts

Lesson 10-1

- To simplify radicals involving products
- To simplify radicals involving quotients

You can simplify some radical expressions by using products or quotients.

The Multiplication Property of Square Roots states that for $a \geq 0$ and $b \geq 0$, $\sqrt{ab} = \sqrt{a} \cdot \sqrt{b}$.

The Division Property of Square Roots states that for $a \geq 0$ and $b > 0$, $\sqrt{\frac{a}{b}} = \frac{\sqrt{a}}{\sqrt{b}}$.

Simplify each radical expression.

10. $\sqrt{32} \cdot \sqrt{144}$

11. $\sqrt{\frac{84}{121}}$

12. $\sqrt{96c^3} \cdot \sqrt{25c}$

13. $\frac{10}{\sqrt{13}}$

14. $\sqrt{5h^3} \cdot \sqrt{50h}$

15. $3\sqrt{20t^6}$

16. $\frac{\sqrt{8}}{\sqrt{32}}$

17. $\frac{2\sqrt{6k^2}}{\sqrt{9k^4}}$

18. $\sqrt{\frac{225}{100}}$

19. A rectangle is 7 times as long as it is wide. Its area is 1400 cm^2. Find the dimensions of the rectangle in simplest radical form.

Lesson 10-2

- To solve problems using the Pythagorean Theorem
- To identify right triangles

Alg1 2.0, 24.2

For a right triangle with **legs** a and b and **hypotenuse** c, the **Pythagorean Theorem** states that $a^2 + b^2 = c^2$. The converse of the Pythagorean Theorem states that if a triangle has sides of lengths a, b, and c, and if $a^2 + b^2 = c^2$, then it is a right triangle with hypotenuse c.

Find the length of the hypotenuse with the given leg lengths. Round to the nearest tenth.

20. $a = 3, b = 5$ **21.** $a = 11, b = 14$ **22.** $a = 7, b = 13$ **23.** $a = 4, b = 9$

Find the missing length to the nearest tenth.

24. **25.** **26.**

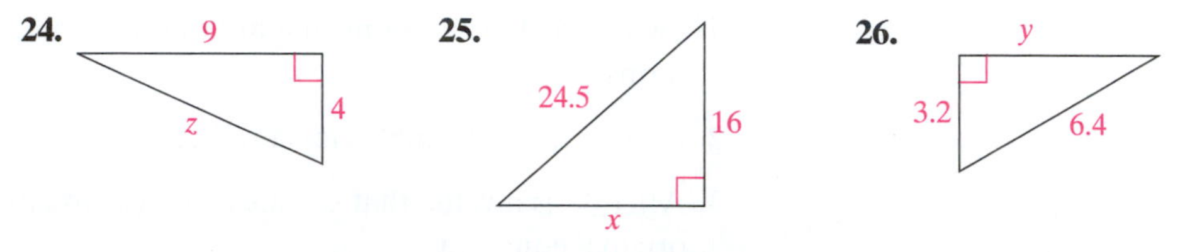

Determine whether the given lengths can be sides of a right triangle.

27. $XY = 16, YZ = 34, XZ = 30$ **28.** $XY = 2.5, YZ = 2.4, XZ = 0.7$

29. The bases on a standard baseball diamond form a square, 90 ft on a side. How far would a catcher standing on home plate need to throw the ball to get a runner out at second base? Round to the nearest foot.

Lesson 10-3

- To simplify sums and differences
- To simplify products and quotients

Alg1 2.0, 25.0

You can use the Distributive Property to simplify expressions with sums and differences of radicals. First, simplify the radicals and check for **like radicals.**

When a denominator contains a sum or a difference including radical expressions, you can **rationalize** the denominator by multiplying the numerator and the denominator by the **conjugate** of the denominator.

Simplify each radical expression.

30. $3\sqrt{2} + 7\sqrt{2}$ **31.** $4\sqrt{21} - 9\sqrt{21}$ **32.** $\sqrt{5} - 14\sqrt{5}$ **33.** $-4\sqrt{37} + 4\sqrt{37}$

Tell whether each pair of expressions can be simplified to like radicals.

34. $\sqrt{10}, \sqrt{40}$ **35.** $\sqrt{6}, \sqrt{38}$ **36.** $\sqrt{5}, \sqrt{60}$

Simplify each radical expression.

37. $6\sqrt{7} - 2\sqrt{28}$

38. $5(\sqrt{20} + \sqrt{80})$

39. $\sqrt{54} - 2\sqrt{6}$

40. $\sqrt{125} - 3\sqrt{5}$

41. $\sqrt{10}(\sqrt{10} - \sqrt{20})$

42. $(\sqrt{2} + \sqrt{7})(3\sqrt{2} - \sqrt{7})$

43. $(\sqrt{5} + 4\sqrt{3})^2$

44. $\frac{3}{\sqrt{6} - \sqrt{3}}$

45. $\frac{\sqrt{7} + \sqrt{28}}{\sqrt{7} - \sqrt{14}}$

46. $\sqrt{28} + 5\sqrt{63}$

47. $\frac{2}{\sqrt{8} + \sqrt{7}}$

48. $3\sqrt{5}(\sqrt{10} - 2\sqrt{15})$

Lesson 10-4

- To solve equations containing radicals
- To identify extraneous solutions

Alg1 2.0, 25.2

A **radical equation** has a variable in the radicand. Sometimes you can solve such an equation by squaring both sides. You may also square both sides of the equation when each side is a square root. Squaring both sides of a radical equation may produce an **extraneous solution.** It is not a solution of the original equation.

Solve each radical equation.

49. $\sqrt{x + 7} = 3$

50. $\sqrt{x} + 3\sqrt{x} = 16$

51. $4 = \sqrt{n - 1}$

52. $\sqrt{p} - 5 = 8$

53. $\sqrt{x + 7} = \sqrt{2x - 1}$

54. $\sqrt{x} - 5 = 4$

55. $\sqrt{n} + 6 = 16$

56. $8\sqrt{b} - \sqrt{b} = 14$

Tell which of the given solutions is extraneous for each equation.

57. $\sqrt{4x} = x - 3$
$x = 1, x = 9$

58. $\sqrt{d - 3} = 5 - d$
$d = 4, d = 7$

Solve each radical equation. Check your solution. If there is no solution, write *no solution.*

59. $\sqrt{2x} = \sqrt{5x + 3}$

60. $\sqrt{2d + 1} = \sqrt{3d - 2}$

61. $5\sqrt{x} = \sqrt{10x + 60}$

62. $\sqrt{-5b + 2} = \sqrt{-4b - 4}$

63. $3\sqrt{x} + 4\sqrt{x} = 0$

64. $\sqrt{k + 1} = \sqrt{7 + 2k}$

65. A rectangle has a width of $2\sqrt{5}$ cm and an area of 50 cm^2. Find the length of the rectangle.

66. The volume V of a cylinder is given by $V = \pi r^2 h$, where r is the radius of a cylinder and h is its height. If the volume of the cylinder is 54 $in.^3$, and its height is 2 in., what is its radius to the nearest 0.01 in.?

Lesson 10-5

- To graph square root functions

Alg1 17.0

The simplest square root function is $y = \sqrt{x}$. To find the domain of a square root function, solve the inequality where the radicand is greater than or equal to zero. To find the range of a function, use the least value in the domain and several other values and make a table. You can graph a square root function by plotting points and then joining the points with a curve.

Find the domain and range of each function.

67. $y = \sqrt{3 - x}$

68. $y = \sqrt{2x} - 1$

69. $y = 5 - \sqrt{x + 4}$

70. $y = 2 + \sqrt{x}$

Make a table of values and graph each function.

71. $y = \sqrt{\frac{x}{2}}$

72. $y = \frac{\sqrt{x}}{2}$

73. $y = \sqrt{2x}$

74. $y = 1 + \sqrt{x}$

Find the domain of each function. Then graph each function.

75. $y = \sqrt{x} + 5$

76. $y = \sqrt{x - 2}$

77. $y = \sqrt{x + 1}$

78. $f(x) = 2\sqrt{x}$

Chapter 10 Test

Go Online PHSchool.com For: Chapter Test Web Code: baa-1052

Simplify each radical expression.

1. $\sqrt{300}$
2. $-\sqrt{90}$
3. $\sqrt{12} \cdot \sqrt{18}$
4. $2\sqrt{7} \cdot 4\sqrt{7}$
5. $\sqrt{5h^3} \cdot \sqrt{2h^5}$
6. $-\sqrt{12b^2} \cdot 2\sqrt{8b}$
7. $\sqrt{\frac{20t^5}{5t}}$
8. $\sqrt{\frac{98m}{2m^9}}$

Solve each radical equation. Check your solution. If there is no solution, write *no solution*.

9. $\sqrt{7n + 3} = \sqrt{n + 15}$
10. $2\sqrt{k - 11} = \sqrt{1 - 5k}$
11. $-8 = \sqrt{4x}$
12. $\sqrt{45 + 3c} = 3$

Determine whether the given lengths can be sides of a right triangle.

13. 6, 7, 9
14. 1.5, 2, 2.5
15. 0.25, 0.6, 0.65
16. 8, 16, 22

17. The length of each leg of an isosceles right triangle is 40.9 cm. Find the length of the hypotenuse to the nearest tenth.

Find the missing length to the nearest tenth.

18.

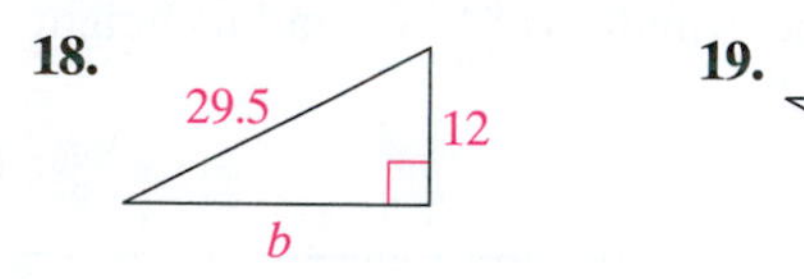

19.

5.8
3.1
z

Simplify each radical expression.

20. $\sqrt{\frac{128}{64}}$
21. $\sqrt{\frac{27}{75}}$
22. $\sqrt{48}$
23. $\sqrt{12} \cdot \sqrt{8}$
24. $3\sqrt{32} + 5\sqrt{2}$
25. $2\sqrt{27} + 5\sqrt{3}$
26. $7\sqrt{125} - 3\sqrt{175}$
27. $\sqrt{128} - \sqrt{192}$
28. $\frac{15}{\sqrt{3}}$
29. $\frac{8}{\sqrt{10} + \sqrt{6}}$

30. Which expression shows $\sqrt{24x^2y^3}$ written in simplest radical form?
A. $2xy\sqrt{12xy^2}$
B. $2xy\sqrt{6y}$
C. $xy\sqrt{24y}$
D. $4xy\sqrt{3y}$

31. Write an expression involving addition of two like radicals. Simplify the sum.

Solve each radical equation.

32. $3\sqrt{x} + 2\sqrt{x} = 10$
33. $8 = \sqrt{5x - 1}$
34. $5\sqrt{x} = \sqrt{15x + 60}$
35. $\sqrt{x} = \sqrt{2x - 7}$
36. $3\sqrt{x + 3} = 2\sqrt{x + 9}$
37. $\sqrt{3x} = x - 6$

38. A rectangle is 5 times as long as it is wide. The area of the rectangle is 100 ft^2. How wide is the rectangle? Express your answer in simplest radical form.

Find the domain and range of each function. Then graph the function.

39. $y = 3\sqrt{x}$
40. $y = \sqrt{x} + 4$
41. $y = \sqrt{x - 4}$
42. $y = \sqrt{x + 9}$

43. The hypotenuse of a right triangle is 26 cm. The length of one leg is 10 cm. Find the length of the other leg.

44. The formula for the volume V of a cylinder with height h and radius r is $V = \pi r^2 h$. Solve for r in terms of V and h.

A right triangle has hypotenuse c and legs a and b. Find the missing side. If necessary, round to the nearest tenth.

45. $a = 4, b = 7$
46. $a = 3.2, b = 6$
47. $a = 6.5, b = 11$
48. $a = 7.2, b = 19$
49. $a = 6, b = 12$
50. $b = 5, c = 8$
51. $a = 1.2, b = 0.5$
52. $c = 16, b = 7$
53. $a = 10, c = 30$
54. $a = \frac{6}{7}, b = \frac{8}{7}$

55. In $\triangle ABC$, $\angle C$ is a right angle, $AB = 7$, and $BC = 6.2$. What is the length of $\overline{AC}$ to the nearest tenth?

56. Ken has a 20-ft ladder to use for washing windows. If he places the base of the ladder on the ground 5 ft from the base of the building, will he be able to reach a window that is 18 ft from the ground? Explain.

Standards Mastery

Cumulative Practice

Some questions ask you to find the lengths of missing sides of right triangles. Read the question at the right. Then follow the tips to answer the sample question.

$\triangle QRS$ is a right triangle with side lengths shown below.

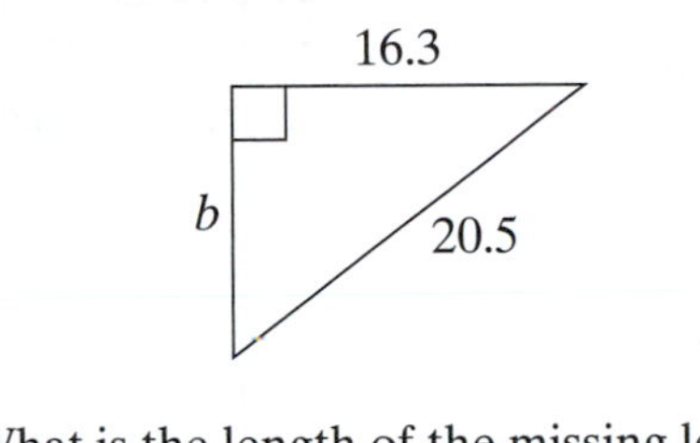

What is the length of the missing leg? Round to the nearest tenth.

Ⓐ 10.8
Ⓑ 12.1
Ⓒ 12.4
Ⓓ 22.6

Tip 1
Make sure you understand the math vocabulary. The hypotenuse is the side opposite the right angle. The legs are the other two sides.

Tip 2
Eliminate answers. The hypotenuse is the longest side of a right triangle, so D is not the correct answer.

Think It Through

Use the Pythagorean Theorem to find side lengths of right triangles. Substitute 16.3 for a and 20.5 for c in the equation $a^2 + b^2 = c^2$. Then solve for b to the nearest tenth. $b = 12.4$. The correct answer is C.

Vocabulary Review

As you solve problems, you must understand the meanings of mathematical terms. Match each term with its mathematical meaning.

A. leg
B. irrational number
C. rational number
D. radicand
E. perfect squares

I. a terminating or repeating decimal
II. one of the sides that form the right angle in a right triangle
III. the squares of integers
IV. the expression under the radical sign in a radical expression or equation
V. a number that cannot be written as a ratio of two numbers

Read each question. Then write the letter of the correct answer on your paper.

1. Which function has y-values that always increase when the corresponding x-values increase? **(Lesson 4-2)**

   Ⓐ $y = |x| + 2$
   Ⓑ $y = x^2 + 2$
   Ⓒ $y = x + 2$
   Ⓓ $y = -2x + 2$

2. Which statement is a correct conclusion about the quantities in the function $y = 2x^2 - 3$? **(Lesson 4-2)**

   Ⓐ The value of y is never less than -3.
   Ⓑ The value of y is never greater than 2.
   Ⓒ The x-value is always greater than the y-value.
   Ⓓ The y-value is always greater than the x-value.

3. Look at the linear function shown below.

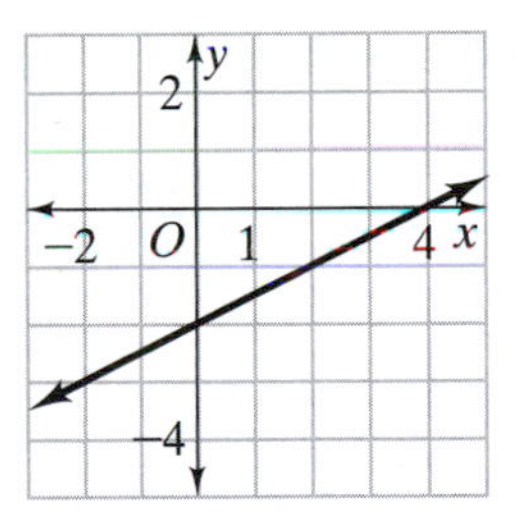

   Which statement is always a correct conclusion about the corresponding values of the function? **(Lesson 4-3)**

   Ⓐ The x-values are always 2 less than the y-values.
   Ⓑ The y-values are always 4 more than the x-values.
   Ⓒ The x-values are always greater than the y-values.
   Ⓓ The y-values are always greater than the x-values.

Cumulative Practice (continued)

4. Simplify $\sqrt{80}$. **(Lesson 10-1)**

Ⓐ $10\sqrt{8}$ Ⓑ $8\sqrt{10}$ Ⓒ $4\sqrt{5}$ Ⓓ 40

5. Simplify $5\sqrt{3x^2} \cdot \sqrt{6x}$. **(Lesson 10-1)**

Ⓐ $15x\sqrt{2x}$ Ⓒ $3x\sqrt{10x}$

Ⓑ $5x\sqrt{18x}$ Ⓓ $6x\sqrt{5x}$

6. Which of the following equals $\frac{2}{3}$? **(Lesson 10-1)**

Ⓐ $\sqrt{\frac{9}{25}}$ Ⓑ $\sqrt{\frac{20}{45}}$ Ⓒ $\sqrt{\frac{4}{27}}$ Ⓓ $\sqrt{\frac{6}{9}}$

7. Four steps to derive the quadratic formula are shown below.

Step 1: $x + \frac{b}{2a} = \pm\sqrt{\frac{b^2 - 4ac}{2a}}$

Step 2: $x^2 + \frac{b}{a}x + \frac{c}{a} = 0$

Step 3: $\left(x + \frac{b}{2a}\right)^2 = -\frac{c}{a} + \left(\frac{b}{2a}\right)^2$

Step 4: $x^2 + \frac{b}{a}x + \left(\frac{b}{2a}\right)^2 = -\frac{c}{a} + \left(\frac{b}{2a}\right)^2$

Which of the following lists the steps in the correct order? **(Lesson 9-7)**

Ⓐ 1, 2, 3, 4 Ⓒ 2, 4, 3, 1

Ⓑ 4, 3, 1, 2 Ⓓ 3, 4, 1, 2

8. What are the solutions of the quadratic equation $3x^2 + 35x - 12 = 0$? **(Lesson 9-7)**

Ⓐ $1, -36$ Ⓑ $-1, 36$ Ⓒ $12, -\frac{1}{3}$ Ⓓ $-12, \frac{1}{3}$

9. Below is a graph of a quadratic function.

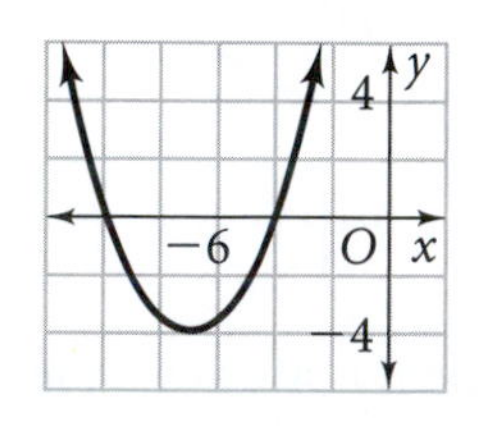

Which of the following is a root of the related equation? **(Lesson 9-4)**

Ⓐ -10 Ⓑ -6.5 Ⓒ -6 Ⓓ 0

10. How many times does the graph of $3x^2 - 6x + 3 = 0$ intersect the x-axis? **(Lesson 9-8)**

Ⓐ 0 Ⓑ 1 Ⓒ 2 Ⓓ 3

11. How many zeros does the quadratic function graphed at the right have? **(Lesson 9-4)**

Ⓐ 0 Ⓒ 2

Ⓑ 1 Ⓓ 3

12. Ellie has \$200 in her wallet. If the sweaters at her favorite store cost \$45 each, how many sweaters can she buy? **(Lesson 1-6)**

Ⓐ 4 Ⓑ 5 Ⓒ 6 Ⓓ 7

13. Rick's car holds 16 gallons of gasoline. When he pulled into the gas station, he had less than half of a tank of gasoline. If gasoline costs \$2.65 per gallon, which of the following is a reasonable amount of money that Rick paid to fill his tank? **(Lesson 1-6)**

Ⓐ \$13.25 Ⓑ \$18.85 Ⓒ \$30.15 Ⓓ \$47.70

14. Mark is laying a 15-square-foot brick walkway. He used 18 bricks for the first 3 square feet. Which is a reasonable number of bricks Mark should buy to finish the walkway? **(Lesson 2-4)**

Ⓐ 100 Ⓑ 200 Ⓒ 300 Ⓓ 400

15. Which of the following is one of the solutions of the equation $3x^2 - 4x - 8 = 0$? **(Lesson 9-7)**

Ⓐ $\frac{2}{3} - \frac{2\sqrt{7}}{3}$ Ⓒ $4 - 4\sqrt{7}$

Ⓑ $\frac{4}{3} - \frac{4\sqrt{7}}{3}$ Ⓓ $2 - 2\sqrt{7}$

16. To solve the equation $x^2 + \frac{b}{a}x = -\frac{c}{a}$ by completing the square, which expression should be added to each side of the equation? **(Lesson 9-7)**

Ⓐ $\left(\frac{b}{a}\right)^2$ Ⓑ $\left(\frac{b}{2a}\right)^2$ Ⓒ $\frac{2b}{a}$ Ⓓ $\frac{b}{2a}$

17. Which of the following is a root of the equation $11x^2 + 3x - 5 = 0$? **(Lesson 9-7)**

Ⓐ $\frac{3 - \sqrt{229}}{22}$ Ⓒ $\frac{-3 - \sqrt{229}}{22}$

Ⓑ $-\frac{-3 - \sqrt{229}}{22}$ Ⓓ $\frac{-3 - \sqrt{229}}{6}$

18. In how many points will the graph of the quadratic function $y = x^2 - x + 6$ intersect the x-axis? **(Lesson 9-8)**

Ⓐ 0 Ⓑ 1 Ⓒ 2 Ⓓ 3

Standards Mastery

19. The graph at the right shows the line $y = x - 1$. Which graph shows a line with the same y-intercept and twice the slope? **(Lesson 5-2)**

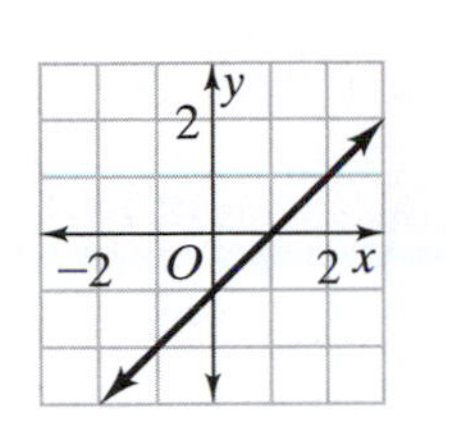

Ⓐ
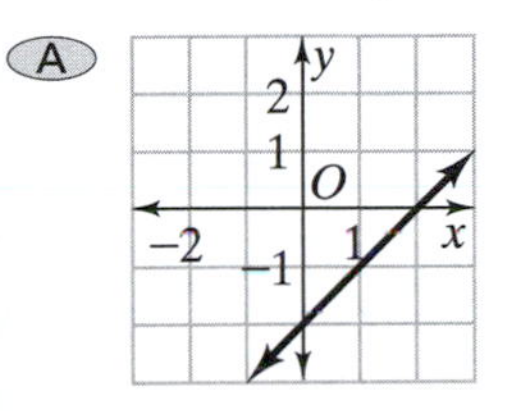

Ⓒ
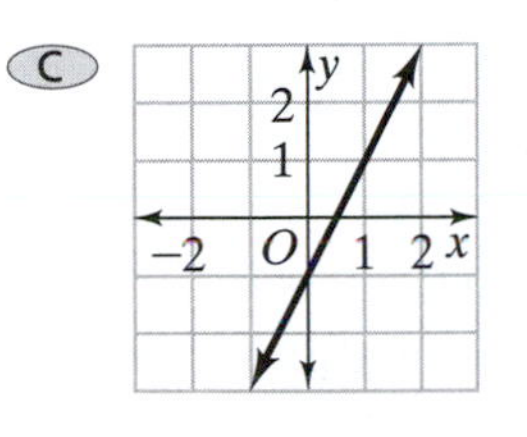

Ⓑ
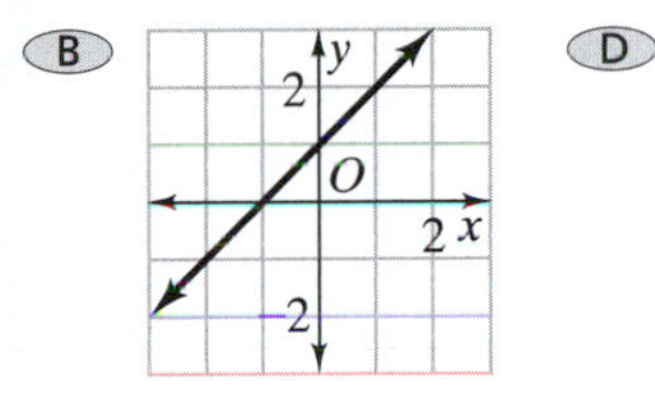

Ⓓ
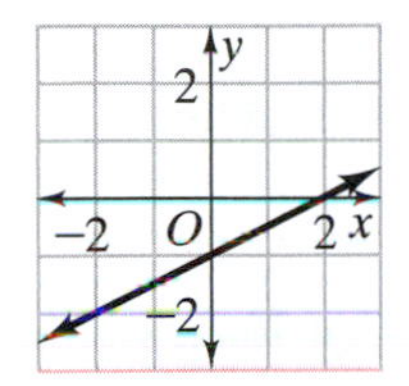

20. Which equation represents a line with a greater slope and smaller y-intercept than the line at the right? **(Lesson 5-2)**

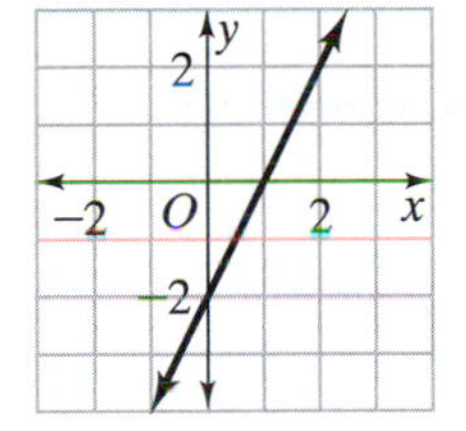

Ⓐ $y = x - 1$

Ⓑ $y = -x - 4$

Ⓒ $y = -2x + 2$

Ⓓ $y = 3x - 3$

21. If the y-intercept of $y = 5x - 4$ is increased by 3, which of the following is true? **(Lesson 5-2)**

Ⓐ The resulting line will have a slope that is greater than the slope of $y = 5x - 4$.

Ⓑ The resulting line will have the same x-intercept as the line $y = 5x - 4$.

Ⓒ The resulting line will be parallel to $y = 5x - 4$.

Ⓓ The resulting line will have a slope of 1.

22. In how many points will the graph of the function of $y = 4x^2 + 21x - 2$ intersect the x-axis? **(Lesson 9-8)**

Ⓐ 0 Ⓑ 1 Ⓒ 2 Ⓓ 3

23. How many x-intercepts does the graph of $y = x^2 - 5x + 16$ have? **(Lesson 9-8)**

Ⓐ 0 Ⓑ 1 Ⓒ 2 Ⓓ 3

24. What is the least possible value for x for the graph of $y = \sqrt{2x - 44} + 3$? **(Lesson 10-5)**

Ⓐ 3 Ⓑ 19 Ⓒ 22 Ⓓ 25

25. What is the solution of $\sqrt{n + 8} = \sqrt{3n}$? **(Lesson 10-4)**

Ⓐ -8 Ⓑ 4 Ⓒ 2, 4 Ⓓ $-2, 4$

26. Suppose the graph of the quadratic function $y = 3x^2 + bx + 4 = 0$ does not intersect the x-axis. Which is a possible value of b? **(Lesson 9-8)**

Ⓐ 6 Ⓑ 7 Ⓒ 8 Ⓓ 9

27. The expression $\frac{-10 \pm \sqrt{10^2 - 4(-3)(-1)}}{2(-3)}$ gives the solutions to which equation? **(Lesson 9-7)**

Ⓐ $-3x^2 + 10x = -1$ Ⓒ $-10x^2 - 3x = 1$

Ⓑ $-10x^2 + 3x = 1$ Ⓓ $-3x^2 + 10x = 1$

Standards Reference Guide

California Content Standard	Item Number(s)
Alg1 2.0	4–6, 25
Alg1 5.0	12–14
Alg1 6.0	19–21
Alg1 16.0	1–3, 24
Alg1 19.0	7, 16
Alg1 20.0	8, 15, 17, 27
Alg1 21.0	9, 11, 18
Alg1 22.0	10, 22, 23, 26

For additional review and practice, see the *California Standards Review and Practice Workbook* or go online to use the

Visit: PHSchool.com, **Web Code:** baq-9045

CHAPTER 11

Rational Expressions and Equations

What You've Learned

California Content Standards

10.0 Add, subtract, and multiply monomials and polynomials. Solve multi-step problems, including word problems, by using these techniques.

11.0 Apply basic factoring techniques to second- and simple third-degree polynomials.

14.0 Solve a quadratic equation by factoring.

15.0 Apply algebraic techniques to solve percent mixture problems.

Check Your Readiness

for Help to the Lesson in green.

Adding and Subtracting Fractions (Skills Handbook page 600)

Add or subtract. Write each answer in simplest form.

1. $\frac{2}{3} + \frac{1}{2}$ **2.** $\frac{3}{13} + \frac{6}{13}$ **3.** $\frac{16}{25} + \frac{3}{10}$ **4.** $\frac{5}{9} - \frac{5}{36}$

Solving Quadratic Equations (Lesson 9-5)

Solve by factoring.

5. $c^2 + 4c - 32 = 0$ **6.** $m^2 - 9m + 14 = 0$ **7.** $p^2 + 6p + 5 = 0$

8. $s^2 - 4s = 12$ **9.** $h^2 - 6h = 27$ **10.** $k^2 = 4k$

Simplifying Expressions (Lesson 7-5)

Simplify each expression.

11. $\frac{6w^3x^2}{2wx}$ **12.** $\frac{81r^{10}s^6}{(3r^2s)^4}$ **13.** $\frac{(5k^5)(2k^3)}{(2k^2)^2}$

Solving Radical Equations (Lesson 10-4)

Solve each radical equation. If there is no solution, write *no solution*.

14. $\sqrt{x} - 4 = 6$ **15.** $\sqrt{3x} + 5 = 2$ **16.** $2x = \sqrt{3x + 1}$

Finding the Domain and Range (Lesson 10-5)

Find the domain and range of each function.

17. $f(x) = 5 - \sqrt{x}$ **18.** $y = -2 + \sqrt{3x}$ **19.** $y = \sqrt{10 - 3x}$

What You'll Learn Next

California Content Standards

10.0 Divide monomials and polynomials. Solve multi-step problems, including word problems, by using these techniques.

12.0 Simplify fractions with polynomials in the numerator and denominator by factoring both and reducing them to the lowest terms.

13.0 Add, subtract, multiply, and divide rational expressions. Solve both computationally and conceptually challenging problems by using these techniques.

15.0 Apply algebraic techniques to solve rate problems and work problems.

▲ When you pluck a guitar string, it vibrates according to the rational equation $f = \frac{k}{L}$, where f is the frequency of string vibration (cycles/s), k is a constant, and L is the length of the string (cm). In Lesson 11-5, you will solve real-world problems involving rational equations.

New Vocabulary

English and Spanish Audio Online

- **rational equation** (p. 550)
- **rational expression** (p. 530)

11-1 Simplifying Rational Expressions

California Content Standards

12.0 Simplify fractions with polynomials in the numerator and denominator by factoring both and reducing them to the lowest terms. ***Introduce, Develop, Master***

What You'll Learn

- To simplify rational expressions

. . . And Why

To find the baking time for bread, as in Example 4

Check Skills You'll Need

GO for Help Skills Handbook page 598 and Lesson 8-5

Write each fraction in simplest form.

1. $\frac{8}{2}$ **2.** $-\frac{15}{24}$ **3.** $\frac{25}{35}$

Factor each quadratic expression.

4. $x^2 + x - 12$ **5.** $x^2 + 6x + 8$ **6.** $x^2 - 2x - 15$

7. $x^2 + 8x + 16$ **8.** $x^2 - x - 12$ **9.** $x^2 - 7x + 12$

New Vocabulary • rational expression

Simplifying Rational Expressions

Fractions like $\frac{5}{9}$, $\frac{7}{12}$, and $\frac{1}{2}$ are rational numbers. An expression that can be written in the form $\frac{\text{polynomial}}{\text{polynomial}}$ is a **rational expression.** Here are some examples:

$$\frac{1}{x} \qquad \frac{x+2}{x-3} \qquad \frac{x^2-5}{x^2-10x+25}$$

Of course, the value of the expression in the denominator cannot be zero, since division by zero is undefined. For the rest of this chapter, assume that the values of the variables that make the denominator zero are excluded from the domain.

Like rational numbers, a rational expression is in simplest form if the numerator and denominator have no common factors except 1. For example, $\frac{z+5}{10z}$ is in simplest form since no factor of $10z$ is a factor of $z + 5$.

1 EXAMPLE Simplifying a Rational Expression

Simplify $\frac{6x+12}{x+2}$.

$\frac{6x+12}{x+2} = \frac{6(x+2)}{x+2}$ Factor the numerator. The denominator cannot be factored.

$= \frac{6(x+2)^1}{_1 x+2}$ Divide out the common factor $x + 2$.

$= 6$ Simplify.

CA Standards Check 1 Simplify each expression.

a. $\frac{15b}{25b^2}$ **b.** $\frac{12c^2}{3c+6}$ **c.** $\frac{4m-2}{2m-1}$ **d.** $\frac{20+4t}{t+5}$

Recall that you learned to factor quadratic expressions in Lessons 8-5 and 8-6. You may need to factor a quadratic expression to simplify a rational expression.

2 EXAMPLE Simplifying a Rational Expression

Simplify $\frac{2x - 12}{x^2 - 7x + 6}$.

$\frac{2x - 12}{x^2 - 7x + 6} = \frac{2(x - 6)}{(x - 6)(x - 1)}$ Factor the numerator and the denominator.

$= \frac{2\cancel{(x - 6)}^1}{{}_1\cancel{(x - 6)}(x - 1)}$ Divide out the common factor $x - 6$.

$= \frac{2}{x - 1}$ Simplify.

CA Standards Check 2 Simplify each expression.

a. $\frac{3x + 12}{x^2 - x - 20}$ b. $\frac{2z - 2}{z^2 - 4z + 3}$ c. $\frac{8a + 16}{2a^2 + 5a + 2}$ d. $\frac{c^2 - c - 6}{c^2 + 5c + 6}$

The numerator and denominator of $\frac{x - 3}{3 - x}$ are opposites. To simplify the expression, you can factor -1 from $3 - x$ to get $-1(-3 + x)$, which you can rewrite as $-1(x - 3)$. Then simplify $\frac{x - 3}{-1(x - 3)}$.

3 EXAMPLE Recognizing Opposite Factors

Simplify $\frac{5x - 15}{9 - x^2}$.

$\frac{5x - 15}{9 - x^2} = \frac{5(x - 3)}{(3 - x)(3 + x)}$ Factor the numerator and the denominator.

$= \frac{5(x - 3)}{-1(x - 3)(3 + x)}$ Factor -1 from $3 - x$.

$= \frac{5\cancel{(x - 3)}^1}{-1_1\cancel{(x - 3)}(x + 3)}$ Divide out the common factor $x - 3$.

$= -\frac{5}{x + 3}$ Simplify.

CA Standards Check 3 Simplify each expression.

a. $\frac{x - 4}{4 - x}$ b. $\frac{8 - m}{m^2 - 64}$ c. $\frac{8 - 4r}{r^2 + 2r - 8}$ d. $\frac{2c^2 - 2}{3 - 3c^2}$

You can use a rational expression to model some real-world situations.

For a given volume of dough, the greater the surface area is, the shorter the baking time.

4 EXAMPLE Evaluating a Rational Expression

The baking time for bread depends, in part, on its size and shape. A good approximation for the baking time, in minutes, of a cylindrical loaf is $\frac{60 \cdot \text{volume}}{\text{surface area}}$, or $\frac{30rh}{r + h}$, where the radius r and the length h of the baked loaf are in inches. Find the baking time for a loaf that is 5 inches long and has a radius of 4 inches. Round your answer to the nearest minute.

$\frac{30rh}{r + h} = \frac{30(4)(5)}{4 + 5}$ Substitute 4 for r and 5 for h.

$= \frac{600}{9}$ Simplify.

≈ 67 Round to the nearest whole number.

The baking time is approximately 67 minutes.

CA Standards Check **4** **a.** Find the baking time for a loaf that is 4 inches long and has a radius of 3 inches. Round your answer to the nearest minute.

b. Critical Thinking The ratio $\frac{60 \cdot \text{volume}}{\text{surface area}}$ for a cylinder is $\frac{60\pi r^2 h}{2\pi r^2 + 2\pi rh}$. Simplify this expression to show that it is the same as the expression evaluated in Example 4.

EXERCISES

Standards Practice

For more exercises, see *Extra Skills and Word Problem Practice.*

Alg1 12.0, 25.3

A Practice by Example

GO for Help

Simplify each expression.

Example 1 (page 530)

1. $\frac{6a + 9}{12}$
2. $\frac{4x^3}{28x^4}$
3. $\frac{2m - 5}{6m - 15}$
4. $\frac{2p - 24}{4p - 48}$
5. $\frac{3x^2 - 9x}{x - 3}$
6. $\frac{3x + 6}{3x^2}$

Example 2 (page 531)

7. $\frac{2x^2 + 2x}{3x^2 + 3x}$
8. $\frac{2b - 8}{b^2 - 16}$
9. $\frac{m + 6}{m^2 - m - 42}$
10. $\frac{w^2 + 7w}{w^2 - 49}$
11. $\frac{a^2 + 2a + 1}{5a + 5}$
12. $\frac{m^2 + 7m + 12}{m^2 + 6m + 8}$
13. $\frac{c^2 - 6c + 8}{c^2 + c - 6}$
14. $\frac{b^2 + 8b + 15}{b + 5}$
15. $\frac{m + 4}{m^2 + 2m - 8}$

Example 3 (page 531)

16. $\frac{5 - 4n}{4n - 5}$
17. $\frac{12 - 4t}{t^2 - 2t - 3}$
18. $\frac{4m - 8}{4 - 2m}$
19. $\frac{m - 2}{4 - 2m}$
20. $\frac{v - 5}{25 - v^2}$
21. $\frac{4 - w}{w^2 - 8w + 16}$

Example 4 (page 531)

Use the expression $\frac{30rh}{r + h}$ to estimate the baking time in minutes for each type of bread. Round your answer to the nearest minute.

22. baguette: $r = 1.25$ in., $h = 26$ in.
23. pita: $r = 3.5$ in., $h = 0.5$ in.

24. biscuit: $r = 1$ in., $h = 0.75$ in.

B Apply Your Skills

Simplify each expression.

25. $\frac{2r^2 + 9r - 5}{r^2 + 10r + 25}$
26. $\frac{7z^2 + 23z + 6}{z^2 + 2z - 3}$
27. $\frac{5t^2 + 6t - 8}{3t^2 + 5t - 2}$
28. $\frac{32a^3}{16a^2 - 8a}$
29. $\frac{3z^2 + 12z}{z^4}$
30. $\frac{2s^2 + s}{s^3}$
31. $\frac{4a^2 - 8a - 5}{15 - a - 2a^2}$
32. $\frac{16 + 16m + 3m^2}{m^2 - 3m - 28}$
33. $\frac{10c + c^2 - 3c^3}{5c^2 - 6c - 8}$

A cylinder with a height of 500 ft and a volume of 1×10^6 ft^3 has about 89% of the surface area of a square prism with the same height and volume.

34. a. To keep heating costs down for a structure, architects want the ratio of surface area to volume as small as possible. Find an expression for the ratio of the surface area to volume for each shape.

i. square prism

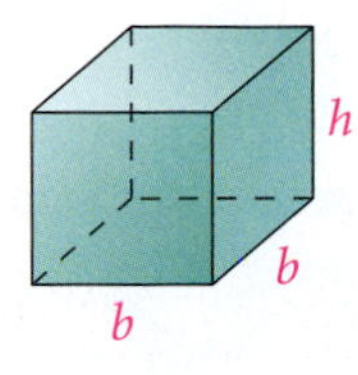

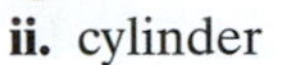
ii. cylinder

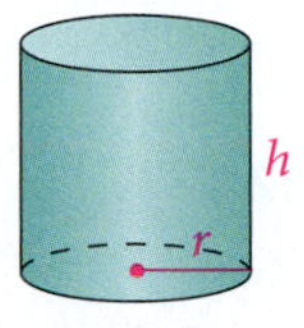

b. Find the ratio for each figure when $b = 12$ ft, $h = 18$ ft, and $r = 6$ ft.

35. Write an expression that has 2 and -3 excluded from the domain.

Error Analysis **Explain the error the student made in simplifying each rational expression. Then simplify the expression correctly.**

36. **37.**

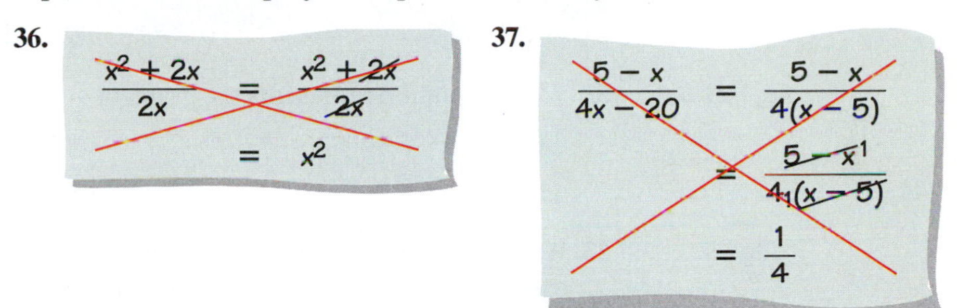

38. Writing Explain why $\frac{x^2 - 9}{x + 3}$ is not the same as $x - 3$.

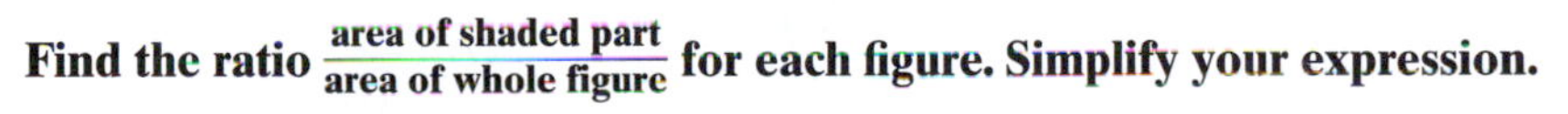
Find the ratio $\frac{\text{area of shaded part}}{\text{area of whole figure}}$ for each figure. Simplify your expression.

39. **40.** **41.** **42.**

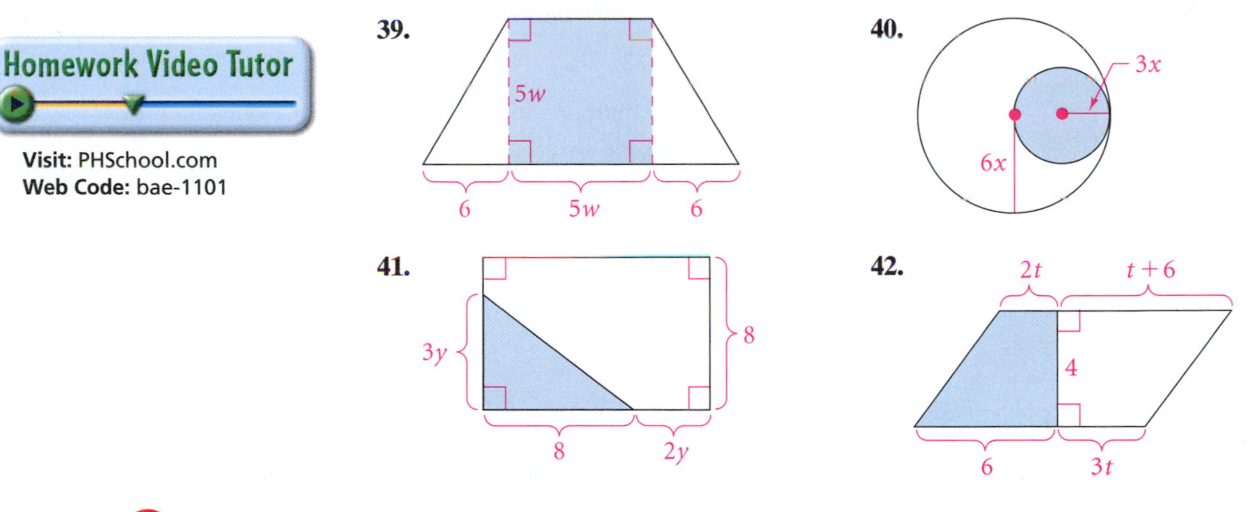

Homework Video Tutor

Visit: PHSchool.com
Web Code: bae-1101

Challenge

Simplify each expression.

43. $\frac{m^2 - n^2}{m^2 + 11mn + 10n^2}$

44. $\frac{a^2 - 5ab + 6b^2}{a^2 + 2ab - 8b^2}$

45. $\frac{36v^2 - 49w^2}{18v^2 + 9vw - 14w^2}$

Math Reasoning **Determine whether each statement is *sometimes*, *always*, or *never* true for real numbers *a* and *b*.**

46. $\frac{2b}{b} = 2$

47. $\frac{ab^3}{b^4} = ab$

48. $\frac{a^2 + 6a - 5}{2a + 2} = \frac{a + 5}{2}$

Multiple Choice Practice

For California Standards Tutorials, visit PHSchool.com. Web Code: baq-9045

Alg1 12.0

49. Which expression is in simplest form?

Ⓐ $\frac{t+1}{t^2-1}$ Ⓑ $\frac{2n-1}{n^2+4}$ Ⓒ $\frac{c-7}{7-c}$ Ⓓ $\frac{2r-4}{8+6r}$

Alg1 12.0

50. What is the ratio of the area of the small circle to the area of the large circle?

Ⓐ $\frac{3}{7}$ Ⓒ $\frac{3}{7}\pi$

Ⓑ $\frac{9\pi}{49x}$ Ⓓ $\frac{9}{49}$

Alg1 17.0

51. Which values of x are NOT in the domain of $\frac{(x+1)(x-3)}{(x-2)(x-5)}$?

Ⓐ -1 and 3 Ⓒ 1 and -3

Ⓑ 2 and 5 Ⓓ -2 and -5

Alg1 21.0

52. Which equation represents the graph of $y = x^2 + 6$ shifted 3 units up?

Ⓐ $y = x^2 + 3$ Ⓒ $y = 3x^2 + 6$

Ⓑ $y = x^2 + 9$ Ⓓ $y = 3x^2 + 9$

Alg1 5.0

53. Water is leaking from a 350-mL container at a rate of 2.5 mL per hour. The equation $w = -2.5h + 350$ gives the number of milliliters of water w in the container after h hours. How long will the container take to empty?

Ⓐ 140 hours Ⓒ 210 hours

Ⓑ 350 hours Ⓓ 490 hours

Alg1 24.0

54. Look at the equations shown below.

$3^1 = 3$ $3^2 = 9$ $3^3 = 27$ $3^4 = 81$ $3^5 = 243$ $3^6 = 729$

Use the pattern in the equations to find the value of the ones digit in 3^{99}.

Ⓐ 1 Ⓑ 3 Ⓒ 7 Ⓓ 9

Multiple Choice Practice

Lesson 10-1

Simplify each radical expression.

55. $\sqrt{20} \cdot \sqrt{10}$ **56.** $\sqrt{a^4b^7c^8}$ **57.** $\frac{\sqrt{80}}{\sqrt{10}}$

58. $\sqrt{\frac{2m}{25m^5}}$ **59.** $\sqrt{90h^2k^4}$ **60.** $\sqrt{6} \cdot \sqrt{8}$

61. $\sqrt{\frac{72}{2a^2}}$ **62.** $\sqrt{9x} \cdot \sqrt{11x}$ **63.** $\sqrt{\frac{28y^5}{7y^2}}$

Lesson 9-1

Order each group of quadratic functions from widest to narrowest graph.

64. $y = x^2, y = 3x^2, y = -2x^2$ **65.** $y = \frac{1}{3}x^2, y = \frac{1}{4}x^2, y = \frac{2}{5}x^2$

66. $y = 2x^2, y = 0.5x^2, y = -4x^2$ **67.** $y = -x^2, y = 2.3x^2, y = -3.8x^2$

Multiplying and Dividing Rational Expressions

California Content Standards

2.0 Understand and use such operations as finding the reciprocal. ***Master***

13.0 Multiply and divide rational expressions. Solve both computationally and conceptually challenging problems by using these techniques. ***Introduce***

What You'll Learn

- To multiply rational expressions
- To divide rational expressions

. . . And Why

To find loan payments, as in Exercises 37–39

Check Skills You'll Need

GO for Help Lessons 7-3 and 8-6

Simplify each expression.

1. $r^2 \cdot r^8$ **2.** $b^3 \cdot b^4$ **3.** $c^7 \div c^2$

4. $3x^4 \cdot 2x^5$ **5.** $5n^2 \cdot n^2$ **6.** $15a^3(-3a^2)$

Factor each polynomial.

7. $2c^2 + 15c + 7$ **8.** $15t^2 - 26t + 11$ **9.** $2q^2 + 11q + 5$

Multiplying Rational Expressions

Multiplying rational expressions is similar to multiplying rational numbers. If a, b, c, and d represent polynomials (with $b \neq 0$ and $d \neq 0$), then $\frac{a}{b} \cdot \frac{c}{d} = \frac{ac}{bd}$.

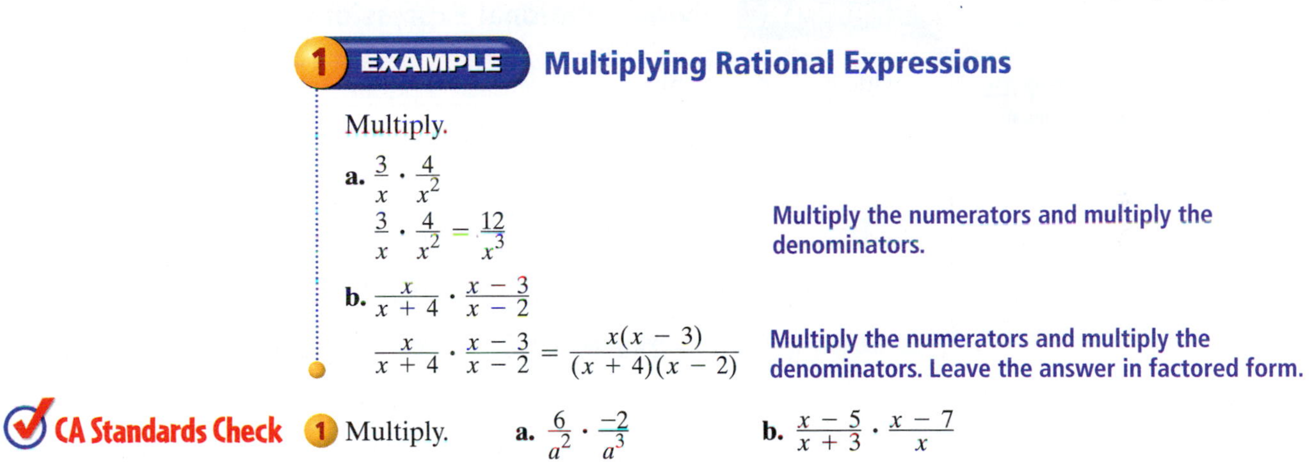

1 EXAMPLE Multiplying Rational Expressions

Multiply.

a. $\frac{3}{x} \cdot \frac{4}{x^2}$

$\frac{3}{x} \cdot \frac{4}{x^2} = \frac{12}{x^3}$ Multiply the numerators and multiply the denominators.

b. $\frac{x}{x+4} \cdot \frac{x-3}{x-2}$

$\frac{x}{x+4} \cdot \frac{x-3}{x-2} = \frac{x(x-3)}{(x+4)(x-2)}$ Multiply the numerators and multiply the denominators. Leave the answer in factored form.

CA Standards Check **1** Multiply. **a.** $\frac{6}{a^2} \cdot \frac{-2}{a^3}$ **b.** $\frac{x-5}{x+3} \cdot \frac{x-7}{x}$

As with rational numbers, the product $\frac{ac}{bd}$ may not be in simplest form. Look for factors common to the numerator and the denominator to divide out.

2 EXAMPLE Using Factoring

Multiply $\frac{2x+1}{3}$ and $\frac{6x}{4x^2-1}$.

$\frac{2x+1}{3} \cdot \frac{6x}{4x^2-1} = \frac{2x+1}{3} \cdot \frac{6x}{(2x+1)(2x-1)}$ Factor the denominator.

$= \frac{\cancel{2x+1}^{1}}{{}_{1}\cancel{3}} \cdot \frac{\cancel{6}^{2}x}{{}_{1}\cancel{(2x+1)}(2x-1)}$ Divide out the common factors.

$= \frac{2x}{2x-1}$ Simplify.

CA Standards Check **2** Multiply $\frac{x-2}{8x}$ and $\frac{-8x-16}{x^2-4}$.

You can also multiply a rational expression by a polynomial.

3 EXAMPLE Multiplying a Rational Expression by a Polynomial

Multiply $\frac{3s+2}{2s+4}$ and $s^2 + 5s + 6$.

$$\frac{3s+2}{2s+4} \cdot (s^2 + 5s + 6) = \frac{3s+2}{2(s+2)} \cdot \frac{(s+2)(s+3)}{1}$$ Factor.

$$= \frac{3s+2}{2_1\cancel{(s+2)}} \cdot \frac{\cancel{(s+2)}^1(s+3)}{1}$$ Divide out the common factor $s + 2$.

$$= \frac{(3s+2)(s+3)}{2}$$ Leave in factored form.

CA Standards Check 3 Multiply.

a. $\frac{3}{c} \cdot (c^3 - c)$ **b.** $\frac{2v}{v+3} \cdot (v^2 - 2v - 15)$ **c.** $(m - 1) \cdot \frac{4m+8}{m^2 - 1}$

Dividing Rational Expressions

Recall that $\frac{a}{b} \div \frac{c}{d} = \frac{a}{b} \cdot \frac{d}{c}$, where $b \neq 0, c \neq 0$, and $d \neq 0$.
When you divide rational expressions that can be factored, first rewrite the expression using the reciprocal before dividing out common factors.

4 EXAMPLE Dividing Rational Expressions

Vocabulary Tip

The vinculum, or fraction bar, is a grouping symbol.

Divide $\frac{a^2 + 7a + 10}{a - 6}$ by $\frac{a+5}{a^2 - 36}$.

$$\frac{a^2 + 7a + 10}{a - 6} \div \frac{a+5}{a^2 - 36} = \frac{a^2 + 7a + 10}{a - 6} \cdot \frac{a^2 - 36}{a + 5}$$ Multiply by $\frac{a^2 - 36}{a + 5}$, the reciprocal of $\frac{a+5}{a^2 - 36}$.

$$= \frac{(a+2)(a+5)}{(a-6)} \cdot \frac{(a-6)(a+6)}{a+5}$$ Factor.

$$= \frac{(a+2)\cancel{(a+5)}^1}{_1\cancel{(a-6)}} \cdot \frac{\cancel{(a-6)}^1(a+6)}{_1\cancel{a+5}}$$ Divide out the common factors.

$$= (a+2)(a+6)$$ Leave in factored form.

CA Standards Check 4 Divide.

a. $\frac{a-2}{ab} \div \frac{a-2}{a}$ **b.** $\frac{5m+10}{2m-20} \div \frac{7m+14}{14m-20}$ **c.** $\frac{6n^2 - 5n - 6}{2n^2 - n - 3} \div \frac{2n-3}{n+1}$

The reciprocal of a polynomial such as $5x^2 + 5x$ is $\frac{1}{5x^2 + 5x}$.

5 EXAMPLE Dividing a Rational Expression by a Polynomial

Divide $\frac{x^2 + 3x + 2}{4x}$ by $(5x^2 + 5x)$.

$$\frac{x^2 + 3x + 2}{4x} \div \frac{5x^2 + 5x}{1} = \frac{x^2 + 3x + 2}{4x} \cdot \frac{1}{5x^2 + 5x}$$ Multiply by the reciprocal of $5x^2 + 5x$.

$$= \frac{(x+1)(x+2)}{4x} \cdot \frac{1}{5x(x+1)}$$ Factor.

$$= \frac{\cancel{(x+1)}^1(x+2)}{4x} \cdot \frac{1}{5x_1\cancel{(x+1)}}$$ Divide out the common factor.

$$= \frac{x+2}{20x^2}$$ Simplify.

CA Standards Check 5 Divide.

a. $\frac{3x^3}{2} \div (-15x^5)$ b. $\frac{y+3}{y+2} \div (y+2)$ c. $\frac{z^2+2z-15}{z^2+9z+20} \div (z-3)$

EXERCISES

Standards Practice

For more exercises, see *Extra Skills and Word Problem Practice.*

Alg1 2.0, 13.0

A Practice by Example

GO for Help

Multiply.

Example 1 (page 535)

1. $\frac{7}{3} \cdot \frac{5x}{12}$
2. $\frac{3}{t} \cdot \frac{4}{t}$
3. $\frac{5}{3a^2} \cdot \frac{8}{a^3}$
4. $\frac{m-2}{m+2} \cdot \frac{m}{m-1}$
5. $\frac{2x}{x+1} \cdot \frac{x-1}{3}$
6. $\frac{6x^2}{5} \cdot \frac{2}{x+1}$

Example 2 (page 535)

7. $\frac{4c}{2c+2} \cdot \frac{c+1}{c-1}$
8. $\frac{5x^3}{x^2} \cdot \frac{3x^4}{6x}$
9. $\frac{3t}{t-2} \cdot \frac{3t-6}{t^2}$
10. $\frac{m-2}{3m+9} \cdot \frac{2m+6}{2m-4}$
11. $\frac{x-5}{4x+6} \cdot \frac{6x+9}{3x-15}$
12. $\frac{4x+1}{5x+10} \cdot \frac{30x+60}{2x-2}$

Example 3 (page 536)

13. $\frac{4t+4}{t-3} \cdot (t^2-t-6)$
14. $\frac{2m+1}{3m-6} \cdot (9m^2-36)$
15. $(x^2-1) \cdot \frac{x-2}{3x+3}$

Example 4 (page 536)

Find the reciprocal of each expression.

16. $\frac{2}{x+1}$
17. $\frac{-6d^2}{2d-5}$
18. c^2-1
19. $s+4$

Divide.

20. $\frac{x-1}{x+4} \div \frac{x+3}{x+4}$
21. $\frac{3t+12}{5t} \div \frac{t+4}{10t}$
22. $\frac{y-4}{10} \div \frac{4-y}{5}$
23. $\frac{x-3}{6} \div \frac{3-x}{2}$
24. $\frac{x^2+6x+8}{x^2+x-2} \div \frac{x+4}{2x+4}$
25. $\frac{2n^2-5n-3}{4n^2-12n-7} \div \frac{4n+5}{2n-7}$

Example 5 (page 536)

26. $\frac{3x+9}{x} \div (x+3)$
27. $\frac{11k+121}{7k-15} \div (k+11)$
28. $\frac{x^2+10x-11}{x^2+12x+11} \div (x-1)$

B Apply Your Skills

Multiply or divide.

29. $\frac{t^2+5t+6}{t-3} \cdot \frac{t^2-2t-3}{t^2+3t+2}$
30. $\frac{c^2+3c+2}{c^2-4c+3} \div \frac{c+2}{c-3}$
31. $\frac{7t^2-28t}{2t^2-5t-12} \cdot \frac{6t^2-t-15}{49t^3}$
32. $\frac{5x^2+10x-15}{5-6x+x^2} \div \frac{2x^2+7x+3}{4x^2-8x-5}$
33. $\frac{x^2+x-6}{x^2-x-6} \div \frac{x^2+5x+6}{x^2+4x+4}$
34. $\left(\frac{x^2-25}{x^2-4x}\right)\left(\frac{x^2+x-20}{x^2+10x+25}\right)$

35. **Error Analysis** In the work shown at the right, what error did the student make in dividing the rational expressions?

$$\frac{3a}{a+2} \div \frac{(a+2)^2}{a-4} = \frac{3a}{a+2} \div \frac{(a+2)^2}{a-4}$$
$$= 3a \div \frac{a+2}{a-4}$$
$$= 3a \cdot \frac{a-4}{a+2}$$
$$= \frac{3a(a-4)}{a+2}$$

36. **Critical Thinking** For what values of x is the expression $\frac{2x^2-5x-12}{6x} \div \frac{-3x-12}{x^2-16}$ undefined?

37. Write two expressions. Find the products.

The formula below gives the monthly payment m on a loan when you know the amount borrowed A, the annual rate of interest r, and the number of months of the loan n. Use this formula for Exercises 37–39.

$$m = \frac{A\left(\frac{r}{12}\right)\left(1 + \frac{r}{12}\right)^n}{\left(1 + \frac{r}{12}\right)^n - 1}$$

FOR SALE
$200,000

38. What is the monthly payment on a loan of \$1500 at 8% annual interest for 18 months?

39. What is the monthly payment on a loan of \$3000 at 6% annual interest for 24 months?

40. Suppose your parents want to buy the house shown at the left. They have \$20,000 for a down payment. Their mortgage will have an annual interest rate of 6%. The loan is to be repaid over a 30-year period.
a. How much will your parents have to borrow?
b. How many monthly payments will there be?
c. What will the monthly payment be?
d. How much will it cost your parents to repay this mortgage over 30 years?

Find the volume of each rectangular solid.

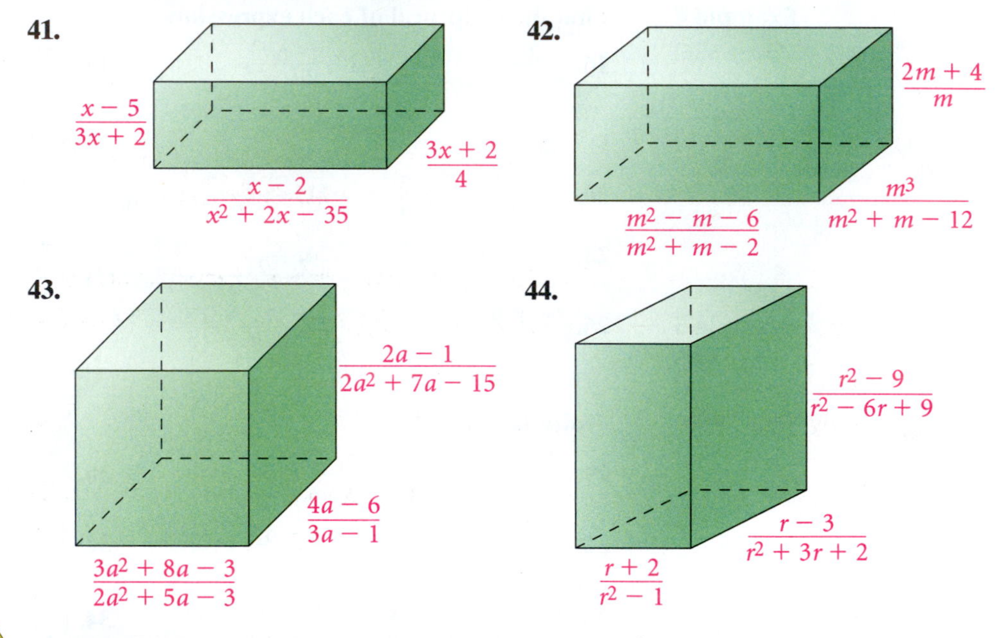

45. Writing Robin's first step in finding the product $\frac{2}{w} \cdot w^5$ was to rewrite the expression as $\frac{2}{w} \cdot \frac{w^5}{1}$. Why do you think Robin did this?

C Challenge

Multiply or divide. (*Hint:* Remember that $\frac{\frac{a}{b}}{\frac{c}{d}} = \frac{a}{b} \div \frac{c}{d}$.)

46. $\frac{3m^3 - 3m}{4m^2 + 4m - 8} \cdot (6m^2 + 12m)$

47. $\frac{t^2 - r^2}{t^2 + tr - 2r^2} \cdot \frac{t^2 + 3tr + 2r^2}{t^2 + 2tr + r^2}$

48. $\frac{5x^2}{y^2 - 25} \div \frac{5xy - 25x}{y^2 - 10y + 25}$

49. $\frac{2a^2 - ab - 6b^2}{2b^2 + 9ab - 5a^2} \div \frac{2a^2 - 7ab + 6b^2}{a^2 - 4b^2}$

50. $\dfrac{\frac{3m}{m-1}}{\frac{6m^2}{m-2}}$

51. $\dfrac{\frac{3x}{x^2-1}}{\frac{6}{x^2-x-2}}$

52. $\dfrac{\frac{w-3}{w^2-4}}{\frac{w^2-9}{w-2}}$

Visit: PHSchool.com
Web Code: bae-1102

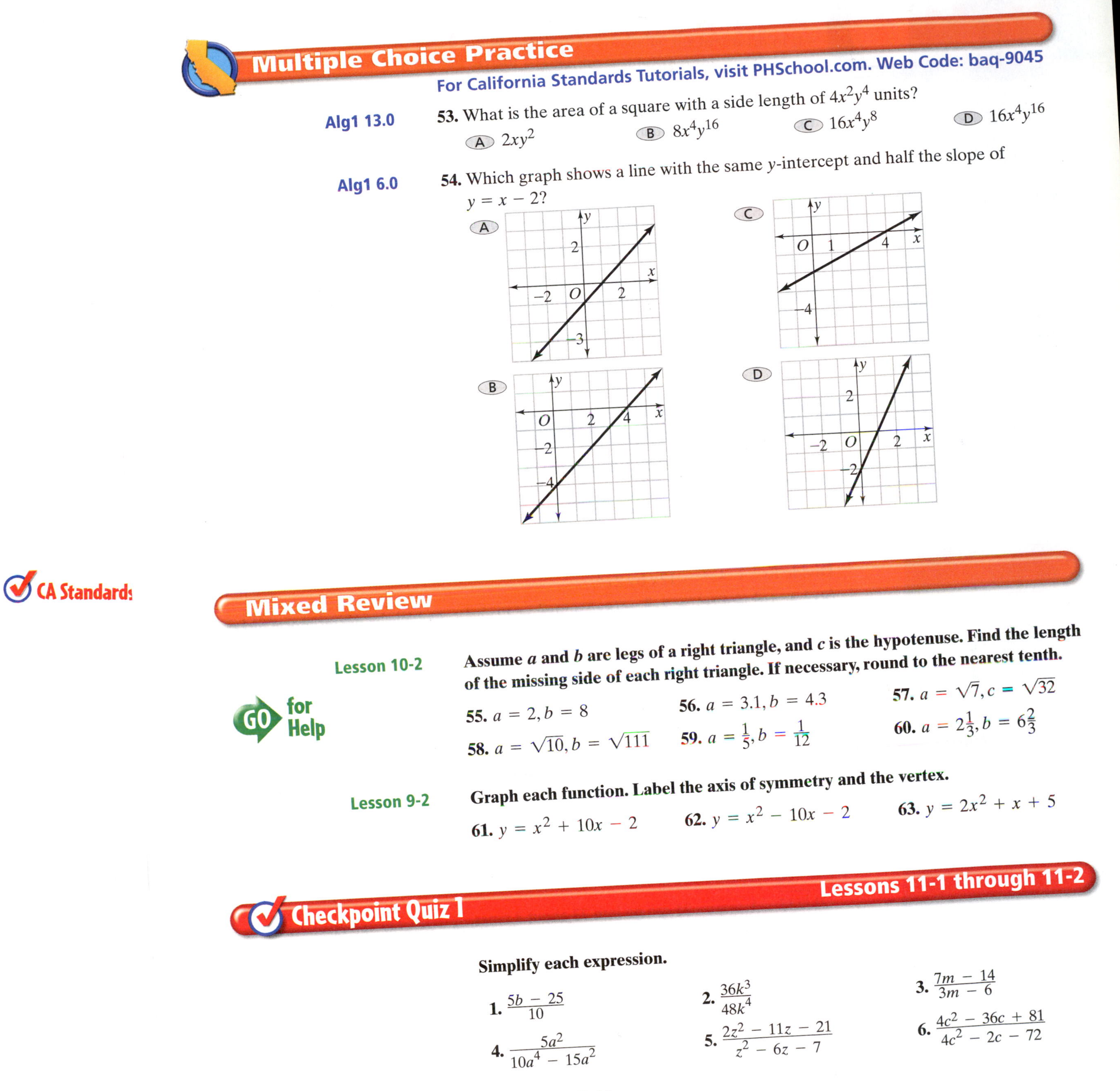

Multiple Choice Practice

For California Standards Tutorials, visit PHSchool.com. Web Code: baq-9045

Alg1 13.0

53. What is the area of a square with a side length of $4x^2y^4$ units?

Ⓐ $2xy^2$ Ⓑ $8x^4y^{16}$ Ⓒ $16x^4y^8$ Ⓓ $16x^4y^{16}$

Alg1 6.0

54. Which graph shows a line with the same y-intercept and half the slope of $y = x - 2$?

Ⓐ Ⓑ Ⓒ Ⓓ

CA Standards

Mixed Review

Lesson 10-2

GO for Help

Assume a and b are legs of a right triangle, and c is the hypotenuse. Find the length of the missing side of each right triangle. If necessary, round to the nearest tenth.

55. $a = 2, b = 8$ **56.** $a = 3.1, b = 4.3$ **57.** $a = \sqrt{7}, c = \sqrt{32}$

58. $a = \sqrt{10}, b = \sqrt{111}$ **59.** $a = \frac{1}{5}, b = \frac{1}{12}$ **60.** $a = 2\frac{1}{3}, b = 6\frac{2}{3}$

Lesson 9-2

Graph each function. Label the axis of symmetry and the vertex.

61. $y = x^2 + 10x - 2$ **62.** $y = x^2 - 10x - 2$ **63.** $y = 2x^2 + x + 5$

Checkpoint Quiz 1

Lessons 11-1 through 11-2

Simplify each expression.

1. $\frac{5b - 25}{10}$ **2.** $\frac{36k^3}{48k^4}$ **3.** $\frac{7m - 14}{3m - 6}$

4. $\frac{5a^2}{10a^4 - 15a^2}$ **5.** $\frac{2z^2 - 11z - 21}{z^2 - 6z - 7}$ **6.** $\frac{4c^2 - 36c + 81}{4c^2 - 2c - 72}$

Multiply or divide.

7. $\frac{3c - 6}{5c} \cdot \frac{c + 4}{c - 2}$ **8.** $\frac{z + 5}{z} \div \frac{3z + 15}{4z}$

9. $\frac{x^2 - 4}{x + 3} \cdot \frac{x^2 + 7x + 12}{x - 2}$ **10.** $\frac{2v^2 + 5v - 3}{4v} \div (12v^2 - 6v)$

CA Standards Chec

GO Online Lesson Quiz Visit: PHSchool.com, Web Code: baa-1102

11-

What You'll Learr

- To divide polynomial:

... And Why

To find the length of a rectangle, as in Example

CA Standards Che

Solve each equation. Be sure to check your answers.

37. $\frac{x-6}{x+3} + \frac{2x}{x-3} = \frac{4x+3}{x+3}$

38. $\frac{n}{n-2} + \frac{n}{n+2} = \frac{n}{n^2-4}$

39. $\frac{2}{r} + \frac{1}{r^2} + \frac{r^2+r}{r^3} = \frac{1}{r}$

40. $\frac{3}{t} - \frac{t^2-2t}{t^3} = \frac{4}{t^2}$

It takes about 1 h 50 min to wash 1000 ft^2 of office windows.

41. Sumi can wash the windows of an office building in $\frac{3}{4}$ the time it takes her apprentice. One day they worked on a building together for 2 h 16 min, and then Sumi continued alone. Sumi took 4 h 32 min more to complete the job. How long would it take her apprentice to wash all the windows alone?

42. A chemist has one solution that is 80% acid and a second solution that is 30% acid. The chemist needs to mix some of both solutions to make 50 liters of a solution that is 62% acid. Let s = the number of liters of the 80% solution used in the mixture.

a. Write an expression for the amount of acid in s liters of the 80% solution.
b. Write an expression for the number of liters of the 30% acid used in the mixture.
c. Write an expression for the amount of acid in a 30% acid solution.
d. Write an equation that combines the amount of acid in each solution to make the total amount of acid in 50 liters of 62% acid solution.
e. Solve the equation you wrote in part (d).
f. How many liters of each solution will the chemist need to make 50 liters of 62% acid solution?

Multiple Choice Practice

For California Standards Tutorials, visit PHSchool.com. Web Code: baq-9045

Alg1 21.0

43. Which graph is the best representation of a quadratic function?

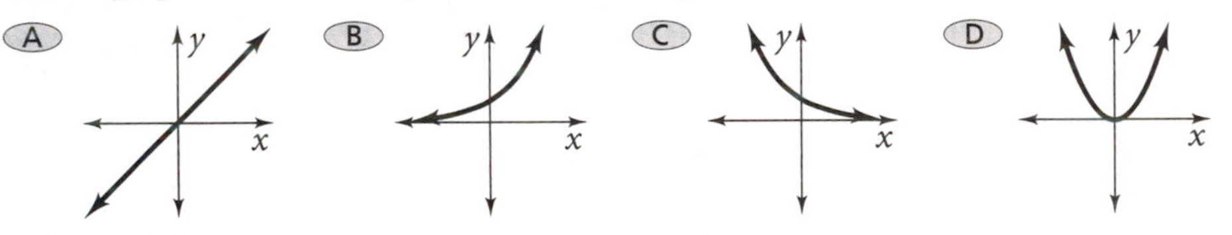

Alg1 7.0

44. Brandon is finding the equation of a line that contains the point (0, −3). Which of the following will NOT be enough information to find the equation?

Ⓐ The slope
Ⓑ The x-intercept
Ⓒ The y-intercept
Ⓓ Another point on the line

Mixed Review

Lesson 10-5

Graph each function.

45. $f(x) = -2\sqrt{x}$
46. $y = \sqrt{x+7}$
47. $f(x) = \sqrt{x-2} - 8$
48. $y = \sqrt{0.25x}$
49. $y = \sqrt{2x} + 3$
50. $y = \sqrt{4x-2} - 2$

Lesson 9-5

Solve each equation by factoring.

51. $x^2 + 23x + 90 = 0$
52. $x^2 - 19x + 88 = 0$
53. $x^2 + 22x - 23 = 0$
54. $x^2 + 2x - 48 = 0$
55. $x^2 + 52 = -17x$
56. $x^2 + 92x - 9 = -100$

GPS Guided Problem Solving

FOR USE WITH PAGE 553, EXERCISE 32

13.0 Add, subtract, multiply, and divide rational expressions. Solve challenging problems by using these techniques. ***Master***

15.0 Apply algebraic techniques to solve rate and work problems. ***Master***

Understanding Word Problems **Read the exercise below and then follow along with what Deon thinks and writes. Check your understanding with the exercise at the bottom of the page.**

Two pipes fill a storage tank in 9 hours. The smaller pipe takes 3 times as long to fill the tank as the larger pipe. How long would it take the larger pipe alone to fill the tank?

What Deon Thinks	What Deon Writes
First I'll write down the important information from the problem.	Time to fill is 9 hours. Large pipe fills the tank 3 times faster than small one.
I'll define a variable. I'll use the time it takes the larger pipe alone to fill the tank as the variable.	n = time in hours for large pipe to fill the tank alone
It would take the small pipe three times longer to fill the tank.	$3n$ = time in hours for small pipe to fill the tank alone
Next I'll write an equation for the amount of work done in one hour.	$\frac{1}{9} = \frac{1}{n} + \frac{1}{3n}$
I'll multiply both sides of the equation by the LCD of 9, *n*, and 3*n*, which is 9*n*. Then I'll simplify and solve the equation.	$9n\left(\frac{1}{9}\right) = 9n\left(\frac{1}{n} + \frac{1}{3n}\right)$ $n = 9 + 3$ $n = 12$
Finally, I write my answer.	It takes 12 hours for the larger pipe alone to fill the tank.

EXERCISES

1. Sam can shovel a driveway in 30 minutes. His cousin Dawn can shovel the same driveway in 50 minutes. How long will it take them if they work together?

2. A homeowner uses two pumps to pump out water from a flooded basement. Together they take 160 minutes to complete the job. The larger pump works twice as fast as the smaller pump. How long would it take the smaller pump alone to complete the job?

Test-Taking Strategies

Answering the Question Asked

When answering a question, be sure to answer the question that is asked. Read the question carefully and identify the quantity that you are asked to find.

1 EXAMPLE

If $5x^2 - x + 4$ is divided by $x + 1$, what is the remainder?

(A) $5x - 6$ (B) $5x + 1$ (C) 10 (D) 0

Use long division.

$$\begin{array}{r} 5x - 6 \\ x + 1\overline{)5x^2 - x + 4} \\ \underline{5x^2 + 5x} \\ -6x + 4 \\ \underline{-6x - 6} \\ 10 \end{array}$$

Choice A is the quotient, and you might be tempted to choose it. The question, however, is asking for the remainder. Choice C is the remainder. That is the correct answer to the question.

2 EXAMPLE

If $\frac{3}{4x} + \frac{5}{x} = 1$, what is the value of $4x$?

(A) $\frac{23}{4}$ (B) $\frac{15}{8}$ (C) 4 (D) 23

$4x\left(\frac{3}{4x} + \frac{5}{x}\right) = 4x(1)$ **Multiply each side by 4x.**

$3 + 20 = 4x$ **Use the Distributive Property.**

$23 = 4x$ **Simplify.**

Choice A is the value of x. The question, however, is asking for the value of $4x$, which is 23. So the correct answer is choice D.

Multiple Choice Practice

1. The graph of $y = \frac{1}{2}x - 2$ is shown at the right. What will the x-intercept be if the y-intercept is increased by 1 but the slope remains the same?

(A) -2 (B) -1 (C) $\frac{1}{2}$ (D) 2

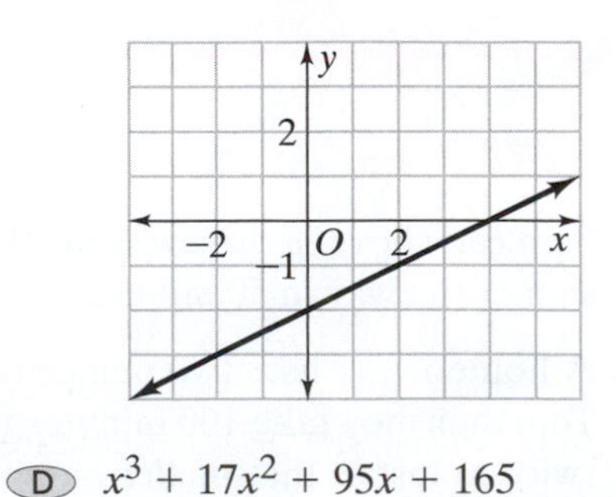

2. The area of a rectangle can be represented by the expression $x^2 + 12x + 35$, and the width by the expression $x + 5$. Which expression could represent the perimeter of the rectangle?

(A) $x + 7$ (B) $x + 12$ (C) $4(x + 6)$ (D) $x^3 + 17x^2 + 95x + 165$

Chapter 11 Review

Vocabulary Review

English and Spanish Audio Online

rational equation (p. 550) **rational expression** (p. 530)

Choose the correct vocabulary term to complete each sentence.

1. A(n) __?__ is in simplest form if the numerator and the denominator have no common factors other than 1.
2. The first step in solving a(n) __?__ is to find the least common denominator.
3. To divide a polynomial by a polynomial using long division, write any divisor or dividend in __?__ form.
4. A(n) __?__ makes a denominator in the original rational equation equal to zero.
5. The rational expressions $\frac{x-3}{x^2+25}$ and $\frac{x^2+25}{x-3}$ are __?__.
6. The numerator and denominator of $\frac{a-b}{b-a}$ are __?__ because the rational expression simplifies to -1.

Go Online PHSchool.com
For: Vocabulary quiz
Web Code: baj-1151

Skills and Concepts

Lesson 11-1

- To simplify rational expressions (p. 520)

A **rational expression** is an expression that can be written in the form $\frac{\text{polynomial}}{\text{polynomial}}$. The domain of a variable is all real numbers excluding the values for which the denominator is zero. A rational expression is in simplest form when the numerator and denominator have no common factors other than 1.

Simplify each expression.

7. $\frac{6t^2}{16t^3}$
8. $\frac{h-9}{3h-27}$
9. $\frac{k-10}{20-2k}$
10. $\frac{x^2-4}{x+2}$
11. $\frac{5x}{20x+15}$
12. $\frac{6x-18}{x-3}$
13. $\frac{-3t}{t^3-t^2}$
14. $\frac{z+2}{2z^2+z-6}$
15. $\frac{x^2-3x-10}{x^2-x-20}$
16. $\frac{6x^2-24}{x+2}$
17. $\frac{3c+9}{3c-9}$
18. $\frac{k-2}{k^2+2k-8}$
19. Which expression simplifies to -1?
   (A) $\frac{x+1}{x-1}$ (B) $\frac{r+3}{3-r}$ (C) $\frac{n-2}{2-n}$ (D) $\frac{4-p}{4+p}$
20. Use the expression $\frac{30rh}{r+h}$ to estimate the baking time in minutes for a loaf of bread with a radius of 2.25 in. and a height of 10 in. Round your answer to the nearest minute.

Lesson 11-2

- To multiply rational expressions (p. 535)
- To divide rational expressions (p. 536)

When you multiply rational expressions, simplify the product by dividing out factors common to the numerator and the denominator. When you divide rational expressions, rewrite the expression using the reciprocal before dividing out common factors. If a, b, c, and d represent polynomials,

- $\frac{a}{b} \cdot \frac{c}{d} = \frac{ac}{bd}$, where b and d are nonzero
- $\frac{a}{b} \div \frac{c}{d} = \frac{a}{b} \cdot \frac{d}{c}$, where b, c, and d are nonzero

Find the reciprocal of each expression.

21. $\frac{3}{x-4}$ **22.** $\frac{t-8}{5t}$ **23.** $\frac{p+1}{3p^2-5p}$

24. $w + 10$ **25.** $s^2 - 7s$ **26.** $\frac{6v^2-12}{v^2+4v-2}$

Multiply.

27. $\frac{8}{m-3} \cdot \frac{3m}{m+1}$ **28.** $\frac{4t-12}{t^2-9} \cdot (3t+9)$

29. $\frac{2x-1}{10x} \cdot \frac{5}{6x^2-7x+2}$ **30.** $\frac{5f}{f+2} \cdot (3f^2+2f-8)$

Divide.

31. $\frac{2x^2+6x-20}{6x} \div \frac{2x}{3x+15}$ **32.** $\frac{z^2+5z-14}{3z^2+21z} \div (z-2)$

33. $\frac{4n+8}{3n} \div \frac{4}{9n}$ **34.** $\frac{2e+1}{8e-4} \div \frac{4e^2+4e+1}{4e-2}$

35. Which *cannot* be the first step in multiplying $\frac{x^2-2x-3}{x+3}$ by $\frac{2x+6}{2x+2}$?

(A) Multiply the numerators.
(B) Find the reciprocal of $\frac{2x+6}{2x+2}$.
(C) Factor each polynomial.
(D) Multiply the denominators.

Lesson 11-3

- To divide polynomials (p. 540)

Alg1 10.0

To divide a polynomial by a monomial, divide each term by the monomial divisor. To divide a polynomial by another polynomial, use long division. Make sure the divisor and dividend are written in standard form. When dividing polynomials, write the answer as quotient + $\frac{\text{remainder}}{\text{divisor}}$.

Divide.

36. $(14x^2 - 28x) \div 7x$ **37.** $(24x^6 + 32x^5 - 8x^2) \div 8x^2$

38. $(50x^5 - 7x^4 + x^2) \div x^3$ **39.** $(x^2 + 8x + 2) \div (x + 1)$

40. $(x^2 + 8x - 16) \div (x + 4)$ **41.** $(8x^3 - 22x^2 - 5x + 12) \div (4x + 3)$

42. $(8x^3 - 8x^2 + 12x - 5) \div (2x - 1)$ **43.** $(4 - 3x^3 + 15x + x^4) \div (x^2 - 5)$

44. $(16x^4 - 32x^3 + 20x - 18) \div (-3 + 2x^2)$ **45.** $(-12x^4 - 1 + 9x^6) \div 3x^4$

46. What is the remainder when $x^2 - 4$ is divided by $x - 3$?

(A) -13 (B) 5 (C) $\frac{-13}{x-3}$ (D) $\frac{5}{x+3}$

47. The length of a rectangle is $(c - 4)$ ft and the area is $(2c^3 - 13c^2 + 29c - 36)$ ft^2. What is the width of the rectangle?

Lesson 11-4

- To add and subtract rational expressions with like denominators
- To add and subtract rational expressions with unlike denominators

 Alg1 13.0

You can add and subtract rational expressions. Restate each expression with the LCD as the denominator, and then add or subtract the numerators.

If a, b, and c represent polynomials (with $c \neq 0$), then $\frac{a}{c} + \frac{b}{c} = \frac{a+b}{c}$.

Find the LCD of each pair of expressions.

48. $\frac{1}{3}; \frac{9}{4x}$ **49.** $\frac{5}{d^2}; \frac{1}{2d}$ **50.** $\frac{h}{6}; \frac{7}{3h^3}$

51. $\frac{1}{11k}; \frac{2}{k}$ **52.** $\frac{4}{8m^4n}; \frac{12}{5m^2n^3}$ **53.** $\frac{1}{2rs^2}; \frac{10}{r^2s}$

Add or subtract.

54. $\frac{8x}{x-7} - \frac{4}{x-7}$ **55.** $\frac{6}{7x} + \frac{1}{4}$

56. $\frac{x}{4+x} - \frac{5}{x-2}$ **57.** $\frac{10x}{6+5x} + \frac{12}{5x+6}$

58. $\frac{9}{3x-1} + \frac{5x}{2x+3}$ **59.** $\frac{7m}{m^2-1} - \frac{10}{m+1}$

60. What is the LCD of $\frac{1}{4}, \frac{2}{x}, \frac{5x}{3x-2}$, and $\frac{3}{8x}$?

Ⓐ $96x^3 - 64x^2$ Ⓒ $24x^2 - 16x$

Ⓑ $12x + 2$ Ⓓ $27x^2 - 6x - 8$

61. Two bicyclists rode a 20-mile round-trip route. On the way back, they had a tail wind and averaged 3 mi/h faster than on the first 10 miles of the trip.

a. Use r for the rate. Write an expression for the total ride time. Simplify the expression.

b. Suppose the bicyclists averaged a rate of 12 mi/h for the first half of the ride. How long did the round trip take?

Lesson 11-5

- To solve rational equations
- To solve proportions

Alg1 13.0, 15.0

You can use the least common denominator (LCD) to solve **rational equations.** Check possible solutions to make sure each answer satisfies the original equation.

Solve each equation. Check your solution.

62. $\frac{1}{2} + \frac{3}{t} = \frac{5}{8}$ **63.** $9 + \frac{1}{t} = \frac{1}{4}$

64. $\frac{3}{m-4} + \frac{1}{3(m-4)} = \frac{6}{m}$ **65.** $\frac{2c}{c-4} - 2 = \frac{4}{c+5}$

66. $\frac{5}{2x-3} = \frac{7}{3x}$ **67.** $\frac{2}{x} = \frac{2}{x^2} + \frac{1}{2}$

68. $\frac{1}{x} + \frac{10}{x^2} = \frac{3}{x}$ **69.** $\frac{4}{10x} = \frac{2}{3x-14}$

70. $\frac{1}{x} + \frac{1}{2x} = 5$ **71.** $\frac{2}{n} + \frac{1}{n+1} = \frac{11}{n^2+n}$

72. $\frac{m}{2} = \frac{24-m}{m}$ **73.** $\frac{10}{3v+6} = \frac{3v}{v+2} + \frac{v^2}{3v+6}$

74. $\frac{3w}{w-1} - \frac{2w}{w+3} = \frac{8w+40}{w^2+2w-3}$ **75.** $\frac{h-5}{h+4} + \frac{h+1}{h+3} = \frac{-6h-6}{h^2+7h+12}$

76. A new photocopier can make 72 copies in 2 min. When an older photocopier is working, the two photocopiers can make 72 copies in 1.5 min. How long will it take the older photocopier working alone to make 70 copies?

Chapter 11 Test

Go Online PHSchool.com For: Chapter Test Web Code: baa-1152

What value of x makes the denominator of each function equal zero?

1. $f(x) = \frac{19 + x}{x - 5}$

2. $y = \frac{x}{7x + 1}$

3. $y = \frac{3}{8 - x}$

4. $f(x) = \frac{2x}{8x - 12}$

Simplify each expression.

5. $\frac{6p - 30}{3p - 15}$

6. $\frac{7p - 8}{8 - 7p}$

7. $\frac{n^2 + 4n - 5}{n + 5}$

8. $\frac{2x + 18}{x^2 + 11x + 18}$

Find the LCD of each pair of expressions.

9. $\frac{5}{h}, \frac{6}{3h}$

10. $\frac{8}{x^2}, \frac{7}{3x}$

11. $\frac{x}{12}, \frac{11}{8x}$

12. $\frac{4}{a^2b^3}, \frac{3}{9ab^4}$

Find the reciprocal of each expression.

13. $\frac{5x}{2 + x}$

14. $\frac{7g^2 - 3}{9g}$

15. $10 - k^2$

16. $r^3 + 2r - 8$

Multiply or divide.

17. $\frac{3}{x - 2} \cdot \frac{x^2 - 4}{12}$

18. $\frac{5x}{x^2 + 2x} \div \frac{30x^2}{x + 2}$

19. $\frac{4w}{3w - 5} \cdot \frac{7}{2w}$

20. $\frac{6c - 2}{c + 5} \div \frac{3c - 9}{c}$

21. $\frac{h}{h + 3} \cdot \frac{h^2 - 9}{h^2 - 3h}$

22. Write a rational expression for which 6 and 3 are excluded from the domain.

Divide.

23. $(12x^4 + 9x^3 - 10x^2) \div 3x^3$

24. $(x^4 - 16) \div (x + 2)$

25. $(4x^4 - 6x^3 + x + 7) \div (2x - 1)$

26. $(6x^3 - 11x^2 - 16x + 13) \div (3x + 2)$

27. If three people working together can clean an office suite in two hours, how long will it take a crew of four people to clean the office?

Solve each equation. Check your solution.

28. $\frac{v}{3} + \frac{v}{v + 5} = \frac{-4}{v + 5}$

29. $\frac{16}{x + 10} = \frac{8}{2x - 1}$

30. $\frac{2}{3} + \frac{t + 6}{t - 3} = \frac{18}{2(t - 3)}$

Add or subtract.

31. $\frac{5}{t} + \frac{t}{t + 1}$

32. $\frac{9}{n} - \frac{8}{n + 1}$

33. $\frac{2y}{y^2 - 9} - \frac{1}{y - 3}$

34. $\frac{4b - 2}{3b} + \frac{b}{b + 2}$

35. $\frac{5}{x^2y^2z} - \frac{8}{x^2y^2z}$

36. $\frac{3h^2}{2t^2 - 8} + \frac{h}{t - 2}$

37. $\frac{k - 11}{k^2 + 6k - 40} - \frac{5}{k - 4}$

38. Which expression is equivalent to $\frac{r^2 - 1}{r} \div (2r^2 - 2)$?

A. $\frac{r^2 - 1}{r} \cdot \frac{1}{2}(r^2 - 1)$

B. $\frac{r^2 - 1}{r} \cdot \frac{2}{r^2 - 1}$

C. $\frac{r^2 - 1}{r} \cdot \left(\frac{1}{2r^2} - 2\right)$

D. $\frac{r^2 - 1}{r} \cdot \frac{1}{2r^2 - 2}$

39. You are trying to find the number you would add to both the numerator and denominator of $\frac{3}{16}$ to make a fraction equation to $\frac{1}{2}$.

a. Write a rational equation that can be used to find this number.

b. Solve the equation to find the number.

Solve each equation. Check your solution.

40. $\frac{4}{x} + \frac{x}{x - 4} = 1$

41. $\frac{2}{z} - \frac{3}{2z} = 5$

42. $\frac{1}{a + 2} + \frac{1}{a - 2} = \frac{10}{a - 2}$

43. $\frac{x}{x + 12} - 1 = \frac{1}{2x}$

44. Critical Thinking Do the equations $x - 2 = 5$ and $\frac{x}{x - 7} - \frac{2}{x - 7} = \frac{5}{x - 7}$ have the same solution(s)? Explain.

Standards Mastery

Cumulative Practice

Read each question. Then write the letter of the correct answer on your paper.

1. The directions on a jar of iced tea mix say that 1 teaspoon of mix should be added to 6 ounces of water. If Ella is using 45 ounces of water, how many teaspoons of iced tea mix should she add? **(Lesson 4-5)**

(A) 7 tsp
(B) 7.5 tsp
(C) 8 tsp
(D) 8.5 tsp

2. Jose's age is 12 less than the square of Mary's age. Which expression best represents the relationship between Jose's age j and Mary's age m? **(Lesson 2-1)**

(A) $j = m^2 - 12$
(B) $j^2 = m - 12$
(C) $m = j^2 - 12$
(D) $m^2 = j - 12$

3. Which graph best represents $y = \frac{1}{2}x - 1$? **(Lesson 5-2)**

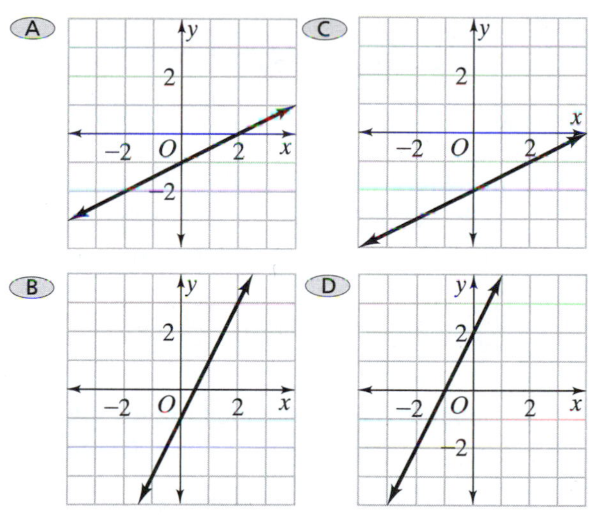

4. What is the solution set of the quadratic equation $2x^2 + 7x + 9 = 0$? **(Lesson 9-7)**

(A) $\left\{\frac{-7 + \sqrt{23}}{4}, \frac{-7 - \sqrt{23}}{4}\right\}$
(B) $\left\{-\frac{9}{2}, 1\right\}$
(C) $\left\{-1, \frac{9}{2}\right\}$
(D) no real solution

5. Mark needs to put yellow caution tape along both diagonals of a doorway. If the doorway is 3.5 feet wide and 7 feet high, about how many feet of caution tape does he need? **(Lesson 10-2)**

(A) 8 ft (B) 11 ft (C) 16 ft (D) 21 ft

6. Which point best represents the intersection of the two lines shown in the graph at the right? **(Lesson 6-1)**

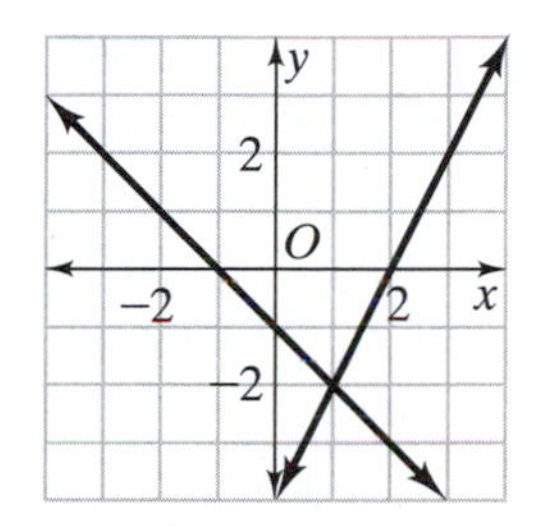

(A) $(-2, 1)$
(B) $(1, -2)$
(C) $(-1, -2)$
(D) $(-2, -1)$

7. Aaron found that the temperature of water on his stove increases at an average rate of 9°F per minute before it boils. The boiling point of water is 212°F. If Aaron puts water that is 68°F on his stove, which equation could be used to find the time, t, in minutes it will take the water to boil? **(Lesson 2-1)**

(A) $212 = 68t + 9$
(B) $212 = 9t + 68$
(C) $68 = 9t - 212$
(D) $9 = 68t - 212$

8. What is $\frac{12x^2 - 4x - 1}{10x^2 - 9x + 2}$ reduced to lowest terms? **(Lesson 11-1)**

(A) $\frac{6x - 1}{5x - 2}$
(B) $\frac{6x + 1}{5x - 2}$
(C) $\frac{6x - 1}{5x + 2}$
(D) $\frac{6x + 1}{5x + 2}$

9. Simplify $\frac{3x}{x + 1} + \frac{5x + 4}{x} + \frac{7x + 4}{x(x + 1)}$. **(Lesson 11-4)**

(A) $\frac{15x + 8}{x(3x + 2)}$
(B) 9
(C) $\frac{8x + 8}{x}$
(D) 16

10. Simplify $\frac{25x^2 - 1}{15x^2 + 22x + 8} \div \frac{20x^2 - 11x - 3}{12x^2 - x - 6}$. **(Lesson 11-2)**

(A) $-\frac{1}{4}$
(B) $\frac{x - 1}{x + 4}$
(C) $\frac{5x + 1}{5x + 4}$
(D) $\frac{5x - 1}{5x + 4}$

11. What is the range of the function $f(x) = x^2 - 1$ for the domain $\{-2, 0, 3, 3.5\}$? **(Lesson 4-2)**

(A) $\{-2, 0, 3, 3.5\}$
(B) $\{-5, -1, 8, 11.25\}$
(C) $\{-1, 3, 8, 11.25\}$
(D) $\{1, 4, 6.25, 9\}$

Cumulative Practice (continued)

12. Carlito's Service Station sells bottles of water for \$1.35 each, including tax. If Sam bought a few bottles of water and paid with a \$20 bill, which of the following could be the amount of change he received? **(Lesson 2-1)**

   A \$1.15 B \$4.05 C \$7.85 D \$12.15

13. Max has \$510 in his savings account and Rose has \$360 in her savings account. Starting today, Max will add \$40 to his account each month, and Rose will add \$55 to her account each month. Which system of equations can be used to find the number of months m it will take for Max and Rose to have the same account balance b? **(Lesson 6-4)**

   A $b = 40m + 510$, $b = 55m + 360$
   C $b = 40m + 360$, $b = 55m + 510$
   B $m = 40b + 510$, $m = 55b + 360$
   D $m = 40b + 360$, $m = 55b + 510$

14. Which function has y-values that always decrease as the corresponding x-values increase? **(Lesson 4-3)**

   A $y = x - 2$ C $y = x^2 - 10$
   B $y = -x + 1$ D $y = -x^2 - 3$

15. Which is a solution of $\frac{x}{x+2} - \frac{8}{x-2} = \frac{6}{x^2-4}$? **(Lesson 11-5)**

   A $x = -5 - \sqrt{47}$ C $x = -\frac{32}{13}$
   B $x = 0$ D $x = 5 + \sqrt{47}$

16. Which statement is an example of deductive reasoning? **(Lesson 4-7)**

   A If $\sqrt{x} + 10 = 19$, then $x = 81$.
   B It rained the last two days, so it will rain today.
   C Both of the above
   D None of the above

17. What is the solution of $8 + |y| - 11 = 3$? **(Lesson 3-6)**

   A $y = -6$ or $y = 6$ C $y = 22$
   B $y = 6$ D $y = -22$ or $y = 22$

18. Which expression is equivalent to $6a^2 \times 6a^5 \div 2a$? **(Lesson 7-5)**

   A $18a^{11}$ B $12a^8$ C $18a^6$ D $12a^{13}$

19. Which equation represents a line that is parallel to $-2x - 4y = 3$? **(Lesson 5-5)**

   A $y = \frac{1}{2}x - 2$ C $y = -\frac{1}{2}x + 5$
   B $y = 2x - 6$ D $y = -2x + 4$

20. An arcade game gives a player game time based on the number of tokens put into the machine. Which equation best represents the relationship between the number of tokens t and the game time g? **(Lesson 5-4)**

Tokens	Game Time (sec)
2	30
4	54
6	78
8	102

   A $g = 12t$ C $g = 12t + 6$
   B $g = 15t$ D $g = 15t + 24$

21. Which statement is NOT always true? **(Lesson 1-2)**

   A $x^2y = xy^2$ when $x = y$
   B $xy = y$ when $x \neq 0$
   C $2x^2 = 8y^2$ when $x = 2y$
   D $y = \frac{y}{x}$ when $x = 1$

22. Which equation represents a line that is perpendicular to the line that passes through the points $(-8, 2)$ and $(-3, 3)$? **(Lesson 5-5)**

   A $(y - 2) = -(x + 8)$ C $y = -5x + 10$
   B $-y = -\frac{1}{5} + 7$ D $x - 5y = -6$

23. What quantity should be added to each side of $t^2 - 14t = 6$ to complete the square? **(Lesson 9-6)**

   A 7 C 49
   B −7 D −49

24. If $4m$ is subtracted from $4m^2$, the difference is 24. Which of the following could be the value of m? **(Lesson 9-5)**

   A −3 C 4
   B −2 D 12

25. What are the solutions of the quadratic equation $2x^2 + 9x = 5$? **(Lesson 9-5)**

   A $-5, -1$ C $5, -\frac{1}{2}$
   B $-5, \frac{1}{2}$ D $5, 1$

Standards Mastery

26. Which graph can be used to find the solution to $2x + 3y = 4$ when $y = -2$? **(Lesson 6-1)**

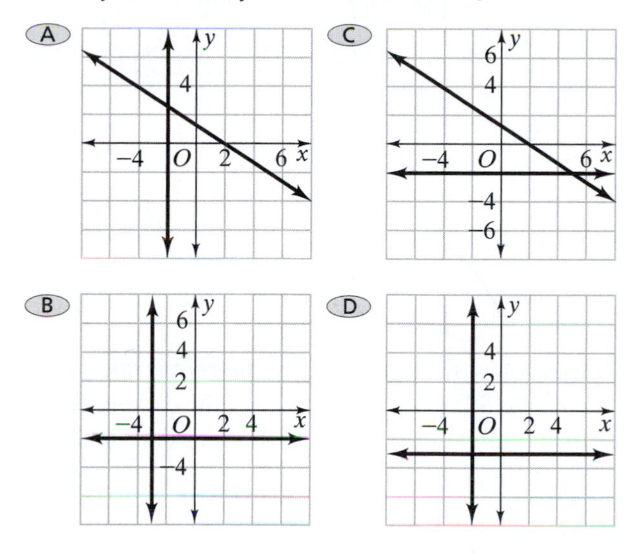

27. Simplify $(x^3 + x^2 + 4x) - (x^2 - 5x + 6)$. **(Lesson 8-1)**

A $4x + 10$
B $x^3 + 9x - 6$
C $4x^2 - 2x$
D $x^3 + 2x^2 - x + 6$

28. Which expression is equivalent to $(8k - 3)(k^2 - k)$? **(Lesson 8-3)**

A $8k^3 + 11k^2 - 11k$
B $8k^3 - 11k^2 + 11k$
C $9k^3 - 8k^2 + 8k$
D $9k^3 - 3k^2 + 3k$

29. What is the remainder when $5x^3 - 14x^2 + 2$ is divided by $x - 3$? **(Lesson 11-3)**

A $\frac{11}{x-3}$
B $-\frac{259}{x-3}$
C $-\frac{7}{x-3}$
D $\frac{263}{x-3}$

30. Which of the following represents a linear function with a slope of 8? **(Lesson 4-2)**

A $y = x + 8$
C $(-5, -6), (-4, 2), (2, 50)$
B

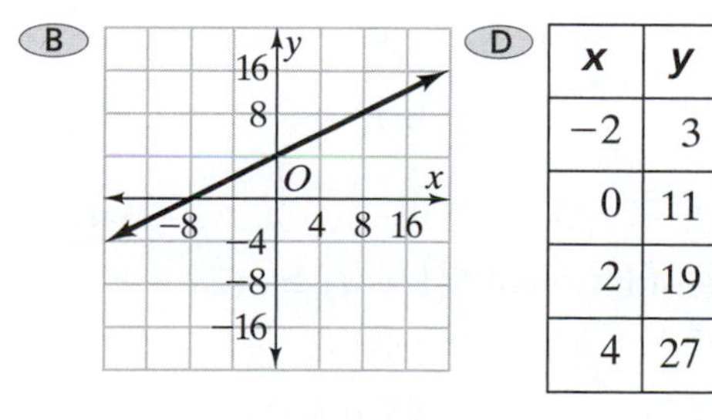

D

x	y
−2	3
0	11
2	19
4	27

31. What is the solution of the equation $|2x + 1| - 3 = 4$? **(Lesson 3-6)**

A $x = 3$ or $x = 0$
B $x = 3$ or $x = -1$
C $x = 3$ or $x = -3$
D $x = 3$ or $x = -4$

32. Which equation is true by the Distributive Property? **(Lesson 1-8)**

A $4(3 - a) = 12 - 3a$
B $9 + 0 = 9$
C $7 + (-7) = 0$
D $(6 \cdot c) \cdot 2 = 6 \cdot (c \cdot 2)$

33. A horizontal line passes through $(5, -2)$. Which other point does it also pass through? **(Lesson 5-1)**

A $(5, 2)$
B $(-5, -2)$
C $(-5, 2)$
D $(5, 0)$

34. Which equation represents a line that fits the data in the table at the right? **(Lesson 5-4)**

x	y
4	11
8	12
12	13
16	14

A $y = -\frac{1}{4}x + 2$
B $y = x + 13$
C $y = \frac{1}{4}x + 10$
D $y = x + 4$

35. Which is one of the solutions to the equation $x^2 - 6x - 11 = 0$? **(Lesson 9-7)**

A -8
B $3 - 4\sqrt{5}$
C 3
D $3 + 2\sqrt{5}$

36. What is $\frac{3x - 9}{x^2 - 6x + 9}$ reduced to lowest terms? **(Lesson 11-1)**

A $\frac{1}{3}x - \frac{1}{3}$
B $\frac{1}{x+3}$
C $\frac{3}{x-3}$
D $x^2 + \frac{1}{3}x - \frac{1}{3}$

37. What is the factored form of $x^2 + 3x - 10$? **(Lesson 8-5)**

A $(x - 2)(x + 5)$
B $(x - 2)(x - 5)$
C $(x + 2)(x - 5)$
D $-(x + 2)(x + 5)$

38. Which of the following shows $16x^2 - 24x + 9$ factored completely? **(Lesson 8-7)**

A $(4x - 3)^2$
B $(4x - 1)(4x - 9)$
C $(2x - 3)(8x - 3)$
D $16x^2 - 24x + 9$

39. Which graph represents the domain of the function $y = x^2 + 1$? **(Lesson 9-1)**

Ⓐ 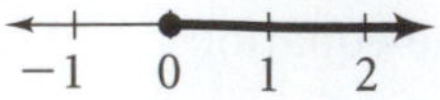

Ⓒ 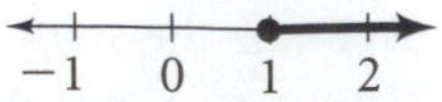

Ⓑ 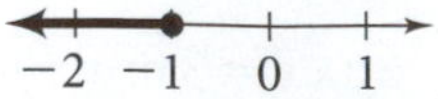

Ⓓ 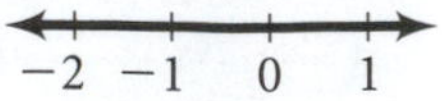

40. What expression gives the approximate area of a circle with a diameter of $6x^2y^4$? **(Lesson 7-4)**

Ⓐ $9x^4y^{16}$ Ⓒ $36x^4y^{16}$

Ⓑ $27x^4y^8$ Ⓓ $108x^4y^8$

41. The area of Square A is 25 in.^{2}, and the area of Square B is 144 in.^{2}. What is the perimeter of Square C to the nearest inch? **(Lesson 10-2)**

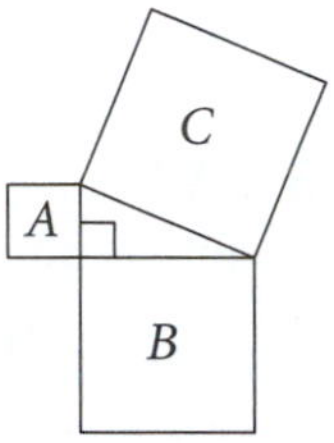

Ⓐ 13 in. Ⓒ 52 in.

Ⓑ 26 in. Ⓓ 169 in.

42. Melissa's height is 5 inches less than 1.5 times Aaron's height. Aaron's height is 3 inches greater than Kira's height. Kira is 46 inches tall. Find Melissa's height. **(Lesson 2-2)**

Ⓐ 46 in. Ⓑ 67 in. Ⓒ 68.5 in. Ⓓ 70 in.

43. The graph of $y = x^2 - 2x - 3$ is shown at the right. For what value or values of x is $y = 0$? **(Lesson 9-4)**

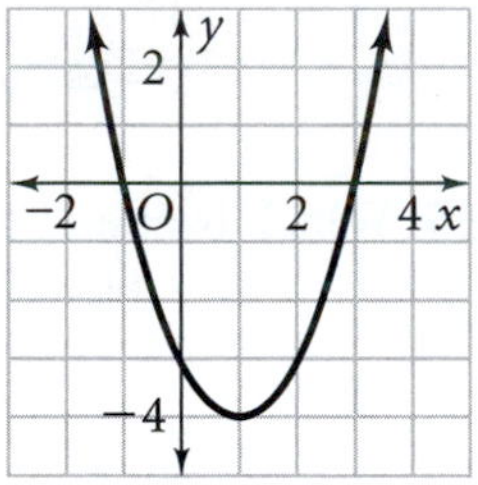

Ⓐ $x = -2$ and $x = 3$

Ⓑ $x = -1$ and $x = -3$

Ⓒ $x = -1$ and $x = 3$

Ⓓ $x = -3$ and $x = 1$

44. A chemist wants to make 500 mL of a 23% acid solution using 10% acid solution and 30% acid solution. How much of the 30% acid solution should he use in the mixture? **(Lesson 2-6)**

Ⓐ 325 mL Ⓒ 150 mL

Ⓑ 175 ml Ⓓ 115 mL

45. Nora can mow the lawn in 75 minutes. Her brother can do the same job in 90 minutes. About how long will it take them to mow the lawn if they work together? **(Lesson 11-5)**

Ⓐ 41 min Ⓒ 60 min

Ⓑ 55 min Ⓓ 82 min

46. Which graph best represents the equation $y = x^2 - c$ if $c > 0$? **(Lesson 9-1)**

Ⓐ 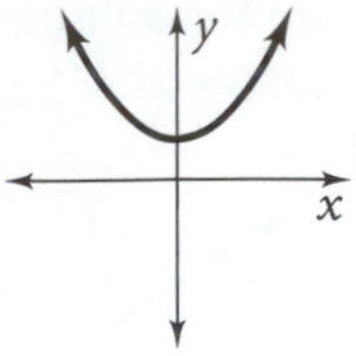

Ⓒ 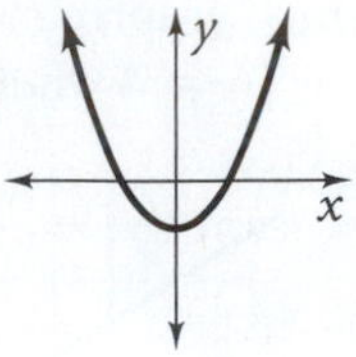

Ⓑ 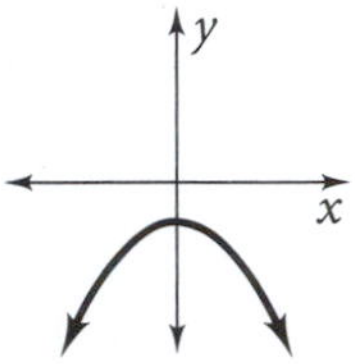

Ⓓ 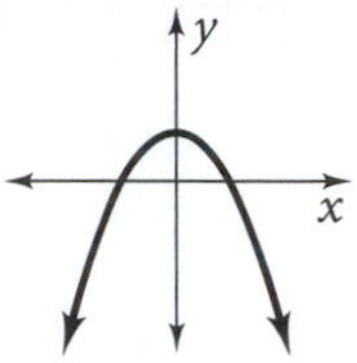

47. Elise paid \$70 to rent a car. The rental rate for the day was \$25 plus \$.30 for each mile driven. How many miles did Elise drive the car? **(Lesson 2-2)**

Ⓐ 268 mi Ⓑ 160 mi Ⓒ 150 mi Ⓓ 45 mi

48. Which equation represents a line with an x-intercept of 4 and a y-intercept of -2? **(Lesson 5-2)**

Ⓐ $y = \frac{1}{2}x - 2$ Ⓒ $y = \frac{1}{2}x + 4$

Ⓑ $y = 2x - 2$ Ⓓ $y = 2x + 4$

49. Which inequality is shown in the graph below? **(Lesson 6-5)**

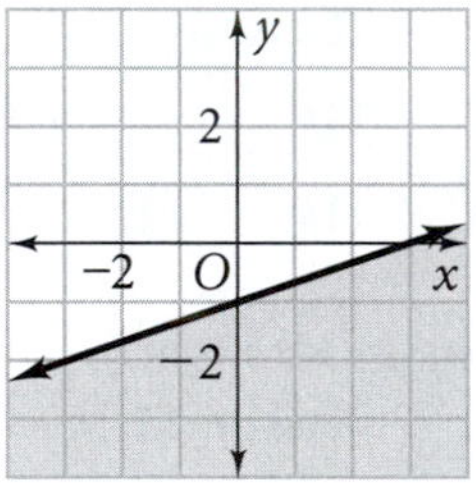

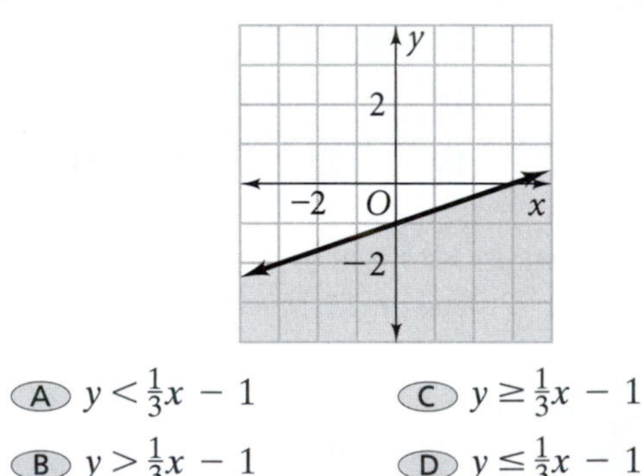

Ⓐ $y < \frac{1}{3}x - 1$ Ⓒ $y \geq \frac{1}{3}x - 1$

Ⓑ $y > \frac{1}{3}x - 1$ Ⓓ $y \leq \frac{1}{3}x - 1$

50. Which statement is true for every solution of the following system? **(Lesson 6-6)**

$$2y > x + 4$$
$$3y + 3x > 13$$

Ⓐ $x \leq -3$ Ⓒ $y < 5$

Ⓑ $x > 4$ Ⓓ $y > 1$

51. What is the solution of $5(1 + d) \geq 3(2d + 9)$? **(Lesson 3-4)**

Ⓐ $d \leq 22$ Ⓒ $d \geq -22$

Ⓑ $d \leq -22$ Ⓓ $d \geq -2$

Standards Mastery

52. The expression $2x^2 + 7x - 15$ represents the area of a rectangle. The dimensions can be represented by the factors of $2x^2 + 7x - 15$. Which expression could represent the length? **(Lesson 8-6)**

   Ⓐ $x - 3$
   Ⓑ $x - 5$
   Ⓒ $2x - 5$
   Ⓓ $2x - 3$

53. Sean is simplifying an expression, as shown below.

   Step 1: $3(x + 2) + 4(2x + 1)$
   Step 2: $3x + 6 + 8x + 4$
   Step 3: $3x + 8x + 6 + 4$
   Step 4: $11x + 10$

   What property did Sean use to get from Step 2 to Step 3? **(Lesson 1-8)**

   Ⓐ Distributive Property
   Ⓑ Commutative Property
   Ⓒ Associative Property
   Ⓓ Addition Property of Equality

54. Which relations are functions? **(Lesson 4-2)**

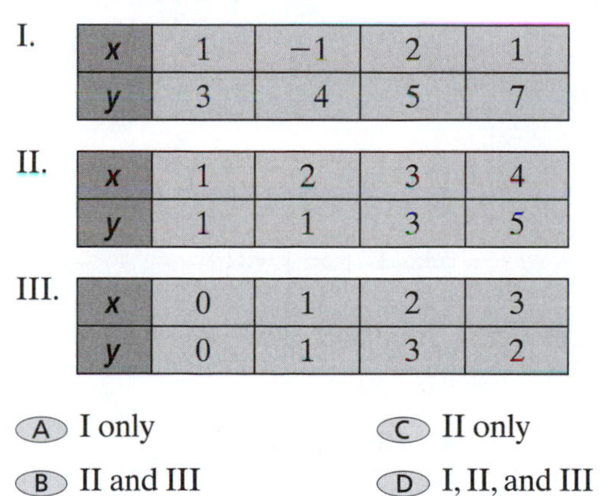

I.

x	1	−1	2	1
y	3	4	5	7

II.

x	1	2	3	4
y	1	1	3	5

III.

x	0	1	2	3
y	0	1	3	2

   Ⓐ I only
   Ⓑ II and III
   Ⓒ II only
   Ⓓ I, II, and III

55. The graph of $y = 15x^2 - 59x - 112$ crosses the x-axis closest to which of the following x-values? **(Lesson 9-7)**

   Ⓐ −1 Ⓑ 0 Ⓒ 3 Ⓓ 6

56. When is the equation $2\sqrt{(x - 4)^2} - 3 = 2x - 5$ true? **(Lesson 10-1)**

   Ⓐ The equation is always true.
   Ⓑ The equation is never true.
   Ⓒ The equation is true for $x \neq 4$.
   Ⓓ The equation is true for $x \geq 4$.

Standards Reference Guide

California Content Standard	Item Number(s)
Alg1 2.0	5, 18, 40, 41
Alg1 3.0	16, 31
Alg1 5.0	2, 7, 12, 42, 47, 51
Alg1 6.0	3, 48, 49
Alg1 7.0	20, 33, 34
Alg1 8.0	19, 22
Alg1 9.0	6, 13, 26, 50
Alg1 10.0	27–29
Alg1 11.0	37, 38, 52
Alg1 12.0	8, 36
Alg1 13.0	9, 10, 15
Alg1 14.0	23–25
Alg1 15.0	1, 44, 45
Alg1 17.0	11, 14, 39
Alg1 18.0	30, 54
Alg1 20.0	4, 35, 55
Alg1 21.0	43, 46
Alg1 24.1	16
Alg1 25.1	32, 53
Alg1 25.3	21, 56

For additional review and practice, see the *California Standards Review and Practice Workbook* or go online to use the

For: PHSchool.com, **Web Code:** baq-9045

Chapter 1

Extra Practice: Skills and Word Problems

Lesson 1-1 **Write an algebraic expression for each phrase.**

1. 4 less than a

2. the quotient of m and n

3. twice y

Define variables and write an equation to model each situation.

4. The total length of the edges of a cube is 12 times the length of an edge.

5. The total cost of lunch is $5.50 times the number of people at the table.

6. The area of a rectangle is 12 cm times the length of the rectangle.

7. The cost of a telephone call is 75 cents plus 25 cents times the number of minutes.

Lesson 1-2 **Simplify each expression.**

8. $4 + 3 \cdot 8$

9. $2 \cdot 3^2 - 7$

10. $6 \cdot (5 - 2) - 9$

11. $2 - 12 \div 3$

12. $4^2 + 8 \div 2$

13. $\frac{1}{2} \div \frac{4}{3}$

14. $-6 \cdot 4.2 - 5 \div 2$

15. $9 - (3 + 1)^2$

16. $2 + 6 \cdot 8 \div 4$

17. $6 + 8 \div 2 - 3$

18. $10 \div 5 \cdot 2 + 6$

19. $5 + 4 \cdot (8 - 6)^2$

Lesson 1-3 **Use <, =, or > to compare.**

20. $0.45 \blacksquare 0.54$

21. $-1.08 \blacksquare -1.008$

22. $\frac{3}{7} \blacksquare \frac{11}{25}$

23. $1.4 \blacksquare \frac{18}{11}$

24. $0.444\ldots \blacksquare \frac{4}{9}$

25. $\frac{4}{13} \blacksquare \frac{4}{15}$

26. $0.101101110\ldots \blacksquare \frac{1}{9}$

27. $\pi \blacksquare \frac{22}{7}$

Lessons 1-4 to 1-6 **Simplify each expression.**

28. $22 + (-33)$

29. $45 + (-54)$

30. $-\frac{4}{3} - \frac{4}{5}$

31. $\frac{4}{13} - \frac{4}{13}$

32. $|12 - 21|$

33. $|12| - |-21|$

34. $-(-(11 - 22))$

35. $\left|\frac{2}{3} + \frac{4}{5}\right|$

36. $(-2)(44)$

37. $(-3)^2$

38. -3^2

39. $\left(\frac{3}{2}\right)\left(-\frac{22}{33}\right)$

40. $\frac{3^2}{2^3}$

41. $\frac{-5^2}{(-5)^2}$

42. $81 \div (-9)$

43. $\frac{4^2}{5^2}$

44. $\frac{2 \cdot 3 + 4}{2(3 + 4)}$

45. $1 + \frac{1}{2 + \frac{1}{3}}$

Lessons 1-7 and 1-8 **Simplify each expression.**

46. $-4(a + 3)$

47. $-12\left(\frac{4}{3}x - 1\right)$

48. $5 + 6(m + 1)$

49. $\frac{4}{9}(18 - 9t)$

50. $1 + 3 + 5 + 7$

51. $1 - 3 + 5 - 7$

52. $-3(7w) + 7(3w)$

53. $2(1 - d) - (2d + 1)$

54. $6c + 2(4c - 3)$

55. $5(2 - j) + (2j - 3)$

56. $\frac{1}{3}(12 - 6r)$

57. $6\left(\frac{1}{2} - \frac{2}{3}y\right)$

Lesson 1-1 Define variables and write an equation for each phrase.

58. The total cost of gas is the number of gallons times $2.25.

59. The length of the trip is 35 minutes plus extra time spent in traffic.

60. The number of tickets available is 4200 minus the number of tickets sold.

Lesson 1-2 Use the formula for the area of a trapezoid $A = h\left(\frac{b_1 + b_2}{2}\right)$, where A is area, b_1 and b_2 are the length of the bases, and h is the height, to answer each question.

61. What is the area of a trapezoidal pool with a height of 15 yd and bases of 14 yd and 26 yd?

62. How many square feet of grass are there on a trapezoidal field with a height of 75 ft and bases of 125 ft and 81 ft?

Lesson 1-3 Is each statement *true* or *false*? If the statement is false, give a counterexample.

63. The product of a rational number and an integer is not an integer.

64. The quotient of two integers is an integer.

65. The sum of two rational numbers is a rational number.

Lessons 1-4 to 1-6 Use addition, subtraction, multiplication, or division to answer each question.

66. A pot of water has a temperature of 25°C. How many degrees should you raise the temperature to boil the water at 100°C?

67. Romana is 68 in. tall and Sophie is 73 in. tall. How much taller is Sophie than Romana?

68. A company buys 1500 small items from a manufacturer for $.02 apiece. What is the total cost of the items?

69. If 36 people are at a pizza party, how many eight-piece pizzas need to be ordered so each person can get two pieces of pizza?

70. Your parents drove the family car 462 miles on 14 gallons of gas. On average, how many miles did the car travel on each gallon of gas?

Lesson 1-7 Use the Distributive Property to find each price.

71. Cereal is on sale for $3.95 per box. What is the cost of seven boxes?

72. The school drama club is putting on a play. If there will be five shows and the auditorium holds 480 people, how many people can see the show?

73. What is the total cost of four CDs on sale for $12.15 each?

Lesson 1-8 Identify the property of real numbers shown in each situation.

74. The cost of one item sold for $14.50 is $14.50.

75. You can find the cost of fish by multiplying the price per pound by the amount or by multiplying the amount by the price per pound.

Chapter 2

Extra Practice: Skills and Word Problems

Lessons 2-1 and 2-2 **Solve each equation.**

1. $8p - 3 = 13$ **2.** $8j - 5 + j = 67$ **3.** $-n + 8.5 = 14.2$

4. $6(t + 5) = -36$ **5.** $m - 9 = 11$ **6.** $\frac{1}{2}(s + 5) = 7.5$

7. $7h + 2h - 3 = 15$ **8.** $\frac{7}{12}x = \frac{3}{14}$ **9.** $3r - 8 = -32$

10. $8g - 10g = 4$ **11.** $-3(5 - t) = 18$ **12.** $3(c - 4) = -9$

Define a variable and write an equation for each situation. Then solve.

13. Your test scores for the semester are 87, 84, and 85. Can you raise your test average to 90 with your next test?

14. You spend $\frac{1}{2}$ of your allowance each week on school lunches. Each lunch costs \$1.25. How much is your weekly allowance?

Lesson 2-3 **Solve each equation. If the equation is an identity, write *identity*. If it has no solution, write *no solution*.**

15. $4h + 5 = 9h$ **16.** $2(3x - 6) = 3(2x - 4)$ **17.** $7t = 80 + 9t$

18. $m + 3m = 4$ **19.** $-b + 4b = 8b - b$ **20.** $6p + 1 = 3(2p + 1)$

21. $10z - 5 + 3z = 8 - z$ **22.** $3(g - 1) + 7 = 3g + 4$ **23.** $17 - 20q = (-13 - 5q)4$

Lesson 2-4 **Solve each proportion.**

24. $\frac{3}{4} = \frac{-6}{m}$ **25.** $\frac{t}{7} = \frac{3}{21}$ **26.** $\frac{9}{j} = \frac{3}{16}$ **27.** $\frac{2}{5} = \frac{w}{65}$

28. $\frac{s}{15} = \frac{4}{45}$ **29.** $\frac{9}{4} = \frac{x}{10}$ **30.** $\frac{10}{q} = \frac{8}{62}$ **31.** $\frac{3}{2} = \frac{18}{y}$

Lesson 2-5 **Find the integers with the given sum.**

32. The sum of two consecutive odd integers is 76.

33. The sum of two consecutive even integers is 106.

34. The sum of three consecutive integers is 126.

35. The sum of three consecutive odd integers is 189.

Find the width and length of each rectangle with the given conditions.

36. The length is 5 in. more than the width. The perimeter is 42 in.

37. The width is one fourth the length. The perimeter is 50 m.

38. The length is 1 ft less than three times the width. The perimeter is 22 ft.

Lesson 2-6 **Determine the amount of each of the two solutions that must be mixed to make 300 L of a 45% acid solution.**

39. solution A: 20%, solution B: 80% **40.** solution A: 35%, solution B: 65%

41. solution A: 30%, solution B: 90% **42.** solution A: 10%, solution B: 70%

43. solution A: 25%, solution B: 50% **44.** solution A: 15%, solution B: 75%

Lessons 2-1 to 2-3 **Write an equation to model each situation. Then solve.**

45. A DVD club charges a monthly membership fee of \$4.95 and \$11.95 for each DVD purchased. If a customer's bill for the month was \$64.70, how many DVDs did the customer purchase?

46. A lawyer charges \$100 per month to be put on retainer for a client. The lawyer also charges an hourly rate of \$75 for work done. How many hours does the lawyer have to work for a client, in one month, to charge \$625?

47. A rectangular pool is twice as long as it is wide. What are the dimensions of the pool if the perimeter is 42 yd?

48. Two friends rent an apartment together. They agree that one person will pay 1.5 times what the other person pays. If the rent is \$850, how much will each friend pay?

49. A shopper's discount club charges a monthly fee of \$15 and sells gasoline for \$2.05 per gallon. The gas station across the street sells gasoline for \$2.35 per gallon and charges no fee. How many gallons of gasoline would you have to buy in one month to spend the same amount at either store?

50. Michael and Kevin are running. Kevin gets a 3-mile head start and runs at a rate of 5.5 mi/h. Michael runs at a rate of 7 mi/h. How many hours will it take Michael to catch up with Kevin?

Lesson 2-4

51. A 12-ounce can of green beans is sold for \$1.45. What is the price per pound?

52. A sailboat is traveling at a speed of 10 nautical miles per hour. If 1 nautical mile is 6076 ft, what is the speed of the sailboat in feet per second?

53. Olivia drove 30 miles in 33 minutes. Juan drove 45 miles in 50 minutes. Who had a faster average speed?

Lesson 2-5

54. Joe and Gayna live 3 miles apart. They both leave their houses at the same time and walk to meet each other. Joe walks at 2.5 mi/h and Gayna walks at 3.5 mi/h. How far will Joe walk before he meets Gayna?

55. A bus traveling 40 mi/h and a car traveling 50 mi/h cover the same distance. The bus travels 1 h more than the car. How many hours did each travel?

Lesson 2-6

56. Cashews cost \$8 per kilogram and pecans cost \$9 per kilogram. How many kilograms of each should you use to make 10 kilograms of a mixture that costs \$8.40 per kilogram?

57. A farmer has one solution that is 30% insecticide and another solution that is 50% insecticide. How many liters of each solution does the farmer need to make 200 liters of a solution that is 44% insecticide?

58. A chemist mixes 128 liters of an 80% chlorinated solution with 92 liters of a 30% chlorinated solution. What percent chlorine is the final solution? Round to the nearest percent.

Chapter 3 Extra Practice: Skills and Word Problems

Lessons 3-1 to 3-4 Solve each inequality. Graph and check your solution.

1. $-8w < 24$
2. $9 + p \leq 17$
3. $\frac{r}{4} > -1$
4. $7y + 2 \leq -8$
5. $t - 5 \geq -13$
6. $9h > -108$
7. $8w + 7 > 5$
8. $\frac{s}{6} \leq 3$
9. $\frac{6c}{5} \geq -12$
10. $-8\ell + 3.7 \leq 31.7$
11. $9 - t \leq 4$
12. $m + 4 \geq 8$
13. $y + 3 < 16$
14. $n - 6 \leq 8.5$
15. $12b - 5 > -29$
16. $4 - a > 15$
17. $4 - x \leq 3$
18. $1 - 4d \geq 4 - d$
19. $n + 7 \leq 3n - 1$
20. $\frac{s}{2} + 1 < s + 2$
21. $3 - \frac{2x}{3} > 5$
22. $8r - \frac{r}{6} > \frac{1}{6} - 8$
23. $1.4 + 2.4x < 0.6$
24. $x - 2 < 3x - 4$

25. The booster club raised $102 in their car wash. They want to buy $18 soccer balls for the soccer team. Write and solve an inequality to find how many soccer balls they can buy.

26. You earn $7.50 per hour and need to earn $35. Write and solve an inequality to find how many hours you must work.

Lesson 3-5 Solve each compound inequality.

27. $8 < w + 3 < 10$
28. $-6 < t - 1 < 6$
29. $6m - 15 \leq 9$ or $10m > 84$
30. $9j - 5j \geq 20$ and $8j > -36$
31. $37 < 3c + 7 < 43$
32. $3 < 5 + 6h < 10$
33. $1 + t < 4 < 2 + t$
34. $2 + 3w < -1 < 3w + 5$
35. $2x - 3 \leq x$ and $2x + 1 \geq x + 3$
36. $3n - 7 > n + 1$ or $4n - 5 < 3n - 3$

Lesson 3-6 Choose a variable and write an absolute value inequality that represents each set of numbers.

37. all real numbers less than 2 units from 0

38. all real numbers more than 0.5 units from 4.5

39. all real numbers less than 1 unit from -4

40. all real numbers 3 or more units from -1

41. all real numbers less than or equal to 5 units from 3

Solve each inequality. Graph and check your solution.

42. $|x| < 5$
43. $|t| > 1$
44. $|t| - 5 \leq 3$
45. $|-6m + 2| > 20$
46. $|3c| - 1 \geq 11$
47. $|8 - w| \leq 8$
48. $|2b + 3| < 7$
49. $|c - 5| \leq 6$
50. $|n| + 4 \leq 5$

51. Write an absolute value inequality that has numbers between 2 and 3 as the solutions.

52. Holes with radius 3 cm must be drilled in sheets of metal. The radius must have an error no more than 0.01 cm. Write an absolute value inequality whose solutions are acceptable radii.

Lesson 3-1 **Define a variable and write an inequality for each situation.**

53. A car dealership sells at least 35 cars each week.

54. No more than 425 tickets to a musical will be sold.

55. You must be at least 18 years old to vote.

56. The party store sold more than 720 balloons in July.

Lessons 3-2 to 3-4 **Write and solve an inequality for each situation.**

57. Suppose you are trying to increase your coin collection to at least 500 coins. How many more coins do you need if you already have a collection of 375 coins?

58. Janet has a balance of $125 on a credit card. On her next statement, she wants to reduce her balance to no more than $60. How much does she need to pay off?

59. A homeroom class with 25 students is holding a fund-raiser to support school sports. Their goal is to raise at least $200. On average, how much money does each student need to contribute to meet or exceed the goal?

60. You are reading a book with 19 chapters. How many chapters should you read each week if you want to finish the book in 5 weeks or less?

61. The sophomore class is putting on a variety show to raise money. It costs $700 to rent the banquet hall they are going to use. If they charge $15 for each ticket, how many tickets do they need to sell in order to raise at least $1000?

62. A technical-support company charges $10 per month plus $35 per hour of phone support. If you need to spend less than $100 per month on support, how many hours can you get?

Lesson 3-5 **Write a compound inequality for each situation. Graph your solution.**

63. Water will be in liquid form when it is warmer than 32°F and colder than 212°F.

64. The width of a parking space needs to be at least 8 feet and no more than 11 feet.

65. A car salesman has been told to sell a particular car for more than $14,500 and no more than the sticker price of $15,755.

Lesson 3-6 **Write and solve an absolute value inequality for each situation.**

66. The ideal diameter of an aircraft tire is 105 inches. The acceptable error for each tire is 0.175 inches. Find the range of acceptable tire diameters.

67. A tractor crankshaft is designed to have a radius of 4.25 cm. The acceptable error for the radius is 0.005 cm. Find the range of acceptable radii for the crankshaft.

68. The ideal weight of an exercise ball is 175 ounces. Each ball can have an error of 0.35 ounces. What is the range of acceptable weights?

Chapter 4

Extra Practice: Skills and Word Problems

Lesson 4-1 **Graph the points on the same coordinate plane.**

1. $(2, 0)$
2. $(-4, -1)$
3. $(0, -2)$
4. $\left(-1, -1\frac{1}{4}\right)$
5. $\left(\frac{1}{2}, \frac{1}{2}\right)$
6. $(3, 3.5)$

In which quadrant or on which axis would you find each point?

7. $(5, 3)$
8. $(-1895, 0)$
9. $(-100, 1)$
10. $(12, -2)$
11. $(0, 3)$
12. $(-3.8, -9.2)$
13. $(6, -6)$
14. $(-3.6, 10.9)$

Lesson 4-2 **Use a mapping diagram to determine whether each relation is a function.**

15. $\{(1, 2), (2, 3), (3, 4), (4, 5), (5, 6)\}$
16. $\{(5, 2), (1, 3), (4, 7), (5, 6), (0, 4)\}$
17. $\{(3.4, 2), (5.6, 2), (0.1, 2), (2.8, 2)\}$
18. $\{(6, 7), (5, 2), (7, 7), (4, 3), (0, 0)\}$

Lesson 4-3 **Graph each function.**

19. $y = 2x + 1$
20. $y = 4 - x$
21. $y = |x| - 3$

Find the range of each function when the domain is $\{-4, -1, 0, 3\}$.

22. $y = 6x - 5$
23. $y = |x| - 2$
24. $y = x^2 + 3x + 1$
25. $y = \frac{1}{2}x + 8$
26. $y = -x^2 - x$
27. $y = \frac{2}{3}x$

Lesson 4-4 **Write a function rule for each table.**

28.

x	f(x)
−3	−1
−1	1
1	3
3	5

29.

x	f(x)
0	0
3	6
6	12
9	18

30.

x	f(x)
21	14
25	18
29	22
33	26

31.

x	f(x)
−8	−4
−6	−3
−4	−2
−2	−1

Lesson 4-5 **Graph the direct variation that includes the given point. Write the equation of the line.**

32. $(5, 4)$
33. $(7, 7)$
34. $(-3, -10)$
35. $(4, -8)$
36. $(-2, 9)$

Lesson 4-6 **Find the constant of variation k for each inverse variation.**

37. $y = 10$ when $x = 7$
38. $y = -8$ when $x = 12$
39. $y = 0.2$ when $x = 4$

Each pair of points is on the graph of an inverse variation. Find the missing value.

40. $(5.4, 3)$ and $(2, y)$
41. $(x, 4)$ and $(5, 6)$
42. $(3, 6)$ and $(9, y)$
43. $(100, 2)$ and $(x, 25)$
44. $(6, 1)$ and $(x, -2)$
45. $(8, y)$ and $(-2, 4)$

Lesson 4-7 **Use inductive reasoning to find the next two numbers in each pattern.**

46. 8, 14, 20, 26, . . .
47. 3, −9, 27, −81, . . .
48. 2, 5, 10, 17, . . .
49. 13, 9, 5, 1, . . .
50. 1, 3, 6, 10, . . .
51. 625, 125, 25, 5, . . .

Lesson 4-1 Write the coordinates of each point.

52. the point 2 units to the right of the y-axis and 1 unit below the x-axis

53. the point on the y-axis and 4 units above the x-axis

54. the point 5 units to the left of the y-axis and 3 units above the x-axis

55. the point 6 units to the right of the y-axis and on the x-axis

Lesson 4-2 Determine whether each relation is a function.

56. (Samantha, 24 years), (Ronak, 15 years), (Pablo, 5 years), (Claire, 11 years)

57. (cheese pizza, \$10), (pepperoni pizza, \$12), (mushroom pizza, \$11), (sausage pizza, \$12)

58. (blue, green), (green, blue), (red, yellow), (orange, red), (purple, green), (blue, purple)

Lesson 4-3 Make a table of values and graph each function.

59. The function $f(x) = 175 + x$ represents the amount of money in a savings account that started with \$175 after a deposit of x dollars.

60. The function $f(x) = 4x$ represents the perimeter of a square with side length x.

Lesson 4-4 Write a function rule for each situation.

61. the circumference of a circle $C(r)$ when you know the radius r

62. the area of a 100-yard-long field $A(w)$ when you know the width w

63. the distance run in feet $D(m)$ when you know the distance in miles m

64. the number of pounds $P(n)$ when you know the number of ounces n

Lessons 4-5 and 4-6 Write a direct or inverse variation to model each situation. Then answer the question.

65. After 30 minutes, a car moving at a constant speed has traveled 25 miles. Moving at the same speed, how far will it travel in 140 minutes?

66. The perimeter of a square depends on the length of a side of the square. What is the perimeter of a square with side length 13.4 in.?

67. Two rectangular fields have the same area. One measures 75 yd by 60 yd. If the other has a length of 72 yd, what is its width?

68. Kevin is training to run in a half marathon. Initially, he could run 6 miles per hour for 2 hours. Two months later he ran the same distance in 1 hour and 45 minutes. What is his new speed?

Lesson 4-7 Use inductive reasoning to answer the question.

69. A train arrives at a subway station at 9:05 A.M. Another train arrives at 9:12 A.M. and a third arrives at 9:19 A.M. If the trains keep running on the same schedule, at what times will each of the next three trains arrive?

70. The balance of a car loan starts at \$9,200 and decreases by \$180 each month. What will the balance be at the end of the next three months?

Chapter 5 Extra Practice: Skills and Word Problems

Lesson 5-1 **Find the rate of change for each situation.**

1. growing from 1.4 m to 1.6 m in one year
2. bicycling 3 mi in 15 min and 7 mi in 55 min
3. growing 22.4 mm in 14 s
4. reading 8 pages in 9 min and 22 pages in 30 min

Find the slope of the line that passes through each pair of points.

5. $(-2, 3), (3, 5)$
6. $(0, -3), (-3, 2)$
7. $(0, 0), (-4, -8)$
8. $(1, -1), (3, 5)$
9. $(9, 7), (3, 7)$
10. $(-1, 8), (-3, 10)$
11. $(-4, -6), (0, -3)$
12. $(4.2, 3.5), (8.7, 2)$

Lesson 5-2 **Find the slope and *y*-intercept of each equation.**

13. $y = 6x + 8$
14. $3x + 4y = -24$
15. $2y = 8$
16. $y = \frac{-3}{4}x - 8$

Write an equation of a line with the given slope and *y*-intercepts.

17. $m = 3, b = -2$
18. $m = 0, b = -5$
19. $m = 4.2, b = 1$
20. $m = 8, b = 0$
21. $m = \frac{1}{2}, b = -4$
22. $m = -\frac{3}{4}, b = 3$

Determine whether the ordered pair lies on the graph of the given equation.

23. $(-2, 5); y = 3x + 1$
24. $(-1, -1); y = -2x - 3$
25. $(0.2, 1.5); 0.5x + 4y = 5.1$
26. $(6, -3); -x - 7y = 13$
27. $(0, 3.5); -5y = 2x - 17.5$
28. $(7.5, 0); -30 = -4x + 9y$

Use the slope and *y*-intercept to graph each equation.

29. $y = 2x - 3$
30. $y = \frac{2}{3}x - 4$
31. $y = -\frac{1}{2}x + 4$
32. $y = -\frac{5}{4}x$

Lesson 5-3 **Find the *x*- and *y*-intercepts for each equation.**

33. $6x + y = 12$
34. $y = -7x$
35. $y = \frac{1}{2}x + 3$
36. $-2y = 5x - 12$

Graph each equation.

37. $x + 4y = 8$
38. $y - 5 = -2(x + 1)$
39. $x + 3 = 0$
40. $4x - 3y = 12$
41. $y = -1$
42. $y + 1 = -\frac{1}{2}(x + 2)$

Lesson 5-4 **Write the equation in point-slope form for the line through the given point with the given slope.**

43. $(4, 6); m = -5$
44. $(3, -1); m = 1$
45. $(8, 5); m = \frac{1}{2}$
46. $(0, -6); m = \frac{4}{3}$

A line passes through the given points. Write an equation for the line in slope-intercept form.

47. $(2, 5)$ and $(4, 8)$
48. $(1, 6)$ and $(7, 3)$
49. $(-2, 4)$ and $(3, 9)$
50. $(1, 6)$ and $(9, -4)$
51. $(0, -7)$ and $(-1, 0)$
52. $(7, 0)$ and $(3, -4)$
53. $(0, 0)$ and $(-7, 1)$
54. $(10, 0)$ and $(0, 7)$

Lesson 5-5 **Write an equation in standard form that satisfies the given conditions.**

55. parallel to $y = 4x + 1$, through $(-3, 5)$
56. perpendicular to $y = -x - 3$, through $(0, 0)$
57. perpendicular to $3x + 4y = 12$, through $(7, 1)$
58. parallel to $2x - y = 6$, through $(-6, -9)$
59. parallel to the *x*-axis and through $(4, -1)$
60. through $(4, 44)$ and parallel to the *y*-axis

Lesson 5-1 **Find the rate of change for each situation.**

61. The cost of four movie tickets is \$30, and the cost of seven tickets is \$52.50.

62. Five seconds after jumping out of the plane, a sky diver is 10,000 ft above the ground. After 30 seconds, the sky diver is 3,750 ft above the ground.

Lesson 5-2 **Write an equation in slope-intercept form for each situation.**

63. A skateboard ramp is 5 ft high and 12 ft long from end to end.

64. An airplane with no fuel weighs 2575 lbs. Each gallon of gasoline added to the fuel tanks weighs 6 lbs.

65. A music store is offering a coupon promotion for its DVDs. The regular price for DVDs is \$14. With the coupon, customers receive \$3 off their total purchase.

66. Expenses for a school dance are \$100. Tickets are \$3 each.

67. A waiter makes \$27 after working for 4 hours. The customers he serves leave an average tip of \$2.50 each.

Lesson 5-3 **Write an equation in standard form for each situation.**

68. Juan can ride his bike at 12 mi/h and walk at 4 mi/h. Write an equation that relates the amount of time he can spend riding or walking combined, to travel 20 miles.

69. You have \$25 to buy supplies for a class party. Juice costs \$3 per bottle, and chips cost \$2 per bag. Write an equation that relates the amount of juice and chips you can buy using \$25.

70. Ticket sales for a school play are \$560. Adult tickets sell for \$5 each. Student tickets sell for \$3 each. Write an equation that relates the number of adult tickets and students tickets sold.

71. A teacher writes an exam that consists of multiple-choice and short-answer questions. She estimates that her students will spend 2 min on each multiple-choice question and 5 min on each short-answer question. Write an equation that relates the number of each type of question the teacher can put on a 60-min exam.

Lesson 5-4 **Write an equation in point-slope form for each situation.**

72. A train travels at a rate of 70 mi/h. Two hours after leaving the station it was 210 miles from its destination.

73. An escalator has a slope of $\frac{3}{4}$. After traveling forward 32 feet, the escalator is 24 feet above the floor.

74. A car travels at a rate of 60 mi/h. Three hours after departing, it is 150 miles from its destination.

Lesson 5-5 **Tell whether each statement is *true* or *false*. Explain your choice.**

75. Two airplanes traveling at the same rate leave an airport 1 hour apart. The graphs of the distance each plane travels will be parallel.

76. Two lines with negative slopes can be perpendicular.

Chapter 6

Extra Practice: Skills and Word Problems

Lesson 6-1 Solve each system by graphing.

1. $x - y = 7$
$3x + 2y = 6$

2. $y = 2x + 3$
$y = -\frac{3}{2}x - 4$

3. $y = -2x + 6$
$3x + 4y = 24$

Lesson 6-2 Solve each system by using substitution.

4. $x - y = 13$
$y - x = -13$

5. $3x - y = 4$
$x + 5y = -4$

6. $x + y = 4$
$y = 7x + 4$

Lesson 6-3 Solve each system by elimination.

7. $x + y = 19$
$x - y = -7$

8. $-3x + 4y = 29$
$3x + 2y = -17$

9. $3x + y = 3$
$-3x + 2y = -30$

10. $6x + y = 13$
$y - x = -8$

11. $4x - 9y = 61$
$10x + 3y = 25$

12. $4x - y = 105$
$x + 7y = -10$

Lesson 6-4 Write a system of equations to model each problem and solve.

13. Suppose you have 12 coins that total 32 cents. Some of the coins are nickels and the rest are pennies. How many of each coin do you have?

14. Claire bought three bars of soap and five sponges for $2.31. Steve bought five bars of soap and three sponges for $3.05. Find the cost of each item.

15. The perimeter of a rectangular lot is 74 feet. The cost of fencing along the two lengths is $1 per foot, and the cost of fencing along the two widths is $3.50 per foot. Find the dimensions of the lot if the total cost of the fencing is $159.

16. A chemist wants to make a 10% solution of fertilizer. How much water and how much of a 30% solution should the chemist mix to get 30 L of a 10% solution of fertilizer?

17. Fruit drink A consists of 6% pure fruit juice and drink B consists of 15% pure fruit juice. How much of each kind of drink should you mix together to get 4 L of a 10% concentration of fruit juice?

18. A motor boat traveled 12 miles with the current, turned around, and returned 12 miles against the current to its starting point. The trip with the current took 2 hours and the trip against the current took 3 hours. Find the speed of the boat and the speed of the current.

Lesson 6-5 Graph each linear inequality.

19. $y < x$

20. $y < x - 4$

21. $y > -6x + 5$

22. $y \leq 14 - x$

23. $y \geq \frac{1}{4}x - 3$

24. $2x + 3y \leq 6$

Lesson 6-6 Solve each system by graphing.

25. $y \leq 5x + 1$
$y > x - 3$

26. $y > 4x + 3$
$y \geq -2x - 1$

27. $y > -x + 2$
$y > x - 4$

28. $y < -2x + 1$
$y > -2x - 3$

29. $y \leq 5$
$y \geq -x + 1$

30. $y \leq 5x - 2$
$y > 3$

Lesson 6-1 **Write and solve a system of equations by graphing.**

31. One calling card has a $.50 connection fee and charges $.02 per minute. Another card has a $.25 connection fee and charges $.03 per minute. After how many minutes would a call cost the same amount using either card?

32. Suppose that you have $75 in your savings account and you save an additional $5 per week. Your friend has $30 in his savings account and saves an additional $10 per week. In how many weeks will you both have the same amount of money in your accounts?

Lesson 6-2 **Write and solve a system of equations by substitution.**

33. A farmer grows corn and soybeans on her 300-acre farm. She wants to plant 110 more acres of soybeans than corn. How many acres of each crop does she need to plant?

34. The perimeter of a rectangle is 34 cm. The length is 1 cm longer than the width. What are the dimensions of the rectangle?

Lesson 6-3 **Write and solve a system of equations using elimination.**

35. Two groups of people order food at a restaurant. One group orders 4 hamburgers and 7 chicken sandwiches for $34.50. The other group orders 8 hamburgers and 3 chicken sandwiches for $30.50. Find the cost of each item.

36. The sum of two numbers is 25. Their difference is 9. What are the two numbers?

Lesson 6-4 **Write and solve a system of equations for each situation by any method. Explain why you chose the method.**

37. The ratio of boys to girls at a college is 4 : 5. How many boys and girls are there if the total number of students is 3321?

38. A boat travels 18 miles downstream in 1.5 hours. It then takes the boat 3 hours to travel upstream the same distance. Find the speed of the boat in still water and the speed of the current.

Lesson 6-5 **Write and graph a linear inequality for each situation.**

39. Suppose you can spend up to $10 on bananas and apples. Apples cost $3 per pound and bananas cost $1 per pound. List three possible combinations of apples and bananas you can buy.

40. Trenton is going to make a rectangular garden in his yard. He wants the perimeter to be no larger than 40 ft. What are three possible sets of dimensions that the garden can have?

Lesson 6-6

41. Hideo plans to spend no more than $60 at an entertainment store on DVDs and CDs. DVDs cost $17 each and CDs cost $14 each. He wants to buy at least two items. Write and graph a system of linear inequalities that describes the situation. What are three possible combinations of CDs and DVDs that he can buy? Write and graph a system of inequalities that describes the situation.

Chapter 7

Extra Practice: Skills and Word Problems

Lesson 7-1 **Simplify each expression. Use only positive exponents.**

1. 9^{-1}
2. 2^{-5}
3. 3.9^{0}
4. $(-5)^{-3}$
5. $\frac{1}{n^{-3}}$
6. $5c^{-4}$
7. $8x^{-5}y^{2}$
8. $7^{-1}r^{-2}s^{6}$

Evaluate each expression for $m = 2, t = -3, w = 4$, and $z = 0$.

9. t^{m}
10. t^{-m}
11. $(w \cdot t)^{m}$
12. $w^{m} \cdot t^{m}$
13. $(w^{z})^{m}$
14. $w^{m}w^{z}$
15. $z^{-t}(m^{t})^{z}$
16. $w^{-t}t^{t}$

Lesson 7-2 **Write each number in scientific notation.**

17. 34,000,000
18. 0.00063
19. 1500
20. 0.0002
21. 360,000
22. 6,200,000,000
23. 0.05
24. 0.000000000891

Write each number in standard notation.

25. 8.05×10^{6}
26. 3.2×10^{-7}
27. 9.0×10^{8}
28. 4.25×10^{-4}
29. 2.35×10^{2}
30. 6.3×10^{4}
31. 2.001×10^{-5}
32. 5.2956×10^{3}

Order the numbers in each list from least to greatest.

33. $4.2 \times 10^{2}, 4.5 \times 10^{-2}, 5.2 \times 10^{6}, 43.8 \times 10^{-1}$
34. $3 \times 10^{8}, 22.4 \times 10^{6}, 2.4 \times 10^{7}, 0.125 \times 10^{9}$
35. $5.6 \times 10^{-2}, 0.32 \times 10^{-1}, 92 \times 10^{-4}, 716 \times 10^{-5}$

Lesson 7-3 **Simplify each expression.**

36. $5m^{5}m^{-8}$
37. $(4.5)^{4}(4.5)^{-2}$
38. $(x^{2}n^{4})(n^{-8})$
39. $(w^{-2}j^{-4})^{-3}(j^{7}j^{3})$

Simplify each expression. Write each answer in scientific notation.

40. $(6 \times 10^{7})(3 \times 10^{2})$
41. $(9 \times 10^{8})(3 \times 10^{-3})$
42. $(1.5 \times 10^{-2})(3 \times 10^{-4})$
43. $(8.4 \times 10^{6})(2 \times 10^{-8})$

Lesson 7-4 **Simplify each expression.**

44. $(2t)^{-6}$
45. $(m^{7}t^{-5})^{2}$
46. $(t^{6})^{3}(m)^{2}$
47. $(3n^{4})^{2}$

Simplify each expression. Write each answer in scientific notation.

48. $(7 \times 10^{5})^{2}$
49. $(4 \times 10^{-3})^{2}$
50. $(8 \times 10^{4})^{2}$
51. $(5 \times 10^{5})^{-2}$

Lesson 7-5 **Simplify each expression.**

52. $\frac{r^{5}}{g^{-3}}$
53. $\frac{1}{a^{-4}}$
54. $\frac{w^{7}}{w^{-6}}$
55. $\frac{6}{t^{-4}}$
56. $\frac{a^{2}b^{-7}c^{4}}{a^{5}b^{3}c^{-2}}$
57. $\frac{(2t^{5})^{3}}{4t^{8}t^{-1}}$
58. $\left(\frac{a^{6}}{a^{7}}\right)^{-3}$
59. $\left(\frac{c^{5}c^{-3}}{c^{-4}}\right)^{-2}$

Simplify each expression. Write each answer in scientific notation.

60. $\frac{7 \times 10^{4}}{2 \times 10^{2}}$
61. $\frac{2.5 \times 10^{-3}}{4 \times 10^{-8}}$
62. $\frac{4 \times 10^{7}}{8 \times 10^{3}}$
63. $\frac{5.4 \times 10^{6}}{6 \times 10^{-7}}$

Lesson 7-1

64. A sample of bacteria triples every week. The expression $3500 \cdot 3^w$ models a population of 3500 bacteria after w weeks of growth. What is the bacteria population after 4 weeks?

65. Suppose an investment doubles in value every 5 years. This year the investment is worth $12,480. How much will it be worth 10 years from now? How much was it worth 5 years ago?

Lesson 7-2 **Write each number in scientific notation.**

66. A bacteria culture has a population of approximately 7,500,000,000.

67. The diameter of a blood cell is about 0.0000082 m.

68. A common house spider weighs about 0.001 kg.

69. Earth's volume is about 259,000,000,000 cubic miles.

70. A human being has about 25,000,000,000,000 red blood cells in his or her bloodstream.

Lesson 7-3 **Write each answer in scientific notation.**

71. A light-year is the distance light travels in one year. If the speed of light is about 3×10^5 km/s, how long is a light-year in kilometers? (Use 365 days for the length of a year).

72. A certain molecule has a mass of 3.01×10^{-23} g. What is the approximate mass of 1.3×10^{21} of these molecules?

73. Find the area of a rectangle with a length of 3.8×10^{-5} cm and a width of 7.1×10^{-3} cm.

74. Find the area of a triangle with a base length of 4.9×10^{-6} ft and a height of 6×10^2 ft.

Lesson 7-4 **Write each answer in scientific notation.**

75. Find the area of a circle with a radius of 8.1×10^{-5} in.

76. The radius of Earth is approximately 6.4×10^6 m. Use the formula $V = \frac{4}{3}\pi r^3$ to find the volume of Earth.

77. A spherical cell has a radius of 2.75×10^{-6} m. Use the formula for the surface area of a sphere $\text{S.A.} = 4\pi r^2$ to find the surface area of a cell.

Lesson 7-5

78. What is the volume of a cube with a side length of $\frac{4}{5}$ m?

79. The speed of sound is approximately 1.2×10^3 km/h. How long does it take for sound to travel 7.2×10^2 km? Write your answer in minutes.

80. Neptune is approximately 2,790,000,000 mi from the sun. Light travels 1.86×10^5 mi/s. About how many seconds does it take light from the sun to reach Neptune?

Extra Practice: Skills and Word Problems

Lesson 8-1 **Simplify. Write each answer in standard form.**

1. $(5x^3 + 3x^2 - 7x + 10) - (3x^3 - x^2 + 4x - 1)$

2. $(x^2 + 3x - 2) + (4x^2 - 5x + 2)$

3. $(4m^3 + 7m - 4) + (2m^3 - 6m + 8)$

4. $(8t^2 + t + 10) - (9t^2 - 9t - 1)$

5. $(-7c^3 + c^2 - 8c - 11) - (3c^3 + 2c^2 + c - 4)$

6. $(6v + 3v^2 - 9v^3) + (7v - 4v^2 - 10v^3)$

7. $(s^4 - s^3 - 5s^2 + 3s) - (5s^4 + s^3 - 7s^2 - s)$

8. $(9w - 4w^2 + 10) + (8w^2 + 7 + 5w)$

9. The sides of a rectangle are $4t - 1$ and $5t + 9$. Write an expression for the perimeter of the rectangle.

10. Three consecutive integers are $n - 1$, n, and $n + 1$. Write an expression for the sum of the three integers.

Lesson 8-2 **Simplify each product.**

11. $4b(b^2 + 3)$

12. $9c(c^2 - 3c + 5)$

13. $8m(4m - 5)$

14. $5k(k^2 + 8k)$

15. $5r^2(r^2 + 4r - 2)$

16. $2m^2(m^3 + m - 2)$

17. $-3x(x^2 + 3x - 1)$

18. $-x(1 + x + x^2)$

Find the common factor of the terms of each polynomial. Factor.

19. $t^6 + t^4 - t^5 + t^2$

20. $3m^2 - 6 + 9m$

21. $16c^2 - 4c^3 + 12c^5$

22. $8v^6 + 2v^5 - 10v^9$

23. $6n^2 - 3n^3 + 2n^4$

24. $5r + 20r^3 + 15r^2$

25. $9x^6 + 5x^5 + 4x^7$

26. $4d^8 - 2d^{10} + 7d^4$

Lessons 8-3 and 8-4 **Simplify each product. Write in standard form.**

27. $(5c + 3)(-c + 2)$

28. $(3t - 1)(2t + 1)$

29. $(w + 2)(w^2 + 2w - 1)$

30. $(3t + 5)(t + 1)$

31. $(2n - 3)(2n + 4)$

32. $(b + 3)(b + 7)$

33. $(3x + 1)^2$

34. $(5t + 4)^2$

35. $(w - 1)(w^2 + w + 1)$

36. $(a + 4)(a - 4)$

37. $(3y - 2)(3y + 2)$

38. $(w^2 + 2)(w^2 - 2)$

39. A rectangle has dimensions $3x - 1$ and $2x + 5$. Write an expression for the area of the rectangle as a product and in standard form.

40. Write an expression for the product of the two consecutive odd integers $n - 1$ and $n + 1$.

Lessons 8-5 to 8-7 **Factor each expression.**

41. $x^2 - 4x + 3$

42. $3x^2 - 4x + 1$

43. $v^2 + v - 2$

44. $5t^2 - t - 18$

45. $m^2 + 9m - 22$

46. $x^2 - 2x - 15$

47. $2n^2 + n - 3$

48. $2h^2 - 5h - 3$

49. $m^2 - 25$

50. $9y^2 - 1$

51. $9y^2 + 6y + 1$

52. $p^2 + 2p + 1$

53. $x^2 + 6x + 9$

54. $25x^2 - 9$

55. $4t^2 + t - 3$

56. $9c^2 - 169$

57. $4m^2 - 121$

58. $3v^2 + 10v - 8$

59. $4g^2 + 4g + 1$

60. $-w^2 + 5w - 4$

61. $9t^2 + 12t + 4$

62. $12m^2 - 5m - 2$

63. $36s^2 - 1$

64. $c^2 - 10c + 25$

Lesson 8-8 **Factor each expression.**

65. $3y^3 + 9y^2 - y - 3$

66. $3u^3 + u^2 - 6u - 2$

67. $w^3 - 3w^2 + 3w - 9$

68. $4z^3 + 2z^2 - 2z - 1$

69. $3x^3 + 8x^2 - 3x$

70. $y^5 - 9y$

71. $2p^3 - 4p^2 + 2p - 4$

72. $3y^3 - 3y^2 - 6y$

Lesson 8-1 **Find an expression for the perimeter of each figure.**

73. A rectangle has side lengths $4k - 3$ and $2k + 2$.

74. A triangle has side lengths $2t^2$, $4t - 3$, and $10 - 2t$.

75. A rhombus has two sides $3d^3 - 2d$ long and two sides $d^2 + 5$ long.

Lesson 8-2

76. A rectangular roof has a length of $13g$ and a width of $4g + 7$. Write an expression for the area of the roof.

77. A cylinder has a base area of $12w^3 + 20w$ and a height of $4w$. Find an expression for the volume.

Lesson 8-3

78. A circular pool has a radius of $5p - 3$ m. Write an expression for the area of the pool.

79. An office building has a rectangular base with side lengths of $12y - 7$ and $22y + 4$. Write an expression for the area of a floor in the office building.

Lesson 8-4

80. Suppose you play a game with two number cubes. Let A represent rolling a number less than 4 and B represent rolling a number greater than 4. The probability of A is $\frac{1}{2}$. The probability of B is $\frac{1}{3}$.

a. Find $\left(\frac{1}{2}A + \frac{1}{3}B\right)^2$.

b. What is the probability that both cubes show a number less than 4?

c. What is the probability that one cube shows a number less than 4 and the other cube shows a number greater than 4?

81. Suppose there are two squares with side lengths of $4x - 3$ and $2x + 4$. Write an expression for the area of each square. Find the area of each square if $x = 6$ cm.

Lesson 8-5

82. Write an expression for the side length of a square that has an area of $h^2 - 12h + 36$.

83. Write an expression for the radius of a circular flower garden with an area of $\pi m^2 + 14\pi m + 49\pi$.

Lessons 8-6 to 8-8 **Use factoring to find expressions for possible dimensions of each figure.**

84. A rectangular parking lot has an area of $10w^2 - 9w - 40$.

85. A rectangular door has an area of $12d^2 - 31d + 14$.

86. A circular window has an area of $49\pi v^2 + 84\pi v + 36\pi$.

87. A rectangular field has an area of $64m^2 - 169n^2$.

88. A rectangular prism has a volume of $6t^3 + 44t^2 + 70t$.

89. A rectangular field has an area of $10k^3 + 25k^2 - 6k - 15$.

Chapter 9

Extra Practice: Skills and Word Problems

Lesson 9-1 **Without graphing, describe how each graph differs from the graph of $y = x^2$.**

1. $y = 3x^2$
2. $y = -4x^2$
3. $y = -0.5x^2$
4. $y = 0.2x^2$
5. $y = x^2 - 4$
6. $y = x^2 + 1$
7. $y = 2x^2 + 5$
8. $y = -0.3x^2 - 7$

Lesson 9-2 **Identify the axis of symmetry and the vertex of each function.**

9. $y = 3x^2$
10. $y = -2x^2 + 1$
11. $y = 0.5x^2 - 3$
12. $y = -x^2 + 2x + 1$
13. $y = 3x^2 + 6x$
14. $y = \frac{3}{4}x^2$
15. $y = 2x^2 - 9$
16. $y = -5x^2 + x + 4$
17. $y = x^2 - 8x$

Graph each quadratic inequality.

18. $y > x^2 - 4$
19. $y < 2x^2 + x$
20. $y \leq x^2 + x - 2$

Lesson 9-3 **Find the square roots of each number.**

21. 25
22. $\frac{4}{9}$
23. 64
24. $\frac{25}{36}$
25. 0.81
26. 900

Tell whether each expression is *rational* or *irrational*.

27. $\sqrt{45}$
28. $-\sqrt{0.16}$
29. -1.010110111

Lessons 9-4 and 9-5 **Solve each equation. If the equation has no solution, write *no solution*.**

30. $x^2 = 36$
31. $x^2 + x - 2 = 0$
32. $c^2 - 100 = 0$
33. $9d^2 = 25$
34. $(x - 4)^2 = 100$
35. $3x^2 = 27$
36. $2x^2 - 54 = 284$
37. $7n^2 = 63$
38. $h^2 + 4 = 0$

Lessons 9-6 and 9-7 **Solve each equation. If the equation has no solution, write *no solution*.**

39. $x^2 + 6x - 2 = 0$
40. $x^2 - 5x = 7$
41. $x^2 - 10x + 3 = 0$
42. $2x^2 - 4x + 1 = 0$
43. $3x^2 + x + 5 = 0$
44. $\frac{1}{2}x^2 - 3x - 8 = 0$
45. $x^2 + 8x + 4 = 0$
46. $x^2 - 2x - 6 = 0$
47. $-3x^2 + x - 7 = 0$
48. $x^2 + 5x + 6 = 0$
49. $d^2 - 144 = 0$
50. $c^2 + 6 = 2 - 4c$
51. $x^2 + 4x = 2x^2 - x + 6$
52. $3x^2 + 2x - 12 = x^2$
53. $r^2 + 4r + 1 = r$
54. $d^2 + 2d + 10 = 2d + 100$
55. $3c^2 + c - 10 = c^2 - 5$
56. $t^2 - 3t - 10 = 0$

57. You are planting a rectangular garden. It is 5 feet longer than 3 times its width. The area of the garden is 250 ft^2. Find the dimensions of the garden.

Lesson 9-8 **Find the number of solutions of each equation.**

58. $3x^2 + 4x - 7 = 0$
59. $5x^2 - 4x = -6$
60. $x^2 - 20x + 101 = 1$
61. $2x^2 - 8x + 9 = 4$
62. $4x^2 - 5x + 6 = 0$
63. $x^2 - 2x + 7 = 0$

Lesson 9-1

64. Water from melting snow drips from a roof at a height of 40 ft. The function $h = -16t^2 + 40$ gives the approximate height h in feet of a drop of water t seconds after it falls. Graph the function.

Lesson 9-2 **The formula $h = -16t^2 + vt + c$ describes the height of an object thrown into the air, where h is the height, t is the time in seconds, v is the initial velocity, and c is the initial height. Use the formula to answer each question.**

65. A football is thrown with an upward velocity of 15 ft/s from an initial height of 5 feet. How long will it take for the football to reach its maximum height?

66. A ball is thrown from the top of a 50-ft building with an upward velocity of 24 ft/s. When will it reach its maximum height? How far above the ground will it be?

Lesson 9-3

67. What is the length of each side of a square garden with an area of 70 ft^2?

68. The formula $t = \sqrt{\frac{d}{16}}$ gives the time t in seconds that it takes for an object to fall d feet. How long does it take an object to fall 6400 ft?

Lesson 9-4 **Model each problem with a quadratic equation. Then solve. If necessary, round to the nearest tenth.**

69. Find the radius of a circular lid with an area of 12 $in.^2$.

70. Find the side length of a square sandbox with an area of 150 ft^2.

71. Find the diameter of a circular pond with an area of 300 m^2.

Lesson 9-5 **Answer each question by factoring a quadratic equation.**

72. The length of an open-top box is 4 cm longer than its width. The box was made from a 480-cm^2 rectangular sheet of material with 6 cm-by-6 cm squares cut from each corner. The height of the box is 6 cm. Find the dimensions of the box.

73. Suppose you throw a rugby ball into the air with an initial upward velocity of 29 ft/s and an initial height of 6 ft. The formula $h = -16t^2 + 29t + 6$ gives the ball's height h in feet at time t seconds. Solve the equation for $h = 0$ to find when the ball will hit the ground.

Lesson 9-6 **Solve by completing the square.**

74. A rectangular patio has a length of $x + 6$ m, a width of $x + 8$ m, and a total area of 400 m^2. Find the dimensions to the nearest tenth.

Lessons 9-7 and 9-8

75. A tennis ball is hit with a vertical velocity of 40 ft/s from an initial height of 7 ft. In how many seconds will the ball hit the ground?

76. A ball is thrown from an initial height of 6 feet at a rate of 42 ft/s to someone standing on a roof 30 feet above the ground. Use the discriminant to determine if the ball will reach the person on the roof.

Chapter 10

Extra Practice: Skills and Word Problems

Lesson 10-1 **Simplify each radical expression.**

1. $\frac{\sqrt{27}}{\sqrt{81}}$
2. $\sqrt{\frac{25}{4}}$
3. $\sqrt{\frac{50}{9}}$
4. $\frac{\sqrt{72}}{\sqrt{50}}$
5. $\sqrt{25} \cdot \sqrt{4}$
6. $\sqrt{27} \cdot \sqrt{3}$
7. $\sqrt{\frac{44x^4}{11}}$
8. $\frac{\sqrt{3c^2}}{\sqrt{27}}$
9. $\sqrt{45} \cdot \sqrt{18}$

Simplify each radical expression by rationalizing the denominator.

10. $\frac{3}{\sqrt{3}}$
11. $\frac{\sqrt{2}}{\sqrt{y}}$
12. $\frac{2}{\sqrt{12}}$
13. $\frac{\sqrt{5}}{\sqrt{8x}}$
14. $\frac{4\sqrt{5}}{\sqrt{16b}}$
15. $\frac{\sqrt{7}}{\sqrt{27x}}$

Lesson 10-2 **Determine whether the given lengths are sides of a right triangle.**

16. 15, 36, 39
17. 3, 7, 10
18. 8, 15, 17
19. $\sqrt{3}$, $\sqrt{4}$, $\sqrt{5}$

For the values given, *a* and *b* are legs of a right triangle. Find the length of the hypotenuse. If necessary, round to the nearest tenth.

20. $a = 6, b = 8$
21. $a = 5, b = 9$
22. $a = 4, b = 10$
23. $a = 9, b = 1$
24. $a = 4, b = 4$
25. $a = 10, b = 4$
26. $a = 5, b = 12$
27. $a = \sqrt{3}, b = \sqrt{5}$

For the values given, find the length of the missing side. If necessary, round to the nearest tenth.

28. $a = 12, c = 20$
29. $b = 5\sqrt{3}, c = 10$
30. $a = 18, c = 30$
31. $a = 1, c = \sqrt{3}$
32. $b = 4, c = 11$
33. $a = 3\sqrt{3}, c = 5\sqrt{3}$
34. $b = 9, c = 27$
35. $a = 8.3, c = 17.2$

Lesson 10-3 **Simplify each radical expression.**

36. $\sqrt{75} - 4\sqrt{75}$
37. $\sqrt{5}(\sqrt{20} - \sqrt{80})$
38. $\sqrt{6}(\sqrt{6} - 3)$
39. $3\sqrt{300} + 2\sqrt{27}$
40. $5\sqrt{2} \cdot 3\sqrt{50}$
41. $\sqrt{8} - 4\sqrt{2}$
42. $\frac{\sqrt{z^3}}{\sqrt{5z}}$
43. $(\sqrt{5} + 1)(\sqrt{5} - 1)$
44. $(\sqrt{3} + \sqrt{2})^2$
45. $\frac{1}{\sqrt{2} + 1}$
46. $\frac{2}{\sqrt{2} - 2}$
47. $\frac{\sqrt{3} + 1}{\sqrt{2} + 1}$

Lesson 10-4 **Solve each radical equation. Check your solution.**

48. $\sqrt{3x + 4} = 1$
49. $6 = \sqrt{8x - 4}$
50. $2x = \sqrt{14x - 6}$
51. $\sqrt{2x + 5} = \sqrt{3x + 1}$
52. $2x = \sqrt{6x + 4}$
53. $\sqrt{5x + 11} = \sqrt{7x - 1}$
54. $\sqrt{3x - 2} = x$
55. $\sqrt{x + 7} = x + 1$
56. $\sqrt{x + 3} = \frac{x + 9}{5}$

Lesson 10-5 **Find the domain of each function. Then graph the function.**

57. $y = \sqrt{x + 5}$
58. $y = \sqrt{x} - 2$
59. $y = \sqrt{x + 1}$
60. $y = \sqrt{x} - 4$
61. $y = \sqrt{x - 3}$
62. $y = \sqrt{x} + 6$

Lesson 10-1 **Use the formula $d = \sqrt{1.5h}$ to estimate the distance d in miles to a horizon when h is the height in feet of the viewer's eyes above the ground. Round your answer to the nearest mile.**

63. Find the distance you can see to the horizon from the top of a building that is 355 ft high.

64. Find the distance you can see to the horizon from an airplane that is 36,000 ft above the ground.

65. Find the distance you can see to the horizon from 15 ft above the ground.

Use the formula $r = 2\sqrt{5L}$ to estimate the speed r in miles per hour of a car that has left a skid mark of length L in feet.

66. Find the speed of a car that leaves a skid mark of 125 ft.

67. Find the speed of a car that leaves a skid mark of 245 ft.

Lesson 10-2 **Use the Pythagorean Theorem to answer each question.**

68. A 20-ft ladder is placed 5 ft from the base of a building. How high on the building will the ladder reach?

69. A soccer field is 80 yd long and 35 yd wide. What is the diagonal distance across the field?

Lesson 10-3 **Find an exact solution. Then find an approximate solution to the nearest tenth.**

70. The ratio of the length of a painting to its width is $(1 + \sqrt{5}) : 1$. The length is 25 in. What is the width?

71. The ratio of the length of a painting to its width is $(1 + \sqrt{3}) : 1$. The length is 40 cm. What is the width?

Lesson 10-4 **Write and solve a radical equation for each situation.**

72. What is the diameter of a circular livestock pen if the area is 450 m^2?

73. On a roller coaster ride, your speed in a loop depends on the height h of the preceding hill and the radius of the loop in feet. The equation $v = 8\sqrt{h - 2r}$ gives the velocity v in feet per second of a car at the top of the loop. Suppose a loop has a radius of 25 ft and you want the car to have a velocity of 25 ft/s at the top of the loop. How high should the preceding hill be?

Lesson 10-5

74. Suppose a motorcycle company uses the function $n = 30\sqrt{4t} + 90$ to model the sales volume n, as a function of time t, the number of months after the start of the advertising camping.
a. Graph the function.
b. Use the graph to estimate when 200 motorcycles will be sold.

Chapter 11

Extra Practice: Skills and Word Problems

Lesson 11-1 **Simplify each expression.**

1. $\frac{4t^2}{16t}$
2. $\frac{c-5}{c^2-25}$
3. $\frac{4m-12}{m-3}$
4. $\frac{a^2+2a-3}{a+3}$
5. $\frac{x+7}{x^2+8x+7}$
6. $\frac{t-4}{4-t}$
7. $\frac{m^2+7m+10}{m^2+8m+15}$
8. $\frac{6b^2+42b}{b^3}$
9. $\frac{5d-10d^2}{5d}$
10. $\frac{y^2+3y+2}{y^2-1}$
11. $\frac{2h^2+h}{2h^2-5h-3}$
12. $\frac{2a^2+3a-2}{4a^2-1}$

Lesson 11-2 **Simplify each expression.**

13. $\frac{5s^4}{10s^3}$
14. $\frac{4n^2}{7} \cdot \frac{14}{2n^3}$
15. $\frac{8b^2-4b}{3b^2} \div \frac{2b-1}{9b}$
16. $\frac{v^5}{v^3} \cdot \frac{4v^{-1}}{v^2}$
17. $\frac{3y}{4y-8} \div \frac{9y}{2y^2-4y}$
18. $\frac{2a+5}{3a-4} \cdot (3a^2+2a-8)$

Lesson 11-3 **Divide.**

19. $(4x^3-6x^2+8x) \div 2x^2$
20. $(8x^2-6x+2) \div (2x-3)$
21. $(x^4+9x^2+20) \div (x^2+4)$
22. $(t^3+t^2+t+1) \div (t+1)$
23. $(2x^3-x^2-13x-6) \div (x-3)$
24. $(3x^3-3) \div (x+1)$
25. $(3x^3+5x^2-22x+24) \div (x+4)$
26. $(3x^3-3) \div (x-1)$
27. $(8x^3+22x^2-5x+12) \div (4x+3)$
28. $(2x^3-9x^2+11x-3) \div (2x-3)$
29. $(x^4+5x^3+3x-10) \div (x+5)$
30. $(5x^5+16x^3+2x^2-1) \div (x^2+4)$

Lesson 11-4 **Simplify each expression.**

31. $\frac{4}{x} - \frac{3}{x}$
32. $\frac{6t}{5} + \frac{4t}{5}$
33. $\frac{6}{c} + \frac{4}{c^2}$
34. $\frac{6}{3d} - \frac{4}{3d}$
35. $\frac{5}{t+4} + \frac{3}{t-4}$
36. $\frac{8}{m^2+6m+5} + \frac{4}{m+1}$
37. $\frac{4}{d^2} - \frac{3}{d^3}$
38. $\frac{5}{6s} + \frac{3}{4}$
39. $\frac{7}{3f^3} - \frac{2}{f^2}$

Lesson 11-5 **Solve each equation. Check your answer.**

40. $\frac{1}{4} + \frac{1}{x} = \frac{3}{8}$
41. $\frac{4}{m} - 3 = \frac{2}{m}$
42. $\frac{1}{b-3} = \frac{1}{4b}$
43. $\frac{4}{x-1} = \frac{3}{x}$
44. $\frac{4}{n} + \frac{5}{9} = 1$
45. $\frac{x}{x+2} = \frac{x-3}{x+1}$
46. $t - \frac{8}{t} = \frac{17}{t}$
47. $\frac{x+2}{x+5} = \frac{x-4}{x+4}$
48. $\frac{1}{5} - \frac{1}{x} = \frac{1}{2}$
49. $\frac{4}{c+1} - \frac{2}{c-1} = \frac{3c+6}{c^2-1}$
50. $\frac{4}{m+3} = \frac{6}{m-3}$
51. $\frac{4}{t+5} + 1 = \frac{15}{t^2-25}$

Lesson 11-1 **The expression $\frac{30rh}{r + h}$ gives the approximate baking time for bread in minutes based on the radius r and the height h of the baked loaf in inches. Use this expression to find the baking time for each loaf.**

52. a roll that will have a radius of 2 in. and a height of 1.5 in.

53. a loaf of Italian bread that will have a length of 18 in. and a radius of 4 in.

Lesson 11-2

54. Find an expression for the area of a rectangular field with a length of $\frac{4y + 10}{3y^2 - 4}$ m and a width of $\frac{y^3 + 6}{2y + 5}$ m.

55. Find an expression for the area of a parallelogram with a base length of $\frac{3}{x - 4}$ yd and a height of $\frac{3x^2 - 7x - 20}{6x}$ yd.

56. Find an expression for the area of a triangle with a base length of $\frac{2}{6b^2 - 10b - 4}$ ft and a height of $10b^2 - 20b$ ft.

Lesson 11-3

57. What is the length of a rectangle with an area of $3d^3 - 24$ cm^2 and a width of $d + 2$ cm?

58. What is the base length of a triangle with an area of $2j^3 - 4j^2 + 3j - 6$ in.^{2} and a height of $j - 2$ in.?

59. What is the area of the base of a hexagonal prism with a volume of $15x^3 - 26x^2 + 43x - 14$ m^3 and a height of $5x - 2$ m?

Lesson 11-4

60. A canoe travels 5 miles downstream at rate r, and then 5 miles back upstream at 70% of its downstream rate. Write and simplify a rational expression for the total time of the trip.

61. Louis walks to get to his friend's house 2 miles away. When he returns home he jogs at a rate that is 160% of his walking rate r. Write and simplify a rational expression for the total time of his trip.

Lesson 11-5

62. Suppose you can clean your kitchen in 30 minutes. Your friend can clean your kitchen in 45 minutes. How long will it take you to clean the kitchen together?

63. One employee of a landscaping company can mow a lawn in 20 minutes. Another employee can do it in 15 minutes. How long will it take them to mow the lawn together?

64. It takes one painter 3 hours to paint a room. It takes another painter 5 hours to paint the same room. How long will it take the painters to paint the room together?

65. It takes 18 hours to fill a tank with water using pipe A. It takes 24 hours to fill the same tank with water using pipe B. How long will it take to fill the tank if both pipes are used?

Skills Handbook

Problem Solving Strategies

You may find one or more of these strategies helpful in solving a word problem.

STRATEGY	WHEN TO USE IT
Draw a Diagram	The problem describes a picture or diagram.
Try, Check, Revise	Solving the problem directly is too complicated.
Look for a Pattern	The problem describes a relationship.
Make a Table	The problem has data that need to be organized.
Solve a Simpler Problem	The problem is complex or has numbers that are too cumbersome to use at first.
Use Logical Reasoning	You need to reach a conclusion using given information.
Work Backward	You need to find the number that led to the result in the problem.

Problem Solving: Draw a Diagram

EXAMPLE

Two cars started from the same point. One traveled east at 45 mi/h and the other west at 50 mi/h. How far apart were the cars after 5 hours?

Draw a diagram.

West ← 50 mi/h • 5 — Start — 45 mi/h • 5 → East

The first car traveled $45 \cdot 5$ or 225 mi. The second car traveled $50 \cdot 5$ or 250 mi.

The diagram shows that the two distances should be added: $225 + 250 = 475$ mi.

After 5 hours, the cars were 475 mi apart.

EXERCISES

1. Jason, Lee, Melda, Aaron, and Bonnie want to play one another in tennis. How many games will be played?
2. A playground, a zoo, a picnic area, and a flower garden will be in four corners of a new park. Straight paths will connect each of these areas to all the other areas. How many pathways will be built?
3. Pedro wants to tack 4 posters on a bulletin board. He will tack the four corners of each poster, overlapping the sides of each poster a little bit. What is the least number of tacks that Pedro can use?

Problem Solving: Try, Check, Revise

When you are not sure how to start, guess an answer and then test it. In the process of testing a guess, you may see a way of revising your guess to get closer to the answer or to get the exact answer.

EXAMPLE

Maria bought books and CDs as gifts. Altogether she bought 12 gifts and spent \$84. The books cost \$6 each and the CDs cost \$9 each. How many of each gift did she buy?

Trial	6 books	**Test**	$6 \cdot \$6 =$	\$36
	6 CDs		$6 \cdot \$9 =$	+\$54
				\$90

Revise your guess. You need fewer CDs to bring the total cost down.

Trial	7 books	**Test**	$7 \cdot \$6 =$	\$42
	5 CDs		$5 \cdot \$9 =$	+\$45
				\$87

The cost is still too high.

Trial	8 books	**Test**	$8 \cdot \$6 =$	\$48
	4 CDs		$4 \cdot \$9 =$	+\$36
				\$84

Maria bought 8 books and 4 CDs.

EXERCISES

1. Find two consecutive odd integers whose product is 323.
2. Find three consecutive integers whose sum is 81.
3. Find four consecutive integers whose sum is 138.
4. Mika bought 9 rolls of film to take 180 pictures on a field trip. Some rolls had 36 exposures and the rest had 12 exposures. How many of each type did Mika buy?
5. Tanya is 18 years old. Her brother Shawn is 16 years younger. How old will Tanya be when she is 3 times as old as Shawn?
6. Steven has 100 ft of fencing and wants to build a fence in the shape of a rectangle to enclose the largest possible area. What should be the dimensions of the rectangle?
7. The combined ages of a mother, her son, and her daughter are 61 years. The mother is 22 years older than her son and 31 years older than her daughter. How old is each person?
8. Kenji traveled 210 mi in a two-day bicycle race. He biked 20 mi farther on the first day than he did on the second day. How many miles did Kenji travel each day?
9. Darren is selling tickets for the school play. Regular tickets are \$4 each, and student tickets are \$3 each. Darren sells a total of 190 tickets and collects \$650. How many of each kind of ticket did he sell?

Problem Solving: Look for a Pattern and Make a Table

Some problems describe relationships that involve regular sequences of numbers or other things. To solve the problem you need to be able to recognize and describe the pattern that gives the relationship for the numbers or things. One way to organize the information given is to make a table.

EXAMPLE

A tree farm is planted as shown at the right. The dots represent trees. The lot will be enlarged by adding larger squares. How many trees will be in the fifth square?

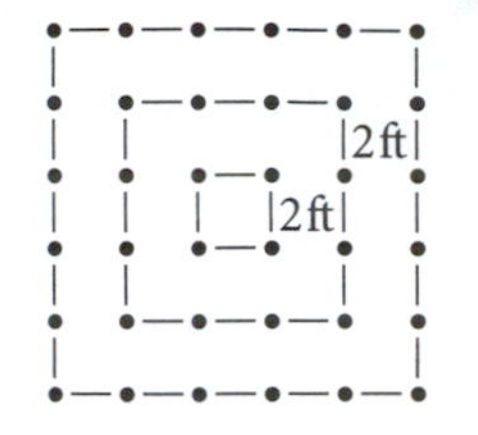

Make a table to help find a pattern.

Square position	1st	2nd	3rd	4th	5th
Number of trees	4	12	20	■	■

Pattern: 8 more trees are planted in each larger square.

The fourth square will have 28 trees. The fifth square will have 36 trees.

EXERCISES

1. Kareem made a display of books at a book fair. One book was in the first row, and each of the other rows had two more books than the row before it. How many books does Kareem have if he has nine rows?
2. Chris is using green and white tiles to cover her floor. If she uses tiles in the pattern G, W, G, G, W, G, G, W, G, G, what will be the color of the twentieth tile?
3. Jay read one story the first week of summer vacation, 3 stories the second week, 6 stories the third week, and 10 stories the fourth week. He kept to this pattern for eight weeks. How many stories did he read the eighth week?
4. Jan has 6 coins, none of which is a half dollar. The coins have a value of $.85. What coins does she have?
5. Sam is covering a wall with rows of red, white, and blue siding. The red siding is cut in 1.8-m strips, the white in 2.4-m strips, and the blue in 1.2-m strips. What is the shortest length that Sam can cover with uncut strips to form equal rows of each color?
6. A train leaves a station at 8:00 A.M. and averages 40 mi/h. Another train leaves the same station one hour later and averages 50 mi/h traveling in the same direction on a parallel track. At what time will the second train catch up with the first train? How many miles would each train have traveled by that time?
7. The soccer team held a car wash and earned $200. They charged $7 per truck and $5 per car. In how many different ways could the team have earned the $200?
8. Students are going to march in a parade. There will be one first-grader, two second-graders, three third-graders, and so on through the twelfth grade. How many students will march in the parade?

Problem Solving: Solve a Simpler Problem

By solving one or more simpler problems you can often find a pattern that will help solve a more complicated problem.

EXAMPLE

How many different rectangles are in a strip with 10 squares?

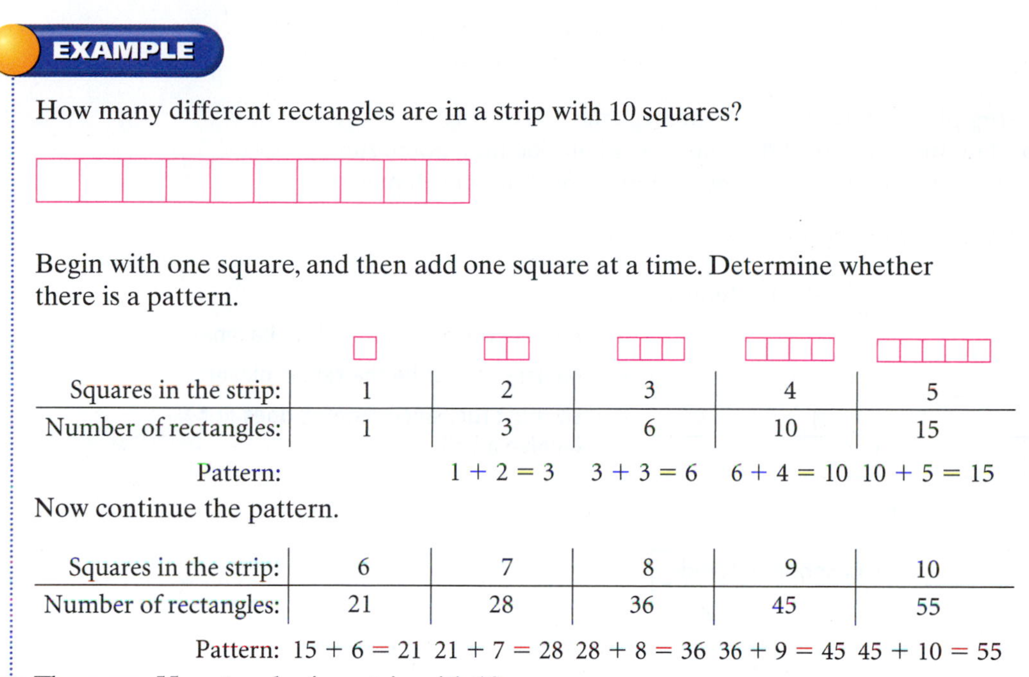

Begin with one square, and then add one square at a time. Determine whether there is a pattern.

Squares in the strip:	1	2	3	4	5
Number of rectangles:	1	3	6	10	15
Pattern:		$1 + 2 = 3$	$3 + 3 = 6$	$6 + 4 = 10$	$10 + 5 = 15$

Now continue the pattern.

Squares in the strip:	6	7	8	9	10
Number of rectangles:	21	28	36	45	55
Pattern:	$15 + 6 = 21$	$21 + 7 = 28$	$28 + 8 = 36$	$36 + 9 = 45$	$45 + 10 = 55$

There are 55 rectangles in a strip with 10 squares.

EXERCISES

1. Lockers in the east wing of Hastings High School are numbered 1–120. How many contain the digit 8?
2. What is the sum of all the numbers from 1 to 100? (*Hint:* What is $1 + 100$? What is $2 + 99$?)
3. Suppose your heart beats 70 times per minute. At this rate, how many times had it beaten by the time you were 10?
4. For a community project you have to create the numbers 1 through 148 using large cardboard digits covered with glitter, which you make by hand. How many cardboard digits will you make?
5. There are 64 teams competing in the state soccer championship. If a team loses a game it is eliminated. How many games have to be played in order to get a single champion team?
6. You work in a supermarket. Your boss asks you to arrange oranges in a pyramid for a display. The pyramid's base should be a square with 25 oranges. How many layers of oranges will be in your pyramid? How many oranges will you need?
7. Kesi has her math book open. The product of the two page numbers on the facing pages is 1056. What are the two page numbers?
8. There are 12 girls and 11 boys at a school party. A photographer wants to take a picture of each boy with each girl. How many photographs must the photographer set up?

Problem Solving: Use Logical Reasoning

Some problems can be solved without the use of numbers. They can be solved by the use of logical reasoning, given some information.

EXAMPLE

Joe, Melissa, Liz and Greg play different sports. Their sports are running, basketball, baseball, and tennis. Liz's sport does not use a ball. Joe hit a home run in his sport. Melissa is the sister of the tennis player. Which sport does each play?

Make a table to organize what you know.

	Running	Basketball	Baseball	Tennis
Joe	✗	✗	✓	✗
Melissa				✗
Liz	✓	✗	✗	✗
Greg				

← A home run means Joe plays baseball.

← Melissa cannot be the tennis player.

← Liz must run, since running does not involve a ball.

Use logical reasoning to complete the table.

	Running	Basketball	Baseball	Tennis
Joe	✗	✗	✓	✗
Melissa	✗	✓	✗	✗
Liz	✓	✗	✗	✗
Greg	✗	✗	✗	✓

← The only option for Greg is tennis.

Greg plays tennis, Melissa plays basketball, Liz runs, and Joe plays baseball.

EXERCISES

1. Juan has a dog, a horse, a bird, and a cat. Their names are Bo, Cricket, K.C., and Tuffy. Tuffy and K.C. cannot fly or be ridden. The bird talks to Bo. Tuffy runs from the dog. What is each pet's name?
2. A math class has 25 students. There are 13 students who are only in the band, 4 students who are only on the swimming team, and 5 students who are in both groups. How many students are not in either group?
3. Annette is taller than Heather but shorter than Garo. Tanya's height is between Garo's and Annette's. Karin would be the shortest if it weren't for Alexa. List the names in order from shortest to tallest.
4. The Robins, Wrens, and Sparrows teams played one another twice in basketball. The Robins won 3 of their games. The Sparrows won 2 of their games. How many games did each team win and lose?
5. The girls' basketball league uses a telephone tree when it needs to cancel its games. The leader takes 1 min to call 2 players. These 2 players take 1 min to call 2 more players, and so on. How many players will be called in 6 min?
6. Miss White, Miss Gray, and Miss Black are wearing single-colored dresses that are white, gray, and black. Miss Gray remarks to the woman wearing a black dress that no woman's dress color matches her last name. What color dress is each woman wearing?

Problem Solving: Work Backward

To solve some problems, you need to start with the end result and work backward to the beginning.

EXAMPLE

On Monday, Rita withdrew $150 from her savings account. On Wednesday, she deposited $400 into her account. She now has $1000. How much was in her account on Monday before she withdrew the money?

money in account now	$1000
Undo the deposit.	−$400
	$600
Undo the withdrawal.	+$150
	$750

Rita had $750 in her account on Monday before withdrawing money.

Skills Handbook

EXERCISES

1. Ned gave Connie the following puzzle: I am thinking of a number. I doubled it, then tripled the result. The final result was 36. What is my number?

2. Fernando gave Maria the following puzzle: I am thinking of a number. I divide it by 3. Then I divide the result by 5. The final result is 8. What is my number?

3. A teacher lends pencils to students. She gave out 7 pencils in the morning, collected 5 before lunch, and gave out 3 after lunch. At the end of the day she had 16 pencils. How many pencils did the teacher have at the start of the day?

4. This week Sandy withdrew $350 from her savings account. She made a deposit of $125, wrote a check for $ 275, and made a deposit of $150. She now has $225 in her account. How much did she have in her account at the beginning of the week?

5. Jeff paid $12.50, including a $1.60 tip, for a taxi ride from his home to the airport. City Cab charges $1.90 for the first mile plus $.15 for each additional $\frac{1}{6}$ mile. How many miles is Jeff's home from the airport?

6. Ben sold $\frac{1}{4}$ as many tickets to the fund-raiser as Charles. Charles sold 3 times as many as Susan. Susan sold 4 fewer than Tom. Tom sold 12 tickets. How many did Ben sell?

7. Two cars start traveling towards each other. One car averages 30 mi/h and the other 40 mi/h. After 4 h the cars are 10 mi apart. How far apart were the cars when they started?

8. Nina has a dentist appointment at 8:45 A.M. She wants to arrive 10 min early. Nina needs to allow 25 min to travel to the appointment and 45 min to dress and have breakfast. What is the latest time Nina should get up?

9. Jordan spent the day exploring her neighborhood and ended up at the park 2 mi east and 1 mi north of the center of town. She started from her house and walked $\frac{1}{2}$ mi north. Next she walked 3 mi west and then $1\frac{1}{2}$ mi south. Finally, she walked $\frac{1}{4}$ mi east to the park. Where is Jordan's house in relation to the center of town?

Prime Numbers and Composite Numbers

A prime number is a whole number greater than 1 that has exactly two factors, the number 1 and itself.

Prime number	2	5	17	29
Factors	1, 2	1, 5	1, 17	1, 29

A composite number is a number that has more than two factors. The number 1 is neither prime nor composite.

Composite number	6	15	48
Factors	1, 2, 3, 6	1, 3, 5, 15	1, 2, 3, 4, 6, 8, 12, 16, 24, 48

1 EXAMPLE

Is 51 prime or composite?

$51 = 3 \cdot 17$ **Try to find factors other than 1 and 51.**

51 is a composite number.

You can use a factor tree to find the prime factors of a number. When all the factors are prime numbers, it is called the prime factorization of the number.

2 EXAMPLE

Use a factor tree to write the prime factorization of 28.

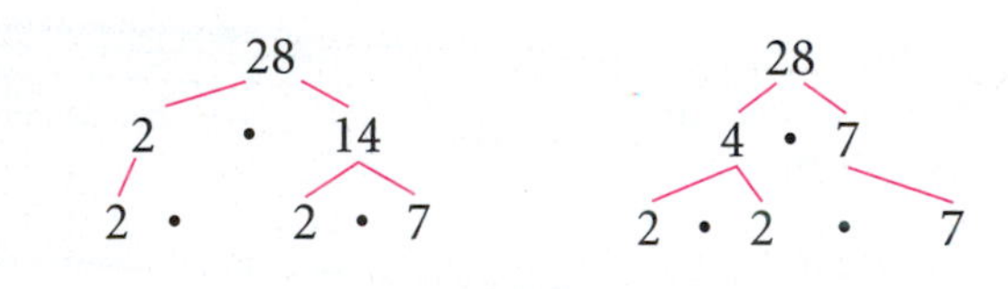

The order of listing the factors may be different, but the end result is the same.

The prime factorization of 28 is $2 \cdot 2 \cdot 7$.

EXERCISES

Is each number prime or composite?

1. 9 **2.** 16 **3.** 34 **4.** 61 **5.** 7 **6.** 13
7. 12 **8.** 40 **9.** 57 **10.** 64 **11.** 120 **12.** 700
13. 39 **14.** 23 **15.** 63 **16.** 19 **17.** 522 **18.** 101

List all the factors of each number.

19. 46 **20.** 32 **21.** 11 **22.** 65 **23.** 27 **24.** 29
25. 205 **26.** 123 **27.** 24 **28.** 162 **29.** 88 **30.** 204
31. 183 **32.** 6 **33.** 98 **34.** 92 **35.** 59 **36.** 47

Use a factor tree to write the prime factorization of each number.

37. 18 **38.** 20 **39.** 27 **40.** 54 **41.** 64 **42.** 96
43. 100 **44.** 125 **45.** 84 **46.** 150 **47.** 121 **48.** 226

Factors and Multiples

A common factor is a number that is a factor of two or more numbers. The greatest common factor or divisor (GCD) is the greatest number that is a common factor of two or more numbers.

1 EXAMPLE

Find the GCD of 24 and 64.

Method 1 List all the factors of each number.

Factors of 24 1, 2, 3, 4, 6, 8, 12, 24 — Find the common factors: 1, 2, 4, 8.

Factors of 64 1, 2, 4, 8, 16, 32, 64 — The greatest common divisor is 8.

GCD (24, 64) = 8

Method 2 Use the prime factorization of each number.

$24 = 2 \cdot 2 \cdot 2 \cdot 3$ — Find the prime factorization of each number.

$64 = 2 \cdot 2 \cdot 2 \cdot 2 \cdot 2 \cdot 2$

$\text{GCD} = 2 \cdot 2 \cdot 2 = 8$ — Use each factor the number of times it appears as a common factor.

A common multiple is a number that is a multiple of two or more numbers. The least common multiple (LCM) is the least number that is a common multiple of two or more numbers.

2 EXAMPLE

Find the LCM of 12 and 18.

Method 1 List the multiples of each number.

Multiples of 12 12, 24, 36, . . .

Multiples of 18 18, 36, . . .

List a number of multiples until you find the first common multiple.

LCM (12, 18) = 36

Method 2 Use the prime factorization of each number.

$12 = 2 \cdot 2 \cdot 3$

$18 = 2 \cdot 3 \cdot 3$

$\text{LCM} = 2 \cdot 2 \cdot 3 \cdot 3 = 36$ — Use each prime factor the greatest number of times it appears in either number.

EXERCISES

Find the GCD of each set of numbers.

1. 12 and 22 **2.** 7 and 21 **3.** 24 and 48 **4.** 17 and 51

5. 9 and 12 **6.** 10 and 25 **7.** 21 and 49 **8.** 27 and 36

9. 10, 30, and 25 **10.** 56, 84, and 140 **11.** 42, 63, and 105 **12.** 20, 28, and 40

Find the LCM of each set of numbers.

13. 16 and 20 **14.** 14 and 21 **15.** 11 and 33 **16.** 8 and 9

17. 5 and 12 **18.** 54 and 84 **19.** 48 and 80 **20.** 25 and 36

21. 10, 15, and 25 **22.** 6, 7, and 12 **23.** 5, 8, and 20 **24.** 18, 21, and 36

Divisibility

An integer is divisible by another integer if the remainder is zero. You can use the following tests to determine whether a number is divisible by the numbers below.

Number	Divisibility Test
2	The ones' digit is 0, 2, 4, 6, or 8.
3	The sum of the digits is divisible by 3.
4	The number formed by the last two digits is divisible by 4.
5	The ones' digit is 0 or 5.
6	The number is divisible by 2 and by 3.
8	The number formed by the last three digits is divisible by 8.
9	The sum of the digits is divisible by 9.
10	The ones' digit is 0.

EXAMPLE

Use the divisibility tests to determine the numbers by which 2116 is divisible.

2: Yes; the ones digit is 6.
3: No; the sum of the digits is $2 + 1 + 1 + 6 = 10$, which is not divisible by 3.
4: Yes; the number formed by the last two digits is 16, which is divisible by 4.
5: No; the ones digit is 6, *not* 0 or 5.
6: No; 2116 is not divisible by 3.
8: No; the number formed by the last three digits is 116, which is *not* divisible by 8.
9: No; the sum of the digits is $2 + 1 + 1 + 6 = 10$, which is not divisible by 9.
10: No; the ones digit is 6, *not* 0.

2116 is divisible by 2 and 4.

EXERCISES

Determine whether each number is divisible by 2, 3, 4, 5, 6, 8, 9, or 10.

1. 236 **2.** 72 **3.** 105 **4.** 108 **5.** 225 **6.** 364

7. 1234 **8.** 4321 **9.** 7848 **10.** 3366 **11.** 1421 **12.** 1071

13. 78,765 **14.** 30,303 **15.** 4104 **16.** 700 **17.** 868 **18.** 1155

19. **Math Reasoning** Since 435 is divisible by both 3 and 5, it is also divisible by what number?

20. Find a number greater than 1000 that is divisible by 4, 5, and 9.

21. **Critical Thinking** If a is divisible by 2, what can you conclude about $a + 1$? Justify your answer.

Using Estimation

To make sure the answer to a problem is reasonable, you can estimate before you calculate. If the answer is close to your estimate, the answer is probably correct.

1 EXAMPLE

Estimate to find whether each answer is reasonable.

a.

Calculation		Estimate
$126.91	≈	$130
$14.05	≈	$10
+$25.14	≈	+$30
$266.10		$170

The answer is not close to the estimate. It is *not* reasonable. The calculation is *incorrect.*

b.

Calculation		Estimate
372.85	≈	370
−227.31	≈	−230
145.54		140

The answer is close to the estimate. It *is* reasonable. The calculation is *correct.*

For some situations, like estimating a grocery bill, you may not need an exact answer. A *front-end estimate* will give you a good estimate that is usually closer to the exact answer than an estimate you would get by rounding. Add the front-end digits, estimate the sum of the remaining digits by rounding, and then combine sums.

2 EXAMPLE

Tomatoes cost $3.54, squash costs $2.75, and lemons cost $1.20. Estimate the total cost of the produce.

Add the front-end digits.			Estimate by rounding.
3.54	→	0.50	
2.75	→	0.80	
+1.20	→	+ 0.20	
6	+	1.50 = 7.50	

The total cost is about $7.50.

EXERCISES

Estimate by rounding.

1. the sum of $15.70, $49.62, and $278.01

2. 563 − 125

3. the sum of $163.90, $107.21, and $33.56

4. 824 − 467

Use front-end estimation.

5. $1.65 + $5.42 + $9.89

6. 1.369 + 7.421 + 2.700

7. 9.563 − 2.480

8. 1.17 + 3.92 + 2.26

9. 8.611 − 1.584

10. $2.52 + $3.04 + $5.25

Estimate using a method of your choice.

11. Ticket prices at an amusement park cost $11.25 for adults and $6.50 for children under 12. Estimate the cost for three children and one adult.

12. Esmeralda has a new checking account. So far, she has deposited $177, $250, and $193. She has also written a check for $26.89. Estimate her current balance.

Simplifying Fractions

A fraction can name a part of a group or region. The region below is divided into 10 equal parts and 6 of the equal parts are shaded.

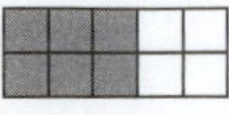

$\frac{6}{10}$ ← Numerator
← Denominator   **Read: six tenths**

A fraction can have many names. Different names for the same fraction are called equivalent fractions. You can find an equivalent fraction for any given fraction by multiplying the numerator and denominator of the given fraction by the same number.

1 EXAMPLE

Write five equivalent fractions for $\frac{3}{5}$.

$\frac{3}{5} = \frac{3 \cdot 2}{5 \cdot 2} = \frac{6}{10}$ $\quad \frac{3}{5} = \frac{3 \cdot 3}{5 \cdot 3} = \frac{9}{15}$ $\quad \frac{3}{5} = \frac{3 \cdot 4}{5 \cdot 4} = \frac{12}{20}$ $\quad \frac{3}{5} = \frac{3 \cdot 5}{5 \cdot 5} = \frac{15}{25}$ $\quad \frac{3}{5} = \frac{3 \cdot 6}{5 \cdot 6} = \frac{18}{30}$

The fraction $\frac{3}{5}$ is in simplest form because its numerator and denominator are relatively prime, that is, their only common factor is the number 1. To write a fraction in simplest form, divide its numerator and denominator by their greatest common divisor (GCD).

2 EXAMPLE

Write $\frac{6}{24}$ in simplest form.

Step 1 Find the GCD of 6 and 24.

$6 = 2 \cdot 3$ **Multiply the common prime factors.**

$24 = 2 \cdot 2 \cdot 2 \cdot 3$ **GCD = $2 \cdot 3 = 6$.**

Step 2 Divide the numerator and denominator of $\frac{6}{24}$ by the GCD, 6.

$\frac{6}{24} = \frac{6 \div 6}{24 \div 6} = \frac{1}{4}$ **simplest form**

EXERCISES

Write five equivalent fractions for each fraction.

1. $\frac{4}{7}$ **2.** $\frac{9}{16}$ **3.** $\frac{3}{8}$ **4.** $\frac{8}{17}$ **5.** $\frac{5}{6}$ **6.** $\frac{7}{10}$

Complete each statement.

7. $\frac{3}{7} = \frac{\blacksquare}{21}$ **8.** $\frac{5}{8} = \frac{20}{\blacksquare}$ **9.** $\frac{11}{12} = \frac{44}{\blacksquare}$ **10.** $\frac{12}{16} = \frac{\blacksquare}{4}$ **11.** $\frac{50}{100} = \frac{1}{\blacksquare}$

12. $\frac{5}{9} = \frac{\blacksquare}{27}$ **13.** $\frac{3}{8} = \frac{\blacksquare}{24}$ **14.** $\frac{5}{6} = \frac{20}{\blacksquare}$ **15.** $\frac{12}{20} = \frac{\blacksquare}{5}$ **16.** $\frac{75}{150} = \frac{1}{\blacksquare}$

Which fractions are in simplest form?

17. $\frac{4}{12}$ **18.** $\frac{3}{16}$ **19.** $\frac{5}{30}$ **20.** $\frac{9}{72}$ **21.** $\frac{11}{22}$ **22.** $\frac{24}{25}$

Write in simplest form.

23. $\frac{8}{16}$ **24.** $\frac{7}{14}$ **25.** $\frac{6}{9}$ **26.** $\frac{20}{30}$ **27.** $\frac{8}{20}$ **28.** $\frac{12}{40}$

29. $\frac{15}{45}$ **30.** $\frac{14}{56}$ **31.** $\frac{10}{25}$ **32.** $\frac{9}{27}$ **33.** $\frac{45}{60}$ **34.** $\frac{20}{35}$

Fractions and Decimals

You can write a fraction as a decimal.

1 EXAMPLE

Write $\frac{3}{5}$ as a decimal.

$$\begin{array}{r} 0.6 \\ 5\overline{)3.0} \\ \underline{-3.0} \end{array}$$ Divide the numerator by the denominator.

The decimal for $\frac{3}{5}$ is 0.6.

You can write a decimal as a fraction.

2 EXAMPLE

Write 0.38 as a fraction.

$0.38 = 38 \text{ hundredths} = \frac{38}{100} = \frac{19}{50}$

Some fractions have decimal forms that do not end, but do repeat.

3 EXAMPLE

Write $\frac{3}{11}$ as a decimal.

Divide the numerator by the denominator. The remainders 8 and 3 keep repeating. Therefore 2 and 7 will keep repeating in the quotient.

$\frac{3}{11} = 0.2727\ldots = 0.\overline{27}$

$$\frac{3}{11} = \begin{array}{r} 0.2727 \\ 11\overline{)3.0000\ldots} \\ \underline{22} \\ 80 \\ \underline{77} \\ 30 \\ \underline{22} \\ 80 \\ \underline{77} \\ 3 \end{array}$$

You can write a repeating decimal as a fraction.

4 EXAMPLE

Write 0.363636 . . . as a fraction.

Let $x = 0.363636\ldots$

Then $100x = 36.36363636\ldots$ When 2 digits repeat, multiply by 100.

$99x = 36$ Subtract the first equation from the second.

$x = \frac{36}{99}$ or $\frac{4}{11}$ Divide each side by 99.

EXERCISES

Write as a decimal.

1. $\frac{3}{10}$ **2.** $\frac{13}{12}$ **3.** $\frac{4}{20}$ **4.** $\frac{25}{75}$ **5.** $\frac{5}{7}$ **6.** $4\frac{3}{25}$

7. $\frac{5}{9}$ **8.** $5\frac{7}{8}$ **9.** $\frac{2}{7}$ **10.** $\frac{3}{15}$ **11.** $\frac{16}{100}$ **12.** $2\frac{2}{5}$

Write as a fraction in simplest form.

13. 0.07 **14.** 0.25 **15.** 0.875 **16.** 0.4545 . . . **17.** 6.333 . . . **18.** 7.2626 . . .

19. 0.77 . . . **20.** 3.1313 . . . **21.** 0.375 **22.** 0.8333 . . . **23.** 6.48 **24.** 0.8

Adding and Subtracting Fractions

You can add and subtract fractions when they have the same denominator. Fractions with the same denominator are called like fractions.

1 EXAMPLE

a. Add $\frac{4}{5} + \frac{3}{5}$.

$\frac{4}{5} + \frac{3}{5} = \frac{4+3}{5} = \frac{7}{5} = 1\frac{2}{5}$ ← **Add or subtract the numerators and keep the same denominator.** →

b. Subtract $\frac{5}{9} - \frac{2}{9}$.

$\frac{5}{9} - \frac{2}{9} = \frac{5-2}{9} = \frac{3}{9} = \frac{1}{3}$

Fractions with unlike denominators are called unlike fractions. To add or subtract fractions with unlike denominators, find the least common denominator (LCD) and write equivalent fractions with the same denominator. Then add or subtract the like fractions.

2 EXAMPLE

Add $\frac{3}{4} + \frac{5}{6}$.

$\frac{3}{4} + \frac{5}{6} = \frac{9}{12} + \frac{10}{12}$ — **Find the LCD. The LCD is the same as the least common multiple (LCM). The LCD of 4 and 6 is 12.**

$= \frac{9+10}{12} = \frac{19}{12}$ or $1\frac{7}{12}$ — **Write equivalent fractions with the same denominator.**

To add or subtract mixed numbers, add or subtract the fractions. Then add or subtract the whole numbers. Sometimes when subtracting mixed numbers you may have to regroup.

3 EXAMPLE

Subtract $5\frac{1}{4} - 3\frac{2}{3}$.

$5\frac{1}{4} - 3\frac{2}{3} = 5\frac{3}{12} - 3\frac{8}{12}$ — **Write equivalent fractions with the same denominator.**

$= 4\frac{15}{12} - 3\frac{8}{12}$ — **Write $5\frac{3}{12}$ as $4\frac{15}{12}$ so you can subtract the fractions.**

$= 1\frac{7}{12}$ — **Subtract the fractions. Then subtract the whole numbers.**

EXERCISES

Add. Write each answer in simplest form.

1. $\frac{2}{7} + \frac{3}{7}$ **2.** $\frac{3}{8} + \frac{7}{8}$ **3.** $\frac{6}{5} + \frac{9}{5}$ **4.** $\frac{4}{9} + \frac{8}{9}$ **5.** $6\frac{2}{3} + 3\frac{4}{5}$

6. $1\frac{4}{7} + 2\frac{3}{14}$ **7.** $4\frac{5}{6} + 1\frac{7}{18}$ **8.** $2\frac{4}{5} + 3\frac{6}{7}$ **9.** $4\frac{2}{3} + 1\frac{6}{11}$ **10.** $3\frac{7}{9} + 5\frac{4}{11}$

11. $8 + 1\frac{2}{3}$ **12.** $8\frac{1}{5} + 3\frac{3}{4}$ **13.** $11\frac{3}{8} + 2\frac{1}{16}$ **14.** $9\frac{1}{12} + 8\frac{3}{4}$ **15.** $33\frac{1}{3} + 23\frac{2}{5}$

Subtract. Write each answer in simplest form.

16. $\frac{7}{8} - \frac{3}{8}$ **17.** $\frac{9}{10} - \frac{3}{10}$ **18.** $\frac{17}{5} - \frac{2}{5}$ **19.** $\frac{11}{7} - \frac{2}{7}$ **20.** $\frac{5}{11} - \frac{4}{11}$

21. $8\frac{5}{8} - 6\frac{1}{4}$ **22.** $3\frac{2}{3} - 1\frac{8}{9}$ **23.** $8\frac{5}{6} - 5\frac{1}{2}$ **24.** $12\frac{3}{4} - 4\frac{5}{6}$ **25.** $17\frac{2}{7} - 8\frac{2}{9}$

26. $7\frac{3}{4} - 3\frac{3}{8}$ **27.** $4\frac{1}{12} - 1\frac{11}{12}$ **28.** $5\frac{5}{8} - 2\frac{7}{16}$ **29.** $11\frac{2}{3} - 3\frac{5}{6}$ **30.** $25\frac{5}{8} - 17\frac{15}{16}$

Multiplying and Dividing Fractions

To multiply two or more fractions, multiply the numerators, multiply the denominators, and simplify the product, if necessary.

1 EXAMPLE

Multiply $\frac{3}{7} \cdot \frac{5}{6}$.

$$\frac{3}{7} \cdot \frac{5}{6} = \frac{3 \cdot 5}{7 \cdot 6} = \frac{15}{42} = \frac{15 \div 3}{42 \div 3} = \frac{5}{14}$$

Sometimes you can simplify before multiplying.

$$\frac{\cancel{3}^{1}}{7} \cdot \frac{5}{\cancel{6}_{2}} = \frac{5}{14}$$ Divide a numerator and a denominator by a common factor.

To multiply mixed numbers, change the mixed numbers to improper fractions and multiply the fractions. Write the product as a mixed number.

2 EXAMPLE

Multiply $2\frac{4}{5} \cdot 1\frac{2}{3}$.

$$2\frac{4}{5} \cdot 1\frac{2}{3} = \frac{14}{{}_{1}\cancel{5}} \cdot \frac{\cancel{5}^{1}}{3} = \frac{14}{3} = 4\frac{2}{3}$$

To divide fractions, change the division problem to a multiplication problem. Remember that $8 \div \frac{1}{4}$ is the same as $8 \cdot 4$.

To divide mixed numbers, change the mixed numbers to improper fractions and divide the fractions.

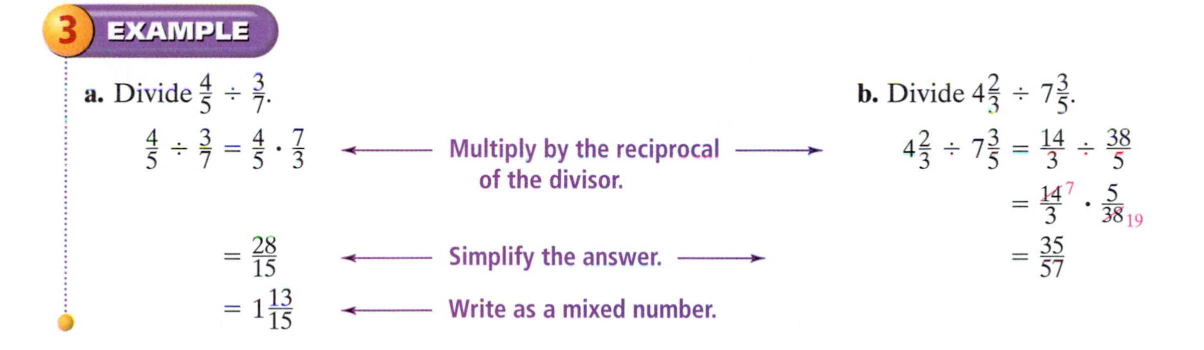

3 EXAMPLE

a. Divide $\frac{4}{5} \div \frac{3}{7}$.

$$\frac{4}{5} \div \frac{3}{7} = \frac{4}{5} \cdot \frac{7}{3}$$ ← Multiply by the reciprocal of the divisor. →

$$= \frac{28}{15}$$ ← Simplify the answer. →

$$= 1\frac{13}{15}$$ ← Write as a mixed number.

b. Divide $4\frac{2}{3} \div 7\frac{3}{5}$.

$$4\frac{2}{3} \div 7\frac{3}{5} = \frac{14}{3} \div \frac{38}{5}$$

$$= \frac{\cancel{14}^{7}}{3} \cdot \frac{5}{\cancel{38}_{19}}$$

$$= \frac{35}{57}$$

EXERCISES

Multiply. Write your answers in simplest form.

1. $\frac{2}{5} \cdot \frac{3}{4}$ **2.** $\frac{3}{7} \cdot \frac{4}{3}$ **3.** $1\frac{1}{2} \cdot 5\frac{3}{4}$ **4.** $3\frac{4}{5} \cdot 10$ **5.** $5\frac{1}{4} \cdot \frac{2}{3}$

6. $4\frac{1}{2} \cdot 7\frac{1}{2}$ **7.** $3\frac{2}{3} \cdot 6\frac{9}{10}$ **8.** $6\frac{1}{2} \cdot 7\frac{2}{3}$ **9.** $2\frac{2}{5} \cdot 1\frac{1}{6}$ **10.** $4\frac{1}{9} \cdot 3\frac{3}{8}$

11. $3\frac{1}{5} \cdot 1\frac{7}{8}$ **12.** $7\frac{5}{6} \cdot 4\frac{1}{2}$ **13.** $1\frac{2}{3} \cdot 5\frac{9}{10}$ **14.** $3\frac{3}{4} \cdot 5\frac{1}{3}$ **15.** $1\frac{2}{3} \cdot 3\frac{9}{16}$

Divide. Write your answers in simplest form.

16. $\frac{3}{5} \div \frac{1}{2}$ **17.** $\frac{4}{5} \div \frac{9}{10}$ **18.** $2\frac{1}{2} \div 3\frac{1}{2}$ **19.** $1\frac{4}{5} \div 2\frac{1}{2}$ **20.** $3\frac{1}{6} \div 1\frac{3}{4}$

21. $5 \div \frac{3}{8}$ **22.** $\frac{4}{9} \div \frac{3}{5}$ **23.** $\frac{5}{8} \div \frac{3}{4}$ **24.** $2\frac{1}{5} \div 2\frac{1}{2}$ **25.** $6\frac{1}{2} \div \frac{1}{4}$

26. $1\frac{3}{4} \div 4\frac{3}{8}$ **27.** $\frac{8}{9} \div \frac{2}{3}$ **28.** $\frac{1}{5} \div \frac{1}{3}$ **29.** $2\frac{2}{5} \div 7\frac{1}{5}$ **30.** $7\frac{2}{3} \div \frac{2}{9}$

Fractions, Decimals, and Percents

Percent means per hundred. 50% means 50 per hundred. $50\% = \frac{50}{100} = 0.50$

You can write fractions as percents by writing the fractions as decimals first. Then move the decimal point two places to the right and write a percent sign.

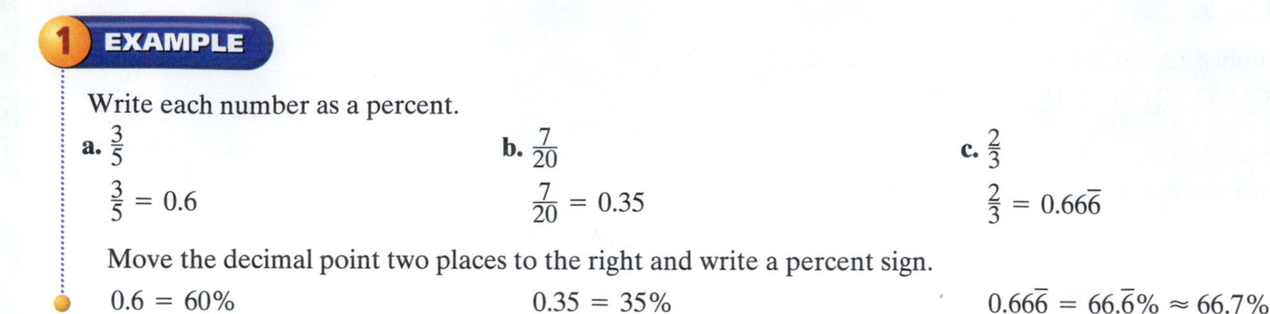

1 EXAMPLE

Write each number as a percent.

a. $\frac{3}{5}$

$\frac{3}{5} = 0.6$

b. $\frac{7}{20}$

$\frac{7}{20} = 0.35$

c. $\frac{2}{3}$

$\frac{2}{3} = 0.66\overline{6}$

Move the decimal point two places to the right and write a percent sign.

$0.6 = 60\%$ $\quad 0.35 = 35\%$ $\quad 0.66\overline{6} = 66.\overline{6}\% \approx 66.7\%$

You can write percents as decimals by moving the decimal point two places to the left and removing the percent sign.

You can write a percent as a fraction with the denominator of 100. You then simplify it, if possible.

2 EXAMPLE

Write each number as a decimal and as a fraction or mixed number.

a. 25%

$25\% = 0.25$

$25\% = \frac{25}{100} = \frac{1}{4}$

b. $\frac{1}{2}\%$

$\frac{1}{2}\% = 0.5\% = 0.005$

$\frac{1}{2}\% = \frac{\frac{1}{2}}{100} = \frac{1}{2} \div 100$

$= \frac{1}{2} \cdot \frac{1}{100} = \frac{1}{200}$

c. 360%

$360\% = 3.6$

$360\% = \frac{360}{100} = \frac{18}{5} = 3\frac{3}{5}$

EXERCISES

Write each number as a percent. If necessary, round to the nearest tenth.

1. 0.56 **2.** 0.09 **3.** 6.02 **4.** 5.245

5. 8.2 **6.** 0.14 **7.** $\frac{1}{7}$ **8.** $\frac{9}{20}$

9. $\frac{1}{9}$ **10.** $\frac{5}{6}$ **11.** $\frac{3}{4}$ **12.** $\frac{7}{8}$

Write each number as a decimal.

13. 7% **14.** 8.5% **15.** 0.9% **16.** 250% **17.** 83% **18.** 110%

19. 15% **20.** 72% **21.** 0.03% **22.** 36.2% **23.** 365% **24.** 101%

Write each number as a fraction or mixed number in simplest form.

25. 19% **26.** $\frac{3}{4}\%$ **27.** 450% **28.** $\frac{4}{5}\%$ **29.** 64% **30.** $\frac{2}{3}\%$

31. 24% **32.** 845% **33.** $\frac{3}{8}\%$ **34.** 480% **35.** 60% **36.** 350%

37. 2% **38.** 16% **39.** 66% **40.** $\frac{4}{7}\%$ **41.** 125% **42.** 84%

Exponents

You can express $2 \cdot 2 \cdot 2 \cdot 2 \cdot 2$ as 2^5. The raised number 5 shows the number of times 2 is used as a factor. The number 2 is the base. The number 5 is the exponent.

2^5 ← **exponent**
↑ **base**

Factored Form	Exponential Form	Standard Form
$2 \cdot 2 \cdot 2 \cdot 2 \cdot 2$	2^5	32

A number with an exponent of 1 is the number itself: $8^1 = 8$.
Any number, except 0, with an exponent of 0 is 1: $5^0 = 1$.

1 EXAMPLE

Write using exponents.

a. $8 \cdot 8 \cdot 8 \cdot 8 \cdot 8$ **b.** $2 \cdot 9 \cdot 9 \cdot 9 \cdot 9 \cdot 9 \cdot 9$ **c.** $6 \cdot 6 \cdot 10 \cdot 10 \cdot 10 \cdot 6 \cdot 6$

Count the number of times the number is used as a factor.

$= 8^5$ $= 2 \cdot 9^6$ $= 6^4 \cdot 10^3$

2 EXAMPLE

Write in standard form.

a. 2^3 **b.** $8^2 \cdot 3^4$ **c.** $10^3 \cdot 15^2$

Write in factored form and multiply.

$2 \cdot 2 \cdot 2 = 8$ $8 \cdot 8 \cdot 3 \cdot 3 \cdot 3 \cdot 3 = 5184$ $10 \cdot 10 \cdot 10 \cdot 15 \cdot 15 = 225{,}000$

In powers of 10, an exponent tells how many zeros are in the equivalent standard form.

$10^1 = 10$
$10^2 = 10 \cdot 10 = 100$
$10^3 = 10 \cdot 10 \cdot 10 = 1000$
$10^4 = 10 \cdot 10 \cdot 10 \cdot 10 = 10{,}000$
$10^5 = 10 \cdot 10 \cdot 10 \cdot 10 \cdot 10 = 100{,}000$
$10^6 = 10 \cdot 10 \cdot 10 \cdot 10 \cdot 10 \cdot 10 = 1{,}000{,}000$

You can use exponents to write numbers in expanded form.

3 EXAMPLE

Write 739 in expanded form using exponents.

$739 = 700 + 30 + 9 = (7 \cdot 100) + (3 \cdot 10) + (9 \cdot 1) = (7 \cdot 10^2) + (3 \cdot 10^1) + (9 \cdot 10^0)$

EXERCISES

Write using exponents.

1. $6 \cdot 6 \cdot 6 \cdot 6$ **2.** $7 \cdot 7 \cdot 7 \cdot 7 \cdot 7$ **3.** $5 \cdot 2 \cdot 2 \cdot 2 \cdot 2$

4. $3 \cdot 3 \cdot 3 \cdot 3 \cdot 3 \cdot 14 \cdot 14$ **5.** $4 \cdot 4 \cdot 3 \cdot 3 \cdot 2$ **6.** $3 \cdot 5 \cdot 5 \cdot 7 \cdot 7 \cdot 7$

Write in standard form.

7. 4^3 **8.** 9^4 **9.** 12^2 **10.** $6^2 \cdot 7^1$ **11.** $11^2 \cdot 3^3$

Write in expanded form using exponents.

12. 658 **13.** 1254 **14.** 7125 **15.** 83,401 **16.** 294,863

Perimeter, Area, and Volume

The perimeter of a figure is the distance around the figure. The area of a figure is the number of square units contained in the figure. The volume of a space figure is the number of cubic units contained in the space figure.

1 EXAMPLE

Find the perimeter of each figure.

a. 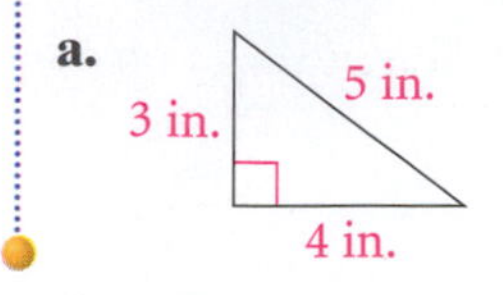

Add the measures of the sides.

$3 + 4 + 5 = 12$

The perimeter is 12 in.

b. 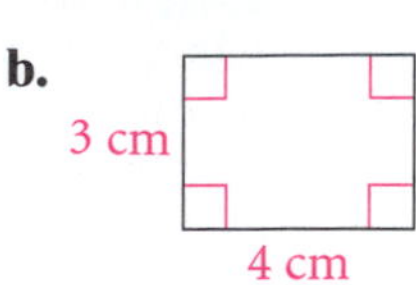

Use the formula $P = 2\ell + 2w$.

$P = 2(3) + 2(4)$

$= 6 + 8 = 14$

The perimeter is 14 cm.

2 EXAMPLE

Find the area of each figure.

a. 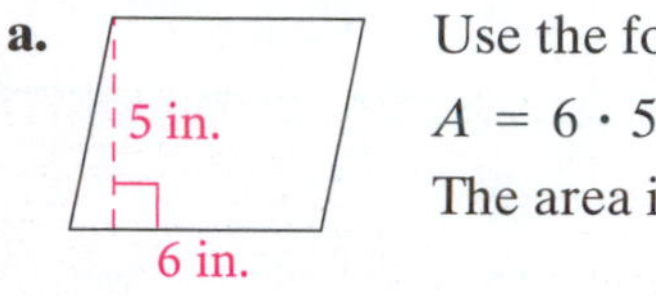

Use the formula $A = bh$.

$A = 6 \cdot 5 = 30$

The area is 30 in.^{2}.

b. 6 in. 7 in.

Use the formula $A = \frac{1}{2}(bh)$.

$A = \frac{1}{2}(7 \cdot 6) = 21$

The area is 21 in.^{2}.

3 EXAMPLE

Find the volume of each figure.

a. 6 in. 3 in. 5 in.

Use the formula $V = Bh$.

(B = area of the base

$= 3 \cdot 5 = 15$).

$V = 15 \cdot 6 = 90$ in.^{3}

The volume is 90 in.^{3}.

b. 5 in. 2 in.

Use the formula $V = \pi r^2 h$.

$V = 3.14 \cdot 2^2 \cdot 5$

$= 3.14 \cdot 4 \cdot 5 = 62.8$ in.^{3}

The volume is 62.8 in.^{3}.

EXERCISES

For Exercises 1–2, find the perimeter of each figure. For Exercises 3–4, find the area of each figure.

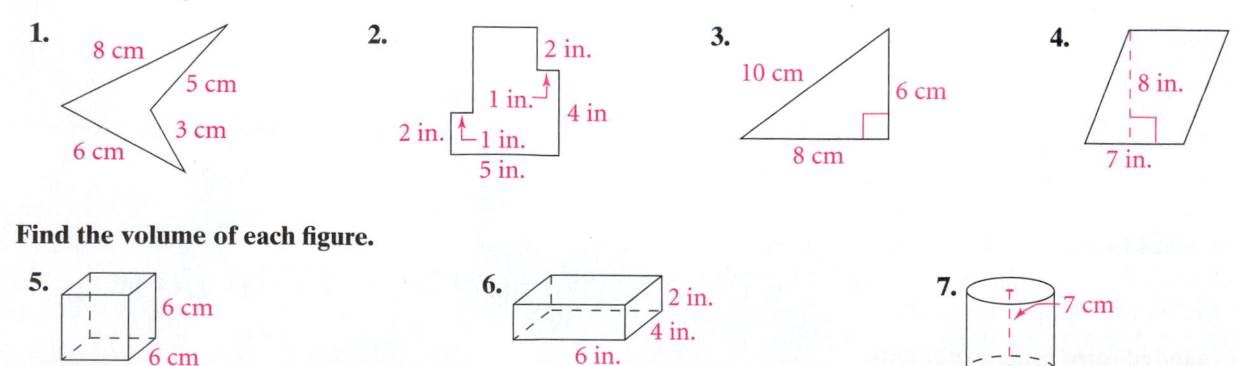

Find the volume of each figure.

Line Plots

A line plot is created by placing a mark above a number line corresponding to the location of each data item. Line plots have two main advantages:

- You can see the frequency of data items.
- You can see how the data items compare.

EXAMPLE

The table at the right gives the heights (in inches) of a group of twenty-five adults. Display the data in a line plot. Describe the data shown in the line plot.

Height of Adults (inches)

59	60	63	63	64
64	64	65	65	65
67	67	67	67	68
68	68	69	70	70
71	72	73	73	77

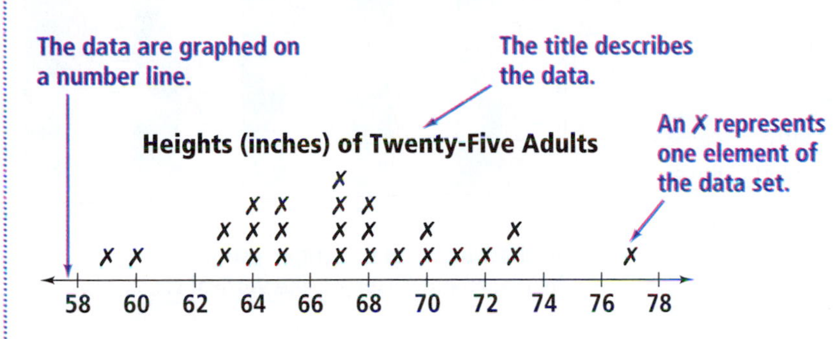

The line plot shows that most of the heights are concentrated around 67 inches, the maximum value is 77, and the minimum value is 59.

EXERCISES

Display each set of data in a line plot.

1. 3, 6, 4, 3, 6, 0, 4, 5, 0, 4, 6, 1, 5, 1, 0, 5, 5, 6, 5, 3
2. 19, 18, 18, 18, 19, 20, 19, 18, 18, 17, 18, 20, 19, 17

Draw a line plot for each frequency table.

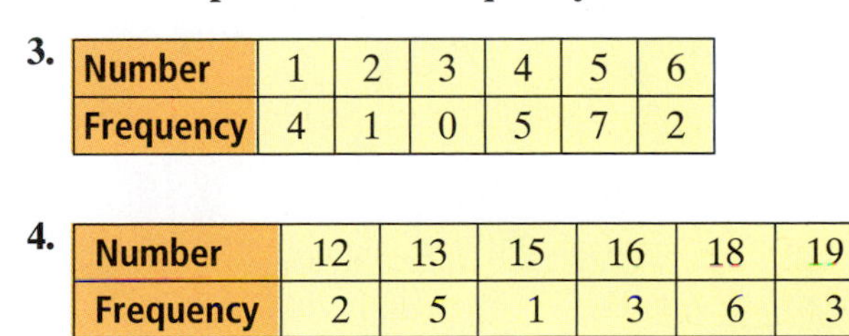

3.

Number	1	2	3	4	5	6
Frequency	4	1	0	5	7	2

4.

Number	12	13	15	16	18	19
Frequency	2	5	1	3	6	3

5. Below are the numbers of gold medals won by different countries during the 1998 Winter Olympics (Bulgaria had the least with 1 gold medal, and Germany had the most with 12 gold medals).
   1, 1, 2, 2, 2, 2, 3, 3, 5, 5, 6, 6, 9, 10, 12
   Display the data in a line plot. Describe the data shown in the line plot.

Bar Graphs

Bar graphs are used to compare amounts. The horizontal axis shows the categories and the vertical axis shows the amounts. A multiple bar graph includes a key.

EXAMPLE

Draw a bar graph for the data in the table below.

Median Household Income

State	2001	2003	2005
Calif.	$47,262	$49,300	$53,629
Col.	$49,397	$49,940	$50,652
Ind.	$40,379	$42,425	$43,993
Tex.	$40,860	$39,271	$42,139
Utah	$47,342	$49,275	$47,934

SOURCE: U.S. Census Bureau

The categories (in the first column) are placed on the horizontal scale. The amounts (in the second, third, and fourth columns) are placed on the vertical scale.

Graph the data for each state. Use the values in the top row to create the key.

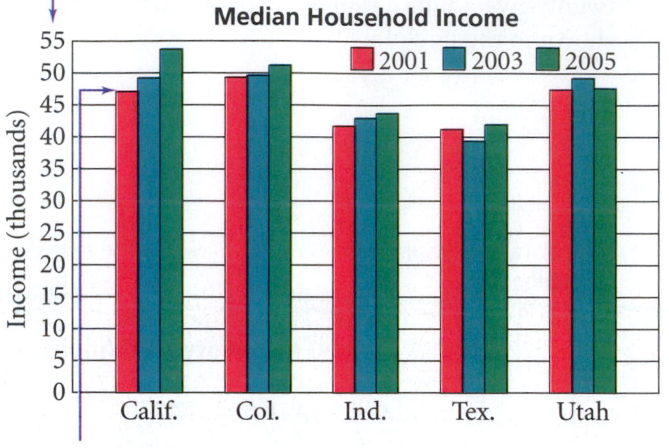

EXERCISES

1. Draw a bar graph for the data in the table below.

Highest Temperatures

City	March	June	August
Juneau, AK	61	86	83
Denver, CO	84	104	101
Atlanta, GA	89	101	102
Honolulu, HI	88	92	93
Detroit, MI	81	104	100
Buffalo, NY	81	96	99
Houston, TX	91	103	107

2. a. **Critical Thinking** If one more column of data were added to the table in the example, how would the bar graph be different?

   b. If one more row of data were added to the table in the example, how would the bar graph be different?

Histograms

A histogram is a bar graph that shows the frequency, or number of times, a data item occurs. Histograms often combine data into intervals of equal size. The intervals do not overlap.

EXAMPLE

The data at the right show the number of hours of battery life for different brands of batteries used in portable CD players. Use the data to make a histogram.

Hours of Battery Life

12	9	10	14	10	11
10	18	21	10	14	22

Step 1 Decide on an interval size.

The data start at 9 hours and go to 22 hours. Use equal-sized intervals of 4 hours, beginning with 8 hours. So the first interval will be 8–11.

Step 2 Make a frequency table.

Battery Life

Hours	Tally	Frequency
8–11	~~IIII~~ I	6
12–15	III	3
16–19	I	1
20–23	II	2

Step 3 Make a histogram.

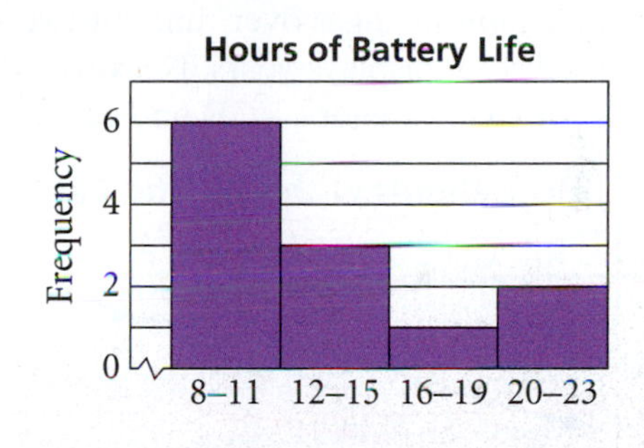

EXERCISES

1. Students answered a survey question about how long it takes to get ready in the morning. The histogram at the right shows the survey results.
   a. Which interval indicates the answers most students gave?
   b. How many students answered the survey question?
   c. Why might no students have given an answer in the interval 50–59?
   d. **Critical Thinking** With the information you have, could you redraw the histogram with intervals half their current size? Explain why or why not.

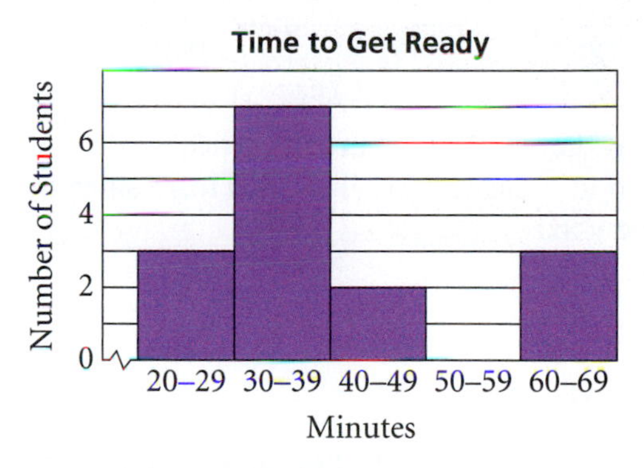

2. a. An Internet company surveyed their users. The first 25 people who responded gave the ages shown at the right. What intervals would you use to make a histogram?
   b. Make a frequency table for the data.
   c. Make a histogram.

Age of Internet Users

25, 43, 65, 12, 8, 30, 44, 68, 18, 21, 25, 33, 37, 54, 61, 29, 31, 38, 22, 48, 19, 34, 55, 14, 21

3. a. Survey your class to find out what day of the month they were born. For example, 12 if a student's birthday is August 12th.
   b. What intervals would you use to make a histogram?
   c. Make a frequency table for the data.
   d. Make a histogram.

Line Graphs

Line graphs are used to display the change in a set of data over a period of time. A multiple-line graph shows change in more than one category of data over time. You can use a line graph to look for trends and make predictions.

EXAMPLE

Graph the data in the table below.

Households with VCR and Cable TV (millions)

Year	1990	1995	2000	2002	2004	2006
VCR	63	77	86	96	98	98
Cable TV	52	60	69	73	74	73

SOURCE: Nielsen Media Research–NTI

Since the data show changes over time for two sets of data, use a double line graph. The horizontal scale displays years. The vertical scale displays the number of households for each category, VCR and cable TV.

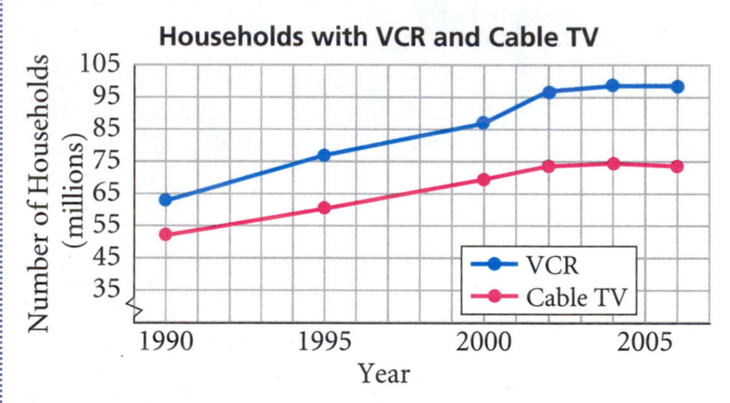

Notice that there is a *break* in the vertical scale, which goes from 0 to 85. A zigzag line is used to indicate a break from 0 to 15 since there is no data to graph in this part of the y-axis.

EXERCISES

Graph the following data.

1. **Market Shares (percent)**

Year	1999	2000	2001	2002	2003	2004	2005
Rap/Hip Hop	10.8	12.9	11.4	13.8	13.3	12.1	13.3
Pop	10.3	11.0	12.1	9.0	8.9	10.0	8.1

SOURCE: The Recording Industry of America

2. **Percents of Schools With Internet Access**

Year	1995	1996	1997	1998	1999	2000	2001
Elementary	46	61	75	88	94	97	99
Secondary	65	77	89	94	98	100	100

SOURCE: U.S. National Center for Education Statistics

Circle Graphs

A circle graph is an efficient way to present certain types of data. The graphs show data as percents or fractions of a whole. The total must be 100% or 1. Circle graphs are used to show the parts of the whole. The angles at the center are central angles, and each angle is proportional to the percent or fraction of the total.

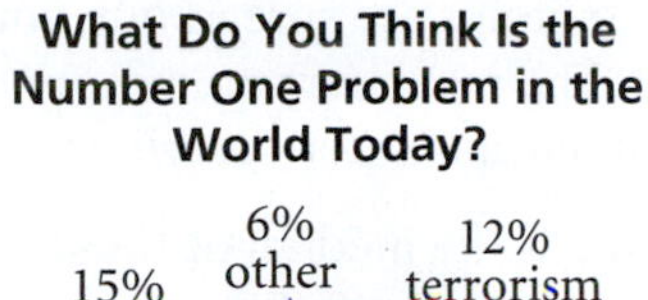

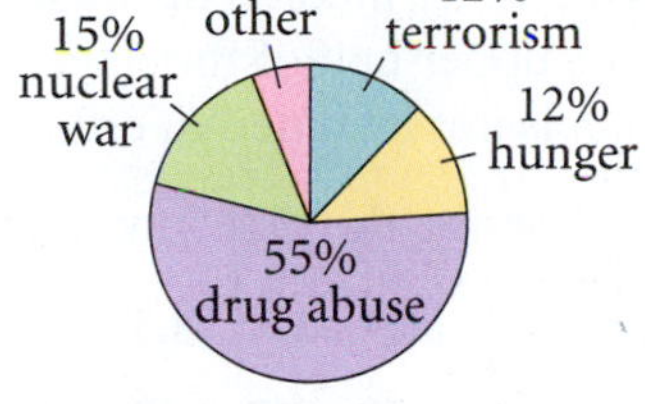

SOURCE: *The Second Kids' World Almanac*

EXAMPLE

The table below shows the number of people in the United States who have at least one grandchild under the age of 18. Draw a circle graph for the data.

Ages of U.S. Grandparents

Age	People (millions)
44 and under	3.6
45–54	10.3
55–64	15.0
65 and over	18.2

Step 1 Add to find the total number.

$3.6 + 10.3 + 15.0 + 18.2 = 47.1$ (million)

Step 2 For each central angle, set up a proportion to find the measure. Use a calculator to solve each proportion.

$\frac{3.6}{47.1} = \frac{a}{360^\circ}$ $a \approx 27.5^\circ$ $\frac{10.3}{47.1} = \frac{b}{360^\circ}$ $b \approx 78.7^\circ$ $\frac{15.0}{47.1} = \frac{c}{360^\circ}$ $c \approx 114.6^\circ$ $\frac{18.2}{47.1} = \frac{d}{360^\circ}$ $d \approx 139.1^\circ$

Step 3 Use a compass to draw a circle. Draw the approximate central angles with a protractor.

139° 115° 27° 79°

Step 4 Label each sector. Add any necessary information.

Ages of U.S. Grandparents

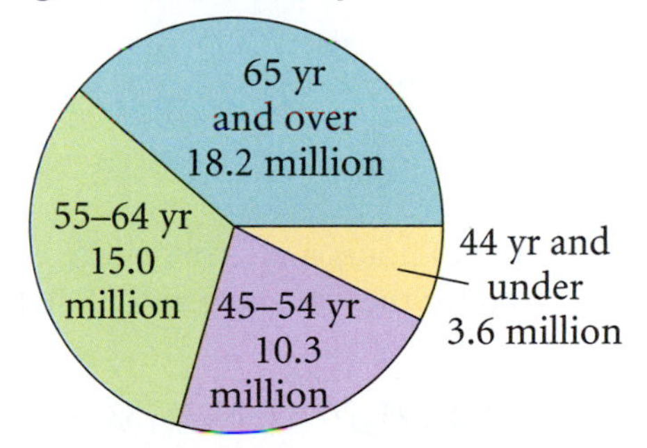

EXERCISES

Transportation Mode	Walk	Bicycle	Bus	Car
Number of Students	252	135	432	81

1. a. Use the data in the table to draw a circle graph.
   b. Approximately what percent of students ride the bus?
   c. Approximately how many times more students walk than ride in a car?
2. Survey your class to find out how they get to school. Use the data to draw a circle graph.

Box-and-Whisker Plots

To show how data items are spread out, you can arrange a set of data in order from least to greatest. The maximum, minimum, and median give you some information about the data. You can better describe the data by dividing it into fourths.

The lower quartile is the median of the lower half of the data. The upper quartile is the median of the upper half of the data. If the data set has an odd number of items, the median is not included in either the upper half or the lower half.

The data below describe the highway gas mileage (mi/gal) for several cars.

minimum ↓ **median = 38.5** ↓ **maximum** ↓

17 19 27 37 40 42 52 58

lower quartile $\frac{19 + 27}{2} = 23$ ↑ ↑ **upper quartile** $\frac{42 + 52}{2} = 47$

A box-and-whisker plot is a visual representation of data. The box-and-whisker plot below displays the gas mileage information.

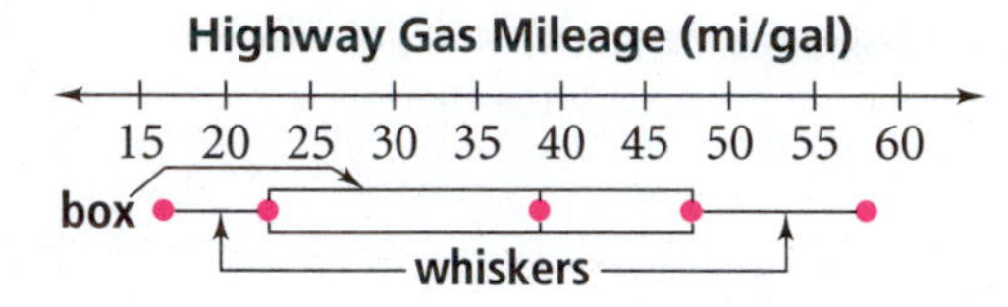

The box represents the data from the lower quartile to the upper quartile. The vertical line segment represents the median. Horizontal line segments called whiskers show the spread of the data to the minimum and to the maximum.

EXERCISES

Create a box-and-whisker plot for each data set.

1. {3, 2, 3, 4, 6, 6, 7}

2. {1, 1.5, 1.7, 2, 6.1, 6.2, 7}

3. {1, 2, 5, 6, 9, 12, 7, 10}

4. {65, 66, 59, 61, 67, 70, 67, 66, 69, 70, 63}

5. {29, 32, 40, 31, 33, 39, 27, 42}

6. {3, 3, 5, 7, 1, 10, 10, 4, 4, 7, 9, 8, 6}

7. {1, 1.2, 1.3, 4, 4.1, 4.2, 7}

8. {1, 3.8, 3.9, 4, 4.3, 4.4, 7, 5}

9. Below are the number of hours a student worked each week at her summer job. When she applied for the job, she was told that the typical work week was 29 hours.

29, 25, 21, 20, 17, 16, 15, 33, 33, 30, 15

a. Make a box-and-whisker plot for the data.

b. How many weeks are above the upper quartile? What are the numbers of hours worked?

c. What is the median number of hours she worked? What is the mean? Compare them to the typical work week.

10. Writing In what ways are histograms and box-and-whisker plots alike, and in what ways are they different?

Choosing an Appropriate Graph

The type of data you want to display can suggest an appropriate graph. You can have data by categories (qualitative data), such as states (page 606), years (page 609), or mode of transportation (page 609). You may also have measurement data (quantitative data), such as height (page 605), time to get ready in the morning (page 607), or gas mileage (page 610).

The table below lists some common types of graphs and how they are frequently used.

Graph	Use
Bar Graph	To display frequency of categories
Circle Graph	To show categories as part of a whole
Line Graph	To show trends over time
Line Plot, Histogram, Stem-and-Leaf Plot	To display frequency distribution of measurement data
Box-and-Whisker Plot	To summarize the distribution of measurement data
Scatter Plot	To display possible relationships in data pairs

EXAMPLE

Would you use a line graph or a circle graph to display the percent of fiction books published each year for the last ten years?

A circle graph shows percents, but it would not allow you to show the change over time. A line graph would be more appropriate.

EXERCISES

Choose the appropriate graph to display each set of data. Explain your choice.

1. circle graph or bar graph
how much the average family spends on rent, food, transportation, utilities, and entertainment in October

2. bar graph or line graph
the number of runners in the Olympic marathon for each of the last five Olympic games

3. scatter plot or double bar graph
the ages of twelve cars and their levels of emissions

4. double box-and-whisker plot or scatter plot
the heights of men and women playing professional basketball in 2004

For each type of graph, describe a set of data that would be appropriate.

5. stem-and-leaf plot

6. double line graph

7. circle graph

Tables

Table 1 Measures

United States Customary	Metric
Length	
12 inches (in.) = 1 foot (ft)	10 millimeters (mm) = 1 centimeter (cm)
36 in. = 1 yard (yd)	100 cm = 1 meter (m)
3 ft = 1 yard	1000 mm = 1 meter
5280 ft = 1 mile (mi)	1000 m = 1 kilometer (km)
1760 yd = 1 mile	
Area	
144 square inches (in.^2) = 1 square foot (ft^2)	100 square millimeters (mm^2) = 1 square centimeter (cm^2)
9 ft^2 = 1 square yard (yd^2)	10,000 cm^2 = 1 square meter (m^2)
43,560 ft^2 = 1 acre (a)	10,000 m^2 = 1 hectare (ha)
4840 yd^2 = 1 acre	
Volume	
1728 cubic inches (in.^3) = 1 cubic foot (ft^3)	1000 cubic millimeters (mm^3) = 1 cubic centimeter (cm^3)
27 ft^3 = 1 cubic yard (yd^3)	1,000,000 cm^3 = 1 cubic meter (m^3)
Liquid Capacity	
8 fluid ounces (fl oz) = 1 cup (c)	1000 milliliters (mL) = 1 liter (L)
2 c = 1 pint (pt)	1000 L = 1 kiloliter (kL)
2 pt = 1 quart (qt)	
4 qt = 1 gallon (gal)	
Weight or Mass	
16 ounces (oz) = 1 pound (lb)	1000 milligrams (mg) = 1 gram (g)
2000 pounds = 1 ton (t)	1000 g = 1 kilogram (kg)
	1000 kg = 1 metric ton
Temperature	
32°F = freezing point of water	0°C = freezing point of water
98.6°F = normal body temperature	37°C = normal body temperature
212°F = boiling point of water	100°C = boiling point of water

Time	
60 seconds (s) = 1 minute (min)	365 days = 1 year (yr)
60 minutes = 1 hour (h)	52 weeks (approx.) = 1 year
24 hours = 1 day (d)	12 months = 1 year
7 days = 1 week (wk)	10 years = 1 decade
4 weeks (approx.) = 1 month (mo)	100 years = 1 century

Table 2 Reading Math Symbols

Symbol	Meaning	Page
$\cdot$	multiplication sign, times ($\times$)	p. 4
$=$	equals	p. 5
( )	parentheses for grouping	p. 9
a^n	nth power of a	p. 9
%	percent	p. 11
[ ]	brackets for grouping	p. 12
. . .	and so on	p. 17
$-a$	opposite of a	p. 17
$\neq$	is not equal to	p. 17
π	pi, an irrational number, approximately equal to 3.14	p. 18
$<$	is less than	p. 19
$>$	is greater than	p. 19
$\leq$	is less than or equal to	p. 19
$\geq$	is greater than or equal to	p. 19
$\lvert a \rvert$	absolute value of a	p. 20
$^\circ$	degree(s)	p. 27
$\frac{1}{a}, a \neq 0$	reciprocal of a	p. 40
$\stackrel{?}{=}$	Is the statement true?	p. 70
$\angle A$	angle A	p. 73
$a:b$	ratio of a to b	p. 92
$\approx$	is approximately equal to	p. 93
(x, y)	ordered pair	p. 176
{ }	set braces	p. 181
$f(x)$	f of x; the function value at x	p. 187
x_1, x_2, etc.	specific values of the variable x	p. 232
y_1, y_2, etc.	specific values of the variable y	p. 232
$\overleftrightarrow{AB}$	line through points A and B	p. 232
m	slope of a linear function	p. 240
b	y-intercept of a linear function	p. 240
$\triangle ABC$	triangle ABC	p. 266
$\overline{AB}$	segment with endpoints A and B	p. 266
a^{-n}	$\frac{1}{a^n}, a \neq 0$	p. 329
$\sqrt{x}$	nonnegative square root of x	p. 440
$\pm$	plus or minus	p. 440

Table 3 Squares and Square Roots

Number n	Square n^2	Positive Square Root $\sqrt{n}$	Number n	Square n^2	Positive Square Root $\sqrt{n}$	Number n	Square n^2	Positive Square Root $\sqrt{n}$
1	1	1.000	**51**	2601	7.141	**101**	10,201	10.050
2	4	1.414	**52**	2704	7.211	**102**	10,404	10.100
3	9	1.732	**53**	2809	7.280	**103**	10,609	10.149
4	16	2.000	**54**	2916	7.348	**104**	10,816	10.198
5	25	2.236	**55**	3025	7.416	**105**	11,025	10.247
6	36	2.449	**56**	3136	7.483	**106**	11,236	10.296
7	49	2.646	**57**	3249	7.550	**107**	11,449	10.344
8	64	2.828	**58**	3364	7.616	**108**	11,664	10.392
9	81	3.000	**59**	3481	7.681	**109**	11,881	10.440
10	100	3.162	**60**	3600	7.746	**110**	12,100	10.488
11	121	3.317	**61**	3721	7.810	**111**	12,321	10.536
12	144	3.464	**62**	3844	7.874	**112**	12,544	10.583
13	169	3.606	**63**	3969	7.937	**113**	12,769	10.630
14	196	3.742	**64**	4096	8.000	**114**	12,996	10.677
15	225	3.873	**65**	4225	8.062	**115**	13,225	10.724
16	256	4.000	**66**	4356	8.124	**116**	13,456	10.770
17	289	4.123	**67**	4489	8.185	**117**	13,689	10.817
18	324	4.243	**68**	4624	8.246	**118**	13,924	10.863
19	361	4.359	**69**	4761	8.307	**119**	14,161	10.909
20	400	4.472	**70**	4900	8.367	**120**	14,400	10.954
21	441	4.583	**71**	5041	8.426	**121**	14,641	11.000
22	484	4.690	**72**	5184	8.485	**122**	14,884	11.045
23	529	4.796	**73**	5329	8.544	**123**	15,129	11.091
24	576	4.899	**74**	5476	8.602	**124**	15,376	11.136
25	625	5.000	**75**	5625	8.660	**125**	15,625	11.180
26	676	5.099	**76**	5776	8.718	**126**	15,876	11.225
27	729	5.196	**77**	5929	8.775	**127**	16,129	11.269
28	784	5.292	**78**	6084	8.832	**128**	16,384	11.314
29	841	5.385	**79**	6241	8.888	**129**	16,641	11.358
30	900	5.477	**80**	6400	8.944	**130**	16,900	11.402
31	961	5.568	**81**	6561	9.000	**131**	17,161	11.446
32	1024	5.657	**82**	6724	9.055	**132**	17,424	11.489
33	1089	5.745	**83**	6889	9.110	**133**	17,689	11.533
34	1156	5.831	**84**	7056	9.165	**134**	17,956	11.576
35	1225	5.916	**85**	7225	9.220	**135**	18,225	11.619
36	1296	6.000	**86**	7396	9.274	**136**	18,496	11.662
37	1369	6.083	**87**	7569	9.327	**137**	18,769	11.705
38	1444	6.164	**88**	7744	9.381	**138**	19,044	11.747
39	1521	6.245	**89**	7921	9.434	**139**	19,321	11.790
40	1600	6.325	**90**	8100	9.487	**140**	19,600	11.832
41	1681	6.403	**91**	8281	9.539	**141**	19,881	11.874
42	1764	6.481	**92**	8464	9.592	**142**	20,164	11.916
43	1849	6.557	**93**	8649	9.644	**143**	20,449	11.958
44	1936	6.633	**94**	8836	9.695	**144**	20,736	12.000
45	2025	6.708	**95**	9025	9.747	**145**	21,025	12.042
46	2116	6.782	**96**	9216	9.798	**146**	21,316	12.083
47	2209	6.856	**97**	9409	9.849	**147**	21,609	12.124
48	2304	6.928	**98**	9604	9.899	**148**	21,904	12.166
49	2401	7.000	**99**	9801	9.950	**149**	22,201	12.207
50	2500	7.071	**100**	10,000	10.000	**150**	22,500	12.247

Properties and Formulas

Chapter 1

Order of Operations

1. Perform any operation(s) inside grouping symbols.
2. Simplify powers.
3. Multiply and divide in order from left to right.
4. Add and subtract in order from left to right.

Identity Property of Addition

For every rational number n, $n + 0 = n$.

Inverse Property of Addition

For every rational number n, there is an additive inverse $-n$ such that $n + (-n) = 0$.

Identity Property of Multiplication

For every real number n, $1 \cdot n = n$.

Multiplication Property of Zero

For every real number n, $n \cdot 0 = 0$.

Multiplication Property of −1

For every real number n, $-1 \cdot n = -n$.

Inverse Property of Multiplication

For every nonzero real number a, there is a multiplicative inverse $\frac{1}{a}$ such that $a\left(\frac{1}{a}\right) = 1$.

Distributive Property

For every real number a, b, and c:

$a(b + c) = ab + ac$

$(b + c)a = ba + ca$

$a(b - c) = ab - ac$

$(b - c)a = ba - ca$

Commutative Property of Addition

For every real number a and b, $a + b = b + a$.

Commutative Property of Multiplication

For every real number a and b, $a \cdot b = b \cdot a$.

Associative Property of Addition

For every real number a, b, and c, $(a + b) + c = a + (b + c)$.

Associative Property of Multiplication

For every real number a, b, and c, $(a \cdot b) \cdot c = a \cdot (b \cdot c)$.

Symmetric Property

If $a = b$, then $b = a$.

Closure Property of Addition

For every real number a and b, $a + b$ is a real number.

Closure Property of Multiplication

For every real number a and b, ab is a real number.

Chapter 2

Addition Property of Equality

For every real number a, b, and c, if $a = b$, then $a + c = b + c$.

Subtraction Property of Equality

For every real number a, b, and c, if $a = b$, then $a - c = b - c$.

Multiplication Property of Equality

For every real number a, b, and c, if $a = b$, then $a \cdot c = b \cdot c$.

Division Property of Equality

For every real number a, b, and c, with $c \neq 0$, if $a = b$, then $\frac{a}{c} = \frac{b}{c}$.

Cross Products of a Proportion

If $\frac{a}{b} = \frac{c}{d}$, then $ad = bc$.

Chapter 3

The following properties of inequality are also true for $\geq$ and $\leq$.

Addition Property of Inequality

For every real number a, b, and c,
if $a > b$, then $a + c > b + c$;
if $a < b$, then $a + c < b + c$.

Subtraction Property of Inequality

For every real number a, b, and c,
if $a > b$, then $a - c > b - c$;
if $a < b$, then $a - c < b - c$.

Multiplication Property of Inequality

For every real number a and b, and for $c > 0$,
if $a > b$, then $ac > bc$;
if $a < b$, then $ac < bc$.

For every real number a and b, and for $c < 0$,
if $a > b$, then $ac < bc$;
if $a < b$, then $ac > bc$.

Division Property of Inequality

For every real number a and b, and for $c > 0$,
if $a > b$, then $\frac{a}{c} > \frac{b}{c}$;
if $a < b$, then $\frac{a}{c} < \frac{b}{c}$.
For every real number a and b, and for $c < 0$,
if $a > b$, then $\frac{a}{c} < \frac{b}{c}$;
if $a < b$, then $\frac{a}{c} > \frac{b}{c}$.

Reflexive Property of Equality

For every real number a, $a = a$.

Symmetric Property of Equality

For every real number a and b,
if $a = b$, then $b = a$.

Transitive Property of Equality

For every real number a, b, and c,
if $a = b$ and $b = c$, then $a = c$.

Transitive Property of Inequality

For every real number a, b, and c,
if $a < b$ and $b < c$, then $a < c$.

Chapter 5

Slope

$$\text{slope} = \frac{\text{vertical change}}{\text{horizontal change}} = \frac{\text{rise}}{\text{run}}$$

Slope-Intercept Form of a Linear Equation

The slope-intercept form of a linear equation is $y = mx + b$, where m is the slope and b is the y-intercept.

Standard Form of a Linear Equation

The standard form of a linear equation is $Ax + By = C$, where A, B, and C are real numbers and A and B are not both zero.

Point-Slope Form of a Linear Equation

The point-slope form of the equation of a nonvertical line that passes through the point (x_1, y_1) with slope m is $y - y_1 = m(x - x_1)$.

Slopes of Parallel Lines

Nonvertical lines are parallel if they have the same slope and different y-intercepts. Any two vertical lines are parallel.

Slopes of Perpendicular Lines

Two lines are perpendicular if the product of their slopes is -1. A vertical and a horizontal line are perpendicular.

Chapter 6

Solutions of Systems of Linear Equations

A system of linear equations can have one solution, no solution, or infinitely many solutions:

- If the lines have different slopes, the lines intersect, so there is one solution.
- If the lines have the same slopes and different y-intercepts, the lines are parallel, so there are no solutions.
- If the lines have the same slopes and the same y-intercepts, the lines are the same, so there are infinitely many solutions.

Chapter 7

Zero as an Exponent

For every nonzero number a, $a^0 = 1$.

Negative Exponent

For every nonzero number a and integer n, $a^{-n} = \frac{1}{a^n}$.

Scientific Notation

A number in scientific notation is written as the product of two factors in the form $a \times 10^n$, where n is an integer and $1 \leq a < 10$.

Multiplying Powers with the Same Base

For every nonzero number a and integers m and n,
$a^m \cdot a^n = a^{m+n}$.

Raising a Power to a Power

For every nonzero number a and integers m and n,
$(a^m)^n = a^{mn}$.

Raising a Product to a Power

For every nonzero number a and b and integer n,
$(ab)^n = a^n b^n$.

Dividing Powers with the Same Base

For every nonzero number a and integers m and n,
$\frac{a^m}{a^n} = a^{m-n}$.

Raising a Quotient to a Power

For every nonzero number a and b and integer n,
$\left(\frac{a}{b}\right)^n = \frac{a^n}{b^n}$.

Chapter 8

Factoring Special Cases

For every nonzero number a and b:
$a^2 - b^2 = (a + b)(a - b)$
$a^2 + 2ab + b^2 = (a + b)(a + b) = (a + b)^2$
$a^2 - 2ab + b^2 = (a - b)(a - b) = (a - b)^2$

Chapter 9

Graph of a Quadratic Function

The graph of $y = ax^2 + bx + c$, where a, b, and c are real numbers and $a \neq 0$, has the line $x = \frac{-b}{2a}$ as its axis of symmetry. The x-coordinate of the vertex is $\frac{-b}{2a}$.

Zero-Product Property

For every real number a and b, if $ab = 0$, then $a = 0$ or $b = 0$.

Quadratic Formula

If $ax^2 + bx + c = 0$ where a, b, and c are real numbers and $a \neq 0$, then $x = \frac{-b \pm \sqrt{b^2 - 4ac}}{2a}$.

Property of the Discriminant

For the quadratic equation $ax^2 + bx + c = 0$, where a, b, and c are real numbers and $a \neq 0$, the value of the discriminant $b^2 - 4ac$ tells you the number of solutions.

- If $b^2 - 4ac > 0$, there are two real solutions.
- If $b^2 - 4ac = 0$, there is one real solution.
- If $b^2 - 4ac < 0$, there are no real solutions.

Chapter 10

Multiplication Property of Square Roots

For every number $a \geq 0$ and $b \geq 0$, $\sqrt{ab} = \sqrt{a} \cdot \sqrt{b}$.

Division Property of Square Roots

For every number $a \geq 0$ and $b > 0$, $\sqrt{\frac{a}{b}} = \frac{\sqrt{a}}{\sqrt{b}}$.

The Pythagorean Theorem

In a right triangle, the sum of the squares of the lengths of the legs is equal to the square of the length of the hypotenuse. $a^2 + b^2 = c^2$

The Converse of the Pythagorean Theorem

If a triangle has sides of lengths a, b, and c, and $a^2 + b^2 = c^2$, then the triangle is a right triangle with hypotenuse of length c.

The Distance Formula

The distance d between any two points (x_1, y_1) and (x_2, y_2) is $d = \sqrt{(x_2 - x_1)^2 + (y_2 - y_1)^2}$.

Formulas of Geometry

You will use a number of geometric formulas as you work through your algebra book. Here are some perimeter, area, and volume formulas.

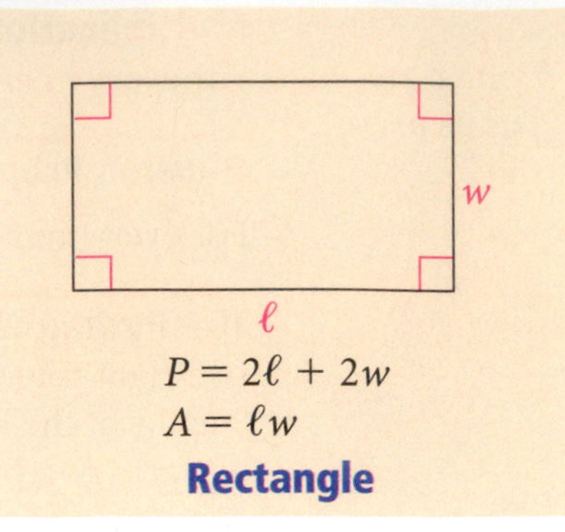

$P = 2\ell + 2w$
$A = \ell w$
Rectangle

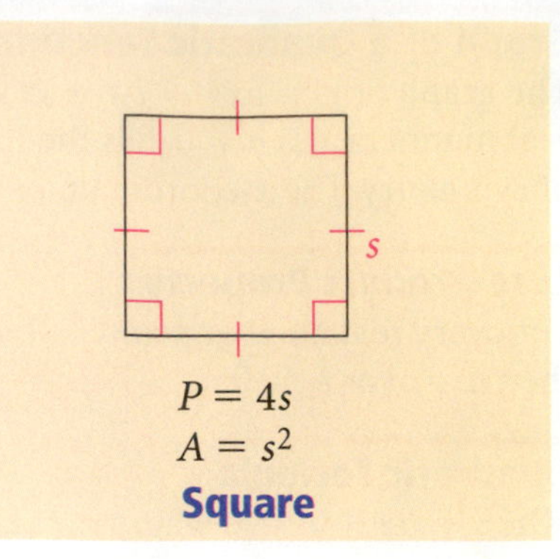

$P = 4s$
$A = s^2$
Square

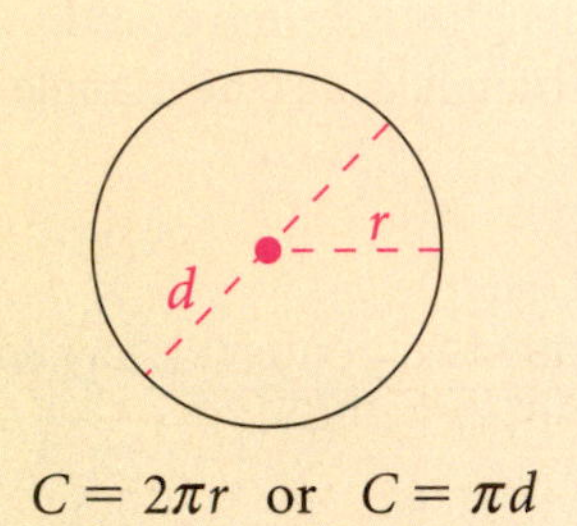

$C = 2\pi r$ or $C = \pi d$
$A = \pi r^2$
Circle

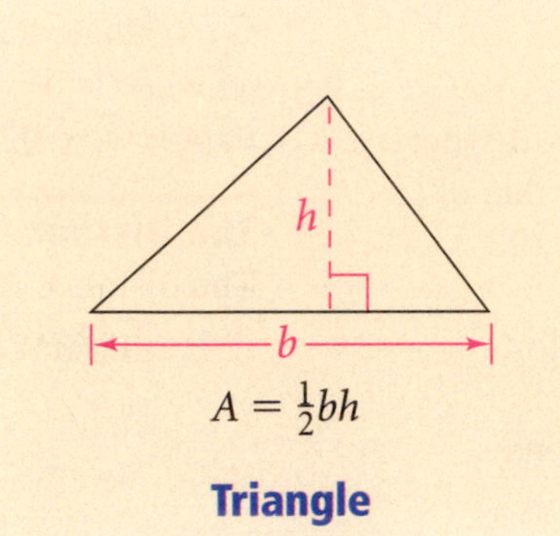

$A = \frac{1}{2}bh$
Triangle

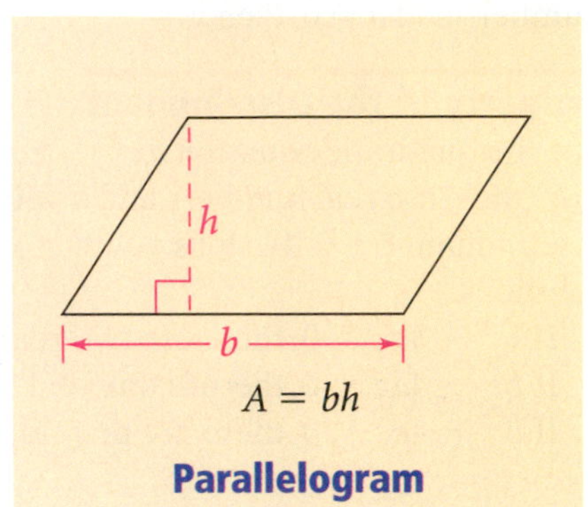

$A = bh$
Parallelogram

b_1
h
b_2

$A = \frac{1}{2}(b_1 + b_2)h$
Trapezoid

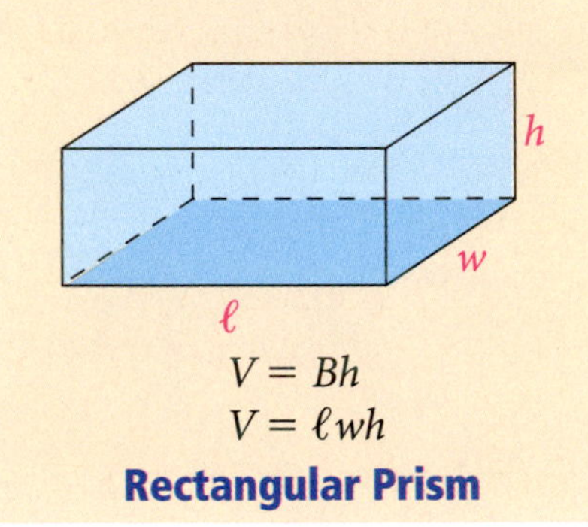

$V = Bh$
$V = \ell wh$
Rectangular Prism

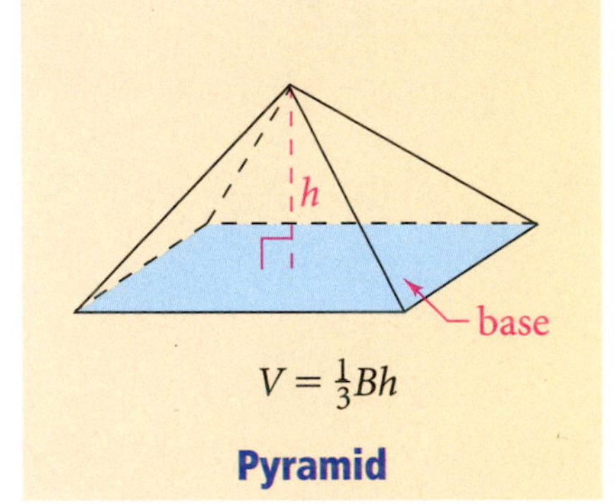

$V = \frac{1}{3}Bh$
Pyramid

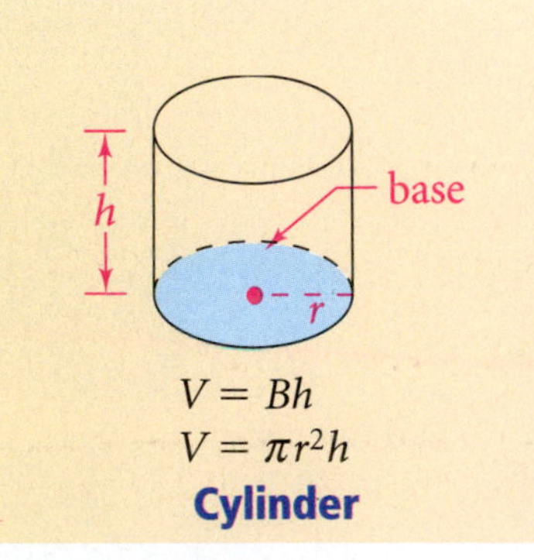

$V = Bh$
$V = \pi r^2 h$
Cylinder

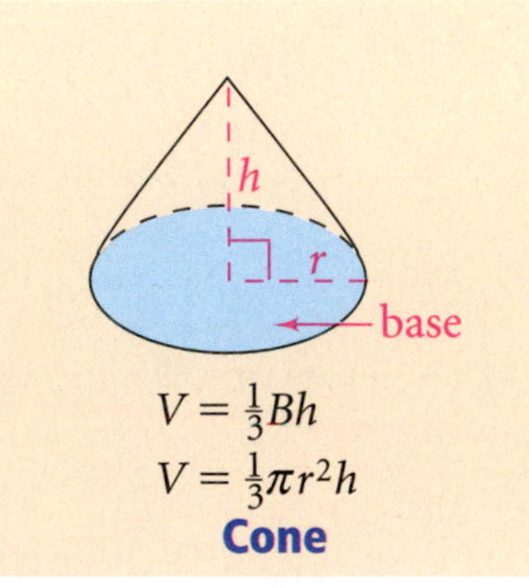

$V = \frac{1}{3}Bh$
$V = \frac{1}{3}\pi r^2 h$
Cone

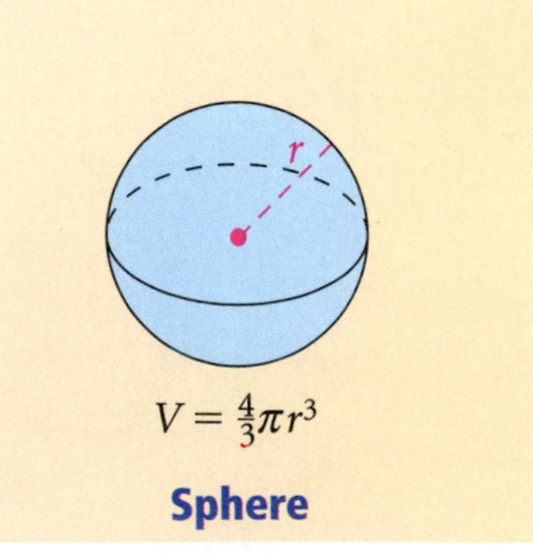

$V = \frac{4}{3}\pi r^3$
Sphere

English/Spanish Illustrated Glossary

A

EXAMPLES

Absolute value (p. 20) The distance that a number is from zero on a number line.

Valor absoluto (p. 20) La distancia a la que un número está del cero en una recta numérica.

-7 is 7 units from 0, so $|-7| = 7$.

Absolute value equation (p. 189) Equation whose graph forms a V that opens up or down.

Ecuación de valor absoluto (p. 189) La ecuación cuya gráfica forma una V que se abre hacia arriba o hacia abajo.

$y = |3 - x|$

Additive inverse (p. 24) The opposite of a number. Additive inverses sum to 0.

Inverso aditivo (p. 24) El opuesto de un número. La suma de inversos aditivos es igual a 0.

-5 and 5 are additive inverses because $-5 + 5 = 0$.

Algebraic expression (p. 4) A mathematical phrase that can include numbers, variables, and operation symbols.

Expresión algebraica (p. 4) Proposición matemática que incluye números, variables y símbolos de operaciones.

$7 + x$ is an algebraic expression.

Axis of symmetry (p. 427) The line that divides a parabola into two matching halves.

Eje de simetría (p. 427) La línea recta que divide una parábola en dos mitades exactamente iguales.

axis of symmetry

B

Base (p. 9) A number that is multiplied repeatedly.

Base (p. 9) El número que se multiplica repetidas veces.

$4^5 = 4 \cdot 4 \cdot 4 \cdot 4 \cdot 4$. The base 4 is used as a factor 5 times.

Binomial (p. 371) A polynomial of two terms.

Binomio (p. 371) Polinomio compuesto de dos términos.

$3x + 7$ is a binomial.

English/Spanish Glossary

C

EXAMPLES

Coefficient (p. 47) The numerical factor when a term has a variable.

Coeficiente (p. 47) Factor numérico de un término que contiene una variable.

In the expression $2x + 3y + 16$, 2 and 3 are coefficients.

Completing the square (p. 457) A method of solving quadratic equations. Completing the square turns every quadratic equation into the form $x^2 = c$.

Completar el cuadrado (p. 457) Método para solucionar ecuaciones cuadráticas. Cuando se completa el cuadrado se transforma la ecuación cuadrática a la fórmula $x^2 = c$.

$x^2 + 6x - 7 = 11$ is rewritten as $(x + 3)^2 = 25$ by completing the square.

Compound inequality (p. 151) Two inequalities that are joined by *and* or *or*.

Desigualdad compuesta (p. 151) Dos desigualdades que están enlazadas por medio de una *y* o una *o*.

$5 < x$ and $x < 10$

$14 < x$ or $x \geq -3$

Conclusion (p. 142) In a conditional, the part following *then*. *See* **conditional**.

Conclusión (p. 142) En un enunciado condicional, la parte que sigue a *entonces*. *Ver* **conditional**.

In the conditional "If an animal has four legs, then it is a horse," the conclusion is "it is a horse."

Conditional (p. 142) An "if-then" statement.

Condicional (p. 142) Un enunciado de la forma "si-entonces".

If an animal has four legs, then it is a horse.

Conjecture (p. 215) Conclusion reached by inductive reasoning.

Conjetura (p. 215) Conclusión a la que se llega mediante el razonamiento inductivo.

Conjugates (p. 501) The sum and the difference of the same two terms.

Valores conjugados (p. 501) La suma y resta de los mismos dos términos.

$(\sqrt{3} + 2)$ and $(\sqrt{3} - 2)$ are conjugates.

Consecutive integers (p. 101) Integers that differ by one.

Números enteros consecutivos (p. 101) Número enteros cuya diferencia es 1.

-5, -4, and -3 are three consecutive integers.

EXAMPLES

Constant (p. 47) A term that has no variable factor.

Constante (p. 47) Un término que tiene un valor fijo.

In the expression $4x + 13y + 17$, 17 is a constant term.

Constant of variation for direct variation (p. 202) The nonzero constant k in the function $y = kx$.

Constante de variación en variaciones directas (p. 202) La constante k cuyo valor no es cero en la función $y = kx$.

For the function $y = 24x$, 24 is the constant of variation.

Constant of variation for inverse variation (p. 209) The nonzero constant k in the function $y = \frac{k}{x}$.

Constante de variación en variaciones inversas (p. 209) La constante k cuyo valor no es cero en la función $y = \frac{k}{x}$.

For the equation $y = \frac{8}{x}$, 8 is the constant of variation.

Converse (p. 142) The statement obtained by reversing the *if* and *then* parts of an if-then statement.

Expresión recíproca (p. 142) La que se obtiene al invertir los componentes *si* y *entonces* de un enunciado condicional.

The converse of "If I was born in Houston, then I am a Texan," would be "If I am a Texan, then I was born in Houston."

Coordinate plane (p. 176) A plane formed by two number lines that intersect at right angles.

Plano de coordenadas (p. 176) Se forma cuando dos rectas numéricas se cortan formando ángulos rectos.

y-axis
2
x-axis
−4
O
4
−2

Coordinates (p. 176) The numbers that make an ordered pair and identify the location of a point.

Coordenadas (p. 176) Números ordenados por pares que determinan la posición de un punto sobre un plano.

y
2
1
R
T
−4 −3 −2 O 1 2 3 x
U
−2
S
−3
−4

Counterexample (p. 18) Any example that proves a statement false.

Contraejemplo (p. 18) Todo ejemplo que pruebe la falsedad de un enunciado.

Statement: All apples are red.

Counterexample: A Granny Smith apple is green.

Cross products (p. 94) In a proportion, $\frac{a}{b} = \frac{c}{d}$, the products ad and bc. These products are equal.

Productos cruzados (p. 94) En una proporción, $\frac{a}{b} = \frac{c}{d}$, los productos ad y bc. Estos productos son iguales.

$\frac{3}{4} = \frac{6}{8}$

The cross products are $3 \cdot 8$ and $4 \cdot 6$.
$3 \cdot 8 = 24$ and $4 \cdot 6 = 24$

English/Spanish Glossary

D

EXAMPLES

Deductive reasoning (p. 54) A process of reasoning logically from given facts to a conclusion.

Razonamiento deductivo (p. 54) Proceso de razonar lógicamente para llegar a una conclusión a partir de datos dados.

Degree of a monomial (p. 371) The sum of the exponents of the variables of a monomial.

$-4x^3y^2$ is a monomial of degree 5.

Grado de un monomio (p. 371) La suma de los exponentes de las variables de un monomio.

Degree of a polynomial (p. 371) The degree of the term with the greatest exponent for a polynomial in one variable.

The degree of $3x^2 + x - 9$ is 2.

Grado de un polinomio (p. 371) El grado del término con el mayor exponente en un polinomio de una variable.

Dependent variable (p. 188) A variable that provides the output values of a function.

In the equation $y = 3x$ the value of y depends upon the value of x.

Variable dependiente (p. 188) Una variable de la que depende los valores de salida de una función.

Difference of squares (p. 390) A difference of squares is an expression of the form $a^2 - b^2$. It can be factored as $(a + b)(a - b)$.

$25a^2 - 4 = (5a + 2)(5a - 2)$
$m^6 - 1 = (m^3 + 1)(m^3 - 1)$

Diferencia de cuadrados (p. 390) La diferencia de cuadrados es una expresión de la forma $a^2 - b^2$. Se puede factorizar como $(a + b)(a - b)$.

Direct variation (p. 202) A linear function that can be expressed in the form $y = kx$, where $k \neq 0$.

$y = 18x$ is a direct variation.

Variación directa (p. 202) Una función lineal que puede expresarse como $y = kx$, donde $k \neq 0$.

Discriminant (p. 470) The quantity $b^2 - 4ac$ is the discriminant of $ax^2 + bx + c = 0$.

The discriminant of $2x^2 + 9x - 2 = 0$ is 65.

Discriminante (p. 470) La cantidad $b^2 - 4ac$ es el discriminante de $ax^2 + bx + c = 0$.

EXAMPLES

Distance Formula (p. 498) The distance d between any two points (x_1, y_1) and (x_2, y_2) is

$d = \sqrt{(x_2 - x_1)^2 + (y_2 - y_1)^2}$.

Fórmula de distancia (p. 498) La distancia d entre dos puntos cualesquiera (x_1, y_1) y (x_2, y_2) es

$d = \sqrt{(x_2 - x_1)^2 + (y_2 - y_1)^2}$.

The distance between $(-2, 4)$ and $(4, 5)$ is

$$d = \sqrt{(4 - (-2))^2 + (5 - 4)^2}$$
$$= \sqrt{(6)^2 + (1)^2}$$
$$= \sqrt{37}$$

Distributive Property (p. 45) For every real number a, b, and c:

$a(b + c) = ab + ac \quad (b + c)a = ba + ca$

$a(b - c) = ab - ac \quad (b - c)a = ba - ca$

Propiedad Distributiva (p. 45) Para cada número real a, b y c:

$a(b + c) = ab + ac \quad (b + c)a = ba + ca$

$a(b - c) = ab - ac \quad (b - c)a = ba - ca$

$3(19 + 4) = 3(19) + 3(4)$

$(19 + 4)3 = 19(3) + 4(3)$

$7(11 - 2) = 7(11) - 7(2)$

$(11 - 2)7 = 11(7) - 2(7)$

Domain (p. 181) The domain of a relation is the set of all inputs, or x-coordinates, of the ordered pairs.

Dominio (p. 181) El dominio de una relación es el conjunto de todos los valores de entrada, o coordenadas x, de los pares ordenados.

In the relation $\{(0, 1), (0, 2), (0, 3), (0, 4), (1, 3), (1, 4), (2, 1)\}$, the domain is $\{0, 1, 2\}$. In the function $f(x) = x^2 - 10$, the domain is all real numbers.

E

Elements (of a set) (p. 75) Members of a set.

Elementos (p. 75) Partes integrantes de un conjunto.

Cats and dogs are elements of the set of mammals.

Elimination method (p. 287) A method for solving a system of linear equations. You add or subtract the equations to eliminate a variable.

Eliminación (p. 287) Método para resolver un sistema de ecuaciones lineales. Se suman o se restan las ecuaciones para eliminar una variable.

$3x + y = 19$

$\underline{2x - y = 1}$

$x + 0 = 18 \qquad x = 18$

$2(18) - y = 1 \rightarrow$ Substitute 18 for x

$36 - y = 1$ in the second equation.

$y = 35 \rightarrow$ Solve for y.

Equation (p. 5) A mathematical sentence that uses an equal sign.

Ecuación (p. 5) Enunciado matemático que tiene el signo de igual.

$x + 5 = 3x - 7$

Equivalent equations (p. 68) Equations that have the same solution.

Ecuaciones equivalentes (p. 68) Ecuaciones que tienen la misma solución.

$\frac{9}{3} = 3$ and $\frac{9}{3} + a = 3 + a$ are equivalent equations.

EXAMPLES

Equivalent inequalities (p. 130) Equivalent inequalities have the same set of solutions.

Desigualdades equivalentes (p. 130) Las desigualdades equivalentes tienen el mismo conjunto de soluciones.

$x + 4 < 7$ and $x < 3$ are equivalent inequalities.

Evaluate (p. 10) Substitute a given number for each variable, and then simplify.

Evaluar (p. 10) Método de sustituir cada variable por un número dado para luego simplificar la expresión.

To evaluate $3x + 4$ for $x = 2$, substitute 2 for x and simplify.

$3(2) + 4$

$6 + 4$

10

Exponent (p. 9) A number that shows repeated multiplication.

Exponente (p. 9) Denota el número de veces que debe multiplicarse.

$3^4 = 3 \cdot 3 \cdot 3 \cdot 3$

The exponent 4 indicates that 3 is used as a factor four times.

Extraneous solution (p. 509) An apparent solution of the equation that does not satisfy the original equation.

Solución extraña (p. 509) Solución aparente de una ecuación que no satisface la ecuación original.

$\frac{b}{b + 4} = 3 - \frac{4}{b + 4}$

Multiply by $(b+4)$.

$b = 3(b + 4) - 4$

$b = 3b + 12 - 4$

$-2b = 8$

$b = -4$

Replace b with -4 in the original equation. The denominator is 0, and so -4 is an extraneous solution.

Extremes of a proportion (p. 94) In the proportion, $\frac{a}{b} = \frac{c}{d}$, a and d are the extremes.

Valores extremos de una proporción (p. 94) En la proporción $\frac{a}{b} = \frac{c}{d}$, a y d son los valores extremos.

The product of the extremes of $\frac{x}{4} = \frac{x + 3}{2}$ is $2x$.

F

Factor by grouping (p. 410) A method of factoring that uses the distributive property to remove a common binomial factor of two pairs of terms.

Factor común por agrupación de términos (p. 410) Método de factorización que aplica la propiedad distributiva para sacar un factor común de dos pares de términos en un binomio.

The expression $7x(x - 1) + 4(x - 1)$ can be factored as $(7x + 4)(x - 1)$.

	EXAMPLES
Function (p. 181) A relation that assigns exactly one value in the range to each value of the domain. **Función (p. 181)** La relación que asigna exactamente un valor del rango a cada valor del dominio.	Earned income is a function of the number of hours worked. If you earn \$4.50/h, then your income is expressed by the function $f(h) = 4.5h$.
Function notation (p. 187) To write a rule in function notation, you use the symbol $f(x)$ in place of y. **Notación de una función (p. 187)** Para expresar una regla en notación de función se usa el símbolo $f(x)$ en lugar de y.	$f(x) = 3x - 8$ is in function notation.
Function rule (p. 187) An equation that describes a function. **Regla de una función (p. 187)** Ecuación que describe una función.	$y = 4x + 1$ is a function rule.

H

Hypotenuse (p. 493) The side opposite the right angle in a right triangle. It is the longest side in the triangle. **Hipotenusa (p. 493)** En un triángulo rectángulo, el lado opuesto al ángulo recto. Es el lado más largo del triángulo.	A, B, C, a, b, c c is the hypotenuse.
Hypothesis (p. 142) The part following *if* in a conditional. *See* **conditional**. **Hipótesis (p. 142)** En un enunciado condicional, la parte que sigue a *si*. *Ver* **conditional**.	In the conditional "If an animal has four legs, then it is a horse," the hypothesis is "an animal has four legs."

I

Identity (p. 86) An equation that is true for every value. **Identidad (p. 86)** Una ecuación que es verdadera para todos los valores.	$5 - 14x = 5\left(1 - \frac{14}{5}x\right)$ is an identity because it is true for any value of x.
Independent variable (p. 188) A variable that provides the input values of a function. **Variable independiente (p. 188)** Una variable de la que dependen los valores de entrada de una función.	In the equation $y = 3x$, x is the independent variable.

	EXAMPLES
Inductive reasoning (p. 215) Making conclusions based on observed patterns. **Razonamiento inductivo (p. 215)** Sacar conclusiones a partir de patrones observados.	
Inequality (p. 19) A mathematical sentence that compares the values of two expressions using an inequality symbol. **Desigualdad (p. 19)** Expresión matemática que compara el valor de dos expresiones con el símbolo de desigualdad.	$3 < 7$
Infinitely many solutions (p. 278) The number of solutions of a system of equations in which the graphs of the equations are the same line. **Infinitamente muchas soluciones (p. 278)** El número de soluciones de un sistema de ecuaciones cuyas gráficas son la misma recta.	The system $2x + 4y = 8$ and $y = -\frac{1}{2}x + 2$ has infinitely many solutions.
Integers (p. 17) Whole numbers and their opposites. **Números enteros (p. 17)** Números que constan exclusivamente de una o más unidades, y sus opuestos.	$\ldots -3, -2, -1, 0, 1, 2, 3, \ldots$
Intersection (p. 75) The set of elements that are common to two or more sets. **Intersección (p. 75)** El conjunto de elementos que son comunes a dos o más conjuntos.	If $C = \{1, 2, 3, 4\}$ and $D = \{2, 4, 6, 8\}$ then the intersection of C and D, or $C \cap D$, equals $\{2, 4\}$.
Inverse operations (p. 68) Operations that undo one another. **Operaciones inversas (p. 68)** Las operaciones que se cancelan una a la otra.	Addition and subtraction are inverse operations. Multiplication and division are inverse operations.
Inverse variation (p. 209) A function that can be written in the form $xy = k$ or $y = \frac{k}{x}$. The product of the quantities remains constant, so as one quantity increases, the other decreases. **Variación inversa (p. 209)** Función que puede expresarse como $xy = k$ ó $y = \frac{k}{x}$. El producto de las cantidades permanece constante, de modo que al aumentar una cantidad, disminuye la otra.	The length x and the width y of a rectangle with a fixed area vary inversely. If the area is 40, $xy = 40$.
Irrational number (p. 18) A number that cannot be written as a ratio of two integers. Irrational numbers in decimal form are nonterminating and nonrepeating. **Número irracional (p. 18)** Número que no puede expresarse como razón de dos números enteros. Los números irracionales en forma decimal no tienen término y no se repiten.	$\sqrt{11}$ and π are irrational numbers.

L

EXAMPLES

Leg (p. 493) Each of the sides that form the right angle of a right triangle.

Cateto (p. 493) Cada uno de los dos lados que forman el ángulo recto en un triángulo rectángulo.

a and *b* are legs.

Like radicals (p. 500) Radical expressions with the same radicands.

Radicales semejantes (p. 500) Expresiones radicales con los mismos radicandos.

$3\sqrt{7}$ and $-5\sqrt{7}$ are like radicals.

Like terms (p. 47) Terms with exactly the same variable factors in a variable expression.

Términos semejantes (p. 47) Términos con los mismos factores variables en una expresión variable.

$4y$ and $16y$ are like terms.

Linear equation (p. 239) An equation whose graph forms a straight line.

Ecuación lineal (p. 239) Ecuación cuya gráfica es una línea recta.

$y = 2x + 1$

Linear function (p. 239) A function whose graph is a line is a linear function. You can represent a linear function with a linear equation.

Función lineal (p. 239) Una función cuya gráfica es una recta es una función lineal. La función lineal se representa con una ecuación lineal.

$y = 2x + 1$

Linear inequality (p. 303) A mathematical sentence that describes a region of the coordinate plane having a boundary line. Each point in the region is a solution of the inequality.

Desigualdad lineal (p. 303) Expresión matemática que describe una región del plano de coordenadas que tiene una recta límite. Cada punto de la región es una solución de la desigualdad.

$y > x + 1$

Linear parent function (p. 239) The simplest form of a linear function.

Función lineal elemental (p. 239) La forma más simple de una función lineal.

$y = x$ or $f(x) = x$

EXAMPLES

Literal equation (p. 90) An equation involving two or more variables.

Ecuación literal (p. 90) Ecuación que incluye dos o más variables.

$4x + 2y = 18$ is a literal equation.

M

Maximum (p. 427) The y-coordinate of the vertex of a parabola that opens downward.

Valor máximo (p. 427) La coordenada y del vértice en una parábola que se abre hacia abajo.

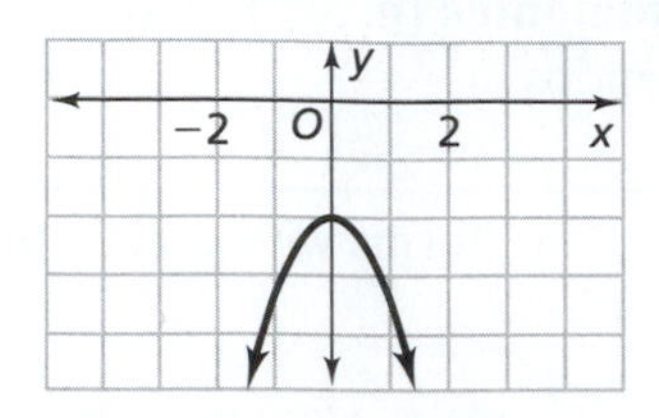

Since the parabola opens downward, the y-coordinate of the vertex is the function's maximum value.

Means of a proportion (p. 94) In the proportion, $\frac{a}{b} = \frac{c}{d}$, b and c are the means.

Valores medios de una proporción (p. 94) En la proporción, $\frac{a}{b} = \frac{c}{d}$, b y c son los valores medios.

The product of the means of $\frac{x}{4} = \frac{x+3}{2}$ is $4(x + 3)$ or $4x + 12$.

Minimum (p. 427) The y-coordinate of the vertex of a parabola that opens upward.

Valor mínimo (p. 427) La coordenada y del vértice en una parábola que se abre hacia arriba.

Since the parabola opens upward, the y-coordinate of the vertex is the function's minimum value.

Monomial (p. 370) An expression that is a number, a variable, or a product of a number and one or more variables.

Monomio (p. 370) Expresión algebraica que puede ser un número, una variable o el producto de un número y una o más variables.

9, n, and $-5xy^2$ are examples of monomials.

Multiplicative inverse (p. 41) Given a nonzero rational number $\frac{a}{b}$, the multiplicative inverse, or reciprocal, is $\frac{b}{a}$. The product of a nonzero number and its multiplicative inverse is 1.

Inverso multiplicativo (p. 41) Dado un número racional $\frac{a}{b}$ distinto de cero, el inverso multiplicativo, o recíproco, es $\frac{b}{a}$. El producto de un número distinto de cero y su inverso multiplicativo es 1.

$\frac{3}{4}$ is a multiplicative inverse of $\frac{4}{3}$ because $\frac{3}{4} \times \frac{4}{3} = 1$.

N

EXAMPLES

Natural numbers (p. 17) The counting numbers.

1, 2, 3, . . .

Números naturales (p. 17) Los números que se emplean para contar.

Negative reciprocal (p. 260) A number of the form $-\frac{b}{a}$, where $\frac{a}{b}$ is a nonzero rational number. The product of a number and its negative reciprocal is -1.

$\frac{2}{5}$ and $-\frac{5}{2}$ are negative reciprocals because $\left(\frac{2}{5}\right)\left(-\frac{5}{2}\right) = -1$.

Recíproco negativo (p. 260) El recíproco negativo de un número racional $\frac{a}{b}$ cuyo valor no es cero es $-\frac{b}{a}$. El producto de un número y su recíproco negativo es -1.

Negative square root (p. 440) A number of the form $-\sqrt{b}$, which is the negative square root of b.

-7 is the negative square root of $\sqrt{49}$.

Raíz cuadrada negativa (p. 440) $-\sqrt{b}$ es la raíz cuadrada negativa de b.

No solution (p. 278) When the graphs of the equations in a system are parallel with no point of intersection.

There is no solution to the system of equations $x + y = 5$ and $x + y = -3$.

Sin solución (p. 278) Cuando las gráficas de las ecuaciones de un sistema son paralelas y no existe entre ellas ningún punto de intersección.

Null set (p. 75) A set that has no elements.

{ } or ∅

Conjunto vacío (p. 75) Conjunto que no tiene elementos.

O

Open sentence (p. 5) An equation that contains one or more variables.

$5 + x = 12$ is an open sentence.

Ecuación abierta (p. 5) Ecuación que contiene una o más variables.

Opposites (p. 20) Opposites are two numbers that are the same distance from 0 on a number line, but in opposite directions.

17 and -17 are opposites.

Opuestos (p. 20) Opuestos son dos números que están a la misma distancia del cero en una recta numérica, pero en direcciones opuestas.

EXAMPLES

Order of operations (p. 10)
1. Perform any operation(s) inside grouping symbols.
2. Simplify powers.
3. Multiply and divide in order from left to right.
4. Add and subtract in order from left to right.

$6 - (4^2 - [2 \cdot 5]) \div 3$
$= 6 - (16 - 10) \div 3$
$= 6 - 6 \div 3$
$= 6 - 2$
$= 4$

Orden de las operaciones (p. 10)
1. Se hacen las operaciones que están dentro de símbolos de agrupación.
2. Se simplifican todos los términos que tengan exponentes.
3. Se hacen las multiplicaciones y divisiones en orden de izquierda a derecha.
4. Se hacen las sumas y restas en orden de izquierda a derecha.

Ordered pair (p. 176) Two numbers that identify the location of a point.

Par ordenado (p. 176) Un par ordenado de números que denota la ubicación de un punto.

The ordered pair $(4, -1)$ identifies the point 4 units to the right on the x-axis and 1 unit down on the y-axis.

Origin (p. 176) The point at which the axes of the coordinate plane intersect.

Origen (p. 176) Punto de intersección de los ejes del plano de coordenadas.

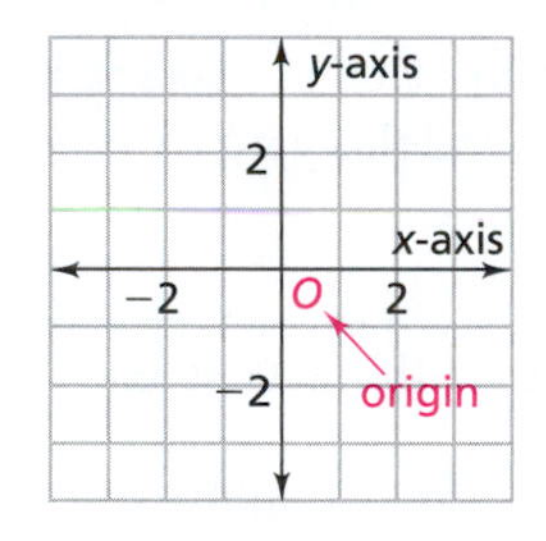

P

Parabola (p. 426) The graph of a quadratic function.

Parábola (p. 426) La gráfica de una función cuadrática.

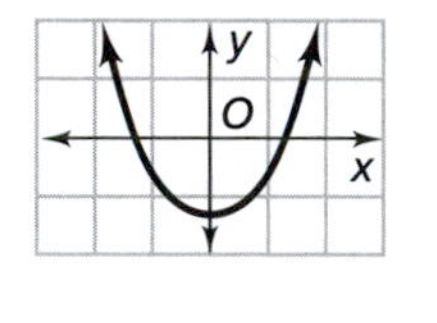

Parallel lines (p. 259) Two lines in the same plane that never intersect. Parallel lines have the same slope.

Rectas paralelas (p. 259) Dos rectas situadas en el mismo plano que nunca se cortan. Las rectas paralelas tienen la misma pendiente.

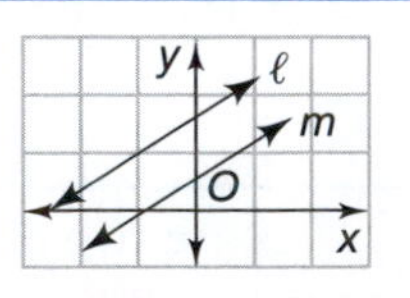

Lines ℓ and m are parallel.

Parent function (p. 239) A family of functions is a group of functions with common characteristics. A parent function is the simplest function with these characteristics.

Función elemental (p. 239) Una familia de functiones es un grupo de funciones con características en común. La función elemental es la función más simple que reúne esas características.

$y = x^2$ is the parent function for the family of quadractic equations of the form $y = ax^2 + bx + c$.

EXAMPLES

Perfect square trinomial (p. 404) Any trinomial of the form $a^2 + 2ab + b^2$ or $a^2 - 2ab + b^2$.

Trinomio cuadrado perfecto (p. 404) Todo trinomio de la forma $a^2 + 2ab + b^2$ ó $a^2 - 2ab + b^2$.

$(x + 3)^2 = x^2 + 6x + 9$

Perfect squares (p. 441) Numbers whose square roots are integers.

Cuadrado perfecto (p. 441) Número cuya raíz cuadrada es un número entero.

The numbers 1, 4, 9, 16, 25, 36, . . . are perfect squares because they are the squares of integers.

Perpendicular lines (p. 260) Lines that intersect to form right angles. Two lines are perpendicular if the product of their slopes is -1.

Rectas perpendiculares (p. 260) Rectas que forman ángulos rectos en su intersección. Dos rectas son perpendiculares si el producto de sus pendientes es -1.

Lines ℓ and m are perpendicular.

Point-slope form (p. 252) A linear equation of a nonvertical line written as $y - y_1 = m(x - x_1)$. The line passes through the point (x_1, y_1) with slope m.

Forma punto-pendiente (p. 252) La ecuación lineal de una recta no vertical que pasa por el punto (x_1, y_1) con pendiente m está dada por $y - y_1 = m(x - x_1)$.

An equation with a slope of $-\frac{1}{2}$ passing through $(2, -1)$ would be written $y + 1 = -\frac{1}{2}(x - 2)$ in point-slope form.

Polynomial (p. 371) A sum of one or more monomials. A quotient with a variable in the denominator is not a polynomial.

Polinomio (p. 371) Una suma de un o más monomios. Un cociente con una variable en el denominador no es un polinomio.

$2x^2$, $3x + 7$, 28, and $-7x^3 - 2x^2 + 9$ are all polynomials.

Power (p. 9) The base and the exponent of an expression of the form a^n.

Potencia (p. 9) La base y el exponente de una expresión de la forma a^n.

5^4

Principal square root (p. 440) A number of the form $\sqrt{b}$. The expression $\sqrt{b}$ is called the principal (or positive) square root of b.

Raíz cuadrada principal (p. 440) La expresión $\sqrt{b}$ se llama raíz cuadrada principal (o positiva) de b.

5 is the principal square root of $\sqrt{25}$.

EXAMPLES

Properties of equality (p. 68) For all real numbers a, b, and c:

Addition: If $a = b$, then $a + c = b + c$.

Subtraction: If $a = b$, then $a - c = b - c$.

Multiplication: If $a = b$, then $a \cdot c = b \cdot c$.

Division: If $a = b$, and $c \neq 0$, then $\frac{a}{c} = \frac{b}{c}$.

Propiedades de la igualdad (p. 68) Para todos los números reales a, b y c:

Suma: Si $a = b$, entonces $a + c = b + c$.

Resta: Si $a = b$, entonces $a - c = b - c$.

Multiplicación: Si $a = b$, entonces $a \cdot c = b \cdot c$.

División: Si $a = b$, y $c \neq 0$, entonces $\frac{a}{c} = \frac{b}{c}$.

Since $\frac{2}{4} = \frac{1}{2}$, $\frac{2}{4} + 5 = \frac{1}{2} + 5$.

Since $\frac{9}{3} = 3$, $\frac{9}{3} - 6 = 3 - 6$.

Proportion (p. 94) An equation that states that two ratios are equal.

$\frac{a}{b} = \frac{c}{d}$ where $b \neq 0$ and $d \neq 0$

Proporción (p. 94) Una ecuación que establece que dos razones son iguales.

$\frac{a}{b} = \frac{c}{d}$ por $b \neq 0$ y $d \neq 0$

$\frac{7.5}{9} = \frac{5}{6}$

Pythagorean Theorem (p. 493) In any right triangle, the sum of the squares of the lengths of the legs is equal to the square of the length of the hypotenuse: $a^2 + b^2 = c^2$.

Teorema de Pitágoras (p. 493) En un triángulo rectángulo, la suma de los cuadrados de los catetos es igual al cuadrado de la hipotenusa: $a^2 + b^2 = c^2$.

$3^2 + 4^2 = 5^2$

Q

Quadrants (p. 176) The four parts into which the coordinate plane is divided by its axes.

Cuadrantes (p. 176) El plano de coordenadas está dividido por sus ejes en cuatro regiones llamadas cuadrantes.

Quadratic equation (p. 446) An equation you can write in the standard form $ax^2 + bx + c = 0$, where a, b, and c are real numbers and $a \neq 0$.

Ecuación cuadrática (p. 446) Una ecuación que puede expresarse de la forma normal como $ax^2 + bx + c = 0$, donde a, b, y c son números reales y $a \neq 0$.

$4x^2 + 9x - 5 = 0$

EXAMPLES

Quadratic formula (p. 463) If $ax^2 + bx + c = 0$, a, b, and c are real numbers, and $a \neq 0$, then $x = \frac{-b \pm \sqrt{b^2 - 4ac}}{2a}$.

Fórmula cuadrática (p. 463) Si $ax^2 + bx + c = 0$, a, b, y c son números reales, y $a \neq 0$, entonces $x = \frac{-b \pm \sqrt{b^2 - 4ac}}{2a}$.

$2x^2 + 10x + 12 = 0$

$x = \frac{-b \pm \sqrt{b^2 - 4ac}}{2a}$

$x = \frac{-10 \pm \sqrt{10^2 - 4(2)(12)}}{2(2)}$

$x = \frac{-10 \pm \sqrt{4}}{4}$

$x = \frac{-10 + 2}{4}$ or $\frac{-10 - 2}{4}$

$x = -2$ or -3

Quadratic function (p. 426) A function of the form $y = ax^2 + bx + c$, where a, b, and c are real numbers and $a \neq 0$. The graph of a quadratic function is a parabola, a U-shaped curve that opens up or down.

Función cuadrática (p. 426) La función $y = ax^2 + bx + c$, donde a, b, y c son números reales y $a \neq 0$. La gráfica de una función cuadrática es una parábola, o curva en forma de U que se abre hacia arriba o hacia abajo.

$y = 5x^2 - 2x + 1$ is a quadratic function.

Quadratic parent function (p. 426) The simplest quadratic function.

Función cuadrática madre (p. 426) La función cuadrática más sencilla.

$y = x^2$ or $f(x) = x^2$

R

Radical equation (p. 507) An equation that has a variable in a radicand.

Ecuación radical (p. 507) Ecuación que tiene una variable en un radicando.

$\sqrt{x} - 2 = 12$

$\sqrt{x} = 14$

Radical expression (p. 486) Expression that contains a radical.

Expresión radical (p. 486) Una expresión que contiene un radical.

$\sqrt{3}$, $\sqrt{5x}$, and $\sqrt{x - 10}$ are examples of radical expressions.

Radicand (p. 440) The expression under the radical sign.

Radicando (p. 440) La expresión que aparece debajo del signo radical.

The radicand of the radical expression $\sqrt{x + 2}$ is $x + 2$.

Range (p. 181) The range of a relation is the set of all outputs or y-coordinates of the ordered pairs.

Rango (p. 181) El rango de una relación es el conjunto de todas las salidas posibles, o coordenadas y, de los pares ordenados.

In the relation $\{(0, 1), (0, 2), (0, 3), (0, 4), (1, 3), (1, 4), (2, 1)\}$, the range is $\{1, 2, 3, 4\}$. In the function $f(x) = |x - 3|$, the range is the set of real numbers greater than or equal to 0.

EXAMPLES

Rate (p. 92) A ratio of a to b where a and b represent quantities measured in different units.

Razón (p. 92) La relación que existe entre a y b cuando a y b son cantidades medidas con distintas unidades.

Traveling 125 miles in 2 hours results in the rate $\frac{125 \text{ miles}}{2 \text{ hours}}$ or 62.5 mi/h.

Rate of change (p. 230) The relationship between two quantities that are changing. The rate of change is also called slope.

$$\text{rate of change} = \frac{\text{change in the dependent variable}}{\text{change in the independent variable}}$$

Tasa de cambio (p. 230) La relación entre dos cantidades que cambian. La tasa de cambio se llama también pendiente.

$$\text{tasa de cambio} = \frac{\text{cambio en la variable dependiente}}{\text{cambio en la variable independiente}}$$

Video rental for 1 day is \$1.99. Video rental for 2 days is \$2.99.

$$\text{rate of change} = \frac{2.99 - 1.99}{2 - 1} = \frac{1.00}{1} = 1$$

Ratio (p. 92) A comparison of two numbers by division.

Razón (p. 92) Una comparación de dos números por división.

$\frac{5}{7}$ and 7 : 3 are ratios.

Rational equation (p. 550) An equation containing rational expressions.

Ecuación racional (p. 550) Una ecuación que contiene expresiones racionales.

$\frac{1}{x} = \frac{3}{2x - 1}$ is a rational equation.

Rational expression (p. 530) A ratio of two polynomials. The value of the variable cannot make the denominator equal to 0.

Expresión racional (p. 530) Una razón de dos polinomios. El valor de la variable no puede hacer el denominador igual a 0.

$\frac{3}{x^3 + x}$ when $x \neq 0$

Rational number (p. 17) A real number that can be written as a quotient of two integers where the denominator is not 0. Rational numbers in decimal form are terminating or repeating.

Número racional (p. 17) Un número racional puede ser escrito como cociente de dos números enteros, donde el denominador es diferente de cero. Los números racionales en forma decimal son exactos o periódicos.

$\frac{2}{3}$, 1.548, and 2.292929 . . . are all rational numbers.

Rationalize (p. 489) Rewrite as a rational number. Rationalizing the denominator of a radical expression may be necessary to obtain the simplest radical form.

Racionalizar (p. 489) Escribir una expresión matemática en forma de número racional. A veces es necesario racionalizar el denominador de una expresión radical a fin de obtener la forma radical más simple.

$$\frac{2}{\sqrt{5}} = \frac{2}{\sqrt{5}} \cdot \frac{\sqrt{5}}{\sqrt{5}} = \frac{2\sqrt{5}}{\sqrt{25}} = \frac{2\sqrt{5}}{5}$$

EXAMPLES

Real number (p. 18) A number that is either rational or irrational.

Número real (p. 18) Un número que no es racional ni irracional.

$5, -3, \sqrt{11}, 0.666\ldots, 5\frac{4}{11}, 0$, and π are all real numbers.

Reciprocal (p. 41) Given a nonzero rational number $\frac{a}{b}$, the reciprocal, or multiplicative inverse, is $\frac{b}{a}$. The product of a nonzero number and its reciprocal is 1.

Recíproco (p. 41) El recíproco, o inverso multiplicativo, de un número racional $\frac{a}{b}$ cuyo valor no es cero es $\frac{b}{a}$. El producto de un número que no es cero y su valor recíproco es 1.

$\frac{2}{5}$ and $\frac{5}{2}$ are reciprocals because $\frac{2}{5} \times \frac{5}{2} = 1$.

Relation (p. 181) Any set of ordered pairs.

Relación (p. 181) Cualquier conjunto de pares ordenados.

$\{(0, 0), (2, 3), (2, -7)\}$ is a relation.

Roots of the equation (p. 446) The solutions of an equation.

Raíces de la ecuación (p. 446) Las soluciones de una ecuación.

S

Scientific notation (p. 334) A number expressed in the form $a \times 10^n$, where n is an integer and $1 < a < 10$.

Notación científica (p. 334) Un número expresado en forma de $a \times 10^n$, donde n es un número entero y $1 < a < 10$.

3.4×10^6

Set (p. 75) A well-defined collection of elements.

Conjunto (p. 75) Un grupo bien definido de elementos.

The set of integers:
$Z = \{\ldots, -3, -2, -1, 0, 1, 2, 3, \ldots\}$

Simplify (p. 9) Replace an expression with its simplest name or form.

Simplificar (p. 9) Reemplazar una expresión por su versión o forma más simple.

$\underbrace{3 + 5}_{8}$

Slope (p. 232) The ratio of the vertical change to the horizontal change.

$$\text{slope} = \frac{\text{vertical change}}{\text{horizontal change}} = \frac{y_2 - y_1}{x_2 - x_1}, \text{ where } x_2 - x_1 \neq 0$$

Pendiente (p. 232) La razón del cambio vertical al cambio horizontal.

$$\text{pendiente} = \frac{\text{cambio vertical}}{\text{cambio horizontal}} = \frac{y_2 - y_1}{x_2 - x_1}, \text{ donde } x_2 - x_1 \neq 0$$

The slope of the line below is $\frac{2}{4} = \frac{1}{2}$.

y
2
(4, 2)
O
4
x

English/Spanish Glossary

EXAMPLES

Slope-intercept form (p. 240) A linear equation of a nonvertical line written as $y = mx + b$, where m is the slope and b is the y-intercept.

Forma pendiente-intercepto (p. 240) La ecuación lineal de una recta no vertical expresada como $y = mx + b$, donde m es la pendiente y b es el intercepto en y.

$y = 8x + 2$

Solution of a system of linear equations (p. 276) Any ordered pair in a system that makes all the equations of that system true.

Solución de un sistema de ecuaciones lineales (p. 276) Todo par ordenado de un sistema que hace verdaderas todas las ecuaciones de ese sistema.

(2, 1) is a solution of the system
$y = 2x - 3$
$y = x - 1$
because the ordered pair makes each equation true.

Solution of a system of linear inequalities (p. 309) Any ordered pair that makes all of the inequalities in the system true.

Solución de un sistema de desigualdades lineales (p. 309) Todo par ordenado que hace verdaderas todas las desigualdades del sistema.

Any point in the shaded purple area is a solution of the system
$y > 2x - 5$
$3x + 4y < 12$.

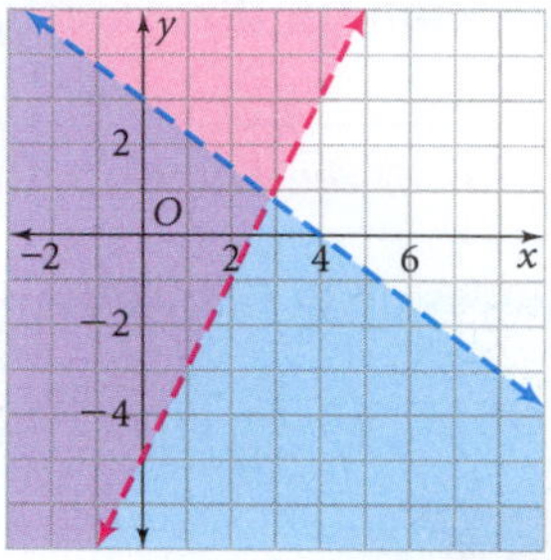

Solution of an equation (p. 68) Any value or values that make an equation true.

Solución de una ecuación (p. 68) Cualquier valor o valores que hagan verdadera una ecuación.

In the equation $y + 22 = 11$, -11 is the solution.

Solution of an inequality (one variable) (p. 124) Any value or values of a variable in the inequality that makes an inequality true.

Solución de una desigualdad (una variable) (p. 124) Cualquier valor o valores de una variable de la desigualdad que hagan verdadera la desigualdad.

The solution of the inequality $x < 9$ is all numbers less than 9.

Solution of an inequality (two variables) (p. 303) Any ordered pair that makes the inequality true.

Solución de una desigualdad (dos variables) (p. 303) Cualquier par ordenado que haga verdadera la desigualdad.

Each ordered pair in the pink area and on the solid pink line is a solution of $3x - 5y \leq 10$.

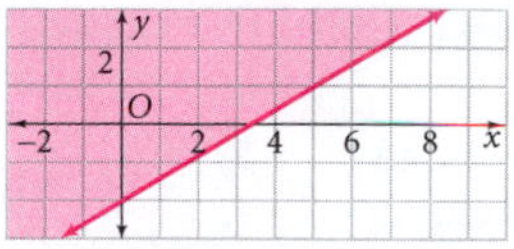

EXAMPLES

Solution set (p. 309) The set of all solutions.

Conjunto de soluciones (p. 309) Conjunto de todas las soluciones.

The shaded purple area shows the solution set of the system $y > 2x - 5$, $3x + 4y < 12$.

Square root (p. 440) A number b such that $a^2 = b$. $\sqrt{b}$ is the principal square root. $-\sqrt{b}$ is the negative square root.

Raíz cuadrada (p. 440) Si $a^2 = b$, entonces a es la raíz cuadrada de b. $\sqrt{b}$ es la raíz cuadrada principal. $-\sqrt{b}$ es la raíz cuadrada negativa.

-3 and 3 are square roots of 9.

Square root function (p. 514) A function that contains the independent variable in the radicand.

Función de raíz cuadrada (p. 514) Una función que contiene la variable independiente en el radicando.

$y = \sqrt{2x}$ is a square root function.

Standard form of a linear equation (p. 246) The form of a linear equation $Ax + By = C$, where A, B, and C are real numbers and A and B are not both zero.

Forma normal de una ecuación lineal (p. 246) La forma normal de una ecuación lineal es $Ax + By = C$, donde A, B y C son números reales, y donde A y B no son iguales a cero.

$6x - y = 12$

Standard form of a polynomial (p. 371) The form of a polynomial in which the degree of the terms decreases from left to right (also *descending order*).

Forma normal de un polinomio (p. 371) Cuando el grado de los términos de un polinomio disminuye de izquierda a derecha, está en forma normal, o en orden descendente.

$15x^3 + x^2 + 3x - 9$

Standard form of a quadratic equation (p. 446) The form of a quadratic equation written $ax^2 + bx + c = 0$, where a, b, and c are real numbers and $a \neq 0$.

Forma normal de una ecuación cuadrática (p. 446) Cuando una ecuación cuadrática se expresa de forma $ax^2 + bx + c = 0$, donde a, b, y c son números reales y $a \neq 0$.

$-x^2 + 2x + 9 = 0$

EXAMPLES

Standard form of a quadratic function (p. 426) The form of a quadratic function written $y = ax^2 + bx + c$, where a, b, and c are real numbers and $a \neq 0$.

$y = 2x^2 - 5x + 2$

Forma normal de una función cuadrática (p. 426) Cuando una ecuación cuadrática se expresa como $y = ax^2 + bx + c$, donde a, b, y c son números reales y $a \neq 0$.

Subset (p. 75) Set A is a subset of set B if every element of set A is an element of set B.

set $A = \{1, 3, 5\}$ is a subset of set $B = \{x: x \text{ is a positive odd integer}\}$.

Subconjunto (p. 75) El conjunto A es un subconjunto del conjunto B si todo elemento del conjunto A es tambien elemento del conjunto B.

Substitution method (p. 282) A method of solving a system of equations by replacing one variable with an equivalent expression containing the other variable.

$y = 2x + 5$
$x + 3y = 7$
$x + 3(2x + 5) = 7$

Método de sustitución (p. 282) Método para resolver un sistema de ecuaciones en el que se reemplaza una variable por una expresión equivalente que contenga la otra variable.

System of linear equations (p. 276) Two or more linear equations using the same variables.

$y = 5x + 7, y = \frac{1}{2}x - 3$

Sistema de ecuaciones lineales (p. 276) Dos o más ecuaciones lineales que usen las mismas variables.

System of linear inequalities (p. 309) Two or more linear inequalities using the same variables.

$y \leq x + 11, y < 5x$

Sistema de desigualdades lineales (p. 309) Dos o más desigualdades lineales que usen las mismas variables.

T

Term (p. 47) A number, variable, or the product or quotient of a number and one or more variables.

The expression $5x + \frac{y}{2} - 8$ has three terms: $5x$, $\frac{y}{2}$, and -8.

Término (p. 47) Un número, una variable o el producto o cociente de un número y una o más variables.

Trinomial (p. 371) A polynomial of three terms.

$3x^2 + 2x - 5$

Trinomio (p. 371) Polinomio compuesto de tres términos.

U

EXAMPLES

Uniform motion (p. 101) The motion of an object moving at a constant rate.

Movimiento uniforme (p. 101) El movimiento de un objeto que se mueve a una velocidad constante.

Union (p. 75) The set that contains all of the elements of two or more sets.

Unión (p. 75) El conjunto que contiene todos los elementos de dos o más conjuntos.

If $A = \{1, 3, 6, 9\}$ and $B = \{1, 5, 10\}$, then the union of A and B, or $A \cup B$, equals $\{1, 3, 5, 6, 9, 10\}$

Unit analysis (p. 93) The process of selecting conversion factors to produce the appropriate units.

Análisis de unidades (p. 93) Proceso de seleccionar factores de conversión para producir las unidades apropiadas.

To change ten feet to yards, multiply by the conversion factor $\frac{1 \text{ yd}}{3 \text{ ft}}$.

$10 \text{ ft}\left(\frac{1 \text{ yd}}{3 \text{ ft}}\right) = 3\frac{1}{3} \text{ yd}$

Unit rate (p. 92) A rate with a denominator of 1.

Razón en unidades (p. 92) Razón cuyo denominador es 1.

The unit rate for 120 miles driven in 2 hours is 60 mi/h.

Unlike radicals (p. 500) Radical expressions that do not have the same radicands.

Radicales no semejantes (p. 500) Expresiones radicales que no tienen radicandos semejantes.

$\sqrt{2}$ and $\sqrt{3}$ are unlike radicals.

V

Variable (p. 4) A symbol, usually a letter, that represents one or more numbers.

Variable (p. 4) Símbolo, generalmente una letra, que representa uno o más valores.

x is a variable in the equation $9 - x = 3$.

Vertex (p. 427) The highest or lowest point on a parabola. The axis of symmetry intersects the parabola at the vertex.

Vértice (p. 427) El punto más alto o más bajo de una parábola. El punto de intersección del eje de simetría y la parábola.

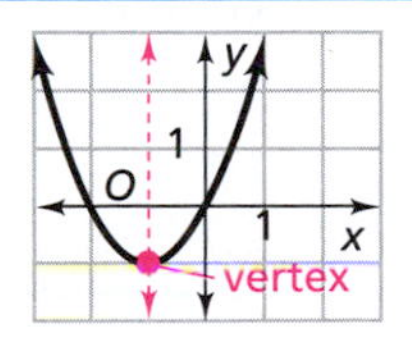

EXAMPLES

Vertical-line test (p. 183) A method used to determine if a relation is a function or not. If a vertical line passes through a graph more than once, the graph is not the graph of a function.

Prueba de la recta vertical (p. 183) Método que permite determinar si una relación es o no es una función. Si una recta vertical corta la gráfica más de una vez, la gráfica no es de función.

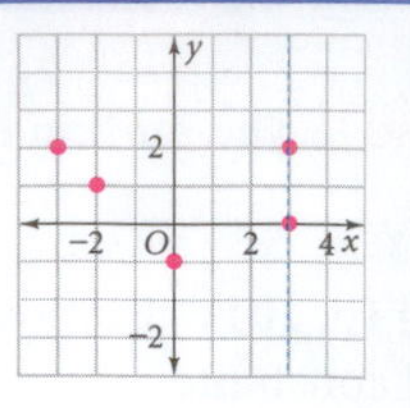

A line would pass through (3, 0) and (3, 2), so the relation is not a function.

W

Whole numbers (p. 17) The nonnegative integers.

Números enteros positivos (p. 17) Todos los números enteros que no son negativos.

0, 1, 2, 3, . . .

X

x-axis (p. 176) The horizontal axis of the coordinate plane.

Eje x (p. 176) El eje horizontal del plano de coordenadas.

x-coordinate (p. 176) The location on the x-axis of a point in the coordinate plane.

Coordenada x (p. 176) La ubicación de un punto sobre el eje x en el plano de coordenadas.

In the ordered pair $(4, -1)$, 4 is the x-coordinate.

x-intercept (p. 246) The x-coordinate of the point where a line crosses the x-axis.

Intercepto en x (p. 246) La coordenada x del punto donde una recta corta el eje x.

The x-intercept of $3x + 4y = 12$ is 4.

Y

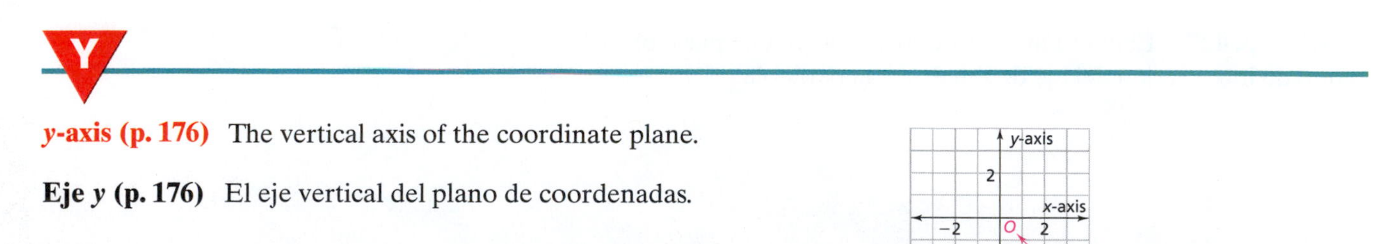

y-axis (p. 176) The vertical axis of the coordinate plane.

Eje y (p. 176) El eje vertical del plano de coordenadas.

EXAMPLES

***y*-coordinate (p. 176)** The location on the *y*-axis of a point in the coordinate plane.

Coordenada *y* (p. 176) La ubicación de un punto sobre el eje *y* en el plano de coordenadas.

In the ordered pair $(4, -1)$, -1 is the *y*-coordinate.

***y*-intercept (p. 239)** The *y*-coordinate of the point where a line crosses the *y*-axis.

Intercepto en *y* (p. 239) La coordenada *y* del punto donde una recta corta el eje *y*.

The *y*-intercept of $y = 5x + 2$ is 2.

Z

Zero-product property (p. 452) For all real numbers *a* and *b*, if $ab = 0$, then $a = 0$ or $b = 0$.

Propiedad del producto cero (p. 452) Para todos los números reales *a* y *b*, si $ab = 0$, entonces $a = 0$ ó $b = 0$.

$x(x + 3) = 0$

$x = 0$ or $x + 3 = 0$

$x = 0$ or $x = -3$

Zeros of the function (p. 446) The *x*-intercepts of the graph of a function.

Cero de una funcion (p. 446) En la gráfica de una función, cada intercepto en *x* representa un cero.

The zeros of $y = x^2 - 4$ are ± 2.

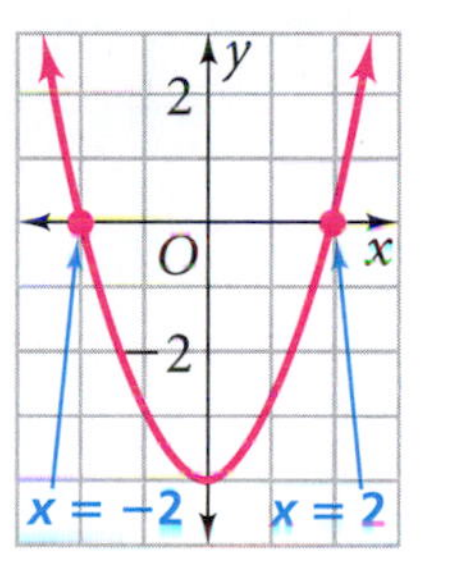

English/Spanish Glossary

Answers to California Check System

Chapter 1

Check Your Readiness — p. 2

1. $\frac{4}{5}$ **2.** $\frac{5}{7}$ **3.** $\frac{3}{7}$ **4.** $\frac{1}{7}$ **5.** $\frac{12}{13}$ **6.** $\frac{7}{24}$ **7.** $\frac{6}{11}$ **8.** $1\frac{9}{20}$ **9.** $\frac{23}{39}$ **10.** $12\frac{23}{40}$ **11.** $4\frac{7}{12}$ **12.** $1\frac{5}{6}$ **13.** $13\frac{13}{28}$ **14.** $\frac{5}{12}$ **15.** $1\frac{1}{9}$ **16.** $\frac{4}{7}$ **17.** $1\frac{3}{4}$ **18.** $3\frac{3}{10}$ **19.** $9\frac{7}{9}$ **20.** $12\frac{1}{12}$ **21.** $3\frac{3}{10}$ **22.** 9^5 **23.** $5 \cdot 7^6$ **24.** $2^2 \cdot 3^6$ **25.** $4^4 \cdot 7^2$ **26.** $5^3 \cdot 8^2 \cdot 3$ **27.** $2^3 \cdot 6^5$ **28.** 125 **29.** 4096 **30.** 121 **31.** 486 **32.** 256

Lesson 1-1 — pp. 4–6

Check Skills You'll Need **1.** Reasonable **2.** Incorrect **3.** Incorrect **4.** Reasonable

CA Standards Check **1a.** $\frac{4.2}{c}$ **b.** $t - 15$ **2.** Let n be the number. **a.** $n - 9$ **b.** $2n + 31$ **3a.** $c = 15n$ **b.** Each CD costs $10.99. **4.** Answers may vary. Sample: e = money earned, s = money saved, $s = \frac{1}{2}e$

Lesson 1-2 — pp. 9–12

Check Skills You'll Need **1.** 4 **2.** 3 **3.** 1 **4.** 4 **5.** 7 **6.** 4 **7.** 8 **8.** 60 **9.** 35 **10.** 9 **11.** 18 **12.** 36

CA Standards Check **1a.** 4 **b.** 10 **c.** 29 **2a.** 3 **b.** 8 **c.** 6

3.

Price p	$p + 0.05p$	Cost c
$5	5 + 0.05(5)	$5.25
$10	10 + 0.05(10)	$10.50
$15	15 + 0.05(15)	$15.75
$20	20 + 0.05(20)	$21.00

$5.25, $10.50, $15.75, $21.00 **4a.** 26 **b.** 10.5 **5a.** 1764 **b.** 1134 **c.** 15,876 **6a.** 95 **b.** 21 **c.** 29 **7.** 63,000 ft^2

Lesson 1-3 — pp. 17–20, 23

Check Skills You'll Need **1.** $\frac{1}{2}$ **2.** $\frac{1}{20}$ **3.** $\frac{13}{4}$ **4.** $\frac{13}{40}$ **5.** 0.4 **6.** 0.375 **7.** $0.\overline{6}$ **8.** $3.\overline{5}$

CA Standards Check **1a.** integers, rational numbers **b.** rational numbers **c.** rational numbers **d.** natural numbers, whole numbers, integers, rational numbers **2.** rational numbers **3a.** true **b.** False; answers may vary. Sample: $\frac{3}{1} = 3$ is a whole number. **4.** $-\frac{2}{3}, -\frac{5}{8}, \frac{1}{12}$ **5a.** 5 **b.** 4 **c.** 3.7 **d.** $\frac{5}{7}$

Checkpoint Quiz 1 **1.** $b + 4$ **2.** $\frac{c}{2}$ **3.** $4.3a$ **4.** $b + c + 2a$ **5.** 28 **6.** 58 **7.** 60 **8.** 252 **9.** False; answers may vary. Sample: The opposite of -2 is 2, but $-2 < 2$. **10.** natural numbers or whole numbers

Lesson 1-4 — pp. 24–27

Check Skills You'll Need **1.** 6 **2.** 17 **3.** 1.3 **4.** 5.2 **5.** $\frac{4}{5}$ **6.** $1\frac{1}{4}$

CA Standards Check **1a.** -2 **b.** -2 **c.** -11 **d.** 6 **2a.** -11 **b.** -17.4 **c.** $-1\frac{1}{4}$ **d.** $\frac{1}{18}$ **3.** $-15 + 18 = 3$, rise of 3° **4a.** -11.4 **b.** -9.1 **c.** 15.6 **d.** 14.59 **5.** Choices of variable may vary. Sample: c = change in temp., $-14 + c$; -25°F

Lesson 1-5 — pp. 32–34

Check Skills You'll Need **1.** -6 **2.** 7 **3.** -3.79 **4.** $\frac{7}{19}$ **5.** 1 **6.** 6 **7.** 5 **8.** $\frac{1}{2}$

CA Standards Check **1a.** -4 **b.** -5 **c.** -11 **d.** 5 **2a.** -8 **b.** 12 **c.** 8.0 **d.** $-\frac{1}{18}$ **3a.** 1 **b.** 1 **c.** 6 **d.** 6 **4a.** -5 **b.** 5 **c.** 9 **d.** 5 **5.** ABC: $32.47; PQR: $15.46

Lesson 1-6 — pp. 37–41

Check Skills You'll Need **1.** -8 **2.** -25 **3.** -24 **4.** -72

CA Standards Check **1a.** -24 **b.** 50 **c.** 39.2 **d.** $-\frac{1}{2}$ **2a.** -56 **b.** 336 **c.** -56 **3a.** -24.75°F **b.** 15.25°F **4a.** -64 **b.** 16 **c.** 0.09 **d.** $-\frac{9}{16}$ **5a.** -6 **b.** 4 **c.** -1 **d.** 13 **6a.** $-4\frac{1}{2}$ **b.** $-\frac{1}{5}$ **c.** $29\frac{1}{2}$ **7.** -10

Lesson 1-7 — pp. 45–47, 51

Check Skills You'll Need **1.** 33 **2.** -22 **3.** 1 **4.** -1 **5.** $3t$ **6.** $-4m$

CA Standards Check **1a.** 1339 **b.** 2121 **c.** 2352 **d.** 1485 **2.** $17.70 **3a.** $6 - 14t$ **b.** $1.2 + 3.3c$ **4a.** $-2x - 1$ **b.** $-3 + 8a$ **5a.** $13y$ **b.** $2t$ **c.** $-12w^3$ **d.** $9d$ **6a.** $-2(t + 7)$ **b.** $14(8 + w)$

Checkpoint Quiz 1 **1.** $-\frac{1}{9}$ **2.** -20 **3.** 5 **4.** 11 **5.** 120 **6.** 1 **7.** -1.6 **8.** t = temperature change; $74 + t$; 87°F **9.** $8x - 12$ **10.** $49t$

Lesson 1-8 pp. 52–54

Check Skills You'll Need **1.** 19 **2.** −30 **3.** 3 **4.** $1 + x$ **5.** $5t - 8$ **6.** $-7m$

CA Standards Check **1a.** Ident. Prop. of Mult.; m is mult. by the mult. identity, 1. **b.** Assoc. Prop. of Add.; the grouping of the terms changes. **c.** Assoc. Prop. of Mult.; the grouping of the factors changes. **d.** Ident. Prop. of Add.; the ident. for add., 0, is added. **e.** Comm. Prop. of Mult.; the order of the factors changes. **f.** Comm. Prop. of Add.; the order of the terms changes. **2.** $8.80

3a. $5a + 6 + a$

$= 5a + a + 6$	Comm. Prop. of Add.
$= (5a + a) + 6$	Assoc. Prop. of Add.
$= (5a + 1a) + 6$	Ident. Prop. of Mult.
$= (5 + 1)a + 6$	Dist. Prop.
$= 6a + 6$	addition

b. $2(3t - 1) + 2$

$= 6t - 2 + 2$	Dist. Prop.
$= 6t + (-2) + 2$	def. of subtr.
$= 6t + [(-2) + 2]$	Assoc. Prop. of Add.
$= 6t + 0$	Inv. Prop. of Add.
$= 6t$	Ident. Prop. of Add.

Chapter 2

Check Your Readiness p. 66

1. $0.45n = 3.60$ **2.** $3s = 124$ **3.** 3 **4.** −10 **5.** 8 **6.** −8 **7.** 7.14 **8.** 16.4 **9.** $-\frac{9}{20}$ **10.** $-\frac{7}{15}$ **11.** 17 **12.** −3 **13.** 576 **14.** −2.75 **15.** $16k^2$ **16.** $13xy$ **17.** $2t + 2$ **18.** $12x - 4$ **19.** Assoc. Prop. of Add. **20.** Dist. Prop. **21.** Comm. Prop. of Add.

Lesson 2-1 pp. 69–71

Check Skills You'll Need **1.** 19; Add. Prop. of Eq. **2.** 5.2; Subtr. Prop. of Eq. **3.** 14; Add. Prop. of Eq. **4.** 33; Add. Prop. of Eq. **5.** 32; Mult. Prop. of Eq. **6.** 3; Div. Prop. of Eq. **7.** $\frac{1}{5}$; **8.** −9; **9.** $3\frac{3}{4}$

CA Standards Check **1a.** 5 **b.** 243 **c.** 3 **2.** 18 bulbs **3a.** −5 **b.** 3 **c.** 7 **4.** $\frac{3}{5}w + 9 = -1$ Original equation $\frac{3}{5}w + 9 - 9 = -1 - 9$ Subtr. Prop. of Eq. $\frac{3}{5}w = -10$ Simplify. $\frac{3}{5}w \cdot \frac{5}{3} = -10 \cdot \frac{5}{3}$ Mult. Prop. of Eq. $w = -16\frac{2}{3}$ Simplify.

5.

$-9 - 4m = 3$	Original equation
$-9 + 9 - 4m = 3 + 9$	Add. Prop. of Eq.
$-4m = 12$	Simplify.
$\frac{-4m}{-4} = \frac{12}{-4}$	Div. Prop. of Eq.
$m = -3$	Simplify.

Lesson 2-2 pp. 76–78

Check Skills You'll Need **1.** $-n$ **2.** $8b - 2$ **3.** $9w - 45$ **4.** $-10b + 120$ **5.** $-3x + 12$ **6.** $30 - 5w$ **7.** 43 **8.** 26 **9.** −45 **10.** −35

CA Standards Check **1.** 3 **2.** 135 ft **3a.** −1 **b.** −1 **4a.** $\frac{5}{6}$ **b.** 624 **5a.** 28 **b.** 4

Lesson 2-3 pp. 84–86, 89

Check Skills You'll Need **1.** $4x$ **2.** $-4x$ **3.** 0 **4.** 0 **5.** −2 **6.** −5 **7.** −7 **8.** $\frac{1}{3}$

CA Standards Check **1a.** $-\frac{4}{7}$ **b.** −2 **c.** $-\frac{5}{2}$ **d.** 10 **2.** at least 15 bottles **3.** no solution

Checkpoint Quiz 1 **1.** 50 **2.** 16 **3.** $3\frac{1}{8}$ **4.** −15 **5.** 2.5 **6.** 2 **7.** no solution **8.** $6\frac{3}{4}$ **9.** 8 ft **10.** 15 h

Lesson 2-4 pp. 92–95

Check Skills You'll Need **1.** $\frac{7}{12}$ **2.** $\frac{4}{7}$ **3.** $\frac{3}{4}$ **4.** 4 **5.** $\frac{3}{4}$ **6.** $\frac{1}{2}$

CA Standards Check **1.** $1.025/rose; $1.25 rose; Main Street Florist **2a.** about 0.5 mi/min; $d = 0.5t$ **b.** 3.75 mi **3.** 13.2 ft/min **4a.** $6\frac{2}{3}$ **b.** $6\frac{6}{7}$ **c.** 5.4 **5a.** $8\frac{1}{3}$ **b.** 33.6 **c.** 48 **6a.** 5 **b.** −21 **c.** −8.75

Lesson 2-5 pp. 100–104, 107

Check Skills You'll Need **1.** $25q$ **2.** $34h$ **3.** $5x$ **4.** $3.99n$

CA Standards Check **1.** 5 cm **2a.** Let x = the first integer. **b.** $x + 1$ is the second integer, and $x + 2$ is the third integer. **c.** $3x + 3 = 48$; 15, 16, 17 **3a.** $3\frac{2}{3}$ h **b.** $1\frac{2}{3}$ h **4.** 1 h **5.** John: 38 mi/h; Sarah: 50 mi/h

Checkpoint Quiz 2 **1.** −20 **2.** 4.4 **3.** $-22\frac{6}{7}$ **4.** 40 **5.** $-5\frac{1}{7}$ **6.** $1\frac{2}{3}$ **7.** 33.6 min **8.** 14 cm **9.** 153, 155, 157 **10.** Marcus: 63 mi/h; Beth: 50 mi/h

Lesson 2-6 pp. 110–111

Check Skills You'll Need **1.** 4 **2.** 40% **3.** 20 **4.** 30 **5.** 15% **6.** 39

CA Standards Check **1.** 25 lb of raisins, 25 lb of nuts **2.** 40 L of 10%, 160 L of 60%

Chapter 3

Check Your Readiness p. 122

1. > **2.** = **3.** > **4.** < **5.** 7 **6.** −4 **7.** 1 **8.** 2 **9.** 3 **10.** −12 **11.** 32.4 **12.** 23 **13.** 29.5 **14.** −28 **15.** −12 **16.** 48 **17.** 5 **18.** −24 **19.** −10 **20.** 1.85 **21.** −24 **22.** −2 **23.** 3 **24.** −4 **25.** 3 **26.** $\frac{1}{2}$ **27.** $\frac{5}{2}$ **28.** 4.1 **29.** 48

Lesson 3-1 pp. 124–126

Check Skills You'll Need **1–5.** −4 −3 −2 −1 0 1 2 3 4

6. > **7.** < **8.** = **9.** = **10.** > **11.** <

CA Standards Check **1a.** no **b.** yes **c.** yes **d.** yes **2a.** no **b.** no **c.** yes **d.** yes

3a. −2 −1 0 1 2 **b.** −5 −4 −3 −2 −1 0 1

c. −1 0 1 2 3 4 5 **4a–b.** Choice of variable may vary. **a.** $x \geq 2$ **b.** $x < 0$ **5a.** No; speeds cannot be negative, so you can't use all real numbers. **b.** No; answers may vary. Sample: Hourly wages are not likely to be in hundreds of dollars.

Lesson 3-2 pp. 130–132

Check Skills You'll Need **1.** > **2.** < **3.** > **4.** 9 **5.** −2 **6.** −9 **7.** $\frac{1}{6}$

CA Standards Check **1.** $m > 2$;

0 1 2 3 4 5 **2.** $n \leq 5$; 3 4 5 6 7 8

3. $t \geq 5$; −1 0 1 2 3 4 5 6

4. $42 + 65 + b \geq 160$, or $b \geq 53$

Lesson 3-3 pp. 136–139, 141

Check Skills You'll Need **1.** 16 **2.** $-\frac{2}{3}$ **3.** −6 **4.** 6.4 **5.** −18 **6.** 18 **7.** $x \leq -1$ **8.** $x > 3$

CA Standards Check **1a.** $b > 2$; −1 0 1 2 3

b. $d \geq 2\frac{1}{2}$; −1 0 1 2 3 4

c. $y \leq -6$; −8 −7 −6 −5 −4

2a. $k < 4$; −1 0 1 2 3 4 5

b. $t > -\frac{1}{2}$; −3 −2 −1 0 1 2

c. $w \leq -10$; −20 −10 0 5

3a. $t > 4$; −2 0 2 4 6 8

b. $w \leq -4$; −7 −6 −5 −4 −3 −2

c. $n > -3$; −4 −3 −2 −1 0 1

4. $0.4c > 327$; 818 calendars

Checkpoint Quiz 1 **1.** $c > 5$; −5 0 5 10 15

2. $x < -6$; −10 −8 −6 −4 −2 0 2

3. $p \leq -6$; −10 −8 −6 −4 −2 0 2

4. $y \geq 2$; −1 0 1 2 3 4

5. $g < -8$; −12 −10 −8 −6 −4 −2 0 2

6. $b \leq -5$; −8 −6 −4 −2 0 2

7a. yes **b.** no **c.** yes **d.** no **8a.** no **b.** no **c.** no **d.** yes **9.** $m \geq 92$ **10** $1.50p \leq 20$; 13 plants

Lesson 3-4 pp. 143–145

Check Skills You'll Need **1.** −2 **2.** no solution **3.** $-3\frac{1}{3}$ **4.** identity **5.** $1\frac{2}{9}$ **6.** −11 **7.** 40 cm **8.** 13 in.

CA Standards Check **1a.** $x \geq -6$ **b.** $t < 1$ **c.** $n > 3$ **2.** $2(12) + 2w \leq 40$, so the banner's width must be 8 feet or less. **3a.** $p < -1$ **b.** $m \leq -3$ **c.** $b > 3$ **4.** $b > 3$ **5.** $x \leq 2\frac{1}{4}$

Lesson 3-5 pp. 151–153, 156

Check Skills You'll Need **1.** 6 7 8 9 10 11 12

2. −6 −5 −4 −3 −2 −1

3. 5 6 7 8 9 10 11 12 13 14

4. 6 **5.** −3 **6.** 14 **7.** 3

CA Standards Check **1a.** $n > -2$ and $n < 9$ or $-2 < n < 9$; −4 −2 0 2 4 6 8 10

b. $3.50 \leq b \leq 6$; 0 1 2 3 4 5 6 7

2a. $-2 \leq x < 5$; −4 −2 0 2 4 6

b. $-1 < x < 4$; −2 −1 0 1 2 3 4 5

c. $-4 \leq n < -2$; −5 −4 −3 −2 −1 0 1

3a. $6.7 \leq p \leq 8.5$ **b.** $5.2 \leq p \leq 7$. No; readings in this range are unlikely if the first readings are high.

4. $n \leq -5$ or $n \geq 3$; −6 −4 −2 0 2 4 6

5. $x < 2$ or $x \geq 3$; −1 0 1 2 3 4

Checkpoint Quiz 2

1. $d < -3$ −5 −4 −3 −2 −1 0 1

2. $n \geq -2$
−4 −3 −2 −1 0 1 2 3 4

3. $-2 \leq m \leq 1$
−3 −2 −1 0 1 2

4. $s < 2$
−1 0 1 2 3

5. $p > 4$
−2 0 2 4 6 8

6. $x \leq -4$ or $x > 4$
−6 −4 −2 0 2 4 6

7. $c < 8$ **8.** $65 \leq t \leq 75$
9. $2(15) + 2(w) \leq 48$, $w \leq 9$ **10.** $x \geq -19$

Lesson 3-6 pp. 159–161

Check Skills You'll Need **1.** 15 **2.** 3 **3.** 6 **4.** −7 **5.** 24 **6.** 2 **7.** = **8.** > **9.** < **10.** > **11.** > **12.** =

CA Standards Check **1a.** −1, 1 **b.** −5, 5 **c.** −2, 2 **d.** No; an absolute value cannot be negative. **2a.** −4, 8 **b.** no solution **c.** −2, 2
3a. $w < -7$ or $w > 3$,
−8 −6 −4 −2 0 2 4 6

4. 33.81 oz to 33.91 oz, inclusive

Chapter 4

Check Your Readiness p. 174

1. Let n = number of pens and t = total price; $t = 0.59n$. **2.** Let h = height of house and t = height of tower; $t = h + 200$. **3.** Let s = length of a side and p = perimeter; $p = 3s$. **4.** −7 **5.** −18 **6.** 2 **7.** −1 **8.** $6\frac{2}{5}$ **9.** 0.6 **10.** 4.5 **11.** −58

12.
−8 −6 −4

13.
0 2 4

14.
2 4 6

15.
−2 0 2

16. −4, 0 **17.** 3, 7 **18.** no solution

Lesson 4-1 pp. 176–178

Check Skills You'll Need

1.
4 6 8

2.
−8 −6 −4 −2

3.
1 2 3 4

4.
−2 0 2

5. 1 **6.** −2.5 **7.** 3.5 **8.** −4

CA Standards Check **1a.** (3, 4) **b.** (−2, −3) **c.** $(-4\frac{1}{2}, 0)$ **d.** (1, −2)

2a–d.

3a. x-axis **b.** IV **c.** III **d.** I

Lesson 4-2 pp. 181–183, 186

Check Skills You'll Need

1–4.

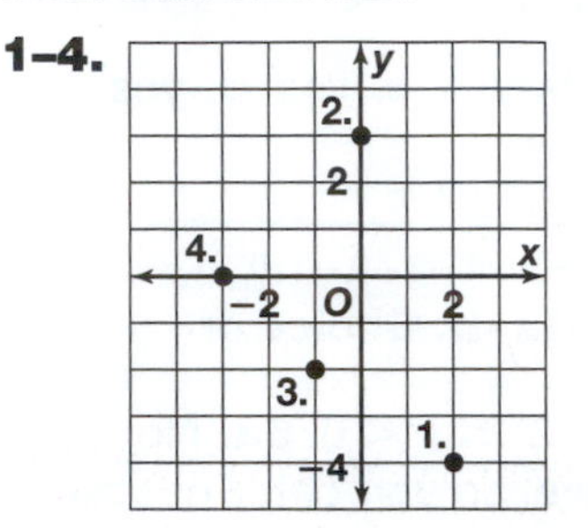

CA Standards Check **1a.** domain: {−4, −2, 3, 5}; range: {−1, 0, 3}; yes **b.** domain: {−3, 6, 8}; range: {−5, −2, 4, 7}; no **2a.** domain: {−4, 3, 8, 9}; range: {−2, 0, 1, 2, 3}; not a function **b.** domain: {2, 5, 6, 6.5, 7}; range: {−1, 0, 2, 6}; function **3a.** domain: {−1, 0, 1, 2}; range: {−3, −1, 1, 2, 4}; not a function **b.** domain: all real numbers; range: $\{y \geq 3\}$; function

Checkpoint Quiz 1 **1.** *C* **2.** *D* **3.** *E* **4.** *A* **5.** (0, 0) **6.** (−4, −2) **7.** (−3, 3) **8.** function **9.** not a function **10.** function

Lesson 4-3 pp. 187–190

Check Skills You'll Need

1. not a function **2.** function **3.** not a function

CA Standards Check **1a.** {−3, 1, 11} **b.** {−3, 2, 4} **c.** {−4, 0, 21}

2. Tables may vary. Sample:

x	$f(x)$
0	4
1	7
−1	1
−2	−2

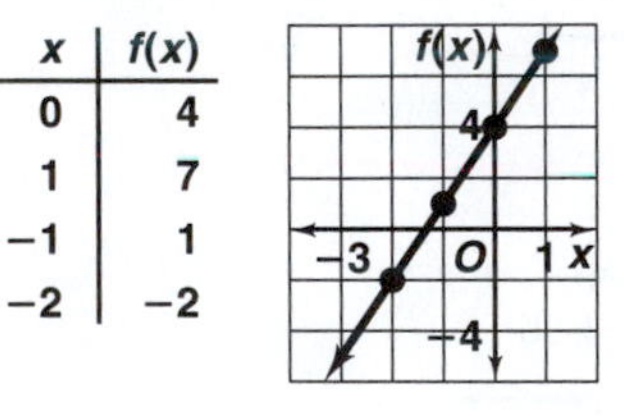

3a. Tables may vary. Sample:

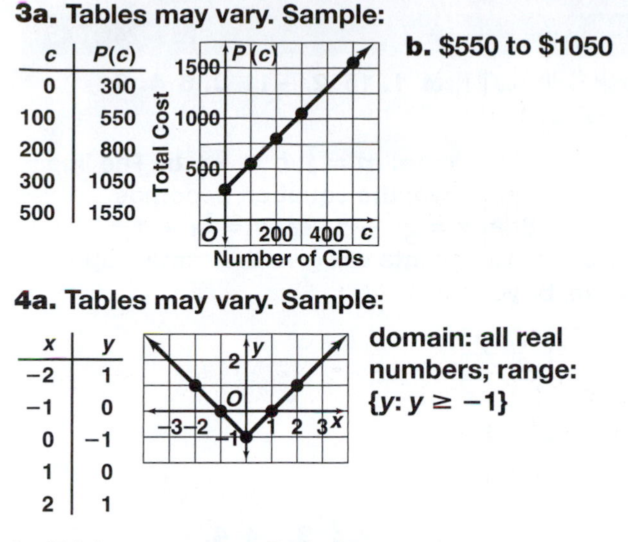

c	P(c)
0	300
100	550
200	800
300	1050
500	1550

b. \$550 to \$1050

4a. Tables may vary. Sample:

x	y
−2	1
−1	0
0	−1
1	0
2	1

domain: all real numbers; range: $\{y: y \geq -1\}$

b. Tables may vary. Sample:

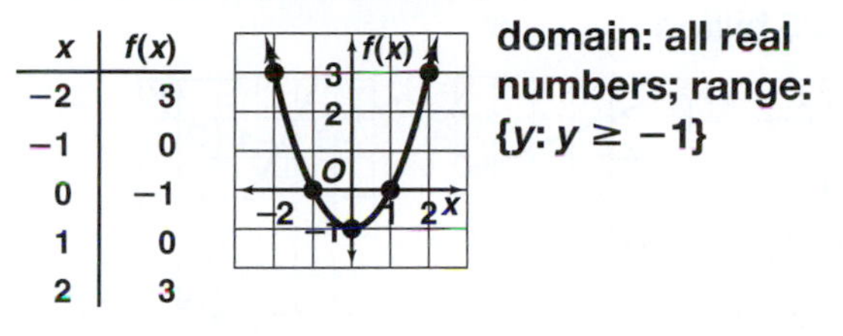

x	f(x)
−2	3
−1	0
0	−1
1	0
2	3

domain: all real numbers; range: $\{y: y \geq -1\}$

5a. all real numbers; function **b.** $\{x: x \neq 5\}$; function **c.** $\{x: x \geq 0\}$; not a function

Lesson 4-4 pp. 194–195

Check Skills You'll Need **1–6.** Tables may vary. Samples are given.

1.

x	f(x)
−1	−6
0	−1
1	4
2	9
3	14

2.

x	y
−2	10
−1	7
0	4
1	1
2	−2

3.

t	g(t)
−2	−7.4
−1	−7.2
0	−7
1	−6.8
2	−6.6

4.

x	y
−2	−7
−1	−3
0	1
1	5
2	9

5.

x	f(x)
−2	8
−1	7
0	6
1	5
2	4

6.

d	c(d)
−2	−1.1
−1	−0.1
0	0.9
1	1.9
2	2.9

7. 3 **8.** −2 **9.** 4

CA Standards Check **1a.** $f(x) = x - 2$ **b.** $y = 2x$ **c.** $y = x + 2$ **2a.** $C(x) = 1.19x$ **b.** \$14.28 **3.** $p(n) = 15n - 199$

Lesson 4-5 pp. 201–204, 207

Check Skills You'll Need **1.** 7.5 **2.** 20 **3.** 5 **4.** 10 **5.** 14.4 **6.** 81

CA Standards Check **1a.** yes; $\frac{2}{7}$ **b.** no **c.** yes; 7.5 **2.** $y = 2x$ **3.** $y = 12x$ **4a.** no **b.** yes; $y = 1.5x$ **5.** 2.5 lb

Checkpoint Quiz 2

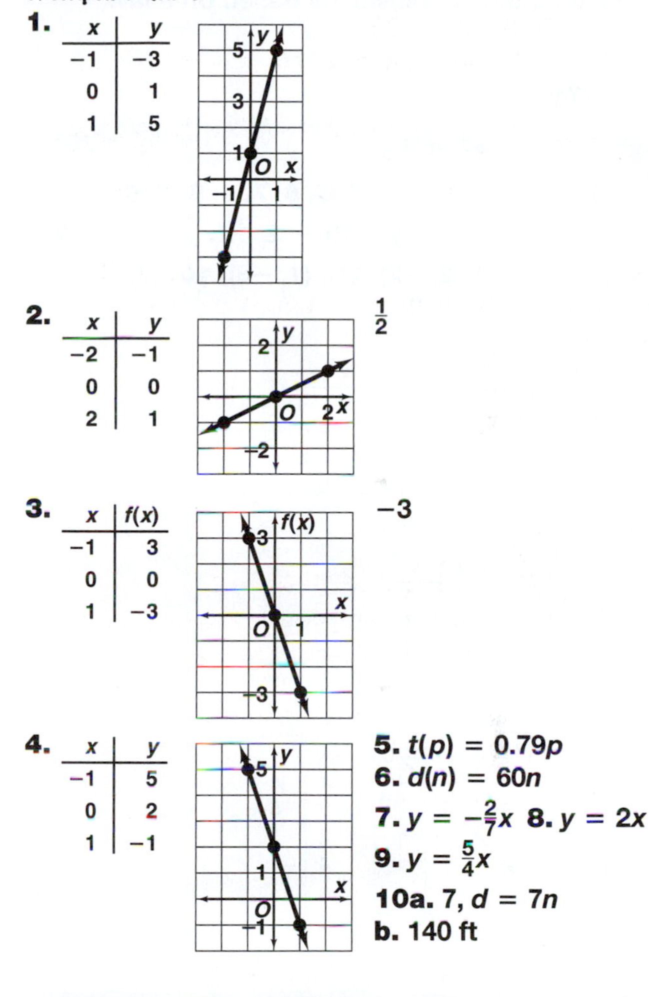

1.

x	y
−1	−3
0	1
1	5

2.

x	y
−2	−1
0	0
2	1

$\frac{1}{2}$

3.

x	f(x)
−1	3
0	0
1	−3

−3

4.

x	y
−1	5
0	2
1	−1

5. $t(p) = 0.79p$ **6.** $d(n) = 60n$ **7.** $y = -\frac{2}{7}x$ **8.** $y = 2x$ **9.** $y = \frac{5}{4}x$ **10a.** 7, $d = 7n$ **b.** 140 ft

Lesson 4-6 pp. 208–211

Check Skills You'll Need **1.** 5 **2.** −7 **3.** $\frac{1}{3}$ **4.** 4 **5.** $y = 2x$ **6.** $y = 0.5x$ **7.** $y = -0.25x$ **8.** $y = 0.4x$

CA Standards Check **1.** $xy = 18$ **2a.** 15 **b.** 5 **3a.** $5.\overline{3}$ ft **b.** 120 lb **4a.** inverse variation; $xy = 36$ **b.** direct variation; $y = 4x$ **5a.** Direct variation, since the ratio $\frac{\text{cost}}{\text{sweater}}$ is constant at \$15 each. **b.** Inverse variation, since the total number of miles walked each day is a constant product of 5.

Lesson 4-7 pp. 215–216

Check Skills You'll Need **1.** 14 **2.** −17 **3.** −1.9 **4.** −10 **5.** −32 **6.** 21 **7.** 36 **8.** −64 **9.** 81

CA Standards Check **1a.** "Multiply the previous term by 3"; 243, 729. **b.** "Add 6 to the previous term"; 33, 39. **c.** "Multiply the previous term by −2"; 32, −64. **2.** $A(n) = n(n + 1)$; 930 **3.** Deductive reasoning; the conclusion is based on a law.

Chapter 5

Check Your Readiness p. 228

1. 2 **2.** 5 **3.** $\frac{1}{12}$ **4.** 7 **5.** 7 **6.** 6 **7.** 1 **8.** 3 **9.** 3 **10.** $y = \frac{1}{2}x + 2$ **11.** $y = 3x - 2$ **12.** $y = -x - 2$ **13.** (4, 3) **14.** (−2, −2) **15.** (1, −3) **16.** (3, 0) **17.** (−4, 2) **18.** (0, 2)

19.

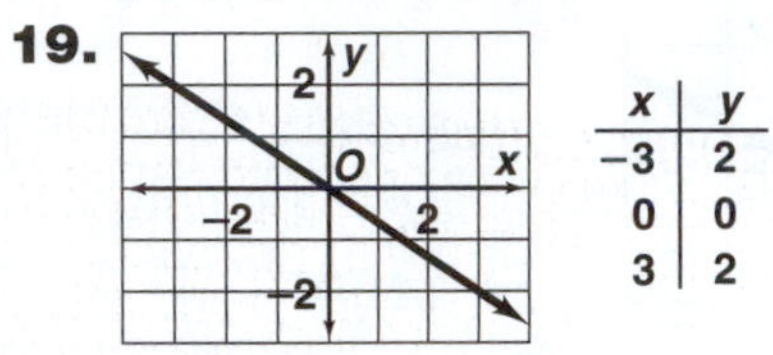

x	y
−3	2
0	0
3	2

20.

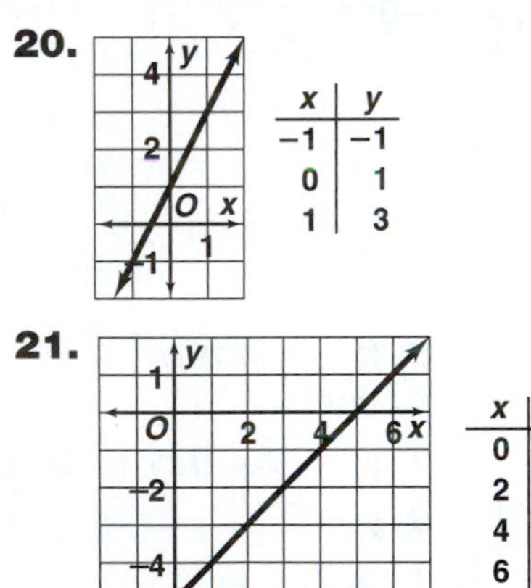

x	y
−1	−1
0	1
1	3

21.

x	y
0	−5
2	−3
4	−1
6	1

Lesson 5-1 pp. 230–233

Check Skills You'll Need **1.** 12 **2.** −5 **3.** 5 **4.** 2 **5.** $-\frac{1}{3}$ **6.** −3 **7.** $\frac{3}{5}$ **8.** $\frac{1}{4}$ **9.** −1

CA Standards Check **1a.** 15 **b.** No; the rate of change for each consecutive pair of days does not have to be the same. **2.** 50 mi/h **3a.** $\frac{3}{5}$ **b.** $-\frac{1}{6}$ **4.** 1 **5a.** 0 **b.** undefined

Lesson 5-2 pp. 239–241, 245

Check Skills You'll Need **1.** 15 **2.** −11 **3.** 6 **4.** 5 **5.** −7 **6.** 1

CA Standards Check **1a.** $m = \frac{7}{6}$; $b = -\frac{3}{4}$ **b.** The line shifts 3 units down; the equation becomes $y = 3x - 8$. **2.** $y = \frac{2}{5}x - 1$ **3a.** $y = \frac{1}{2}x + 1$ **b.** No; any two points will give the same slope. **4a.** no **b.** yes

5.

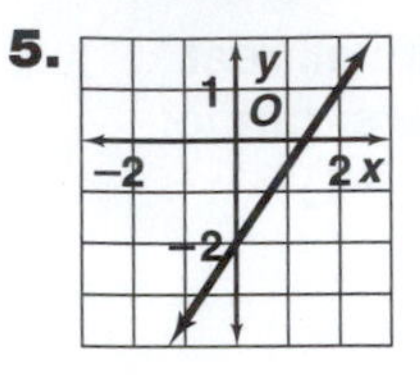

Checkpoint Quiz 1 **1.** $-\frac{5}{7}$ **2.** $\frac{3}{4}$ **3.** −4 **4.** −1 **5.** $121.75 billion per year

6. **7.**

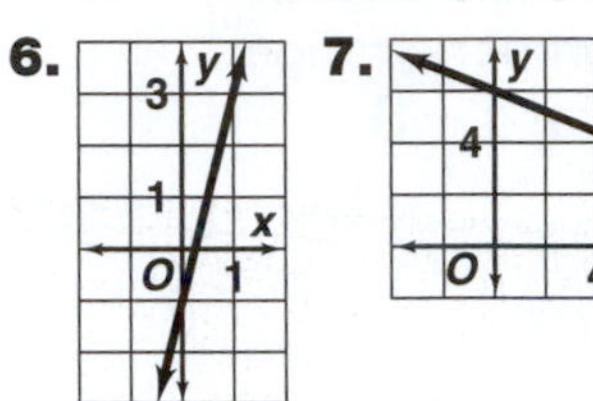

8.

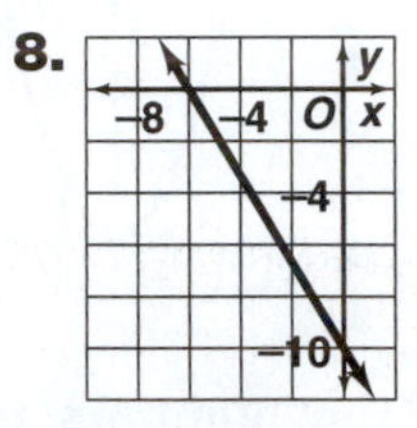

9.

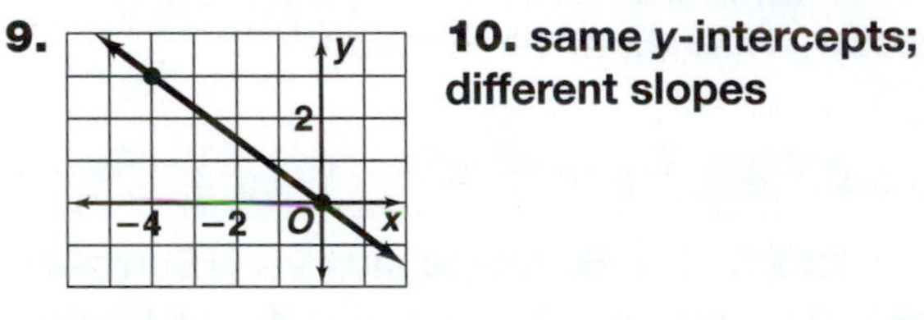

10. same y-intercepts; different slopes

Lesson 5-3 pp. 246–248

Check Skills You'll Need **1.** $y = -3x + 5$ **2.** $y = 2x + 10$ **3.** $y = x - 6$ **4.** $y = -5x + 2$ **5.** $y = -\frac{1}{3}x + \frac{1}{9}$ **6.** $y = \frac{2}{5}x + \frac{4}{5}$ **7.** $625x + 850 = 775$ **8.** $4 = 2x - 50$ **9.** $900 - 222x = 1000$

CA Standards Check **1.** −3; $\frac{4}{3}$

2. **3a.**

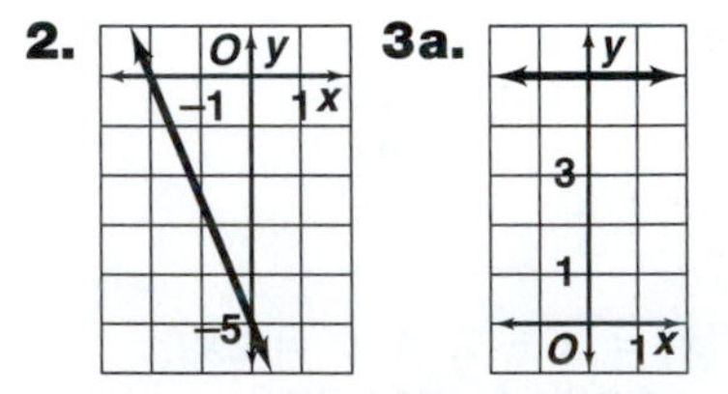

b. **4.** $2x + 5y = 5$ **5.** $4x + 5y = 250$

Lesson 5-4 pp. 252–255

Check Skills You'll Need **1.** -2 **2.** $\frac{1}{2}$ **3.** 2 **4.** $-3x + 15$ **5.** $5x + 10$ **6.** $-\frac{4}{9}x + \frac{8}{3}$

CA Standards Check

1.

2. $y + 8 = \frac{2}{5}(x - 10)$
3a. $y + 5 = \frac{8}{3}(x + 1)$
b. $y = \frac{8}{3}x - 2\frac{1}{3}$

4. Yes; answers may vary. Sample: $y - 5 = \frac{2}{5}(x - 19)$
5. Yes; answers may vary. Sample: $y - 3030 = -\frac{50}{3}(x - 68)$

Lesson 5-5 pp. 259–261, 265

Check Skills You'll Need **1.** $\frac{2}{1}$ **2.** $\frac{3}{4}$ **3.** $-\frac{5}{2}$ **4.** $-\frac{5}{7}$ **5.** $\frac{5}{3}$; 4 **6.** $\frac{5}{3}$; -8 **7.** 6; 0 **8.** 6; 2

CA Standards Check **1.** yes; same slope, different y-intercepts **2.** $y = 3x - 12$ **3.** $y = -\frac{4}{3}x + 9\frac{1}{3}$ **4.** $y = 2x + 4$

Checkpoint Quiz 2 **1.** $y - 4 = -\frac{1}{4}(x - 3)$ **2.** 3; 3; $y - 4 = -(x - 5)$ **3.** $\frac{1}{3}$; $\frac{1}{2}$; $y - 6 = -\frac{3}{2}(x + 2)$ **4.** $y - 2 = \frac{1}{4}x$ **5.** $y - 2 = -\frac{3}{2}(x + 6)$

Chapter 6

Check Your Readiness p. 274

1. identity **2.** 1 **3.** no solution **4.** 3 **5.** $\frac{3}{2}$ **6.** no solution **7.** $y = \frac{3}{2}x + 1$ **8.** $y = -\frac{1}{5}x + 2$ **9.** $y = -x - 4$

10. $-10 < x < 3$;

11. $x < 12$ or $x > 60$

12a. $C(t) = 39.50t$ **b.** \$118.50 **c.** 6

13. **14.**

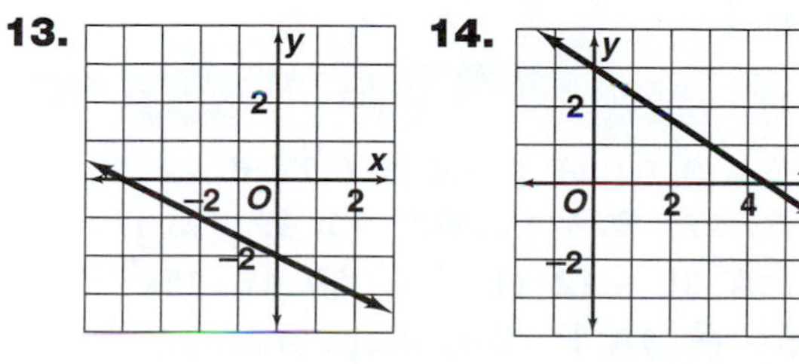

15.

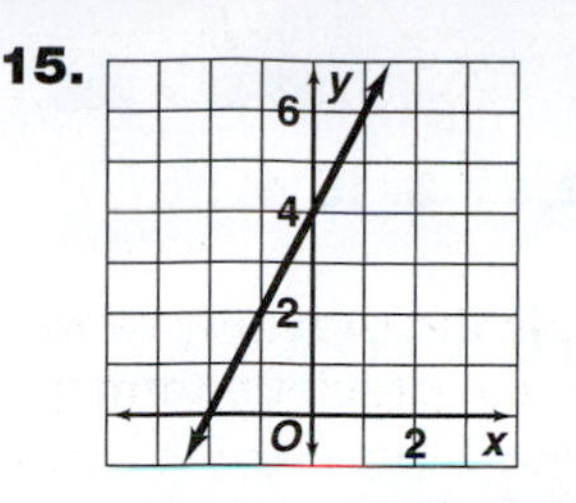

Lesson 6-1 pp. 276–278

Check Skills You'll Need **1.** $1\frac{2}{3}$ **2.** $3\frac{1}{2}$ **3.** 7

4.

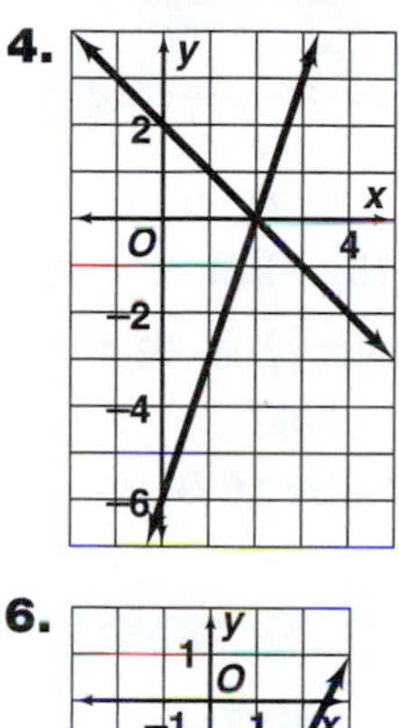

5.

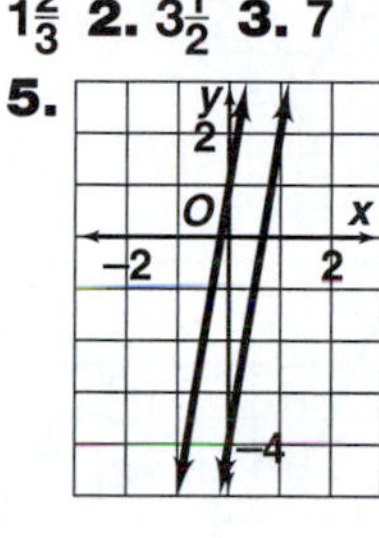

6.

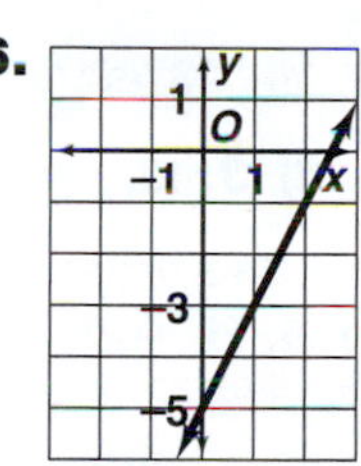

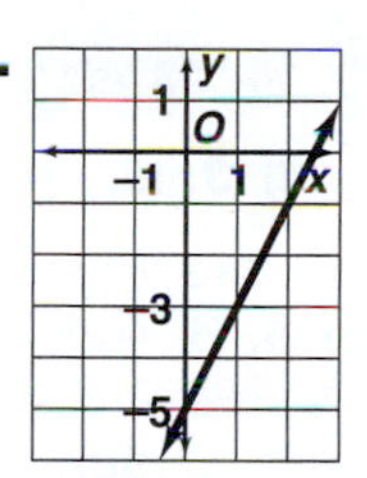

CA Standards Check

1a. $(-1, 4)$; **b.** $(-2, 3)$;

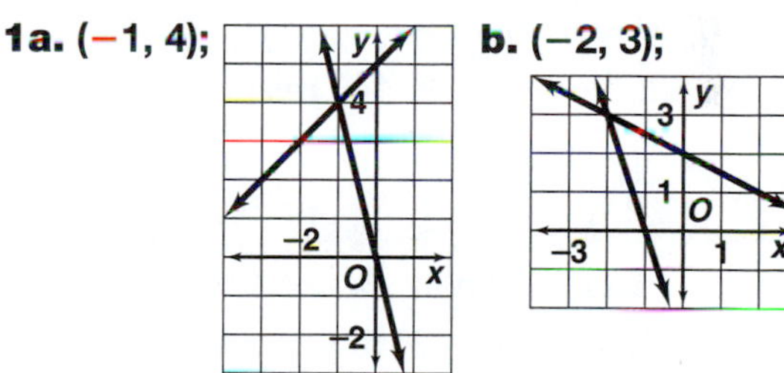

2. $(H)d = 3d + 5$; $(H)d = 4d + 1$
3a. (1.5, 6) **b.** 1.5h after the second walker starts, both have walked 6 mi. **4.** The slopes are the same, and the y-intercepts are not. Ex.: $y = x - 1$, $y = x + 3$ **5.** all the ordered pairs (x, y) such that $y = \frac{1}{5}x + 9$

Lesson 6-2 pp. 282–283, 286

Check Skills You'll Need **1.** $-4\frac{2}{3}$ **2.** $1\frac{1}{2}$ **3.** 15 **4.** no **5.** no

CA Standards Check **1.** (3, 6) **2.** (2.3, 1.6) **3.** 47 games

Checkpoint Quiz 1

1. (1, −1); **2.** (3, 2);

3. (−4, −2);

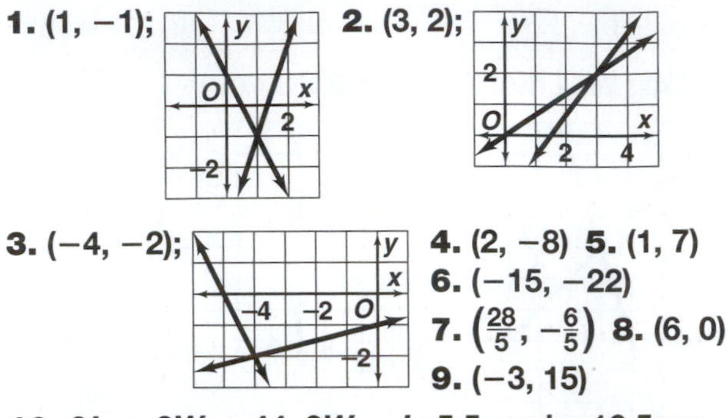

4. (2, −8) **5.** (1, 7) **6.** (−15, −22) **7.** $\left(\frac{28}{5}, -\frac{6}{5}\right)$ **8.** (6, 0) **9.** (−3, 15)

10. $2L + 2W = 44$, $3W = L$; 5.5 cm by 16.5 cm

Lesson 6-3 pp. 287–290

Check Skills You'll Need **1.** (8, 29) **2.** (2, −6) **3.** (3, −4)

CA Standards Check **1.** (2, 3) **2.** 30 adult; 34 student **3.** (1, −2) **4.** 85 cards, 135 gift wrap **5.** (1, −2)

Lesson 6-4 pp. 294–296

Check Skills You'll Need **1.** 2.75 h **2.** 275 mi

CA Standards Check **1.** 32 kg 50% alloy; 8 kg 25% alloy **2.** 3850 copies **3.** 440 mi/h; 40 mi/h

Lesson 6-5 pp. 302–304, 308

Check Skills You'll Need **1.** never **2.** always **3.** sometimes **4.** $y = \frac{2}{3}x - 3$ **5.** $y = -3x + 6$ **6.** $y = \frac{3}{4}x + \frac{1}{4}$

CA Standards Check

1. **2.**

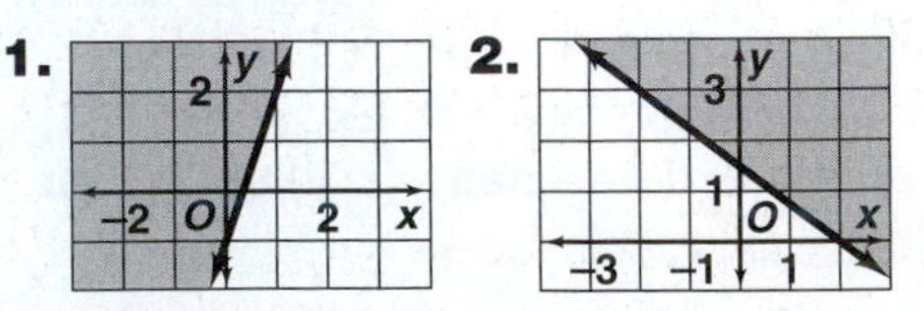

3. Answers may vary. Sample: 6 lb hamburger and 2 lb chicken, 3 lb hamburger and 6 lb chicken, 5 lb hamburger and 3 lb chicken

Checkpoint Quiz 2 **1.** (11, −4) **2.** (−9, 1) **3.** (3.5, 10) **4.** no solution **5.** $\left(15, -\frac{1}{2}\right)$ **6.** $n + d = 21$, $0.05n + 0.10d = 1.70$; 8 nickels, 13 dimes **7.** $y = 200 + 0.35x$, $y = 1.20x$; about 236 ice cream cones **8.** $x + y = 4$, $x - y = 3$; 3.5 mi/h, 0.5 mi/h

9. **10.**

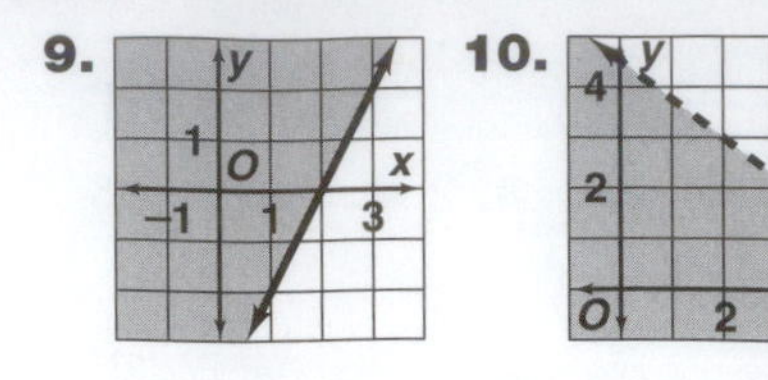

Lesson 6-6 pp. 309–312

Check Skills You'll Need **1.** (2, 0);

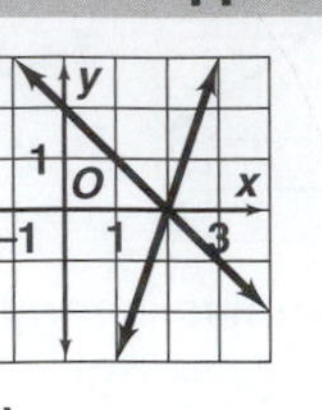

2. no solution; **3.** (4, 0);

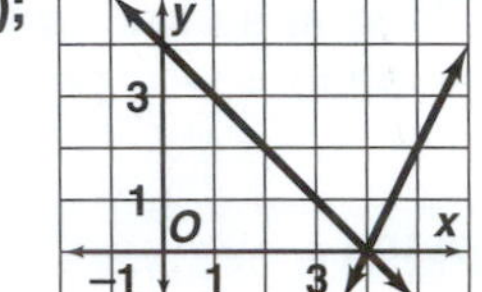

4. **5.** **6.**

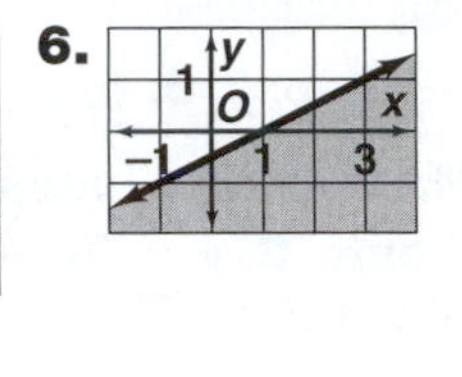

CA Standards Check

1.

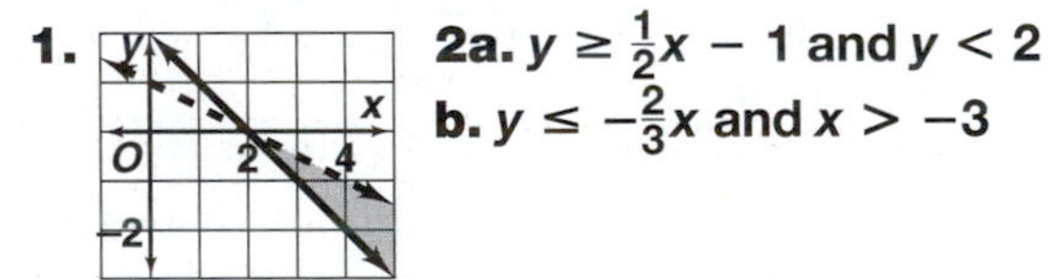

2a. $y \geq \frac{1}{2}x - 1$ and $y < 2$ **b.** $y \leq -\frac{2}{3}x$ and $x > -3$

3.

4a. Answers may vary. Sample: 2 24¢ stamps and 6 39¢ stamps; 4 24¢ stamps and 5 39¢ stamps **b.** no **c.** You cannot have a negative or fractional number of stamps.

Chapter 7

Check Your Readiness p. 326

1. 0.7 **2.** 6.4 **3.** 0.008 **4.** 3.5 **5.** $0.\overline{27}$ **6.** 49 **7.** 5.027 **8.** 0.75 **9.** 4 **10.** 100 **11.** 49 **12.** 17 **13.** −31 **14.** $9b + 12$ **15.** $\frac{1}{2} - \frac{3}{16}h$ **16.** $15x^2$ **17.** $10rst - t^2$ **18.** Identity Prop. of Mult. **19.** Inverse Prop. of Mult. **20.** Distributive Property **21.** {−24.5, −8, 0} **22.** {−32.875, 10, 18} **23.** {−11, −1, 16.5}

Check **1a.** $12h^2 + 4h - 21$ **b.** $40m^2 +$
. $63a^2 - 20a - 32$ **2a.** $6x^2 + 23x + 20$
$- 20$ **c.** $6x^2 - 7x - 20$
$3x + 20$ **3a.** $25x^2 + 28x + 16$
$- 2$ **4.** $12n^3 - 10n^2 + 34n - 56$

uiz 1 **1.** $9x^2 + 10x + 1$ **2.** $6b^2 - 13b + 9$
$11w$ **4.** $-48k^3 + 42k^2$ **5.** $x^2 - 2x - 15$
$2n^4 - 30n^2 - 5n$ **7.** $2(6y^2 - 5)$
$5t^2 - 2)$ **9.** $9v^2(2v^2 + 3v + 4)$
$m^2 + 2 + m^6)$

4 pp. 388–391

You'll Need **1.** $49x^2$ **2.** $9v^2$ **3.** $16c^2$ **4.** $25g^6$
$j + 35$ **6.** $6b^2 - 34b + 48$
$3y - 2$ **8.** $x^2 - x - 12$
$78c^2 - 20$ **10.** $54y^4 - 21y^2 - 3$

rds Check **1a.** $t^2 + 12t + 36$
$10y + 1$ **c.** $49m^2 - 28mp + 4p^2$
$144c + 64$ **2a.** $\frac{1}{9}A^2 + \frac{4}{9}AB + \frac{4}{9}B^2$
d. $\frac{4}{9}$ **3a.** 961 **b.** 841 **c.** 9604
9 **4a.** $d^2 - 121$ **b.** $c^4 - 64$ **c.** $81v^6 - w^8$
b. 399 **c.** 3599 **d.** 8091

8-5 pp. 395–397

lls You'll Need **1.** 1, 2, 3, 4, 6, 8, 12, 24 **2.** 1, 2,
12 **3.** 1, 2, 3, 6, 9, 18, 27, 54 **4.** 1, 3, 5, 15
3, 4, 6, 9, 12, 18, 36 **6.** 1, 2, 4, 7, 8, 14, 28,
, 2, 4, 8, 16, 32, 64 **8.** 1, 2, 3, 4, 6, 8, 12, 16,
48, 96

dards Check **1a.** $(g + 5)(g + 2)$ **b.** $(v + 20)\cdot$
c. $(a + 10)(a + 3)$ **2a.** $(k - 5)(k - 5)$
$2)(x - 9)$ **c.** $(q - 12)(q - 3)$ **3a.** $(m + 10)\cdot$
$)$ **b.** $(p - 8)(p + 5)$ **c.** $(y + 7)(y - 8)$
$+ 8y)(x + 3y)$ **b.** $(v + 8w)(v - 6w)$
$- 20n)(m + 3n)$

n 8-6 pp. 400–401

kills You'll Need **1.** $6x$ **2.** 7 **3.** 2 **4.** $(x + 1)(x + 4)$
$- 7)(y + 4)$ **6.** $(t - 5)(t - 6)$

ndards Check **1a.** $(2y + 1)(y + 2)$
$- 1)(2n - 7)$ **c.** $(2y - 1)(y - 2)$
$5d + 1)(d - 3)$ **b.** $(2n + 3)(n - 1)$
$- 9)(4p + 1)$ **3a.** $2(v - 1)(v - 5)$
$2y + 1)(y + 3)$ **c.** $6(3k + 1)(k - 1)$

Lesson 8-7 pp. 404–406, 409

Check Skills You'll Need **1.** $9x^2$ **2.** $25y^2$ **3.** $225h^4$
4. $4a^2b^4$ **5.** $c^2 - 36$ **6.** $p^2 - 22p + 121$
7. $16d^2 + 56d + 49$

CA Standards Check **1a.** $(x + 4)^2$ **b.** $(n + 8)^2$
c. $(n - 8)^2$ **2a.** $(3g - 2)^2$ **b.** $(2t + 9)^2$
c. $(2t - 9)^2$ **3a.** $(x + 6)(x - 6)$
b. $(m + 10)(m - 10)$ **c.** $(p + 7)(p - 7)$
4a. $(3v + 2)(3v - 2)$ **b.** $(5x + 8)(5x - 8)$
c. $(2w + 7)(2w - 7)$ **5a.** $2(2y + 5)(2y - 5)$
b. $3(c + 5)(c - 5)$ **c.** $7(2k + 1)(2k - 1)$

Checkpoint Quiz 2 **1.** $k^2 - 14k + 49$ **2.** $25t^2 +$
$90t + 81$ **3.** $h^2 - 22h + 121$ **4.** $5x^5 + x^3y^2$
$- 10x^2y - 2y^3$ **5.** $(v + 10)^2$ **6.** $(k - 12)(k - 5)$
7. $(2x + 11)(x + 1)$ **8.** $(5m + 7)(2m + 1)$
9. $3(w + 2)(w - 4)$ **10.** $(3t + 5)(3t - 5)$

Lesson 8-8 pp. 410–412

Check Skills You'll Need **1.** 2 **2.** $3r$ **3.** $5h$ **4.** $4m$
5. $v^3 + 3v^2 + 5v + 15$ **6.** $2q^3 - 10q^2 - 4q + 20$
7. $6t^2 - 7t - 20$ **8.** $4x^3 + 7x^2 + 10x - 3$

CA Standards Check **1a.** $(5t^3 + 6)(t + 4)$
b. $(w^2 - 7)(2w + 1)$ **2.** $3m(3m^2 + 2)(5m - 1)$
3a. $(9d + 5)(7d + 1)$ **b.** $(11k + 5)(k + 4)$
c. $(4y - 7)(y + 10)$ **4a.** Answers may vary.
Sample: $2g$, $(3g + 4)$, and $(g + 2)$ **b.** m, $(3m + 1)$,
and $(m + 3)$

Chapter 9

Check Your Readiness p. 424

1. -13 **2.** $-\frac{7}{2}$ **3.** -9 **4.** $-\frac{1}{2}$ **5.** -23 **6.** -3 **7.** -108
8. 26 **9.** 0 **10.** 49 **11.** -67 **12.** 25 **13.** 24 **14.** 144

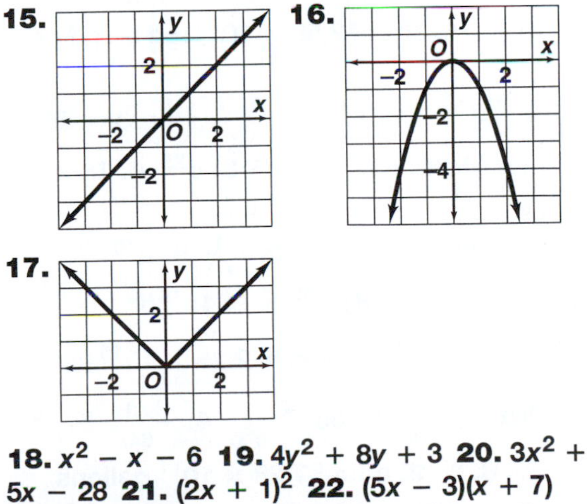

18. $x^2 - x - 6$ **19.** $4y^2 + 8y + 3$ **20.** $3x^2 +$
$5x - 28$ **21.** $(2x + 1)^2$ **22.** $(5x - 3)(x + 7)$
23. $(4x - 3)(2x - 1)$ **24.** $(m - 9)(m + 2)$
25. $(6y - 5)(2y + 3)$ **26.** $(x - 9)^2$

Lesson 7-1 pp. 328–330

Check Skills You'll Need **1.** 8 **2.** $\frac{1}{16}$ **3.** 4 **4.** −27 **5.** −27 **6.** 3 **7.** $\frac{1}{2}$ **8.** −1 **9.** 4

CA Standards Check **1a.** $\frac{1}{81}$ **b.** 1 **c.** $-\frac{1}{64}$ **d.** $\frac{1}{7}$ **e.** $-\frac{1}{9}$ **2a.** $\frac{11}{m^5}$ **b.** $\frac{7t^2}{s^4}$ **c.** $2a^3$ **d.** $\frac{1}{n^5v^2}$ **3a.** $-\frac{1}{8}$ **b.** $-\frac{1}{50}$ **c.** $\frac{1}{16}$ **d.** $-12\frac{1}{2}$ **4.** 600; 5400; for $x = -2$, the population is 600, 2 months before the population is 5400. For $x = 0$, it is the population when time is 0.

Lesson 7-2 pp. 334–336, 338

Check Skills You'll Need **1.** 60,000 **2.** 0.07 **3.** 820,000 **4.** 0.003 **5.** 34 **6.** 524 **7.** 367.8

CA Standards Check **1a.** yes **b.** No; $52 > 10$. **c.** No; $0.04 < 1$. **2a.** 2.67×10^5 **b.** 4.6205×10^7 **c.** 3.25×10^{-5} **d.** 9.0×10^{-9} **e.** 436 is 436 times greater than 1, and $436 = 4.36 \times 10^2$. Then $(4.36 \times 10^2) \cdot 10^9 = 4.36 \times 10^{11}$. **3a.** 3,200,000,000,000 **b.** 50,700 **c.** 0.00056 **d.** 0.083 **4.** electron, proton, neutron **5.** 60.2×10^{-5}, 61×10^{-2}, 0.067×10^3, 63×10^4 **6a.** 1.5×10^4 **b.** 8×10^{-10}

Checkpoint Quiz 1 **1.** $\frac{1}{45}$ **2.** $\frac{1}{r^5s^4}$ **3.** $\frac{6x^5}{y^{12}}$ **4.** $\frac{mq^2}{n^4}$ **5.** $\frac{a^2}{c^3}$ **6.** $36m^2$ **7.** $\frac{2s^2}{3}$ **8.** $\frac{3n^6}{25}$ **9.** 500; 2000; 16,000 **10.** Saturn

Lesson 7-3 pp. 339–341

Check Skills You'll Need **1.** t^7 **2.** $(6 - m)^3$ **3.** $(r + 5)^5$ **4.** 5^3s^3 **5.** −625 **6.** 625 **7.** 1 **8.** $\frac{1}{625}$

CA Standards Check **1a.** 5^9 **b.** 2^1 **c.** 7^5 **2a.** $7n^6$ **b.** $28x^2y^7$ **c.** $\frac{7m^3}{n^2}$ **3a.** 1.5×10^{12} **b.** 4.5×10^2 **c.** 6.3×10^{-14} **4.** about 2.56×10^{13} red blood cells

Lesson 7-4 pp. 345–347

Check Skills You'll Need **1.** 3^6 **2.** 2^{12} **3.** 5^{28} **4.** 7^3 **5.** x^6 **6.** a^6 **7.** $\frac{1}{y^6}$ **8.** $\frac{1}{n^6}$

CA Standards Check **1.** a^{28}; $\frac{1}{a^{28}}$ **2a.** $\frac{1}{t^{12}}$ **b.** a^{18} **3a.** $16z^4$ **b.** $\frac{1}{16g^{10}}$ **4a.** $81c^{26}$ **b.** $864a^{18}b^6$ **c.** $\frac{5400n^3}{m^3}$ **5a.** 9×10^{11} joules. **b.** 2.25×10^{15} joules.

Checkpoint Quiz 2 **1.** $\frac{1}{m^2}$ **2.** 35 **3.** $\frac{1}{a^3b}$ **4.** $-\frac{3}{64r^5}$ **5.** p^8 **6.** a^6 **7.** $\frac{9b^3}{32}$ **8.** $\frac{c^6}{d^6}$ **9.** about 7.28×10^{11} gallons **10a.** about 3.63×10^{13} km^2 **b.** about 2.06×10^{19} km^3

Lesson 7-5

Check Skills You'll Need
7. $\frac{2}{7}$ **8.** $\frac{2}{7}$ **9.** $\frac{y}{3}$ **10.**

CA Standards Check **1**
e. $\frac{xz^7}{y^5}$ **2a.** 2.5×10
d. about $9.59 \times 10^{-}$
4a. $\frac{64}{27}$ **b.** −32 **c.** $\frac{s}{2r}$

Chapter 8

Check Your Readiness

1. 1, 2, 3, 4, 6, 12 **2.** 1,
4. 1, 3, 9, 27 **5.** 1, 2, 5,
13, 65 **7.** 1, 2, 5, 10, 25
25, 40, 50, 100, 200 **9.**
21, 42 **11.** 1, 2, 3, 6, 11
13. $3x^2 - 4x$ **14.** $2b +$
16. $-\frac{2}{3}w^2 + \frac{7}{6}w$ **17.** $7z$
19. $-6t^2 + 10t$ **20.** $-p$
23. $9z^4$ **24.** $10t^7$ **25.** 1
28. $36p^8$ **29.** x^2y^4 **30.**

Lesson 8-1

Check Skills You'll Need **1.** $19t$
5. $-3n^2$ **6.** $7x^2$

CA Standards Check **1.** Degre
7; fourth degree trinomial
cubic trinomial **c.** $-4v + 8$
3a. $20m^2 + 9$ **b.** $4t^2 + 5$ **c**
d. $11p^3 + 17p^2 + 13p$ **4a.**
b. $28d^3 - 30d^2 - 3d$

Lesson 8-2

Check Skills You'll Need **1.** 906 **2**
4. $24 + 20x$ **5.** $-16y - 8$ **6.**
8. $54 - 9x$ **9.** $-8x + 2$

CA Standards Check **1a.** $20b^3 +$
b. $-21h^3 + 56h^2 + 7h$ **c.** $2x^3$
2a. $5v^3$ **b.** 3 **c.** $2b$ **3a.** $4x(2x$
c. $6m(m^2 - 2m - 4)$

Lesson 8-3

Check Skills You'll Need **1.** $4r^2 - 4r$
3. $2y^5 - 7y^2$ **4.** $x^3 + 8x^2 + 2x$
6. $5w^2 - 27w$ **7.** $-2b^2 - 15b$
8. $7m^3 + 27m^2 - 6m$ **9.** $d^5 - 4$

CA Standards
$11m - 2$
b. $6x^2 + 7$
d. $6x^2 - 2$
b. $x^2 + 2x$

Checkpoint Q
3. $36w^2 -$
6. $12n^5 +$
8. $5t(t^5 +$
10. $6m^2(6$

Lesson 8-

Check Skills
5. $j^2 + 1$
7. $20y^2 -$
9. $8c^4 -$

CA Standa
b. $25y^2$
d. $81c^2 -$
b. $\frac{1}{9}$ **c.** $\frac{4}{9}$
d. 41,20
5a. 396

Lesson

Check Ski
3, 4, 6,
5. 1, 2,
56 **7.** 1
24, 32,

CA Stan
$(v + 1)$
b. $(x -$
$(m - 2$
4a. $(x$
c. $(m$

Lesso

Check S
5. $(y$

CA Sta
b. $(3$
2a. $($
c. $(5$
b. $2($

Lesson 9-1 pp. 426–429

Check Skills You'll Need **1.** -24 **2.** 18 **3.** 12 **4.** 35

5. **6.** **7.**

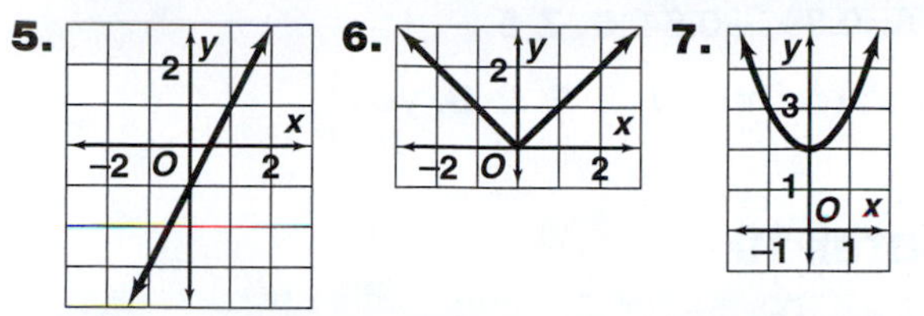

CA Standards Check **1a.** (4, 3); max. **b.** $(-3, -3)$; min.

2.

x	$f(x) = -2x^2$	(x, y)
0	$-2(0)^2 = 0$	(0, 0)
1	$-2(1)^2 = -2$	$(1, -2)$
2	$-2(2)^2 = -8$	$(2, -8)$

3. $y = \frac{1}{2}x^2, y = x^2, y = -2x^2$

4a. The graph of $y = x^2 - 4$ has the same shape as the graph of $y = x^2$, and it is shifted down 4 units.

b. Positive values of c shift the vertex up. Negative values of c shift the vertex down.

5a.

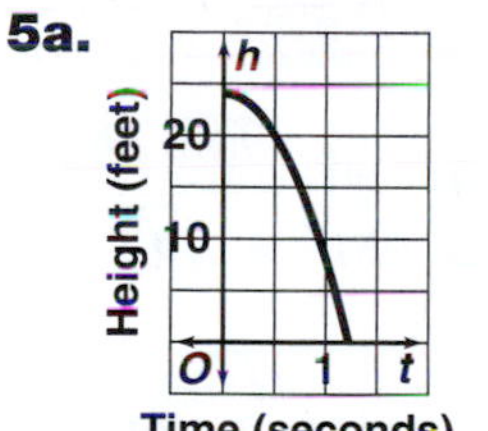

b. Domain: 0 to about 1.5 seconds; range: 0 to 30 feet.

Lesson 9-2 pp. 433–435

Check Skills You'll Need **1.** $\frac{1}{3}$ **2.** $-\frac{2}{3}$ **3.** $-3\frac{1}{2}$ **4.** 6

5. **6.**

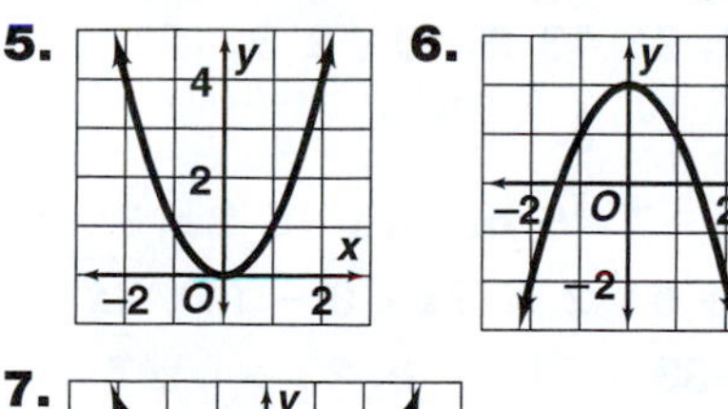

7.

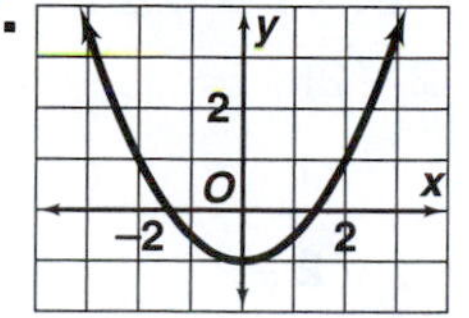

CA Standards Check

1. **2a.** 1.5 s **b.** 40 ft

3a. **b.**

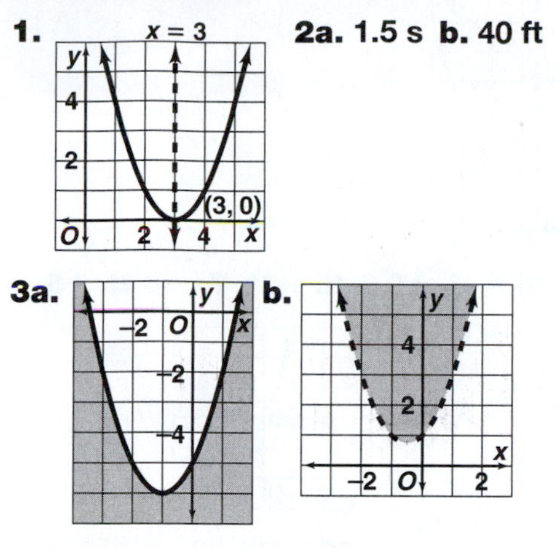

Lesson 9-3 pp. 440–441

Check Skills You'll Need **1.** 121 **2.** 144 **3.** -144 **4.** 2.25 **5.** 0.36 **6.** $\frac{1}{4}$ **7.** $\frac{4}{9}$ **8.** $\frac{16}{25}$

CA Standards Check **1a.** 7 **b.** ± 6 **c.** -11 **d.** $\frac{1}{5}$

2a. irrational **b.** rational **c.** irrational **d.** rational **3.** -11 and -10 **4.** 156.5 ft

Lesson 9-4 pp. 445–447, 450

Check Skills You'll Need **1.** 6 **2.** -9 **3.** ± 11 **4.** 1.2 **5.** 0.5 **6.** ± 1.1 **7.** $\frac{1}{2}$ **8.** $\pm\frac{1}{3}$ **9.** $\frac{7}{10}$

CA Standards Check

1a. ± 1 **b.** no solution

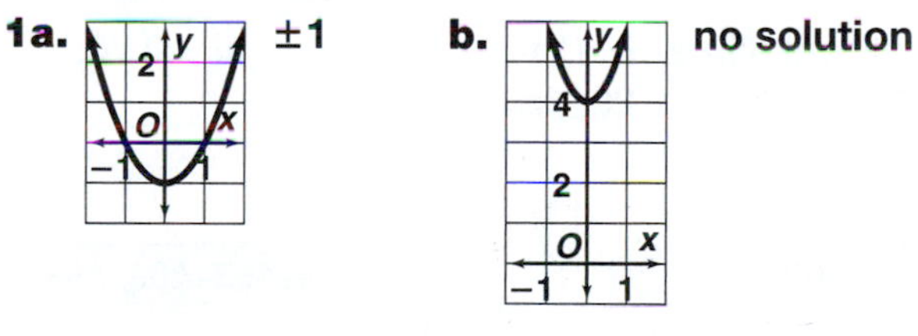

c. $x = 0$

2a. ± 5 **b.** 0 **c.** no solution **3.** about 14 ft

Checkpoint Quiz 1

1. **2.**

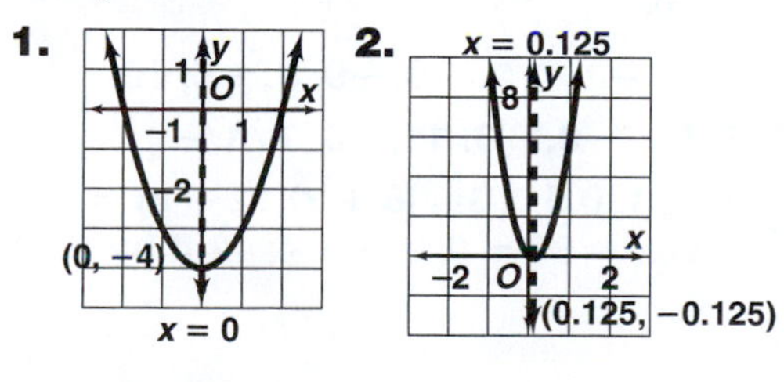

3.

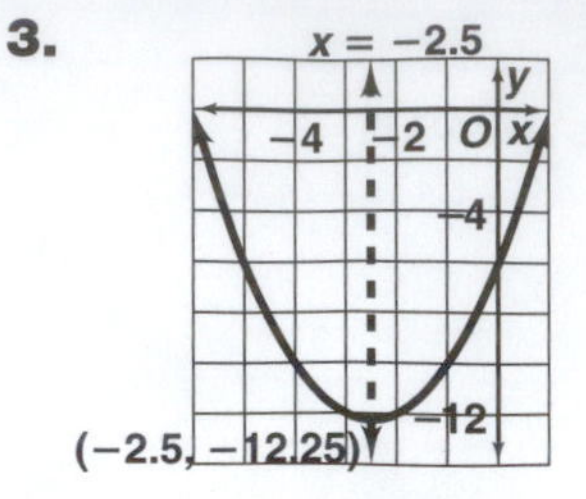

4a. 0.75 s **b.** 15 ft **5.** ±0.6 **6.** −21 **7.** ±8 **8.** ±5

9.

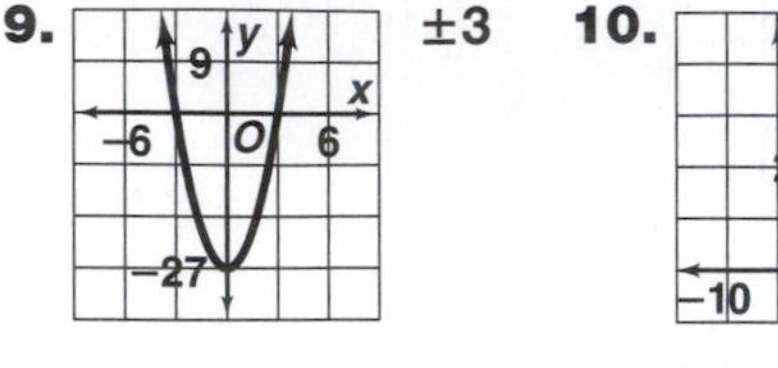

±3

10.

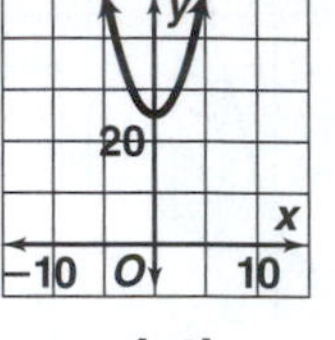

no solution

Lesson 9-5 pp. 452–453

Check Skills You'll Need **1.** −1 **2.** 104 **3.** $-2\frac{5}{7}$
4. $(2c + 1)(c + 14)$ **5.** $(3p + 2)(p + 10)$
6. $(4x + 3)(x - 6)$

CA Standards Check **1a.** −7, 4 **b.** $\frac{5}{3}$, 2 **c.** $-\frac{3}{2}$, $\frac{11}{4}$
d. $-\frac{1}{5}$, −6 **2.** −4, 12 **3.** 6 **4.** 9 in. × 10 in. × 2 in.

Lesson 9-6 pp. 457–459

Check Skills You'll Need **1.** $d^2 - 8d + 16$
2. $x^2 + 22x + 121$ **3.** $k^2 - 16k + 64$ **4.** $(b + 5)^2$
5. $(t + 7)^2$ **6.** $(n - 9)^2$

CA Standards Check **1.** 121 **2.** 19, −13 **3a.** −0.70, −4.30 **b.** 12.74, 1.26 **4a.** −1.65, 3.65
b. 2.56, −1.96

Lesson 9-7 pp. 463–466, 468

Check Skills You'll Need **1.** 9 **2.** $\frac{49}{4}$ **3.** $\frac{81}{4}$ **4.** 6, 4
5. 2, −18 **6.** 1, −5 **7.** −7, 8

CA Standards Check **1a.** 4, −2 **b.** 13, −9 **2a.** 0.67, 1
b. 1.22, −0.94 **3a.** $0 = -16t^2 + 38.4t + 3.5$
b. $t \approx 2.5$; 2.5 s **4a.** Quadratic formula; the equation cannot be factored. **b.** Factoring; the equation is easily factorable. **c.** Square roots; there is no x term.

Checkpoint Quiz 2 **1.** −3, 7 **2.** −3, −9 **3.** −5, 10
4. 0.4, −2.4 **5.** 5.7, −0.7 **6.** 11, −3 **7.** 1, $-\frac{3}{4}$
8. no solution **9.** 1, 0.5 **10a.** $(8 + x)(12 + x) = 2 \cdot (8 \cdot 12)$ or $x^2 + 20x - 96 = 0$ **b.** $x = 4$; 12 ft by 16 ft

Lesson 9-8 pp. 470–472

Check Skills You'll Need **1.** −80 **2.** 72 **3.** −283 **4.** 2.18, 0.15 **5.** 0.39, −0.64 **6.** 7, 5

CA Standards Check **1.** 2 **2.** 2 **3.** yes

Chapter 10

Check Your Readiness p. 484

1. 3 **2.** 13 **3.** 30 **4.** 4 **5.** 45 **6.** 17 **7.** 3
8. 66 **9.** 11 **10.** $\frac{16}{9}$ **11.** $\frac{1}{y^6}$ **12.** $\frac{m}{6}$ **13.** a^3
14. 2 **15.** 15 **16.** $\frac{3}{5}$ **17.** −0.06 **18.** 6.32
19. 9.17 **20.** 10.20 **21.** 1.79 **22.** 2 **23.** 2
24. 0 **25.** 1 **26.** 2 **27.** 2

Lesson 10-1 pp. 486–489

Check Skills You'll Need **1.** 1 **2.** 1 **3.** 3 **4.** 4 **5.** 2 **6.** 13 **7.** 5 **8.** 7

CA Standards Check **1a.** $5\sqrt{2}$ **b.** $-50\sqrt{3}$ **c.** $3\sqrt{2}$
2a. $3n\sqrt{3}$ **b.** $-2a^4\sqrt{15a}$ **c.** $xy^2\sqrt{y}$ **3a.** 26
b. $15c\sqrt{2}$ **c.** $60a^2\sqrt{2a}$ **4.** 6 mi **5a.** 4 **b.** $\frac{5p\sqrt{p}}{q}$
c. $\frac{5\sqrt{3}}{4t}$ **6a.** $3\sqrt{2}$ **b.** $\frac{4}{5}$ **c.** $3x$ **7a.** $\sqrt{3}$ **b.** $\frac{\sqrt{10t}}{6t}$
c. $\frac{\sqrt{70m}}{10}$

Lesson 10-2 pp. 493–495

Check Skills You'll Need **1.** 61 **2.** 65 **3.** $25t^2$ **4.** 14
5. $\frac{5}{7}$ **6.** 1.2

CA Standards Check **1.** 25 cm **2.** 6.9 miles **3.** yes
4. no

Lesson 10-3 pp. 500–502, 506

Check Skills You'll Need **1.** $2\sqrt{13}$ **2.** $10\sqrt{2}$ **3.** $12\sqrt{6}$
4. $5x\sqrt{5}$ **5.** $\frac{\sqrt{33}}{11}$ **6.** $\frac{\sqrt{10}}{4}$ **7.** $\frac{\sqrt{30x}}{2x}$

CA Standards Check **1a.** $-7\sqrt{5}$ **b.** $-4\sqrt{10}$ **2a.** $8\sqrt{5}$
b. $-3\sqrt{3}$ **3a.** $2\sqrt{5} + 5\sqrt{2}$ **b.** $2x\sqrt{3} - 11\sqrt{2x}$
c. $5a + 3\sqrt{5a}$ **4a.** $-33 - 21\sqrt{2}$ **b.** $23 + 8\sqrt{7}$
5a. $2(\sqrt{7} - \sqrt{5})$ **b.** $-2(\sqrt{10} - 2\sqrt{2})$
c. $\frac{-5(\sqrt{11} + \sqrt{3})}{8}$ **6.** 55 in.

Checkpoint Quiz 1 **1.** $-8\sqrt{7}$ **2.** $4 - 5\sqrt{2}$
3. $2\sqrt{5} + 15$ **4.** $3\sqrt{2}$ **5.** $5 + 2\sqrt{6}$
6. $4\sqrt{3} + 2\sqrt{10} - 9\sqrt{2} - 3\sqrt{15}$ **7.** yes
8. no **9.** no **10.** 15 mi

Lesson 10-4 pp. 507–509

Check Skills You'll Need **1.** 1 **2.** 4 **3.** 4 **4.** 3 **5.** $x + 1$ **6.** $2x - 5$

CA Standards Check **1a.** 25 **b.** 81 **c.** 38 **2a.** about 67 ft **b.** No; $h - 2r$ decreases as r increases. **3.** 5 **4a.** A principal square root must be a nonnegative number. **b.** 2 **5.** no solution

Lesson 10-5 pp. 514–515, 519

Check Skills You'll Need

1. **2.**

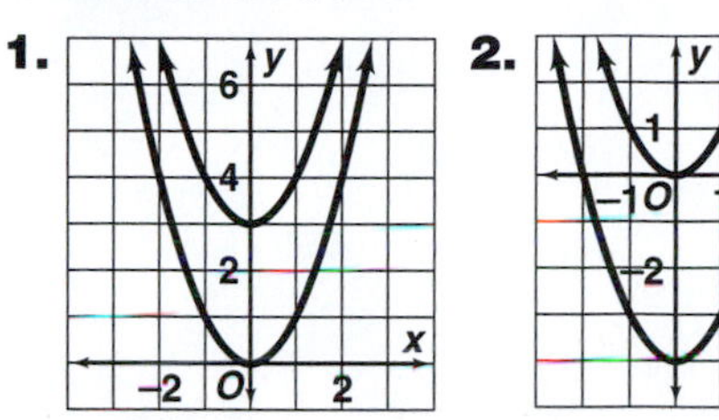

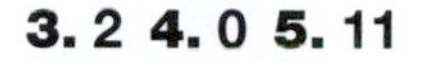

3. 2 **4.** 0 **5.** 11

CA Standards Check **1a.** $\{x: x \geq 7\}$; $\{y: y \geq 0\}$ **b.** $\{x: x \geq \frac{1}{3}\}$; $\{y: y \geq 0\}$

2a. **b.**

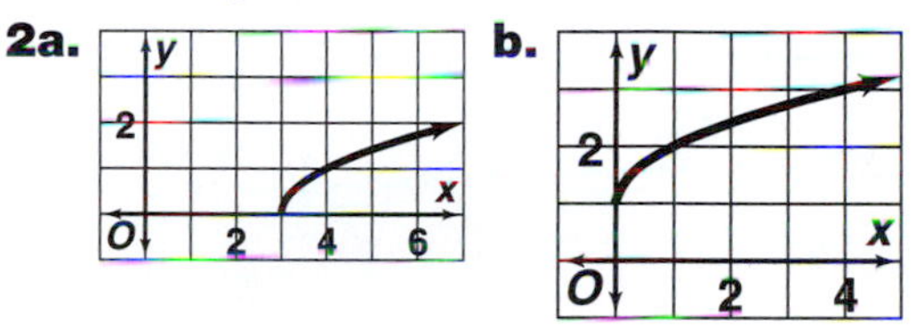

3a.

b. 361.25 ft

Checkpoint Quiz 2 **1.** 256 **2.** 8 **3.** 5 **4.** $\frac{1}{4}$ **5.** domain: $\{x: x \geq 0\}$; range $\{y: y \geq 3\}$ **6.** domain: $\{x: x \geq -3\}$; range $\{y: y \geq 0\}$ **7.** domain: $\{x: x \geq 1\}$; range $\{y: y \geq -2\}$

8.

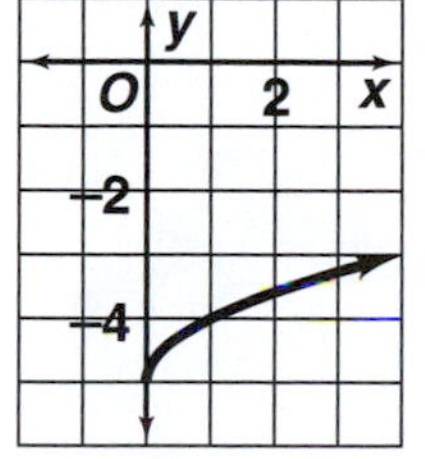

9.

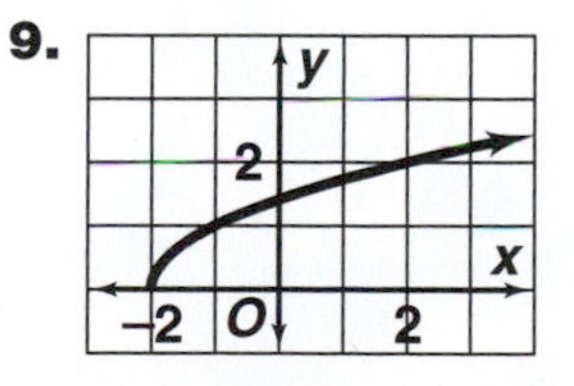

10.

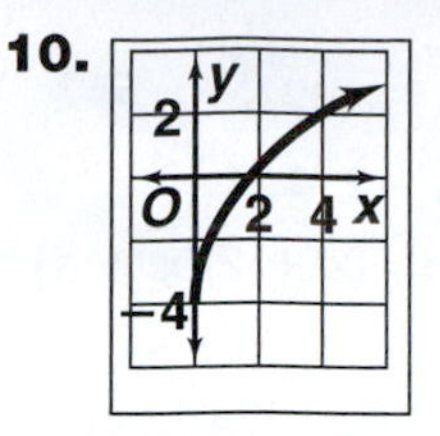

Chapter 11

Check Your Readiness p. 528

1. $1\frac{1}{6}$ **2.** $\frac{9}{13}$ **3.** $\frac{47}{50}$ **4.** $\frac{5}{12}$ **5.** $-8, 4$ **6.** $2, 7$ **7.** $-5, -1$ **8.** $-2, 6$ **9.** $-3, 9$ **10.** $0, 4$ **11.** $3w^2x$ **12.** r^2s^2 **13.** $\frac{5}{2}k^4$ **14.** 100 **15.** no solution **16.** 1 **17.** $\{x: x \geq 0\}$; $\{y: y \leq 5\}$ **18.** $\{x: x \geq 0\}$; $\{y: y \geq -2\}$ **19.** $\{x: x \leq \frac{10}{3}\}$; $\{y: y \geq 0\}$

Lesson 11-1 pp. 530–532

Check Skills You'll Need **1.** 4 **2.** $-\frac{5}{8}$ **3.** $\frac{5}{7}$ **4.** $(x + 4)(x - 3)$ **5.** $(x + 4)(x + 2)$ **6.** $(x - 5)(x + 3)$ **7.** $(x + 4)^2$ **8.** $(x + 3)(x - 4)$ **9.** $(x - 3)(x - 4)$

CA Standards Check **1a.** $\frac{3}{5b}$ **b.** $\frac{4c^2}{c + 2}$ **c.** 2 **d.** 4 **2a.** $\frac{3}{x - 5}$ **b.** $\frac{2}{z - 3}$ **c.** $\frac{8}{2a + 1}$ **d.** $\frac{c - 3}{c + 3}$ **3a.** -1 **b.** $-\frac{1}{m + 8}$ **c.** $-\frac{4}{r + 4}$ **d.** $-\frac{2}{3}$ **4a.** 51 min **b.** $\frac{30rh}{r + h}$

Lesson 11-2 pp. 535–537, 539

Check Skills You'll Need **1.** r^{10} **2.** b^7 **3.** c^5 **4.** $6x^9$ **5.** $5n^4$ **6.** $-45a^5$ **7.** $(2c + 1)(c + 7)$ **8.** $(15t - 11)(t - 1)$ **9.** $(2q + 1)(q + 5)$

CA Standards Check **1a.** $\frac{-12}{a^5}$ **b.** $\frac{(x - 5)(x - 7)}{x(x + 3)}$ **2.** $-\frac{1}{x}$ **3a.** $3(c - 1)(c + 1)$ **b.** $2v(v - 5)$ **c.** $\frac{4(m + 2)}{m + 1}$ **4a.** $\frac{1}{b}$ **b.** $\frac{5(7m - 10)}{7(m - 10)}$ **c.** $\frac{3n + 2}{2n - 3}$ **5a.** $-\frac{1}{10x^2}$ **b.** $\frac{y + 3}{(y + 2)^2}$ **c.** $\frac{1}{z + 4}$

Checkpoint Quiz 1 **1.** $\frac{b - 5}{2}$ **2.** $\frac{3}{4k}$ **3.** $\frac{7}{3}$ **4.** $\frac{1}{2a^2 - 3}$ **5.** $\frac{2z + 3}{z + 1}$ **6.** $\frac{2c - 9}{2c + 8}$ **7.** $\frac{3(c + 4)}{5c}$ **8.** $\frac{4}{3}$ **9.** $(x + 2)(x + 4)$ **10.** $\frac{v + 3}{24v}$

Lesson 11-3 pp. 540–542

Check Skills You'll Need **1.** $-4a^2 + 9a + 1$ **2.** $-x^3 + 3x^2 + 5x - 6$ **3.** $8t - 2$ **4.** $2x^2 + 10x + 12$ **5.** $-3n^2 + 11n + 20$ **6.** $6a^3 - 21a^2 + 2a - 7$

CA Standards Check **1a.** $m - 2 + \frac{1}{3m}$ **b.** $2t^3 + 4t - 1 + \frac{1}{2t}$ **2a.** $2b - 3$ **b.** $3m - 4 - \frac{3}{2m + 1}$ **3a.** $t^3 + t^2 + 2t + 3$ **b.** $c^2 - 3c + 5 - \frac{3}{c + 3}$ **4a.** $4x + 3 - \frac{4}{2x + 1}$ **b.** $-2a - 5 - \frac{1}{3a - 2}$

Lesson 11-4 pp. 545–547

Check Skills You'll Need **1.** $\frac{2}{3}$ **2.** $-\frac{2}{7}$ **3.** -2 **4.** $1\frac{1}{18}$ **5.** $-\frac{1}{12}$ **6.** $-\frac{1}{3}$ **7.** $\frac{2x}{3}$ **8.** $\frac{x}{2}$ **9.** $\frac{1}{2y}$ **10.** $(x + 2)(x + 1)$ **11.** $(y + 3)(y + 4)$ **12.** $(t - 2)^2$

CA Standards Check **1a.** $\frac{5}{x + 2}$ **b.** $\frac{4y}{y - 5}$ **c.** $\frac{7n}{n + 1}$ **2a.** $-\frac{1}{t - 2}$ **b.** $\frac{2b - 3}{b + 2}$ **c.** $\frac{-c + 5}{5m + 2}$ **3a.** $\frac{9 + 14y^2}{21y^4}$ **b.** $\frac{16 - 49x}{100x}$ **c.** $\frac{5(b + 1)}{12b^2}$ **4a.** $\frac{8t + 7}{(t + 4)(t - 1)}$ **b.** $\frac{m^2 + 5m + 3}{(2m + 1)(m - 1)}$ **c.** $\frac{3a^2 + 2a + 2}{(a + 2)(2a - 1)}$ **5.** $\frac{1270}{r} + \frac{1270}{1.12r} \approx \frac{2404}{r}$

Checkpoint Quiz 2 **1.** $a^2 + 5a + 15 + \frac{44}{a - 3}$ **2.** $5g - 12 + \frac{15}{g + 2}$ **3.** $\frac{5}{x - 3}$ **4.** $\frac{2(7m - 6)}{(m + 2)(m - 3)}$ **5.** $\frac{3(2t + 1)}{t^2}$

Lesson 11-5 pp. 550–552

Check Skills You'll Need **1.** $1\frac{2}{3}$ **2.** $1\frac{1}{5}$ **3.** $-9, 9$ **4.** $4n$ **5.** $15x$ **6.** $24y^2$

CA Standards Check **1a.** -2 **b.** $-\frac{25}{2}$ **2a.** $\frac{1}{2}, 2$ **b.** $-2, 3$ **3.** $28\frac{1}{8}$ min **4a.** -3 **b.** $-5, 4$ **5a.** no solution **b.** -1

Selected Answers

Chapter 1

Lesson 1-1 pp. 6–8

EXERCISES **1.** $p + 4$ **3.** $12 - m$ **5.** $\frac{n}{8}$ **7.** $x - 23$ **9–11.** Choice of variable for the number may vary. **9.** $2n + 2$ **11.** $9 - n$ **13.** $5n$ **15.** $\frac{n}{6}$ **17–19.** Choice of variable may vary. **17.** c = total cost, n = number of cans, $c = 0.70n$ **19.** ℓ = total length in feet, n = number of tents, $\ell = 60n$ **21–23.** Choices of variables may vary. Samples are given. **21.** w = number of workers, r = number of radios, $r = 13w$ **23.** n = number of sales, t = total earnings, $t = 0.4n$ **25.** $9 + k - 17$ **27.** $37t - 9.85$ **29.** $15 + \frac{60}{w}$ **31.** $5m - \frac{t}{7}$ **33.** $8 - 9r$ **35–37.** Answers may vary. Samples are given. **35.** the difference of 3 and t **37.** the quotient of y and 5 **39.** Choices of variables may vary. Sample is given. n = number of days, c = change in height (m), $c = 0.165n$ **41a.** i. yes; $6 = 3 \cdot 2$ ii. yes; $6 = 3 + 3$ **b.** Answers may vary. Sample: i; it makes sense that an equation relating lawns mowed and hours worked would be a multiple of the number of lawns mowed. **43.** Choices of variables may vary. Samples are given. **a.** d = drop height (ft), f = height of first bounce (ft), $f = \frac{1}{2}d$ **b.** 10 ft **45 and 47.** Answers may vary. Samples are given. **45.** You jog at a rate of 5 miles per hour. How far do you jog in 2 hours? Let d = distance in miles and t = time in hours. **47.** The Merkurs have budgeted $40 for a baby sitter. What hourly rate can they afford to pay if they need the sitter for 5 hours? Let h = the number of hours and c = the cost per hour. **49.** A **51.** C **53.** $\frac{31}{35}$ **55.** $\frac{11}{24}$ **57.** $\frac{14}{45}$ **59.** $2\frac{2}{3}$ **61.** $(4 \cdot 10^2) + (8 \cdot 10^1) + (6 \cdot 10^0)$ **63.** $(3 \cdot 10^4) + (6 \cdot 10^3) + (2 \cdot 10^1) + (1 \cdot 10^0)$

Lesson 1-2 pp. 12–15

EXERCISES **1.** 59 **3.** 7 **5.** 32 **7.** 21 **9.** 124 **11.** 180

13.

Original Price P	$P - 0.15P$	Sale Price S
$ 12	12 – 0.15(12)	$ 10.20
$ 16	16 – 0.15(16)	$ 13.60
$ 20	20 – 0.15(20)	$ 17.00
$ 25	25 – 0.15(25)	$ 21.25

15. 22 **17.** 44 **19.** 16 **21.** 704 **23.** 185 **25.** 57 **27.** 1936 **29.** 18 **31.** 0 **33.** 81 **35.** 8 cm^3 **37.** 21 ft^3 **39.** 15,000 ft^3 **41.** 15 **43.** 111 **45.** 50.4 **47a.** left side = 1, right side = 1 **b.** left side = 4, right side = 2 **c.** Answers may vary. Sample: For $a = 2$ and $b = 3$, left side = 25, right side = 13 **d.** No; as seen in part (b), $(a + b)^2 = a^2 + b^2$ is not true for all values of a and b. **49.** 17 **51.** 143 **53.** 143 **55.** $14\frac{3}{4}$ **57.** The student should have divided 14 by 30 before adding 1. The correct answer is $1\frac{7}{15}$. **59a.** 523.60 cm^3 **b.** 381.70 cm^3 **61.** 1.2, 0.9, 0.5, 0.2 **63.** $(10 + 6) \div 2 - 3 = 5$ **65.** $(3^2 + 9) \div 9 = 2$ **67a.** 22; 22 **b.** No; part (a) shows the value is unaffected for the given numbers. **69.** Answers may vary. Samples: $2(4 - 1) - 5 = 1$, $5 + 2 - (1 + 4) = 2$, $(2^4 - 1) \div 5 = 3$, $1 + 2 + 5 - 4 = 4$, $2 \cdot 5 - (1 + 4) = 5$, $(5^2 - 1) \div 4 = 6$, $5 + 4 - 1 \cdot 2 = 7$, $2^5 \div (4 \cdot 1) = 8$, $2^5 \div 4 + 1 = 9$, $4^2 - (1 + 5) = 10$, $(4^2 - 5) \div 1 = 11$, $1 + 2 + 4 + 5 = 12$, $2^{(4-1)} + 5 = 13$, $2 \cdot 5 + 1 \cdot 4 = 14$, $5(4 - 1^2) = 15$, $2(1 + 5) + 4 = 16$, $5 + 4(2 + 1) = 17$, $4(5 - 1) + 2 = 18$, $4 \cdot 5 - 1^2 = 19$, $4^2 + 5 - 1 = 20$ **71.** C **73.** D **75.** $c + 2$ **77.** $t - 21$ **79.** 50% **81.** 95% **83.** 6% **85.** $\frac{1}{8}$ **87.** $\frac{5}{12}$ **89.** $\frac{5}{24}$

Lesson 1-3 pp. 20–23

EXERCISES **1.** integers, rational numbers **3.** rational numbers **5.** rational numbers **7.** whole numbers, integers, rational numbers **9.** rational numbers **11.** Answers may vary. Sample: −17 **13.** Answers may vary. Sample: 0.3 **15.** whole numbers **17.** whole numbers **19.** true **21.** False; answers may vary. Sample: 6 **23.** False; answers may vary. Sample: $-6 < |-6|$ **25.** $<$ **27.** $=$ **29.** $-9\frac{3}{4}, -9\frac{2}{3}, -9\frac{7}{12}$ **31.** −1.01, −1.001, −1.0009 **33.** $\frac{22}{25}$; 0.8888, $\frac{8}{9}$ **35.** 9 **37.** 0.5 **39.** 0 **41.** $\frac{4}{5}$ **43.** Answers may vary. Sample: $\frac{5}{1}$ **45.** Answers may vary. Sample: $\frac{1034}{1000}$ **47.** natural numbers, whole numbers, integers, rational numbers **49.** rational numbers **51.** $=$ **53.** $<$ **55.** $=$ **57.** 6 **59.** a **61.** −48 **63a.** irrational **b.** No; π has no final digit. **65.** Yes; all can be expressed as ratios of themselves to 1. **67.** sometimes; $1 - 0.5 = 0.5$ **69.** always **71.** 17 **73.** 10 **75a.** −2.2 **b.** −2.81 **c.** $-2\frac{1}{8}$ **d.** Yes; find the average of the two given numbers. **77.** C **79.** D **81.** D **83.** 48 **85.** 7 **87.** $7\frac{1}{2}$ **89.** c = total cost, n = number of books, $c = 3.5n$

Lesson 1-4 pp. 27–30

EXERCISES **1.** $6 + (-3)$; 3 **3.** $-5 + 7$; 2 **5.** 15 **7.** −19 **9.** −4 **11.** −8 **13.** 2.2 **15.** −7.49 **17.** $\frac{14}{15}$ **19.** $6\frac{3}{16}$ **21.** 0 **23.** $5\frac{1}{6}$ **25.** $-47 + 12 = -35$, 35 ft **27.** $-6 + 13 = 7$, 7°F **29.** −1.7 **31.** −8.7 **33.** −5.6 **35.** −12.6 **37.** Choices of variable may vary. c = change in amount of money, $74 + c$ **a.** \$92 **b.** \$45 **c.** \$27 **d.** \$1.94 **39.** $-5, -3, -1\frac{1}{2}, 9$ **41.** 13.8 million people **43.** Weaving; add the numbers in each column. **45.** 0 **47.** 1 **49.** 7 **51.** −1 **53.** The sum of −227 and 319; the sum of −227 and 319 is positive, while the sum of 227 and −319 is negative. **55.** −0.3 **57.** −0.6 **59.** 0.1 **61.** D **63.** $-1\frac{5}{12}, -\frac{1}{4}, \frac{5}{24}, \frac{9}{10}$ **65.** \$7 **67.** $\frac{w}{10}$ **69.** $\frac{58a}{21}$ **71.** $\frac{x}{12}$ **73.** Pos.; if m is neg., $-m$ is pos. and the sum of two pos. is pos. **75.** Pos.; if m is neg., $-m$ is pos. and the sum of two pos. is pos. **77.** B **79.** D **81.** C **83.** = **85.** > **87.** = **89.** 2.2 **91.** 21

Lesson 1-5 pp. 34–36

EXERCISES **1.** −1 **3.** −6 **5.** 1 **7.** 14

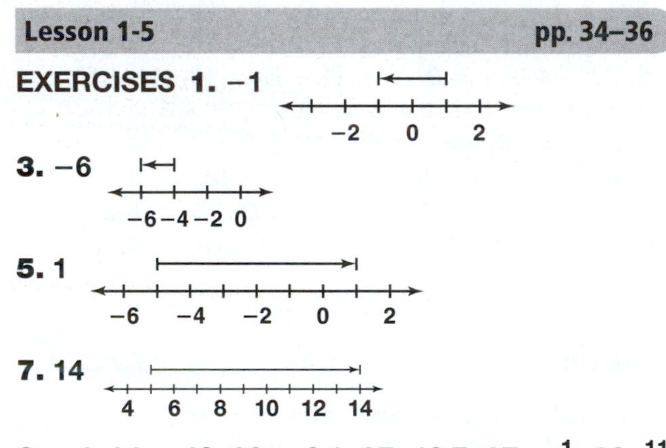

9. −4 **11.** −10 **13.** −2.1 **15.** 13.7 **17.** $-\frac{1}{6}$ **19.** $\frac{11}{12}$ **21.** 3 **23.** 6 **25.** 13 **27.** 6 **29.** 21 **31.** 7 **33.** 1 **35.** 0 **37.** −13 **39.** −9.5 **41.** −2 **43.** 1.5 **45.** 16 **47.** 11 **49.** −2 **51.** A **53.** false; $2 - (-1) = 3$, $3 \not< 2$ or −1 **55a.** −0.4, −1.4, −2.2 **b.** 1.4, 0.3, 0 **c.** Answers may vary. Sample: Invest in soccer; it has not lost any participants. **57.** $-\frac{9}{20}$ **59.** $-12t - m$ **61.** A **63.** A **65.** −9 **67.** −4.1 **69.** whole numbers **71–73.** Choices of variables may vary. **71.** t = total cost, p = pounds of pears, $t = 1.19p$ **73.** c = check (\$), s = your share, $s = \frac{c}{6}$

Lesson 1-6 pp. 41–44

EXERCISES **1.** −15 **3.** 15 **5.** −34.4 **7.** −120 **9.** −80 **11.** −78 **13.** −12 **15.** −15 **17.** −8 **19.** 48 **21.** 12 **23.** −432 **25.** −64 **27.** 4 **29.** 36 **31a.** −9°F **b.** −53.2°F **c.** −32.4°F **d.** −43°F **33.** 8 **35.** 81 **37.** −192 **39.** 675 **41.** −4 **43.** 6 **45.** $12\frac{4}{5}$ **47.** −8 **49.** −7 **51.** 0 **53.** $3\frac{1}{2}$ **55.** −15 **57.** $-\frac{6}{25}$ **59.** $-8, -7\frac{1}{4}, -3\frac{1}{2}, 4$ **61a.** i. 1 ii. −1 iii. 2 iv. −6 v. 24 vi. −120 **b.** pos. **c.** neg. **d.** No; answers may vary. Sample: The sign of the product is not affected by the number of pos. factors, only by the number of neg. factors. **63.** −6 **65.** $-\frac{1}{10}$ **67–71.** Answers may vary. Sample answers are given. **67.** $ac + b$ **69.** $ab - c$ **71.** $-bc + a$ **73.** Yes; whatever the signs of a and b, $|ab|$, $|a|$, and $|b|$ are pos., and $|ab| = |a| \cdot |b|$. **75.** 0.1 is the multiplicative inverse of 10 because $0.1(10) = 1$. (−10 is the opposite of 10.) **77.** always **79.** sometimes; $-2 \cdot (-3)]$ **81.** sometimes; 1 **83.** D **85.** $\frac{1}{16}$ **87.** $\frac{1}{64}$ **89.** −8 **91.** $-\frac{9}{16}$ **93.** $\frac{1}{2}$ **95.** D **97.** C **99.** C **101.** −20 **103.** 9.8 **105.** $\frac{1}{72}$ **107.** 56 **109.** $\frac{3}{4}$ **111.** 121

Lesson 1-7 pp. 48–51

EXERCISES **1.** 2412 **3.** 5489 **5.** 686 **7.** 20,582 **9.** \$3.96 **11.** \$29.55 **13.** \$98.97 **15.** $7t - 28$ **17.** $3m + 12$ **19.** $-2x - 6$ **21.** $1.5q + 8$ **23.** $\frac{5}{2} + \frac{15}{16}r$ **25.** $2w + 4$ **27.** $-x - 3$ **29.** $-3 - x$ **31.** $-6k - 5$ **33.** $-2 + 7x$ **35.** $4m - 8$ **37.** $20k^2$ **39.** $24w$ **41.** $6m$ **43.** $-45x$ **45.** $3(m - 7)$ **47.** $2(b + 9)$ **49.** 44,982 **51.** 14.021 **53.** $18.6 + 15m$ **55.** −28; −18; −3; 4 **57.** −18; −6; 0; 5 **59.** $6\frac{7}{100}\left(8 + \frac{4}{3}p\right)$ **61.** $\frac{17}{z - 34}$ **63.** A **65.** The student did not mult. the second number in parentheses, 10, by 4 to get the correct answer, $12x + 40$. **67.** $4.78d$ **69.** $-6.1t^2 + 13.7t$ **71.** $\frac{71}{42}n + n^3$ **73.** $7m^2 - mz + 4$ **75.** $1.4b - 5b^2 + 5c$ **77.** terms: $-7t$, $6v$, 7, $-19y$, coefficients: −7, 6, −19, constant: 7 **79.** 10 pennies, 7 nickels, 4 quarters, 1 dime **81.** $27 + 3t$ **83.** $-3m - 9$ **85.** $14b + 42b^2$ **87.** $\frac{3x - 10}{3}$ **89a.** 30; −8 **b.** 12; −6 **c.** No; parts (a) and (b) show the expressions are not equal. **91.** D **93.** D **95.** A **97.** B **99.** −4 **101.** 7 **103.** $-\frac{5}{4}$ **105.** −17 **107.** 12.127 **109.** 45.7 **111.** 0.92 **113.** 23

Lesson 1-8 pp. 54–56

EXERCISES **1.** Ident. Prop. of Add.; 0, the identity for addition, is added. **3.** Assoc. Prop. of Add.; the grouping of the terms changes. **5.** Comm. Prop. of Mult.; the order of the factors changes. **7.** Assoc. Prop. of Mult.; the grouping of the factors changes. **9.** 100 **11.** 14.95 **13.** −5 **15.** \$6.00 **17a.** Comm. Prop. of Mult. **b.** Assoc. Prop. of Mult. **c.** mult. **d.** mult.

19. $-5(7y)$
$= [-5(7y)]y$ Assoc. Prop. of Mult.
$= -35y$ mult.

21. $12x - 3 + 6x$
$= 12x + (-3) + 6x$ def. of subtr.
$= 12x + 6x + (-3)$ Comm. Prop. of Add.
$= (12 + 6)x + (-3)$ Dist. Prop.
$= 18x + (-3)$ add.
$= 18x - 3$ def. of subtr.

23. $43\left(\frac{1}{43}\right) + 1 = 1 + 1$ Inv. Prop. of Mult.
$= 2$ add.

25. $36jkm - 36mjk$
$= 36jkm + (-36)mjk$ def. of subtr.
$= 36jkm + (-36)jmk$ Comm. Prop. of Mult.
$= 36jkm + (-36)jkm$ Comm. Prop. of Mult.
$= [36 + (-36)]jkm$ Dist. Prop.
$= (0)jkm$ Inv. Prop. of Add.
$= (0)jkm$ Mult. Prop. of Zero

27. $(7^6 - 6^5)(8 - 8)$
$= (7^6 - 6^5)[8 + (-8)]$ def. of subtr.
$= (7^6 - 6^5) \cdot 0$ Inv. Prop. of Add.
$= 0$ Mult. Prop. of Zero

29. $5\left(w - \frac{1}{5}\right) - w(9)$
$= 5\left(w - \frac{1}{5}\right) - 9w$ Comm. Prop. of Mult.
$= 5(w) - 5\left(\frac{1}{5}\right) - 9w$ Dist. Prop.
$= 5w - 1 - 9w$ Inv. Prop. of Mult.
$= 5w + (-1) + (-9w)$ def. of subtr.
$= 5w + (-9w) + (-1)$ Comm. Prop. of Add.
$= [5w + (-9)w] + (-1)$ Assoc. Prop. of Add.
$= [5 + (-9)]w + (-1)$ Dist. Prop.
$= -4w + (-1)$ add.
$= -4w - 1$ def. of subtr.

31. no **33.** no **35.** no **37.** yes
39. No; $3 - 5 = -2$, while $5 - 3 = 2$.
41. No; $1 \div 2 = \frac{1}{2}$, while $2 \div 1 = 2$.
43a. Dist. Prop. **b.** Comm. Prop. of Add.
c. Assoc. Prop. of Add. **d.** add. **e.** Dist. Prop.
f. add. **45.** C **47.** Inverse Prop. of Mult.
49. Inverse Prop. of Mult.; Inverse Prop. of Add.
51. A **53.** B **55.** B **57.** $11 - \frac{1}{3}b$ **59.** $28 - 4n$
61. $-18v + 31.2$ **63.** -18.3 **65.** $-1\frac{1}{5}$ **67.** 9.2
69. $\frac{1}{2}\left(\frac{b}{4}\right)$

Chapter Review pp. 59–6 1

1. term **2.** Evaluate **3.** algebraic expression
4. rational **5.** absolute value **6.** rational number
7. additive inverse **8.** Distributive Property
9. Commutative **10.** power **11.** Counterexample
12. reciprocal **13.** whole **14.** variable
15. like terms **16.** Let n = the number; $5 + 3n$.
17. Let n = the number; $30 - n$. **18.** Let n = the number; $\frac{7}{n}$. **19.** Let n = the number; $n(12)$. **20.** 9
21. 64 **22.** 4 **23.** 8 **24.** real numbers, rational numbers **25.** real numbers, irrational numbers
26. real numbers, rational numbers **27.** real numbers, rational numbers, natural numbers, whole numbers, integers **28.** real numbers, rational numbers, natural numbers, whole numbers, integers **29.** -17 **30.** -5 **31.** 9.9
32. 24.9 **33.** -12 **34.** 0 **35.** $\frac{1}{2}$ **36.** $-1\frac{1}{2}$ **37.** 6.7
38. 10 **39.** -40 **40.** $-\frac{5}{9}$ **41.** 2 **42.** $-\frac{5}{4}$ **43.** $\frac{15}{8}$
44. -144 **45.** 54 **46.** $4m + 3$ **47.** $b + 10$

48. $-5w + 20$ **49.** $36 - 27j$ **50.** $-3 + 30y$
51. $-2r + 1$ **52.** $35b + 5$ **53.** $7 - 25v$ **54.** $9t - \frac{6}{5}$
55. $-18 + 9m$ **56.** $-4 + x$ **57.** $10g + 1.5$
58. Assoc. Prop. of Add. **59.** Ident. Prop. of Add.
60. Comm. Prop. of Mult. **61.** Dist. Prop.

62. $19 + 56\left(\frac{1}{56}\right)$
$= 19 + 1$ Inv. Prop. of Mult.
$= 20$ Add.

63. $-12p + 45 - 7p$
$= -12p + 45 + (-7p)$ def. of subtr.
$= -12p + (-7p) + 45$ Comm. Prop. of Add.
$= [-12 + (-7)]p$ Dist. Prop.
$= -19p + 45$ Add.

64. $2(7 - v) - 3v$
$= (14 - 2v) - 3v$ Dist. Prop.
$= 14 + (-2v) + (-3v)$ def. of. subtr.
$= 14 + [(-2v + (-3v)]$ Assoc. Prop. of Add.
$= 14 + [(-2) + (-3)]v$ Dist. Prop.
$= 14 + (-5v)$ Add.
$= 14 - 5v$ def. of subtr.

65. $24abc - 24bac$
$= 24abc - 24abc$ Comm. Prop of Mult.
$= 24abc + (-24abc)$ def. of subtr.
$= 0$ Inv. Prop. of Add.

66. $4 \cdot 13 \cdot 25 \cdot 1$
$= 4 \cdot 13 \cdot (25 \cdot 1)$ Assoc. Prop. of Mult.
$= 4 \cdot 13 \cdot 25$ Ident. Prop. of Mult.
$= 4 \cdot 25 \cdot 13$ Comm. Prop. of Mult.
$= (4 \cdot 25) \cdot 13$ Assoc. Prop. of Mult.
$= 100 \cdot 13$ Mult.
$= 1300$ Mult.

67. $4[m - 2(2m + 3)]$
$= 4(m - 4m - 6)$ Dist. Prop.
$= 4[m + (-4m) + (-6)]$ def. of subtr.
$= 4[1m + (-4m) + (-6)]$ Ident. Prop. of Mult.
$= 4[m(1 + (-4)) - 6]$ Dist. Prop. of Mult.
$= 4[(-3m) - 6]$ Add.
$= -12m - 24$ Dist. Prop.

Chapter 2

Lesson 2-1 pp. 72–74

EXERCISES **1.** -10 **3.** -1 **5.** -3 **7.** -60 **9.** 96
11. 3 **13.** $6\frac{2}{5}$ **15.** 45 **17.** m = number of minutes; $2m + 18 = 60$; 21 min **19.** -16
21. -85 **23.** 25 **25.** Add. Prop. of Eq., Simplify., Mult. Prop. of Eq., Simplify. **27.** Subtr. Prop. of Eq., Simplify., Div. Prop. of Eq., Simplify. **29.** 75
31. 1 **33.** 0 **35.** -6.4 **37.** 2 **39.** 2.6

41. $7 - 3k - 7 = -14 - 7$ Subtr. Prop. of Eq.
$-3k = -21$ Simplify.
$\frac{-3k}{-3} = \frac{-21}{-3}$ Div. Prop. of Eq.
$k = 7$ Simplify.

43. A **45.** d = number of days, c = number of items; $c = 10{,}000d + 128{,}000{,}000$; about 2200 days **47.** 5 **49.** 19 **51.** 87 **53.** -34 **55.** 15.5 **57.** 31.5 **59.** The neg. sign was dropped in the term $-3y$; -1. **61.** Answers may vary. **63.** 100°; 98.6°; 20°; 32°; $-40°$ **65.** $x = 8 - y$; 5 **67.** $x = 12 - y$; 7 **69.** C **71.** 24 **73.** -15 **75.** 4 **77.** -11

Lesson 2-2 pp. 79–82

EXERCISES **1.** 9 **3.** $5\frac{4}{7}$ **5.** $2\frac{6}{7}$ **7.** 3 **9.** 3 **11.** $x + \frac{1}{2}x = 1725$; 150 **13.** 3 **15.** -2 **17.** 2 **19.** 4 **21.** $13\frac{2}{5}$ **23.** $1\frac{1}{2}$ **25.** 7 **27.** $33\frac{3}{5}$ **29.** $\frac{1}{3}$ **31.** 2 **33.** 0.5 **35.** 9 **37.** 6 **39.** 28 **41.** 2 **43.** 5 **45.** 1 **47.** $5\frac{3}{5}$ **49.** 9 **51.** -3 **53.** The student forgot to multiply -1 by 8. **55.** Answers may vary. Sample: multiply by -2 to eliminate fractions. **57.** $4\frac{2}{3}$ **59.** 92 mi **61.** Answers may vary. Sample: $3x + 5 - 4x + 9$ **63.** 25 **65.** $11.68 **67.** about 15 gal **69.** $100,000 **71.** C **73.** B **75.** A **77.** 16 **79.** -19 **81.** $-4\frac{1}{2}$ **83.** -7 **85.** 1400 **87.** 0 **89.** 80 **91.** -4 **93.** -11 **95.** -10 **97.** -30

Lesson 2-3 pp. 86–89

EXERCISES **1.** 3 **3.** 7 **5.** 3 **7.** 7 **9.** -3 **11.** 2 **13.** 4 **15.** $16.95 + 0.05m = 22.95 + 0.02m$; 200 min **17a.** Answers may vary. Sample:

0: $9 = 9$
3: $-9 = -9$
-4: $33 = 33$
-6: $45 = 45$ **b.** identity

19. no solution **21.** identity **23.** no solution **25.** 0 **27.** 10 **29.** identity **31.** 0 **33.** $1200 + 9b = 25b$; 75 bags **35.** 7 **37.** The student subtracted y from both sides instead of adding y to both sides; 5.3. **39a.** no **b.** 1 and 3; at 3, $4 - 3(x + 1)$ is less than $5(x - 3)$, while at 1 the opposite is true. The values must be the same for some value of x between 1 and 3. **c.** for values of x greater than 2 **41–45.** Answers may vary. Samples are given. **41.** $4x + 4 = 3x + 7$ **43.** $3x + 1 = 3\left(x + \frac{1}{3}\right)$ **45.** $7x - 2 = 5x$ **47.** 6 units, 2 units; 4 units, 4 units **49.** C **51.** D **53.** D **55.** 7 **57.** 1.68 **59.** 20.84 **61.** $4\frac{1}{4}$ in. **63.** 5.009, 5.04, 5.043 **65.** -100, -87, 93, 500 **67.** -9.8, 0.9, 8.6, 9.7

Lesson 2-4 pp. 95–98

EXERCISES **1.** $9.50/h **3.** 131 cars/week **5.** $.24/oz.; $.22/oz.; 12-oz. **7a.** $.97/mile, $c = 0.97m$ **b.** $1164 **c.** 845 miles **9.** A **11.** B **13.** 480 **15.** 10,800 **17.** 6 **19.** 25.2 **21.** 11.25 **23.** 14.4 **25.** 105.6 km **27.** $8\frac{11}{12}$ **29.** $-3\frac{1}{2}$ **31.** 165 **33.** 18.75 **35.** 18.25 **37.** 2520 **39.** 15 mi/h **41.** 1 mi/h **43.** about 0.28 mi/h **45.** $5.\overline{3}$ **47.** 0.35 mm/day; $g = 0.35n$; 10.55 mm **49.** about 646 students **51.** about 1000 students **53.** A **55.** Check students' work. **57.** 48 V **59.** 9 **61a.** 5.47 min/mi **b.** 5.37 min/mi **63.** B **65.** 4 **67.** -6 **69.** -110 **71.** 18 **73.** 25.5 **75.** false; $1 = 1^2$

Lesson 2-5 pp. 104–107

EXERCISES **1.** 6 in.; 9 in. **3.** 5 yd; 13 yd **5.** 58, 60 **7.** 27, 29 **9.** $t - \frac{1}{2}$ **11.** $t = 1\frac{1}{2}$; $t - \frac{1}{2} = 1$; The car catches the van after traveling 1 hour.

t	van	car
1	40	30
$1\frac{1}{2}$	60	60

13. 15 mi/h; 20 mi/h **15a.** $1.5 + 2x + x$ **b.** 15.5 ft **c.** $3x + 1.5 = 15.5$; $10\frac{5}{6}$ ft or 10 ft 10 in. **17.** 3:45 P.M. **19.** 2:30 P.M. **21a.** 4:00 P.M. **b.** the distance traveled **25a.** $n + n + 1 + n + 2 = 126$; 41; 42, 43 **b.** Yes; if n is the middle integer, $n - 1$ is the previous integer, and $n + 1$ is the next integer. The three integers would be consecutive. **27.** $x + 2x - 65 + x - 10 = 165$; 60; 55 cm, 60 cm, 50 cm **29.** $-9, -7, -5, -3, -1$ **31.** B **33.** -2 **35.** 0.3 **37.** no solution **39.** $4\frac{1}{2}$ h

Lesson 2-6 pp. 111–113

EXERCISES **1.** 15; 7.50; 10.00; 8.95; $7.50c$; $10.00(15 - c)$; $8.95(15)$; 4.5 lb of $7.50/lb coffee; 10.5 lb of $10/lb coffee **3.** 75; 50; 20; 30; $0.5a$; $0.2(75 - a)$; $0.3(75)$; 25 L of 50%, 50 L of 20% **5.** 35; 85; 75; $0.35x$; $0.85(120)$; $0.75(120 + x)$ **7.** 30 mL **9.** $8.99/lb **11.** about 32% **13.** 77 mL **15.** D **17.** $1\frac{17}{30}$ **19.** Comm. Prop. of Add. **21.** Distributive Property **23.** Distributive Property **25.** -1 **27.** 38 **29.** -2

Chapter Review pp. 115–117

1. inverse operations **2.** Solutions of equivalent equations **3.** rate **4.** cross products **5.** identity **6.** uniform motion **7.** 4 **8.** 3 **9.** 5 **10.** 3 **11.** 2 **12.** 11 **13.** Let p = number of people; $6p + 3 = 27$; 4 people

14.

$314 = -n + 576$	
$314 - 576 = -n + 576 - 576$	Subtr. Prop. of Eq.
$-262 = -n$	Simplify.
$-1(-262) = -1(-n)$	Mult. Prop. of Eq.
$262 = n$	Simplify.

15.

$-\frac{1}{4}w - 1 = 6$	
$-\frac{1}{4}w - 1 + 1 = 6 + 1$	Add. Prop. of Eq.
$-\frac{1}{4}w = 7$	Simplify.
$-4\left(-\frac{1}{4}w\right) = -4(7)$	Mult. Prop. of Eq.
$w = -28$	Simplify.

16. $3h - 4 = 5$

$3h - 4 + 4 = 5 + 4$ Add. Prop. of Eq.

$3h = 9$ Simplify.

$\frac{3h}{3} = \frac{9}{3}$ Div. Prop. of Eq.

$h = 3$ Simplify.

17. −18 **18.** 4 **19.** $-\frac{1}{2}$ **20.** $\frac{3}{2}$ **21.** 2 **22.** 2.5 **23.** 20 **24.** 10 **25.** $2(\ell + \ell - 6) = 72$; 21 cm by 15 cm **26.** 0 **27.** 7 **28.** 3 **29.** 2 **30.** 4 **31.** −2. **32.** no solution **33.** no solution **34.** no solution **35.** identity **36.** 4 books **37.** 3 channels **38.** 150 mi/h **39.** 3.4 mi/h **40.** 0.2 mi/h **41.** 7.1 mi/h **42.** 2 **43.** 2.3 **44.** −6 **45.** 20 **46.** 6 **47.** 5 **48a.** 0.6 pages/min; $p = 0.6m$ **b.** 325 min **49.** $4r = 7.6$; 1.9 h or 1 h 54 min **50.** $n + (n + 1) + (n + 2) = 582$; 193, 194, 195 **51.** $10t + 18(t - 2) = 209$; 6.75 h or 6 h 45 min **52.** $22x = 72 - 32x$; $1\frac{1}{3}$ h **53.** x; $50 - x$; 50; 2.50; 7.00; 4.30; $2.50x$; $7.00(50 - x)$; 4.30(50); 30 lb of dried fruit; 20 lb of nuts **54.** 60 mL of 30%, 40 mL of 65%

Chapter 3

Lesson 3-1 pp. 126–129

EXERCISES **1.** yes **3.** yes **5.** no **7.** no **9a.** no **b.** no **c.** yes **11a.** no **b.** no **c.** no **13a.** no **b.** yes **c.** no **15.** C **17.** D

19. 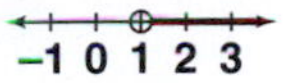 −1 0 1 2 3 **21.** 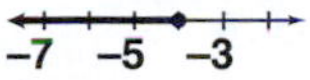 −7 −5 −3

23. 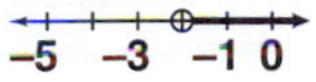 −5 −3 −1 0 **25.** 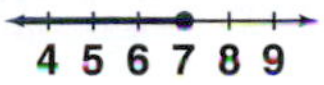 4 5 6 7 8 9

27–35. Choice of variable may vary. **27.** $x > -3$ **29.** $x \geq 1$ **31.** $x \geq 4.5$ **33.** Let s = number of students. $s \leq 48$ **35.** Let w = safe number of watts. $w \leq 60$ **37.** Let a = number of appearances. $a > 75$ **39.** b is greater than 0. **41.** z is greater than or equal to −5.6. **43.** −1 is greater than or equal to m, or m is less than or equal to −1. **45.** g minus 2 is less than 7. **47.** 6 plus r is greater than −2. **49.** 1.2 is greater than k, or k is less than 1.2. **51.** Answers may vary. Sample: Every class has at least 18 students.

53. $x > 2$; −1 0 1 2 3

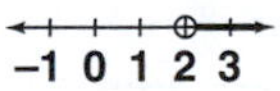

55. $r \geq 0$; −2 −1 0 1 2

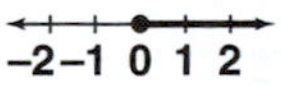

57. 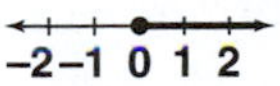 −2 −1 0 1 2 **59.** 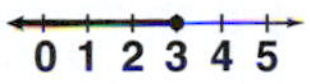 0 1 2 3 4 5

61. 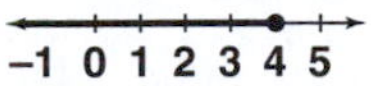 −1 0 1 2 3 4 5

63. "At least" is translated as ≥. "At most" is translated as ≤. **65.** Since 1231 < 1513, Option A < Option B. **67.** Put an open dot at 3 and color the rest of the number line. **69.** C; the inequality is true for $x = 3$ but not true for $x = 5$, so C is correct. **71.** a is negative, and a and b are opposites.

73. 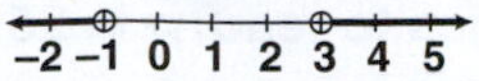 −2 −1 0 1 2 3 4 5

75. C **77.** B **79.** 4 oz of 2% milk, 8 oz of 0.5% milk **81.** $-\frac{1}{8}$ **83.** 36 **85.** 9 **87.** Commutative Property of Multiplication

Lesson 3-2 pp. 132–135

EXERCISES **1.** 5 **3.** 4.3 **5.** $t < 1$; −1 0 1 2

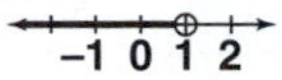

7. $d \geq 10$; 8 9 10 11 12 13

9. $r \leq 9$; 6 7 8 9 10 11

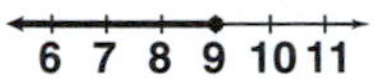

11. $d > 3$; −1 0 1 2 3 4

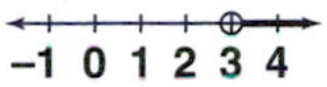

13. $q < 3\frac{1}{3}$; 0 1 2 3 4 5

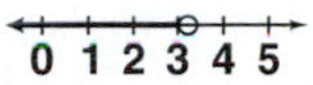

15. $r < 4.5$; −1 0 1 2 3 4 5

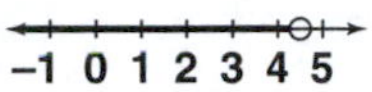

17. $b < \frac{1}{2}$; −1 0 1 2

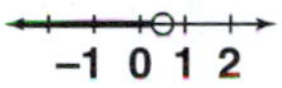

19. 2 **21.** 3.1

23. $m > -8$; −10 −8 −6

25. $a \leq -6$; −8 −6 −4

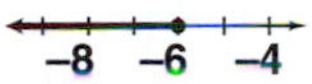

27. $x < -1$; −1 0 1 2

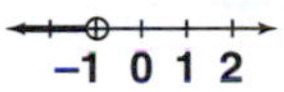

29. $z \geq -1$; −1 0 1 2

31. $m > -1\frac{1}{2}$; −2 0 1

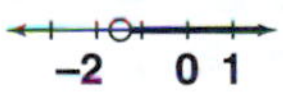

33. $p > -7$; −10 −6 −2 0 2

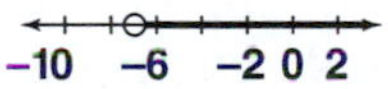

35. $d > -1.5$; −3 −1 0 1

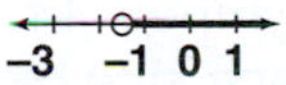

37. $s + 637 \leq 2000$, \$1363 **39.** $r + 17 + 12 \geq 50$, 21 reflectors **41.** Subtract 9 from each side. **43.** $w \geq 11$ **45.** $y < 3.1$ **47.** $z < -9.7$ **49.** $t > \frac{1}{6}$ **51.** $k \geq -8.1$ **53.** $m \leq -3.5$ **55.** $h \geq -\frac{1}{2}$ **57.** $w < -14$ **59a.** yes **b.** no **c.** Answers may vary. Sample: The = sign indicates that each side is equal, so the two sides may be interchanged. The < sign does not indicate equality. One side cannot be both greater than and less than the other side. **61.** 51.2 MB **63a–b.** Check students' work. **65.** $x \geq 1$ **67.** $t \leq -3$ **69.** $a \leq 24$ **71.** The inequality symbol was not reversed when n was moved to the left side; $n \leq -2$. **73.** not true; sample counterexample: for $a = 5$ and $b = -6$, $5 - (-6) \nless 5 + (-6)$ **75.** true **77.** Answers may vary. Sample: For $x = 2$, $y = 1$, $z = 4$, and $w = 3$, $2 > 1$ and $4 > 3$, but $2 - 4 \ngtr 1 - 3$.

Selected Answers

79. B **81.** A **83.** D **85.** Let h = distance in miles a hummingbird migrates. $h > 1850$
87. Let p = number of pages to read. $p \geq 25$
89. 7 **91.** 31 **93.** 73

Lesson 3-3 pp. 139–141

EXERCISES **1.** $t \geq -4$; −4 0 2
3. $w \leq -2$; −2 0 1
5. $y > -4$; −6 −5 −4 −3 −2 −1
7. $x < 6$; 0 2 4 6 8
9. $x < 0$; −3 −1 0 1 2
11. $x < 7$; −2 0 2 4 6 8
13. $c > -\frac{2}{3}$; −1 0 1 2 3
15. $u < -\frac{1}{2}$; −2 0 1
17. $t < -3$; −5 −3 −1 0 1
19. $w \leq -5$; −8 −4 0 2
21. $z \leq -9$; −12 −8 −4 0 2
23. $d < -\frac{2}{3}$; −3 −1 0 1
25. $q > -3\frac{1}{2}$; −4 −2 0 1
27. $d > 4$; −2 0 2 4 6 8
29. $4.5c \geq 300$, 67 cars **31–37.** Answers may vary. Samples are given. **31.** −2, −3, −4, −5 **33.** −3, −4, −5, −6 **35.** −6, −7, −8, −9 **37.** 5, 4, 3, 2 **39.** Multiply each side by −4 and reverse the inequality symbol. **41.** Divide each side by 5. **43.** Divide each side by 4. **45.** −2 **47.** 4 **49.** −10 **51.** x and y are equal. **53–55.** Estimates may vary. **53.** $j > -6$ **55.** $s \geq 28$ **57.** For both the equation and the inequality, you multiply each side by −3. For the inequality, you must reverse the inequality symbol. **59.** $d \leq -7$ **61.** $s < -\frac{1}{4}$ **63.** $y < 9$ **65.** $h \leq -4$ **67.** $x < -9$ **69.** $p > -2\frac{1}{2}$ **71.** $g < -\frac{2}{3}$ **73.** $m < 3.5$ **75.** Yes; in each case, y is greater than 6. **77a.** She should have divided each side by −15. **b.** 150 satisfies the original inequality $-15q \leq 135$. **c.** Answers may vary. Sample: −15 **79.** $a > 0$ **81.** $a < 0$ **83.** $\frac{9}{16}x \geq 18(15)$, 480 tiles **85.** B **87.** A **89.** $w < -\frac{1}{8}$ **91.** $d > 4$ **93.** $y < 8$ **95.** $k \leq 3$ **97.** −2 **99.** Inv. Prop. of Add. **101.** Ident. Prop. of Add. **103.** Assoc. Prop. of Mult.

Lesson 3-4 pp. 146–149

EXERCISES **1.** $d \leq 4$ **3.** $x > -2\frac{1}{2}$ **5.** $q \geq 4$ **7.** $a \leq 3$ **9.** $c < 2$ **11.** $-6x + 9$ **13.** $b < \frac{1}{3}$ **15.** $x \geq 3$ **17.** $w \leq 4\frac{1}{2}$ **19.** $r \leq 2\frac{1}{2}$ **21.** $w < 3$ **23.** $d \leq 6$ **25.** $k \geq -4$ **27.** $p > 3$ **29.** $m > -\frac{1}{4}$ **31.** $q \leq -2$ **33.** $x < 1\frac{1}{3}$ **35.** $v \geq 2$ **37.** Subtract 7 from each side. **39.** Add 2 to each side, then multiply each side by −5, and reverse the inequality sign. **41.** C **43a.** maximum **b.** no more than 135 **45.** E **47.** A **49.** C **51.** $r < 5\frac{1}{2}$ **53.** $s \leq 4.4$ **55.** $s < 8$ **57.** $n > -2$ **59.** $x > 1$ **61.** $m \geq 1$ **63.** $n \geq -23$ **65.** $a < -6\frac{2}{3}$ **67a.** $-3t \leq -9, t \geq 3$ **b.** $9 \leq 3t, t \geq 3$ **c.** The results are the same. **69.** For x = amount of sales, $250 + 0.03x \geq 460$, so to reach her goal, she must have at least $7000 in sales. **71.** Add $2x$ to each side rather than subtract $2x$, so $x \leq \frac{2}{5}$. **73a.** $x > \frac{c-b}{a}$ **b.** $x < \frac{c-b}{a}$ **75.** 8.8 in. × 14.2 in. **77.** 10 h **79.** A **81.** B **83.** A **85.** $y \geq -8$ **87.** $t \geq -3$ **89.** $w > -98$ **91.** $d \geq 7$ **93.** $s \geq -0.7$ **95.** −16 **97.** 24

Lesson 3-5 pp. 153–156

EXERCISES **1.** $-4 < x$ and $x < 6$ or $-4 < x < 6$; −4 0 2 4 6 8
3. $23 < c < 23.5$; 22 23 24
5. $-5 < j < 5$; −5 0 5 10
7. $2 < n \leq 6$; 0 2 4 6 8
9. $1 < x < 3$; 0 1 2 3 4
11. $5 < x < 8$; 4 5 6 7 8 9
13. $3 \leq s < 4$; 2 3 4 5
15. $1 < x < 7$; −2 0 2 4 6 8 10
17. $n \leq -3$ or $n \geq 5$; −4 0 2 4 6
19. $h < 1$ or $h > 3$; 0 1 2 3 4 5
21. $b < -2$ or $b > 2$; −2 0 1 2 3
23. $c < 2$ or $c \geq 3$; −1 0 1 2 3 4
25. $c \leq 2$ or $c \geq 3$; 0 1 2 3 4 5
27. $d \leq -3$ or $d \geq 0$; −5 −3 −1 0 1 2
29. $-2 < x < 3$ **31.** $x \leq 0$ or $x > 2$ **33.** $q \leq -2\frac{2}{3}$ or $q > 4$ **35.** $4 \leq t \leq 14$ **37.** $-6 \leq t < 1$ **39.** D **41.** The word "and" means both statements must be true. The word "or" means that at least one of the statements must be true.

43. $15 \le D \le 30$ **45.** Answers may vary. Sample: Elevation near a coastline varies between 2 m below and 8 m above sea level.
47. $-2 < x < 0$ or $0 < x < 3$
49a. $130 \le R \le 157$ **b.** 20 years old
51. 10, 12, 14 **53.** B **55.** B **57.** B **59.** $n \le 3$
61. −1 **63.** identity

Lesson 3-6 pp. 161–164

EXERCISES **1.** −2, 2 **3.** $-\frac{1}{2}, \frac{1}{2}$ **5.** −3, 3 **7.** −5, 5 **9.** 0 **11.** −3, 3 **13.** 3, 13 **15.** −3, 1 **17.** −5, 9 **19.** −7, 1 **21.** −0.6, 0.6
23. $k < -2.5$ or $k > 2.5$; −3 −1 0 1 2 3 4
25. $-8 < x < 2$; −8 −6 −4 −2 0 2
27. $1 \le y \le 3$; −1 0 1 2 3 4 5
29. $-2 < c < 7$; −2 0 2 4 6 8
31. $t < -3$ or $t > 2\frac{1}{3}$; −3 −1 0 1 2 3 4
33. $t \le -2.4$ or $t \ge 4$; −3 −1 0 1 2 3 4 5
35. between 12.18 mm and 12.30 mm, inclusive
37. −9, 9 **39.** $-1\frac{1}{2}, 1\frac{1}{2}$ **41.** −5, 3
43. $d \le -2$ or $d \ge 2$ **45.** $c < -16$ or $c > 2$
47. $-6 < x < 6$ **49.** −8, 8 **51.** $-8 < m < 4$
53. $|n| > 7.5$ **55.** $|n + 1| \ge 3$
57. $|w - 16| \le 0.05$, $15.95 \le w \le 16.05$
59. $|g - 6.27| \le 0.02$ **61.** Sample: $|5x - 12| = 3$; $1\frac{4}{5}$, 3 **63.** 4 was subtracted from 3 instead of added to 11; 6, −9 **65a.** 11°F, 39°F **b.** $|t - 25| = 14$
67. $\frac{2}{3}$, 3 **69.** $\le$ **71.** $=$ **73.** $|x + 1| > 3$
75. A **77.** D **79.** A **81.** Let e = elevation (ft); $-282 \le e \le 20{,}320$. **83.** −3 **85.** 5 **87.** $\frac{1}{3}$
89. −2.5, −2, 0, 3, π **91.** 0.001, 0.009, 0.01, 0.011

Chapter Review pp. 167–169

1. C **2.** B **3.** A **4.** C **5.** D **6.** −1 0 1 2 3 4
7. −6 −5 −4 −3 −2 −1 0 1
8. 5 6 7 8 9 10 11 12
9. −2 −1 0 1 2 3 4
10. $n < -2$ **11.** $n \ge -3.5$ **12.** $n > -6$ **13.** $n \ge 2$
14. Let p = number of people, $p \ge 600$.
15. Let n = number of people, $n \le 15$. **16.** Let t = temperature in degrees Fahrenheit, $t < 32$.
17. $h > -1$; −3 −2 −1 0 1 2
18. $t < -5$; −8 −7 −6 −5 −4 −3
19. $m \ge -3$; −4 −3 −2 −1 0 1
20. $w \ge -2$; −4 −3 −2 −1 0 1
21. $q > -2.5$; −4 −3 −2 −1 0 1
22. $y > -14$; −15 −10 −5 0 5
23. $n \le 15$; −5 0 5 10 15 20
24. $d \ge 4$; −2 0 2 4 6
25. $-2 \le t$; −6 −4 −2 0 2 4 6
26. $0 < c$; −2 −1 0 1 2
27. $2.5 \ge u$; −1 0 1 2 3 4
28. $-9 < p$; −10 −8 −6 −4 −2 0 2
29. $3.50 + 2.75 + x \le 12.00$, $x \le 5.75$
30. $7.25h \ge 200$, $h \ge 27.586$
You must work at least 28 h.
31. $n > -2$ **32.** $k \le -\frac{1}{2}$ **33.** $b < 40$ **34.** $c \le -2$
35. $m < -6$ **36.** $t > 3$ **37.** $x \ge 2$ **38.** $y \le -56$
39. $x < \frac{8}{3}$ **40.** $190 + 0.04x \ge 500$, $x \ge 7750$
41. −4 −2 0 2 4 **42.** −4 −3 −2 −1 0 1 2 3
43. −4 −2 0 2 4 6
44. $-2 \le z < 4$, −4 −2 0 2 4 6
45. $-\frac{5}{2} \le d < 4$, −3 −2 −1 0 1 2 3 4 5
46. $-\frac{3}{2} \le b < 0$, −4 −3 −2 −1 0 1
47. $t \le -2$ or $t \ge 7$, −2 0 2 4 6 8
48. $2 \le a < 5$, 1 2 3 4 5 6
49. $2 \le a < 4$, 0 1 2 3 4 5 **50.** $75 \le t \le 89$
51. $|n + 2| > 3$
52. $|n - 12| \le 5$ **53.** 5 or −5
54. $n \le -6$ or $n \ge 2$ **55.** $-3 \le x \le 3$
56. $-9.6 < m < 9.6$ **57.** $x < 3$ or $x > 4$
58. 6.5 or −12.5 **59.** 8 **60.** all real numbers
61. no solution **62.** $k < -7$ or $k > -3$
63. −5 or 1 **64.** $z \le -0.25$ or $z \ge 0.25$
65. $2.74 \le d \le 2.86$ **66.** $19.6 \le \ell \le 20.4$

Chapter 4

Lesson 4-1 pp. 178–180

EXERCISES **1.** (4, 5) **3.** (5, −3) **5.** $\left(-3, 2\frac{1}{2}\right)$ **7.** (0, −5) **9.** (5, 4)

11–13.

15. II **17.** IV **19.** (−3, 4) **21.** (6, −6) **23.** I **25.** *y* **27.** always **29.** $V\left(3, 3\frac{1}{2}\right)$, $W(2, 0)$, $X(0, -3)$, $Y\left(-4\frac{1}{2}, -3\right)$, $Z\left(-2\frac{1}{2}, 1\frac{1}{2}\right)$ **31.** The point (x, y) is on the *x*- or *y*-axis. Since $xy = 0$, one or both coordinates is equal to 0. **33.** Answers will vary. Sample: (−1, 1), (−2, 2), (−10, 10)

35. 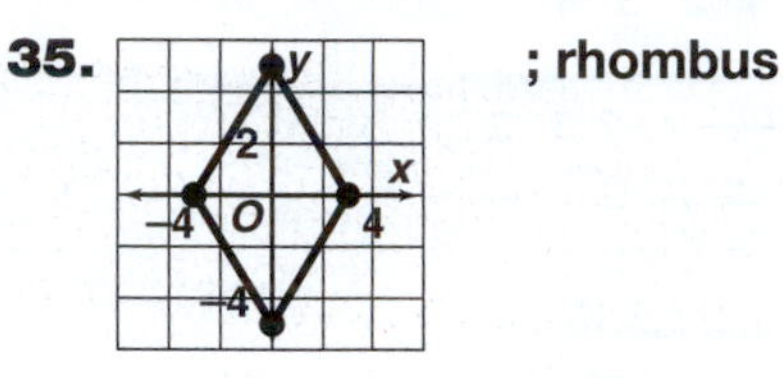

; rhombus

37. 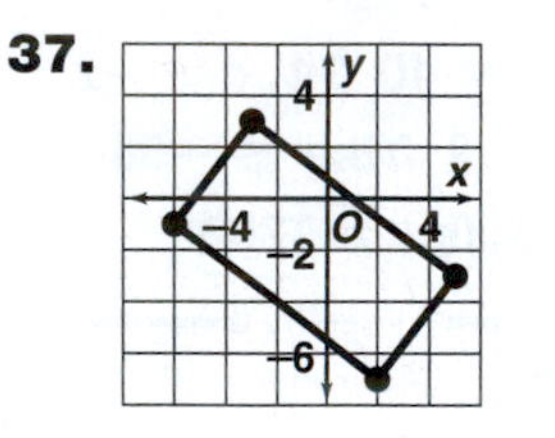

; rectangle

39. 7.5 square units **41.** C **43.** D **45.** D **47a.** $|w - 7.09| \leq 0.015$ **b.** $7.075 \leq w \leq 7.105$ **49.** $x < 8$ **51.** $x > -4$ **53.** $x < \frac{2}{3}$ **55.** 167 mL of 30%, 83 mL of 60% **57.** 36 mL of 10%, 214 mL of 45%

Lesson 4-2 pp. 184–186

EXERCISES **1.** domain: {1, 6, 9}; range: {−3, −2, −1, 3}; no **3.** domain: {−4, −1, 0, 3}; range: {−4}; yes **5.** domain: {1, 5, 6}; range: {−8, −7, 4, 5}; not a function **7.** domain: {4, 1, 0}; range: {−2, −1, 0, 1, 2}; not a function **9.** domain: {0, 1, 5}; range: {0, 1, 5}; not a function **11.** domain: {−2, −0.5, 3, 4}; range: {9}; function **13.** domain: $\{x: x \leq 2\}$; range: all real numbers; not a function **15.** Answers may vary. Sample: A relation is not a function if two range values have the same domain value. **17a.** domain: {1, 4, 6, 8, 9, 10, 19}; range: {45, 70, 80, 90, 115, 150, 185, 245}

b. 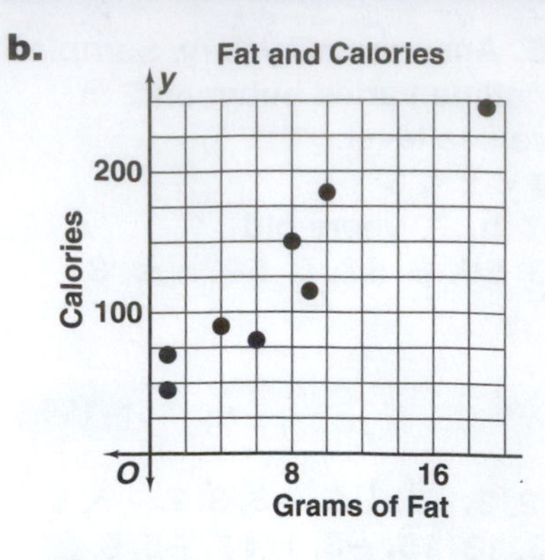

c. No; both corn and broccoli have 1 gram of fat, but they have different numbers of calories. **19.** domain: all real numbers; range: $\{y: -2 \leq y \leq 3\}$; function **21.** No; two 4-year-old iguanas may have different lengths. **23.** no **25.** yes **27–29.** Explanations may vary. Samples are given. **27.** always; a function is a kind of relation **29.** always; the *x*-value 0 would have more than one *y*-value **31.** No, a domain value cannot correspond to more than one range value. **33.** D **35.** D **37.** $r > 14$ **39.** $s > 8$ **41.** $c \leq 5$ **43.** $h > 8$ **45.** no **47.** yes

Lesson 4-3 pp. 190–192

EXERCISES

1. {3, 8, 10} **3.** {1, 9, 16} **5.** {12, 14, 19} **7.** $\left\{-1, \frac{1}{4}, \frac{3}{4}\right\}$ **9–17.** Tables may vary. Samples are given.

9.

x	f(x)
−1	3
0	0
1	−3

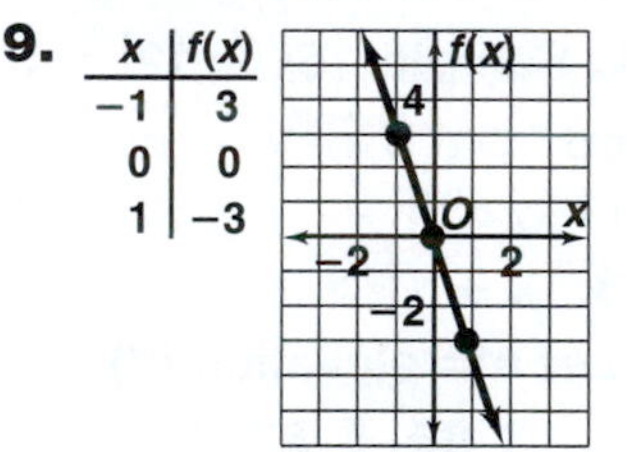

11.

x	f(x)
−2	4
−1	1
0	−2
1	−5

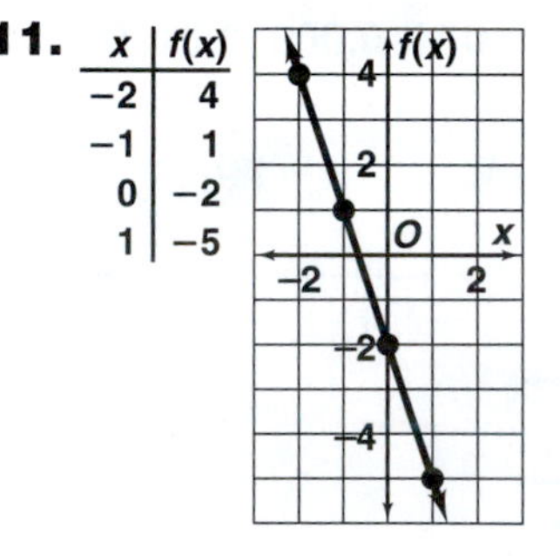

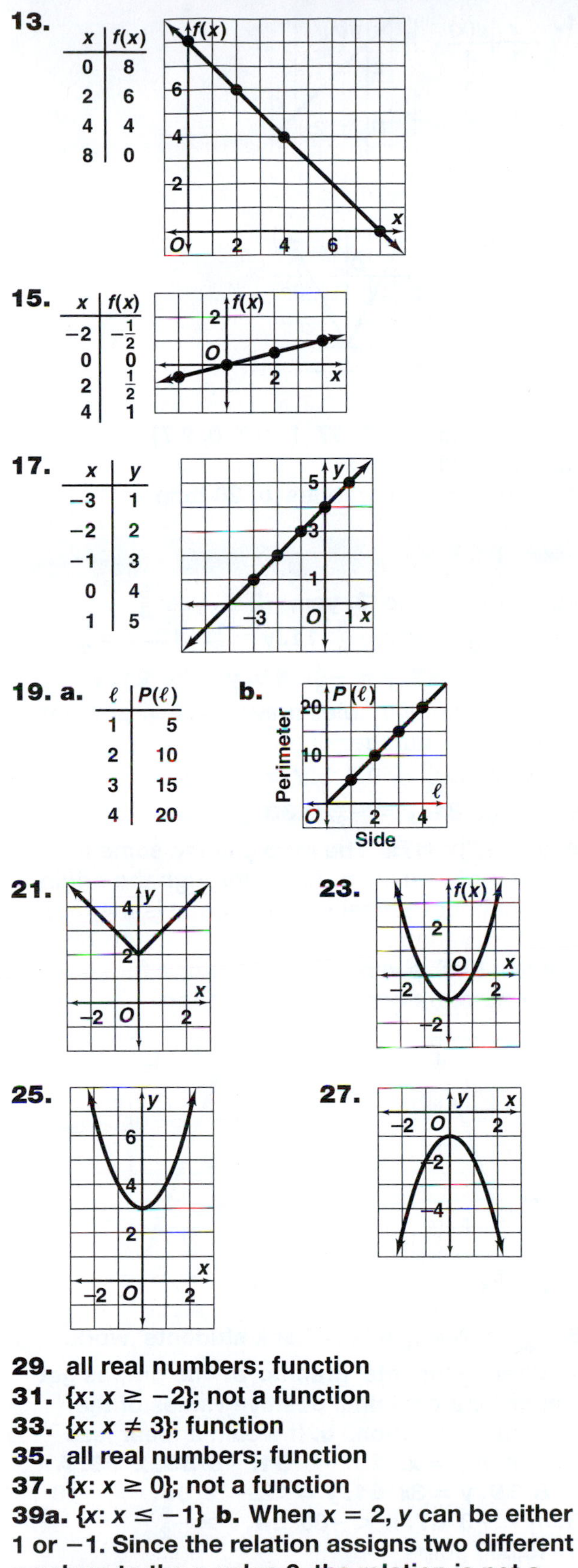

13.

x	$f(x)$
0	8
2	6
4	4
8	0

15.

x	$f(x)$
−2	$-\frac{1}{2}$
0	0
2	$\frac{1}{2}$
4	1

17.

x	y
−3	1
−2	2
−1	3
0	4
1	5

19. a.

ℓ	$P(\ell)$
1	5
2	10
3	15
4	20

b.

21. **23.** **25.** **27.**

29. all real numbers; function
31. $\{x: x \geq -2\}$; not a function
33. $\{x: x \neq 3\}$; function
35. all real numbers; function
37. $\{x: x \geq 0\}$; not a function
39a. $\{x: x \leq -1\}$ **b.** When $x = 2$, y can be either 1 or -1. Since the relation assigns two different y-values to the x-value 2, the relation is not a function. **41.** $\{-11, -5, 5.5\}$ **43.** $\{-5, -3, -1.5\}$
45. $\{-20, -10, 7.5\}$

47. 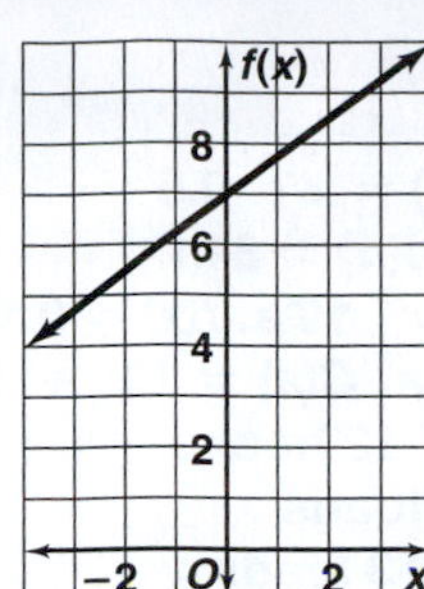 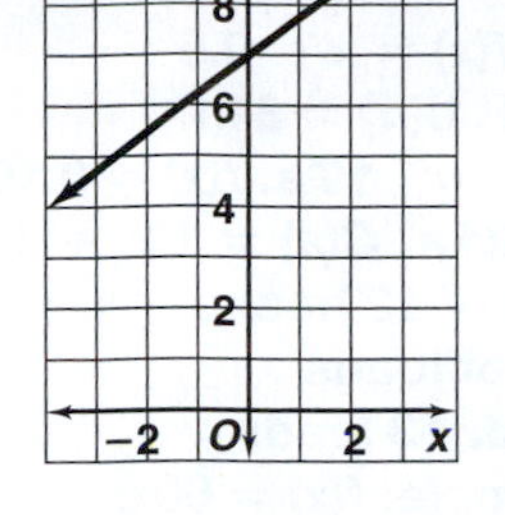 domain: all real numbers; range: all real numbers

49. domain: all real numbers; range: $\{y: y \geq 0\}$

51. domain: all real numbers; range: all real numbers

53. domain: all real numbers; range: $\{y: y \geq 1\}$

55. 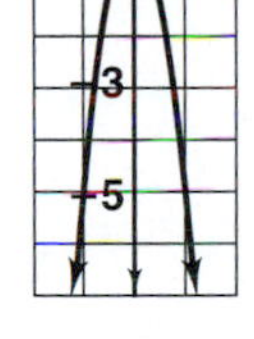 domain: all real numbers; range: $\{y: y \leq 0\}$

57. a. **b.** It makes the graph wider or narrower.

59. D **61.** domain: $\{-4, -1, 0, 1, 2\}$; range: $\{-5, 0, 3, 6, 7\}$
63. domain: $\{-7, -3.5, 0.4, 6.9\}$; range: $\{0, 1.1, 3, 8\}$
65. $a < -3$ or $a > 5$
67. $c < -6$ or $c > -2$

Selected Answers

Lesson 4-4 pp. 196–199

EXERCISES **1.** B **3.** C **5.** $f(x) = x - 0.5$ **7.** $f(x) = -3x$ **9.** $y = x^2$ **11.** $d(n) = 34n$ **13.** $e(n) = 6.37n$ **15.** $V(n) = n^3$ **17a.** $f(x) = 0.19x$ **b.** \$1.52 **19.** $f(x) = 1000x$ **21a.** $C(a) = 10a + 1$ **b.** \$31 **c.** 61; the total cost of 12 books **23a.** gal of water, number of loads **b.** $w(n) = 34n$ **c.** 238 gal **d.** 13 loads **25.** Answers may vary. Sample: $f(x) = 60x$; $f(3) = 180$, 180 mi in 3 h, the distance you can travel at a constant speed of 60 mi/h

27.

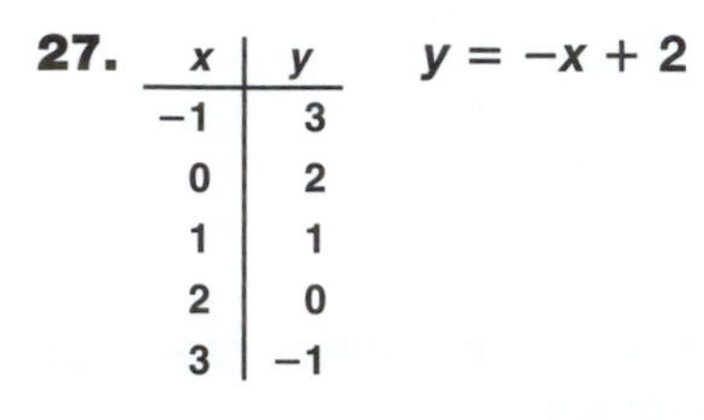

x	y
−1	3
0	2
1	1
2	0
3	−1

$y = -x + 2$

29.

x	y
−3	0
−2	1
−1	2

$y = x + 3$

31. a.

h	Process	A(h)
1	$1 \cdot 3 \cdot \frac{1}{2}$	$\frac{3}{2} = 1\frac{1}{2}$
2	$2 \cdot 3 \cdot \frac{1}{2}$	3
3	$3 \cdot 3 \cdot \frac{1}{2}$	$\frac{9}{2} = 4\frac{1}{2}$

b. $A(h) = \frac{3}{2}h$

c.

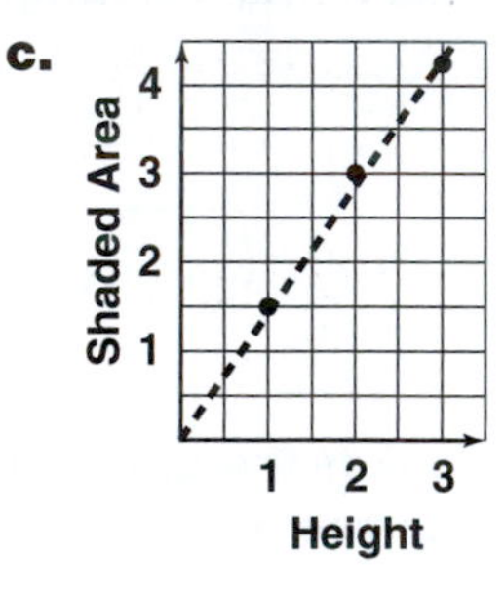

33. $f(x) = -x^3$ **35a.** $c(m) = 44 + 0.38m$ **b.** \$70.60, \$89.60 **c.** 38 mi **d.** \$202 **37.** A

39.

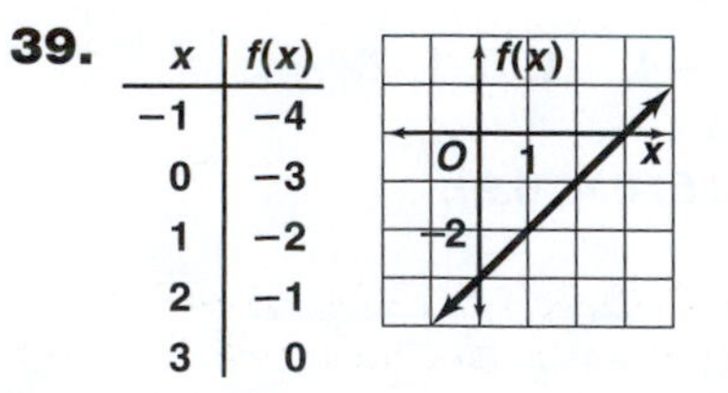

x	f(x)
−1	−4
0	−3
1	−2
2	−1
3	0

41. **43.**

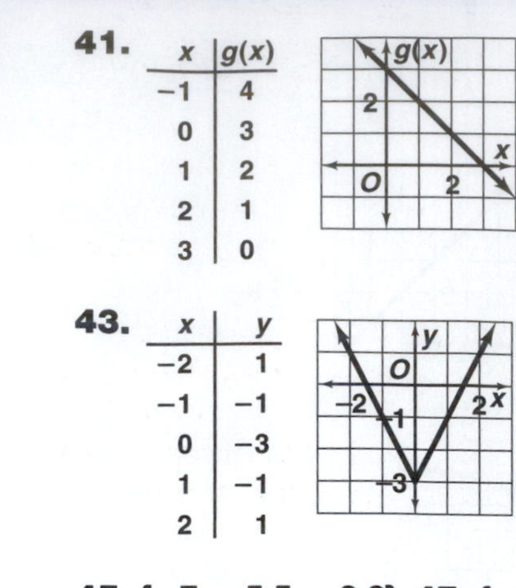

x	g(x)
−1	4
0	3
1	2
2	1
3	0

x	y
−2	1
−1	−1
0	−3
1	−1
2	1

45. {−7, −5.5, −2.3} **47.** {−0.5, 0, 2.7} **49.** {−5, 4, 23.2} **51a.** 2 oranges; 3 oranges **b.** 28 tbsp

Lesson 4-5 pp. 204–207

EXERCISES **1.** no **3.** yes; −2 **5.** yes; $\frac{5}{6}$ **7.** yes; $-\frac{1}{10}$ **9.** yes; $-\frac{3}{2}$ **11.** $y = \frac{1}{5}x$ **13.** $y = \frac{9}{5}x$ **15.** $y = -\frac{1}{6}x$ **17.** $y = -\frac{4}{3}x$ **19.** $y = 2x$ **21.** $y = \frac{1}{5}x$ **23.** Choices of variables may vary. E = amount you earn, h = number of hours, $E(h) = 7.10h$ **25.** no **27a.** $\frac{20}{50}$ or 0.4 **b.** $f = 0.4w$, 52 lb **29.** $y = \frac{1}{6}x$ **31.** $y = -\frac{36}{25}x$ **33.** $y = 9x$ **35.** $y = -\frac{15}{52}x$ **37a.** The ratio $\frac{y}{x}$ is the same for each pair of values. **b.** A line through the origin that is neither vertical nor horizontal is the graph of a direct variation. **39.** False; the line through (0, 3) and (0,0) is vertical, so it is not a function and is therefore not a direct variation.

41. **43.**

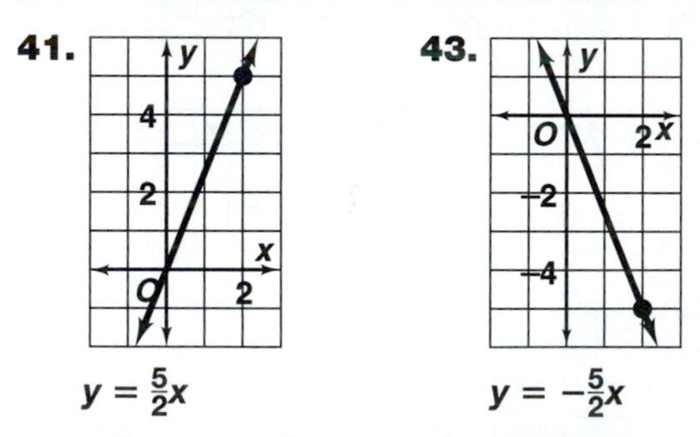

$y = \frac{5}{2}x$ $y = -\frac{5}{2}x$

45a. $\frac{1}{32}$ **b.** $b = \frac{1}{32}w$ **c.** Check students' work. **47.** Check students' graphs. **a.** The graphs get steeper for increasing, positive values of the constant of variation. **b.** It would appear less steep than $y = x$. **49.** −8 **51.** −6 **53.** 2 **55.** A **57.** B **59.** $y = 3x$ **61.** $y = 12 - x$ **63.** $r > -18$ **65.** $m < -3$ **67.** $n < -80$ **69.** $v \geq -\frac{5}{2}$ **71.** 15,600 ships

Lesson 4-6 pp. 212–214

EXERCISES **1.** $xy = 18$ **3.** $xy = 56$ **5.** $xy = 24$ **7.** $xy = 2$ **9.** $xy = 0.06$ **11.** 15 **13.** 7 **15.** 130 **17.** 96 **19.** 2 **21.** 20 **23.** $13.\overline{3}$ mi/h **25.** inverse variation; $xy = 60$ **27.** Direct variation; the ratio $\frac{\text{cost}}{\text{pound}}$ is constant at \$1.79. **29.** Inverse variation; the product of the length and width remains constant with an area of 24 square units. **31.** 1.1; $rt = 1.1$ **33.** 1; $ab = 1$ **35.** 375; $xy = 375$ **37.** Inverse variation; the product of the rate and the time is always 150. **39.** 121 ft **41.** direct variation; $y = 0.4x$; 8 **43.** inverse variation; $xy = 48$; 0.5 **45a.** 16 h; 10 h; 8 h; 4 h **b.** hours worked, rate of pay **c.** $rt = 80$ **47.** $612 = PV$ **49a.** y is doubled. **b.** y is halved. **51a.** $x^4y = k$ **b.** $\frac{x^4y}{z} = k$ **53.** C **55.** A **57.** $y = 6x$ **59.** $y = -0.1x$ **61.** $y = \frac{11}{7}x$

63–65.

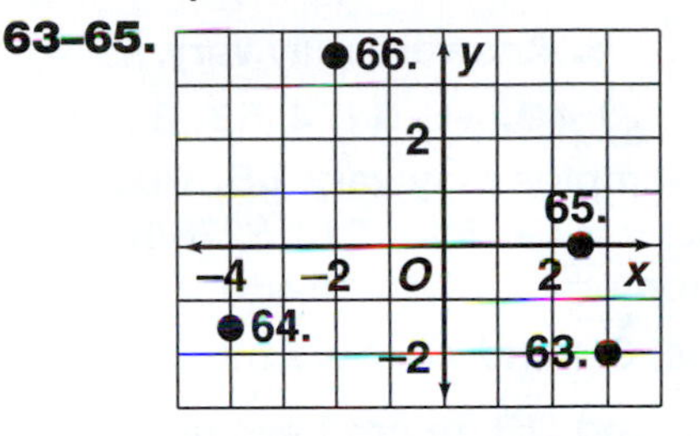

67. II **69.** I **71.** $-x - 1$ **73.** $6n + 10.5$ **75.** $6 - 4t$

Lesson 4-7 pp. 217–219

EXERCISES **1.** "Add 2 to the previous term"; 12, 14. **3.** "Add 2 to the first term, 3 to the second term and continue, adding 1 more each time"; 18, 24. **5.** "Multiply the previous term by 1.1"; 4.3923, 4.83153. **7.** "Add 1.1 to the previous term"; 5.5, 6.6. **9.** "Multiply the previous term by 4"; 512, 2048. **11.** "Add −14 to the previous term"; −47, −61. **13.** $A(n) = 1 - \left(\frac{1}{2}\right)^n$; $\frac{1023}{1024}$ **15.** Inductive reasoning; the conclusion is based on an observed pattern. **17.** Deductive reasoning; the conclusion is based on a property of triangles. **19.** Inductive reasoning; the conclusion is based on the pattern of points. **21.** $3\frac{1}{4}$, $3\frac{1}{2}$ **23.** $\frac{4}{27}$, $\frac{4}{81}$ **25.** 31, 40 **27.** 8, $8\frac{1}{4}$ **29a.** Answers may vary. Sample: Inductive reasoning is making conclusions based on patterns, while deductive reasoning is making conclusions based on given facts. **b.** Answers may vary. Check students' work. **31.** Answers may vary. Sample: $A(n) = 2 - 4n$ **33.** \$4500, \$4350, \$4200, \$4050, \$3900; the balance after 4 payments **35a.** 1, 5, 10, 10, 5, 1 **b.** 1, 2, 4, 8, 16; 32 **37a.** Yes; for each input there is only one output value. **b.** For every increase of 7 in the key position, the frequency doubles. **39.** $4x + 4$

41. a.

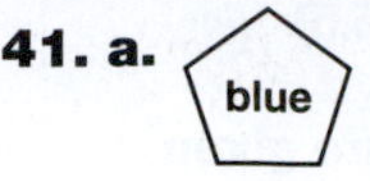

b. Blue; the colors rotate red, blue, and purple. Every third figure is purple. Since 21 is divisible by 3, the 21st figure is purple. The figure just before a purple figure is blue.

c. 12 sides; the figures show this pattern for number of sides.

Figure		Number of Sides
1–3	→	3
4–6	→	4
7–9	→	5
10–12	→	6
13–15	→	7
16–18	→	8
19–21	→	9
22–24	→	10
25–27	→	11
28	→	12

43. A **45.** A **47.** $xy = 9.6$ **49.** $xy = 42.7$ **51.** $y = 24x$ **53.** $y = 0.14x$ **55.** $y = -\frac{31}{110}x$ **57.** $y = \frac{2}{3}x$ **59.** {−19, −3, 9} **61.** {2, 4, 10} **63.** $\left\{-6\frac{1}{2}, -4\frac{1}{4}, -1\frac{1}{4}\right\}$

Chapter Review pp. 221–223

1. C **2.** D **3.** A **4.** E **5.** B **6.** G **7.** (−4, 1) **8.** (2, −2) **9.** (3, 0) **10.** (−1, −1)

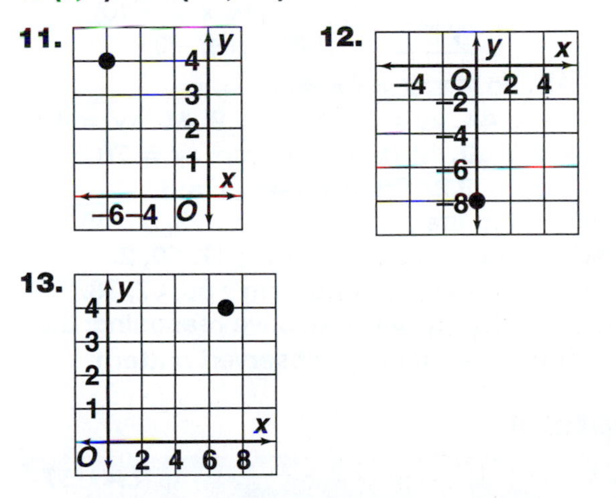

14. II **15.** IV **16.** y-axis **17.** III **18.** domain: {0, 1, 2}; range: {1, 2, 3, 4}; no **19.** domain: {−2, 0, 2, 4}; range: {−4, −2, 0, 2}; yes **20.** domain: {−1, 0, 2, 5}; range: {−3}; yes **21.** domain: {−1, 1, 3, 5}; range: {0}; function **22.** domain: {3, 4, 6, 9}; range: {−5, −1, 2, 3}; function **23.** no **24.** A relation is a function when each value of the domain corresponds to exactly one value of the range.

25. {−23, −7, −3, 13} **26.** {1, 3, 3.5, 5.5}
27. {1, 2, 17, 26} **28.** {−10, 2, 5, 17}
29–32. Tables may vary. Samples are given.

29.

x	$f(x)$
−1	−2
0	−3
1	−2

30.

x	$f(x)$
−2	−2
0	−3
2	−4

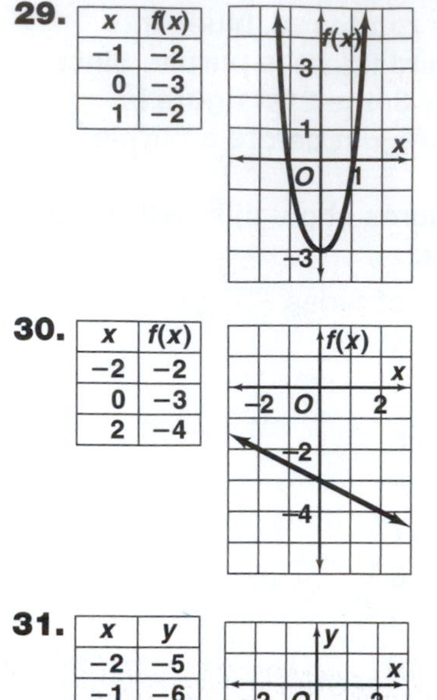

31.

x	y
−2	−5
−1	−6
0	−7
1	−6
2	−5

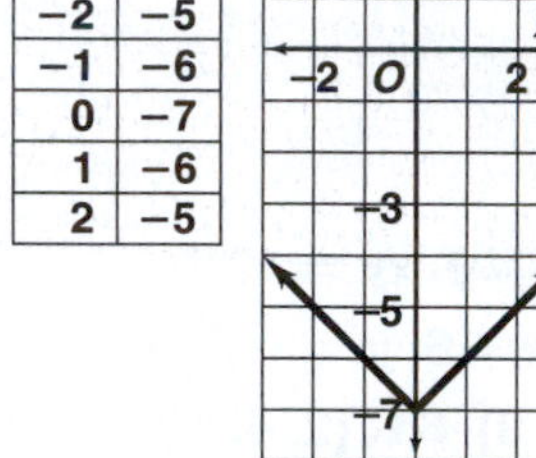

32.

x	y
−2	−3
−1	−1
0	1
1	3

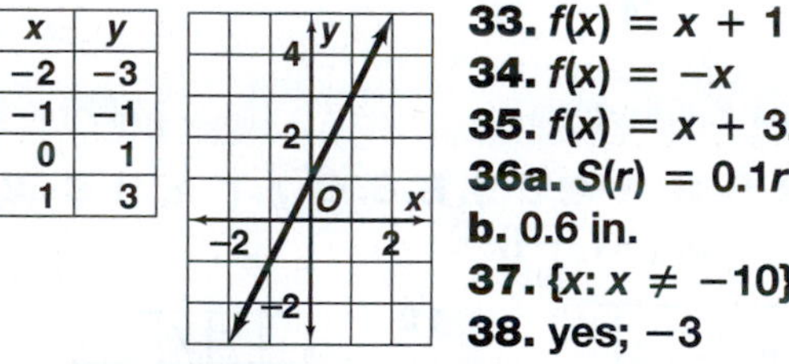

33. $f(x) = x + 1$
34. $f(x) = -x$
35. $f(x) = x + 3.5$
36a. $S(r) = 0.1r$
b. 0.6 in.
37. $\{x: x \neq -10\}$
38. yes; −3

39. no **40.** no **41.** $y = \frac{1}{5}x$ **42.** $y = x$
43. $y = -3x$ **44.** $xy = 6$ **45.** $xy = 9$ **46.** $xy = 4.4$
47. 4 **48.** 2.5 **49.** 18.75 **50.** inverse; $xy = 70$
51. direct; $y = 8.2x$ **52.** inverse; $xy = 3$
53. "Add −9 to the previous term"; 63, 54, 45.
54. "Add 3 to the previous term"; 17, 20, 23.
55. "Add 11 to the previous term"; 56, 67, 78.
56. $A(n) = \frac{n}{n+1}$; $\frac{20}{21}$ **57.** Inductive reasoning; the conclusion is based on an observed pattern.

Chapter 5

Lesson 5-1 pp. 234–237

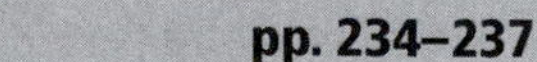

EXERCISES **1.** 3; the temperature increases 3°F each hour. **3.** $-\frac{1}{15}$ gal/mi; the amount of fuel consumed each mile is $\frac{1}{15}$ gal. **5.** $-16\frac{2}{3}$; the skydiver descends $16\frac{2}{3}$ ft/s. **7.** $\frac{1}{2}$ **9.** $\frac{2}{3}$ **11.** 2
13. $-\frac{3}{2}$ **15.** −1 **17.** $\frac{5}{3}$ **19.** $-\frac{2}{5}$ **21.** −5
23. undefined **25.** undefined **27.** $\frac{9}{10}$ in./month
29. 30 mi/h **31.** $\frac{1}{6}$ **33.** −20 **35.** −3
37. **39.**

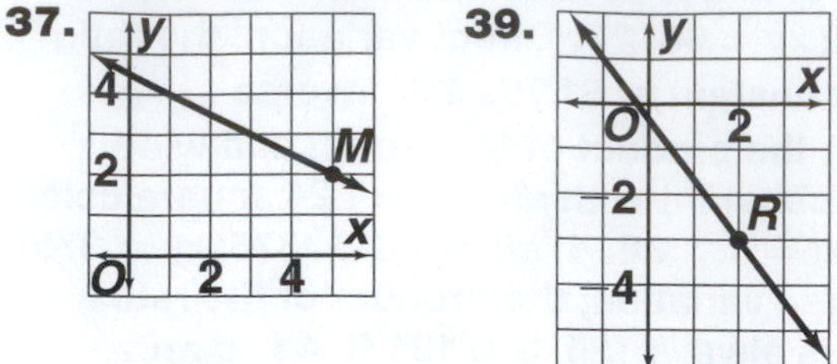

41a. $\frac{2}{3}$ **b.** $\frac{2}{3}$ **c.** Answers may vary. Sample: $\frac{y_2 - y_1}{x_2 - x_1} = \frac{y_2 - y_1}{x_2 - x_1}$ **43.** No; for example, the line passing through two points such as (1, 6) and (2, 5) has a slope of −1. **45.** $\overline{JK}$: $-\frac{1}{2}$; $\overline{KL}$: 2; $\overline{ML}$: $-\frac{1}{2}$; $\overline{MJ}$: 2 **47a.** Answers may vary. Sample: (0, 0), $\left(1, \frac{3}{4}\right)$ **b.** Answers may vary. Sample: (0, 0), $\left(1, -\frac{1}{2}\right)$ **49.** −6 **51.** 4 **53.** 3
55–59. Counterexamples may vary. **55.** true
57. true **59.** false; $y = 0x$ **61a.** 278; \$278/h
b. about 138 customers per hour **63.** 0
65. $\frac{2d - b}{c - 2a}$ **67.** Yes; $\overleftrightarrow{GH}$ and $\overleftrightarrow{HI}$ have the same slope. **69.** No; $\overleftrightarrow{PQ}$ and $\overleftrightarrow{QR}$ do not have the same slope. **71.** No; $\overleftrightarrow{ST}$ and $\overleftrightarrow{TX}$ do not have the same slope. **73.** A **75.** $c = 3.5n$ **77.** no solution **79.** −5, 5 **81.** −4 **83.** 7 **85.** −10

Lesson 5-2 pp. 242–245

EXERCISES **1.** −2; 1 **3.** 1; $-\frac{5}{4}$ **5.** $\frac{2}{3}$; 1 **7.** −1; −7
9. $-\frac{3}{4}$; −5 **11.** $y = 3x + \frac{2}{9}$ **13.** $y = 1$
15. $y = -\frac{2}{3}x + 5$ **17.** $y = 0.4x + 0.6$
19. $y = -\frac{1}{5}x - \frac{2}{5}$ **21.** $y = \frac{8}{3}x + \frac{2}{3}$
23. $y = \frac{3}{4}x + 2$ **25.** $y = \frac{1}{2}x + \frac{1}{2}$ **27.** $y = \frac{5}{4}x - \frac{1}{2}$
29. yes **31.** no **33.** no

35.

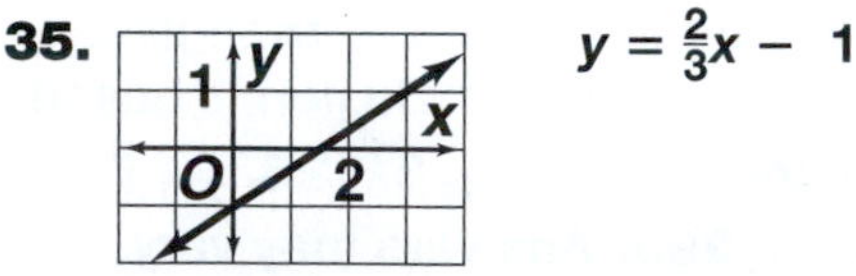

$y = \frac{2}{3}x - 1$

37. $y = 2x + 5$

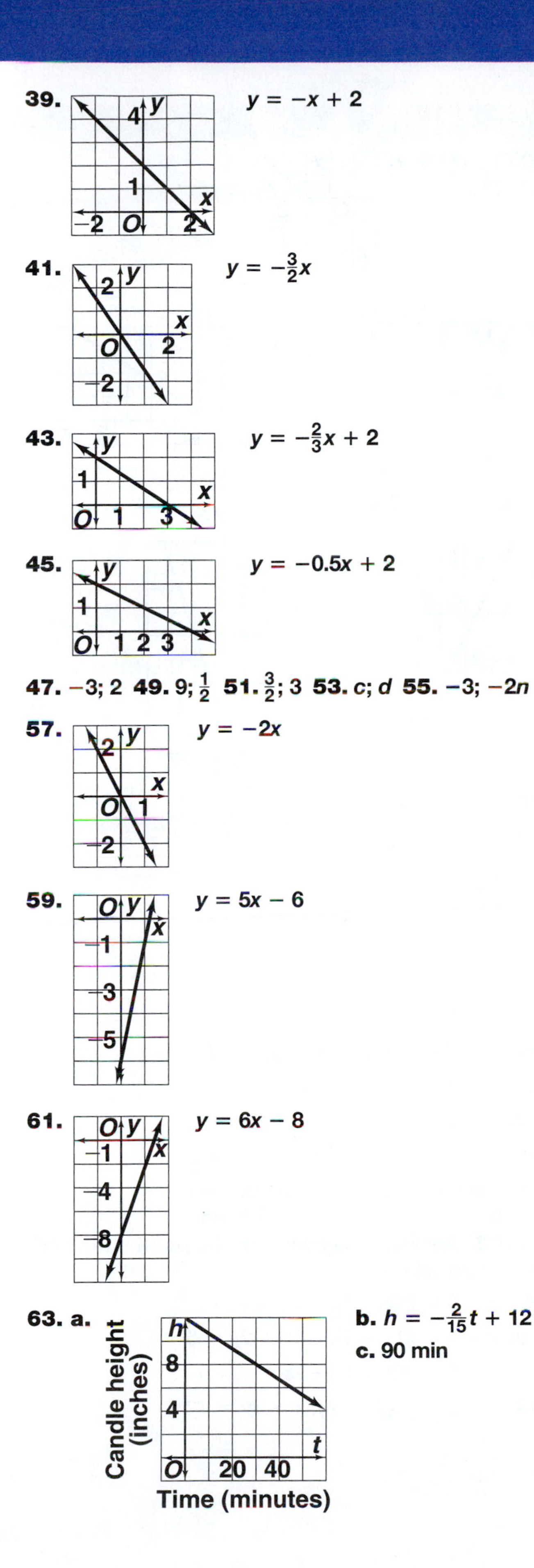

39. $y = -x + 2$

41. $y = -\frac{3}{2}x$

43. $y = -\frac{2}{3}x + 2$

45. $y = -0.5x + 2$

47. -3; 2 **49.** 9; $\frac{1}{2}$ **51.** $\frac{3}{2}$; 3 **53.** c; d **55.** -3; $-2n$

57. $y = -2x$

59. $y = 5x - 6$

61. $y = 6x - 8$

63. a. (graph: Candle height (inches) vs. Time (minutes)) **b.** $h = -\frac{2}{15}t + 12$ **c.** 90 min

65. The student substituted for x and y incorrectly. (2.4, -0.8) is not a solution. **67.** yes **69.** C **71.** Answers may vary. Sample: Plot point (0, 5), then move up 3 and right 4. Plot (4, 8) and connect the two points. **73.** $y = 2x - 1$ **75.** $y = -\frac{1}{2}x + 8$ **77.** $y = -x - 3$ **79.** Always true; substitute (0, b) into the equation. $b = m(0) + b$; $b = 0 + b$; $b = b$; b is always equal to itself. **81.** Check students' work. **83.** -5

85. a.

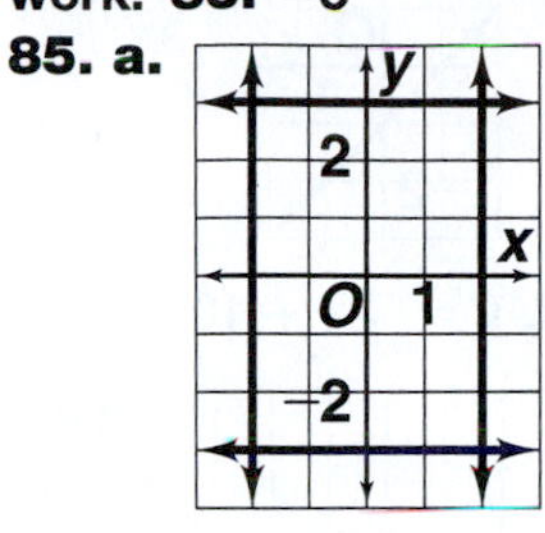

$x = -2$; $x = 2$
$x = 3$; $y = -3$
b. Rectangle; Check students' work.
c. $y = \frac{3}{2}x$ OR $y = -\frac{3}{2}x$; explanations may vary.

87. D **89.** C **91.** $\frac{3}{5}$ **93.** $10\frac{1}{2}$ **95.** $3\frac{3}{4}$ **97.** $x > 1\frac{3}{4}$ **99.** $x > -1$ **101.** $x > \frac{3}{2}$

Lesson 5-3 — pp. 249–251

EXERCISES **1.** 18; 9 **3.** -6; 30 **5.** $-\frac{9}{2}$; $-\frac{3}{2}$ **7.** 6; 4 **9.** -5; 4 **11.** C

13.

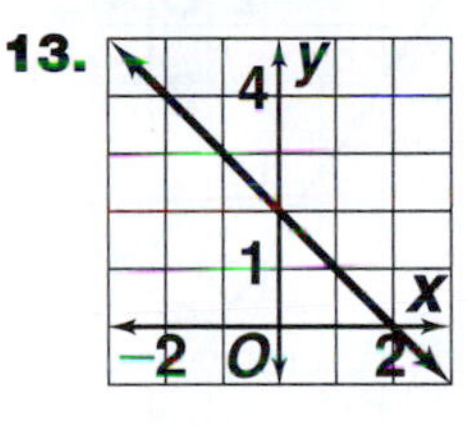

15.

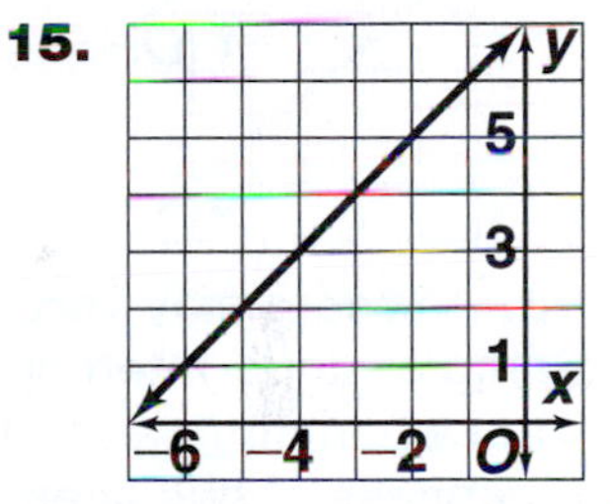

17.

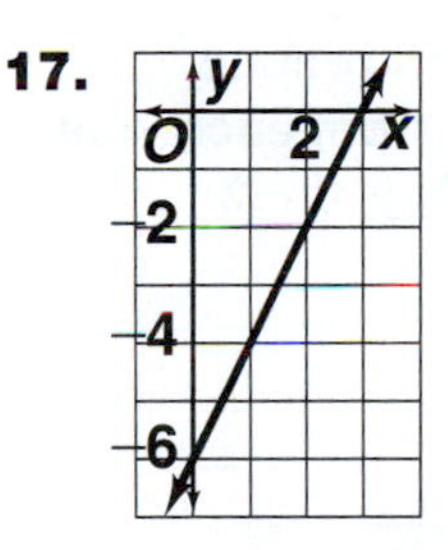

19. horizontal
21. horizontal
23.

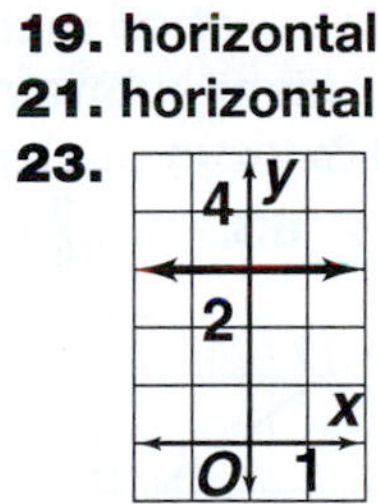

25.

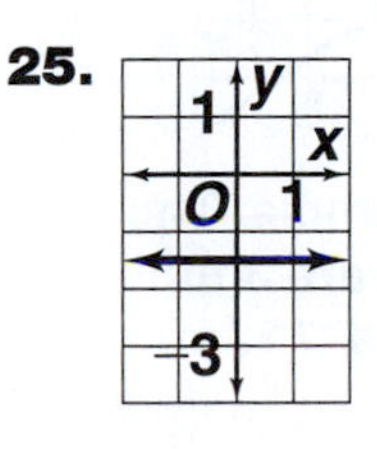

27. $-3x + y = 1$ **29.** $x - 2y = 6$ **31.** $-3x - 4y = 16$ **33.** $-14x + 4y = 1$ **35.** $3x + y = 0$ **37a.** Answers may vary. Sample: x = time walking; y = time running **b.** $3x + 8y = 15$

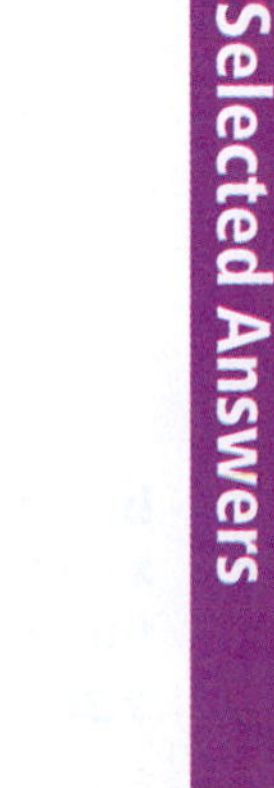

39.

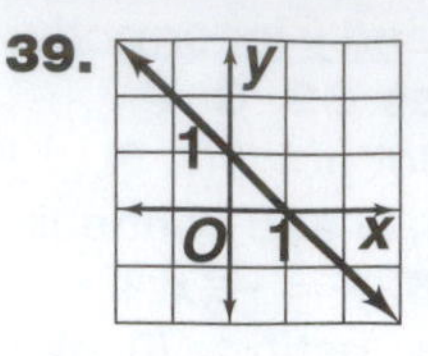

41.

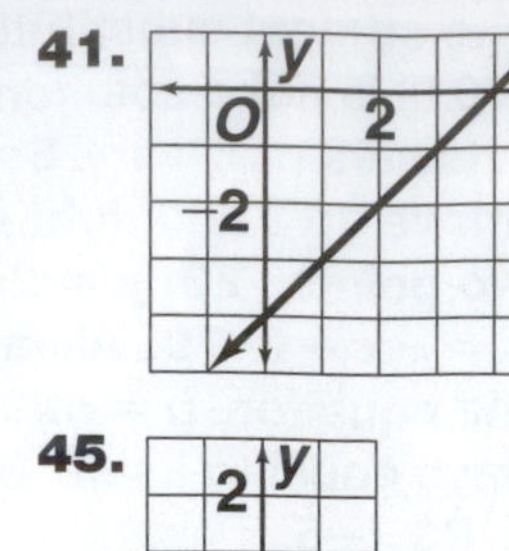

43.

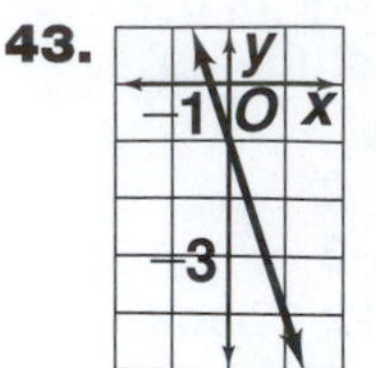

45.
2 y
O x
1
−2

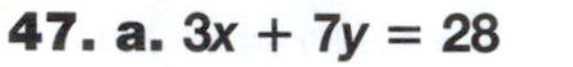

47. a. $3x + 7y = 28$

b.

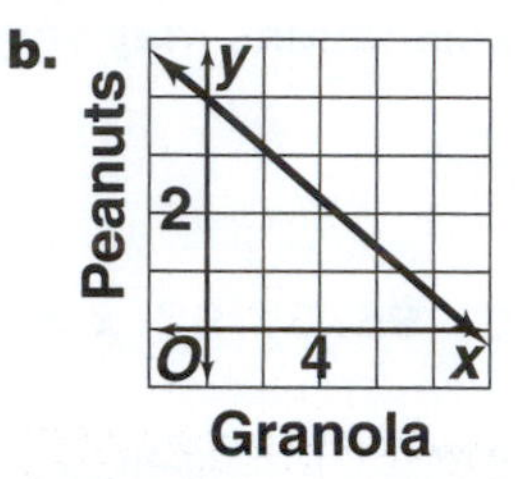

7 oz

49. $y = \frac{4}{5}x + 10$

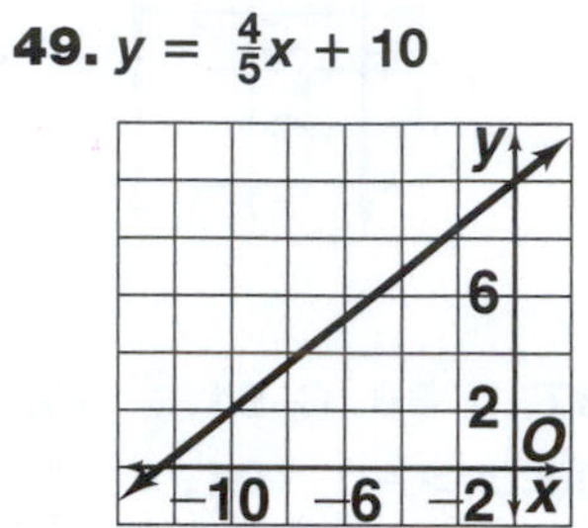

51. $y = -\frac{4}{5}x - 3$

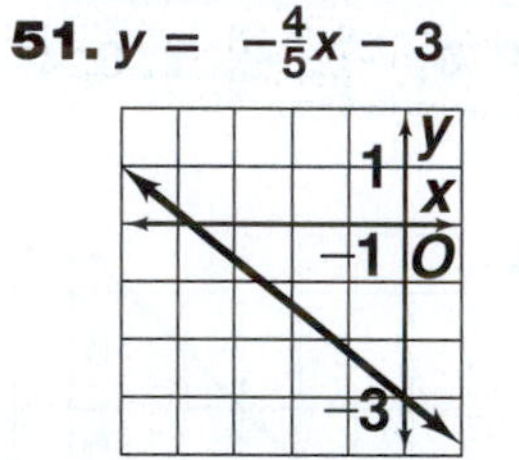

53. $y = -\frac{16}{11}x - 8$

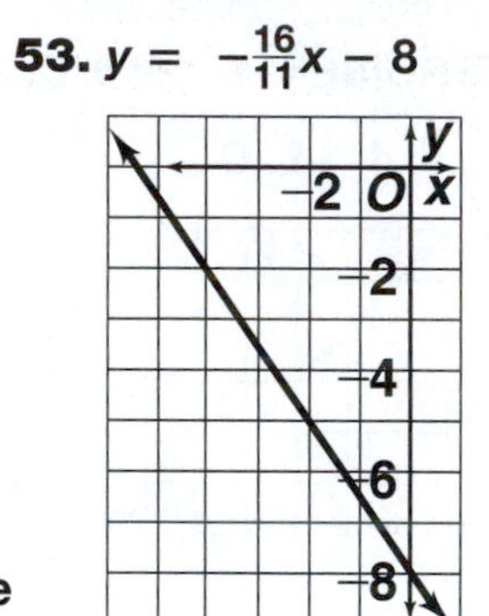

55. Answers may vary. Sample: slope-intercept form when comparing the steepness of two lines; standard form when making quick graphs
57. The student subtracted $-3x$ from each side instead of $3x$ from each side. **59.** $y = -2$
61. $x = -2$ **63.** $y = \frac{3}{5}x + 4$

65. a.

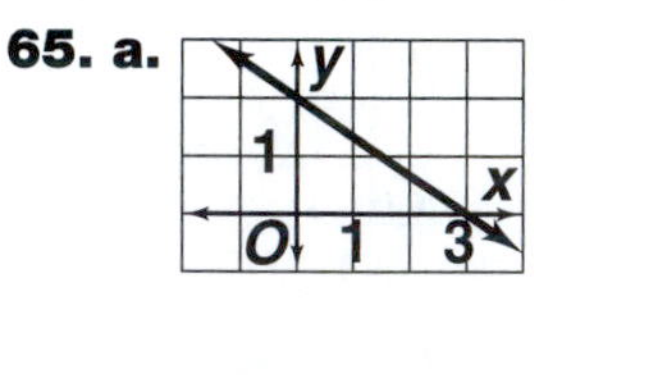

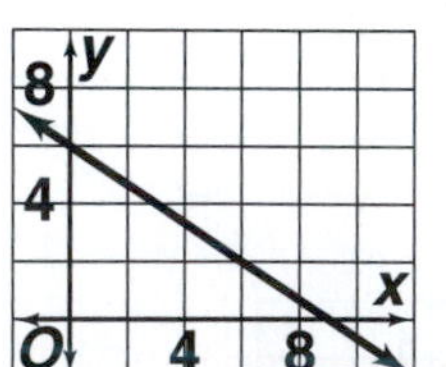

b. $-\frac{2}{3}$; $-\frac{2}{3}$ **c.** Answers may vary. Sample: The x- and y-intercepts of $2x + 3y = 18$ are 3 times those of $2x + 3y = 6$. **67.** A **69.** yes **71.** no
73. $y = \frac{2}{3}x - 1$ **75.** 4 **77.** −0.5

Lesson 5-4 pp. 255–257

EXERCISES 1.

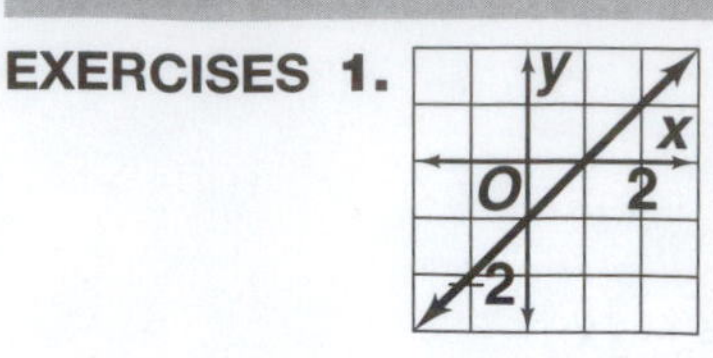

3.

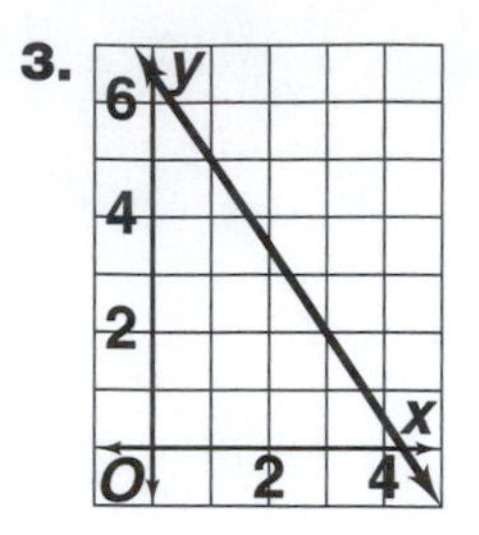

5.

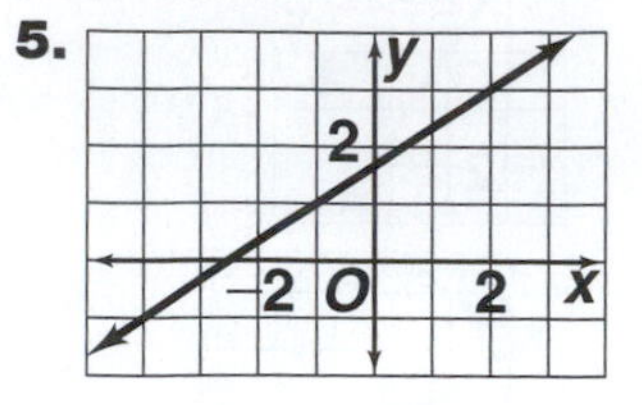

7.

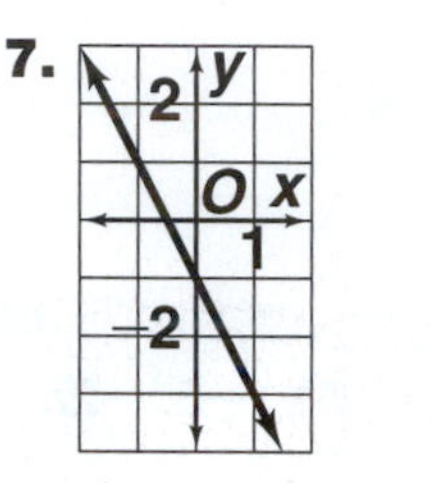

9.

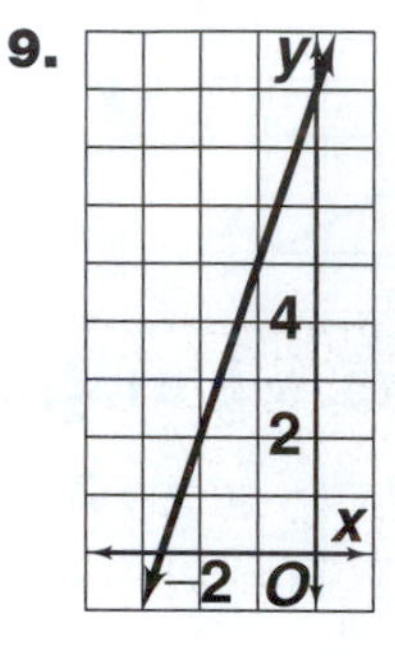

11. $y - 2 = -\frac{5}{3}(x - 4)$
13. $y + 7 = -\frac{3}{2}(x + 2)$
15. $y + 8 = -3(x - 5)$
17. $y + 8 = -\frac{1}{5}(x - 1)$
19–29. Answers may vary for the point indicated by the equation.
19. $y = 1(x + 1)$; $y = x + 1$
21. $y + 2 = -\frac{6}{5}(x - 4)$; $y = -\frac{6}{5}x + \frac{14}{5}$
23. $y + 5 = \frac{1}{6}(x + 1)$; $y = \frac{1}{6}x - \frac{29}{6}$
25. $y - 7 = 11(x - 2)$; $y = 11x - 15$
27. $y + 8 = -\frac{13}{5}(x - 3)$; $y = -\frac{13}{5}x - \frac{1}{5}$
29. $y - 2 = -1\left(x - \frac{1}{2}\right)$; $y = -x + \frac{5}{2}$
31. Yes; answers may vary. Sample: $y - 9 = -2(x + 4)$ **33.** no **35.** no
37–53. Answers may vary for the point indicated by the equation.
37. $y + 3 = \frac{2}{5}(x - 1)$
39. $y - 4 = \frac{3}{2}(x - 1)$; $-3x + 2y = 5$
41. $y + 2 = 2(x + 1)$; $-2x + y = 0$
43. $y - 6 = -\frac{1}{3}(x + 6)$; $x + 3y = 12$

45. $y + 3 = -\frac{7}{2}(x - 5)$; $7x + 2y = 29$
47. $y - 1 = -\frac{1}{6}(x + 7)$; $x + 6y = -1$
49. $y - 4 = 2(x - 2)$; $-2x + y = 0$
50. $y - 1 = \frac{1}{3}x$; $-x + 3y = 3$
53. $y - 2 = \frac{3}{5}(x - 6)$; $-3x + 5y = -8$
55. $y = -2.6x + 315.6$
57. y-intercept changes from -4 to 4
59. Answers may vary. Sample:
a. $y - 332 = \frac{3}{5}(x - 0)$ **b.** 341 m/s **c.** 368 m/s
61. $y = 3$ **63a.** 14.75 **b.** 57.5 **c.** -4 **d.** 100
65. C

67.

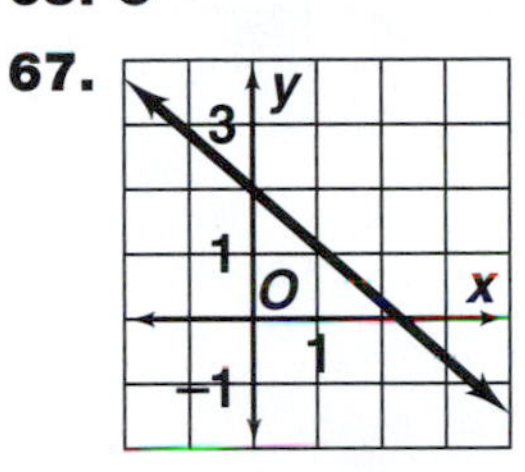

69.

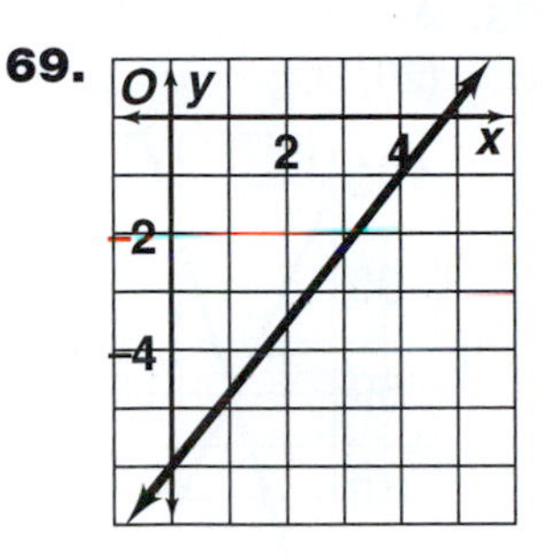

71. y, x, −2, O, 1, −2

73. 3, 8
75. 2.66, 2.73
77. 144, 288

Lesson 5-5 pp. 262–265

EXERCISES **1.** $\frac{1}{2}$ **3.** 1 **5.** $-\frac{3}{4}$ **7.** no, different slopes **9.** yes, same slopes and different y-intercepts **11.** yes, same slopes and different y-intercepts **13.** $y = 6x$ **15.** $y = -2x - 1$ **17.** $y = 0.5x - 9$ **19.** $-\frac{1}{2}$ **21.** $-\frac{5}{7}$ **23.** $\frac{3}{2}$ **25.** $y = -\frac{1}{2}x$ **27.** $y = 3x - 10$ **29.** $y = -\frac{4}{5}x + 24$ **31.** $y = \frac{5}{4}x + 1$ **33.** parallel **35.** neither **37.** perpendicular **39.** neither **41.** $y = -\frac{4}{5}x - \frac{19}{5}$; $y = -\frac{4}{5}x + \frac{3}{5}$ **43.** $y = -\frac{1}{2}x$; $y = 2x$ **45.** $y = 4$; $y = 2$ **47.** about $\frac{5}{4}$ **49.** Answers may vary. Sample: $\frac{5}{4} \cdot \left(-\frac{1}{2}\right) \neq -1$ **51.** No; the slopes are not equal. **53.** yes; same slopes and different y-intercepts **55.** False; the product of two positive numbers can't be -1. **57.** False; all direct variations go through the point (0, 0). If they have the same slope, they are the same line, not parallel lines.
59. The slope of $\overleftrightarrow{JK}$ is $\frac{1}{5}$. The slope of $\overleftrightarrow{KL}$ is -2. The slope of $\overleftrightarrow{LM}$ is $\frac{1}{6}$. The slope of $\overleftrightarrow{JM}$ is -4. The quadrilateral is not a parallelogram.
61. The slopes of $\overleftrightarrow{AB}$ and $\overleftrightarrow{CD}$ are both $\frac{2}{5}$. The slopes of $\overleftrightarrow{BC}$ and $\overleftrightarrow{AD}$ are both $-\frac{5}{2}$. The product is -1, so the quadrilateral is a rectangle.
63. The slopes of $\overleftrightarrow{PQ}$ and $\overleftrightarrow{RS}$ are both $\frac{1}{2}$. The slopes of $\overleftrightarrow{PS}$ and $\overleftrightarrow{QR}$ are both -2. The product is -1, so the quadrilateral is a rectangle.
65. perpendicular
67. $y = \frac{1}{2}x - 3$; $y = -2x + 7$
69. $\overleftrightarrow{BC}$ and $\overleftrightarrow{AD}$ both have a slope of zero. $\overleftrightarrow{BC}$ and $\overleftrightarrow{AD}$ are parallel. $\overleftrightarrow{AB}$ and $\overleftrightarrow{CD}$ both have a slope of $\frac{4}{3}$. $\overleftrightarrow{AB}$ and $\overleftrightarrow{CD}$ are parallel. The diagonal $\overleftrightarrow{BD}$ has a slope of -2. The diagonal $\overleftrightarrow{AC}$, has a slope of $\frac{1}{2}$. The diagonals are perpendicular. ▱$ABCD$ is a rhombus. **71.** A **73.** C **75.** $-\frac{1}{5}$
77. yes **79.** no

Chapter Review pp. 267–269

1. perpendicular lines **2.** parallel lines **3.** point-slope **4.** slope **5.** y-intercept **6.** 8 oz/mo **7.** 3.375 in./wk **8.** 5; the speed is 5 mi/h. **9.** -1.25; gasoline decreases 1.25 gal for each hour of driving time. **10.** 0; the height is at a constant level of 150 ft. **11.** $\frac{1}{4}$ **12.** undefined **13.** 1

14. $y = -3$ **15.** $y = -7x + \frac{1}{2}$ **16.** $y = \frac{2}{5}x$

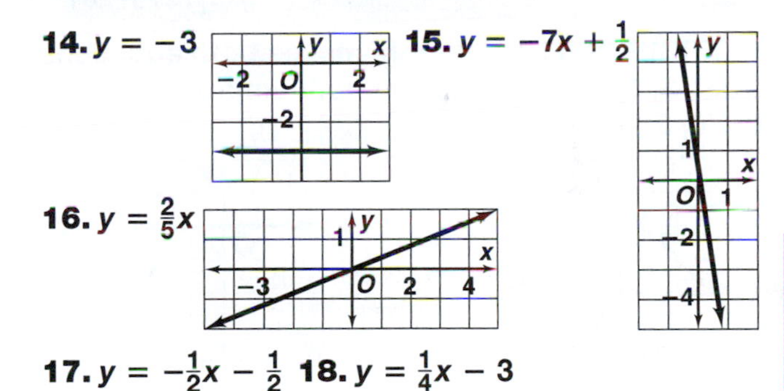

17. $y = -\frac{1}{2}x - \frac{1}{2}$ **18.** $y = \frac{1}{4}x - 3$
19. no **20.** yes **21.** yes **22.** no **23.** no **24.** yes

25. 2; 5 **26.** 8; -13 **27.** -1; $-\frac{1}{3}$

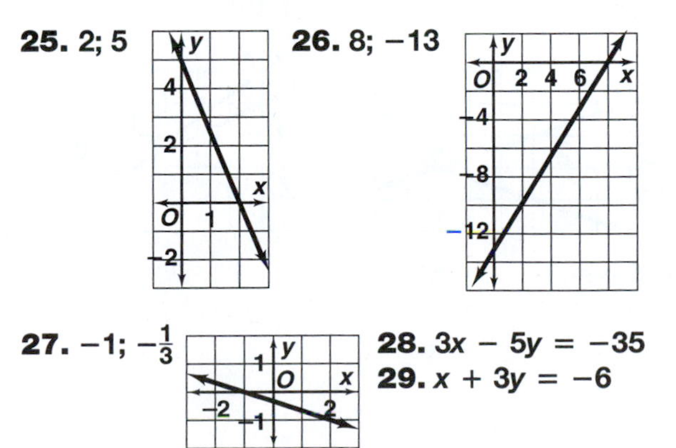

28. $3x - 5y = -35$
29. $x + 3y = -6$

30. $4x - 3y = 15$ **31.** C **32.** A **33.** B
34. horizontal **35.** vertical **36.** horizontal
37. $y + 2 = 2(x - 1)$
38. $y + 2 = \frac{3}{4}(x - 1)$
39. $y + 2 = -3(x - 1)$ **40.** $y + 2 = 0$
41. $y - 3 = \frac{1}{3}(x - 4)$ or $y - 1 = \frac{1}{3}(x + 2)$
42. $y + 4 = -\frac{6}{5}(x - 5)$ or $y - 2 = -\frac{6}{5}x$
43. $y = \frac{1}{2}(x + 1)$ or $y + 1 = \frac{1}{2}(x + 3)$
44. Yes; answers may vary. Sample: $y - 4 = \frac{1}{3}(x - 6)$. **45.** no **46.** Yes; answers may vary. Sample: $y - 7 = -2(x + 1)$ **47.** yes; same slopes and different y-intercepts **48.** yes; same slopes and different y-intercepts **49.** no; different slopes **50.** yes; product of slopes is -1 **51.** no; product of slopes is not -1 **52.** yes; product of slopes is -1
53. $y + 1 = 5(x - 2)$ or $y = 5x - 11$
54. $y - 5 = \frac{1}{3}(x - 3)$ or $y = \frac{1}{3}x + 4$
55. $y + 5 = 9x$ or $y = 9x - 5$
56. $y - 10 = -\frac{1}{8}(x - 4)$ or $y = -\frac{1}{8}x + 10\frac{1}{2}$
57. $y = -\frac{3}{4}x + \frac{7}{2}$; $y = -\frac{3}{4}x - \frac{1}{2}$
58. $y = \frac{1}{5}x + \frac{9}{5}$; $y = -5x - 12$

Chapter 6

Lesson 6-1 pp. 279–281

EXERCISES **1.** Yes. $(-1, 5)$ makes both equations true. **3.** Yes. $(-1, 5)$ makes both equations true.

5. (0, 2);

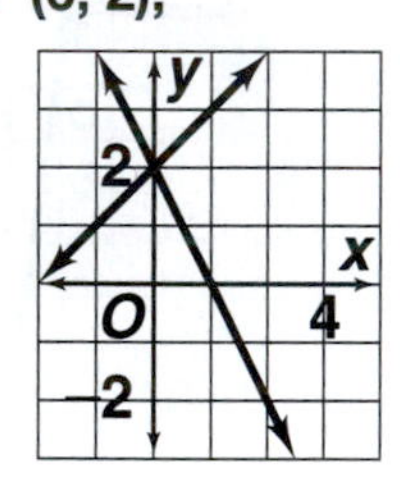

7. (1, 1);

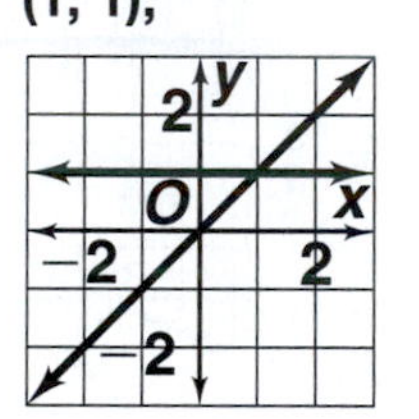

9. (6, −1);

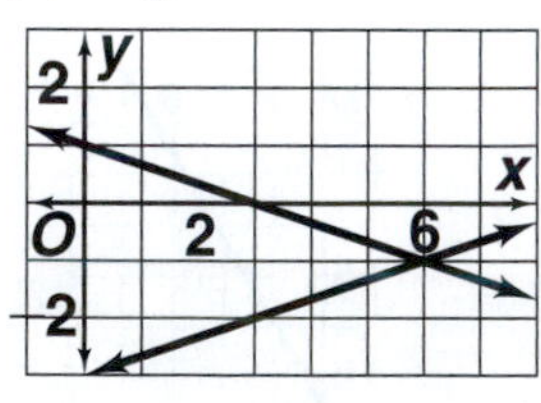

11. (4, 0);

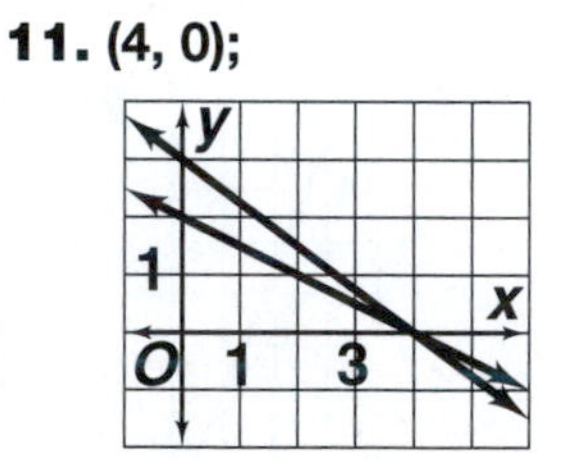

13a. 3 weeks **b.** $35

15. no solution;

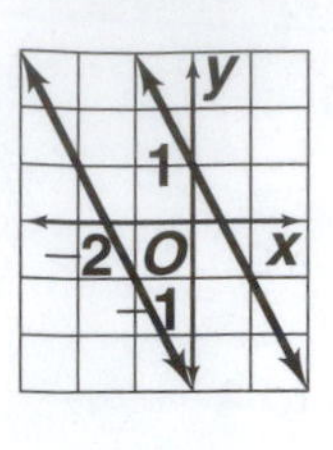

17. infinitely many solutions;

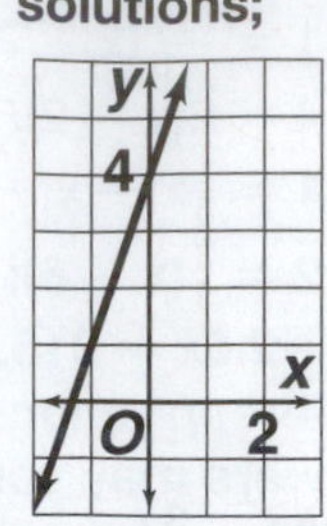

19. no solution; same slope, different y-int.
21. one solution; different slopes
23. A
25. (20, 60);

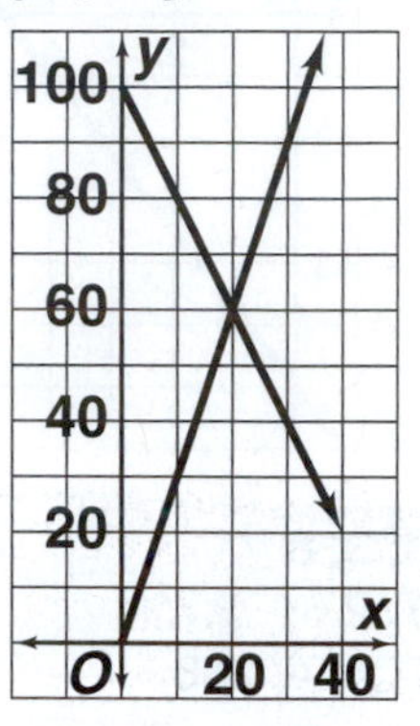

27. Answers may vary. Sample: $y = 2x - 1$, $y = 2x + 5$
29. (2, 20)

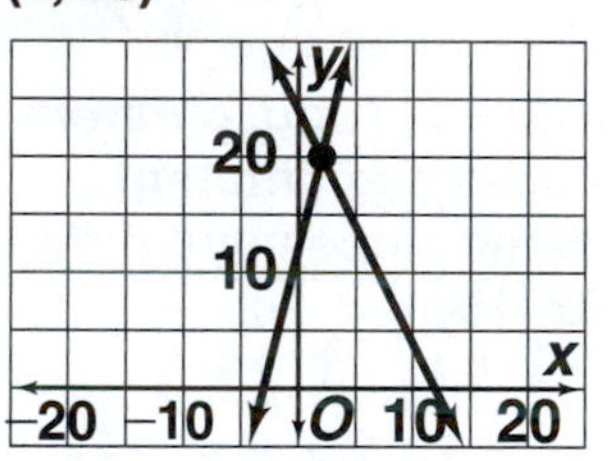

31. (12, 30)

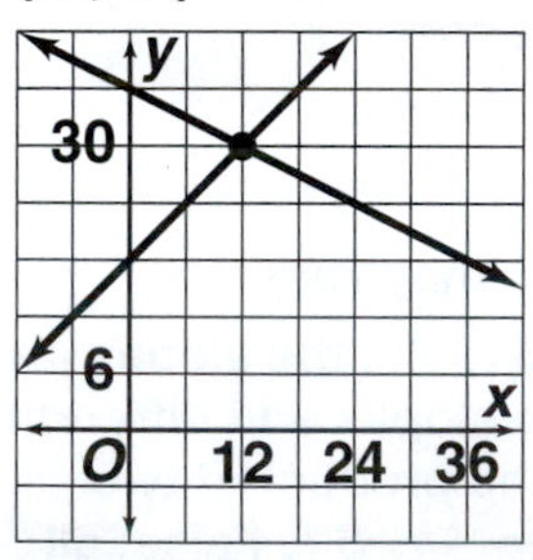

33a. time on the horizontal and distance on the vertical **b.** Red represents the tortoise because it shows distance changing steadily over time. Blue represents the hare because it is steeper than the other line at the ends but shows no change in distance while the hare is napping. **c.** The point of intersection shows when the tortoise passed the sleeping hare. **35a.** $c = 100 + 50t$; $c = 50 + 75t$; (2, 200);

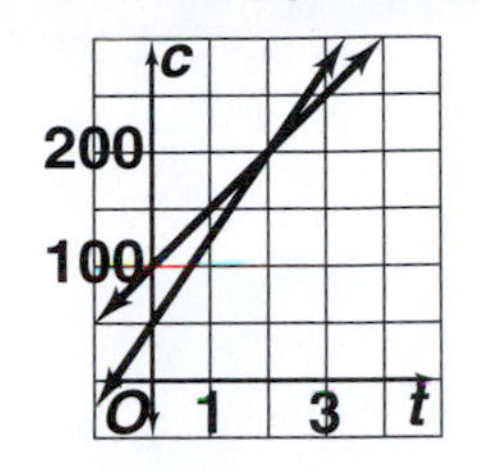

b. The cost of renting either studio for 2 h is the same, \$200.
37. a. sometimes **b.** never **39.** B **41.** B
43. −12, 4 **45.** 1, 3 **47.** 42 **49.** 4 **51.** 18

Lesson 6-2 pp. 284–286

EXERCISES **1.** D **3.** B **5–15.** Coordinates given in alphabetical order. **5.** (9, 28) **7.** $\left(6\frac{1}{3}, -\frac{1}{3}\right)$ **9.** (4, 20) **11.** (2, 0) **13.** (6, −2) **15.** (8, −2) **17.** 4 cm by 13 cm **19.** (15, 15) **21.** (−4, −4) **23.** 9 yr

25. estimate: (−3.5, −3.5); $\left(-\frac{10}{3}, -\frac{3}{11}\right)$

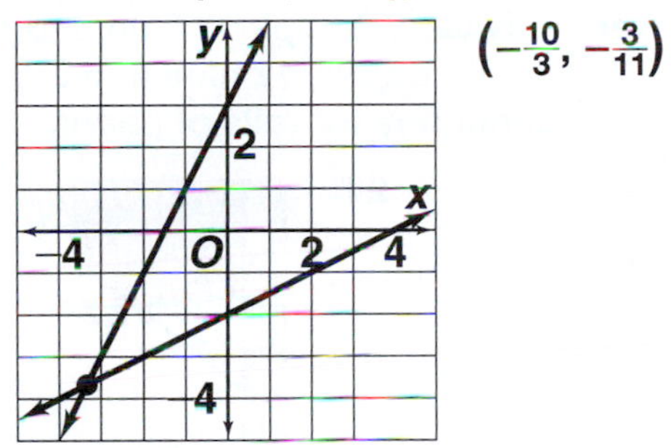

27. estimate: (−4, 0); $\left(-\frac{50}{11}, -\frac{2}{11}\right)$

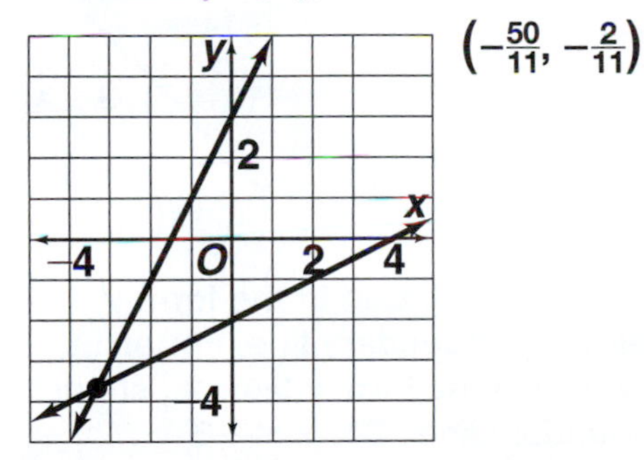

29. The student added $5 + (-y)$ instead of multiplying $5(-y)$. The correct solution is (−1, 1).
31. (2, 4) **33.** (2, −4) **35.** $\left(-\frac{1}{2}, 0\right)$
37a. $g = \frac{23}{22}b$ **b.** $(b, g) = (572, 598)$ **c.** 26
39. B **41.** D **43.** (2, 1)

45. **47.** **49.**

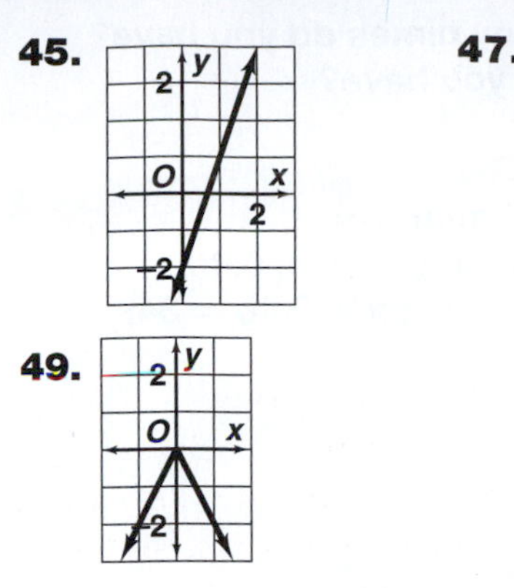

Lesson 6-3 pp. 290–293

EXERCISES **1.** (1, 3) **3.** (5, −17) **5.** $\left(-9, \frac{1}{2}\right)$
7a. $x + y = 20, x - y = 4$ **b.** 12 and 8 **9.** (−5, 1)
11. $\left(-2, -\frac{5}{2}\right)$ **13.** $\left(\frac{1}{2}, 1\right)$ **15a.** $30w + \ell = 17.65$, $20w + 3\ell = 25.65$ **b.** \$.39 for a wallet size, \$5.95 for an 8 × 10 **17.** (−1, −3) **19.** (2, −2) **21.** $\left(-1, \frac{3}{2}\right)$
23–27. Methods may vary. Samples are given.
23. (−1, −2); substitution; both solved for *y*
25. (10, 2); substitution; one eq. solved for *x*
27. (5, 1); substitution; one eq. solved for *x*
29. one night: \$81.25; one meal: \$8.13
31. She forgot to multiply −8 by 6. **33.** (10, −6)
35. (−15, −1) **37.** (−2, 16) **39.** 9 **41.** $B_1 = 3$ volts; $B_2 = 1.5$ volts **43.** $\left(\frac{c}{a}, 0\right)$ $(a \neq 0, b \neq 1)$
45. CD: \$3.40, cassette: \$1.80 **47.** C **49.** C
51. (−1, 4) **53.** no **55.** yes **57.** $a > -\frac{3}{5}$
59. $h > -25$ **61.** $p < 7$

Lesson 6-4 pp. 297–300

EXERCISES **1a.** $4a + 5b = 61$ **b.** $5a + 3b = 7.12$
c. pen; \$1.19, pencil: \$.39

3. a.

a	*b*	24
0.04*a*	0.08*b*	0.05(24)

b. $a + b = 24$; $0.04a + 0.08b = 1.2$ **c.** 18 kg A, 6 kg B **5.** 600 games **7. a.** $s + c = 2.75$ **b.** $s - c = 1.5$ **c.** 2.125 mi/h **d.** 0.625 mi/h **9–13.** Answers may vary. Samples are given. **9.** Substitution; one eq. is solved for *t*. **11.** Elimination; subtract to eliminate *m*. **13.** Elimination; mult. first eq. by 3 and add to elim. *y*. **15a.** $t = 99 - 3.5m$; $t = 0 + 2.5m$; $t = 41.25°$, $m = 16.5$ min **b.** After 16.5 min, the temp. of either piece will be 41.25°C.
17. Answers may vary. Sample: You have 10 coins, all dimes and quarters. The value of the

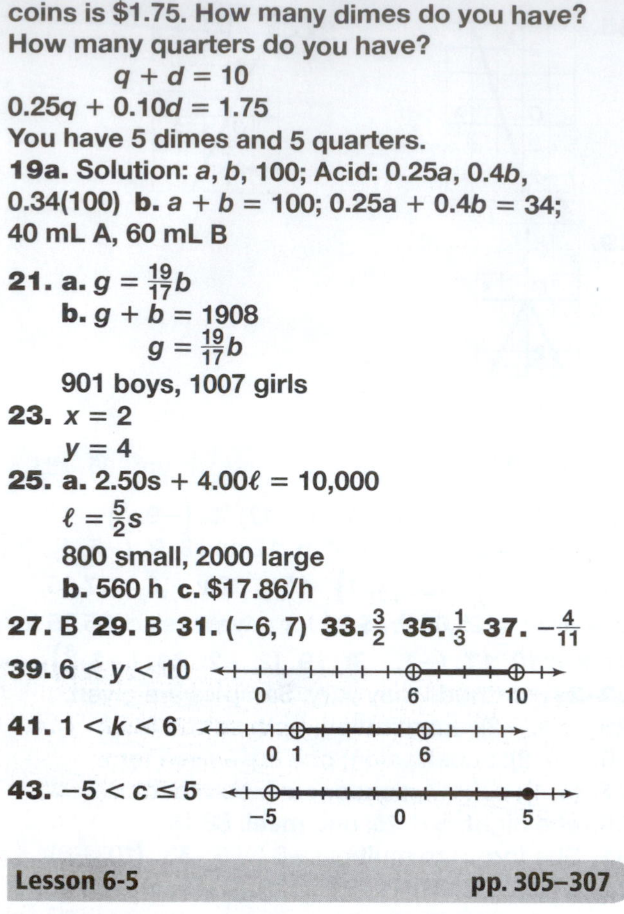

coins is \$1.75. How many dimes do you have? How many quarters do you have?

$q + d = 10$

$0.25q + 0.10d = 1.75$

You have 5 dimes and 5 quarters.

19a. Solution: a, b, 100; Acid: $0.25a$, $0.4b$, $0.34(100)$ **b.** $a + b = 100$; $0.25a + 0.4b = 34$; 40 mL A, 60 mL B

21. a. $g = \frac{19}{17}b$

b. $g + b = 1908$

$g = \frac{19}{17}b$

901 boys, 1007 girls

23. $x = 2$

$y = 4$

25. a. $2.50s + 4.00\ell = 10{,}000$

$\ell = \frac{5}{2}s$

800 small, 2000 large

b. 560 h **c.** \$17.86/h

27. B **29.** B **31.** $(-6, 7)$ **33.** $\frac{3}{2}$ **35.** $\frac{1}{3}$ **37.** $-\frac{4}{11}$

39. $6 < y < 10$

41. $1 < k < 6$

43. $-5 < c \le 5$

Lesson 6-5 pp. 305–307

EXERCISES **1.** no **3.** yes **5.** no **7.** A **9.** B

11.

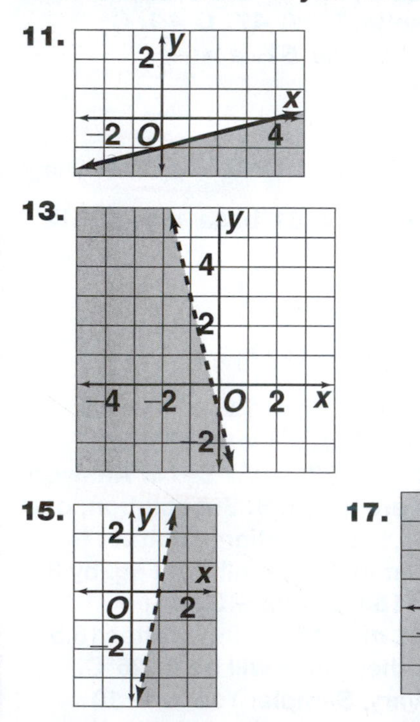

13.

15.

17.

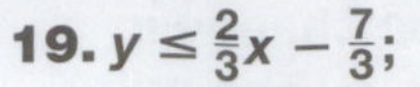

19. $y \le \frac{2}{3}x - \frac{7}{3}$;

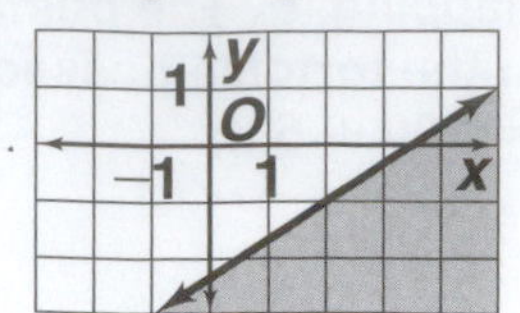

21. $y \le \frac{2}{3}x - \frac{8}{3}$;

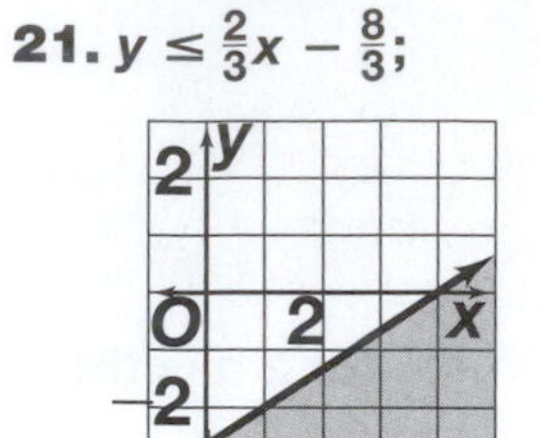

23. a. $3x + 5y \le 48$

b.

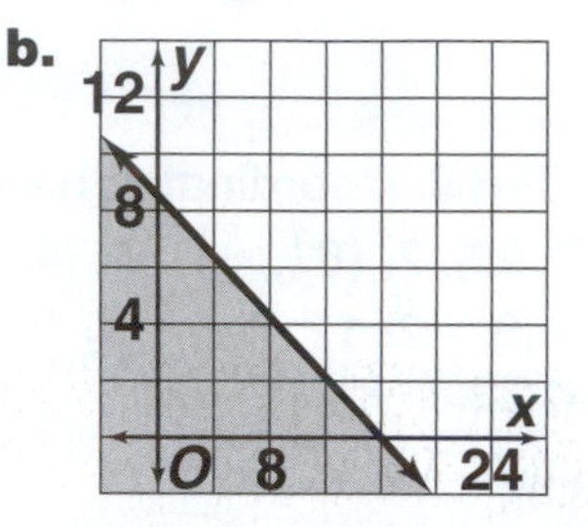

c. Answers may vary. Sample: 8 blue and 4 gold, 2 blue and 8 gold, 12 blue and 2 gold

d. No; you cannot buy -2 rolls of paper.

25.

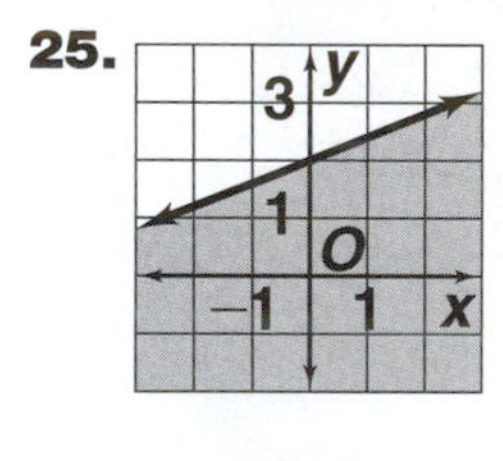

27.

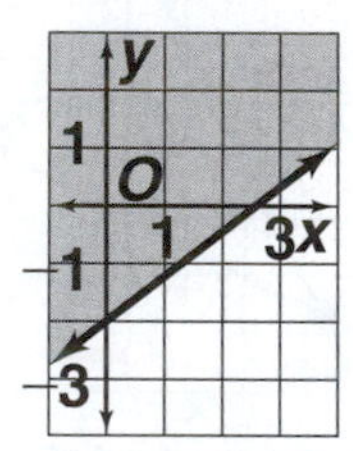

29.

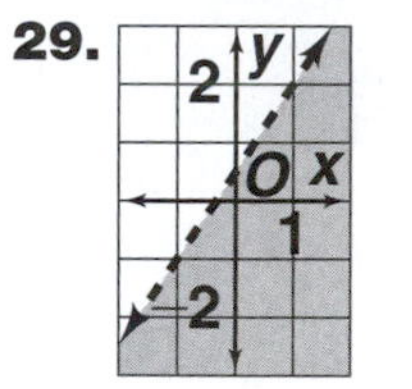

31.

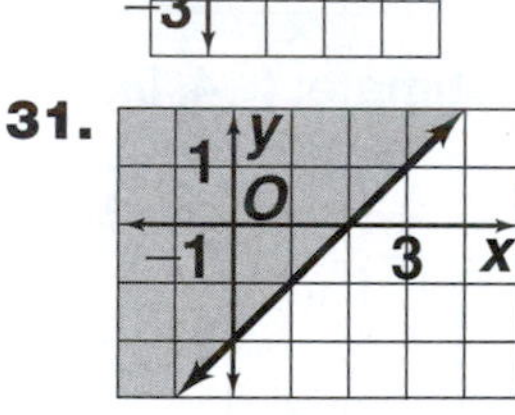

33. For an inequality written in the form $y <$ or $y \le$, shade below the boundary line. For an inequality written in the form $y >$ or $\ge$, shade above the boundary line. **35.** $x \le -3$

37. a. $12x + 8y \le 180$

b.

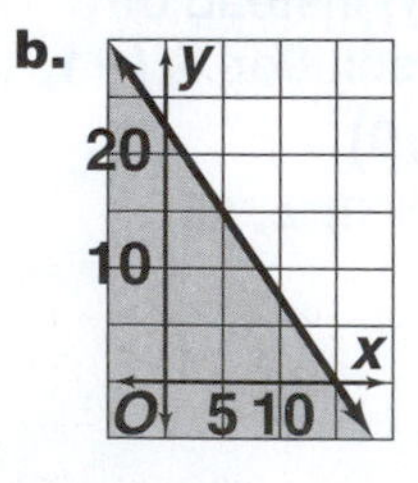

c. Yes; you can buy 8 CDs and 9 tapes.

d. 43

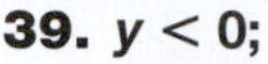

39. $y < 0$;

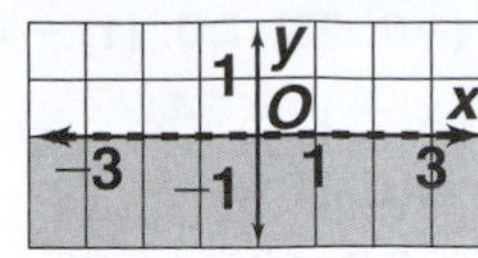

41. $x < y$;

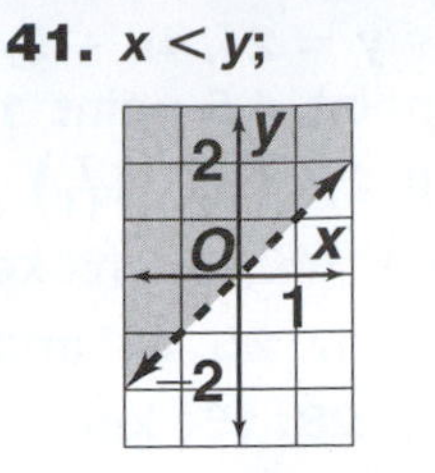

43. a. $y \geq \frac{100}{8} - \frac{5}{8}x$;

b. No; the point (5, 8) does not lie in the shaded region.
c. Answers will vary. Sample: (0, 13), (8, 8), (16, 4).

45. a. $2w + 2\ell \leq 50$;

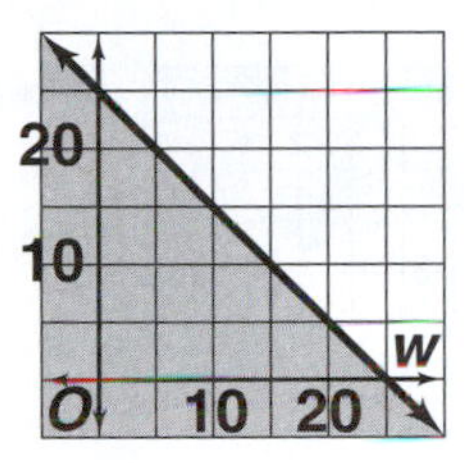

b. Answers may vary. Sample: 10 ft by 10 ft, 5 ft by 5 ft
c. No; (12, 15) is not in the shaded region and is not a solution of the inequality.

47. $y \geq 2x - 2$ **49a.** yes **b.** yes **c.** Answers may vary. Sample: (2, 3)

d.

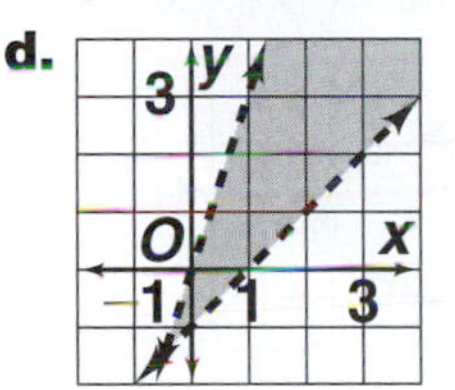

51. A **53.** D **55.** 0.75 mi/h, 3.25 mi/h **57.** 25, 32
59. −7, −13 **61.** 28 **63.** $16\frac{2}{3}$
65. 4 **67.** 6.5

Lesson 6-6 pp. 312–316

EXERCISES **1.** no **3.** no

5.

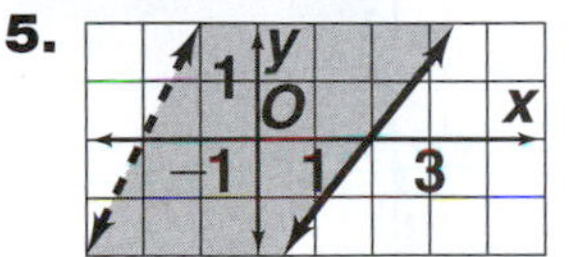

7.

9.

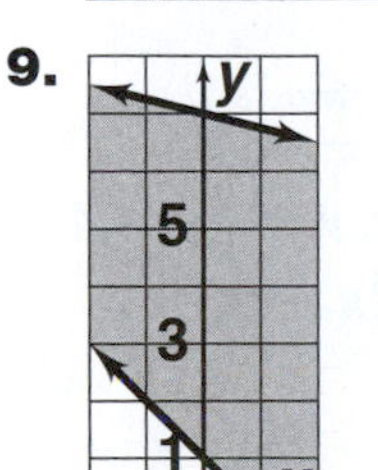

11.

13.

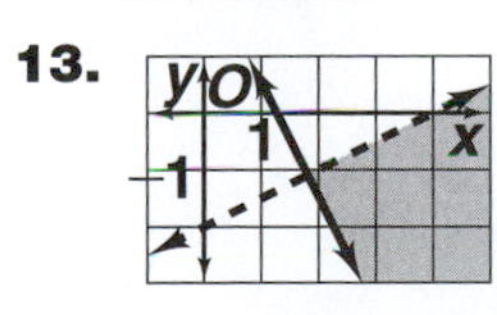

15.

17. $y \geq -\frac{1}{2}x - 2$ and $y \leq \frac{1}{2}x + 2$
19. $y \leq -\frac{2}{3}x - 4$ and $y \geq \frac{1}{5}x - 3$
21.

23. $x + y \geq 30$, $1.25x + 3y \leq 60$

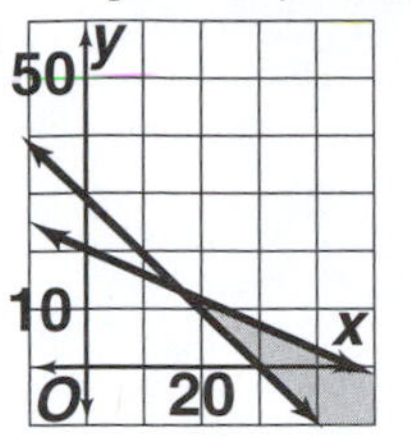

25. $y \geq \frac{2}{3}x - 2$, $y < \frac{2}{3}x + 2$
27. $x \leq 3$, $y \geq -3$
29–31. Answers may vary. Samples are given.
29. $x \leq 1$, $y \leq 2$ **31.** $y > 5$ and $y < 3$
33. $x > 0$ and $y < 0$
35. a. $x \geq 1$, and $y \geq 0$, $10.99x + 4.99y \leq 45$

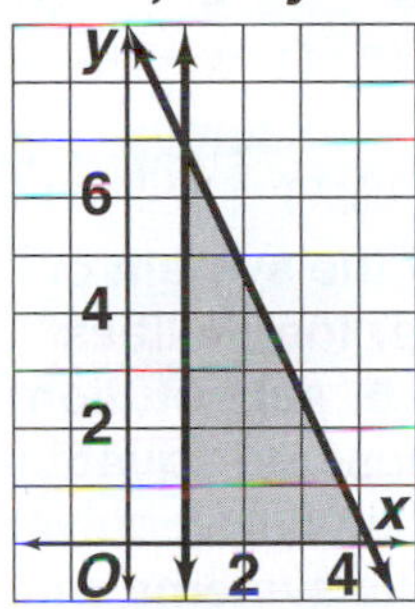

b. (3, 0), (3, 1), (3, 2), (4, 0)

37. a.

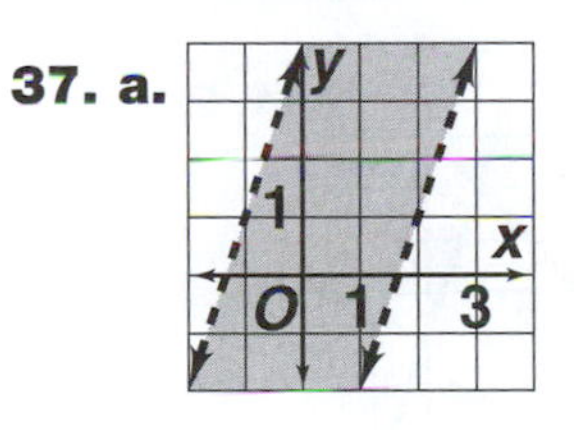

b. No; they are parallel.
c. It is a strip between the lines.
39a. −1 **b.** 8 units^2
41a. square **b.** (1, −1), (5, −1), (1, 3), (5, 3)
c. 16 units^2
43a. triangle **b.** (2, −3), (2, 2), (7, −3)
c. 12.5 units^2
45.

47. Answers may vary. Sample:
$y > x + 1$
$y > -x + 1$
49. A **51.** D

53.

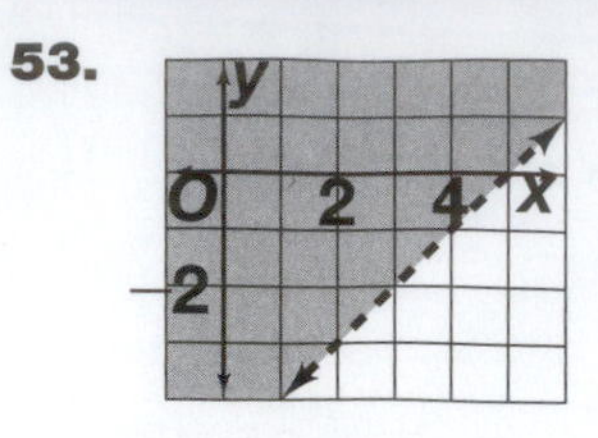

55.

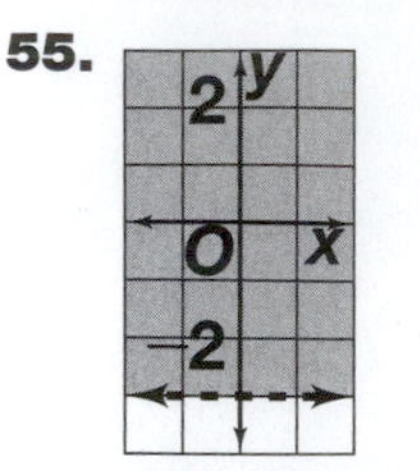

57.

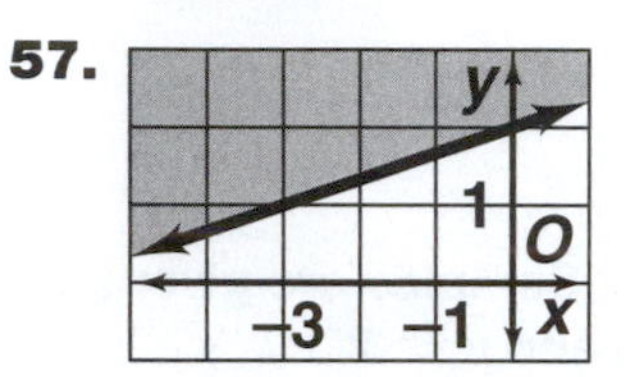

59. $\frac{5}{2}$ **61.** -8 **63.** $-\frac{1}{5}$ **65.** $\frac{10}{9}$ **67.** $\frac{15}{4}$
69. $f(x) = x + 6$

Chapter Review pp. 319–321

1. elimination **2.** solution of the system of linear equations **3.** system of linear inequalities **4.** solution of the inequality **5.** substitution **6.** A **7.** No; (2, 5) only satisfies one equation. **8.** Infinitely many; the equations are equivalent. **9.** Answers may vary. Sample: systems with noninteger solutions

10. (1, 2) **11.** (−1, 2)

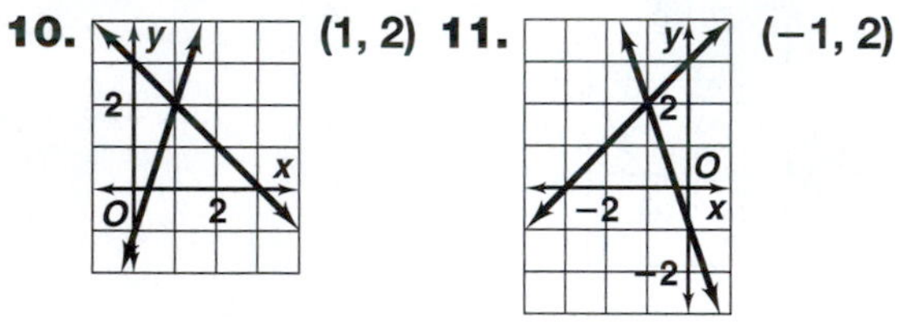

12.

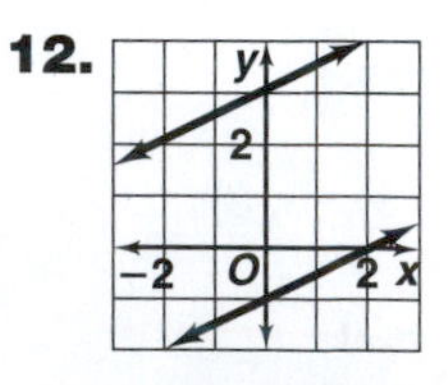

no solution

13. $(-2, 5)$ **14.** $\left(-4\frac{1}{2}, -6\right)$ **15.** $\left(-1\frac{1}{9}, -\frac{5}{9}\right)$ **16.** $(2, 2)$

17. Answers may vary. Sample: There is no solution when you get a false equation such as $0 = 2$. There are infinitely many solutions when you get a true equation such as $5 = 5$.

18a. $x + y = 24$, $4x + 5y = 100$ **b.** (20, 4) **c.** 20 4-point, 4 5-point **19.** $(-6, 23)$ **20.** $(1, -1)$ **21.** $(6, 4)$ **22.** $\left(5\frac{5}{11}, 1\frac{7}{11}\right)$ **23.** $x + y = 34$, $2x + 4y = 110$; 13 chickens and 21 cows **24.** $10\frac{2}{3}$ fl oz **25.** 63° and 27° **26.** 18 ft by 39 ft **27.** \$1.29 **28.** 154 km/h

29. **30.**

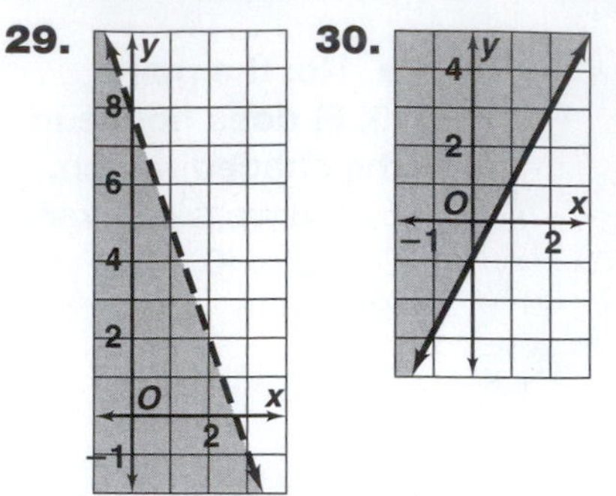

31. **32.**

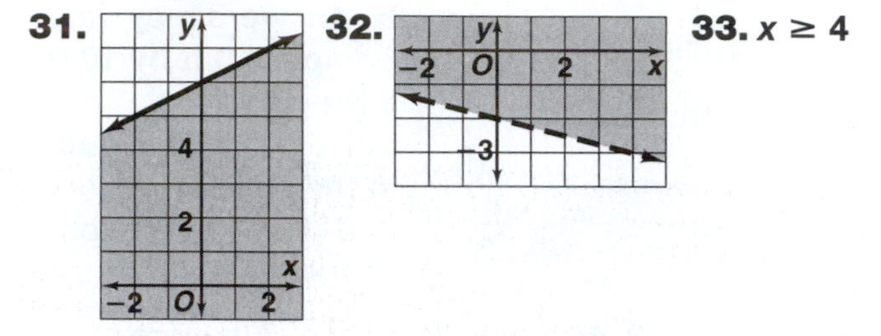

33. $x \geq 4$

34. $y \leq 3x + 3$ **35.** $2x + 3y \geq -6$

36. **37.**

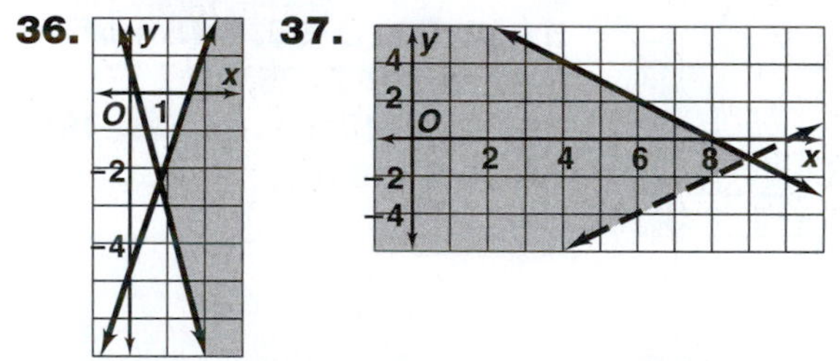

38. **39.**

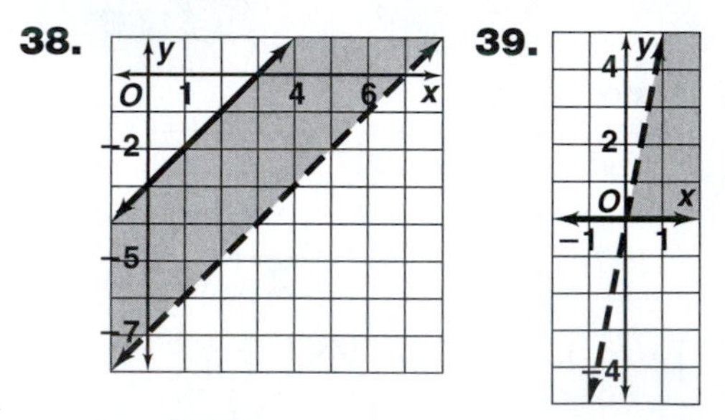

40. $y \leq 3, y > x$ **41.** $y > -2x + 2, y > \frac{4}{5}x - 4$ **42.** $x > -1, y \leq x + 5$ **43.** $y \leq -\frac{3}{2}x + 3$, $y \geq -\frac{1}{2}x - 1$

Chapter 7

Lesson 7-1 pp. 331–333

EXERCISES **1.** -1 **3.** $\frac{1}{25}$ **5.** $\frac{1}{16}$ **7.** $\frac{1}{64}$ **9.** 1 **11.** $-\frac{1}{64}$ **13.** -2 **15.** 0; -3 **17.** $3a$ **19.** x^7 **21.** $\frac{1}{25p}$ **23.** $\frac{3}{x^2y}$ **25.** $\frac{1}{x^5y^7}$ **27.** $4c^3$ **29.** $\frac{6}{ac^3}$ **31.** $\frac{y^7}{t^{11}}$ **33.** $\frac{1}{25}$ **35.** $-\frac{1}{9}$ **37.** $\frac{3}{25}$ **39.** $\frac{25}{81}$ **41.** $-\frac{25}{27}$ **43.** -27 **45.** \$20.48; \$.32 **47.** pos. **49.** neg. **51.** 10^{-1} **53.** 10^{-3} **55.** 10^{-5} **57.** 0.000001 **59.** 0.03 **61a.** $5^{-2}, 5^{-1}, 5^0, 5^1, 5^2$ **b.** 5^4 **c.** $\frac{a^n}{1}$ **63.** 45 **65.** 40 **67.** $-\frac{1}{243}$ **69.** $\frac{2}{9}$ **71.** $\frac{1}{16}$

73.

a	4	$\frac{1}{3}$	6	$\frac{7}{8}$	2
a^{-1}	$\frac{1}{4}$	3	$\frac{1}{6}$	$\frac{8}{7}$	0.5

75. A, B, D **77.** No; $3x^{-2} \cdot 3x^2 = 9 \cdot x^0 = 9$. The product of reciprocals should be 1. **79.** The student multiplied b by zero instead of raising b to the zero power, which would equal 1; a^nx^n. **81.** about 4 students; about 16 students; about 29 students **83.** 21 **85.** 2.9375 **87.** $-7\frac{1}{4}$ **89.** $\frac{1}{9}$ **91.** C **93.** B

95.

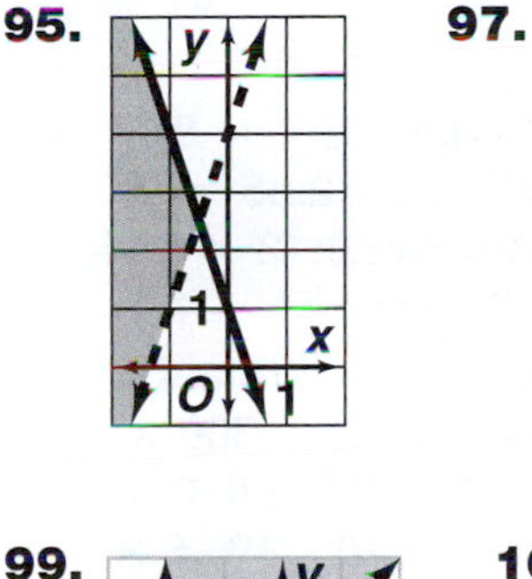

97.

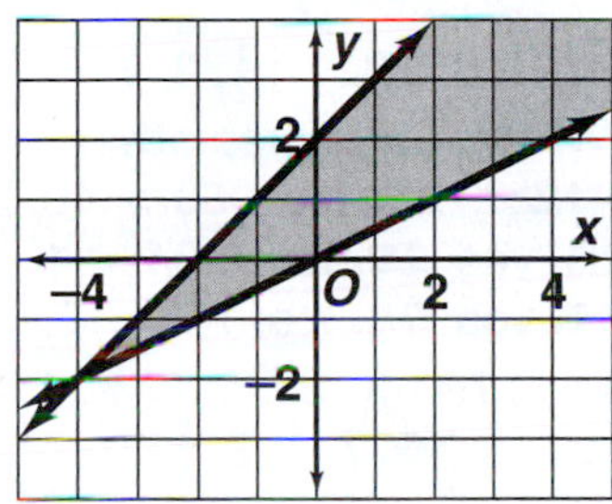

99.

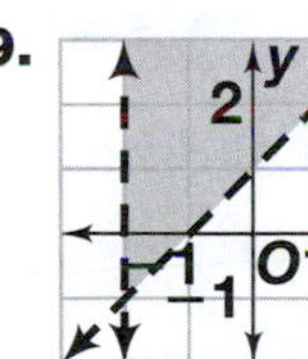

101. $y = 5x$
103. $y = -2x + 8$
105. $y = -x + 4$
107. $y = \frac{2}{5}x - 3$
109. $y = \frac{5}{9}x + \frac{1}{3}$

Lesson 7-2 pp. 336–338

EXERCISES **1.** No; $55 > 10$. **3.** No; $0.9 < 1$. **5.** yes **7.** 9.04×10^9 **9.** 9.3×10^6 **11.** 3.25×10^{-3} **13.** 9.2×10^{-4} **15.** 500 **17.** 2040 **19.** 0.897 **21.** 0.0000274 **23.** $10^{-3}, 10^{-1}, 10^0, 10^1, 10^5$ **25.** $0.52 \times 10^{-3}, 50.1 \times 10^{-3}, 4.8 \times 10^{-1}, 56 \times 10^{-2}$ **27.** C, A, B **29.** 2.4×10^{15} **31.** 3.18×10^{-3} **33.** 3.4×10^5 **35.** 7×10^1 **37.** 4.6×10^{-2} **39.** 3×10^{-26} **41.** 48 million $= 48 \times 10^6$. Write 48 in scientific notation; then add the powers of 10: $4.8 \times 10^1 \times 10^6 = 4.8 \times 10^7$. 48 millionths $= 48 \times 10^{-6}$. So $4.8 \times 10^1 \times 10^{-6} = 4.8 \times 10^{-5}$. **43.** 2.796×10^{10} instructions; 1.6776×10^{12} instructions **45.** about 1.6×10^8 years **47.** $3.\overline{3} \times 10^{-3}$ **49.** D **51.** 4 **53.** $\frac{2}{3}$ **55.** $\frac{1}{9}$

57.

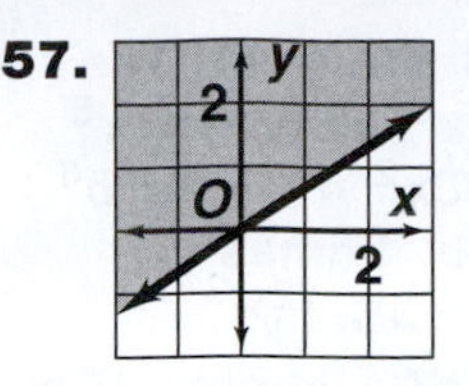

59. $2.5 \le a < 6.5$ **61.** $-3.5 < m < -0.25$ **63.** $p > 7$ or $p \le -3$

Lesson 7-3 pp. 341–343

EXERCISES **1.** 2^{10} **3.** 1 **5.** 6^9 **7.** c^5 **9.** $\frac{10}{t^7}$ **11.** $3x^4$ **13.** b^3 **15.** $-45a^4$ **17.** $45x^7y^6$ **19.** $x^{10}y^2$ **21.** $-\frac{240m^3}{r}$ **23.** 6×10^9 **25.** 3.4×10^{-5} **27.** 1.5×10^{22} **29.** 1.08×10^{21} dollars **31.** 9 **33.** -3 **35.** -5 **37.** -4 **39.** 2, -3 **41.** $12a^7$ **43.** $3^4 \cdot 2^2$ **45.** $4x^4$ **47.** $4c^4$ **49.** 8.0×10^5 **51.** 1.2×10^{-4} **53.** 1.5×10^8 **55a.** y^1y^7; y^2y^6; y^3y^5; y^4y^4 **b.** Answers may vary. Sample: $y^{-1}y^9$; $y^{-2}y^{10}$; $y^{-3}y^{11}$; $y^{-4}y^{12}$ **c.** An infinite number; there are an infinite number of integer pairs with a sum of 8. **57.** Answers may vary. Sample: The property of multiplying powers only applies when 2 terms have the same base. **59.** 7.65×10^{14} **61.** 6.9715×10^{-7} **63.** about 4.7×10^{37} molecules **65.** x^3 **67.** $5c^3$ **69.** $8m^5 + 56m^3$ **71.** 81 **73.** $2^{x+y} \cdot 3^{x+2}$ **75.** $(t + 3)^2$ **77a.** 1.833×10^{-9} km^3 **b.** 1.833 m^3 **79.** B **81.** C **83.** 1.28×10^6 **85.** 9.0×10^{-5} **87.** 876,000,000 **89.** 910,000,000,000

91.

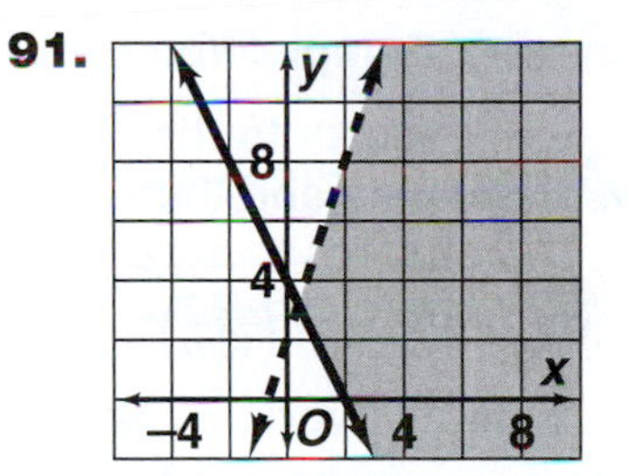

93.

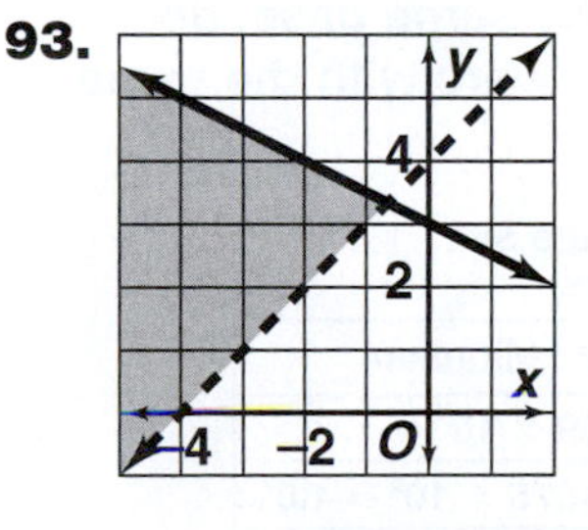

Lesson 7-4 pp. 347–350

EXERCISES **1.** c^{10} **3.** n^{32} **5.** c^{19} **7.** $\frac{1}{t^{14}}$ **9.** $625y^4$ **11.** $49a^2$ **13.** $36y^4$ **15.** $\frac{1}{8y^{12}}$ **17.** x^{16} **19.** 1 **21.** $9a^6b^8$ **23.** 1.6×10^{11} **25.** 8×10^{-30} **27.** 4.9×10^9 **29.** 6.25×10^{-18} **31.** $8.57375 \times$

10^{-10} m^3 **33.** −4 **35.** −3 **37.** 8 **39.** 0 **41.** The student who wrote $x^5 + x^5 = 2x^5$ is correct; x^5 times x^5 is x^{10}. **43.** $243x^3$ **45.** $30x^2$ **47.** $-8a^9b^6$ **49.** 4.3×10^4 **51a.** $24x^2$; $96x^2$ **b.** 4 times **c.** $8x^3$; $64x^3$ **d.** 8 times **53.** $(ab)^5$ **55.** $\left(\frac{2x}{y}\right)^2$ **57a.** 10^6 **b.** 10^9 **c.** 10^9 **d.** 10^{18} **59a.** about 5.15×10^{14} m^2 **b.** about 3.60×10^{14} m^2 **c.** about 1.37×10^{18} m^3 **61.** Add exponents for products of powers as in a^2a^4. Multiply exponents for powers of powers, as in $(a^2)^4$. **63.** 6 **65.** 3 **67.** −5 **69.** D **71.** B **73.** C **75.** a^8b^3 **77.** $-4t^5$ **79.** $\left(4\frac{2}{3}, 1\frac{1}{3}\right)$ **81.** (−9, −5) **83.** 6 **85.** $-\frac{9}{11}$ **87.** −2

Lesson 7-5 pp. 354–357

EXERCISES **1.** 7 **3.** −3 **5.** $\frac{1}{4}$ **7.** $\frac{1}{c^3}$ **9.** $\frac{s^2}{2}$ **11.** $\frac{1}{cd^2}$ **13.** 5×10^7 **15.** 6×10^2 **17.** 1.5×10^{-6} **19a.** 3.86×10^{11} h; 2.65×10^8 people **b.** about 1457 h **c.** about 4.0 h **21.** $\frac{9}{25}$ **23.** $\frac{32x^5}{y^5}$ **25.** $\frac{64}{125}$ **27.** $\frac{36}{n^{12}}$ **29.** $\frac{3}{2}$ **31.** $\frac{9}{4}$ **33.** $\frac{x^8}{25}$ **35.** $\frac{1}{c^{12}}$ **37.** 5^3 simplifies to 125. **39.** Each factor should be raised to the 4th power and simplified. **41.** The base d should appear only once. **43.** $\frac{1}{16m^{12}}$ **45.** a^6 **47.** $\frac{1}{n^{28}}$ **49.** 49 **51a.** Answers may vary. Sample: $\frac{c^4}{c^6}$ can be written as c^{4-6} or c^{-2}; $c^{-2} = \frac{1}{c^2}$. **b.** Check students' work. **53.** $\frac{a^5c^5}{b^3}$ **55.** 5 **57.** 20,736 **59.** $\frac{3b^5}{5a}$ **61.** Answers may vary. Sample: You can raise the numerator and denominator to the power and then simplify, or simplify and then raise to the power. **63a.** The student treated $\frac{5^4}{5}$ as $\left(\frac{5}{5}\right)^4$. **b.** 125 **65.** $\left(\frac{m}{n}\right)^7$ **67.** 10^{10} **69.** $\left(\frac{2}{13m}\right)^2$ **71.** $\left(\frac{5c}{6}\right)^3$ **73a–b.** Check students' work. **c.** No, the power may remain the same or be one less. **75.** dividing powers with the same base, def. of neg. exponent **77.** mult. powers with the same base **79.** n^2 **81.** x^4

83a.

Distance From the Sun (kilometers)

Planet	Maximum : Minimum
Mercury	$6.97 \times 10^7 : 4.59 \times 10^7 \approx 1.52$
Venus	$1.089 \times 10^8 : 1.075 \times 10^8 \approx 1.01$
Earth	$1.521 \times 10^8 : 1.471 \times 10^8 \approx 1.03$
Mars	$2.491 \times 10^8 : 2.067 \times 10^8 \approx 1.21$
Jupiter	$8.157 \times 10^8 : 7.409 \times 10^8 \approx 1.10$
Saturn	$1.507 \times 10^9 : 1.347 \times 10^9 \approx 1.12$
Uranus	$3.004 \times 10^9 : 2.735 \times 10^9 \approx 1.10$
Neptune	$4.537 \times 10^9 : 4.457 \times 10^9 \approx 1.02$

b. The closer the ratio is to 1, the more circular the orbit. **c.** Mercury, Venus **85.** C **87.** B **89.** $\frac{8}{m^{21}}$ **91.** $\frac{2s^6}{27}$ **93.** $9r^6$ **95.** 1

97. (0, 0) **99.** (3, 5)

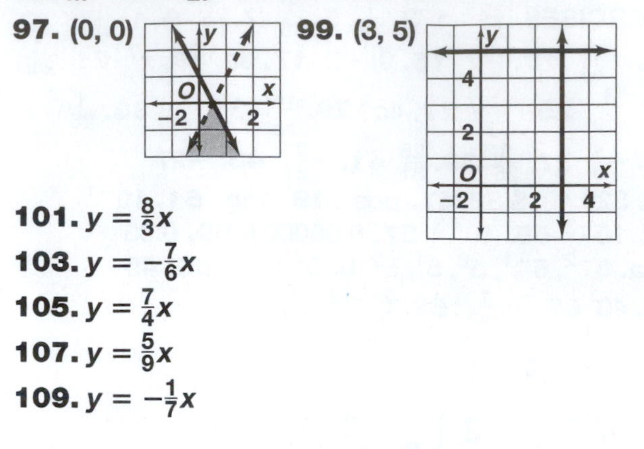

101. $y = \frac{8}{3}x$
103. $y = -\frac{7}{6}x$
105. $y = \frac{7}{4}x$
107. $y = \frac{5}{9}x$
109. $y = -\frac{1}{7}x$

Chapter Review pp. 361–363

1. Scientific notation **2.** exponent **3.** −2 **4.** 0; −5 **5.** −6, 4 **6.** $\frac{d^6}{b^4}$ **7.** $\frac{y^8}{x^2}$ **8.** $\frac{7h^3}{k^8}$ **9.** $\frac{q^4}{p^2}$ **10.** $\frac{625}{16}$ or $39\frac{1}{16}$ **11.** $-\frac{1}{8}$ **12.** $-\frac{1}{8}$ **13.** $\frac{1}{49y^4}$ **14.** $\frac{9x^2}{w^4y^7}$ **15.** $\frac{m^6}{25n^{11}}$ **16.** $\frac{8k^6}{g^3}$ **17.** $\frac{16y^5}{x^3z}$ **18.** 36 **19.** $\frac{4}{9}$ **20.** $\frac{9}{8}$ or $1\frac{1}{8}$ **21.** 1 **22.** 108 **23.** 2^a: $\frac{1}{2}$, 2; 2^{-a}: $\frac{1}{4}$, $\frac{1}{8}$, 4 **24.** C **25.** No; for values other than 0, $(-3b)^4 = 81b^4 \neq -12b^4$. **26.** No; 950 > 10. **27.** No; 72.35 > 10. **28.** yes **29.** No; 0.84 < 1. **30.** No; 0.12 < 1. **31.** yes **32.** No; 10 ≥ 10. **33.** No; 0.71 < 1. **34.** 2.793×10^6 mi **35.** 1.89×10^8 cars and trucks **36.** $7^{-4}, 7^{-2}, 7^0, 7^1, 7^6, 7^{12}$ **37.** 300×10^{-4}, 30×10^{-1}, 3.1×10^2, 0.3×10^4 **38.** 0.6×10^3, 60.8×10^1, 6.73×10^2, 5.6×10^3 **39.** 5×10^{-3}, 100×10^{-4}, 150×10^{-3}, 50×10^{-2} **40.** 3.3×10^{13} **41.** 1.5×10^{-2} **42.** 1.96×10^{-3} **43.** $\frac{1}{a^2}$ **44.** st^{10} **45.** $4x^5$ **46.** n^3 **47.** $4p^9$ **48.** $2a^4b^6$ **49.** r^9s^6 **50.** $44x^2y^4$ **51.** qw^{14} **52.** $\frac{240z^9}{v}$ **53.** $-\frac{26a^8}{25n^2}$ **54.** $-2b^6c$ **55.** 1.2×10^6 **56.** 1.2×10^0 **57.** 2.2×10^9 **58.** 2×10^2 **59.** 7.2×10^{-6} **60.** 1.35×10^0 **61.** 9 **62.** 4 **63.** −3 **64.** −2 **65.** 3 **66.** −3; 3 **67.** about 7.8×10^3 pores **68.** m^{12} **69.** b^{-28} **70.** h^{-3} **71.** $1269y^{12}$ **72.** $\frac{1}{10h^7}$ **73.** 25 **74.** $2d^5$ **75.** $q^{12}r^4$ **76.** $-20c^4m^2$ **77.** 1.34^2 or 1.7956 **78.** $\frac{243x^2y^{14}}{64}$ **79.** $-\frac{4}{3r^{10}z^8}$ **80.** 9×10^8 **81.** 1.6×10^{-9} **82.** 8×10^{21} **83.** 2×10^2 **84.** 4.4×10^1 **85.** 2.16×10^{-4} **86.** $(3xy)^3$ **87.** Answers may vary. Sample: Simplify $(2a^{-2})^{-2}(-3a)^2$; $\frac{9a^6}{4}$. **88.** 2 **89.** −5 **90.** −7 **91.** 0 **92.** 10 **93.** 3 **94.** $\frac{1}{w^3}$ **95.** $\frac{1}{64}$ **96.** $7x^2$ **97.** $\frac{n^{35}}{v^{21}}$ **98.** $\frac{c^3}{e^{11}}$ **99.** b^6 **100.** 1

101. $\frac{t^{12}}{s^8}$ **102.** $\frac{x^5}{y}$ **103.** $\frac{16}{m^4}$ **104.** $6dg^{12}$ **105.** $64v^{10}$ **106.** 2×10^{-3} **107.** 2.5×10^1 **108.** 5×10^{-5} **109.** 3×10^3 **110.** Answers may vary. Sample: Simplify and use div. prop.: $\left(\frac{a^2}{2}\right)^{-3}$; use raising a quot. to a power prop.: $\frac{a^{-6}}{2^{-3}}$; use the def. of neg. exp.: $\frac{2^3}{a^6}$ or $\frac{8}{a^6}$.

Chapter 8

Lesson 8-1 pp. 373–375

EXERCISES **1.** 1 **3.** 0 **5.** 4 **7.** 4 **9.** quadratic trinomial **11.** cubic trinomial **13.** constant monomial **15.** $-3x^2 + 4x$; quadratic binomial **17.** $c^2 + 4c - 2$; quadratic trinomial **19.** $15y^8 - 7y^3 + y$; eighth degree trinomial **21.** $8m^2 + 15$ **23.** $8w^2 - 3w + 4$ **25.** $10g^4 + 11g$ **27.** $8y^4 + 7y^3 + 4y$ **29.** $b + 1$ **31.** $7n^4 + n^3$ **33.** $5w^2 - 4w + 10$ **35.** $18y^2 + 8y$ **37.** $-7z^3 + 6z^2 + 2z - 5$ **39.** $28c - 16$ **41.** Kwan did not take the opposite of each term in the polynomial being subtracted. **43.** $-x^4 + x^3 + 15x$ **45.** $-h^{10} - 5h^9 + 8h^5 + 2h^4$ **47.** $-5b^9 + 3b^8 - 4b^7 + 8b$ **49.** $5x + 18$ **51.** No; both terms of a binomial cannot be constants. **53.** $5a^3b - 5ab$ **55a.** $p(t) = 31.7t + 1674.8$ **b.** 1,801,600 **c.** the difference between the number of men and the number of women enrolled in a college **57.** C **59.** $\frac{1}{b^5}$ **61.** $\frac{m^{12}}{n^{30}}$ **63.** Each term should be raised to the 4th power and simplified. **65.** r^0 simplifies to 1. **67.** $\frac{1}{2}$ **69.** $3a^3b^2$ **71.** 9 **73.** $10q^7$ **75.** 16; -8 **77.** 10.5; -63 **79.** $1\frac{1}{3}$; 1

Lesson 8-2 pp. 377–379

EXERCISES **1.** $8m^2 + 48m$ **3.** $63k^2 + 36k$ **5.** $18x^2 + 2x^3$ **7.** $12x^4 - 2x^3 + 10x^2$ **9.** $-45c^5 + 40c^4 + 25c^3$ **11.** $-3g^{11} + 18g^9 - 15g^7$ **13.** 3 **15.** 12 **17.** 5 **19.** $2(3x - 2)$ **21.** $5(2x^3 - 5x^2 + 4)$ **23.** $3n(5n^2 - n + 4)$ **25.** Karla; Kevin multiplied $-2x$ by 3 instead of -3. **27.** $-12a^3 + 15a^2 - 27a$ **29.** $-60c^3 + 36c^2 - 48c$ **31.** $x^2 + x$ **33a.** $A = 16\pi x^2 - 4x^2$ **b.** $A = 4x^2(4\pi - 1)$ **35.** $24x(x^2 - 4x + 2)$ **37.** $x^2(5x^2 + 4x + 3)$ **39.** $7g^2k^2(k - 5g^3)$ **41a.** $n(n - 1)$ **b.** Always; the product of two consecutive integers is always even since one of the integers is even. **43a.** 6; 3 **b.** $n - 3$ **c.** $\frac{1}{2}n^2 - \frac{3}{2}n$ **d.** 20 **45.** B **47.** A **49.** $-3x^2 + 10$ **51.** $5g^2 - g$ **53.** $t^4 + 5t^2 - 9$ **55.** $\frac{1}{5}$ **57.** $-\frac{1}{8}$ **59.** $\frac{m^2}{n^3}$ **61.** $4c^3$ **63.** (3, 2) **65.** (1, 6)

Lesson 8-3 pp. 383–386

EXERCISES **1.** 30 **3.** 7 **5.** $x^2 + 7x + 10$ **7.** $k^2 + k - 42$ **9.** $2x^2 + 3x - 2$ **11.** $r^2 + 2r - 24$ **13.** $x^2 - x - 42$ **15.** $4b^2 + 10b - 6$ **17.** $x^2 + 2x - 63$ **19.** $p^2 + 9p - 10$ **21.** $-2x^2 + 5x + 48$ **23.** $a^3 - 6a^2 + 9a - 4$ **25.** $3k^3 + 19k^2 - 33k + 56$ **27.** $2t^3 - 17t^2 + 36t - 15$ **29.** $48w^3 - 28w^2 - 2w + 2$ **31.** $p^2 + p - 56$ **33.** $25c^2 - 40c - 9$ **35.** $15k^4 + 3k^3 + 10k^2 + 2k$ **37.** $9y^4 - 9y^3 - 7y^2 - 2y - 2$ **39a.** $2x^2 + 12x + 16$ **b.** $12x + 16$ **c.** 10 ft by 5 ft **41.** Answers may vary. Sample: vertical method, so you can keep terms aligned **43.** $1.5x^2 + 2.5x - 1$ **45.** $n^3 + 15n^2 + 56n$ **47.** Never; the expression equals $(x - 4)^2$ and the square of any number is never negative. **49.** Sometimes; the degree of $(x + 1)(x^2 + 2x - 3)$ is 3, but the degree of $(x^2 + 1)(x^2 + 2x - 3)$ is 4. **51.** The student forgot to multiply the outer terms; $16x^2 + 38x - 5$. **53.** $6x^2 + 36x + 54$ **55.** $24w^4 + 168w^2 + 294$ **57a.** $2000r^3 + 6000r^2 + 6000r + 2000$ **b.** \$2185.45 **59.** B **61.** B **63.** $3c^2 - 27c$ **65.** $3y^2 - 10y$ **67.** $-6t^4 + t^3$ **69.** $9b^5 + 18b^3$ **71.** $x(3x - 11)$ **73.** $n^2(9 - n)$ **75.** $9v(7v + 5)$ **77.** $11k(1 + 7k^5)$ **79.** $\frac{1}{27}$ **81.** $\frac{1}{3w^5}$ **83.** $\frac{3}{5}$ **85.** 1 **87.** $64y^4$

Lesson 8-4 pp. 391–393

EXERCISES **1.** $c^2 + 2c + 1$ **3.** $4v^2 + 44v + 121$ **5.** $w^2 - 24w + 144$ **7.** $36x^2 - 96x + 64$ **9a.** $\frac{1}{16}C^2 + \frac{3}{8}CD + \frac{9}{16}D^2$ **b.** $\frac{1}{16}$ **c.** It is the coefficient of C^2. **11.** 9801 **13.** 91,204 **15.** $x^2 - 16$ **17.** $d^2 - 49$ **19.** $y^2 - 144$ **21.** 899 **23.** 2496 **25.** 89,999 **27.** $(10x + 15)$ units^2 **29.** $25p^2 - 10pq + q^2$ **31.** $x^2 - 14xy + 49y^2$ **33.** $4y^2 - 36xy + 81x^2$ **35.** $36a^2 + 132ab + 121b^2$ **37.** $36h^2 - 96hp + 64p^2$ **39.** $64k^2 + 64kh + 16h^2$

41a.

$4^2 = 16$	$3 \cdot 5 = 15$
$5^2 = 25$	$4 \cdot 6 = 24$
$6^2 = 36$	$5 \cdot 7 = 35$
$7^2 = 49$	$6 \cdot 8 = 48$

b. n^2 is one more than the product $(n - 1)(n + 1)$. **c.** The product $(n - 1)(n + 1)$ is $n^2 - 1$. **43.** No; $\left(3\frac{1}{2}\right)^2 = \left(3 + \frac{1}{2}\right)^2 = \left(3 + \frac{1}{2}\right)\left(3 + \frac{1}{2}\right) = 3^2 + 2(3)\left(\frac{1}{2}\right) + \left(\frac{1}{2}\right)^2 = 9 + 3 + \frac{1}{4} = 12\frac{1}{4} \neq 9\frac{1}{4}$. **45.** $p^2 - 81q^2$ **47.** $49b^2 - 64c^2$ **49.** $g^6 - 49h^4$ **51.** $121x^2 - y^6$ **53.** $a^2 + b^2 + c^2 + 2ab + 2bc + 2ac$ **55a.** $(3n + 1)^2 = (3n + 1)(3n + 1) = 9n^2 + 6n + 1 = 3(3n^2 + 2n) + 1$; since $3n^2 + 2n$ is an integer, then $3(3n^2 + 2n)$ is a multiple of three and $3(3n^2 + 2n) + 1$ is one more than a multiple of three. **b.** No; its square is one more than a multiple of three.

57a.

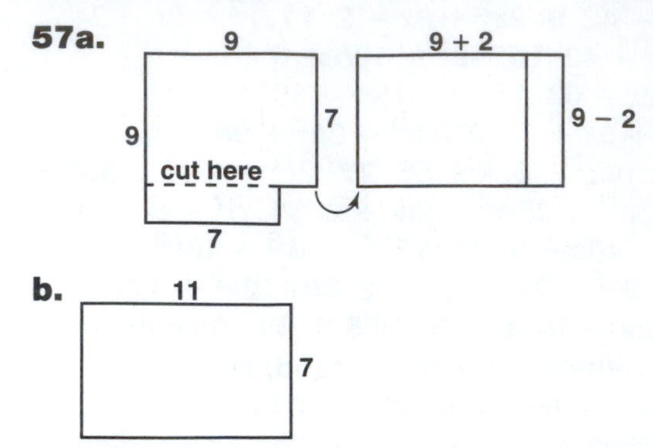

59. B **61.** B **63.** $2x^2 - 23x + 66$ **65.** $3y^2 + 4y + 1$ **67.** $72b^2 + 74b + 14$ **69.** $r^3 - 4r^2 - 30r + 63$ **71.** 8.713×10^3 **73.** 6.8952×10^4 **75.** 1.1×10^1 **77.** 6×10^9

Lesson 8-5 pp. 397–399

EXERCISES **1.** 5 **3.** 7 **5.** $(r + 3)(r + 1)$ **7.** $(k + 3) \cdot (k + 2)$ **9.** $(x - 1)(x - 1)$ **11.** $(k - 14)(k - 2)$ **13.** $(m - 1)(m - 8)$ **15.** $(t - 7)(t - 6)$ **17.** 5 **19.** 9 **21.** $(x + 4)(x - 1)$ **23.** $(y + 5)(y - 4)$ **25.** $(x - 16) \cdot (x + 2)$ **27.** $(m + 2)(m - 15)$ **29.** $(p + 3)(p - 18)$ **31.** B **33.** $(t + 9v)(t - 2v)$ **35.** $(p - 8q)(p - 2q)$ **37.** $(h + 17j)(h + j)$ **39–41.** Answers may vary. Samples are given. **39.** 18; $(x - 6)(x + 3)$ 28; $(x - 7)(x + 4)$ 10; $(x - 5)(x + 2)$ **41.** 7; $(x + 4)(x + 3)$, 8; $(x + 6)(x + 2)$, 13; $(x + 12)(x + 1)$ **43.** $(k + 2) \cdot (k + 8)$ **45.** $(n - 4)(n + 14)$ **47.** $(x - 5)(x + 13)$ **49.** $(x - 14)(x + 3)$ **51.** $(m - 3)(m + 17)$ **53.** $(t - 15)(t + 5)$ **55.** $4x^2 + 12x + 5$; $(2x + 1) \cdot (2x + 5)$ **57a.** The signs of a and b must be opposite. **b.** Since the middle term is negative, the number with the larger absolute value must be negative. Therefore, a must be a negative integer. **59.** $(x^6 + 7)(x^6 + 5)$ **61.** $(r^3 - 16) \cdot (r^3 - 5)$ **63.** $(x^6 - 24)(x^6 + 5)$ **65.** D **67.** B **69.** $x^2 + 8x + 16$ **71.** $r^2 - 25$ **73.** $64v^2 - 4$ **75.** $9a^2 - 25$ **77.** $4x^2 - 64y^2$ **79.** 7, 35

81.

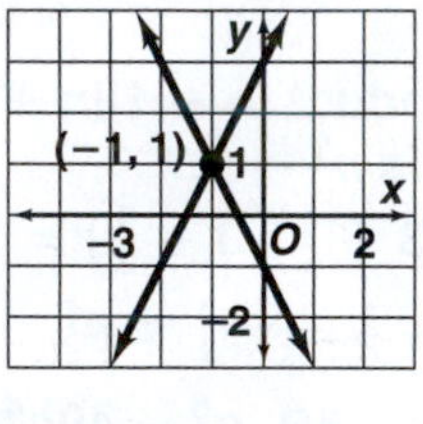

83.

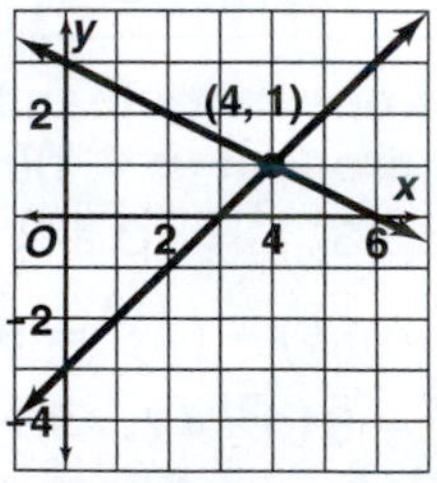

Lesson 8-6 pp. 401–403

EXERCISES **1.** $(2n + 1)(n + 7)$ **3.** $(11w - 3)(w - 1)$ **5.** $(3t + 11)(2t + 1)$ **7.** $(2m + 1)(8m + 9)$ **9.** $(2y + 1) \cdot (4y + 13)$ **11.** $(x - 3)(7x - 9)$ **13.** $(2t - 3)(t + 1)$ **15.** $(2q + 3)(q - 7)$ **17.** $(13p - 5)(p + 1)$ **19.** $(5w + 8)(2w - 1)$ **21.** $(7n + 15)(2n - 1)$ **23.** $7(3v - 7)(v - 1)$ **25.** $5(5x + 3)(x - 1)$ **27.** $2(4v + 3)(3v - 1)$ **29.** Answers may vary. Sample: 18; $(5m - 4)(3m + 6)$, 54; $(5m - 2) \cdot (3m + 12)$, 117; $(5m - 1)(3m + 24)$ **31a.** $(2x + 2) \cdot (x + 2)$; $(x + 1)(2x + 4)$ **b.** $2x^2 + 6x + 4$; $2x^2 + 6x + 4$; yes **c.** Answers may vary. Sample: Neither factoring is complete. Each one has a common factor, 2. **33.** $(9p + 4)(6p + 7)$ **35.** $(7x - 2)(2x - 7)$ **37.** $3(7h - 4)(h + 4)$ **39.** $2(6y - 1)(3y + 10)$ **41.** $(9q - 1)(11q - 9)$ **43.** Answers may vary. Sample: $5x^2 - 12x + 4 = (5x - 2)(x - 2)$; $9x^2 - 12x + 3 = 3(3x - 1)(x - 1)$; $16x^2 - 12x + 2 = 2(4x - 1)(2x - 1)$ **45.** $(7p - 3q)(7p + 12q)$ **47a.** -2 and -3 **b.** $(x + 2)(x + 3)$ **c.** Answers may vary. Sample: Each x-intercept is the opposite of the last term in a binomial factor. **49.** C **51.** C **53.** $(t - 4)(t - 3)$ **55.** $(m - 3)(m - 12)$ **57.** $(g + 9) \cdot (g + 8)$ **59.** $(x - 15)(x + 2)$ **61.** 7921 **63.** 815,409 **65.** 1599 **67.** 39,996 **69.** $g \leq 7$ **71.** $m < 4$ **73.** $b \geq 0.7$ **75–77.** Answers may vary. Samples ae given. **75.** 2, 3, 4 **77.** $-3.5, -4, -4.5$

Lesson 8-7 pp. 407–409

EXERCISES **1.** $(c + 5)^2$ **3.** $(h + 6)^2$ **5.** $(k - 8)^2$ **7.** $(2m + 5)$ **9.** $(5g - 4)$ **11.** $(8r - 9)^2$ **13.** $(x + 2) \cdot (x - 2)$ **15.** $(k + 14)(k - 14)$ **17.** $(h + 10)(h - 10)$ **19.** $(w + 16)(w - 16)$ **21.** $(y + 30)(y - 30)$ **23.** $(7y + 2)(7y - 2)$ **25.** $(2m + 9)(2m - 9)$ **27.** $(12p + 1)(12p - 1)$ **29.** $(20n + 11)(20n - 11)$ **31.** $3(m + 2)(m - 2)$ **33.** $3(x + 8)^2$ **35.** $6r(r + 5) \cdot (r - 5)$ **37.** Answers may vary. Sample: Rewrite the first and last terms as a square. Check to see if the middle term is $2ab$. Factor as a square binomial: $4x^2 + 12x + 9 = (2x)^2 + 12x + 3^2 = (2x)^2 + 2(2x)(3) + 3^2 = (2x + 3)^2$; $9x^2 - 30x + 25 = (3x)^2 - 30x + 5^2 = (3x)^2 - 2(3x)(5) + 5^2 = (3x - 5)^2$. **39.** 11, 9 **41.** 15, 5 **43.** 16, 14 **45.** $25(2v + w)(2v - w)$ **47.** $7(2c + 5d)^2$ **49.** $\left(x + \frac{1}{2}\right)^2$ **51.** $\left(\frac{1}{2}p - 2\right)^2$ **53.** $\left(\frac{1}{5}k + 3\right)^2$ **55a.** $4(x + 5)(x - 5)$ **b.** $4(x + 5)(x - 5)$ **c.** The polynomial has a common factor that has two identical factors. **d.** $3(x + 5)(x - 5)$; no, because 3 does not have a pair of identical factors **57.** $(p^3 + 20q)^2$ **59.** $(9p^5 + 11)^2$ **61.** $(x^{10} - 2y^5)^2$ **63.** $5(3x^2 - 2y)^2$ **65a.** $t - 3$; 4 **b.** $(t + 1)(t - 7)$ **67.** D **69.** D **71.** $(2d + 1)(d + 5)$ **73.** $(2t + 1) \cdot (2t + 7)$ **75.** $(3t + 8)(2t + 1)$ **77.** $(7x - 9) \cdot (2x + 1)$ **79.** $(3k - 2)(4k + 1)$ **81.** $f(x) = x - 5$ **83–85.** Answers may vary. Samples are given. **83.** $(-2, 3)$ **85.** $(5, 1)$

Lesson 8-8 pp. 413–415

EXERCISES **1.** $2m^2$; 3 **3.** $2z^2$; -5 **5.** $(2n^2 + 1) \cdot (3n + 4)$ **7.** $(3t + 1)(3t - 1)(3t + 5)$ **9.** $(5x^2 + 1) \cdot (9x + 4)$ **11.** $2(2v^2 + 1)(3v - 8)$ **13.** $2(m^2 + 2) \cdot (10m - 9)$ **15.** $2(2y^2 + 5)(3y - 5)$ **17.** $(6p + 5) \cdot (2p + 1)$ **19.** $(6n - 1)(3n + 10)$ **21.** $2(6m - 1) \cdot (2m + 1)$ **23.** $(3x - 2)(2x + 5)$ **25.** $(7q + 2) \cdot (9q - 10)$ **27.** $5k$, $(k + 2)$, and $(k + 4)$ **29.** $2(10t^2 - 11)(3t - 10)$ **31.** $4(3x - 7y)(x + 2y)$ **33.** $10(5k^2 + 6)(3k + 7)$ **35.** $(7w^2 - 4)(2w + 7)$ **37.** $2(2t^2 + 3)(11t - 1)$ **39.** $2w$, $(6w + 5)$, and $(7w + 1)$ **41.** Answers may vary. Sample: Split the expression into two groups. Remove the common factor from each group, and then factor again. **43.** $(6m^3 - 7n^2)(5m^2 + 4n)$ **45.** $(h + 2)(h - 2) \cdot (h + 11)$ **47a.** $2\pi x(x + 3)^2$ **b.** $x + 3$ **49.** $(2^4 + 2^2 + 2^0)(2^1 + 2^0)$; (21)(3) **51.** D **53.** B **55.** $(k + 7)^2$ **57.** $(y - 8)^2$ **59.** $(m + 8)(m - 8)$ **61.** $(2d + 5) \cdot (2d - 5)$ **63.** $(5q + 4)^2$ **65.** x^2 **67.** $c^{35}d^7$ **69.** 1 **71.** $81w^8v^{12}$ **73.** 9×10^{12} **75.** 3.2×10^{36} **77.** 6.561×10^{-5} **79.** 6.25×10^4 **81.** $(4, -8)$ **83.** $(2, -30)$ **85.** $(7, 2)$

Chapter Review pp. 417–419

1. A **2.** D **3.** E **4.** C **5.** B **6.** $-6y^2 + 8y + 2$; quadratic trinomial **7.** $9h^2 + 1$; quadratic binomial **8.** $3k^5 + k$; fifth degree binomial **9.** $7t^2 + 8t + 9$; quadratic trinomial **10.** x^2y^2; fourth degree monomial **11.** $x^3 + x^2 + 5$; cubic trinomial **12.** $-b^5 + 2b^3 + 6$
13. $8g^4 - 5g^2 + 11g + 5$
14. $7x^3 + 8x^2 - 3x + 12$
15. $t^3 - 5t^2 + 12t - 8$
16. $7w^5 - 5w^4 - 7w^3 + w^2 + 3w - 3$
17. $-40x^2 + 16x$ **18.** $35g^3 + 15g^2 - 45g$
19. $-40t^4 + 24t^3 - 32t^2$ **20.** $5m^3 + 15m^2$
21. $-6w^4 - 8w^3 + 20w^2$ **22.** $-3b^3 + 5b^2 + 10b$
23. $3x$; $3x(3x^3 + 4x^2 + 2)$
24. $4t^2$; $4t^2(t^3 - 3t + 2)$
25. $10n^3$; $10n^3(4n^2 + 7n - 3)$
26. $3d$; $3d(d - 2)$ **27.** 2; $2(k^4 + 2k^3 - 3k - 4)$
28. $2m^2$; $2m^2(5m^2 - 6m + 2)$ **29.** 5; $5(2v - 1)$
30. $4w$; $4w(3w^2 + 2w + 5)$
31. $3d^3$; $3d^3(6d^2 + 2d + 3)$ **32.** 12; if the common factor of x and y is 3, the common factor of $4x$ and $4y$ is $4 \cdot 3$ or 12. **33.** $x^2 + 8x + 15$
34. $15v^2 - 29v - 14$ **35.** $6b^2 + 11b - 10$
36. $-k^2 + 5k - 4$ **37.** $p^3 + 3p^2 + 3p + 2$
38. $4a^2 - 21a + 5$ **39.** $3x^2 + 10x + 8$
40. $y^3 - 9y^2 + 18y + 8$ **41.** $-2h^3 + 11h^2 - 6h + 5$
42. $q^2 - 8q + 16$ **43.** $4k^6 + 20k^3 + 25$
44. $64 - 9t^4$ **45.** $w^2 - 16$ **46.** $4m^4 - 25$
47. $16g^4 - 25h^8$ **48.** $(2x + 1)(x + 4)$; $2x^2 + 9x + 4$
49. No; $(x - y)^2 = x^2 - 2xy + y^2 \neq x^2 - y^2$.
50. $(x + 2)(x + 1)$ **51.** $(y - 7)(y - 2)$
52. $(x - 5)(x + 3)$ **53.** $(2w - 3)(w + 1)$
54. $(b - 3)(b - 4)$ **55.** $(2t - 1)(t + 2)$
56. $(x + 6)(x - 1)$ **57.** $2(3x + 2)(x + 1)$
58. $(7x + 2)(3x - 4)$ **59.** $(3x - 2)(x + 1)$
60. $(15y + 1)(y + 1)$ **61.** $(15y - 1)(y - 1)$
62. $(q + 1)^2$ **63.** $(b + 4)(b - 4)$ **64.** $(x - 2)^2$
65. $(2t + 11)(2t - 11)$ **66.** $(2d - 5)^2$
67. $(3c + 1)^2$ **68.** $(3k + 5)(3k - 5)$ **69.** $(x + 3)^2$
70. $6(2y + 1)(2y - 1)$ **71.** $\frac{1}{2}d + 1$
72. No; only the square $(5u + 6)^2$ would have $25u^2$ and 36 as the first and last terms. However $2(5u)(6) \neq 65u$. **73.** $4x^2$; 2 **74.** $3k^2$; 2
75. $24y^2$; 4 **76.** $10n^3$; 7 **77.** $(3x^2 + 4)(2x + 1)$
78. $5y^2(2y + 3)(2y - 3)$ **79.** $3(3g - 1)(g + 2)$
80. $(3c - d)(2c - d)$ **81.** $(5p + 3)(3p + 1)$
82. $3(u - 6)(u - 1)$ **83.** $(h^2 - 3)(15h + 11)$
84. $(5x + 7)(6x^2 - 1)$ **85.** $4s^2t(3s - 1)(s + 2)$
86. $(x^2 + 2)(2x + 7)$ **87.** $2p$, $(p + 5)$, and $(3p + 4)$

Chapter 9

Lesson 9-1 pp. 429–432

EXERCISES **1.** $(2, 5)$; max. **3.** $(2, 1)$; min.

5. **7.** **9.**

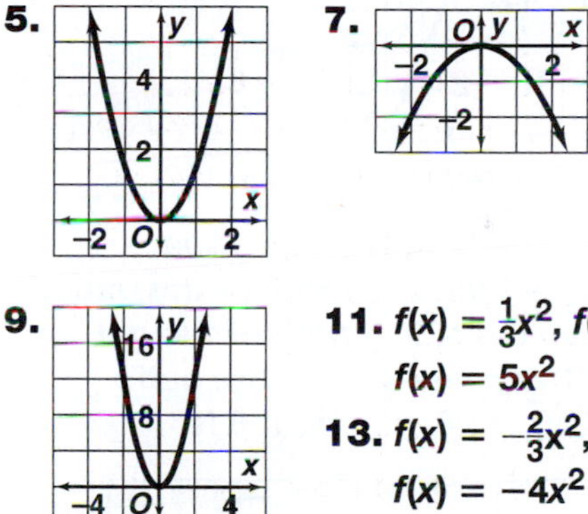

11. $f(x) = \frac{1}{3}x^2$, $f(x) = x^2$, $f(x) = 5x^2$
13. $f(x) = -\frac{2}{3}x^2$, $f(x) = -2x^2$, $f(x) = -4x^2$

15.

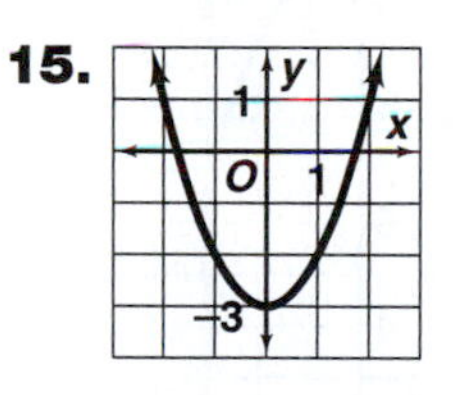

17.

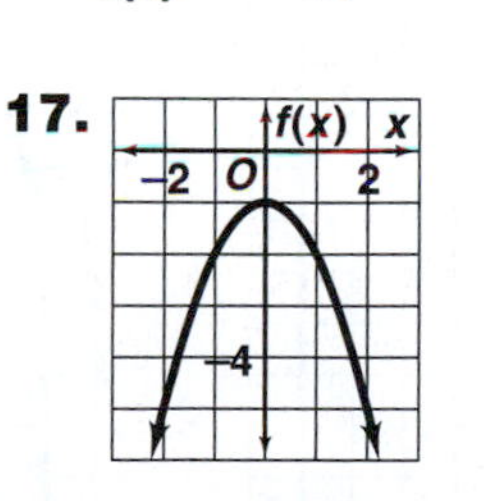

19.

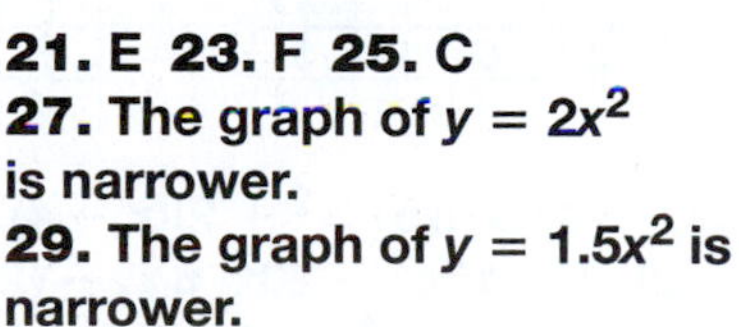

21. E **23.** F **25.** C
27. The graph of $y = 2x^2$ is narrower.
29. The graph of $y = 1.5x^2$ is narrower.

31.

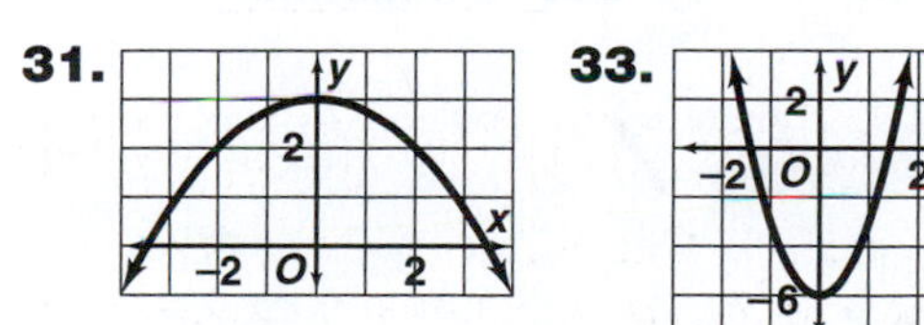

33.

35.

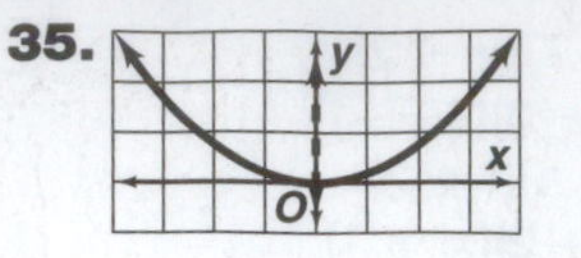

37.

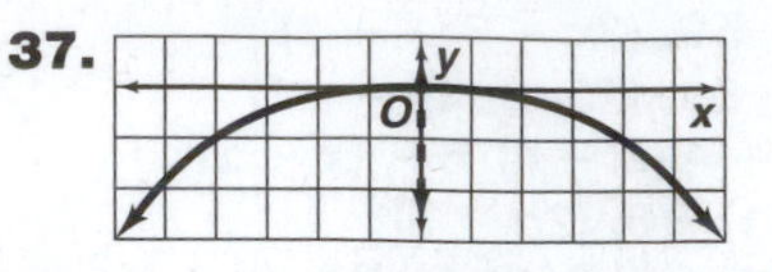

39a. $0 < r < 6$ **b.** $0 < A < 36\pi \approx 113.1$

c.

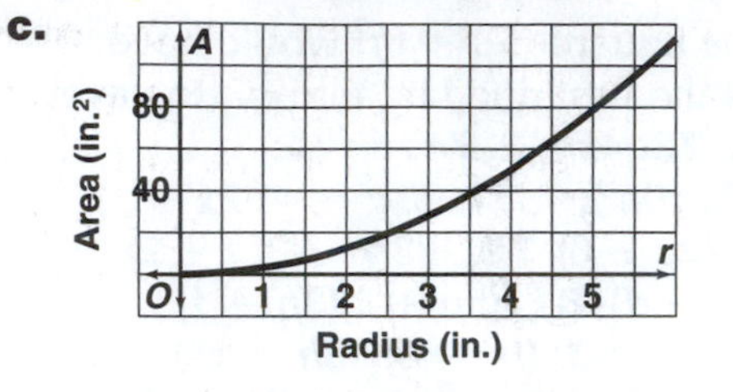

41. *M* **43.** *M* **45.** B

47a.

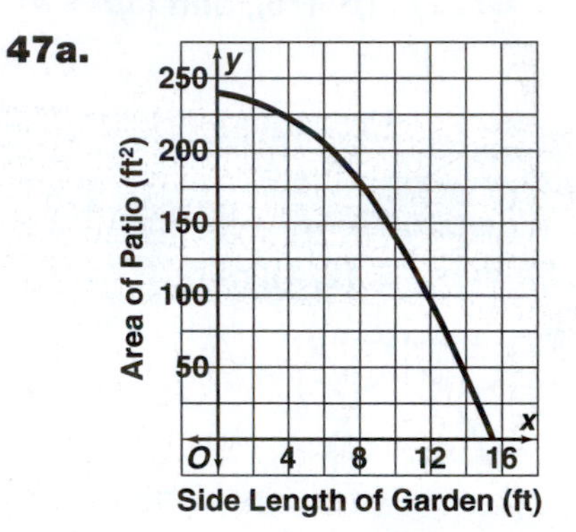

b. $0 < x < 12$; the side length of the square garden must be less than the width of the patio. **c.** $96 < A < 240$; as the side length of the garden increases from 0 to 12, the area of the patio decreases from 240 to 96. **d.** about 6 ft

49a.

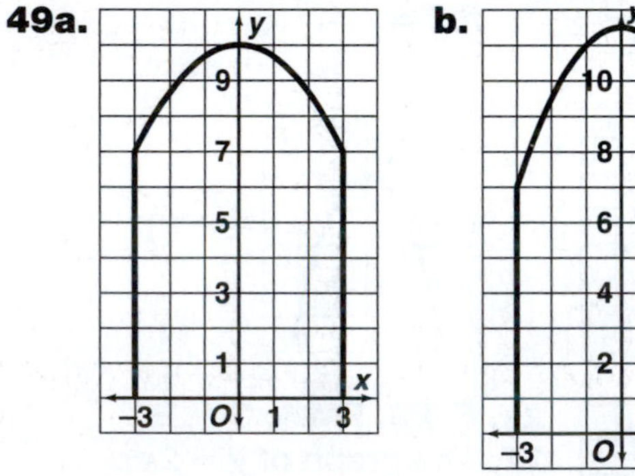

b.

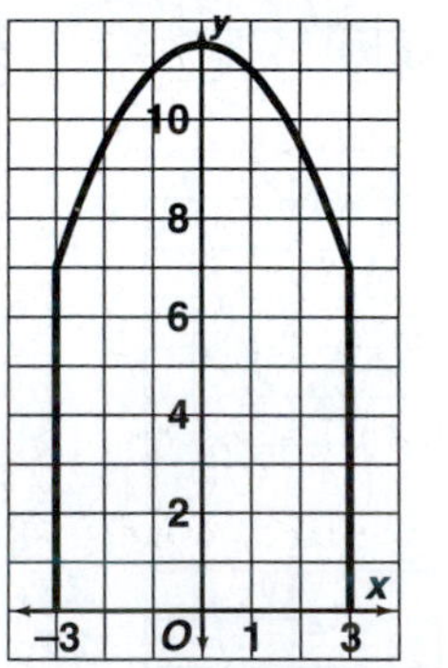

51. C **53.** B **55.** $(x^2 + 2)(x - 4)$ **57.** $(7b^2 + 1) \cdot (b + 2)$ **59.** $15x^2 - 20x$ **61.** $-12t^3 + 22t^2$ **63.** $-15y^6 - 10y^4 + 20y$ **65.** 15 balloons

Lesson 9-2 pp. 436–439

EXERCISES **1.** $x = 0$, (0, 4); domain: set of all real numbers; range: $\{y: y \geq 4\}$ **3.** $x = 4$, (4, −25); domain: set of all real numbers; range: $\{y: y \geq 25\}$ **5.** B **7.** C **9.** A

11.

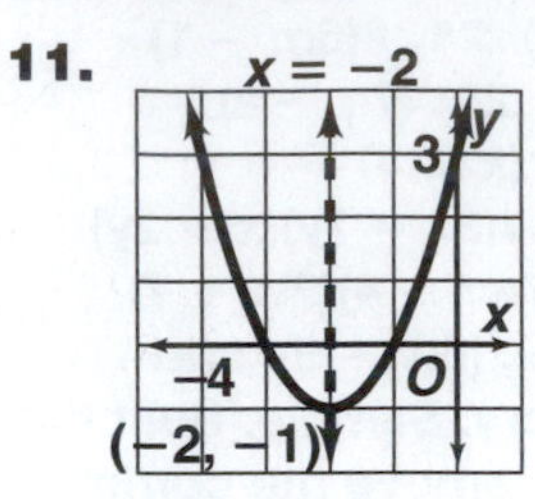

13.

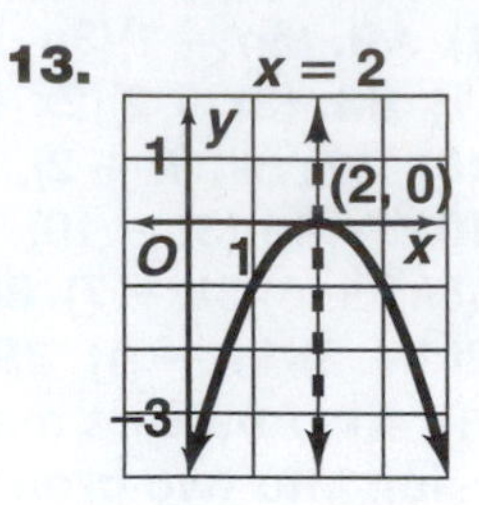

15a. 20 ft **b.** 400 ft²

17.

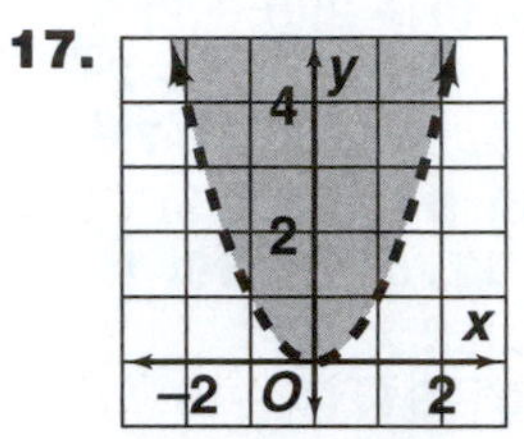

19.

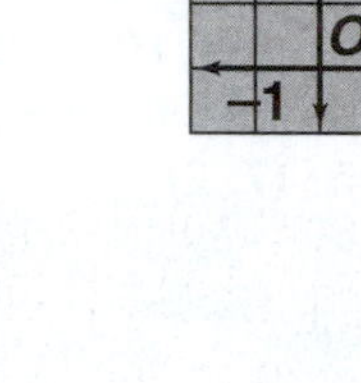

21.

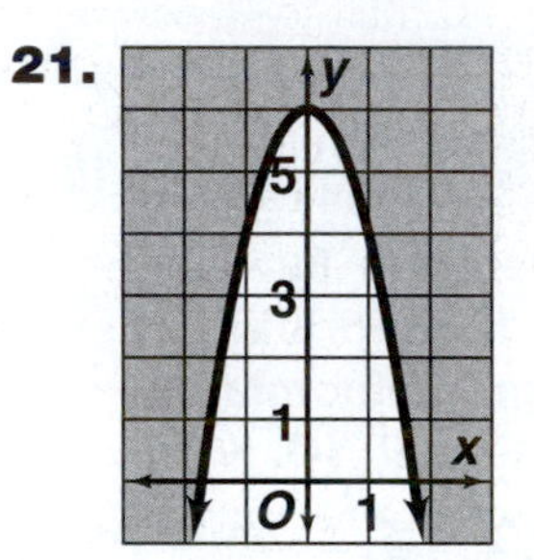

23. $x = 4.5$ domain: set of all real numbers; range: $\{y: y \geq -17.25\}$

25. $f(x)$ $x = 1$

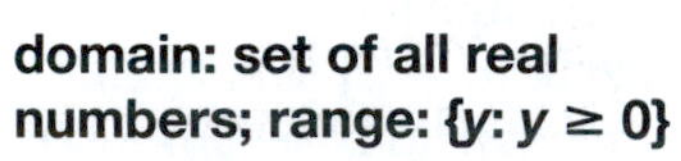

domain: set of all real numbers; range: $\{y: y \geq 0\}$

27.

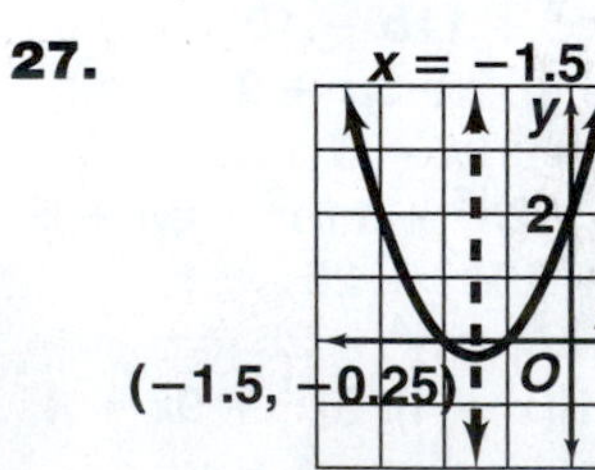

domain: set of all real numbers; range: $\{y: y \geq -0.25\}$

29.

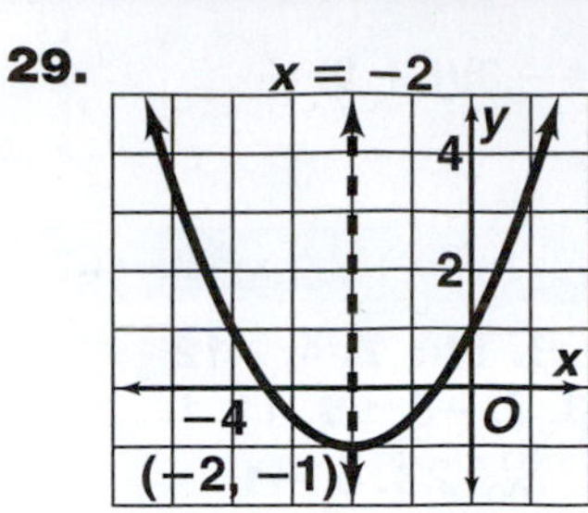

domain: set of all real numbers; range: $\{y: y \geq 1\}$

31.

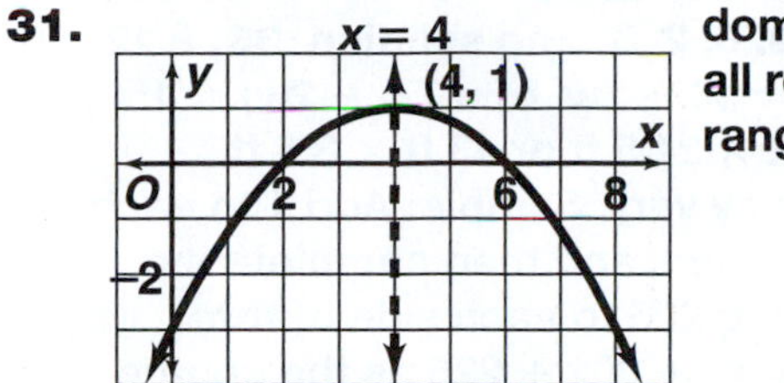

domain: set of all real numbers; range: $\{y: y \leq 1\}$

33. Answers may vary. Sample: $y = -3x^2$
35a. 1.3 m **b.** 5.0 m **37.** C **39.** 26 units^2

41a. $y \leq -0.1x^2 + 12$

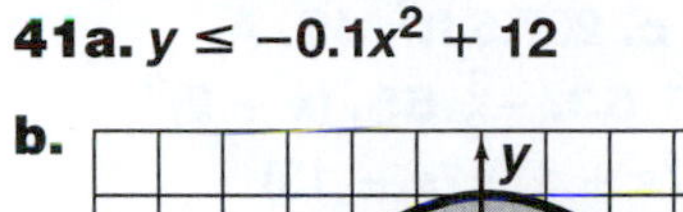

b.

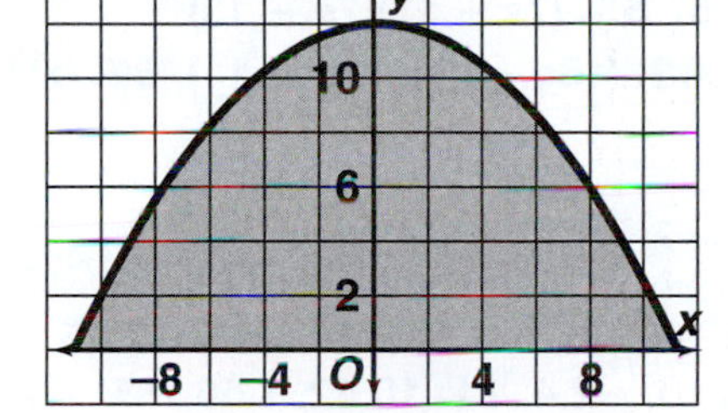

c. Yes; when $x = 6$, $y = 8.4$, so the camper will fit.

43.

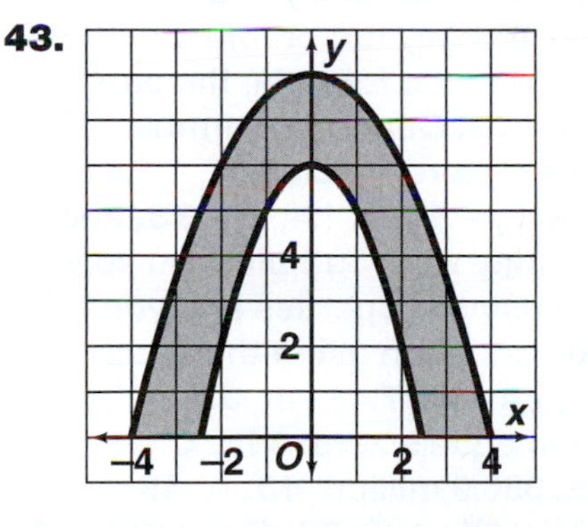

45a. (0, 2) **b.** $x = -2.5$ **c.** 5 **d.** $y = x^2 + 5x + 2$
e. Answers may vary. Sample: Test (−4, −2).

$-2 \stackrel{?}{=} (-4)^2 + 5(-4) + 2$
$-2 \stackrel{?}{=} 16 - 20 + 2$
$-2 = -2$ ✓

f. No; you would not be able to determine the b value using the vertex formula. **47.** A **49.** C
51. A **53.** D **55.** E **57.** $2x^2 + 7x - 30$

Lesson 9-3 pp. 442–444

EXERCISES **1.** 13 **3.** $\frac{1}{3}$ **5.** 0.5 **7.** −1.1 **9.** 0.6
11. $\frac{5}{4}$ **13.** irrational **15.** irrational **17.** 5 and 6
19. −12 and −11 **21.** 0.93 **23.** 0 **25.** $\pm\frac{3}{7}$
27. $\pm\frac{1}{9}$ **29.** ±1.5 **31.** ±0.1 **33.** ±202 **35.** C
37. $-\frac{2}{5}$ **39.** 1.26 **41.** −33 **43.** 6.40
45. Answers may vary. Sample: The first expression means the neg. square root of 1 and the second expression means the pos. square root of 1. **47.** 4 **49.** False; zero has one square root. **51.** true **53a.** 4 units^2 **b.** $\frac{1}{2}$ unit^2 **c.** 2 units^2
d. $\sqrt{2}$ units **55.** C **57.** B **59.** $(x + 8)(x - 3)$
61. $(m - 9)(m - 2)$

63. $8 \cdot 7 \cdot 5 = 8 \cdot 5 \cdot 7$ Comm. Prop. of Mult.
$= 40 \cdot 7$ Multiply.
$= 280$ Multiply.

65. $16\left(\frac{1}{16}\right) + 5 = 1 + 5$ Inv. Prop. of Mult.
$= 6$ Add.

67. $-7(3w) = (-7 \cdot 3)w$ Assoc. Prop. of Mult.
$= (-1 \cdot 7 \cdot 3)w$ Mult. Prop. of −1
$= -21w$ Multiply.

Lesson 9-4 pp. 447–450

EXERCISES

1.

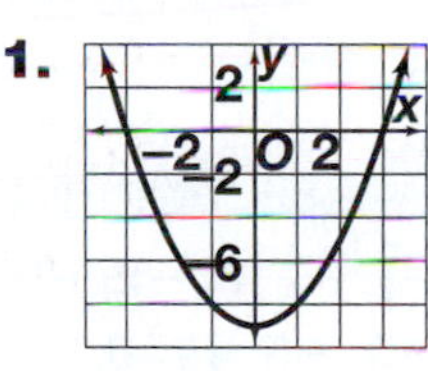

±3

3.

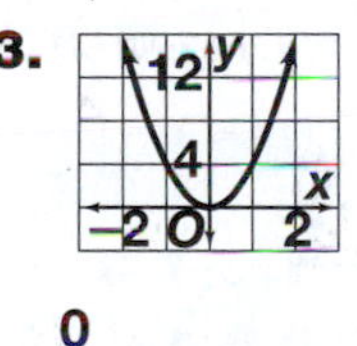

0

5.

20
y
12
4
x
−2
O
2

no solution

7.

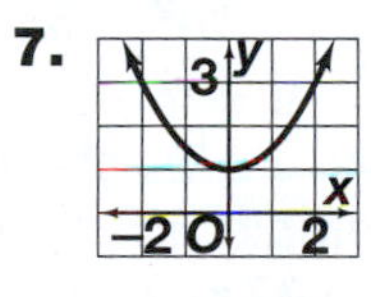

no solution

9.

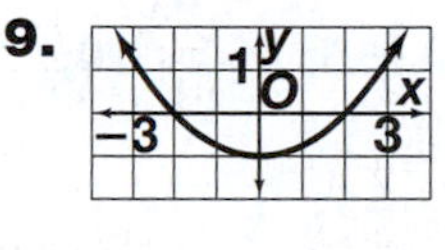

±2

Selected Answers

11. ± 21 **13.** 0 **15.** $\pm\frac{5}{2}$ **17.** ± 2 **19.** $x^2 = 256$; 16 m **21.** $\pi r^2 = 80$; 5.0 cm **23.** none **25.** one **27a.** 11.3 ft **b.** 16.0 ft **29.** $\pm\frac{3}{7}$ **31.** ± 2.8 **33.** ± 3.5 **35.** 121 **37.** Answers may vary. Sample: Michael subtracted 25 from the left side of the equation but added 25 to the right side. **39a.** square: $4r^2$, circle: πr^2 **b.** $4r^2 - \pi r^2 = 80$ **c.** 9.7 in., 19.3 in. **41.** 6.3 ft **43a.** 0.2 m **b.** 2.5 s **c.** 3.0 s **d.** Shorten; as ℓ decreases, t decreases. **45.** 28 cm **47.** C **49.** B

51. **53.**

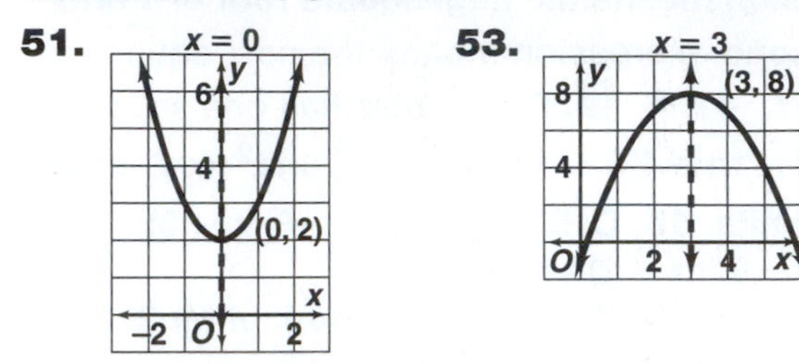

55.

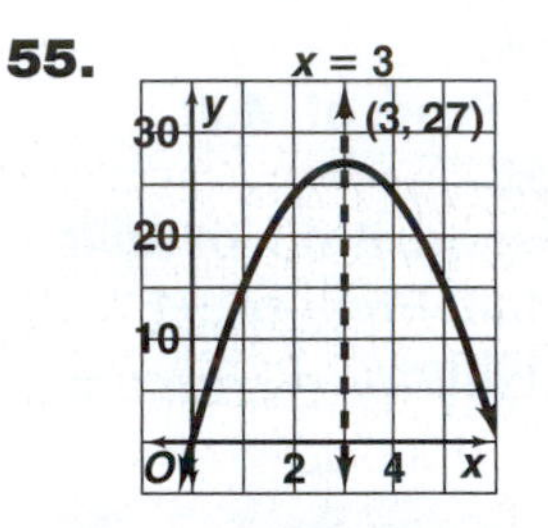

57. $(y - 13)(y - 2)$ **59.** $(z - 12)(z + 6)$ **61.** $(t + 2u)(t - u)$ **63.** 3.48×10^{-5} **65.** 31,000 **67.** 0.00062

Lesson 9-5 pp. 454–456

EXERCISES **1.** 3, 7 **3.** 0, -1 **5.** $-\frac{2}{7}, -\frac{4}{5}$ **7.** $-2, -5$ **9.** 1, -4 **11.** 0, 8 **13.** -2, 5 **15.** $-3, -5$ **17.** 0, 6 **19.** $-5, -\frac{1}{3}$ **21.** 5 cm **23.** 6 ft × 15 ft **25.** 2 and 3 or 7 and 8 **27.** $6n^2 - 5n - 4 = 0$; $\frac{4}{3}, -\frac{1}{2}$ **29.** $a^2 + 6a + 9 = 0$; -3 **31.** $x^2 - 10x + 24 = 0$; 4, 6 **33a.** 2 s **b.** about 19 ft **35.** Answers may vary. Sample: $x = 6$, $a = 2$, $b = 1$; $x = 3$, $a = 1$, $b = 11$ **37a.** 0, 1; -1, 0 **b.** 0 **39.** 0, 1, 4 **41.** 0, 7, -10 **43.** 0, 4, -5 **45.** Answers may vary. Samples: **a.** $x^2 - 3x - 40 = 0$ **b.** $x^2 - x - 6 = 0$ **c.** $2x^2 + 19x - 10 = 0$ **d.** $21x^2 + x - 10 = 0$ **47.** $-2, 2, -1$ **49.** B **51.** B **53.** A **55.** $x^2 = 320$; 17.9 ft

57. **59.** **61.**

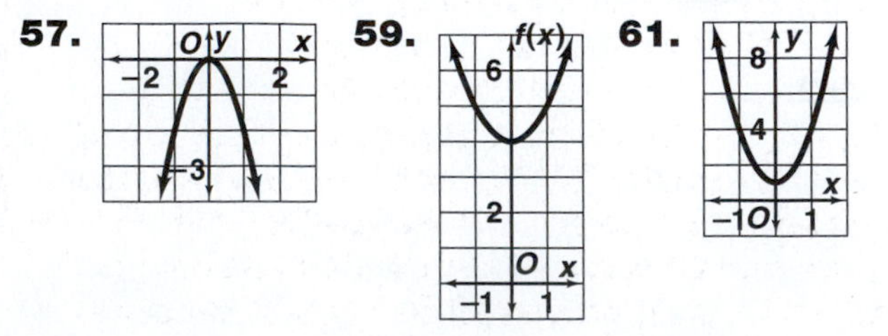

63. $(2x + 3)(x + 5)$ **65.** $(4t - 3)(t + 2)$ **67.** $5a(3a + 2)(a - 4)$

Lesson 9-6 pp. 460–462

EXERCISES **1.** 49 **3.** 400 **5.** 144 **7.** 4, -12 **9.** $-5, -17$ **11.** 9, -29 **13.** 7, -5 **15.** 11, 1 **17.** 4.82, -5.82 **19.** 1 **21.** $\frac{81}{100}$ **23.** 5, -1 **25a.** $(2x + 1)(x + 1)$ **b.** $2x^2 + 3x + 1 = 28$ **c.** 3 **27.** $-3, -4$ **29.** 6, 2 **31.** no solution **33.** 8.12, -0.12 **35a.** $\ell = 50 - 2w$ **b.** $w(50 - 2w) = 150$; 21.5, 3.5 **c.** 7 ft × 21.5 ft or 43 ft × 3.5 ft **37.** Answers may vary. Sample: Add 1 to each side of the equation, and then complete the square by adding 225 to each side of the equation. Write $x^2 + 30x + 225$ as the square $(x + 15)^2$ and add 1 and 225 to get 226. Then take square roots and solve the resulting equations. **39.** 5.16, -1.16 **41.** 5.6 ft by 14.2 ft **43a.** $A = \frac{7}{2}x^2 + 5x + 1$ **b.** about 6.86 **c.** 207.5 ft^2 **45.** A **47.** B **49.** -3, 7 **51.** 0, 5 **53.** $-\frac{3}{2}$ **55.** $(x + 2)^2$ **57.** $(b + 5)(b - 5)$ **59.** $(7s + 13)(7s - 13)$ **61.** $(5m + 12)^2$ **63.** $(16g - 11)(16g + 11)$ **65.** p^{13} **67.** $\frac{1}{m^{40}}$ **69.** t^{29}

Lesson 9-7 pp. 466–468

EXERCISES **1.** $-1, -1.5$ **3.** 1.5 **5.** 6.67, -0.25 **7.** 2.67, -16 **9.** 16, -2.4 **11.** 10.42, 1.58 **13.** 1.14, -0.77 **15.** 3.84, -0.17 **17a.** $0 = -16t^2 + 50t + 3.5$ **b.** $t \approx 3.2$; 3.2 s **19.** Factoring or square roots; the equation is easily factorable and there is no x term. **21.** Quadratic formula; the equation cannot be factored. **23.** Quadratic formula; the equation cannot be factored. **25.** 0.87, -1.54 **27.** 1.28, -2.61 **29.** 3, -3 **31.** 1.4, -1 **33.** about 2.1 s **35.** Answers may vary. Sample: You solve the linear equation using properties and you solve the quadratic equation using the quadratic formula. **37.** 13.44 cm and 7.44 cm **39.** if the expression $b^2 - 4ac$ equals zero **41a.** Check students' work. **b.** 356.9 million **43.** A **45.** D **47.** $-1, -2$ **49.** $(2c + 5)(c + 3)$ **51.** $(5n + 2)(n - 7)$ **53.** $(2x - 1)(3x - 5)$

Lesson 9-8 pp. 472–474

EXERCISES **1.** A **3.** B **5.** 0 **7.** 2 **9.** 2 **11.** 0 **13.** 0 **15.** 2 **17.** 2 **19.** 2 **21.** 0 **23.** No; the discriminant is negative. **25.** 0 **27.** 2 **29.** 0 **31a.** $S = -0.75p^2 + 54p$ **b.** no **c.** \$36 **d.** If a product is too expensive, fewer people will buy it.

33. no **35a.** 16; 5, 1 **b.** 81; 4, −5 **c.** 73; 3.89, −0.39 **d.** Rational; the square root of a discriminant that is a perfect square is a pos. integer. **37.** no **39.** yes; −1, $\frac{2}{3}$ **41.** yes; 2.5, −1 **43.** never **45.** always **47.** $y = 2x^2 + 8x + 10$ has a vertex closer to the x-axis; its discriminant is closer to zero. **49.** C **51.** C **53.** D **55.** 1.83, −3.83 **57.** 1.79, −2.79 **59.** 2, 1.5 **61.** no solution **63.** $-\frac{7}{2} \pm \frac{\sqrt{97}}{2}$ **65.** 5, 13 **67.** $(x - 15)^2$ **69.** $\left(\frac{1}{\sqrt{2}}d - \frac{3}{2}\right)\left(\frac{1}{\sqrt{2}}d + \frac{3}{2}\right)$

Chapter Review pp. 477–479

1. parabola **2.** completing the square **3.** principal **4.** vertex **5.** discriminant **6–9.** Answers may vary. Samples are given. **6.** $y = -2x^2$ **7.** $y = 2x^2$ **8.** $y = x^2$ **9.** $y = \frac{1}{2}x^2$

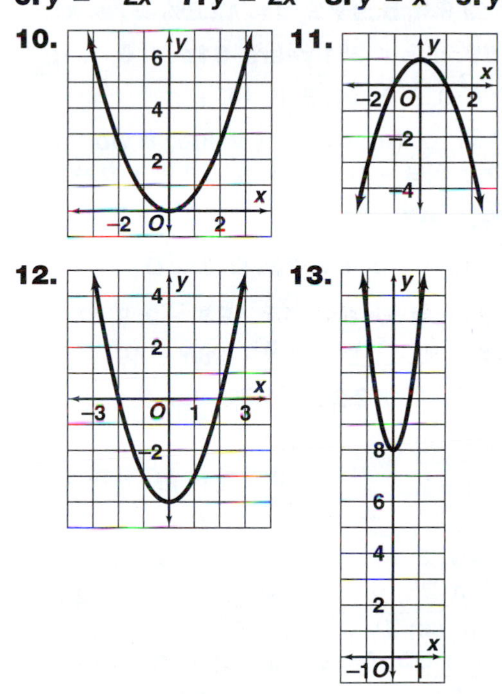

14. min. **15.** max. **16.** min. **17.** max.

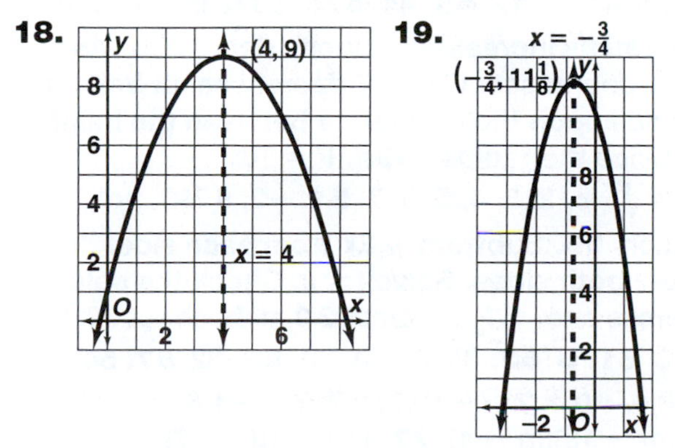

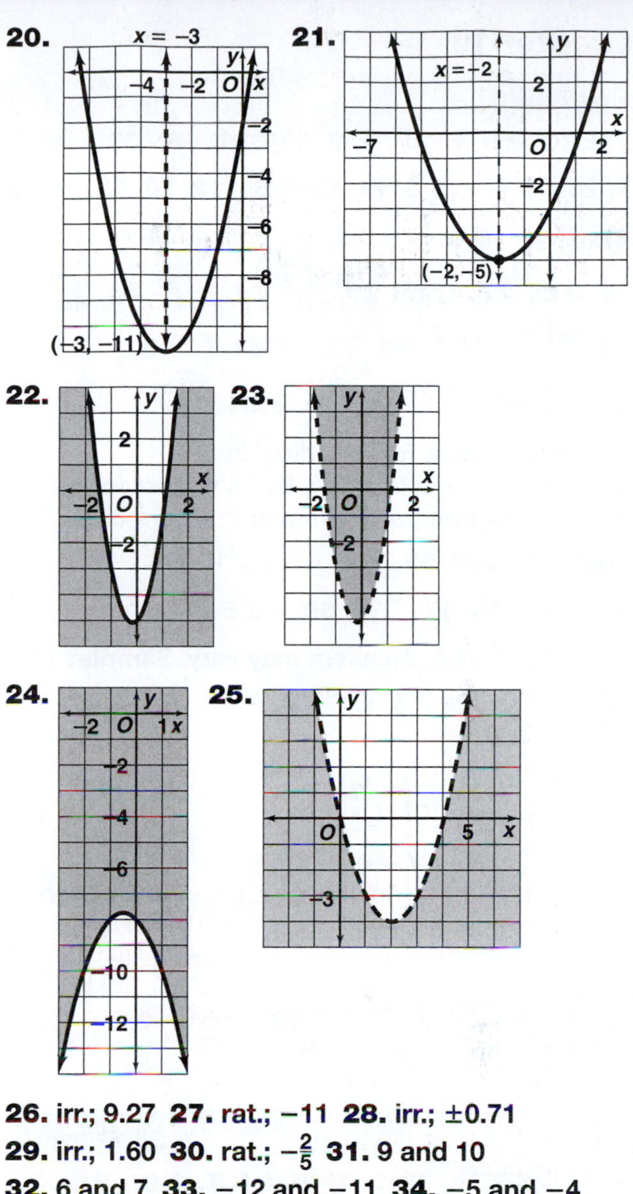

26. irr.; 9.27 **27.** rat.; −11 **28.** irr.; ±0.71 **29.** irr.; 1.60 **30.** rat.; $-\frac{2}{5}$ **31.** 9 and 10 **32.** 6 and 7 **33.** −12 and −11 **34.** −5 and −4 **35.** 2, −2 **36.** 5, −5 **37.** 0 **38.** no solution **39.** $-\frac{2}{3}, \frac{2}{3}$ **40.** −4, 4 **41.** −4, −3 **42.** 0, 2 **43.** 4, 5 **44.** $-3, \frac{1}{2}$ **45.** $-\frac{2}{3}, 1\frac{1}{2}$ **46.** 1, 4 **47.** 2.3 in. **48.** 25 **49.** 4 **50.** 225 **51.** 81 **52.** 169 **53.** 441 **54.** 16 **55.** 64 **56.** $\frac{49}{64}$ **57.** −6.74, 0.74 **58.** 0.38, 2.62 **59.** $-2, -1\frac{1}{2}$ **60.** 10 ft × 17 ft **61.** 2 **62.** 2 **63.** 0 **64.** 1 **65.** −1.84, 1.09 **66.** 0.5, 3 **67.** 0.13, 7.87 **68.** −5.48, 5.48 **69.** −5, 5; use factoring, because the equation is easily factorable. **70.** −4.12, 0.78; use the quadratic formula, because the trinomial does not factor easily. **71.** 4, 5; use factoring, because the equation is easily factorable. **72.** 3; use factoring, because the equation is easily factorable. **73.** −15, 15; use square roots, because the equation has no x term. **74.** −8.47, 0.47; complete the square, because the equation is in the form $x^2 + bx = c$. **75.** 18 ft; 324 ft^2 **76.** 1.5 s

Selected Answers

Chapter 10

Lesson 10-1 pp. 489–491

EXERCISES **1.** $10\sqrt{2}$ **3.** $5\sqrt{3}$ **5.** $-6\sqrt{30}$ **7.** $2n\sqrt{7}$ **9.** $6x\sqrt{3}$ **11.** $2a^2\sqrt{5a}$ **13.** 20 **15.** $11\sqrt{2}$ **17.** $7\sqrt{3}$ **19.** $6n\sqrt{2}$ **21.** $3x^2\sqrt{17}$ **23.** $3a^3\sqrt{2}$ **25.** 3 mi **27.** 17 mi **29.** $\frac{3\sqrt{3}}{2}$ **31.** $\frac{2\sqrt{30}}{11}$ **33.** $\frac{\sqrt{7}}{4c}$ **35.** $\frac{2n\sqrt{2n}}{9}$ **37.** $\frac{3}{2}$ **39.** $-2\sqrt{5}$ **41.** $\frac{s}{3}$ **43.** $\frac{3}{y}$ **45.** $\sqrt{5}$ **47.** $\frac{2\sqrt{10n}}{5n}$ **49.** $2\sqrt{3}$ **51.** $\frac{\sqrt{55y}}{2y}$

53. not simplest form; radical in the denominator of a fraction **55.** Simplest form; radicand has no perfect-square factors other than 1. **57.** 30 **59.** $\frac{3\sqrt{2}}{4}$ **61.** $2\sqrt{15}$ **63.** $-\sqrt{3}$ **65.** $2ab\sqrt{5b}$ **67.** $\frac{\sqrt{3m}}{4m}$ **69.** $-3 \pm 3\sqrt{2}$ **71.** $\frac{2 \pm \sqrt{10}}{3}$ **73.** Answers may vary. Sample: 12, 27, 48. **75.** $12x$ **77.** $30a^4$ **79.** A **81.** A **83.** 2 **85.** 1 **87.** 0

89. **91.**

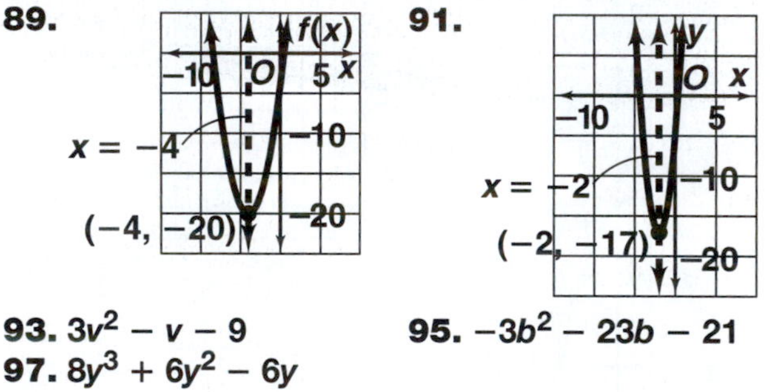

93. $3v^2 - v - 9$ **95.** $-3b^2 - 23b - 21$ **97.** $8y^3 + 6y^2 - 6y$

Lesson 10-2 pp. 496–499

EXERCISES **1.** 10 **3.** 17 **5.** 2.5 **7.** 4 **9.** 12 **11.** 7.5 **13.** 1.2 m **15.** about 5.8 km **17.** no **19.** yes **21.** yes **23.** no **25.** yes **27.** $\frac{4}{15}$ **29.** 1.25 **31.** 7.0 **33a.** 13.4 ft **b.** 80.4 ft^2 **35.** 1000 lb **37.** 9.0 **39a.** These lengths could be 2 legs or one leg and the hypotenuse. **b.** about 12.8 in. or 6 in. **41a.** 6.9 ft **b.** about 89.2 ft^2 **c.** 981 watts **43a.** Answers may vary. Sample: $\sqrt{5}$, $\sqrt{20}$, 5 **b.** 5 units^2 **45.** An integer has 2 as a factor; the integer is even; if an integer is even, then it has 2 as a factor; true. **47.** You are in Brazil; you are south of the equator; if you are south of the equator you are in Brazil; false. **49.** 52 units^2 **51.** 15 **53.** 10 **55.** 2.8 **57.** 10 **59.** 5

61a.

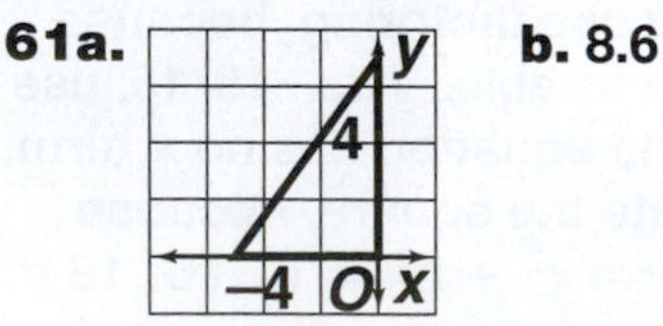

b. 8.6

63. D **65.** B **67.** 3 and 4 **69.** −8 and −7 **71.** rational **73.** irrational **75.** $7p^4 + p^3 + 2p^2 + p$ **77.** $2m^3 - 2m$

Lesson 10-3 pp. 503–506

EXERCISES **1.** $5\sqrt{6}$ **3.** $-2\sqrt{5}$ **5.** $14\sqrt{2}$ **7.** yes **9.** no **11.** $-3\sqrt{3}$ **13.** $-2\sqrt{5}$ **15.** $8\sqrt{10}$ **17.** $9 + \sqrt{3}$ **19.** $3\sqrt{5} + 2\sqrt{3}$ **21.** $6 - 5\sqrt{6}$ **23.** $58 - 10\sqrt{30}$ **25.** $43 + 4\sqrt{30}$ **27.** $23 - 5\sqrt{13}$ **29** $-6\sqrt{2}$ **31.** $\frac{3\sqrt{10} + 3\sqrt{5}}{5}$ **33.** $18\sqrt{3} + 9\sqrt{11}$ **35.** $-\frac{4}{3}$; −1.3 **37.** 7.4 ft **39.** $6\sqrt{2} + 6\sqrt{3}$ **41.** $8 + 2\sqrt{15}$ **43.** $15 + 4\sqrt{14}$ **45.** $-\sqrt{2}$ **47.** $\frac{\sqrt{10}}{2}$ **49.** $(10 + 10\sqrt{2})$ units **51.** The student simplified $2\sqrt{8} \cdot 7\sqrt{8}$ as $14\sqrt{8}$; $115 + 18\sqrt{6}$ **53a.** $2\sqrt{2}$ or 2.8 ft **b.** $s\sqrt{2}$ **55.** 12.8% **57a.** $x^{\frac{n}{2}}$ **b.** $x^{\frac{n-1}{2}}\sqrt{x}$ **59.** about 251 years **61a.** 1, 0, 1, 1; 4, 1, 5, $\sqrt{17}$; 5, 3, 8, $\sqrt{34}$; 8, 6, 14, 10; 10, 9, 19, $\sqrt{181}$ **b.** No; the only values it works for are $a = b = 0$; $a = 0, b = 1$; and $a = 1, b = 0$. **63.** B **65.** $\frac{23\sqrt{7}}{21}$ **67.** $\frac{13\sqrt{3}}{6}$ **69.** $10\sqrt{2}$ **71.** $2\sqrt{2} - \sqrt{6} - \sqrt{3} + 3$ **73.** D **75.** D **77.** $\frac{\sqrt{6}}{3}$ **79.** $2b^2\sqrt{10b}$ **81.** $\frac{2\sqrt{6v}}{v^4}$ **83.** −2, 9, 84 **85.** −4, 6 **87.** $-3, -\frac{1}{2}$ **89.** $4p^2 + 28p + 49$ **91.** $9x^2 - 1$ **93.** $d^2 - 2.2d + 1.21$

Lesson 10-4 pp. 510–512

EXERCISES **1.** 4 **3.** 36 **5.** 15 **7.** 576 ft **9.** 4.5 **11.** 7 **13.** 4 **15.** 2 **17.** none **19.** −7 **21.** 3 **23.** no solution **25.** no solution **27.** 1.25 or $\frac{5}{4}$ **29.** true **31.** false; $3\sqrt{24} > \sqrt{150}$ **33.** about 2.5 in **35.** Answers may vary. Sample: $x - 2 = \sqrt{7 - 2x}$, $\sqrt{3x} = 3$ **37.** 3 **39.** no solution **41.** 1.5 **43.** 0, 12 **45.** 44 **47a.** 68 ft **b.** 20.5 mi/h **c.** As radius increases, velocity decreases. As height decreases, velocity decreases. **d.** Velocity depends upon the difference between the height and twice the radius. **49a.** $V = 10x^2$ **b.** $x = \frac{V}{10}$ **c.** 2, 3, 4, 5, 6, 7 **51.** −2, 8 **53.** no solution **55.** Subtract $\sqrt{2x}$ from each side. Square both sides. Solve for x. Check the solution if there is one. **57. a.** about 2.0 m **b.** about 32.4 m **59.** C **61.** D **63.** $3\sqrt{2} + 4\sqrt{3}$ **65.** 32 **67.** $54\sqrt{2}$ **69.** 8.4, −0.4 **71.** −10.7, 0.7 **73.** −1.6, 3.1 **75.** $(m - 13)(m - 1)$ **77.** $(2p + 1)(p + 7)$ **79.** $(4v - 5)(v - 5)$ **81.** $(3k + 7)(k + 1)$

Lesson 10-5 pp. 516–519

EXERCISES **1.** $x \geq 2$ **3.** $x \geq 0$ **5.** $x \geq -3$ **7.** $x \geq -\frac{5}{3}$ **9.** $x \geq \frac{4}{3}$ **11.** A **13.** B

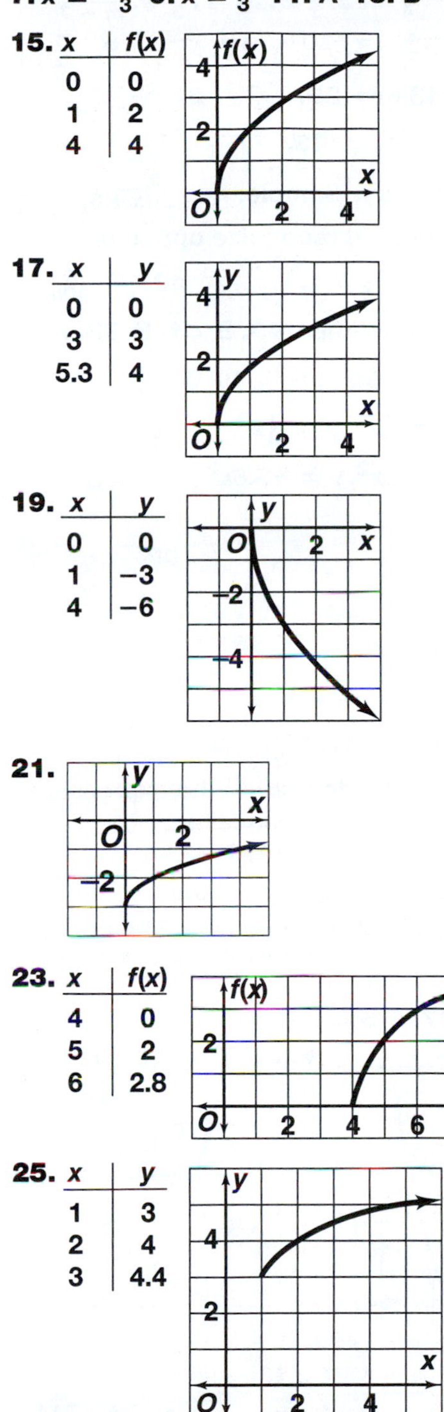

15.

x	$f(x)$
0	0
1	2
4	4

17.

x	y
0	0
3	3
5.3	4

19.

x	y
0	0
1	−3
4	−6

21.

23.

x	$f(x)$
4	0
5	2
6	2.8

25.

x	y
1	3
2	4
3	4.4

27. $\{x: x \geq 4\}$, $\{y: y \geq 0\}$

29. Form an inequality setting the radicand ≥ 0. Solve for x. Answers may vary.

Sample: $y = \sqrt{x - 2}$

Domain: $x - 2 \geq 0$

$x \geq 2$

31. Translate the graph of $y = \sqrt{x}$ 8 units to the left.

33. Translate the graph of $y = \sqrt{x}$ 12 units up.

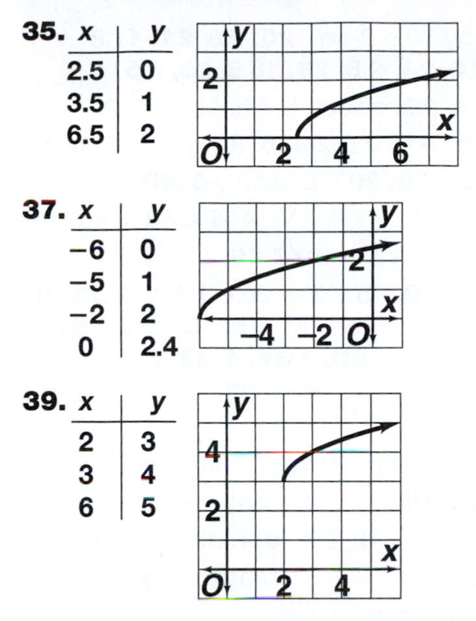

35.

x	y
2.5	0
3.5	1
6.5	2

37.

x	y
−6	0
−5	1
−2	2
0	2.4

39.

x	y
2	3
3	4
6	5

41. D **43a.** no **b.** Answers may vary. Sample: The graph of $y = \sqrt{x}$ is the first quadrant portion of the graph $x = y^2$. **c.** $y = -\sqrt{x}$

45. Never; x must equal 81.

47. always

49a. about 213 cameras **b.** month 4

51a. i. ii. iii. iv.

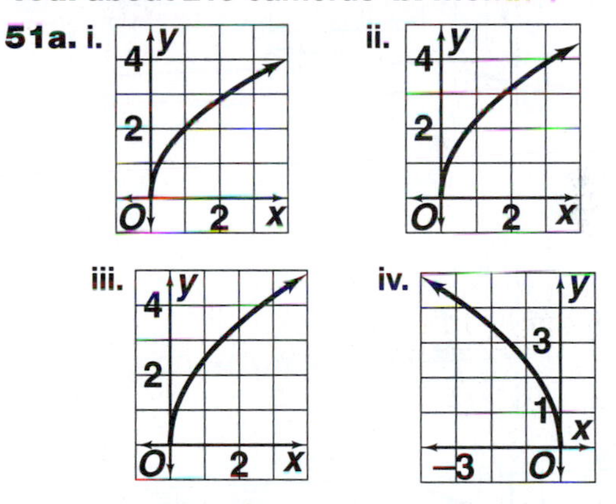

b. The greater the absolute value of n, the steeper the graph. If $n < 0$, then the graph lies in Quadrant II. If $n > 0$, the graph lies in Quadrant I.

53. D **55.** D **57.** 16 **59.** 169 **61.** no solution **63.** $\frac{-2 - 3\sqrt{2}}{2}$, $\frac{-2 + 3\sqrt{2}}{2}$ **65.** no solution **67.** no solution **69.** $(2x + 1)(x - 4)$ **71.** $(2x + 1)(2x + 9)$ **73.** $4(x^2 - x - 15)$

Chapter Review pp. 521–523

1. conjugates **2.** rationalize **3.** extraneous solution **4.** like radicals **5.** hypotenuse **6.** square root function **7.** Pythagorean Theorem **8.** unlike radicals **9.** radical expression **10.** $48\sqrt{2}$ **11.** $\frac{2\sqrt{21}}{11}$ **12.** $20c^2\sqrt{6}$ **13.** $\frac{10\sqrt{13}}{13}$

14. $5h^2\sqrt{10}$ **15.** $6t^3\sqrt{5}$ **16.** $\frac{1}{2}$ **17.** $\frac{2\sqrt{6}}{3k}$ **18.** $\frac{3}{2}$ **19.** $10\sqrt{2}$ cm by $70\sqrt{2}$ cm **20.** 5.8 **21.** 17.8 **22.** 14.8 **23.** 9.8 **24.** 9.8 **25.** 18.6 **26.** 5.5 **27.** yes **28.** yes **29.** about 127 ft **30.** $10\sqrt{2}$ **31.** $-5\sqrt{21}$ **32.** $-13\sqrt{5}$ **33.** 0 **34.** yes **35.** no **36.** no **37.** $2\sqrt{7}$ **38.** $30\sqrt{5}$ **39.** $\sqrt{6}$ **40.** $2\sqrt{5}$ **41.** $10 - 10\sqrt{2}$ **42.** $-1 + 2\sqrt{14}$ **43.** $53 + 8\sqrt{15}$ **44.** $\sqrt{6} + \sqrt{3}$ **45.** $-3 - 3\sqrt{2}$ **46.** $17\sqrt{7}$ **47.** $4\sqrt{2} - 2\sqrt{7}$ **48.** $15\sqrt{2} - 30\sqrt{3}$ **49.** 2 **50.** 16 **51.** 17 **52.** 169 **53.** 8 **54.** 81 **55.** 100 **56.** 4 **57.** 1 **58.** 7 **59.** no solution **60.** 3 **61.** 4 **62.** no solution **63.** 0 **64.** no solution **65.** $5\sqrt{5}$ cm **66.** 2.93 in.

67. domain: $\{x: x \le 3\}$; range: $\{y: y \ge 0\}$ **68.** domain: $\{x: x \ge 0\}$; range: $\{y: y \ge -1\}$

69. domain: $\{x: x \ge -4\}$; range: $\{y: y \le 5\}$ **70.** domain: $\{x: x \ge 0\}$; range: $\{y: y \ge 2\}$

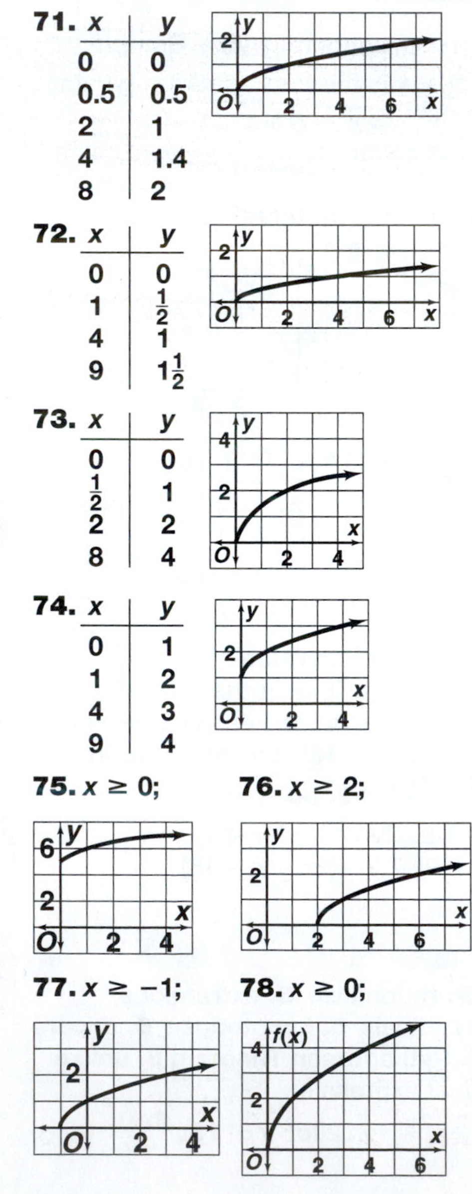

71.

x	y
0	0
0.5	0.5
2	1
4	1.4
8	2

72.

x	y
0	0
1	$\frac{1}{2}$
4	1
9	$1\frac{1}{2}$

73.

x	y
0	0
$\frac{1}{2}$	1
2	2
8	4

74.

x	y
0	1
1	2
4	3
9	4

75. $x \ge 0$; **76.** $x \ge 2$;

77. $x \ge -1$; **78.** $x \ge 0$;

Chapter 11

Lesson 11-1 pp. 532–534

EXERCISES 1. $\frac{2a+3}{4}$ **3.** $\frac{1}{3}$ **5.** $3x$ **7.** $\frac{2}{3}$ **9.** $\frac{1}{m-7}$ **11.** $\frac{a+1}{5}$ **13.** $\frac{c-4}{c+3}$ **15.** $\frac{1}{m-2}$ **17.** $\frac{-4}{t+1}$ **19.** $-\frac{1}{2}$ **21.** $-\frac{1}{w-4}$ **23.** 13 min **25.** $\frac{2r-1}{r+5}$ **27.** $\frac{5t-4}{3t-1}$ **29.** $\frac{3(z+4)}{z^3}$ **31.** $-\frac{2a+1}{a+3}$ **33.** $\frac{-c(3c+5)}{5c+4}$ **35.** Answers may vary. Sample: $\frac{3}{(x-2)(x+3)}$ **37.** The student did not recognize opposite factors; $-\frac{1}{4}$. **39.** $\frac{5w}{5w+6}$ **41.** $\frac{3y}{4(y+4)}$ **43.** $\frac{m-n}{m+10n}$ **45.** $\frac{6v-7w}{3v-2w}$ **47.** sometimes **49.** B **51.** B **53.** A **55.** $10\sqrt{2}$ **57.** $2\sqrt{2}$ **59.** $3hk^2\sqrt{10}$ **61.** $\frac{6}{a}$ **63.** $2y\sqrt{y}$ **65.** $y = \frac{1}{4}x^2, y = \frac{1}{3}x^2, y = \frac{2}{5}x^2$ **67.** $y = -x^2, y = 2.3x^2, y = -3.8x^2$

Lesson 11-2 pp. 537–539

EXERCISES 1. $\frac{35x}{36}$ **3.** $\frac{40}{3a^5}$ **5.** $\frac{2x(x-1)}{3(x+1)}$ **7.** $\frac{2c}{c-1}$ **9.** $\frac{9}{t}$ **11.** $\frac{1}{2}$ **13.** $4(t+1)(t+2)$ **15.** $\frac{(x-1)(x-2)}{3}$ **17.** $-\frac{2d-5}{6d^2}$ **19.** $\frac{1}{s+4}$ **21.** 6 **23.** $-\frac{1}{3}$ **25.** $\frac{n-3}{4n+5}$ **27.** $\frac{11}{7k-15}$ **29.** $t + 3$ **31.** $\frac{3t-5}{7t^2}$ **33.** $\frac{x-2}{x-3}$ **35.** The student forgot to rewrite the expression using the reciprocal before canceling. **37.** Check students' work. **39.** \$132.96 **41.** $\frac{x-2}{4(x+7)}$ **43.** $\frac{2}{a+5}$ **45.** She wrote w^5 as a fraction so she could easily see what she could cancel. **47.** 1 **49.** $\frac{-(2a+3b)(a+2b)}{(5a+b)(2a-3b)}$ **51.** $\frac{x(x-2)}{2(x-1)}$ **53.** C **55.** 8.2 **57.** 5 **59.** 0.2

61.

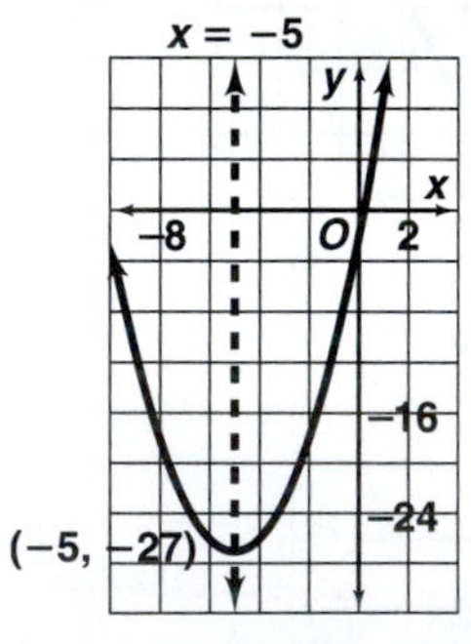

63.

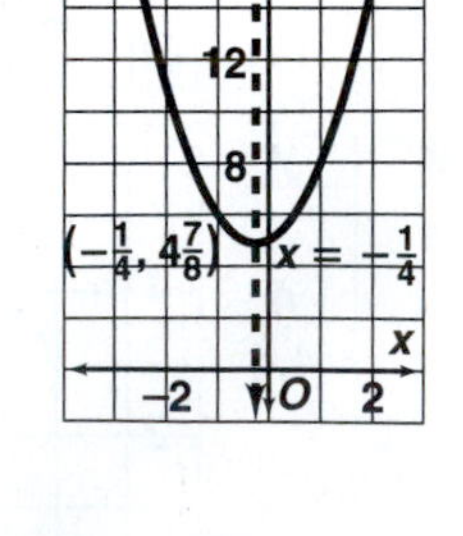

Lesson 11-3 pp. 542–544

EXERCISES 1. $x^4 - x^3 + x^2$ **3.** $3c^2 + 2c - \frac{1}{3}$ **5.** $4 - \frac{16}{q}$ **7.** $x - 3$ **9.** $n - 1$ **11.** $3x - 1$ **13.** $4a - 2 + \frac{16}{a+2}$ **15.** $5t - 50$ **17.** $b^2 - 3b - 1 + \frac{3}{3b-1}$ **19.** $t^2 - 2t - 2$ **21.** $(r^2 + 5r + 1)$ cm **23.** $b + 12 + \frac{1}{b+4}$ **25.** $10w - 681 + \frac{49{,}046}{w+72}$ **27.** $2x^2 + 5x + 2$

29. $3x + 2 - \frac{1}{2x}$ **31.** $2b^2 + 2b + 10 + \frac{10}{b - 1}$
33. $28a - 12$ **35.** $k^2 - 0.3k - 0.4$
37. $-2z^2 + 3z - 4 + \frac{5}{z + 1}$
39. $-16c^2 - 20c - 25$ **41.** $t - 1 + \frac{2t}{2t^3 + 1}$
43a. Answers may vary. Sample: $(c^3 + 3c^2 - 2c - 4)$; $(c + 1)$ **b.** $(c^3 + 3c^2 - 2c - 4) \div (c + 1) = c^2 + 2c - 4$ **45.** The binomial is a factor of the polynomial if there is no remainder from the division. **47a.** $d - 2 + \frac{3}{d + 1}$ **b.** $d^2 - 2d + 3 - \frac{4}{d + 1}$ **c.** $d^3 - 2d^2 + 3d - 4 + \frac{5}{d + 1}$
d. Answers may vary. Sample:
$d^4 - 2d^3 + 3d^2 - 4d + 5 - \frac{6}{d + 1}$
e. $d^4 - 2d^3 + 3d^2 - 4d + 5 - \frac{6}{d + 1}$
49a. $t = \frac{d}{r}$ **b.** $t^2 - 7t + 12$ **51.** $3x + 2y$
53. $2b^3 - 2b^2 + 3$ **55.** B **57.** $n + 2$ **59.** $\frac{3c + 8}{2c + 7}$
61. 0 **63.** 2 **65.** 0 **67.** 5.38 **69.** −12.7 **71.** 6.32

Lesson 11-4 pp. 547–549

EXERCISES **1.** $\frac{9}{2m}$ **3.** $\frac{n + 2}{n + 3}$ **5.** $\frac{2s^2 + 1}{4s^2 + 2}$ **7.** $\frac{-3}{2 - b}$
9. $\frac{-2t}{2t - 3}$ **11.** 2 **13.** $2x^2$ **15.** $7z$ **17.** $\frac{35 + 6a}{15a}$
19. $\frac{18 + 20x^2}{15x^8}$ **21.** $\frac{189 - 9n}{7n^3}$ **23.** $\frac{17m - 47}{(m + 2)(m - 7)}$
25. $\frac{a^2 + 12a + 15}{4(a + 3)}$ **27.** $\frac{4t^2 + 5t + 5}{t^2(t + 1)}$ **29a.** $\frac{1}{r} + \frac{1}{0.7r}$
b. $\frac{17}{7r}$ **c.** about 0.8 h **31.** $\frac{h^2 + h + 1}{2t^2 - 7}$ **33.** $\frac{-3 - x - z}{xy^2z}$
35. $\frac{12c - 15a}{abc}$ **37.** $\frac{-21t + 33}{2t - 3}$ **39.** $\frac{k - 1}{k - 6}$
41a. $\frac{2}{r} + \frac{2}{1.25r}$; $\frac{18}{5r}$ **b.** $\frac{2}{d} + \frac{2}{0.8d}$; $\frac{9}{2d}$
c. Yes; they both represent the time it takes to make a round trip.
43. Answers may vary. Sample:
$\frac{2w}{w + 3}, \frac{3w^2}{w - 3}$; $\frac{3w^3 + 11w^2 - 6w}{(w + 3)(w - 3)}$ **45.** 8 **47.** $\frac{32x}{x - 5}$
49. $\frac{1}{2x(x - 5)}$ **51.** $\frac{-x^3 + 6x^2 + 35x - 50}{x(x + 5)(x^2 + x - 10)}$
53. $\frac{5a - 8}{(a + 2)(a - 5)}$ **55.** D **57.** $\frac{x^2}{2} + 2x - 1$ **59.** 6
61. no solution **63.** ±3.9

Lesson 11-5 pp. 553–554

EXERCISES **1.** −2 **3.** −1 **5.** $-\frac{1}{3}$ **7.** 1, 4 **9.** 1, 3
11. $\frac{16}{3}$ **13.** −2 **15.** $-\frac{2}{3}$ **17.** ≈12.7 min
19. 10, −10 **21.** 4 **23.** 6 **25.** $\frac{1}{2}$, 2 **27.** −5, 2
29. $\frac{1}{2}$ **31.** 0, 2 **33a.** 32 **b.** Answers may vary. Sample: Cross-multiplying; I think it's quicker. **c.** No; it only works for rational equations that are proportions. **35.** 40 mi/h **37.** 9 **39.** −1
41. $11\frac{1}{3}$ h **43.** D

45. **47.** **49.**

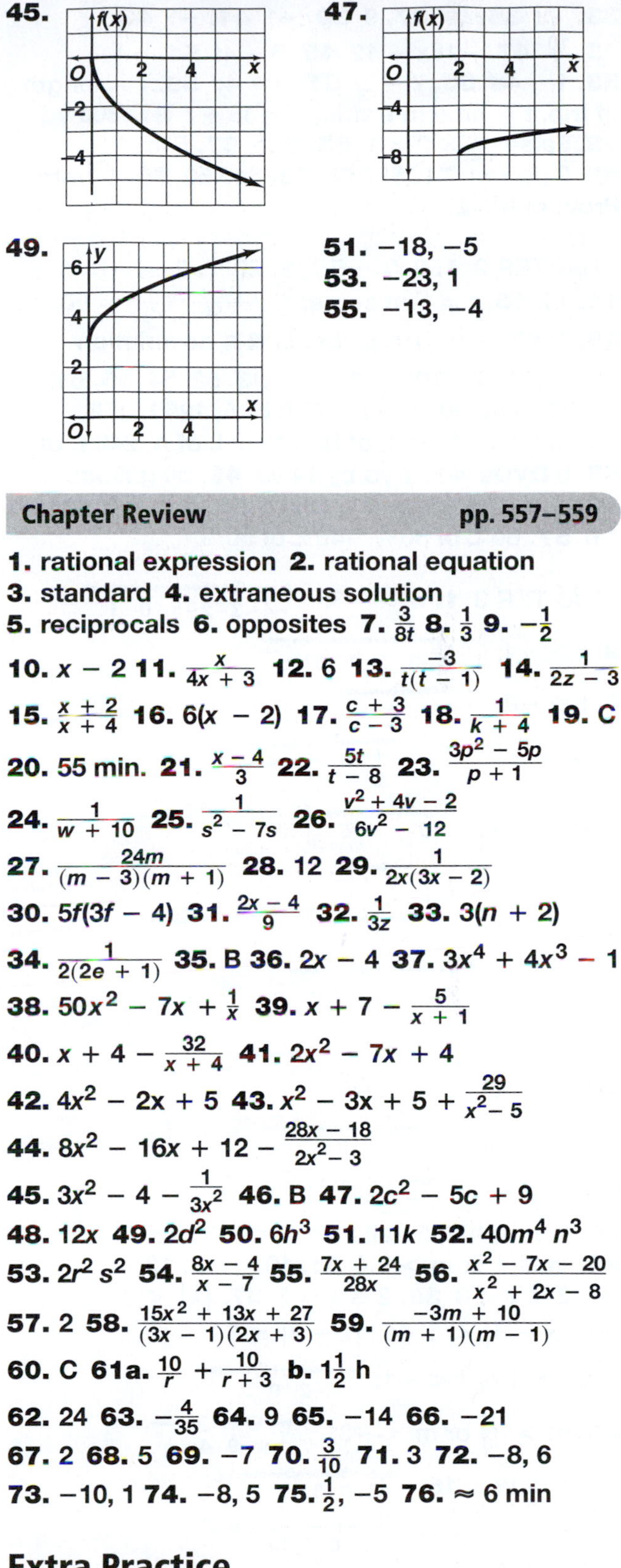

51. −18, −5
53. −23, 1
55. −13, −4

Chapter Review pp. 557–559

1. rational expression **2.** rational equation
3. standard **4.** extraneous solution
5. reciprocals **6.** opposites **7.** $\frac{3}{8t}$ **8.** $\frac{1}{3}$ **9.** $-\frac{1}{2}$
10. $x - 2$ **11.** $\frac{x}{4x + 3}$ **12.** 6 **13.** $\frac{-3}{t(t - 1)}$ **14.** $\frac{1}{2z - 3}$
15. $\frac{x + 2}{x + 4}$ **16.** $6(x - 2)$ **17.** $\frac{c + 3}{c - 3}$ **18.** $\frac{1}{k + 4}$ **19.** C
20. 55 min. **21.** $\frac{x - 4}{3}$ **22.** $\frac{5t}{t - 8}$ **23.** $\frac{3p^2 - 5p}{p + 1}$
24. $\frac{1}{w + 10}$ **25.** $\frac{1}{s^2 - 7s}$ **26.** $\frac{v^2 + 4v - 2}{6v^2 - 12}$
27. $\frac{24m}{(m - 3)(m + 1)}$ **28.** 12 **29.** $\frac{1}{2x(3x - 2)}$
30. $5f(3f - 4)$ **31.** $\frac{2x - 4}{9}$ **32.** $\frac{1}{3z}$ **33.** $3(n + 2)$
34. $\frac{1}{2(2e + 1)}$ **35.** B **36.** $2x - 4$ **37.** $3x^4 + 4x^3 - 1$
38. $50x^2 - 7x + \frac{1}{x}$ **39.** $x + 7 - \frac{5}{x + 1}$
40. $x + 4 - \frac{32}{x + 4}$ **41.** $2x^2 - 7x + 4$
42. $4x^2 - 2x + 5$ **43.** $x^2 - 3x + 5 + \frac{29}{x^2 - 5}$
44. $8x^2 - 16x + 12 - \frac{28x - 18}{2x^2 - 3}$
45. $3x^2 - 4 - \frac{1}{3x^2}$ **46.** B **47.** $2c^2 - 5c + 9$
48. $12x$ **49.** $2d^2$ **50.** $6h^3$ **51.** $11k$ **52.** $40m^4n^3$
53. $2r^2s^2$ **54.** $\frac{8x - 4}{x - 7}$ **55.** $\frac{7x + 24}{28x}$ **56.** $\frac{x^2 - 7x - 20}{x^2 + 2x - 8}$
57. 2 **58.** $\frac{15x^2 + 13x + 27}{(3x - 1)(2x + 3)}$ **59.** $\frac{-3m + 10}{(m + 1)(m - 1)}$
60. C **61a.** $\frac{10}{r} + \frac{10}{r + 3}$ **b.** $1\frac{1}{2}$ h
62. 24 **63.** $-\frac{4}{35}$ **64.** 9 **65.** −14 **66.** −21
67. 2 **68.** 5 **69.** −7 **70.** $\frac{3}{10}$ **71.** 3 **72.** −8, 6
73. −10, 1 **74.** −8, 5 **75.** $\frac{1}{2}$, −5 **76.** ≈ 6 min

Extra Practice

CHAPTER 1 **1.** $a - 4$ **3.** $2y$ **5.** n = number of people; $c = 5.50n$ **7.** t = time in minutes; $c = 75 + 25t$ **9.** 11 **11.** −2 **13.** $\frac{3}{8}$ **15.** −7 **17.** 7
19. 21 **21.** $<$ **23.** $<$ **25.** $>$ **27.** $<$ **29.** −9 **31.** 0

33. -9 **35.** $\frac{22}{15}$ **37.** 9 **39.** -1 **41.** -1 **43.** $\frac{16}{25}$ **45.** $\frac{10}{7}$ **47.** $-16x + 12$ **49.** $8 - 4t$ **51.** -4 **53.** $1 - 4d$ **55.** $7 - 3j$ **57.** $3 - 4y$ **59.** ℓ = length of trip, t = time in traffic, $\ell = 35 + t$ **61.** 300 yd^2 **63.** False; $\frac{1}{2} \times 2 = 1$ **65.** true **67.** 5 in. **69.** 9 pizzas **71.** \$27.65 **73.** \$48.60 **75.** Comm. Prop. of Mult.

CHAPTER 2 **1.** 2 **3.** -5.7 **5.** 20 **7.** 2 **9.** -8 **11.** 11 **13.** t = test score; $\frac{87 + 84 + 85 + t}{4} = 90$; no **15.** 1 **17.** -40 **19.** 0 **21.** $\frac{13}{14}$ **23.** no solution **25.** 1 **27.** 26 **29.** $\frac{45}{2}$ **31.** 12 **33.** 52, 54 **35.** 61, 63, 65 **37.** 5 m, 20 m **39.** 175 L of A, 125 L of B **41.** 225 L of A, 75 L of B **43.** 60 L of A, 240 L of B **45.** 5 DVDs **47.** 7 yd by 14 yd **49.** 50 gallons **51.** about \$1.93/lb **53.** Olivia **55.** bus: 5 h; car: 4 h **57.** 60 L of 30%, 140 L of 50%

CHAPTER 3 **1.** $w > -3$;
3. $r > -4$;
5. $t \geq -8$;
7. $w > -\frac{1}{4}$;
9. $c \geq -10$;
11. $t \geq 5$;
13. $y < 13$;
15. $b > -2$;
17. $x \geq 1$;
19. $n \geq 4$;
21. $x < -3$;
23. $x < -\frac{1}{3}$;
25. $18x \leq 102$, 5 balls **27.** $5 < w < 7$ **29.** $m \leq 4$ or $m > 8.4$ **31.** $10 < c < 12$ **33.** $2 < t < 3$ **35.** $2 \leq x \leq 3$ **37.** $|x| < 2$ **39.** $|x + 4| < 1$ **41.** $|x - 3| \leq 5$
43. $t > 1$ or $t < -1$;
45. $m > 3\frac{2}{3}$ or $m < -3$;
47. $0 \leq w \leq 16$;
49. $-1 \leq c \leq 11$;
51. $|x - 2.5| < 0.5$
53. c is the number of cars sold; $c \geq 35$
55. y is age in years; $y \geq 18$
57. $375 + c \geq 500$; $c \geq 125$ **59.** $25c \geq 200$; $c \geq 8$

61. $15n - 700 \geq 1000$; $n \geq 114$
63. $32 \leq t \leq 212$
65. $14{,}500 < p \leq 15{,}755$
67. $|r - 4.25| \leq 0.005$; $4.245 \leq r \leq 4.255$

CHAPTER 4 **1–6.**

7. I **9.** II **11.** y-axis **13.** IV **15.** yes **17.** yes
19. **21.**

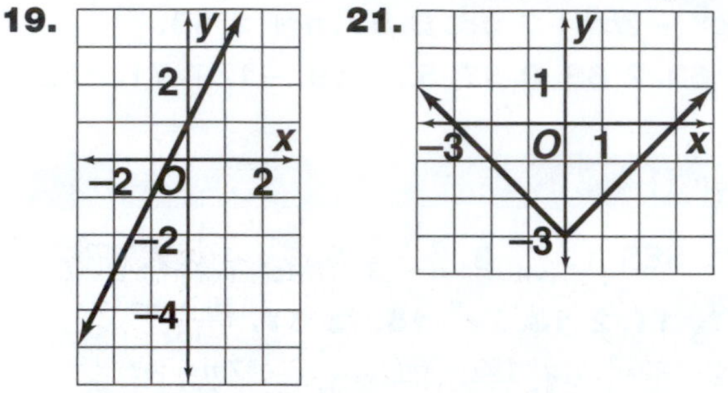

23. {2, −1, −2, 1} **25.** {6, 7.5, 8, 9.5} **27.** $\left\{-\frac{8}{3}, -\frac{2}{3}, 0, 2\right\}$ **29.** $f(x) = 2x$ **31.** $f(x) = \frac{1}{2}x$
33. **35.**

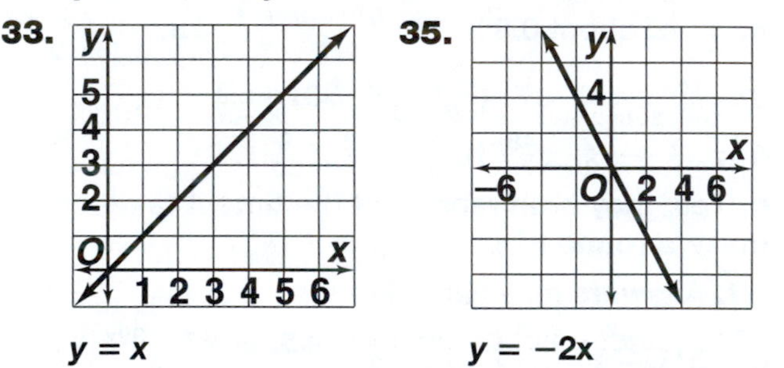

$y = x$ $y = -2x$

37. 70 **39.** 0.8 **41.** 7.5 **43.** 8 **45.** -1 **47.** 243, -729 **49.** -3, -7 **51.** 1, $\frac{1}{5}$ **53.** (0, 4) **55.** (6, 0) **57.** yes **59.**

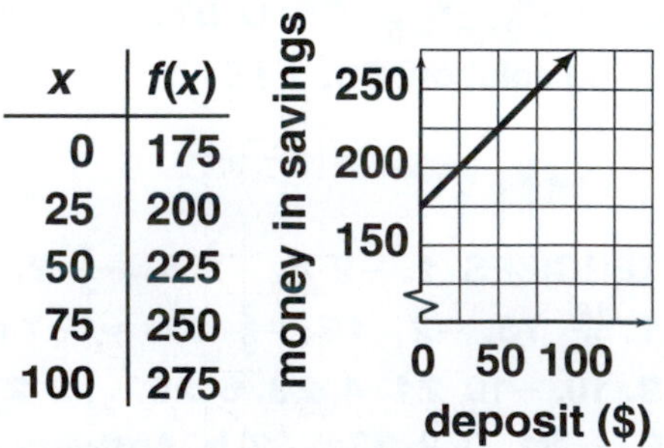

x	$f(x)$
0	175
25	200
50	225
75	250
100	275

61. $C(r) = 2\pi r$ **63.** $D(m) = 5280m$ **65.** $d = \frac{5}{6}t$ about 117 mi **67.** $\ell w = 4500$; 62.5 yd **69.** 9:26 A.M., 9:33 A.M., 9:40 A.M.

CHAPTER 5

1. 0.2 m/yr **3.** 1.6 mm/s **5.** $\frac{2}{5}$ **7.** 2 **9.** 0 **11.** $\frac{3}{4}$ **13.** slope = 6, y-intercept = 8 **15.** slope = 0, y-intercept = 4 **17.** $y = 3x - 2$ **19.** $y = 4.2x + 1$ **21.** $y = \frac{1}{2}x - 4$ **23.** no **25.** no **27.** yes

29. **31.**

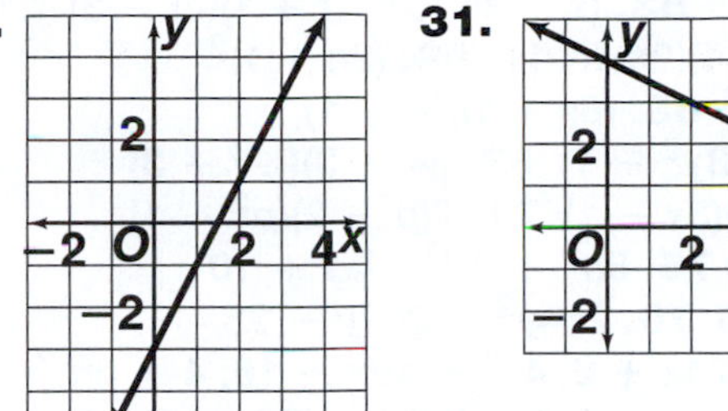

33. x-intercept = 2, y-intercept = 12
35. x-intercept = −6, y-intercept = 3

37. **39.**

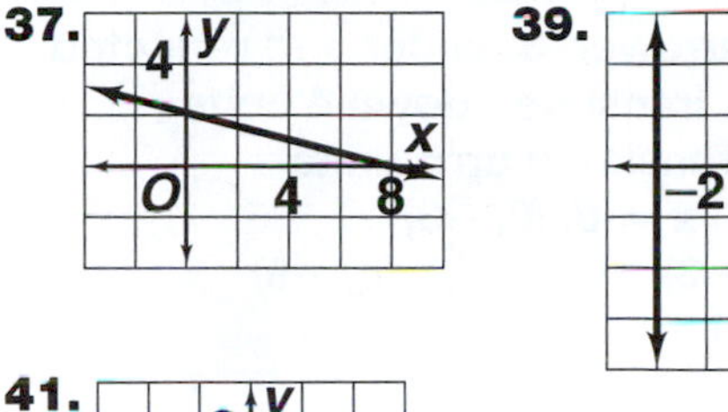

41.

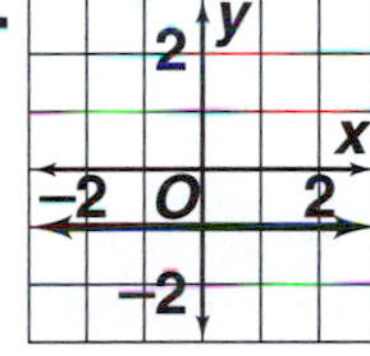

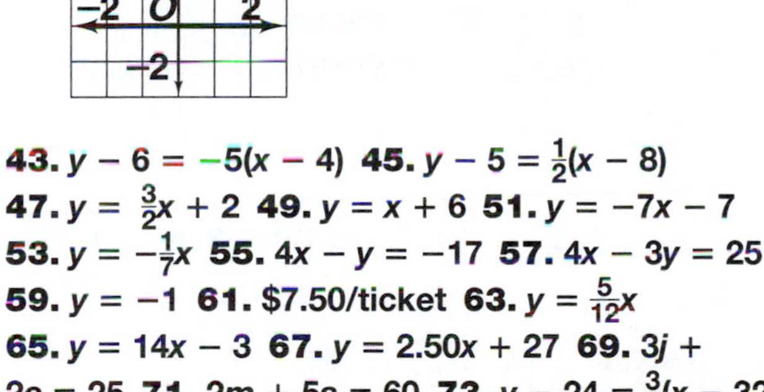

43. $y - 6 = -5(x - 4)$ **45.** $y - 5 = \frac{1}{2}(x - 8)$ **47.** $y = \frac{3}{2}x + 2$ **49.** $y = x + 6$ **51.** $y = -7x - 7$ **53.** $y = -\frac{1}{7}x$ **55.** $4x - y = -17$ **57.** $4x - 3y = 25$ **59.** $y = -1$ **61.** \$7.50/ticket **63.** $y = \frac{5}{12}x$ **65.** $y = 14x - 3$ **67.** $y = 2.50x + 27$ **69.** $3j + 2c = 25$ **71.** $2m + 5s = 60$ **73.** $y - 24 = \frac{3}{4}(x - 32)$ **75.** True; the same rate of travel means that slopes of the graphs are the same, so the lines are parallel.

CHAPTER 6

1. (4, −3);

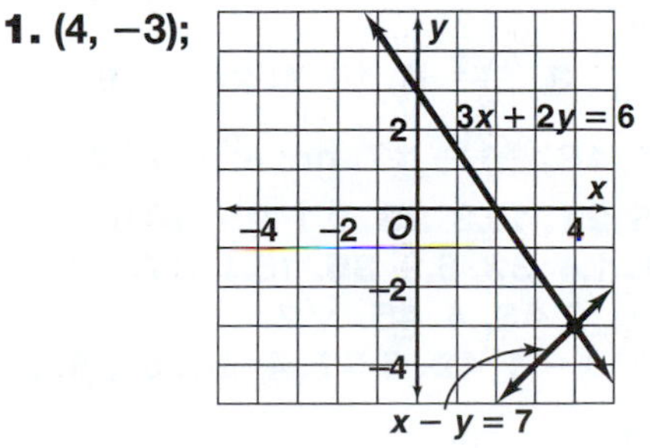

3. (0, 6);

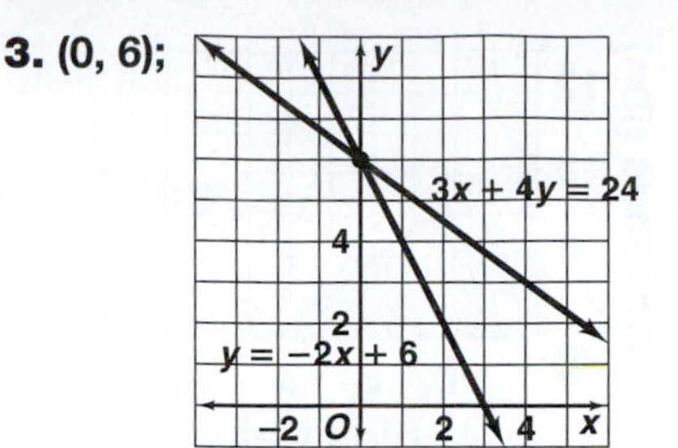

5. $x = 1, y = -1$ **7.** $x = 6, y = 13$ **9.** $x = 4, y = -9$ **11.** $x = 4, y = -5$ **13.** $x + y = 12$; $5x + y = 32$; 5 nickels, 7 pennies **15.** $2x + 2y = 74$; $7x + 2y = 159$; length: 20 ft, width: 17 ft **17.** $x + y = 4$; $0.06x + 0.15y = 0.1(4)$; A: $2\frac{2}{9}$ L, B: $1\frac{7}{9}$ L

19. **21.**

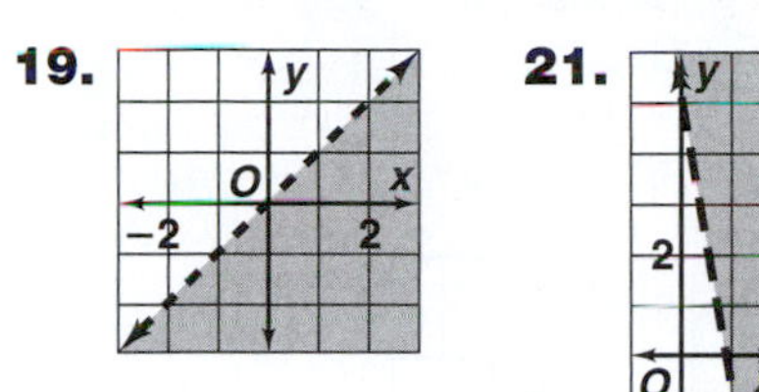

23.

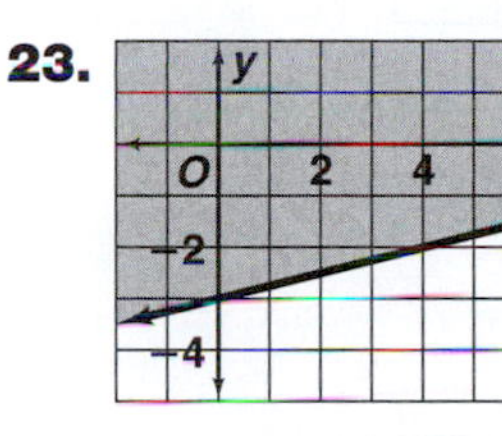

25.

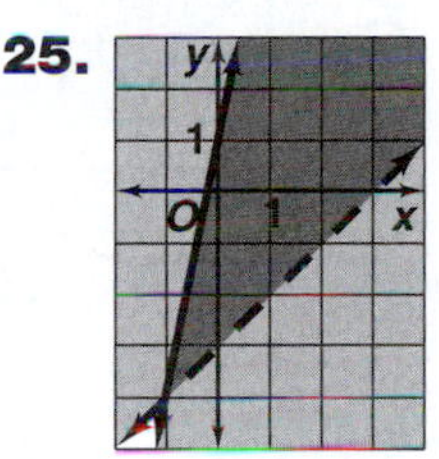

27.

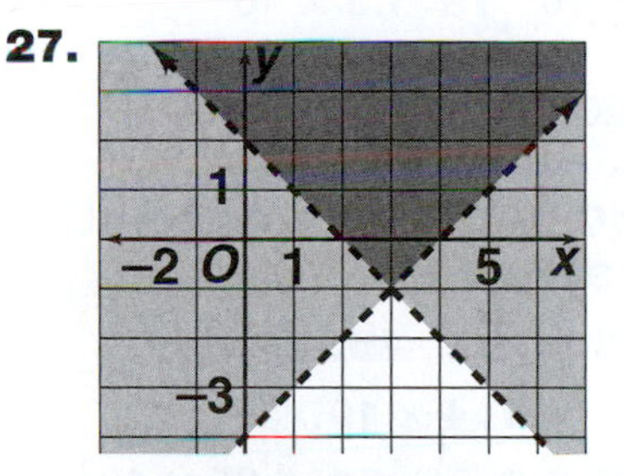

29.

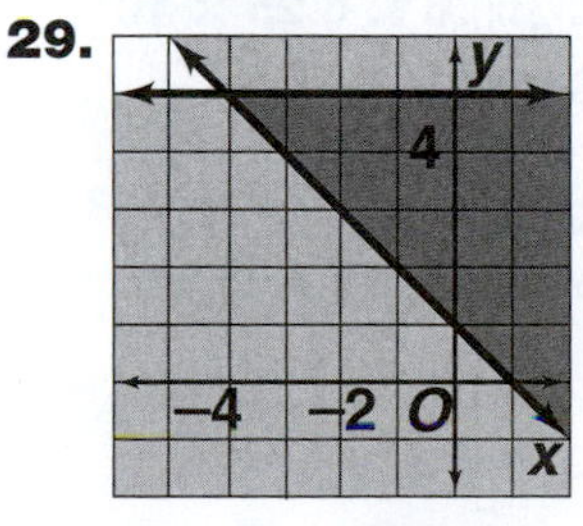

31. $y = 0.5 + 0.02x$; $y = 0.25 + 0.03x$; 25 minutes **33.** $c + s = 300$, $s = c + 110$; corn: 95 acres; soybeans: 205 acres **35.** $4h + 7c = 34.50$, $8h + 3c = 30.50$; h: \$2.50; c: \$3.50 **37.** $b = \frac{4}{5}g$, $b + g = 3321$; 1476 boys, 1845 girls

39. $3a + b \leq 10$

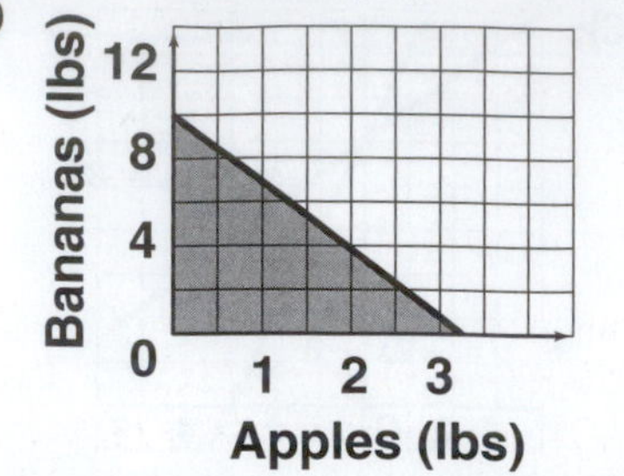

Answers may vary. Sample: 1 lb of apples and 3 lbs of bananas, or 2 lbs of apples and 2 lbs of bananas, or 1 lb of apples and 4 lbs of bananas. **41.** Answers may vary. Sample: He can buy 3 CDs and 1 DVD, or 1 CD and 2 DVDs, or 2 CDs and 1 DVD.

$17d = 14c \leq 60$
$d + c \geq 2$

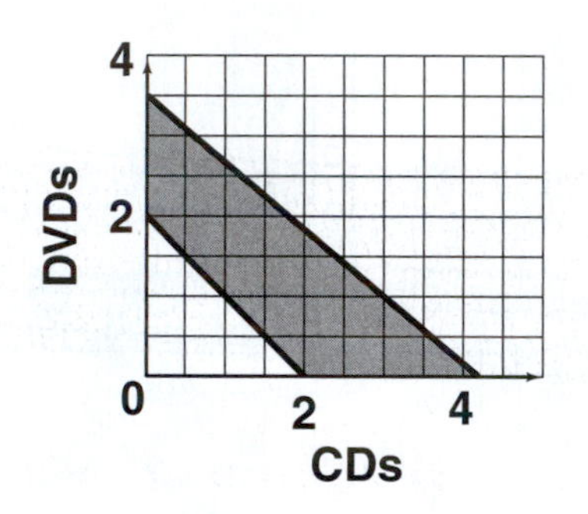

CHAPTER 7 **1.** $\frac{1}{9}$ **3.** 1 **5.** n^3 **7.** $\frac{8y^2}{x^5}$ **9.** 9 **11.** 144 **13.** 1 **15.** 0 **17.** 3.4×10^7 **19.** 1.5×10^3 **21.** 3.6×10^5 **23.** 5×10^{-2} **25.** 8,050,000 **27.** 900,000,000 **29.** 235 **31.** 0.00002001 **33.** 4.5×10^{-2}, 4.38×10^{-1}, 4.2×10^2, 5.2×10^6 **35.** 716×10^{-5}, 92×10^{-4}, 0.32×10^{-1}, 5.6×10^{-2} **37.** $(4.5)^2$ **39.** w^6j^{22} **41.** 2.7×10^6 **43.** 1.68×10^{-1} **45.** $\frac{m^{14}}{t^{10}}$ **47.** $9n^8$ **49.** 1.6×10^{-5} **51.** 4×10^{-12} **53.** a^4 **55.** $6t^4$ **57.** $2t^8$ **5 9.** $\frac{1}{c^{12}}$ **61.** 6.25×10^4 **63.** 9×10^{12} **65.** \$49,920; \$6240 **67.** 8.2×10^{-6} m **69.** 2.59×10^{11} mi^3 **71.** about 9.5×10^{12} km **73.** 2.698×10^{-7} cm^2 **75.** 2.1×10^{-8} in.^{2} **77.** about 9.5×10^{-11} m^2 **79.** 36 min

CHAPTER 8 **1.** $2x^3 + 4x^2 - 11x + 11$ **3.** $6m^3 + m + 4$ **5.** $-10c^3 - c^2 - 9c - 7$ **7.** $-4s^4 - 2s^3 + 2s^2 + 4s$ **9.** $18t + 16$ **11.** $4b^3 + 12b$ **13.** $32m^2 - 40m$ **15.** $5r^4 + 20r^3 - 10r^2$ **17.** $-3x^3 - 9x^2 + 3x$ **19.** $t^2(t^4 - t^3 + t^2 + 1)$ **21.** $4c^2(3c^3 - c + 4)$ **23.** $n^2(2n^2 - 3n + 6)$ **25.** $x^5(4x^2 + 9x + 5)$ **27.** $-5c^2 + 7c + 6$ **29.** $w^3 + 4w^2 + 3w - 2$ **31.** $4n^2 + 2n - 12$ **33.** $9x^2 + 6x + 1$ **35.** $w^3 - 1$ **37.** $9y^2 - 4$ **39.** $(3x - 1)(2x + 5)$, $6x^2 + 13x - 5$ **41.** $(x - 3)(x - 1)$ **43.** $(v - 1)(v + 2)$ **45.** $(m - 2)(m + 11)$ **47.** $(n - 1)(2n + 3)$ **49.** $(m - 5)(m + 5)$ **51.** $(3y + 1)^2$ **53.** $(x + 3)^2$ **55.** $(t + 1)(4t - 3)$ **57.** $(2m + 11)(2m - 11)$ **59.** $(2g + 1)^2$ **61.** $(3t + 2)^2$ **63.** $(6s + 1)(6s - 1)$ **65.** $(y + 3)(3y^2 - 1)$ **67.** $(w - 3)(w^2 + 3)$ **69.** $x(x + 3)(3x - 1)$ **71.** $2(p - 2)(p^2 + 1)$ **73.** $12k - 2$ **75.** $6d^3 + 2d^2 - 4d + 10$ **77.** $3w^2 + 5$ **79.** $264y^2 + 202y - 28$ **81.** $16x^2 - 24x + 9$, $4x^2 + 16x + 16$; 441 cm^2, 256 cm^2 **83.** $m + 7$ **85.** $(12d - 7)$ by $(d - 2)$ **87.** $(8m - 13n)$ by $(8m + 13n)$ **89.** $(5k^2 - 3)$ by $(2k + 5)$

CHAPTER 9 **1.** narrower **3.** wider and reflected over the x-axis **5.** translated down 4 units **7.** narrower and translated up 5 units **9.** $x = 0$, $(0, 0)$ **11.** $x = 0$, $(0, -3)$ **13.** $x = -1$, $(-1, -3)$ **15.** $x = 0$, $(0, -9)$ **17.** $x = 4$, $(4, -16)$

19.

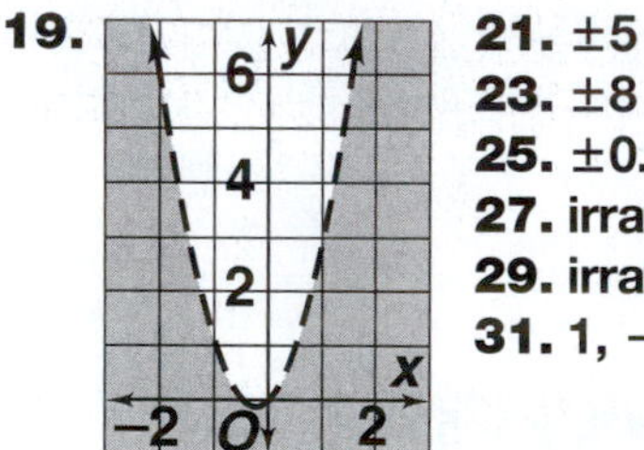

21. ± 5 **23.** ± 8 **25.** ± 0.9 **27.** irrational **29.** irrational **31.** 1, −2

33. $\frac{5}{3}, -\frac{5}{3}$ **35.** 3, −3 **37.** 3, −3 **39.** $-3 \pm \sqrt{11}$ **41.** $5 \pm \sqrt{22}$ **43.** no solution **45.** $-4 \pm 2\sqrt{3}$ **47.** no solution **49.** 12, −12 **51.** 3, 2 **53.** $\frac{-3 \pm \sqrt{5}}{2}$ **55.** $\frac{-1 \pm \sqrt{41}}{4}$ **57.** $\frac{25}{3}$ ft by 30 ft **59.** 0 **61.** 2 **63.** 0 **65.** 0.46875 s **67.** about 8.4 ft **69.** $12 = \pi r^2$; 2.0 in. **71.** $\left(\frac{D}{2}\right)^2\pi = 300$; 19.6 m **73.** 2 s **75.** about 2.66 s

CHAPTER 10 **1.** $\frac{\sqrt{3}}{3}$ **3.** $\frac{5\sqrt{2}}{3}$ **5.** 10 **7.** $2x^2$ **9.** $9\sqrt{10}$ **11.** $\frac{\sqrt{2y}}{y}$ **13.** $\frac{\sqrt{10x}}{4x}$ **15.** $\frac{\sqrt{21x}}{9x}$ **17.** no; $3^2 + 7^2 \neq 10^2$ **19.** no; $3 + 4 \neq 5$ **21.** 10.3 **23.** 9.1 **25.** 10.8 **27.** 2.8 **29.** 5 **31.** 1.4 **33.** 6.9 **35.** 15.1 **37.** −10 **39.** $36\sqrt{3}$ **41.** $-2\sqrt{2}$ **43.** 4 **45.** $\sqrt{2} - 1$ **47.** $\sqrt{6} + \sqrt{2} - \sqrt{3} - 1$ **49.** 5 **51.** 4 **53.** 6 **55.** 2

57. $x \geq -5$;

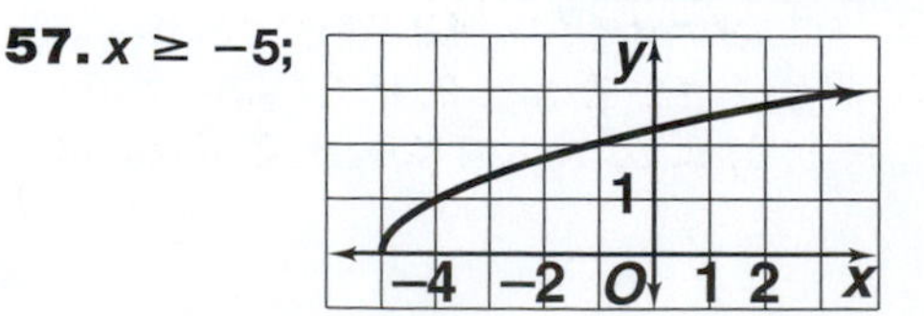

59. $x \geq -1$;

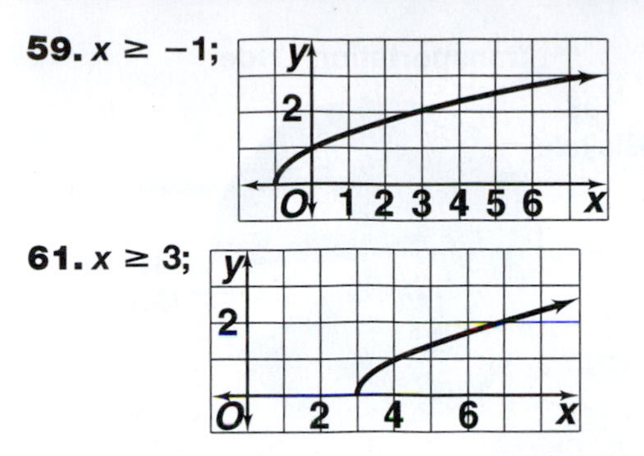

61. $x \geq 3$;

63. 23 mi **65.** 5 mi **67.** 70 mi/h **69.** about 87.3 ft **71.** $-40(1 - \sqrt{3})$; 29.3 cm **73.** about 60

CHAPTER 11 **1.** $\frac{t}{4}$ **3.** 4 **5.** $\frac{1}{x+1}$ **7.** $\frac{m+2}{m+3}$ **9.** $1 - 2d$ **11.** $\frac{h}{h-3}$ **13.** $\frac{s}{2}$ **15.** 12 **17.** $\frac{y}{6}$ **19.** $2x - 3 + \frac{4}{x}$ **21.** $x^2 + 5$ **23.** $2x^2 + 5x + 2$ **25.** $3x^2 - 7x + 6$ **27.** $2x^2 + 4x - 4 - \frac{x}{4x+3}$ **29.** $x^3 + 3 - \frac{25}{x+5}$ **31.** $\frac{1}{x}$ **33.** $\frac{6c+4}{c^2}$ **35.** $\frac{8(t-1)}{t^2-16}$ **37.** $\frac{4d-3}{d^3}$ **39.** $\frac{7-6f}{3f^3}$ **41.** $\frac{2}{3}$ **43.** -3 **45.** -3 **47.** $-\frac{28}{5}$ **49.** -12 **51.** 6, -10 **53.** about 98 min **55.** $\frac{3x+5}{2x}$ yd^2 **57.** $3d^2 - 6d - 12$ cm **59.** $3x^2 - 4x + 7$ m^2 **61.** $\frac{2}{r} + \frac{2}{1.6r} = \frac{3.25}{r}$ **63.** $8\frac{4}{7}$ min **65.** $10\frac{2}{7}$ h

Algebra Skills Handbook

p. 588 **1.** 10 games **3.** 9 tacks

p. 589 **1.** 17 and 19, or –19 and –17 **3.** 33, 34, 35, and 36 **5.** 24 years old **7.** mother: 38 yr; son: 16 yr; daughter: 7 yr **9.** regular tickets: 80; student tickets: 110

p. 590 **1.** 81 books **3.** 36 stories **5.** 7.2 m **7.** 6 ways

p. 591 **1.** 21 lockers **3.** about 370,000,000 times **5.** 63 games **7.** 32 and 33

p. 592 **1.** dog: K. C.; horse: Bo; bird: Cricket; cat: Tuffy **3.** Alexa, Karin, Heather, Annette, Tanya, Garo **5.** 126 players

p. 593 **1.** 6 **3.** 21 pencils **5.** 11 mi **7.** 290 mi **9.** $4\frac{3}{4}$ mi east, 2 mi north

p. 594 **1.** composite **3.** composite **5.** prime **7.** composite **9.** composite **11.** composite **13.** composite **15.** composite **17.** composite **19.** 1, 2, 23, 46 **21.** 1, 11 **23.** 1, 3, 9, 27 **25.** 1, 5, 41, 205 **27.** 1, 2, 3, 4, 6, 8, 12, 24 **29.** 1, 2, 4, 8, 11, 22, 44, 88 **31.** 1, 3, 61, 183 **33.** 1, 2, 7, 14, 49, 98 **35.** 1, 59 **37.** $2 \cdot 3 \cdot 3$ **39.** $3 \cdot 3 \cdot 3$ **41.** $2 \cdot 2 \cdot 2 \cdot 2 \cdot 2 \cdot 2$ **43.** $2 \cdot 2 \cdot 5 \cdot 5$ **45.** $2 \cdot 2 \cdot 3 \cdot 7$ **47.** $11 \cdot 11$p. 595 **1.** 2 **3.** 24 **5.** 3 **7.** 7 **9.** 5 **11.** 21 **13.** 80 **15.** 33 **17.** 60 **19.** 240 **21.** 150 **23.** 40

p. 596 **1.** 2, 4 **3.** 3, 5 **5.** 3, 5, 9 **7.** 2 **9.** 2, 3, 4, 6, 8, 9 **11.** none **13.** 3, 5 **15.** 2, 3, 4, 6, 8, 9 **17.** 2, 4 **19.** 15 **21.** Answers may vary. Sample: $a + 1$ is not divisible by 2. Dividing by 2 will leave a remainder of 1.

p. 597 **1.** \$350 **3.** \$300 **5.** \$17.00 **7.** 7.10 **9.** 7.00 **11.** \$30.80

p. 598 **1.** $\frac{8}{14}, \frac{12}{21}, \frac{16}{28}, \frac{20}{35}, \frac{24}{42}$ **3.** $\frac{6}{16}, \frac{9}{24}, \frac{12}{32}, \frac{15}{40}, \frac{18}{48}$ **5.** $\frac{10}{12}, \frac{15}{18}, \frac{20}{24}, \frac{25}{30}, \frac{30}{36}$ **7.** 9 **9.** 48 **11.** 2 **13.** 9 **15.** 3 **17.** no **19.** no **21.** no **23.** $\frac{1}{2}$ **25.** $\frac{2}{3}$ **27.** $\frac{2}{5}$ **29.** $\frac{1}{3}$ **31.** $\frac{2}{5}$ **33.** $\frac{3}{4}$

p. 599 **1.** $0.\overline{3}$ **3.** 0.2 **5.** $0.\overline{714285}$ **7.** $0.\overline{5}$ **9.** $0.\overline{285714}$ **11.** 0.16 **13.** $\frac{7}{100}$ **15.** $\frac{7}{8}$ **17.** $6\frac{1}{3}$ **19.** $\frac{7}{9}$ **21.** $\frac{3}{8}$ **23.** $6\frac{12}{25}$

p. 600 **1.** $\frac{5}{7}$ **3.** 3 **5.** $10\frac{7}{15}$ **7.** $6\frac{2}{9}$ **9.** $6\frac{7}{33}$ **11.** $9\frac{2}{3}$ **13.** $13\frac{7}{16}$ **15.** $56\frac{11}{15}$ **17.** $\frac{3}{5}$ **19.** $1\frac{2}{7}$ **21.** $2\frac{3}{8}$ **23.** $3\frac{1}{3}$ **25.** $9\frac{4}{63}$ **27.** $2\frac{1}{6}$ **29.** $7\frac{5}{6}$

p. 601 **1.** $\frac{3}{10}$ **3.** $8\frac{5}{8}$ **5.** $3\frac{1}{2}$ **7.** $25\frac{3}{10}$ **9.** $2\frac{4}{5}$ **11.** 6 **13.** $9\frac{5}{6}$ **15.** $5\frac{15}{16}$ **17.** $\frac{8}{9}$ **19.** $\frac{18}{25}$ **21.** $13\frac{1}{3}$ **23.** $\frac{5}{6}$ **25.** 26 **27.** $1\frac{1}{3}$ **29.** $\frac{1}{3}$

p. 602 **1.** 56% **3.** 602% **5.** 820% **7.** 14.3% **9.** 11.1% **11.** 75% **13.** 0.07 **15.** 0.009 **17.** 0.83 **19.** 0.15 **21.** 0.0003 **23.** 3.65 **25.** $\frac{19}{100}$ **27.** $4\frac{1}{2}$ **29.** $\frac{16}{25}$ **31.** $\frac{6}{25}$ **33.** $\frac{3}{800}$ **35.** $\frac{3}{5}$ **37.** $\frac{1}{50}$ **39.** $\frac{33}{50}$ **41.** $1\frac{1}{4}$

p. 603 **1.** 6^4 **3.** $5 \cdot 2^4$ **5.** $4^2 \cdot 3^2 \cdot 2$ **7.** 64 **9.** 144 **11.** 3267 **13.** $(1 \cdot 10^3) + (2 \cdot 10^2) + (5 \cdot 10^1) + (4 \cdot 10^0)$ **15.** $(8 \cdot 10^4) + (3 \cdot 10^3) + (4 \cdot 10^2) + (1 \cdot 10^0)$

p. 604 **1.** 22 cm **3.** 24 cm^2 **5.** 216 cm^3 **7.** 351.68 cm^3

p. 605 **1.** **3.**

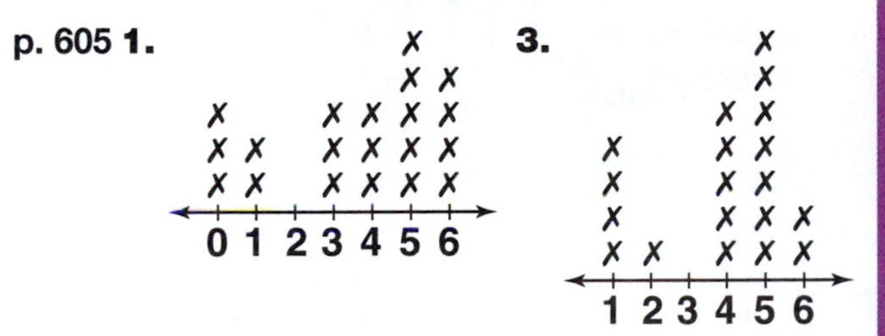

Selected Answers

5.

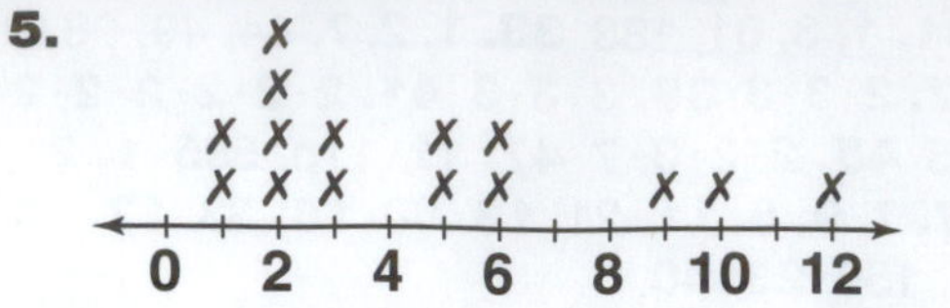

The line plot shows that most of the numbers are concentrated around 2, the maximum is 12, and the minimum is 1.

p. 606 1.

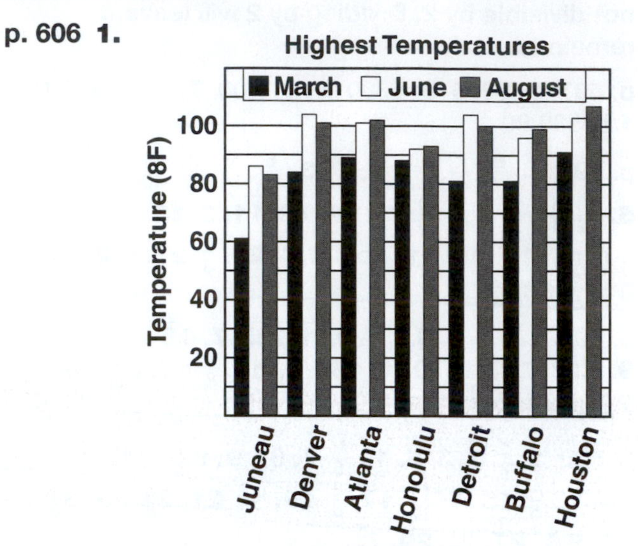

p. 607 1a. 30–39 minutes **b.** 15 students **c.** Answers may vary. Sample: If it actually took 50–59 minutes, the student might estimate by saying 1 hour. **d.** No; you don't know where inside each interval the answers are.
3a–d. Check students' work.

p. 608 1.

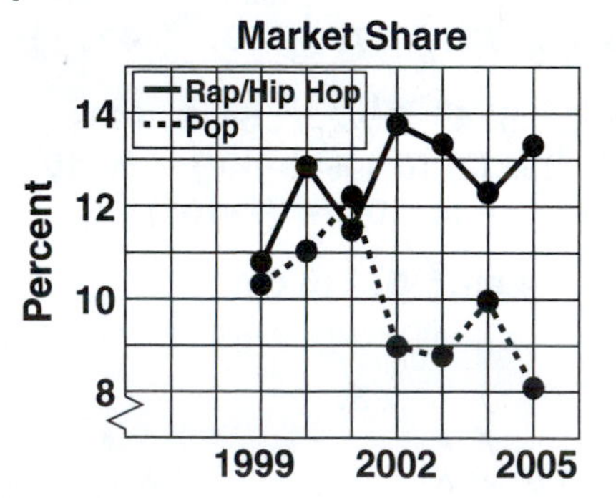

p. 609 1a.

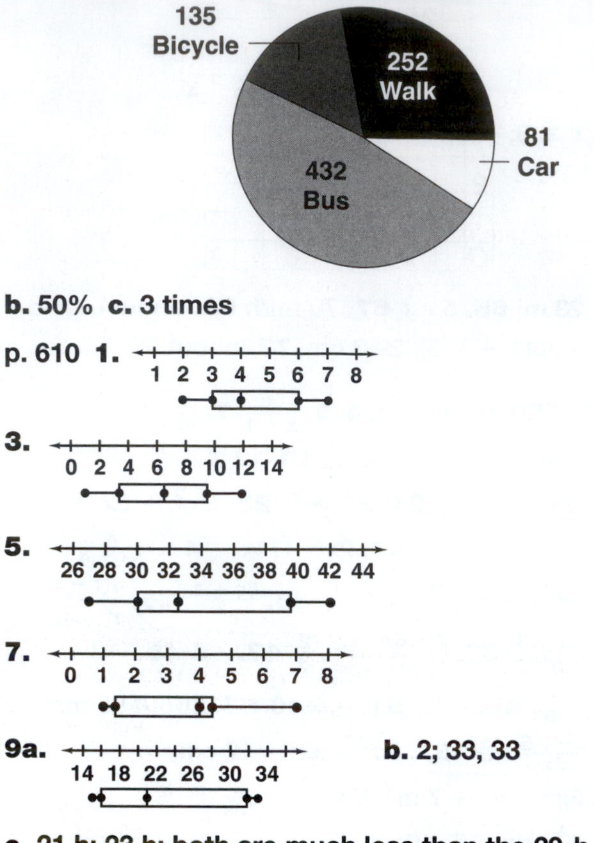

b. 50% **c.** 3 times

p. 610 1. 1 2 3 4 5 6 7 8

3. 0 2 4 6 8 10 12 14

5. 26 28 30 32 34 36 38 40 42 44

7. 0 1 2 3 4 5 6 7 8

9a. 14 18 22 26 30 34 **b.** 2; 33, 33

c. 21 h; 23 h; both are much less than the 29-h typical week.

p. 611 1. Circle graph; the categories seem to cover how an average family spends all of its money in October. A circle graph also shows the percentage of a category more easily than a bar graph. **3.** Scatter plot; the levels of emissions most likely increase as the age of a car increases. A double bar graph would only be used if the data had an additional subject.
5. the scores of ten volleyball games **7.** the distribution of kinds of nuts in a jar of mixed nuts

Index

A

Index

B

C

F

G

H

I

J

L

M

N

Q

R

S

T

U

V

W

X

Y

Z

Acknowledgments

Staff Credits

The people who made up the California Mathematics team—representing design services, editorial, editorial services, education technology, image services, marketing, market research, production services, publishing processes, and strategic markets—are listed below. Bold type denotes the core team members.

Dan Anderson, **Scott Andrews,** Carolyn Artin, Judith D. Buice, Kerry Cashman, Sarah Castrignano, Allison Cook, Carl Cottrell, Bob Craton, Patrick Culleton, Sheila DeFazio, Kathleen J. Dempsey, Frederick Fellows, **Suzanne Finn,** Patricia Fromkin, David J. George, **Patricia K. Gilbert,** Sandy Graff, **Ellen Welch Granter,** Richard Heater, Jayne Holman, Jennifer King, Betsy Krieble, Christopher Langley, Lisa LaVallee, Christine Lee, **Elizabeth Lehnertz,** Catherine Maglio, Cheryl Mahan, **Ann Mahoney,** Constance McCarty, **Carolyn McGuire,** Anne McLaughlin, Richard McMahon, Eve Melnechuk, Terri Mitchell, Michael Oster, Jeffrey Paulhus, Marcy Rose, Rashid Ross, Siri Schwartzman, Vicky Shen, **Dennis Slattery,** Nancy Smith, Mark Tricca, Paul Vergith, Teresa Whitney, Merce Wilczek, Joe Will, Kristin Winters, Heather Wright, Helen Young

Additional Credits: J.J. Andrews, Sarah J. Aubry, Deborah Belanger, Beth Blumberg, Casey Clark, Patty Fagan, Tom Greene, Karmyn Guthrie, Gillian Kahn, Jonathan Kier, Mary Landry, Mary Beth McDaniel, Anakin Steuart Michele, Hope Morley, Carol Roy, Jewel Simmons, Ted Smykal, Richard Sullivan, Dan Tanguay, Steve Thomas, Michael Torocsik, Alwyn Velasquez, Allison Wyss

Cover Design

Nancy Smith

Cover Photos

Building, Ted Soqui/Corbis;
Artichoke, Ed Young/Corbis.

Illustration

XNR Productions

Photography

Front matter: Page CA6, Ralph A. Clevenger/Corbis; **CA7,** Jon Riley/Getty Images, Inc.; **CA8,** Frank Lane/Parfitt/Stone/Getty Images, Inc.; **CA9,** Corbis/Stock Market; **CA10,** Rob Atkins/Image Bank/Getty Images, Inc.; **CA11,** Alan Thornton/Getty Images, Inc.; **CA12,** Wilfried Krecichwost/Stone/Getty Images, Inc.; **CA13,** John Lund/Getty Images, Inc.; **CA14,** Ron Kimball/Ron Kimball Stock; **CA15,** R.D. Rubic/Precision Chromes, Inc.; **CA16,** Zefa/London/Corbis; **CA17,** Jeff Greenberg/Photo Edit; **CA29,** David McNew/Getty Images; **CA33,** David McNew/Getty Images; **CA34,** Steve Vidler/SuperStock.

Chapter One: Page 3, Galen Rowell/Corbis; **5,** Jon Riley/Stone/Getty Images, Inc.; **7,** Bob Daemmrich/Stock Boston; **12,** Steve Bronstein/The Image Bank/Getty Images, Inc.; **13,** PhotoEdit; **27,** Getty Images, Inc.; **39,** Nicholas Devore III/Bruce Coleman, Inc.; **43,** Courtesy of Cedar Point/Photo by Dan Feicht; **53,** Russ Lappa.

Chapter Two: Page 67, V.C.L./FPG/Getty Images, Inc.; **70,** Russ Lappa; **80,** VCL/Alistair Berg/Getty Images, Inc.; **85,** Michelle Bridwell/Photoedit; **97,** Pedro Coll/Superstock; **102,** The Image Works.

Chapter Three: Page 123 ml, Sinibaldi/Corbis; **126,** Tony Freeman/PhotoEdit; **128,** Poulides/Thatcher/Getty Images, Inc.; **133,** Clive Brunskill/Allsport/Getty Images, Inc.; **134,** Corbis; **140,** Doug Sokell/Visuals Unlimited; **144,** Russ Lappa; **147,** Robin L. Sachs/PhotoEdit; **148,** Stone/Getty Images, Inc.; **152,** Bob Daemmrich/Stock Boston; **155,** Michael Newman/PhotoEdit; **161,** Dave King/Dorling Kindersley; **162,** Juan Silva/Getty Images.

Chapter Four: Page 175, Steve Hamblin/Alamy; **181,** Daryl Balfour/Stone/Getty Images, Inc.; **195,** Seth Resnick/Stock Boston; **203,** Rob Atkins/Getty Images, Inc.; **205,** Jim West/The Image Works; **208,** Nancy Richmond/The Image Works; **210,** David Young-Wolff/PhotoEdit; **213,** CLOSE TO HOME ©John McPherson. Reprinted with permission of Universal Press Syndicate. All rights reserved.

Chapter Five: Page 229, Superstock; **232,** Mark Richards/Photo Edit; **236 l,** Gail Mooney/Masterfile; **241,** David Young-Wolff/PhotoEdit, Inc.; **244,** Tim Davis/Stone/Getty Images, Inc.; **248,** Myrleen Ferguson/PhotoEdit; **250,** Kenneth W. Fink/Photo Researchers, Inc.; **254,** Tom Stock/Getty Images, Inc.; **259,** Alan Thornton/Getty Images, Inc.; **261,** Robert Landau/Corbis.

Chapter Six: Page 275, Phil Klein/Corbis; **277,** SuperStock, Inc.; **284,** Wilfried Krecichwost/Getty Images, Inc.; **288,** Robert Brenner/PhotoEdit; **294,** Index Stock Imagery, Inc.; **299,** Steve McCutcheon/Visuals Unlimited; **305,** Ilan Rosen/Alamy; **306,** Aaron Stevenson/Prentice Hall; **311,** Steven Kline/Bruce Coleman, Inc.; **312 t,** Pearson Education; **312 b,** Leonard de Selva/Corbis; **314,** Frank Pedrick/The Image Works; **315,** Omni-Photo Communications, Inc.

Chapter Seven: Page 327, John Lund/Getty Images, Inc.; **337,** Frans Lanting/Minden Pictures; **341,** Andrew Syred/Science Photo Library/Photo Researchers, Inc.; **343,** Maxine Hall/Corbis; **347,** Bettmann/Corbis; **352,** Royalty-Free/Corbis; **355,** Artiga Photo/Corbis; **359,** AP Photo/Paul Sakuma.

Chapter Eight: Page 369, Mark Bacon/Alamy; **370,** Getty Images, Inc.; **374,** Chuck Savage/Corbis; **385,** Cesar Lucas Abreu/Getty Images, Inc.; **389,** Ron Kimball/Ron Kimball Stock; **392,** Lynn M. Stone.

Chapter Nine: Page 425, Craig Aurness/Corbis; **427,** Richard Megna/Fundamental Photographs; **430 l,** Getty Images, Inc.; **430 r,** Prentice Hall; **431,** C Squared Studios/PhotoDisc, Inc./Getty Images, Inc.; **435,** R.D. Rubic/Precision Chromes, Inc.;

437, Agence Vandystadt/Getty Images, Inc.; **438,** Jose Carrillo/PhotoEdit; **441,** David Austen/Getty Images, Inc.; **442 t,** NASA; **442 b,** Reprinted by permission: Tribune Media Services; **448,** A. Ramey/Stock Boston; **454,** Michael Keller/Getty Images, Inc.; **463,** David Cannon/Getty Images; **467,** CLOSE TO HOME by John McPherson/Universal Press Syndicate; **472,** Jeff Sherman/Getty Images, Inc.

Chapter Ten: Page 485, Doug Dreyer/AP/Wide World Photos; **494,** Spencer Jones/Getty Images, Inc.; **497,** AFP/Corbis; **502,** ©ABC/Mondrian Estate/Holtzman Trust/Haags Gemeentemuseum; **505,** ©Tribune Media Services, Inc. All Rights Reserved. Reprinted with permission; **511,** David Young-Wolff/PhotoEdit; **515,** James Shaffer/PhotoEdit; **517,** Kelly-Mooney Photography/Corbis; **518,** David Young-Wolff/PhotoEdit.

Chapter Eleven: Page 529, John William Banagan/Getty Images, Inc.; **531,** Antman/The Image Works; **533,** SuperStock, Inc.; **548,** Jeff Greenberg/Photo Edit; **554,** AP Photo/Charles Krupa.